SYNTHETIC
ORGANIC CHEMISTRY

SYNTHETIC
ORGANIC CHEMISTRY

ROMEO B. WAGNER

Former Assistant Professor of Chemistry
The Pennsylvania State College

HARRY D. ZOOK

Assistant Professor of Chemistry
The Pennsylvania State College

NEW YORK · JOHN WILEY & SONS, INC.
LONDON

Preface

Synthetic Organic Chemistry is designed to summarize in a single volume methods of organic syntheses most frequently employed in the preparation of mono- and di-functional compounds. The methods are collected in chapters each of which is devoted to the formation of compounds containing a particular functional group or related groups. In order to present a wide coverage of organic chemistry, detailed discussions were omitted; however, frequent references to the original literature as well as to other books and review articles are given. An effort has been made to include among these references examples of the better preparative procedures. Tables supplement the text in recording additional references and other examples. Moreover, the tabular material stands alone as a handy index to the literature for the preparation of starting materials of relatively simple structure.

In the selection of compounds for the tables, the original literature was read for clarity of directions along with statements of yield and physical constants. With few exceptions, a compound is listed in the tables only if its preparation appears adequately described. Also, the compound had to fit into an arbitrarily chosen scheme of structure simplicity. The reader will find that this scheme is quite liberal. Some compounds and their preparations serve as models in testing the generality of a particular method; hence, these substances are included even though they may be available commercially.

The following books and journals from 1919 to 1950 inclusive have been reviewed page by page:

Annalen der Chemie
Annales de chimie
Archiv der Pharmazie
Berichte der deutschen
  chemischen Gesellschaft
Bulletin de la société
  chimique de France
Chemical Reviews
Chemische Berichte
Helvetica Chimica Acta
Industrial and Engineering
  Chemistry

Journal of Biological
  Chemistry
Journal of Chemical Education
Journal of the Chemical
  Society of London
Journal of Organic Chemistry
Journal für praktische Chemie
Journal of the Society of
  Chemical Industry (London)
Monatshefte für Chemie
Organic Reactions
Organic Syntheses

v

| *Journal of the American* | *Recueil des travaux* |
| *Chemical Society* | *chimiques* |

Numerous other books and articles have also been examined. Although the survey is not complete, an attempt has been made to include those journals most readily accessible and most frequently consulted.

Because the methods and compounds have been arranged in a systematic manner already familiar to chemists, information concerning the formation of a particular functional compound may be found rapidly by consulting the table of contents, the individual chapter contents, or the tables. The index has been prepared with particular emphasis on the reactions of organic compounds. In the interest of economy the compounds listed in the tables are not repeated in the index.

We acknowledge with gratitude the assistance of Dr. James A. Moore, who has read the entire manuscript and has given many helpful suggestions. We are grateful to Elizabeth F. Wagner and Margaret H. Zook for their valuable assistance in the preparation of the manuscript.

Hercules Powder Company	ROMEO B. WAGNER
Wilmington, Delaware	
The Pennsylvania State College	HARRY D. ZOOK
State College, Pennsylvania	

January, 1953

Contents

List of Tables

Explanation of Tables

Arrangement. The compounds are classified according to functional groups and are arranged with respect to their carbon content. For convenience, the larger classes are subdivided into aliphatic, alicyclic, aromatic, and heterocyclic series.

Nomenclature. For the most part, compounds are listed under the name used in the original literature; hence, they can readily be found in the articles cited and the inconvenience of seeking a compound under a new name is avoided. Since common names are used to a large extent in the literature, the compounds can be found in the tables under the appropriate series arranged according to the carbon content.

Method. Each number listed under this heading refers to a particular method which is discussed in the accompanying text and is described in the reference cited. The methods are numbered consecutively throughout the text. Certain methods, not general enough to warrant description, are designated as miscellaneous by a dash.

Yield. The yield is stated for a single-step process (final step) unless a dagger (†) is attached; then it is based on a multiple-step process.

Reference. The references are listed as superscripts to the number of the chapter in which they appear. The page on which the description of the compound appears is cited, unless more than one compound is selected from the article, in which case the initial page of the article is cited.

Physical Constants. The data are taken from the literature reference cited unless an asterisk (*) is attached; the asterisk indicates that they have been obtained from another source. *Boiling points* (B.p./mm.) are given in °C and are at "atmospheric pressure" unless the investigator has been specific in recording the actual pressure (millimeters of mercury). *Melting points* (M.p.) are given in °C and are enclosed in parentheses to set them off from boiling points. Decomposition points are indicated by the abbreviation "d." *Indices of refraction* (n_D) are for sodium light and at 20°C unless a superscript denotes another temperature.

Derivatives. Melting-point data for the derivatives are taken from the cited reference unless marked by an asterisk (*), which indicates that

the data have been obtained from another source.   Various derivatives
are represented by the following symbols:

Ac	Acetate or acetyl derivative	Ox	Oxime
Am	Amide	*p*B	*p*-Bromophenacyl ester
An	Anilide	Ph	Phenylhydrazone
Bz	Benzoate or benzoyl derivative	Phz	Phenylhydrazide
Cu	Copper salt	Pi	Picrate
Db	3,5-Dinitrobenzoate	*p*N	*p*-Nitrophenylhydrazone
Di	Dibromide	*p*P	*p*-Phenylphenacyl ester
Dn	2,4-Dinitrophenylhydrazone	Pu	Phenylurethane
Du	Diphenylurethane	Sb	S-Benzylthiouronium salt
HBr	N-Hydrobromide	Se	Semicarbazone
HCl	N-Hydrochloride	Te	Tetrabromide
NBz	*p*-Nitrobenzoate	To	*p*-Toluide
Nu	α-Naphthylurethane		

1

Paraffinic, Naphthenic, and Aromatic* Hydrocarbons

CONTENTS

The common reactions for the preparation of hydrocarbons have been divided into eighteen types. Of these, methods 3, 5, 8, and 9 are most general for aliphatic hydrocarbons; methods 3, 4, and 9 for alicyclic hydrocarbons; and methods 3, 5, and 10 for the introduction of an alkyl group into the aromatic nucleus. Biaryls are usually made by methods 11 or 12, and polynuclear aromatic hydrocarbons with fused rings by methods 2, 3, or 17.

No attempt has been made to include "best values" for the physical constants of the hydrocarbons in Table 1. For the most part, the constants listed are those corresponding to the yield of material prepared. Data for more highly purified materials may be found in the several ex-

* Aryl-substituted olefins and acetylenes are discussed in Chapters 2 and 3.

1

cellent works on this subject.[255] A review of the properties of alkylbenzenes is worthy of mention.[5]

1. Alkylation of Hydrocarbons (Friedel-Crafts)

$$ArH + RX \xrightarrow{AlCl_3} ArR + HX$$

Alkylation of aromatic hydrocarbons has been accomplished by a variety of reagents including alkyl halides, alcohols, olefins, ethers,[9,24,46] esters,[22,30] and alkyl sulfates.[10,27] Catalysts for the reaction are those which tend to produce carbonium ions (R^+) from the alkylating agents.[47] Isomerization frequently occurs within the alkyl group.[1,33] Thus, s-alkyl derivatives are obtained when n-alkyl halides or primary alcohols are employed as alkylating agents. Similarly, isobutyl halides give t-butyl compounds. The reaction, therefore, cannot be used to prepare pure n-alkyl-substituted aromatic hydrocarbons containing more than two carbon atoms in the side chain. An exception is the formation of n-propylbenzene from cyclopropane, benzene, and aluminum chloride.[33,35,50] Racemization of the s-butyl radical occurs to the extent of 95% in the boron trifluoride-catalyzed alkylation of benzene by optically active s-butyl alcohol.[26,47]

Alkyl halides are common alkylating agents in this reaction. Benzene is converted to toluene at atmospheric pressure by methyl chloride in the presence of aluminum chloride.[15] Nitroparaffins have been used as solvents for the aluminum chloride catalyst.[50] An amalgamated aluminum catalyst is more effective than aluminum chloride in certain alkylations by alkyl chlorides.[38] Boron trifluoride must be accompanied by water, alcohol, or some other polar compound in order to be effective in similar alkylations.[14] Hydrogen chloride,[39] hydrogen fluoride,[44] ferric chloride,[41] and beryllium chloride[42] also have been used as catalysts.

Alkylation of benzene by an olefin occurs when the olefin is stirred with a cold mixture of benzene and sulfuric acid.[4] The type of product formed depends upon the concentration of sulfuric acid; high concentrations (90—96%) are required for alkylations.[28] Alkylation by olefins is also catalyzed by aluminum chloride,[32,50] ferric chloride,[45] silicophosphoric acid,[248] and hydrogen fluoride.[23,24,44] The last catalyst is the best of four studied for the preparation of phenylcycloheptane from benzene and cycloheptene.[43]

Acetylene adds two molecules of benzene or other aromatic hydrocarbon in the presence of sulfuric acid and a little mercuric sulfate to give 1,1-diarylethanes.[52]

Benzene has been alkylated by several series of secondary and tertiary alcohols in the presence of aluminum chloride.[2,11] Ferric chloride is. recommended over aluminum chloride for alkylation by t-butyl alcohol.[20]

n- and s-Butyl alcohols are not condensed with benzene by this catalyst. Primary alcohols serve as alkylating agents when boron trifluoride is used with "assistants" such as phosphorus pentoxide or sulfuric acid.[19] The products, however, are secondary-alkyl benzenes formed by isomerization of the alkyl radical. Benzylation of aromatic compounds may be accomplished by refluxing with benzyl alcohol and p-toluenesulfonic acid in an apparatus equipped with a water separator.[9]

The alkylations are reversible. Alkyl groups can be transferred from one position to another on the aromatic nucleus[21,36,37,48] or from one molecule to another.[3,29] t-Butylbenzene is formed in 85% yield from benzene and p-di-t-butylbenzene in the presence of ferric chloride.[31]

Many di- and poly-alkylated benzenes have been prepared by the Friedel-Crafts reaction. Alkyl groups on the nucleus do not exert a strong directive influence upon the orientation, nor do they greatly affect the rate of further alkylation.[18] The composition of the alkylated product varies widely, depending upon the conditions of the reaction. Appreciable quantities of m-dialkylated[48,49] and sym-trialkylated[25] products are obtained under vigorous conditions. The composition of many products is in doubt, as has been shown by later, more accurate analyses.[40] Methylation of xylene gives 1,2,4,5-tetramethylbenzene (durene), pentamethylbenzene, and hexamethylbenzene.[7]

Alkylation of naphthalene gives both α- and β-monoalkyl products, the β-compound usually predominating.[13,17]

Excellent reviews of the alkylation of aromatic hydrocarbons have been published.[17,18,34,47] The production of paraffins by the alkylation of isoparaffins by olefins is important industrially[50,51] but is not common on a laboratory scale for the preparation of pure hydrocarbons.

Alkylation of aryl halides (method 76) and phenols (method 106) is discussed elsewhere as is the application of the Friedel-Crafts reaction to the synthesis of ketones (method 178) and carboxylic acids (method 273). Nitro and alkoxy groups also have been present on the aromatic nucleus during alkylations.[24]

2. Aromatic Hydrocarbons by Dehydrogenation

Saturated and partially saturated alicyclic compounds having six-membered rings are readily converted to the corresponding aromatic compounds by several dehydrogenation procedures. The more nearly saturated compounds are the most difficult to dehydrogenate. Alicyclic rings containing more than six carbon atoms undergo ring contraction to six-membered aromatic rings.[242] Compounds containing quaternary carbon atoms in the ring such as compounds with angular methyl groups or gem-dialkyl groups are aromatized with difficulty. The reaction proceeds, however, at high temperatures by elimination or migration of an alkyl group.[60,67,72] Other carbon-skeleton changes are described in a critical review of the dehydrogenation techniques.[243]

The usual hydrogenation catalysts may be used to effect dehydrogenation. The reaction is carried out in the liquid phase by heating the substance with the catalyst until evolution of hydrogen ceases or in the vapor phase by passing the substance through the catalyst heated to a suitable temperature. Mechanical disturbances caused by boiling (ebullition) are desirable.[73] Benzene is an effective hydrogen acceptor for liquid-phase dehydrogenation.[62,64] Platinum and palladium catalysts have been widely used for the preparation of alkylbenzenes from cyclohexanes[74] and alkylnaphthalenes from di-, tetra-, octa-, and deca-hydro derivatives.[58,59,65,67,251] Nickel catalysts have also been used.[63] Thiophene or diphenyl sulfide are necessary promoters for nickel catalysts.[62] A comparison of platinum and nickel catalysts on various supports has been made; the most active is nickel on chromium oxide.[64] Ten metallic oxide catalysts have been studied in the dehydrogenation of acenaphthene to acenaphthylene (90%).[68] The use of steam as a diluent in the acenaphthene vapor is beneficial. Chromia-alumina catalysts at 450–470° have proved valuable in the preparation of large quantities of pure di- and tri-alkylbenzenes from the corresponding cyclohexenes.[54] At higher temperatures (600–650°) alkylbenzenes are dehydrogenated to styrenes[53] and polynuclear hydrocarbons[244] over catalysts of this type.

Among the better non-catalytic procedures are dehydrogenations by sulfur or selenium. The hydrogen is removed as hydrogen sulfide or hydrogen selenide. Dehydrogenation by heating a mixture of the alicyclic hydrocarbon and sulfur to 210–270° is described for 1-phenylnaphthalene (94%)[57] and 2-ethylbiphenyl (42%).[55] Sulfur dehydrogenation is superior to dehydrogenation over a palladium catalyst for the conversion of 1,3-dimethyltetralin to 1,3-dimethylnaphthalene (98%).[65] Isoamyl disulfide dehydrogenates tetralin to naphthalene at 250–260°.[66] Higher temperatures (300–350°) are required when selenium is used in place of sulfur. Phenanthrene has been synthesized from 3,4-dihydronaphthalene-1,2-dicarboxylic anhydride and butadiene by a Diels-Alder reaction followed by decarboxylation and finally dehydrogenation of the resulting hydrophenanthrenes by selenium.[69]

Low-temperature-dehydrogenation techniques have been described. Biphenyl and terphenyl compounds have been made by dehydrogenations with chloroanil in refluxing xylene.[56] Bromination-dehydrobromination with N-bromosuccinimide in boiling carbon tetrachloride has been used successfully to make naphthalene, anthracene, and phenanthrene.[61] Cyclic nuclei containing hydroxyl, alkoxyl, keto, carboxyl, and ester groups have been dehydrogenated.[63,64,70,71,73] Secondary and tertiary hydroxyl groups are often eliminated as water.[245,246] Cyclic ketones are converted to phenols (method 108).

3. Reduction of Aldehydes and Ketones

$$RCOR' \xrightarrow{(H)} RCH_2R'$$

Three common procedures are available for the transformation of aldehydes and ketones to hydrocarbons: (1) reduction by zinc and hydrochloric acid (Clemmensen), (2) reduction by hydrazine in the presence of a base (Wolff-Kishner), and (3) catalytic hydrogenation. In view of the complicated mixtures obtained by the polyalkylation of benzene by the Friedel-Crafts reaction (method 1), reduction of alkyl aryl ketones is the most reliable method for the preparation of di- and poly-alkylbenzenes.

The Clemmensen reduction is carried out by refluxing the carbonyl compound for a long period of time with a large excess of amalgamated zinc and hydrochloric acid. Solvents both miscible and immiscible with the aqueous phase have been used to advantage. Many of the yields recorded in Table 1 have been obtained by Clemmensen's original procedure[136] and very likely could be improved by the use of solvents.[154] The yields of paraffins and alicyclic hydrocarbons are poor, and the products are frequently contaminated with olefins.[141,144,135,137] Acyl derivatives of benzene,[151,247] toluene,[150] naphthalene,[154,155] tetralin,[59] and polyalkylated aromatic hydrocarbons are reduced in somewhat better yields (40-90%). Benzophenone and p-halo derivatives undergo bimolecular reduction to pinacols, whereas the p-methyl and p-hydroxy derivatives are reduced normally to the corresponding diarylmethanes.[12] The method has been used extensively in the preparation of polynuclear hydrocarbons by reduction of cyclic ketones obtained by internal Friedel-Crafts reactions of γ-arylbutyryl chlorides.[58,152] A review of the Clemmensen reduction with 476 references has been published.[135]

It has been known for some time that hydrazones or semicarbazones of aldehydes and ketones are decomposed by alkali to give nitrogen gas and hydrocarbons corresponding to the carbonyl compounds.

$$RR'C{=\!=}NNH_2 \xrightarrow{KOH} RCH_2R' + N_2$$

Several modified procedures have been described whereby excellent yields of paraffins, alkylbenzenes, and alicyclic hydrocarbons have been obtained.[138–140,158] In one improved procedure the carbonyl compound is merely refluxed with 85% aqueous hydrazine hydrate and potassium hydroxide in triethylene glycol solution, distilling excess water and hydrazine hydrate to a temperature of 180–200°.[138] The reaction has been reviewed.[256]

Catalytic hydrogenation of alkyl aryl ketones and diaryl ketones to hydrocarbons is most convenient provided that high-pressure apparatus is available. Copper-alumina and copper-chromium oxide catalysts have been used. At 100–130° alcohols are formed, but at 180–250° excellent yields of the corresponding hydrocarbons are obtained.[145–149]

Various groups on the aromatic nucleus including halo,[135,157,159] hydroxyl,[135,157,160] alkoxyl,[135] and amino[157] groups are stable during reduction of the carbonyl group by one or more of the above procedures. The Clemmensen reduction of keto acids is treated in method 269.

4. Reduction of the Aromatic Nucleus

Benzene and alkylbenzenes are quantitatively converted to cyclohexanes by catalytic hydrogenation. Modern procedures employ liquid-phase hydrogenation over nickel catalysts at 100–200°[76,78,81] or over platinum catalysts at room temperature.[75,81] Nickel catalysts are poisoned by traces of thiophene and water.[79] Small quantities of hydrogen halide increase the effectiveness of platinum catalysts.[241] Isomerization occurs during the reduction of benzene over nickel at 170°; the cyclohexane formed is probably contaminated with methylcyclopentane.[77] Partial reduction of benzene to 1,4-dihydrobenzene is accomplished by sodium in liquid ammonia at −45°.[80]

Naphthalene is reduced to 1,4-dihydronaphthalene by sodium and alcohol.[83] Isomerization of this product to 3,4-dihydronaphthalene occurs with sodamide in liquid ammonia. Tetrahydronaphthalene (tetralin) is formed from naphthalene by sodium in amyl alcohol or by reduction with nickel-aluminum alloy and aqueous alkali.[92] Catalytic hydrogenation of naphthalene can be stopped at the tetralin stage over copper chromite,[63] Raney nickel,[63] or alkali metal[84] catalysts. cis-Decahydronaphthalene is produced by high-pressure hydrogenation of tetralin over Adams catalyst, whereas a mixture of cis- and trans-decalins is obtained from naphthalene under the same conditions.[75,85]

Anthracene and phenanthrene may be partly or completely reduced by the above procedures. Sodium in either amyl alcohol[88] or ammonia[90] converts anthracene to its 9,10-dihydro derivative. Catalytic hydrogenation over copper chromite catalyst can be stopped at the dihydro or tetrahydro stages.[88] Octahydroanthracene is formed over nickel catalysts.[87] Copper chromite catalyst is best for the preparation of 9,10-dihydrophenanthrene.[86,89] Raney nickel is preferred for further reduction to the tetrahydro, octahydro, and dodecahydro derivatives.[86,91]

Reductions of aromatic nuclei containing hydroxyl (method 86), carboxyl (method 270), ester (method 304), and amino (method 430) groups are discussed elsewhere. Hydrogenation of 2-methoxynaphthalene over Raney nickel occurs in the ring containing the methoxyl group.[93]

5. Reduction of Olefinic Compounds

$$RCH = CHR + H_2 \xrightarrow{\text{Pt or Ni}} RCH_2CH_2R$$

Most paraffin hydrocarbons are best prepared by catalytic hydrogenation of olefins. The preparation of catalysts and the procedure for hydrogenation are well described.[81] Platinum oxide catalyst effects hydrogenation at room temperature and low pressure.[194,195] Nickel-on-kieselguhr[192,196] or Raney nickel catalysts are less expensive but require high-pressure equipment. Temperatures required for hydrogenation with these catalysts vary from 25° to 250°. In general the yields are quantitative, although a second hydrogenation over fresh catalyst is sometimes required to remove last traces of olefin. Simultaneous dehydration and hydrogenation of alcohols over activated alumina and nickel oxide has been described[194] (method 6).

This reaction is valuable for the preparation of certain pure alkylbenzenes which cannot be made by direct alkylation (method 1). Thus, p-s-butyltoluene is obtained from p-bromotoluene and methyl ethyl ketone via the Grignard reagent, tertiary carbinol, and olefin.[147] Other examples of the introduction of an alkyl group into the benzene ring by this procedure include the preparations of various alkylbiphenyls[249] and alkylbromobenzenes.[202] In the selective hydrogenation of the double bond of 11-phenyl-10-heneicosene, it is necessary to purify the olefin by passage through silica gel and to use a very active Raney nickel catalyst.[198]

Studies have been made on the influence of various groups on the rate of hydrogenation of the double bond.[197] Reductions of olefinic alcohols (method 85), olefinic aldehydes (method 161), olefinic ketones (method 196), olefinic acids (method 267), olefinic esters (method 303), olefinic cyanides (method 394), and olefinic amines (method 460) are treated separately.

6. Reduction of Alcohols and Phenols

$$(CH_3)_2CHC(CH_3)_2CH_2OH \xrightarrow[\text{Catalyst}]{H_2} (CH_3)_2CHC(CH_3)_3$$

This method shows much promise for the direct conversion of alcohols to hydrocarbons. In the above example, triptane is prepared without rearrangement from an alcohol which would undergo carbon-skeleton change by the ordinary dehydration-hydrogenation route (method 19). The hydrogenolysis is effected at 300° over a cobalt-on-alumina catalyst.[177] Similar reductions have been carried out over vanadium pentoxide-aluminum oxide catalyst.[179] Hydrogenation over nickel catalysts converts straight-chain primary alcohols to paraffins having one less carbon atom.[178]

Hydroxyl groups *alpha* to the aromatic nucleus are reduced by sodium in liquid ammonia[181] or by catalytic hydrogenation as in the reduction of 2,3-dimethylbenzyl alcohol to hemimellitene (92%).[174] 6-Isopropyltetralin is prepared in a similar manner from the corresponding tertiary carbinol.[59] Phosphorus and iodine have been used for reduction of alkylarylcarbinols and diarylcarbinols containing stable nuclear halogen atoms.[185,202]

The reduction of phenols by dry distillation with zinc dust is illustrated by the conversion of 9-phenanthrol to phenanthrene (72%).[182] The reaction is seldom of preparative value.

7. Reduction of Halides

$$RX \xrightarrow{(H)} RH$$

Most reducing agents which yield nascent hydrogen have been used to effect elimination of halogen from organic halides. Zinc is probably the most common metal employed. It is used with acetic acid saturated with hydrogen chloride in the reduction of cetyl iodide,[187] with hydrogen chloride alone in the reduction of tertiary aliphatic iodides,[104] and with aqueous sodium hydroxide for the preparation of durene from the corresponding chloromethyl compound.[184] 5-Chloromethylindane is reduced catalytically over palladium to 5-methylindane (90%).[191] Lithium aluminum hydride readily reduces alkyl bromides in refluxing tetrahydrofuran solution.[257]

$$4RX + LiAlH_4 \rightarrow 4RH + LiAlX_4$$

Lithium hydride can be substituted for most of the lithium aluminum hydride.[186] Aryl halogen atoms have been successfully removed in certain cases by magnesium and methanol,[189] sodium and amyl alcohol,[188] and nickel-aluminum alloy in aqueous alkali.[190]

8. Hydrolysis of Organometallic Compounds

$$RMgX \xrightarrow[H^+]{H_2O} RH$$

This method furnishes an indirect route for the conversion of an organic halide to a hydrocarbon. The reaction is general, and the yields of hydrocarbons are usually excellent. The chloromethylation of naphthalene followed by the formation and hydrolysis of 1-naphthylcarbinylmagnesium chloride gives 1-methylnaphthalene (80%).[201] An aryl bromine atom is removed in the preparation of p-cymene (73%).[199] The Grignard reagent is prepared in dibutyl ether when the products are low-boiling hydrocarbons such as n-pentane[200] or cyclobutane.[100] n-Butyl alcohol has been used to decompose the Grignard reagent in the case of cyclobutane. n-Octane prepared from n-octyl bromide by this procedure contains some octene formed by elimination of hydrogen bromide from the halide during the formation of the Grignard reagent. Pure n-octane may be obtained by hydrogenation of the crude product.

9. Coupling of Organometallic Compounds with Halides

$$R_3CX + R'M \rightarrow R_3CR' + MX$$

This reaction is valuable in the preparation of certain monoalkyl aromatic hydrocarbons and aliphatic hydrocarbons having quaternary carbon atoms. The organometallic reagents most frequently used are Grignard reagents, zinc alkyls, and alkali-metal alkyls.

Primary Grignard reagents couple with tertiary alkyl halides in low yields (30–50%).[97] This reaction represents the best laboratory preparation for highly branched hydrocarbons such as neopentane,[99] neohexane,[103] and hexamethylethane.[101] The yields of paraffins are no better when dialkylzinc compounds are substituted for the Grignard reagents.[95,98,105] Dimethylzinc is superior to methylmagnesium iodide, however, for the conversion of 1-chloro-1,3-dimethylcyclopentane to 1,1,3-trimethylcyclopentane (35%).[94] Aryl Grignard reagents such as 9-anthryl- and 9-phenanthryl-magnesium bromides couple in moderate yields with primary alkyl halides to give the corresponding 9-alkyl derivatives.[90,109,111] Benzyl halides are extremely active in the coupling reaction. Benzyl chloride[117] and α-phenylethyl chloride[107] are readily converted to the corresponding Grignard reagents which couple with the original halide in each case to give the symmetrical diphenylethane. Highly substituted benzenes are made from chloromethylpolyalkylbenzenes by this method. Alkyl groups in the ortho position to the chloromethyl radical do not hinder the coupling.[119]

The Wurtz or Wurtz-Fittig synthesis is usually thought of as a coupling reaction of two molecules of a halide or different halides by metallic sodium. In the liquid phase, as the reaction is generally carried out, alkylsodium compounds are intermediates and the coupling stage or second step is comparable to the reactions discussed above.[110]

$$RX + 2Na \rightarrow RNa + NaX$$
$$RX + RNa \rightarrow RR + NaX$$

Olefins and paraffins corresponding to the alkyl halide are formed as by-products by dehydrohalogenation of the halide by the basic organosodium compounds.[110,123] The synthesis has little value as a preparative method and has been used infrequently. The factors influencing the yield of n-octane from n-butyl bromide have been studied.[102] Although preparations of several alkylbenzenes from mixtures of alkyl halides and phenyl bromide are described,[106,114,247] good yields of pure products are difficult to obtain.[8] The reaction has been used with some success to prepare α,ω-diphenylparaffins from α,ω-dibromides, phenyl bromide, and sodium.[118] With ethylene bromide, only ethylene and biphenyl are formed. Arylalkali compounds have been used in the preparation of polyphenylparaffins. Potassium triphenylmethide reacts with methyl iodide to give 1,1,1-triphenylethane (94%).[113] The formation of tetraphenylmethane from this potassium alkyl and phenyl chloride is catalyzed by alkali amides.[112]

$$(C_6H_5)_3CK + C_6H_5Cl \xrightarrow{KNH_2} (C_6H_5)_4C + KCl$$

Halogen-metal interconversion sometimes occurs prior to the coupling reaction.[258] Thus, phenyllithium and benzyl bromide react to give bromobenzene and bibenzyl rather than diphenylmethane.[115]

The action of metals on 1,3-dihalides is an important method of ring closure for cyclopropanes. Cyclopropane is made by the action of zinc dust at 125° on an acetamide solution of 1,3-dichloropropane. A small amount of sodium iodide is used as a catalyst, and sodium carbonate is added to regenerate iodide ions from the precipitated zinc iodide.[134] Zinc dust in aqueous ethanol is employed in the preparation of 1,1-dialkylcyclopropanes from the corresponding 1,3-dibromides[96] and spiropentane from pentaerythrityl tetrabromide.[133]

The closing of a six-membered ring by this process is possible when favored by structural rigidity of the molecule as in the preparation of 9,10-dihydrophenanthrene from phenyllithium and 2,2′-di-(bromomethyl)-biphenyl.[120]

Under the proper conditions, two molecules of 1,6-dibromohexane are coupled by magnesium to give 1,12-dibromododecane.[121]

Few functional groups are stable during the above coupling reactions. Ether linkages are occasional exceptions.[110,122]

10. Action of Organometallic Compounds on Alkyl Sulfates and Sulfonates

$$RMgX + R'_2SO_4 \rightarrow RR' + R'(MgX)SO_4$$

Dimethyl and diethyl sulfates have been widely employed in the synthesis of alkylbenzenes[126,192] and alkylnaphthalenes[127,131] from aryl- and benzyl-type organometallic reagents. The final methyl groups of isodurene[125] and pseudocumene[132] are introduced in this manner. The reaction is superior to the Wurtz synthesis (method 9) for the preparation of o- and p-diethylbenzenes.[108] n-Propylbenzene obtained from benzylmagnesium chloride and diethyl sulfate[130] is contaminated with a "rearranged" product, p-ethyltoluene.[129]

Alkyl esters of arylsulfonic acids react similarly with Grignard reagents to give hydrocarbons.[128] Some of the arylsulfonic ester is converted to an alkyl halide by a simultaneous reaction.

$$RMgX + ArSO_3R' \rightarrow RR' + ArSO_3MgX$$
$$ArSO_3MgX + ArSO_3R' \rightarrow R'X + (ArSO_3)_2 Mg$$

Accordingly, the yield of hydrocarbon is increased when two moles of ester are used for each mole of organometallic compound. Alkyl esters of p-toluenesulfonic acid are generally employed. The yield of n-amylbenzene from benzylmagnesium chloride and n-butyl p-toluenesulfonate is 59%.[124] For the preparation of alkylbenzenes, the phenyl group must be a part of the Grignard reagent since aryl esters of sulfonic acids give sulfones and phenols by this reaction.

11. Coupling of Aryl Halides

$$2ArMgX + CuX_2 \rightarrow Ar-Ar + 2MgX_2 + Cu$$

The coupling of two aryl radicals is effected by treating an arylmagnesium halide with an equimolar quantity of cupric chloride,[120,164] silver bromide,[162] or other metallic halide.[172] Certain halides, e.g., cobalt and nickel chlorides, are required in catalytic amounts only, provided that a quantity of an organic bromide equivalent to the Grignard reagent is present. In these reactions, organocobalt compounds are formed which decompose to biaryls, and the bromide serves to regenerate the catalyst.[163]

$$2ArCoCl \rightarrow Ar-Ar + 2CoCl\cdot$$
$$CoCl\cdot + RBr \rightarrow CoClBr + R\cdot$$

The fate of the free radical, R·, depends upon its nature. It is frequently stabilized by coupling, disproportionation, or reaction with the solvent.

A related reaction is the coupling of two molecules of aryl halide by metallic copper at temperatures above $100°$ (Ullmann). Activated copper bronze or freshly precipitated copper is used. The order of activity of the aryl halides is I > Br > Cl. Both symmetrically and unsymmetrically substituted biaryls may be prepared in fair yields. An excellent review of the literature to 1945 has been made. Most functional groups do not interfere; hydroxyl, carboxyl, amino, and acetamino groups are exceptions.[166]

Additional procedures which produce biaryls from aryl halides include catalytic hydrogenation,[167] the action of the binary mixture magnesium-magnesium iodide,[165] and the use of powdered iron in hydroxylated media.[161]

12. Biaryls by Coupling of Diazo Compounds with Aromatic Nuclei

$$ArN_2^+X^- + Ar'H + NaOH \rightarrow ArAr' + N_2 + NaX + H_2O$$

Biaryls are produced in low yields by several related coupling reactions. When benzenediazonium chloride is treated with aqueous sodium hydroxide in the presence of benzene, nitrogen is eliminated and biphenyl is formed in 22% yield.[215] Better results are sometimes obtained when the sodium hydroxide is replaced by sodium acetate[221] or when stabilized diazonium salts are employed.[216] In the former modification the aryldiazoacetate, $ArN=NOCOCH_3$, is an intermediate product. The tautomeric forms of the aryldiazoacetates are N-nitrosoamides, $ArN(NO)COCH_3$, which are obtained by the action of nitrous fumes or nitrosyl chloride on acetyl derivatives of arylamines. The nitroso compounds couple in a similar manner with aromatic compounds to produce biaryls.[217,222]

$$ArN(NO)COCH_3 + Ar'H \longrightarrow ArAr' + N_2 + CH_3CO_2H$$

The two coupling reactions appear to have a common free-radical intermediate. Functional groups already in the aromatic compound, Ar'H, orient *ortho-para* regardless of their nature. The reactions are most valuable for the preparation of biaryls of unequivocal structure when the hydrocarbon, Ar'H, is unsubstituted. Good directions are given for the synthesis of *p*-bromobiphenyl (35%),[212] and the literature of the reaction has been reviewed.[211] Among the hydrocarbons prepared in this way are α- and β-phenylnaphthalenes,[216,217] *o*-, *m*-, and *p*-methylbiphenyls[214] and *m*- and *p*-terphenyls.[220,222] Thiophene and pyridine nuclei also have been arylated.[211,219]

A related reaction for the production of symmetrical biaryls in low yields involves reduction of the diazonium salt with various metals, metallic ions, or simple organic compounds.[213,218]

Intramolecular arylation is an important step in the Pschorr synthesis of phenanthrene from *cis-o*-aminostilbene.[223]

13. Decarboxylation of Carboxylic Acids

$$ArCO_2H \xrightarrow[\text{Quinoline}]{Cu} ArH + CO_2$$

Several polynuclear aromatic hydrocarbons may be synthesized by procedures involving decarboxylation.[69,237] The dry distillation of 3-phenanthrylacetic acid and powdered soda lime furnishes the best method of synthesis of 3-methylphenanthrene (84%).[235] Heating aryl carboxylic acids with copper powder or copper oxide in quinoline or quinaldine is also an effective method of decarboxylation.[238,239]

The decarboxylation of simple aliphatic acids by fusion of their sodium salts with sodium hydroxide does not give pure hydrocarbons.[234] By heating the barium salts of 1-phenylcycloalkane-1-carboxylic acids with dry sodium methoxide, 1-phenylcycloalkanes are obtained in 6–64% yields, the yield increasing with the size of the alicyclic ring.[236] The coupling of the organic radicals sometimes occurs during the electrolysis of alkali salts of carboxylic acids (Kolbe, cf. method 317).[240,250]

$$2RCO_2^- \rightarrow R-R + 2CO_2 + 2e$$

However, the reaction is not general.

14. Replacement of the Diazonium Group by Hydrogen

$$ArN_2^+X^- + H_3PO_2 + H_2O \rightarrow ArH + H_3PO_3 + HX + N_2$$

The successful removal of the diazonium group from the aromatic nucleus is an important step in many indirect syntheses of aromatic compounds which cannot be made by direct substitution reactions. Substituents are introduced into the nucleus under the directive influence of an acetamido or ammonium grouping. The former orients to the *ortho* and *para* positions, whereas the latter is strongly *meta* directing. Both groups are readily formed from and reconverted to the amino group. Since diazotization of most arylamines can be effected in excellent yield, there remains the problem of removal of the diazonium group from the ring.

The classical reagent for this reduction is ethyl alcohol, which is oxidized to acetaldehyde in the reaction. This reagent is unsatisfactory for the preparation of hydrocarbons; a simultaneous reaction occurs to give ethyl aryl ethers.

$$ArN_2^+X^- + C_2H_5OH \rightarrow ArOC_2H_5 + N_2 + HX$$

Satisfactory procedures are described, however, for the deamination when halo, nitro, or carboxyl groups are on the nucleus.[225] Metals or metallic oxides are sometimes added as catalysts.[228,230]

The best general reagent for the reductive elimination of the diazonium group is hypophosphorus acid.[224,227] Reduction proceeds readily at 0–5° with an aqueous solution of the reagent. The yields of hydrocarbons are in the range of 60–85%. Hydrochloric acid is recommended for the diazotization except in certain cases in which nuclear halogenation occurs as a side reaction when this acid is used.

Several other reducing agents have been employed in this reaction. Alkaline formaldehyde converts aromatic diazonium salts to the corresponding hydrocarbons in 60–80% yields.[226] The preparation of *p*-xylene from *p*-xylidene by reduction of the corresponding diazonium chloride by sodium stannite is described in 67% over-all yield.[229] These procedures involving alkaline media suffer from the danger of hydrolytic cleavage of halo, nitro, alkoxyl, and sulfonic acid groups if these substituents are present on the aromatic nucleus.[224]

Aromatic amino groups are selectively diazotized below a pH of 3 in the presence of aliphatic amino groups. Reduction of the aminodiazonium salt by hypophosphorus acid then completes the selective removal of the aryl amino group.[231] The amino group can also be removed from an aromatic ring containing a dimethylamino group.[232]

15. Replacement of the Sulfonic Acid Group by Hydrogen

$$ArSO_3H + H_2O \overset{H^+}{\rightleftharpoons} ArH + H_2SO_4$$

Sulfonation of the aromatic nucleus (method 540) is a reversible reaction. The removal of a sulfonic acid group is important in the preparation of alkylated benzenes by the Jacobsen reaction (method 16).[168] Orthodisubstituted benzenes are sometimes prepared by using the sulfonic acid group to block the *para* position.[233] The removal of the sulfonic acid group is usually effected by heating the arylsulfonic acid with aqueous sulfuric acid.

16. Rearrangements of Polyalkylarylsulfonic Acids (Jacobsen)

The formation of prehnitene from durene (above) illustrates the general tendency of alkyl groups to rearrange to vicinal orientation when polymethyl- and polyethyl-benzenes are heated with concentrated sulfuric acid. Intermolecular migration also occurs leading to 1,2,4-trimethyl-, pentamethyl-, and hexamethyl-benzenes. *sym*-Octahydroanthracene rearranges to *sym*-octahydrophenanthrene.[173] To date the reaction is important for the syntheses of vicinal derivatives of benzene where only methyl, ethyl, and halo groups are rearranged.[170,171] Detailed reviews of the reaction have been made[168] as well as a study of its extension to the rearrangement of 6,7-dialkyltetralins.[59]

17. Cyclodehydration of Aromatic Alcohols and Ketones

Certain phenylated alcohols are dehydrated with ring closure to alkyl-tetralins. Considerable variation in the structure of the reacting alcohols is possible. Thus, 1-methyltetralin is formed from 2-, 3-, 4-, or 5-hydroxy-1-phenylpentane as well as from 5-phenyl-1-pentene.[206] Branching on the third carbon from the phenyl group leads partly to indane formation (five-membered ring closure). Phosphorus pentoxide is used for the cyclode-hydration of 2-β-phenylethylcyclohexanol and related alcohols to as-octahydrophenanthrenes. An angular methyl group has been introduced into the phenanthrene nucleus at position 12 by this reaction.[210]

Many completely aromatic polynuclear hydrocarbons are readily formed by cyclization of aryl-substituted aldehydes, ketones, or related com-pounds. The simplest case is the formation of naphthalene by refluxing β-styrylacetaldehyde, $C_6H_5CH=CHCH_2CHO$, with hydrobromic acid-acetic acid mixture.[204] The ring closure has found extensive use in the synthesis of 9-alkyl- and 9-aryl-anthracenes and phenanthrenes.[207,209]

Cyclodehydration of diaryl ketones through an *ortho* methyl or methylene group by pyrolysis at 400-450° gives low yields of certain substituted anthracenes and their benzologs (Elbs reaction).[208]

18. 9-Alkylfluorenes by Alkylation of 9-Formylfluorene [254]

TABLE 1. HYDROCARBONS 17

TABLE 1. PARAFFINIC, NAPHTHENIC, AND AROMATIC HYDROCARBONS

C_n	Compound	Method	Yield (%)	Chapter[ref.]	B.p./mm., n_D^t, (M.p.), Deriv.
		Aliphatic Hydrocarbons			
C_1	Methane	7	100	1[186]	-161*
C_5	n-Pentane	8	53	1[200]	36, 1.3576*
	Tetramethylmethane (neopentane)	9	50	1[99]	9/760
C_6	n-Hexane	5	50 †	1[192]	69/760, 1.3748
	2-Methylpentane	5	....	1[194]	60, 1.3718
	2,2-Dimethylbutane (neohexane)	5	....	1[194]	50, 1.3692
		9	45	1[95]	50, 1.3675
		9	39	1[103]	50/740, 1.3688
	2,3-Dimethylbutane	5	....	1[194]	58, 1.3750
C_7	n-Heptane	3	54	1[140]	98, 1.3877
		3	72	1[136]	96/741
		6	64	1[178]	96, 1.3854[25]
		7	92	1[186]	
	2-Methylhexane	5	65 †	1[192]	90/760, 1.3850
		7	24	1[104]	90/760, 1.3851
	3-Methylhexane	5	50 †	1[192]	92/760, 1.3888
	2,2-Dimethylpentane	9	40	1[95]	81, 1.3828
		9	20	1[97]	79/760, 1.3822
		5	40 †	1[192]	79/760, 1.3822
	3,3-Dimethylpentane	9	51	1[95]	87, 1.3908
		9	31	1[97]	86/760, 1.3910
	3-Ethylpentane	5	60 †	1[192]	93/760, 1.3938
	2,2,3-Trimethylbutane (triptane)	6	56	1[177]	82, 1.3895 *
C_8	n-Octane	3	75	1[139]	125, 1.401[21]
		5	60 †	1[192]	126/760, 1.3975
		7	96	1[186]	125, 1.3975
		9	70	1[102]	125, 1.3961
	2,2-Dimethylhexane	9	36	1[95]	107, 1.3931
	3,3-Dimethylhexane	9	24	1[95]	112, 1.3998
	2,3,3-Trimethylpentane	3	72	1[140]	113, 1.4074
	3-Methyl-3-ethylpentane	9	31	1[98]	118/760, 1.4081
	Hexamethylethane	9	38	1[101]	106/760, (101)
C_9	2,4-Dimethylheptane	3	36	1[140]	80, 1.3815
C_{16}	n-Hexadecane	7	85	1[187]	157/14, (17)
C_{20}	n-Eicosane	3	73	1[158]	153/1.8, (37.5)
C_{21}	n-Heneicosane	3	30	1[137]	172/3, (41)
		Alicyclic Hydrocarbons			
C_3	Cyclopropane	9	80	1[134]	-33
C_4	Cyclobutane	8	83	1[100]	11/760

For explanations and symbols see pages xi–xii.

TABLE 1. (*continued*)

C_n	Compound	Method	Yield (%)	Chapter[ref.]	B.p./mm., n_D^t, (M.p.), Deriv.
		Alicyclic Hydrocarbons (*continued*)			
C_5	Cyclopentane	3	50	1[141]	51, 1.4064*
	1,1-Dimethylcyclopropane	9	96	1[96]	21/760, 1.3668
	Ethylcyclopropane	3	60	1[140]	36, 1.3784
		3	72	1[142]	36, 1.3786
	Spiropentane	9	26	1[133]	39/760, 1.4122
C_6	Cyclohexane	3	80	1[138]	81, 1.4245[25]
		4	95	1[75]	79/752, 1.4242
		4	85	1[77]	1.4264
	Methylcyclopentane	3	60	1[141]	72*, 1.4098*
C_7	Methylcyclohexane	3	60	1[144]	100/750, 1.4232
		4	92	1[75]	100/742, 1.4198
	1,3-Dimethylcyclopentane	5	60 †	1[192]	91/760, 1.4095
	Ethylcyclopentane	5	75	1[195]	104/760, 1.4196
	1,1-Diethylcyclopropane	9	92	1[96]	89/760, 1.4042
C_8	Ethylcyclohexane	4	93	1[78]	131/740, 1.4332*
	cis- and trans-1,3-Dimethylcyclohexanes	4	92	1[75]	119/747, 1.4230[25]
	1,1,3-Trimethylcyclopentane	9	35	1[94]	105/760, 1.4109
C_9	1,3,5-Trimethylcyclohexane	4	92	1[82]	137/740
	1-Ethyl-1-butylcyclopropane	9	94	1[96]	140/760, 1.4183
C_{10}	Bicyclopentyl	5	62	1[193]	190/762, 1.4642
	cis-Decahydronaphthalene (cis-decalin)	4	91	1[75]	195*, 1.4811*
	trans-Decahydronaphthalene	....	100	1[252]	186*, 1.4697*
C_{12}	Bicyclohexyl (cyclohexylcyclohexane)	4	95	1[78]	119/20, 1.4795*
C_{14}	Tetradecahydrophenanthrene	4	89	1[86]	148/20, 1.5003[25]
C_{19}	Tricyclohexylmethane	4	90	1[82]	165/3, (59)
		Aromatic Hydrocarbons			
C_6	Benzene	14	60	1[226]	80*, 1.5012*
C_7	Toluene	1	58	1[15]	111/760, 1.4968*
		3	46	1[136]	111
		7	98	1[186]	
		13	92	1[238]	111, 1.4978[22]
		14	80	1[226]	

TABLE 1. HYDROCARBONS 19

TABLE 1. (*continued*)

C_n	Compound	Method	Yield (%)	Chapter ref.	B.p./mm., n_D^t, (M.p.), Deriv.
		Aromatic Hydrocarbons (*continued*)			
C_8	Ethylbenzene	1	50	1^{32}	135
		1	76	1^{38}	133/732, 1.4953
		3	83	1^{145}	
		3	38	1^{151}	136/765, 1.4960
	o-Xylene	19	61	1^{183}	142, 1.5054*, 264Te
	m-Xylene	2	88	1^{54}	139/760, 1.4972
	p-Xylene	14	67	1^{229}	138/760, (13)
C_9	n-Propylbenzene	1	25	1^{35}	157/760, 1.4921
		3	82	1^{138}	160–163, 1.4908^{25}
		10	75	1^{130}	155–160, 1.4919*
	Isopropylbenzene	1	71	1^{11}	151/759, 1.4913*
		1	75	1^{24}	151
		1	83	1^{38}	151/740, 1.4918
		1	91	1^{45}	153, 1.4930
	Phenylcyclopropane	13	6	1^{236}	80/37, 1.5285
	o-Ethyltoluene	19	71	1^{183}	161/738, 1.5010^{21}
	m-Ethyltoluene	2	82	1^{54}	161/760, 1.4965
	p-Ethyltoluene	3	80	1^{150}	161/748
		3	91	1^{145}	
		3	95	1^{148}	162, 1.4943
	1,2,3-Trimethylbenzene (hemimellitene)	6	92	1^{174}	172/741, 1.5085^{31}
		2	79	1^{54}	176/760, 1.5138
	1,2,4-Trimethylbenzene	10	37	1^{132}	68/22, 1.5048*
	1,3,5-Trimethylbenzene (mesitylene)	1	63	1^{25}	165, 1.4991*
		17	15	1^{203}	163–167
C_{10}	n-Butylbenzene	3	74	1^{145}	183*, 1.4880*
		5	25 †	1^{192}	183/760, 1.4900
		9	70	1^{106}	181/750
	Isobutylbenzene	5	35 †	1^{192}	173/760, 1.4865
	s-Butylbenzene	1	81	1^{11}	171/759, 1.4900*
	t-Butylbenzene	1	75	1^{38}	169/731, 1.4934
		1	70	1^{2}	169/740
		1	89	1^{45}	168, 1.4960
	Phenylcyclobutane	13	28	1^{236}	102/41, 1.5277
	p-Isopropyltoluene (p-cymene)	8	73	1^{199}	178/760, 1.4888^{25}
	o-Diethylbenzene	10	49	1^{108}	184/760, 1.5034
	m-Diethylbenzene	1	30	1^{49}	181, 1.4955
	p-Diethylbenzene	3	73	1^{146}	179
		10	58	1^{108}	184/760, 1.4950
	1,2,3,4-Tetramethyl-benzene (prehnitene)	16	88	1^{170}	98/25, 1.5201*

For explanations and symbols see pages xi–xii.

TABLE 1. (*continued*)

C_n	Compound	Method	Yield (%)	Chapter[ref.]	B.p./mm., n_D^t, (M.p.), Deriv.
		Aromatic Hydrocarbons (*continued*)			
C_{10}	1,2,3,5-Tetramethyl-benzene (isodurene)	10	60	1^{125}	86/18, 1.5134 *
	1,2,4,5-Tetramethyl-benzene (durene)	1	25	1^7	(80)
		7	45	1^{184}	(80)
	Naphthalene	2	53	1^{244}	(80), 150Pi *
		2	70	1^{66}	
		2	100	1^{64}	
		17	25	1^{204}	(81)
	1,4-Dihydronaphthalene	4	48	1^{83}	75/2, (25)
	1,2,3,4-Tetrahydronaph-thalene	4	81	1^{63}	78/10, 1.5395^{25}
		4	74	1^{92}	204
	2-Methylindene	19	55	1^{176}	98/24, 1.5646^{23}, 79Pi
	5-Methylindane	7	90	1^{191}	74/11, 1.5332
C_{11}	n-Amylbenzene	10	59	1^{124}	200, 1.4883 *
	Neopentylbenzene	3	58	1^{143}	186/755, 1.4850^{25}
	Phenylcyclopentane	13	57	1^{236}	117/37, 1.5309
	p-n-Butyltoluene	3	83	1^{145}	198 *, 1.4916 *
	p-Isobutyltoluene	3	74	1^{147}	192/752, 1.4888
	p-s-Butyltoluene	5	82 †	1^{147}	190, 1.4900
	Pentamethylbenzene	1		1^7	128/22, (53)
	1-Methylnaphthalene	2	62	1^{58}	141Pi
		2	95	1^{59}	95/5, 1.6037, 142Pi
		8	80	1^{201}	239, 1.6140^{25}, 141Pi
		10	51	1^{131}	240
	2-Methylnaphthalene	2	91	1^{60}	(38), 116Pi
		3	36	1^{155}	240, (37), 115Pi
	1-Methyltetralin	17	60	1^{206}	219
	6-Methyltetralin	4	94	1^{59}	102/12, 1.5358
	1-Ethylindane	5	80	1^{206}	212
C_{12}	n-Hexylbenzene	9	35	1^{114}	224–228, 1.4902 *
	Isohexylbenzene	9	50	1^{116}	93/13
	sym-Triethylbenzene	1	87	1^{25}	74/3, 1.4956^{18}
	Hexamethylbenzene	....	70	1^{253}	(165)
		1		1^7	(165) *
	Biphenyl	2	94	1^{62}	
		11	86	1^{163}	145/22, (71) *
		12	22	1^{215}	(71)
	Phenylcyclohexane	1	68	1^4	115/15
		13	64	1^{236}	128/30, 1.5329
	1-Ethylnaphthalene	10	55	1^{127}	248/742, 1.6089 *, 99Pi *
	2-Ethylnaphthalene	2	94	1^{60}	1.6028^{15}, 77Pi
		3	85	1^{153}	101/2

TABLE 1. HYDROCARBONS 21

TABLE 1. *(continued)*

C_n	Compound	Method	Yield (%)	Chapter[ref.]	B.p./mm., n_D^t, (M.p.), Deriv.
	Aromatic Hydrocarbons (continued)				
C_{12}	1-Ethyltetralin	17	65	1[206]	238, 1.5388 *
	6-Ethyltetralin	3	84	1[58]	121–125/20
	Acenaphthene	3	35	1[156]	279 *, (96)*, 162Pi *
	Acenaphthylene	2	93	1[68]	95/2, (93)*, 202Pi*
C_{13}	*n*-Heptylbenzene	9	62	1[114]	245, 1.4860 *
	Phenylcycloheptane	1	71	1[43]	108/7, 1.5280
	2-Methylbiphenyl	2	32	1[249]	255/760, 1.5914
		2	72	1[56]	133/27 *
	3-Methylbiphenyl	12	28	1[214]	268
	4-Methylbiphenyl	12	22	1[214]	268, (48)
	Diphenylmethane	1	78	1[9]	
		1	60	1[42]	(26)
		1	53	1[38]	(25)
		3	83	1[138]	149/29, 1.5752[25]
		3	100	1[149]	
	1-*n*-Propylnaphthalene	3	45	1[206]	276, 92Pi
	2-Isopropylnaphthalene	2	70	1[59]	128/10, 1.5730, 94Pi
	6-*n*-Propyltetralin	3	92	1[169]	124/10, 1.5253[29]
	6-Isopropyltetralin	6	86	1[59]	122/12, 1.5246[29]
C_{14}	1,1-Diphenylethane	1	45	1[52]	270, 1.562[25] *
		1	25	1[16]	148/15
	1,2-Diphenylethane	3	100	1[149]	
		5	95	1[197]	(53)
		9	82	1[117]	158/10, (51)
	2-Ethylbiphenyl	2	42	1[55]	94/3, 1.5808
		10	42	1[249]	266/760, 1.5805
	2,2′-Dimethylbiphenyl	11	75	1[163]	255, (18)
	4,4′-Dimethylbiphenyl	11	95	1[163]	(118) *
	t-Butylnaphthalene	1	41	1[13]	145/15, 1.5795
	9-Methylfluorene	18	75	1[254]	(45)
	Phenanthrene	2	86	1[69]	(97)
		6	72	1[182]	(100)
		19	100	1[175]	(97), 144Pi
	9,10-Dihydrophenanthrene	4	67	1[89]	154/8, (33)
		9	86	1[120]	174/17, (35)
	1,2,3,4-Tetrahydrophenanthrene	3	68	1[152]	(33), 111Pi
		4	40	1[86]	170/10
	s-Octahydrophenanthrene	4	85	1[91]	180/20, 1.5669[17]
		4	94	1[86]	173/20, (17), 1.5640[25]
	as-Octahydrophenanthrene	4	29	1[86]	150/13, 1.5528[25]
		17	85	1[210]	147/10

For explanations and symbols see pages xi–xii.

TABLE 1. (*continued*)

C_n	Compound	Method	Yield (%)	Chapter[ref.]	B.p./mm., n_D^t, (M.p.), Deriv.
		Aromatic Hydrocarbons (*continued*)			
C_{14}	9,10-Dihydroanthracene	4	76	1[90]	(105)
		4	84	1[88]	(109)
	1,2,3,4-Tetrahydro-anthracene	4	43	1[88]	(101), 117Pi*
	Octahydroanthracene	4	....	1[87]	(73)
C_{15}	1,2-Diphenylpropane	1	52	1[24]	109/2
	1,3-Diphenylpropane	9	69	1[118]	157/14
	2-*n*-Propylbiphenyl	5	86	1[249]	277/760, 1.5696
	9-Ethylfluorene	9	65	1[90]	(107)
	1-Methylphenanthrene	2	90	1[246]	(121), 136Pi
	3-Methylphenanthrene	13	84	1[235]	(62), 138Pi*
	4-Methylphenanthrene	2	85	1[245]	(50), 141Pi*
	9-Methylphenanthrene	9	73	1[109]	(91), 153Pi*
		17	50	1[209]	(91)
	9-Methylanthracene	3	78	1[157]	(81), 137Pi*
		9	41	1[111]	(79)
		17	80	1[185]	(81)
C_{16}	*dl*-2,3-Diphenylbutane	9	39	1[107]	155/14
	meso-2,3-Diphenylbutane	9	25	1[107]	(124)
	9-Isopropylfluorene	18	60	1[254]	(55)
	1-Phenylnaphthalene	2	67	1[56]	
		2	94	1[57]	135/2
		12	30	1[216]	
	2-Phenylnaphthalene	2	72	1[56]	
		12	25	1[217]	(102)
		17	80	1[205]	187/5, (104)
	1-Phenyl-3,4-dihydro-naphthalene	19	48	1[57]	135–140/2
	1-Ethylphenanthrene	2	90	1[246]	(64), 110Pi
	9-Ethylphenanthrene	17	54	1[209]	(63), 124Pi
	9-Ethylanthracene	17	69	1[185]	(59)
C_{17}	9-*n*-Butylfluorene	9	41	1[90]	(101)
	1-*n*-Propylphenanthrene	2	100	1[246]	(33), 101Pi
	9-*n*-Propylphenanthrene	9	47	1[90]	(59), 99Pi
		17	51	1[209]	(58), 99Pi
	1-Isopropylphenanthrene	2	65	1[246]	(88), 126Pi
C_{18}	*m*-Terphenyl (1,3-di-phenylbenzene)	12	32	1[220]	(89)
	p-Terphenyl (1,4-di-phenylbenzene)	2	47	1[56]	(211)
		12	60	1[222]	(211)
	1-*n*-Butylphenanthrene	2	59	1[246]	(42), 100Pi

TABLE 1. HYDROCARBONS   23

TABLE 1. *(continued)*

C_n	Compound	Method	Yield (%)	Chapter[ref.]	B.p./mm., n_D^t, (M.p.), Deriv.
		Aromatic Hydrocarbons *(continued)*			
C_{19}	Triphenylmethane	1	84	1[6]	(92)
C_{20}	1,1,1-Triphenylethane	9	94	1[113]	(95)
	1,1,2-Triphenylethane	5	95	1[197]	210, (55)
	1-Phenylphenanthrene	2	94	1[246]	(80), 118Pi
	9-Phenylanthracene	17	75	1[185]	(155)
		19	70	1[180]	(153)
C_{24}	Quaterphenyl	13	31	1[237]	(312)
C_{25}	Tetraphenylmethane	9	45	1[112]	(285)
C_{26}	1,1,2,2-Tetraphenyl-	5	95	1[197]	(209)
	ethane	9	90	1[115]	(208)

For explanations and symbols see pages xi–xii.

REFERENCES FOR CHAPTER 1

[1] Gilman and Meals, *J. Org. Chem.*, **8**, 126 (1943).

[2] Huston et al., *J. Org. Chem.*, **3**, 250 (1938), **6**, 252 (1941); cf. ref. 20.

[3] Nightingale, *Chem. Revs.*, **25**, 329 (1939).

[4] Corson and Ipatieff, *Org. Syntheses*, Coll. Vol. II, 151 (1943); Buu-Hoi and Cagniant, *Bull. soc. chim. France*, (5) **11**, 131 (1944); Neunhoeffer, *J. prakt. Chem.*, **133**, 105 (1932).

[5] Francis, *Chem. Revs.*, **42**, 107 (1948).

[6] Norris, *Org. Syntheses*, Coll. Vol. I, 548 (1941).

[7] Smith, *Org. Syntheses*, Coll. Vol. II, 248 (1943); cf. ref. 8.

[8] Birch et al., *J. Am. Chem. Soc.*, **71**, 1362 (1949).

[9] Pratt, Preston, and Draper, *J. Am. Chem. Soc.*, **72**, 1367 (1950).

[10] Epelberg and Lowy, *J. Am. Chem. Soc.*, **63**, 101 (1941).

[11] Huston and Kaye, *J. Am. Chem. Soc.*, **64**, 1576 (1942); cf. ref. 19.

[12] Bradlow and Vanderwerf, *J. Am. Chem. Soc.*, **69**, 1254 (1947).

[13] Bromby, Peters, and Rowe, *J. Chem. Soc.*, 144 (1943); Price and Ciskowski, *J. Am. Chem. Soc.*, **60**, 2499 (1938); Whitmore and James, *ibid.*, **65**, 2088 (1943).

[14] Hennion and Kurtz, *J. Am. Chem. Soc.*, **65**, 1001 (1943).

[15] Hardy, *J. Soc. Chem. Ind.*, **67**, 81 (1948).

[16] Spilker and Schade, *Ber.*, **65**, 1686 (1932).

[17] Price in *Organic Reactions*, Vol. 3, John Wiley & Sons, New York, 1946, pp. 1, 16–19.

[18] Francis, *Chem. Revs.*, **43**, 257 (1948).

[19] Toussaint and Hennion, *J. Am. Chem. Soc.*, **62**, 1145 (1940).

[20] Potts and Dodson, *J. Am. Chem. Soc.*, **61**, 2553 (1939).

[21] Norris et al., *J. Am. Chem. Soc.*, **61**, 2128, 2131 (1939).

[22] Simons, Archer, and Randall, *J. Am. Chem. Soc.*, **61**, 1821 (1939).

[23] Spiegler and Tinker, *J. Am. Chem. Soc.*, **61**, 1002 (1939).

[24] Calcott, Tinker, and Weinmayr, *J. Am. Chem. Soc.*, **61**, 1012 (1939).

[25] Norris and Rubinstein, *J. Am. Chem. Soc.*, **61**, 1163 (1939); Smith and Guss, *ibid.*, **62**, 2628 (1940); cf. Ref. 17.

[26] Price and Lund, *J. Am. Chem. Soc.*, **62**, 3105 (1940).

[27] Kane and Lowy, *J. Am. Chem. Soc.*, **58**, 2605 (1936).

[28] Ipatieff, Corson, and Pines, *J. Am. Chem. Soc.*, **58**, 920 (1936).

[29] Smith, *J. Am. Chem. Soc.*, **59**, 899 (1937).

[30] McKenna and Sowa, *J. Am. Chem. Soc.*, **59**, 1204 (1937).

[31] Ipatieff and Corson, *J. Am. Chem. Soc.*, **59**, 1417 (1937).

[32] Francis and Reid, *Ind. Eng. Chem.*, **38**, 1194 (1946).

[33] Ipatieff, Pines, and Schmerling, *J. Org. Chem.*, **5**, 253 (1940).

[34] Calloway, *Chem. Revs.*, **17**, 327 (1935).

[35] Grosse and Ipatieff, *J. Org. Chem.*, **2**, 447 (1937).

[36] Egloff et al., *Chem. Revs.*, **20**, 387–411 (1937).

[37] Nightingale and Wadsworth, *J. Am. Chem. Soc.*, **63**, 3514 (1941).

[38] Diuguid, *J. Am. Chem. Soc.*, **63**, 3527 (1941); Hartman and Phillips, *Org. Syntheses*, Coll. Vol. II, 232 (1943).

[39] Simons and Hart, *J. Am. Chem. Soc.*, **66**, 1309 (1944); cf. ref. 40.

[40] Simons and Hart, *J. Am. Chem. Soc.*, **69**, 979 (1947).

[41] Wertyporoch, *Ber.*, **66**, 1232 (1933).

[42] Bredereck et al., *Ber.*, **72**, 1414 (1939).

[43] Pines, Edeleanu, and Ipatieff, *J. Am. Chem. Soc.*, **67**, 2193 (1945).

[44] Simons and Archer, *J. Am. Chem. Soc.*, **60**, 2952, 2953 (1938).
[45] Potts and Carpenter, *J. Am. Chem. Soc.*, **61**, 663 (1939).
[46] Norris and Sturgis, *J. Am. Chem. Soc.*, **61**, 1413 (1939).
[47] Price, *Chem. Revs.*, **29**, 44–51 (1941).
[48] Newton, *J. Am. Chem. Soc.*, **65**, 320 (1943).
[49] Copenhaver and Reid, *J. Am. Chem. Soc.*, **49**, 3159 (1927).
[50] Schmerling, *Ind. Eng. Chem.*, **40**, 2072 (1948).
[51] Thompson and Chenicek, *Ind. Eng. Chem.*, **40**, 1265 (1948).
[52] Reichert and Nieuwland, *J. Am. Chem. Soc.*, **45**, 3090 (1923); *Org. Syntheses,* Coll. Vol. I, 229 (1941).
[53] Mavity, Zetterholm, and Hervert, *Ind. Eng. Chem.*, **38**, 829 (1946); Nickels et al., *ibid.*, **41**, 563 (1949).
[54] Reynolds et al., *Ind. Eng. Chem.*, **40**, 1751 (1948).
[55] Orchin, *J. Am. Chem. Soc.*, **68**, 571 (1946).
[56] Arnold, Collins, and Zenk, *J. Am. Chem. Soc.*, **62**, 983 (1940).
[57] Weiss, *Org. Syntheses,* **24**, 84 (1944).
[58] Kloetzel and Herzog, *J. Am. Chem. Soc.*, **72**, 1993 (1950).
[59] Smith and Lo, *J. Am. Chem. Soc.*, **70**, 2209 (1948); cf. ref. 60.
[60] Adkins et al., *J. Am. Chem. Soc.*, **71**, 2955, 2958, 2962 (1949).
[61] Barnes, *J. Am. Chem. Soc.*, **70**, 145 (1948).
[62] Adkins et al,, *J. Am. Chem. Soc.*, **70**, 381 (1948); cf. ref. 64.
[63] Adkins and Reid, *J. Am. Chem. Soc.*, **63**, 741 (1941).
[64] Adkins, Richards, and Davis, *J. Am. Chem. Soc.*, **63**, 1320 (1941).
[65] Kloetzel, *J. Am. Chem. Soc.*, **62**, 1708 (1940).
[66] Ritter and Sharpe, *J. Am. Chem. Soc.*, **59**, 2351 (1937).
[67] Linstead et al., *J. Chem. Soc.*, 1146 (1937).
[68] Kynaston and Jones, *J. Soc. Chem. Ind.*, **68**, 225, 228 (1949); Flowers and Miller, *J. Am. Chem. Soc.*, **69**, 1388 (1947).
[69] Fieser and Hershberg, *J. Am. Chem. Soc.*, **57**, 2192 (1935); cf. ref. 64.
[70] Marler and Turner, *J. Chem. Soc.*, 266 (1937); Hill et al., *ibid.*, 510 (1937); Haworth and Sheldrick, *ibid.*, 1950 (1934).
[71] Newman and Zahn, *J. Am. Chem. Soc.*, **65**, 1097 (1943); Newman and O'Leary, *ibid.*, **68**, 258 (1946).
[72] Linstead and Thomas, *J. Chem. Soc.*, 1127 (1940).
[73] Linstead and Michaelis, *J. Chem. Soc.*, 1134 (1940).
[74] Zelinsky, *Ber.*, **44**, 3121 (1911); **56**, 787 (1923).
[75] Baker and Schuetz, *J. Am. Chem. Soc.*, **69**, 1250 (1947); Adams and Marshall, *ibid.*, **50**, 1970 (1928).
[76] Serijan, Wise, and Gibbons, *J. Am. Chem. Soc.*, **71**, 2265 (1949).
[77] Seyer, Wright, and Bell, *Ind. Eng. Chem.*, **31**, 759 (1939).
[78] Adkins and Cramer, *J. Am. Chem. Soc.*, **52**, 4354 (1930).
[79] Truffault, *Bull. soc. chim. France*, (5) 2, 244 (1935).
[80] Wibaut and Haak, *Rec. trav. chim.*, **67**, 94 (1948).
[81] Adkins, *Reactions of Hydrogen*, University of Wisconsin Press, Madison, Wisconsin, 1937; Adkins and Shriner in Gilman's *Organic Chemistry*, 2nd ed., Vol. I, John Wiley & Sons, New York, 1943, p. 779.
[82] Adkins, Zartman, and Cramer, *J. Am. Chem. Soc.*, **53**, 1425 (1931).
[83] Hock and Depke, *Chem. Ber.*, **83**, 331 (1950); Cook and Hill, *J. Am. Chem. Soc.*, **62**, 1996 (1940); Hückel and Bretschneider, *Ann.*, **540**, 157 (1939).
[84] Bergstrom and Carson, *J. Am. Chem. Soc.*, **63**, 2934 (1941).
[85] Waterman, Clausen, and Tulleners, *Rec. trav. chim.*, **53**, 821 (1934).

[86] Durland and Adkins, *J. Am. Chem. Soc.*, **59**, 135 (1937); **60**, 1501 (1938).
[87] Waterman, Leendertse, and Cranendonk, *Rec. trav. chim.*, **58**, 83 (1939).
[88] Garlock and Mosettig, *J. Am. Chem. Soc.*, **67**, 2256 (1945); Orchin, *ibid.*, **66**, 535 (1944).
[89] Fieser and Johnson, *J. Am. Chem. Soc.*, **61**, 169 (1939); Burger and Mosettig, *ibid.*, **57**, 2731 (1935).
[90] Bachman et al., *J. Am. Chem. Soc.*, **57**, 768 (1935); **63**, 621 (1941).
[91] van de Kamp and Mosettig, *J. Am. Chem. Soc.*, **57**, 1107 (1935).
[92] Papa, Schwenk, and Breiger, *J. Org. Chem.*, **14**, 369 (1949).
[93] Arbit, *J. Am. Chem. Soc.*, **68**, 1662 (1946).
[94] McKinley, Stevens, and Baldwin, *J. Am. Chem. Soc.*, **67**, 1455 (1945).
[95] Noller, *J. Am. Chem. Soc.*, **51**, 594 (1929).
[96] Whitmore et al., *J. Am. Chem. Soc.*, **63**, 127 (1941); Shortridge et al., *ibid.*, **70**, 946 (1948).
[97] Soroos and Willis, *J. Am. Chem. Soc.*, **63**, 881 (1941).
[98] Wibaut et al., *Rec. trav. chim.*, **58**, 329 (1939).
[99] Whitmore and Fleming, *J. Am. Chem. Soc.*, **55**, 3804 (1933).
[100] Cason and Way, *J. Org. Chem.*, **14**, 31 (1949).
[101] Calingaert et al., *J. Am. Chem. Soc.*, **66**, 1389 (1944).
[102] Lewis, Hendricks, and Yohe, *J. Am. Chem. Soc.*, **50**, 1993 (1928).
[103] Whitmore, Bernstein, and Mixon, *J. Am. Chem. Soc.*, **60**, 2539 (1938).
[104] Whitmore and Orem, *J. Am. Chem. Soc.*, **60**, 2573 (1938).
[105] Whitmore and Southgate, *J. Am. Chem. Soc.*, **60**, 2571 (1938).
[106] Read et al., *Org. Syntheses*, **25**, 11 (1945); Read and Foster, *J. Am. Chem. Soc.*, **48**, 1606 (1926).
[107] Barber, Slack, and Woolman, *J. Chem. Soc.*, 100 (1943).
[108] Karabinos, Serijan, and Gibbons, *J. Am. Chem. Soc.*, **68**, 2107 (1946).
[109] Bachmann, *J. Am. Chem. Soc.*, **56**, 1363 (1934); cf. ref. 90.
[110] Morton et al., *J. Am. Chem. Soc.*, **62**, 123 (1940); **63**, 324, 327 (1941); **64**, 2239, 2240, 2242, 2250 (1942).
[111] Bachmann and Kloetzel, *J. Org. Chem.*, **3**, 55 (1938).
[112] Seibert and Bergstrom, *J. Org. Chem.*, **10**, 544 (1945).
[113] Wooster and Mitchell, *J. Am. Chem. Soc.*, **52**, 688 (1930).
[114] Wegand and Mensdorf, *Ber.*, **68**, 1830 (1935).
[115] Wittig and Witt, *Ber.*, **74**, 1474 (1941).
[116] Stenzl and Fichter, *Helv. Chim. Acta*, **17**, 679 (1934).
[117] Reichstein and Oppenauer, *Helv. Chim. Acta*, **16**, 1377 (1933).
[118] Van Alphen, *Rec. trav. chim.*, **59**, 580 (1940); Sirks, *ibid.*, **62**, 193 (1943).
[119] Fuson et al., *J. Am. Chem. Soc.*, **63**, 2652 (1946); **68**, 533 (1946).
[120] Hall, Lesslie, and Turner, *J. Chem. Soc.*, 711 (1950).
[121] Müller and Schütz, *Ber.*, **71**, 691 (1938).
[122] Dewar and Read, *J. Soc. Chem. Ind.*, **55**, 347T (1936).
[123] Whitmore and Zook, *J. Am. Chem. Soc.*, **64**, 1783 (1942).
[124] Gilman and Robinson, *Org. Syntheses*, Coll. Vol. II, 47 (1943).
[125] Smith, *Org. Syntheses*, Coll. Vol. II, 360 (1943); Smith and MacDougall, *J. Am. Chem. Soc.*, **51**, 3002 (1929); cf. ref. 8.
[126] Gilman and Hoyle, *J. Am. Chem. Soc.*, **44**, 2621 (1922).
[127] Gilman and Kirby, *J. Am. Chem. Soc.*, **51**, 3477 (1929); cf. ref. 126.
[128] Gilman et al., *J. Am. Chem. Soc.*, **47**, 518, 2047 (1925); **50**, 2223 (1928).
[129] Burtle and Shriner, *J. Am. Chem. Soc.*, **69**, 2059 (1947).
[130] Gilman and Catlin, *Org. Syntheses*, Coll. Vol. I, 471 (1941); cf. ref. 129.

[131] Wibaut and van Dijk, *Rec. trav. chim.*, **65**, 413 (1946); Plattner and Ronco, *Helv. Chim. Acta,* **27**, 402 (1944).

[132] Maxwell and Adams, *J. Am. Chem. Soc.*, **52**, 2962 (1930); Smith and Lund, *ibid.*, **52**, 4147 (1930).

[133] Murray and Stevenson, *J. Am. Chem. Soc.*, **66**, 812 (1944); Slabey, *ibid.*, **68**, 1335 (1946).

[134] Hass et al., *Ind. Eng. Chem.*, **28**, 1178 (1936).

[135] Martin in *Organic Reactions,* Vol. 1, John Wiley & Sons, New York, 1942, p. 155.

[136] Clemmensen, *Ber.*, **46**, 1837 (1913).

[137] Strating and Backer, *Rec. trav. chim.*, **55**, 903 (1936).

[138] Huang-Minlon, *J. Am. Chem. Soc.*, **68**, 2487 (1946).

[139] Soffer, Soffer, and Sherk, *J. Am. Chem. Soc.*, **67**, 1435 (1945).

[140] Herr, Whitmore, and Schiessler, *J. Am. Chem. Soc.*, **67**, 2061 (1945).

[141] Nenitzescu and Cantuniari, *Ber.*, **65**, 810 (1932).

[142] Volkenburgh et al., *J. Am. Chem. Soc.*, **71**, 172 (1949).

[143] Berliner and Berliner, *J. Am. Chem. Soc.*, **71**, 1196 (1949).

[144] Cowan, Jeffery, and Vogel, *J. Chem. Soc.*, 1862 (1939).

[145] Nightingale and Radford, *J. Org. Chem.*, **14**, 1089 (1949).

[146] Ross et al., *J. Am. Chem. Soc.*, **72**, 1136 (1950).

[147] Pines, Strehlau, and Ipatieff, *J. Am. Chem. Soc.*, **72**, 1563 (1950).

[148] Pines, Strehlau, and Ipatieff, *J. Am. Chem. Soc.*, **71**, 3536 (1949).

[149] Adkins and Connor, *J. Am. Chem. Soc.*, **53**, 1091 (1931).

[150] Brady and Day, *J. Chem. Soc.*, 116 (1934).

[151] Dolliver et al., *J. Am. Chem. Soc.*, **59**, 831 (1937).

[152] Bachmann and Struve, *J. Org. Chem.*, **4**, 475 (1939).

[153] Bachmann, Cronyn, and Struve, *J. Org. Chem.*, **12**, 600 (1947); cf. ref. 154.

[154] Martin, *J. Am. Chem. Soc.*, **58**, 1438 (1936).

[155] Sah, *Rec. trav. chim.*, **59**, 1026 (1940).

[156] Goldstein and Glauser, *Helv. Chim. Acta,* **17**, 788 (1934).

[157] Lock and Stach, *Ber.*, **76**, 1252 (1943); Waldmann and Marmorstein, *ibid.*, **70**, 106 (1937).

[158] Sherk, Augur, and Soffer, *J. Am. Chem. Soc.*, **67**, 2240 (1945).

[159] Speer and Hill, *J. Org. Chem.*, **2**, 142 (1937); Pope and Bogert, *ibid.*, **2**, 280 (1937); Mann and Watson, *J. Chem. Soc.*, 508 (1947).

[160] Read and Wood, *Org. Syntheses,* **20**, 57 (1940); Dohme, Cox, and Miller, *J. Am. Chem. Soc.*, **48**, 1691 (1926).

[161] Buu-Hoi and Hoan, *J. Org. Chem.*, **14**, 1023 (1949).

[162] Gardner and Borgstrom, *J. Am. Chem. Soc.*, **51**, 3375 (1929).

[163] Kharasch and Urry, *J. Org. Chem.*, **13**, 101 (1948); Kharasch and Fields, *J. Am. Chem. Soc.*, **63**, 2316 (1941); cf. ref. 120.

[164] Conant and Blatt, *J. Am. Chem. Soc.*, **50**, 555 (1928).

[165] Fuson and Armstrong, *J. Am. Chem. Soc.*, **63**, 2650 (1941).

[166] Fanta, *Chem. Revs.*, **38**, 139 (1946).

[167] Busch and Weber, *J. prakt. Chem.*, **146**, 23 (1936).

[168] Smith in *Organic Reactions,* Vol. 1, John Wiley & Sons, New York, 1942, pp. 370, 381–384; Moyle and Smith, *J. Org. Chem.*, **2**, 112 (1937).

[169] Hart and Robinson, *J. Am. Chem. Soc.*, **70**, 3731 (1948); cf. ref. 59.

[170] Smith and Lux, *J. Am. Chem. Soc.*, **51**, 2994 (1929); Smith and MacDougall, *ibid.*, **51**, 3004 (1929); cf. ref. 168.

[171] Smith and Moyle, *J. Am. Chem. Soc.*, **58**, 1 (1936).

[172] Gilman and Lichtenwalter, *J. Am. Chem. Soc.*, **61**, 957 (1939).
[173] Schroeter and Götzky, *Ber.*, **60**, 2035 (1927).
[174] Smith and Spillane, *J. Am. Chem. Soc.*, **62**, 2641 (1940).
[175] Brown and Bluestein, *J. Am. Chem. Soc.*, **62**, 3256 (1940).
[176] Koelsch and Johnson, *J. Am. Chem. Soc.*, **65**, 571 (1943).
[177] Ford, Jacobson, and McGrew, *J. Am. Chem. Soc.*, **70**, 3793 (1948); cf. ref. 194.
[178] Adkins and Burks, *J. Am. Chem. Soc.*, **70**, 4174 (1948); Ipatieff et al., *Ind. Eng. Chem.*, **41**, 1802 (1949).
[179] Komarewsky, Price, and Coley, *J. Am. Chem. Soc.*, **69**, 238 (1947).
[180] Julian et al., *J. Am. Chem. Soc.*, **71**, 2060 (1949).
[181] Birch, *J. Chem. Soc.*, 809 (1945).
[182] Schönberg and Warren, *J. Chem. Soc.*, 1840 (1939).
[183] Grundmann, *Chem. Ber.*, **81**, 513 (1948).
[184] Aitken, Badger, and Cook, *J. Chem. Soc.*, 331 (1950); Braun and Nelles, *Ber.*, **67**, 1094 (1934).
[185] Bradsher, *J. Am. Chem. Soc.*, **62**, 486 (1940).
[186] Johnson, Blizzard, and Carhart, *J. Am. Chem. Soc.*, **70**, 3664 (1948); Nystrom and Brown, *ibid.*, **70**, 3778 (1948).
[187] Levene, *Org. Syntheses*, Coll. Vol. II, 320 (1943); cf. ref. 186.
[188] Buehler, Cooper, and Scrudder, *J. Org. Chem.* **8**, 316 (1943).
[189] Zechmeister and Rom, *Ann.*, **468**, 127 (1929).
[190] Hart, *J. Am. Chem. Soc.*, **71**, 1966 (1949).
[191] Plattner and Roniger, *Helv. Chim. Acta*, **25**, 593 (1942).
[192] Boord et al., *Ind. Eng. Chem.*, **41**, 609, 613 (1949).
[193] Goheen, *J. Am. Chem. Soc.*, **63**, 747 (1941).
[194] Schmerling, Friedman, and Ipatieff, *J. Am. Chem. Soc.*, **62**, 2448 (1940); Cramer and Mulligan, *ibid.*, **58**, 374 (1936).
[195] Crane, Boord, and Henne, *J. Am. Chem. Soc.*, **67**, 1237 (1945); Pines and Ipatieff, *ibid.*, **61**, 1076 (1939); cf. ref. 192.
[196] Ipatieff and Corson, *Ind. Eng. Chem.*, **30**, 1039 (1938).
[197] Zartman and Adkins, *J. Am. Chem. Soc.*, **54**, 1668 (1932); Kern, Shriner, and Adams, *ibid.*, **47**, 1147 (1925).
[198] Whitmore et al., *J. Am. Chem. Soc.*, **64**, 1801 (1942).
[199] LeFevre, LeFevre, and Robertson, *J. Chem. Soc.*, 481 (1935).
[200] Noller, *Org. Syntheses*, Coll. Vol. II, 478 (1943).
[201] Grummitt and Buck, *J. Am. Chem. Soc.*, **65**, 295 (1943).
[202] Marvel et al., *J. Am. Chem. Soc.*, **59**, 1177 (1937); **63**, 1482, 1894 (1941); **68**, 1089 (1946).
[203] Tistchenko, *Bull. soc. chim. France*, **47**, 1137 (1930); Adams and Hufferd, *Org. Syntheses*, Coll. Vol. I, 341 (1941).
[204] Bradsher, *J. Am. Chem. Soc.*, **64**, 1007 (1942).
[205] Carter and Van Loon, *J. Am. Chem. Soc.*, **60**, 1077 (1938).
[206] Roblin, Davidson, and Bogert, *J. Am. Chem. Soc.*, **57**, 151 (1935).
[207] Bradsher and Smith, *J. Am. Chem. Soc.*, **65**, 451, 1643 (1943); cf. ref. 185.
[208] Fieser in *Organic Reactions*, Vol. 1, John Wiley & Sons, New York, 1942, p. 129.
[209] Bradsher et al., *J. Am. Chem. Soc.*, **63**, 493 (1941); **61**, 2184 (1939); **65**, 2016 (1943); **68**, 1094 (1946).
[210] Bardhan and Sengupta, *J. Chem. Soc.*, 2523 (1932); Nenitzescu et al., *Ber.*, **74**, 687 (1941); Perlman, Davidson, and Bogert, *J. Org. Chem.*, **1**, 288 (1936).

[211] Bachmann and Hoffman in *Organic Reactions*, Vol. 2, John Wiley & Sons, New York, 1944, pp. 224, 247–252.

[212] Gomberg and Bachmann, *Org. Syntheses*, Coll. Vol. I, 113 (1941).

[213] Atkinson et al., *J. Am. Chem. Soc.*, **63**, 730 (1941); **65**, 476 (1943); **67**, 1513 (1945); Waters, *J. Chem. Soc.*, 864 (1939).

[214] Gomberg and Pernert, *J. Am. Chem. Soc.*, **48**, 1372 (1926); cf. ref. 211.

[215] Gomberg and Bachmann, *J. Am. Chem. Soc.*, **46**, 2343 (1924); cf. ref. 221.

[216] Hodgson and Marsden, *J. Chem. Soc.*, 208 (1940).

[217] Hey and Lawton, *J. Chem. Soc.*, 374 (1940).

[218] Hodgson and Crook, *J. Chem. Soc.*, 573 (1937).

[219] Haworth, Heilbron, and Hey, *J. Chem. Soc.*, 349 (1940).

[220] France, Heilbron, and Hey, *J. Chem. Soc.*, 1288 (1939); 371 (1940).

[221] Elks, Haworth, and Hey, *J. Chem. Soc.*, 1284 (1940).

[222] France, Heilbron, and Hey, *J. Chem. Soc.*, 1364 (1938).

[223] Johnson in *Organic Reactions*, Vol. 1, John Wiley & Sons, New York, 1942, pp. 246–247; cf. ref. 211, p. 239.

[224] Kornblum in *Organic Reactions*, Vol. 2, John Wiley & Sons, New York, 1944, p. 262.

[225] Coleman and Talbot, *Org. Syntheses*, Coll. Vol. II, 592 (1943); Wallingford and Krueger, *ibid.*, Coll. Vol. II, 353 (1943); Bigelow, Johnson, and Sandborn, *ibid.*, Coll. Vol. I, 133 (1941); Clarke and Taylor, *ibid.*, Coll. Vol. I, 415 (1941).

[226] Brewster and Poje, *J. Am. Chem. Soc.*, **61**, 2418 (1939); cf. ref. 224, p. 295.

[227] Kornblum, *Org. Syntheses*, **21**, 32 (1941).

[228] Hodgson et al., *J. Chem. Soc.*, 744, 748 (1942); 86 (1943); 8, 21, 112 (1944).

[229] Clemo, Haworth, and Walton, *J. Chem. Soc.*, 2375 (1929).

[230] Hodgson and Marsden, *J. Chem. Soc.*, 207 (1940).

[231] Kornblum and Iffland, *J. Am. Chem. Soc.*, **71**, 2137 (1949).

[232] Ayling, Gorvin, and Hinkel, *J. Chem. Soc.*, 618 (1941).

[233] Huston and Ballard, *Org. Syntheses*, Coll. Vol. II, 97 (1943); Ehrenfeld and Puterbaugh, *ibid.*, Coll. Vol. I, 388 (1941).

[234] Oakwood and Miller, *J. Am. Chem. Soc.*, **72**, 1849 (1950).

[235] Bachmann and Cortes, *J. Am. Chem. Soc.*, **65**, 1332 (1943).

[236] Case, *J. Am. Chem. Soc.*, **56**, 716 (1934).

[237] Bergmann and Weizman, *J. Org. Chem.*, **9**, 415 (1944).

[238] Hughes and Reid, *J. Org. Chem.*, **14**, 522 (1949).

[239] Akin, Stamatoff, and Bogert, *J. Am. Chem. Soc.*, **59**, 1272 (1937).

[240] Fichter et al., *Helv. Chim. Acta*, **22**, 970 (1939); **23**, 807 (1940).

[241] Brown, Durand, and Marvel, *J. Am. Chem. Soc.*, **58**, 1594 (1936).

[242] Ruzicka and Seidel, *Helv. Chim. Acta*, **19**, 424 (1936).

[243] Plattner in *Newer Methods of Preparative Organic Chemistry*, Interscience Publishers, New York, 1948, p. 21.

[244] Mattox and Grosse, *J. Am. Chem. Soc.*, **67**, 84 (1945).

[245] Bachmann and Edgerton, *J. Am. Chem. Soc.*, **62**, 2220 (1940).

[246] Bachmann and Wilds, *J. Am. Chem. Soc.*, **60**, 624 (1938); Johnson, Goldman, and Schneider, *ibid.*, **67**, 1357 (1945).

[247] Fahim and Mustafa, *J. Chem. Soc.*, 519 (1949).

[248] Pines, LaZerte, and Ipatieff, *J. Am. Chem. Soc.*, **72**, 2850 (1950).

[249] Goodman and Wise, *J. Am. Chem. Soc.*, **72**, 3076 (1950).

[250] Swann in Weissberger's *Technique of Organic Chemistry*, Vol. 2, Interscience Publishers, New York, 1948, p. 195.

[251] Luther and Wächter, *Chem. Ber.*, **82**, 161 (1949).

[252] Seyer and Yip, *Ind. Eng. Chem.*, **41**, 378 (1949).

[253] Cullinane and Chard, *J. Chem. Soc.*, 823 (1945); Backer, *Rec. trav. chim.*, **54**, 746 (1935).

[254] Brown and Bluestein, *J. Am. Chem. Soc.*, **65**, 1082 (1943).

[255] Doss, *Physical Constants of the Principal Hydrocarbons*, The Texas Co., New York, 1943; Egloff, *Physical Constants of Hydrocarbons*, Reinhold Publishing Corp., New York, 1947; Faraday, *Encyclopedia of Hydrocarbon Compounds*, Chemical Publishing Co., Brooklyn, N. Y.; Rossini et al., *Selected Values of Properties of Hydrocarbons*, U. S. Government Printing Office, Washington, D. C., 1947.

[256] Todd in *Organic Reactions*, Vol. 4, John Wiley & Sons, New York, 1948, p. 378.

[257] Brown in *Organic Reactions*, Vol. 6, John Wiley & Sons, New York, 1951, p. 469.

[258] Jones and Gilman in *Organic Reactions*, Vol. 6, John Wiley & Sons, New York, 1951, p. 339.

2

Olefinic Compounds

CONTENTS

In this chapter are brought together twenty-four reactions for the introduction of a double bond into an organic compound. Olefinic hydrocarbons prepared by these methods are listed in Tables 2 and 3. Olefinic compounds containing an additional functional group but prepared by these methods are found in tables in the following chapters.

19. Dehydration of Hydroxy Compounds

$$RCHOHCH_2R \xrightarrow{-H_2O} RCH = CHR$$

The formation of olefins by removal of the elements of water from simple aliphatic alcohols is not always a straightforward process. Dehydration of n-butyl alcohol by heating with aqueous sulfuric or phosphoric acids gives both 1- and 2-butenes.[26] Certain alcohols with branching on the a-carbon atoms exhibit extensive carbon-skeleton rearrangement upon dehydration with acid catalysts. For example, methyl-t-butylcarbinol gives a mixture of tetramethylethylene and unsym-methylisopropylethylene rather than t-butylethylene.[2, 17, 32]

$$(CH_3)_3CCHOHCH_3 \xrightarrow[CH_3\sim]{-H_2O} (CH_3)_2C = C(CH_3)_2 + H_2C = C(CH_3)CH(CH_3)_2$$

Fission of the carbon chain sometimes occurs during dehydration. Thus, di-t-butylcarbinol gives trimethylethylene and isobutylene when heated to 180° with chloronaphthalenesulfonic acid.[33]

$$(CH_3)_3CCHOHC(CH_3)_3 \xrightarrow{-H_2O} (CH_3)_2C = CHCH_3 + (CH_3)_2C = CH_2$$

These isomerizations, rearrangements, and cleavages are best explained by a carbonium-ion mechanism.[432] Vapor-phase dehydration of alcohols over aluminum oxide greatly reduces the tendency for isomerization and rearrangement. The alcohol vapors are passed over the catalyst at 300-420°. In this manner, pure 1-butene is prepared from n-butyl alcohol[34] and t-butylethylene is obtained from methyl-t-butylcarbinol (54%).[17] The relative rates of dehydration of the simpler alcohols over alumina have been studied.[39] The main side reaction is dehydration to ethers[428] (method 118).

Tertiary alcohols are more easily dehydrated than primary or secondary alcohols. The action of heat and a trace of iodine is usually sufficient.[2, 25, 37] Other catalysts for this purpose include 15% sulfuric acid,[24] formic acid,[21] oxalic acid,[2, 36, 165] and zinc chloride.[11] When the carbinol contains different alkyl radicals, a mixture of isomeric olefins is usually obtained. Studies to determine the ease with which the simple alkyl radicals donate a hydrogen atom to form water have been made.[24, 25] Very often, pure olefins can be obtained from the isomeric mixtures by modern methods of fractional distillation.[430]

Symmetrical secondary or tertiary alicyclic alcohols are readily dehydrated to only one olefin in each case. Examples include cyclopentene from cyclopentanol and phosphoric acid,[435] cyclohexene from cyclohexanol over alumina,[13] cycloheptene from cycloheptanol and β-naphthalenesulfonic acid,[18] and various alkylcyclohexenes from the corresponding tertiary carbinols.[31, 426]

Styrenes are available by dehydration of either α-arylethyl or β-arylethyl alcohols. The procedures were reviewed in 1949.[445] β-Phenylethyl alcohol loses water at 140° over a mixture of molten sodium and potassium hydroxides to give styrene, $C_6H_5CH\!=\!CH_2$, in 57% yield.[49] The 2,4-dimethyl derivative has been prepared in a similar manner from the primary alcohol.[107] Many substituted styrenes have been made by dehydration of methylarylcarbinols with potassium hydrogen sulfate,[22, 23, 62] phosphorus pentoxide,[23, 106] or activated alumina.[53, 61, 166] 1,1-Diphenylethylene[14] and 2-phenyl-2-butene[427] are easily obtained by boiling the corresponding tertiary alcohols with dilute sulfuric acid.

Preparation of *dienes* is accomplished by dehydration of diols or olefinic alcohols. Pinacol, $(CH_3)_2COHCOH(CH_3)_2$, is converted to 2,3-dimethyl-1,3-butadiene by heating with 48% hydrobromic acid[43] or by passing the vapors over activated alumina at 420–470°.[44] Yields of the diene are 60% and 86%, respectively. Aniline hydrobromide is used as a catalyst in the dehydration of 3-methyl-2,4-pentanediol to 3-methyl-1,3-pentadiene (42%).[54] An excellent laboratory preparation of isoprene from acetone in 65% over-all yield has been described. The last step involves catalytic dehydration of dimethylvinylcarbinol over aluminum oxide at 300° to give isoprene in 88% yield.[47]

$$CH_3COCH_3 \xrightarrow{NaC\equiv CH} (CH_3)_2COHC \equiv CH \xrightarrow[Pd]{H_2} (CH_3)_2COHCH\!=\!CH_2 \xrightarrow{Al_2O_3}$$
$$CH_2\!=\!C(CH_3)CH\!=\!CH_2$$

Olefinic tertiary alcohols obtained by the action of Grignard reagents on mesityl oxide, $(CH_3)_2C\!=\!CHCOCH_3$, have been dehydrated over iodine[46] or potassium hydrogen sulfate[48] and by distilling with phthalic anhydride.[3] The yields of dienes are in the range of 58–65%. The product from the addition of methylmagnesium chloride to crotonaldehyde is the ether, $CH_3CH\!=\!CHCH(CH_3)\!-\!O\!-\!CH(CH_3)CH\!=\!CHCH_3$, formed from two molecules of the expected 2-penten-4-ol. By passing the vapors of this ether over alumina at 280–290°, 1,3-pentadiene is obtained in 72% yield.[49]

Dehydration of β,γ- and γ,δ-olefinic alcohols does not always lead to large amounts of the expected conjugated dienes.[55, 109] Treatment of dimethylallylcarbinol with hydrobromic acid gives a 37% yield of the nonconjugated diene, $H_2C\!=\!C(CH_3)CH_2CH\!=\!CH_2$, along with 43% of the two possible conjugated isomers.[55] Oftentimes, ketones are formed by isomerization of the olefinic alcohols under the conditions of the dehydration. In the dehydration of 2-ethyl-3-hydroxy-1-butene,

$$H_2C\!=\!C(C_2H_5)CHOHCH_3,$$

by potassium hydrogen sulfate, some methyl s-butyl ketone is formed.[167] The diene obtained from this alcohol is 3-methyl-1,3-pentadiene rather than the expected 2-ethyl-1,3-butadiene.[173]

Olefinic acetylenes are made by the dehydration of acetylenic carbinols.[111, 436]

Several *olefinic halides* containing aliphatic halogen are prepared by dehydration of halo alcohols. For example, 3,3,3-trichloropropene, $Cl_3CCH = CH_2$, is made by heating the corresponding secondary alcohol with a 10% excess of phosphorus pentoxide; the yield is 84%.[57] Other unsaturated halogen compounds prepared by this method are β-chlorostyrene, $C_6H_5CH = CHCl$, from styrene chlorohydrin and phosphoric acid on silica gel at 400° (63%)[60] and various nuclear halogenated styrenes by dehydration of the corresponding arylmethylcarbinols.[61, 437, 455]

Few *olefinic alcohols* or *olefinic ethers* have been made by this method. The procedure for the dehydration and reduction of glycerol to allyl alcohol[65] by heating with formic acid has been applied to the preparation of vinylglycol, $H_2C = CHCHOHCH_2OH$, from erythritol (35%).[66] α-Hydroxy ethers of the type $R_2C(OH)CH(OC_2H_5)R'$ are dehydrated to α,β-olefinic ethers, $R_2C = C(OC_2H_5)R'$, by refluxing with phosphorus pentoxide in pyridine.[112, 113] Dehydration by oxalic acid produces ketones of the type R_2CHCOR'(method 202). 3-Methoxystyrene and 4-phenoxystyrene are prepared by passing the vapors of the corresponding primary carbinols over potassium hydroxide pellets heated to 250° in stainless-steel or copper tubes.[145]

α,β-*Olefinic aldehydes* are made by treatment of β-hydroxy acetals with acidic reagents.[439, 440] The dehydration of β-hydroxy aldehydes and ketones from the aldol condensation is discussed in method 36.

Olefinic acids and olefinic esters are prepared by dehydration of hydroxy acids and esters. Cis- and trans-α-methylcrotonic acids have been made in small yields by pyrolysis of the corresponding α-hydroxy acids.[83] Certain halogen atoms are stable during the dehydration, as in the preparation of ethyl 3-chlorocrotonate by dehydration of the chlorohydrin, $CH_3CHClCHOHCO_2C_2H_5$.[88] A vinyl group may be formed on the benzene ring in the presence of an ester group by dehydration of the hydroxyethyl group with potassium hydrogen sulfate.[96, 97]

The condensation of aldehydes and ketones with α-halo esters may lead directly to *olefinic acids* and *esters* by dehydration of the intermediate β-hydroxy compounds (Reformatsky).[407, 408] More often, the hydroxy esters are isolated and purified prior to dehydration (method 103).

$$RCH_2CR'(OH)CH_2CO_2C_2H_5 \longrightarrow \left[\begin{array}{l} RCH = C(R')CH_2CO_2C_2H_5 \\ \\ RCH_2C(R') = CHCO_2C_2H_5 \end{array} \right.$$

When an alkyl substituent is present on the β-carbon atom, a mixture of α,β- and β,γ-olefinic compounds is produced, the ratio depending on the nature of the alkyl group and the dehydrating agent.[93, 94] This tendency for the formation of appreciable amounts of the non-conjugated β,γ-olefinic ester is often not fully appreciated. The best work along these lines indicates that efficient fractionation is necessary to insure a pure product. Even when both R groups on the β-carbon atom are methyl groups, $(CH_3)_2COHCHRCO_2C_2H_5$, considerable dehydration to the non-conjugated β,γ-olefinic ester occurs.[94, 420] It was formerly believed that this structure gave only α,β-olefinic esters.[87] Also, the tertiary hydroxyl group in this compound is surprisingly stable. Neither iodine nor hydrochloric acid is an effective catalyst for dehydration, although phosphorus pentoxide has proved satisfactory.

The mode of dehydration can sometimes be controlled from a practical standpoint.[171, 417-419] Thus, ethyl 1-hydroxycyclohexylacetate is converted to 1-cyclohexeneacetic acid in 80% yield by anhydrous hydrogen chloride, whereas dehydration by acetic anhydride followed by saponification leads to cyclohexylidenacetic acid (68%).[86]

A wide variety of dehydrating agents have been employed. In addition to those already mentioned are sulfuric acid,[89, 418] potassium bisulfate,[418, 421] formic acid,[410] thionyl chloride,[90, 92] iodine,[419] acetic anhydride,[418, 419] phosphorus oxychloride,[411, 416, 418] and phosphorus pentoxide.[94, 420] It should be noted that the free olefinic acids are sometimes decarboxylated under conditions similar to those described for certain of these dehydrations (cf. method 27).

β-Hydroxy esters are also obtained by reduction of β-keto esters and may be dehydrated over phosphorus pentoxide.[441]

Dehydration of cyanohydrins to α,β-olefinic nitriles has been accomplished by thionyl chloride,[91, 98, 101] phosphorus pentoxide,[100] or anhydrous potassium carbonate.[99] A typical example is the preparation of 1-cyano-1-cyclopentene from cyclopentanone cyanohydrin (75%).[98] Aluminum powder is the best of many catalysts studied for the dehydration of ethylene cyanohydrin to acrylonitrile, $H_2C{=}CHCN$ (80%).[442]

The *amino* group on the benzene ring is unaffected by catalytic dehydration with iodine of the tertiary alcohol, dimethyl-(o-aminophenyl)-carbinol, to 2-(o-aminophenyl)-1-propene (87%).[103]

The direct dehydration of aliphatic β-nitro alcohols to nitro olefins is usually unsatisfactory.[443] The latter compounds are obtained by method 24 or by treating the nitro alcohols with thionyl chloride and pyridine.[444]

20. Dehydrohalogenation of Halogen Compounds

$$RCHXCH_2R' \xrightarrow{\text{Base}} RCH{=}CHR'$$

The formation of a double bond by removal of the elements of hydrogen halide is a very general method. Basic reagents such as alkali hydroxides and alkoxides or a variety of amines are usually employed. The reaction is of limited application for the preparation of simple olefins, however, since the alcohols are usually more readily available and in most cases yield the same olefins by dehydration.

In general, primary halides show a greater tendency to react meta-thetically with most bases than to undergo the elimination reaction. Treatment of isoamyl chloride with alcoholic potassium hydroxide gives only an 11% yield of 3-methyl-1-butene, the remainder appearing as ethyl isoamyl ether.[116] On the other hand, a 90% yield of 2-pentene is obtained by adding the secondary halide, 3-bromopentane, to a concentrated methanolic solution of potassium hydroxide at 115°.[114] The ratio of dehydrohalogenation to metathesis has been studied for many aliphatic and alicyclic halides in the presence of a variety of bases such as piperidine,[125] pyridine,[126] sodium alkoxides,[120] potassium cresolate,[119] and inorganic hydroxides.[127, 128] The catalytic dehydrohalogenation of dodecyl chloride over alumina at 250° gives all six possible isomeric straight-chain dodecenes.[118]

The dehydrohalogenation of a β-chloroalkylbenzene is readily accomplished by refluxing with excess aqueous methanolic potassium hydroxide. Substituted α-alkylstyrenes which are difficult to obtain by other methods are prepared in this way by a two-step process involving catalytic condensation of aromatic compounds with aliphatic chlorohydrins followed by removal of hydrogen halide from the resulting haloalkylated derivatives.[121]

$$ArH \xrightarrow[BF_3]{RCHOHCH_2Cl} ArCHRCH_2Cl \xrightarrow[CH_3OH]{KOH} ArC(R)=CH_2$$

A bromine atom in the *alpha* position of the side chain is removed by quinoline at 160° in the preparation of 1-(β-naphthyl)-1-butene (81%).[446] Dehydrohalogenation of halides to styrenes has been reviewed.[445]

Several conjugated *diolefins* have been made by heating bromo olefins with solid potassium hydroxide[123] or excess quinoline.[124] In the latter case, the bromo olefins were made available by allylic bromination of olefins with N-bromosuccinimide. β-phenylbutadiene is obtained in 46% yield by the action of pyridine on the corresponding secondary chloride.[518] Chlorination of *n*-butyl chloride gives an isomeric mixture of dichlorides from which low yields (18–30%) of butadiene are obtained by passing the vapors over soda lime at about 700°.[122]

Certain *olefinic halogen* compounds are best prepared by this method. Isobutylene bromide is dehydrohalogenated by hot potassium hydroxide solution to give isobutenyl bromide. $(CH_3)_2C \!=\! CHBr$ (27%).[448] A primary halogen atom of 1,2,3-trichloropropane or 1,2,3-tribromopropane is removed in preference to the secondary halogen atom upon treatment with alkali hydroxides. Yields of 2,3-dibromopropene[131] and 2,3-dichloropropene[132, 133] are 80–87%). 1,1-Dichlorocyclohexane prepared from cyclohexanone and phosphorus pentachloride loses hydrogen chloride upon distillation to give 1-chloro-1-cyclohexene (40%).[136] Nuclear halogenated styrenes have been made by dehydrohalogenation of either α- or β-chloroalkylhalobenzenes.[61, 121, 137]

Two techniques are commonly used in the preparation of *olefinic ethers* from halo ethers. The first involves heating a β-halo ether with fused or powdered potassium hydroxide.[253] This method is typified by the conversion of β-phenoxyethyl bromide to phenyl vinyl ether (69%)[143] and β,β'-dichlorodiethyl ether to divinyl ether (61%).[141] In the latter case, yields are improved in the presence of ammonia gas. In the second procedure, an aliphatic[144] or aromatic[145, 146] chloro ether is heated with pyridine to 115°. This method is of value in the preparation of several methoxystyrenes. Chloroalkylation of the aromatic ether is followed by dehydrohalogenation.

The elimination of a molecule of halogen acid from halo acetals of acetaldehyde with powdered potassium hydroxide gives ketene acetals.[453] However, the α-bromo acetals of the homologs of acetaldehyde on similar treatment with potassium hydroxide or potassium *t*-butoxide are converted into α,β-*olefinic acetals.*[454]

$$CH_2BrCH(OR)_2 \longrightarrow H_2C \!=\! C(OR)_2$$

$$RCH_2CHBrCH(OR)_2 \longrightarrow RCH \!=\! CHCH(OR)_2$$

1-Cyclohexenealdehyde is prepared from the saturated aldehyde by bromination in the presence of finely powdered calcium carbonate followed by dehydrohalogenation of the resulting bromo aldehyde by diethylaniline.[451]

α,β-*Olefinic ketones* result from the loss of hydrogen halide from either α- or β-halo ketones. 2,4-Dinitrophenylhydrazine shows promise as a reagent for the dehydrohalogenation of α-halo ketones.[452] Alcoholic potassium hydroxide, sodium carbonate,[152] sodium acetate,[151] and tertiary amines[149,150] have been used to remove hydrogen halide from β-halo ketones. In the acylation of olefins by acyl chlorides (method 178), dehydrohalogenation sometimes occurs spontaneously to give olefinic ketones. An alcoholic solution of β-chloropropiophenone containing an equivalent amount of potassium acetate is used in synthetic work in place of the readily polymerizable phenyl vinyl ketone. The olefinic ketone may be isolated in 78% yield by a chloroform extraction of this solution.[148]

A variety of bases have been used to effect dehydrohalogenation of halo acids and halo esters. α-Bromo esters or α-bromo acyl halides give α,β-olefinic acids with alcoholic potassium hydroxide.[154,156] Yields are poor with the higher-molecular-weight α-bromo acids; other products are those formed by substitution of the halogen atom by the basic anions. Ethyl α-methyl- and α-ethyl-crotonates are prepared in 80% yields by refluxing the corresponding α-bromo esters with dimethylaniline.[155] β-Chloro esters in which the chlorine atom is tertiary readily lose hydrogen chloride upon heating[163] or upon treatment with alcoholic ammonia. By the latter procedure a series of β,β-dialkylacrylic esters have been prepared in 80–96% yield.[159] α-Haloacrylic acids and esters are made in good yield from α,β-dihalopropionic esters and bases such as barium hydroxide,[158] sodium ethoxide,[164] and quinoline.[162] Excess sodium alkoxide replaces the α-bromine atom in the product by an alkoxyl group.[424] γ-Halocrotonic esters are prepared in 60–65% yields by the dehydrohalogenation of β,γ-dihalobutyric esters.[160]

Certain olefinic nitriles are readily available from α-chloro-β-arylpropionitriles obtained by the addition of diazonium salts to acrylonitrile. Dehydrohalogenation is effected by boiling with diethylaniline.[275]

$$H_2C = CHCN \xrightarrow{C_6H_5 \overset{+}{N_2}\overset{-}{Cl}} C_6H_5 CH_2CHClCN \longrightarrow C_6H_5 CH = CHCN$$

21. Elimination of Halo and Alkoxyl Groups (Boord)

$$RCH_2CHO \xrightarrow[HCl]{C_2H_5 OH} RCH_2CHClOC_2H_5 \xrightarrow{Br_2} RCHBrCHBrOC_2H_5$$

$$\downarrow R'MgBr$$

$$RCHBrCR'BrOC_2H_5 \xleftarrow{Br_2} RCH = CR'OC_2H_5 \xleftarrow[C_2H_5 OH]{KOH} RCHBrCHR'OC_2H_5$$

$$\downarrow R''MgBr \qquad\qquad\qquad\qquad\qquad\qquad\qquad \downarrow Zn$$

$$RCHBrCR'R''OC_2H_5 \xrightarrow{Zn} RCH = CR'R'' \qquad\qquad RCH = CHR'$$

This combination of reactions represents the best general method for the preparation of olefins of unequivocal structure. Many mono-,[244,245] di-,[138, 139, 246] and tri-substituted[246] ethylenes have been made by various modifications of this procedure. Typical examples include various hexenes,[138] heptenes,[246] 1-hexadecene (63%),[243] and styrene (89%).[247] The formation of α-chloro and α,β-dibromo ethers from aldehydes is treated elsewhere (methods 117 and 65). When used for the preparation of olefins these compounds are not isolated or purified.[244] In coupling with the Grignard reagent, advantage is taken of the inert nature of halogen atoms in the *beta* position of ethers. An excess of 10-30% of organomagnesium compound is recommended.[138] Coupling in the *alpha* position takes place readily at 0°.[245] In order to introduce a second alkyl group, hydrogen bromide is eliminated (cf. method 20) and the resulting olefinic ether is treated with bromine at 0° followed by coupling of the dibromide with another Grignard reagent.

Elimination of bromine and ethoxyl groups with zinc is much the same as the elimination of two adjacent halogen atoms. The β-bromo ether is heated with a stirred suspension of powdered zinc[138, 244, 245] or zinc-copper couple[139, 247] in 90-95% ethanol,[139, 244, 247] n-propyl alcohol,[138] or isopropyl alcohol.[246] The preparation of 3-octene fails in n-propyl alcohol.[245] In several cases the products have been shown to be mixtures of cis and trans isomers.[209, 246] The yields for the first two steps of the synthesis are 70-90%. The coupling of the α,β-dibromo ethers with primary Grignard reagents takes place in 50-80% yields, whereas with secondary Grignard reagents only 30-55% yields are obtained.

The method has been adapted to the synthesis of 1,4-*diolefins* by coupling the bromo ethers with allylmagnesium bromide. Yields vary from 42% to 67% for C_5-C_7 compounds.[244, 248] n-Propyl and n-butyl alcohols as solvents are preferred for the decomposition of the β-bromo ethers.

Olefinic acetylenes of the general formula $RCH=CHC\equiv CR'$ are prepared by coupling the α,β-dibromo ethers with an acetylenic Grignard reagent followed by elimination of halogen and alkoxyl groups. Over-all yields are approximately 60%.[249, 250]

The action of zinc and alcohol on dibromo acetals, $CHBr_2CH(OR)_2$, gives olefinic halo ethers, $BrCH=CHOR$ (50-78%).[251] A similar elimination from α-halo ortho esters by means of sodium sand in boiling benzene leads to ketene acetals.

$$RCHBrC(OC_2H_5)_3 + Na \rightarrow RCH=C(OC_2H_5)_2 + NaBr + C_2H_5ONa$$

The method has been applied widely, and the yields are good (65-90%).[210]

22. Dehalogenation of Dihalides

$$RCHBrCH_2Br \xrightarrow{Zn} RCH=CH_2$$

This reaction is sometimes an important step in the purification of olefinic compounds prepared by other methods or for the protection of the double bond during oxidation of some other functional group in the molecule. The dihalides are usually unavailable except from the reaction of halogens with olefinic compounds (method 74). The reagent most commonly used for the regeneration of the double bond is zinc dust in 95% ethanol.[180, 474] The reaction is carried out at the boiling point of the solution or at lower temperatures if possible. No isomerization or carbonskeleton rearrangement takes place in the regeneration of simple olefins. Other reagents are magnesium in ether and sodium iodide in acetone.

Certain bases in non-alcoholic solvents cause debromination rather than dehydrohalogenation of chalcone dibromides[475] and stilbene dibromides (cf. method 13).

An isolated halogen atom is unaffected by zinc under the conditions of the reaction. Thus, 1,2,5-tribromopentane gives the *halo olefin*, 5-bromo-1-pentene (71%).[266]

A mixture of magnesium and magnesium iodide in ether is used to prepare the cyclic *olefinic ethers*, dioxene and dioxadiene, from the corresponding dichloro- and tetrachloro-dioxanes, respectively.[267]

The *allenes*, $RC = C = CR'$, are readily prepared by this method from tetrahalides and dihalo olefins. Typical procedures are given for methylallene (72%)[263] and 1-phenyl-1,2-butadiene (77%).[264] A convenient route to the allenes from allyl halides is as follows:[265]

$$RCH = CHCH_2Br \xrightarrow{Br_2} \underset{100\%}{RCHBrCHBrCH_2Br} \xrightarrow{KOH} \underset{70-80\%}{RCHBrC(Br) = CH_2} \xrightarrow[C_2H_5OH]{Zn}$$

$$\underset{70\%}{RCH = C = CH_2}$$

23. Elimination of Alcohol from Ethers and Acetals

$$RCH_2CH_2OR' \longrightarrow RCH = CH_2 + R'OH$$

The elimination of a molecule of alcohol from an ether has not been developed as a laboratory synthesis of simple olefins, although several olefinic compounds are conveniently made by this method. 1,3-Pentadiene is obtained in 72% yield by passing the ether of 2-penten-4-ol over alumina at 290°.[49] A series of α,β-olefinic esters has been made by heating alkyl α-alkoxyisobutyrates with phosphorus pentoxide at 60–100°. The yields range from 85% to 100%.[503]

Loss of alcohol from acetals occurs upon catalytic thermal decomposition[504] or when these compounds are heated to 140–170° with phosphorus pentoxide and quinoline or with phthalic anhydride.[507] α,β-Olefinic ethers including several alkoxy styrenes are formed in widely varying yields (36-86%).

$$RCH_2CH(OR')_2 \rightarrow R'OH + RCH = CHOR'$$

A platinum-on-asbestos catalyst at 290° is used in the conversion of diethyl acetal to ethyl vinyl ether (42%).[140] Ketals of the type $RC(OCH_3)_2CH_3$ are readily split by heating with a small amount of p-toluenesulfonic acid to yield substituted vinyl ethers of the type $RC(OCH_3)=CH_2$ (92%). In the presence of excess of a higher alcohol, $R'OH$, the olefinic ether corresponding to this alcohol, $RC(OR')=CH_2$, is formed in high yield.[506] Similarly, treatment of alkoxy ketals with acid catalysts gives alkoxy dienes and dialkoxy olefins.[505]

24. Pyrolysis of Esters

$$R_3CCH(OCOR')CH_2R \xrightarrow{\text{Heat}} R_3CCH = CHR + R'COOH$$

Vapor-phase pyrolysis or destructive distillation of esters is of value for the preparation of simple olefins in cases where direct dehydration of the alcohol leads to extensive isomerization or carbon-skeleton rearrangement (cf. method 19). The older literature has been reviewed, and the reaction has been applied to the preparation of nine straight-chain and branched olefins ranging in complexity from 1-butene to 2,2,4-trimethyl-2-pentene (75%).[229] Acetates of primary and secondary alcohols are generally used, although esters of boric acid are reportedly more easily pyrolyzed.[466] Pure t-butylethylene is obtained by the pyrolysis of the acetate of pinacolyl alcohol at 300-400°. Yields vary from 35% to 80%, depending upon the temperature and time of heating.[49, 223] The product contains no rearranged olefins. Pyrolysis of ethyl-t-butylcarbinol gives 7% rearranged olefins along with 4,4-dimethyl-2-pentene (77%).[224] Higher-molecular-weight 1-alkenes have been obtained in good yields by pyrolysis of the palmitates or stearates of the corresponding primary alcohols.[225, 227] Most products have been straight-chain olefins, e.g., 1-hexadecene (69%),[226] although a few branched compounds have been made in this way, e.g., 3,7-dimethyl-1-octene (84%).[222] Several styrenes have been made by pyrolysis of the corresponding α-phenethyl acetates.[445, 492]

Both conjugated and non-conjugated *dienes* have been made by this method from the acetates of diols and olefinic alcohols. A pyrolysis temperature of 575° is required for the conversion of 1,5-pentanediol

diacetate to 1,4-pentadiene (91%).[230] 2-Alkyl-1,3-butadienes are best
made by this method.[167,173] Direct dehydration of the olefinic alcohols
gives extensive rearrangement.

Pyrolysis of the acetate of benzyl-*o*-chlorophenylcarbinol at 300° gives
the *unsaturated halide, o*-chlorostilbene. This carbinol is resistant to
direct dehydration by potassium hydrogen sulfate at 180°.[233] This method
is also superior for the preparation of the olefinic aldehyde, α-isopropyl-
acrolein (50%),[167] and the *olefinic ketone,* methyl isopropenyl ketone
(98%).[488]

β-Lactones formed by the addition of ketene or ketene dimer to aldehydes are decarboxylated to α,β-olefinic methyl ketones (50–65%). The
over-all process is carried out by passing ketene into the aldehyde at
room temperature.[523]

Esters of acrylic acid are made by pyrolytic decomposition of α-
acetoxypropionates.[234,235,236] Direct dehydration of the α-hydroxy esters
fails.

Methoxyl, cyano, and *nitro* groups may also be present in the molecule
during pyrolysis. Examples are γ-methoxycrotononitrile (83%),[99] acrylonitrile (64%),[239] 1-cyano-1,3-butadiene (70%),[238] and a series of conjugated nitroalkenes. The esters of β-nitro alcohols are pyrolyzed at
195°[240] or merely refluxed with sodium bicarbonate in dilute aqueous
methanol. By the latter procedure the yields of conjugated nitro alkenes
are 90–95%.[241] Direct dehydration by heating the nitro alcohols to 180°
with phthalic anhydride has also been used.[443]

25. Pyrolysis of Methyl Xanthates (Chugaev)

$$RCH_2CH_2OH \xrightarrow[CS_2]{NaOH} RCH_2CH_2OCS_2Na \xrightarrow{CH_3I} RCH_2CH_2OCS_2CH_3 \xrightarrow{Heat}$$

$$RCH=CH_2$$

Thermal decomposition of methyl xanthates is similar to the pyrolysis
of acetates for the formation of the double bond. Olefins are obtained
from primary,[242] secondary,[165] and tertiary[170] alcohols without extensive
isomerization or structural rearrangement. The other products of the
pyrolysis of the methyl xanthates are methyl mercaptan and carbon oxy-
sulfide. The xanthates prepared from primary alcohols are more difficult
to decompose than those prepared from secondary and tertiary alcohols.
Over-all yields of 22–51% have been obtained for a number of tertiary
alkyl derivatives of ethylene.[165] Originally the xanthates were made by
successive treatment of the alcohol with sodium or potassium, carbon disulfide, and methyl iodide. In a modification of this procedure sodium

hydroxide is used in place of the metal.[242] A study of the stereochemistry
of the reaction supports the view that the mechanism involves intramolecular bonding of a β-hydrogen atom with a sulfur atom in *quasi* six-
membered ring formation.[427, 469]

26. Pyrolysis of Substituted Amines and Ammonium Salts

$$RCH(CH_3)N(CH_3)_3^+ \bar{O}H \longrightarrow \begin{array}{l} \xrightarrow{A} RCH(CH_3)N(CH_3)_2 + CH_3OH \\ \xrightarrow{B} RCH{=}CH_2 + (CH_3)_3N + H_2O \end{array}$$

Thermal decomposition of quaternary ammonium salts and bases is
most valuable in structural investigations of amines, particularly heterocyclic secondary amines (Hofmann exhaustive methylation).[282] The course
of the elimination (A or B) is determined by the nature of the four alkyl
groups on the nitrogen atom.[281] The reaction has found little use in the
synthesis of pure olefins. The yields are low even when three of the
alkyl groups are methyl radicals. Carbon-skeleton rearrangement does
not occur. Thus, the only olefin obtained by pyrolysis of pinacolyltri-
methylammonium hydroxide, $(CH_3)_3CCH(CH_3)N(CH_3)_3^+ \bar{O}H$, is *t*-butylethylene
(50%).[279]

Pyrolysis is accomplished by concentrating an aqueous solution of the
quaternary hydroxide at temperatures ranging from 30° to 200°. Thermal
decomposition on a platinum catalyst at an optimum temperature of
325° has been studied in detail in the preparation of cyclopropene (45%).[280]

Mannich bases formed by dialkylaminomethylation of various compounds
containing an active hydrogen atom are useful intermediates in the synthesis of certain olefinic compounds. The tertiary amine group of the
Mannich base is eliminated upon steam distillation or low-temperature
pyrolysis (120°) of the hydrochloride. The over-all reaction is illustrated
by the following preparation of an α,β-olefinic ketone.[285]

$$RCOCH_2R \xrightarrow[R'_2NH \cdot HCl]{HCHO} RCOCHRCH_2NR'_2 \cdot HCl \longrightarrow RCOC(R){=}CH_2$$

$$+ R'_2NH \cdot HCl$$

The methylene group of methyl ethyl ketone is active in the condensation
to give, upon pyrolysis, only methyl isopropenyl ketone (92%).[478] Olefinic
aldehydes,[167] acids,[283] esters,[286] and nitro compounds[284] have been prepared in a similar manner. The literature of the Mannich reaction has
been reviewed.[283]

27. Decarboxylation of Olefinic Acids

$$\text{ArCH}{=}\text{CHCO}_2\text{H} \xrightarrow[\text{Cu powder}]{\text{Quinoline}} \text{ArCH}{=}\text{CH}_2$$

As a preparative method the direct decarboxylation of olefinic acids is almost limited to the formation of styrenes and stilbenes from substituted cinnamic acids. Thermal decomposition of cinnamic acid gives styrene (41%).[252] The yield is nearly quantitative if the reaction is carried out in quinoline at 220° in the presence of a copper catalyst.[255] The yields of substituted styrenes where the aryl radical contains halo, methoxyl, aldehyde,[493] cyano, and nitro groups are in the range of 30–76%.[255–258] cis-Stilbene and cis-p-nitrostilbene are prepared in this way from the corresponding α-phenylcinnamic acids (65%).[254, 259] One aliphatic compound worthy of mention is 2-ethoxypropene, prepared by heating β-ethoxycrotonic acid at 165° (91% yield).[140] The mechanism of acid-catalyzed decarboxylations of this type has been studied.[473] Isomerization of the double bond from the α,β- to the β,γ-position before decarboxylation very likely occurs in many instances.[472]

A related reaction is the dehydrohalogenation and decarboxylation of β-halo acids to olefins.

$$\overset{\beta}{\text{R}}\text{CHX}\overset{\alpha}{\text{CHR}'}\text{CO}_2\text{H} \xrightarrow{\text{Na}_2\text{CO}_3} \text{RCH}{=}\text{CHR}'$$

Decarboxylation precedes dehydrohalogenation, however, as noted by analysis of the gas formed in the preparation of 2-butene. Decarboxylation occurs at 20–30° in sodium carbonate solution. Butene is then evolved at higher temperatures.[83] The reaction is important in the preparation of cis- and trans-2-alkenes from cis- and trans-alkylacrylic acids, RCH=CR'CO$_2$H, respectively.[83, 84, 260] Either the β-iodo or β-bromo acids prepared by the addition of hydrogen halide are suitable sources.

α,β-Dibromo and α,β,β-tribromo acids give bromo and dibromo olefins, respectively. A study of the influence of structure upon yield has been made.[261] Best yields are obtained when two alkyl groups are in the beta position or when two bromine atoms are in the alpha position. Decomposition to the bromo olefins is effected by refluxing the bromo acids with aqueous sodium carbonate solution or pyridine. β-Bromostyrenes, ArCH=CHBr and ArCH=CRBr, are similarly prepared from substituted cinnamic acid dibromides by heating with alcoholic sodium acetate solution.[262]

28. Coupling of Olefinic Acids and Diazonium Compounds

$$\text{ArCH} = \text{CHCO}_2\text{H} + \text{Ar}'\text{N}_2\text{X} \xrightarrow[\text{CuCl}_2]{\text{NaOAc}} \text{ArCH} = \text{CHAr}' + \text{N}_2 + \text{CO}_2 + (\text{HX})$$

This relatively new synthesis uses readily available materials and, although the yields are low, is preferred for obtaining certain stilbenes. A cooled solution of the diazonium salt is treated with sodium acetate and an acetone solution of the cinnamic acid. Then aqueous cupric chloride is added and the mixture is stirred at room temperature. The aryl radical may carry alkyl, halo, ether, ester, or nitro groups.[233, 272, 273, 477]

The synthesis has been extended to the preparation of substituted 1,4-diphenylbutadienes[233, 274, 277] and triarylethylenes[278] by the use of cinnamalacetic acid, $\text{C}_6\text{H}_5\text{CH} = \text{CHCH} = \text{CHCO}_2\text{H}$, and diarylacrylic acids, $\text{Ar}_2\text{C} = \text{CHCO}_2\text{H}$, respectively.

In the above reactions the aryl group adds to the α- rather than to the β-carbon atom of the α,β-olefinic acid. The reverse addition occurs in the conversion of acrylonitrile to cinnamonitrile (33%)[275] (cf. method 20).

29. Coupling of Organometallic Compounds with Halogen Compounds

$$\text{RMgX} + \text{CH}_2 = \text{CHCH}_2\text{X} \rightarrow \text{RCH}_2\text{CH} = \text{CH}_2 + \text{MgX}_2$$

This reaction affords an excellent method for the preparation of 1-alkenes. The halogen compound must be of the allylic or some other active type. The double bond is sometimes contained in the organometallic compound.[190, 193] The reaction is exothermic and takes place readily at room temperature. Short periods of heating are sometimes required to complete the coupling. For the preparation of the lower olefins, butyl ether is employed as the solvent for the Grignard reagent[178] or most of the ethyl ether is removed before the addition of the unsaturated halide.[177] In certain cases the olefins have been purified through the corresponding dibromides.[179, 180]

Allyl bromide has been used to prepare allylbenzene (82%),[185] allylcyclopentane (71%),[184] and neopentylethylene (85%).[180] Coupling with methallyl halides, $\text{CH}_2 = \text{C(CH}_3)\text{CH}_2\text{X}$, gives branched structures,[117, 203] and the use of 3-chlorocyclopentene leads to 3-substituted cyclopentenes such as 3-cyclopentylcyclopentene (73%).[195] Coupling of the latter halogen compound is catalyzed by copper vessels.[183] Crotyl chloride, $\text{CH}_3\text{CH} = \text{CHCH}_2\text{Cl}$, undergoes an allylic-type rearrangement during coupling.[197] However, since the allylic system in 4-bromo-2-pentene,

$CH_3CH = CHCHBrCH_3$, is symmetrically substituted, certain 2-alkenes may be prepared from this compound in good yields.[51]

The relatively inactive vinyl halides have been employed with some success in this reaction. α-Thienylmagnesium bromide is coupled with vinyl chloride in the presence of cobaltous chloride to give α-vinylthiophene (29%).[455] Also, the coupling of vinyl and allyl bromides by magnesium-copper alloy produces the diolefin, 1,4-pentadiene, in 15% yield.[199] Other *diolefins* have been prepared by this method.[51, 203] Biallyl is made in a one-step process from allyl chloride and magnesium (65%).[194] Either crotyl or methylvinylcarbinyl chloride gives 3-methyl-1,5-heptadiene, $CH_2 = CHCH(CH_3)CH_2CH = CHCH_3$, when the Grignard reagent is coupled with an excess of the chloride.[198]

Olefinic acetylenes are prepared by the use of acetylenic Grignard reagents. This coupling is catalyzed by copper salts.[181] 2,3-Dibromopropene, $BrCH_2C(Br) = CH_2$, gives *olefinic halides* of the type $RCH_2C(Br) = CH_2$ (45–65%).[196, 200–202] The remaining vinyl-type halogen atom is not affected. Coupling reactions of the homologs of 2,3-dibromopropene are complicated by allylic-type rearrangements.[459] *Olefinic ethers* may be prepared when the ether group is in either the halide or the Grignard reagent.[191, 192] The *olefinic amine*, 5-diethylamino-1-pentene, is obtained in 85% yield by refluxing a suspension of allylmagnesium chloride with diethylaminoethyl chloride.[193]

30. Partial Reduction of Acetylenic Compounds

$$RC \equiv CR' \xrightarrow{(H)} RCH = CHR'$$

An acetylene may be reduced to an olefin by sodium in liquid ammonia,[204, 206] by electrolytic reduction at a spongy nickel cathode,[205] or by partial hydrogenation over metal catalysts. Catalysts for the hydrogenation include nickel,[204, 207] iron,[208] colloidal palladium,[209] and palladium on barium sulfate[211] or calcium carbonate.[212, 214] Pure *trans* olefins are obtained from dialkylacetylenes by reduction with sodium in liquid ammonia. The yields are better than 90%. Catalytic hydrogenation leads to mixtures of *cis* and *trans* olefins in which the *cis* isomers predominate.[204, 206] Mono- and di-arylacetylenes have also been reduced.[205, 207, 220]

Diolefins have been prepared from diacetylenes and olefinic acetylenes;[212] for example, reduction of 2,7-nonadiyne by sodium and liquid ammonia gives *trans,trans*-2,7-nonadiene (72%).[204]

Olefinic alcohols,[213, 215, 463] *ethers*,[216, 217] and *acids*[218, 219, 462] have been prepared by this method. The nitro group is reduced to the *amino* group as in the formation of symmetrical diaminostilbenes from the corresponding dinitrotolanes.[220, 221]

31. Isomerization of Olefinic Compounds

$$RCH = CHCH_2R' \longrightarrow RCH_2CH = CHR'$$

Migrations of the double bond and carbon-skeleton rearrangements are important in the preparation of several olefinic compounds. A number of alkyl cyclopentenes are available in quantities suitable for synthetic work by the isomerization of cyclohexene and its homologs over alumina at 470–480°.[508] o-Allylphenol is isomerized by methanolic potassium hydroxide at 110° to o-propenylphenol (75%).[209] Several β,γ-olefinic acids are conveniently obtained from the corresponding α,β-isomers by equilibration in basic media. The two isomeric acids are readily separated by partial esterification of the resulting mixtures since the β,γ-isomers are more easily esterified.[510]

32. Symmetrical Diarylethylenes from Thiocarbonyl Compounds

$$ArC(=S)R \xrightarrow{\text{Ni or Cu}} ArRC = CRAr$$

Thiobenzaldehyde trimer, $(C_6H_5CHS)_3$, is decomposed at 230° by freshly reduced copper powder to give stilbene, $C_6H_5CH = CHC_6H_5$ (45%).[287] Several benzologs and alkoxyl derivatives of stilbene have been prepared by this method in low yields. The trimers of the thioaldehydes are readily prepared from their oxy analogs, hydrochloric acid, and hydrogen sulfide.

A similar condensation of thioacetophenone fails with copper powder but is accomplished over Raney nickel.[288] Copper bronze, however, is successfully used in the preparation of tetraphenylethylene from thiobenzophenone.[289]

33. Condensation of Halides by Sodium Amide

$$H_2C = C(CH_3)CH_2Cl \xrightarrow[\text{NH}_3]{\text{NaNH}_2} H_2C = C(CH_3)CH = CHC(CH_3) = CH_2$$

Allyl and methallyl chlorides have been condensed to trienes in 30% yields by adding sodium amide to a liquid ammonia solution of the halide.[268, 269] The low yields are due partly to dimerization of the products. Under the same conditions, α-chloroethylbenzene gives cis-α,α'-dimethylstilbene (40%).[276]

34. Additions to Conjugated Dienes (Diels-Alder)

$$
\begin{array}{ccc}
\overset{\displaystyle /\!\!/ CHR}{\underset{\displaystyle \diagdown CHR}{\overset{\displaystyle |}{\underset{\displaystyle |}{\overset{CH}{\underset{CH}{}}}}}}
&
\overset{CHR}{+\ \underset{CHZ}{\overset{\|}{}}}
& \rightarrow
\end{array}
$$

This reaction furnishes the best means of preparation of hundreds of cyclic olefinic compounds, most of which are beyond the scope of this book. In its simplest form, the reaction may be looked upon as a 1,4-addition of an olefinic compound to a conjugated diene. The scope of the reaction is inadequately represented by the above equation. The diene system may be a part of an aromatic or heterocyclic nucleus such as α-vinylnaphthalene or furan, or the double bonds may be parts of two independent molecules. The olefinic compound (dienophile) usually contains one or more groups (Z) which activate the double bond,[502] although this is not necessary; e.g., ethylene is condensed with butadiene at 200° to give cyclohexene (18%).[499] Triple bonds may replace double bonds in both the diene and dienophile. Excellent reviews of the reaction have been published.[496] *Cis* addition of the dienophile to the diene occurs, and several of the reactions have been shown to be truly reversible.[500] Butadiene is conveniently prepared in the laboratory by passing the vapors of cyclohexene over a hot filament.[511]

A related reaction is the substituting addition shown by acceptors such as maleic anhydride with simple olefins.[501]

$$
CH_3CH\!=\!CH_2\ +\ \underset{CHCO}{\overset{CHCO}{\left.\vphantom{\Big|}\right\|}}\!\!\diagdown\!\!O\ \rightarrow\ H_2C\!=\!CHCH_2CHCO\!\diagup\!O\!\diagup\!CH_2CO
$$

35. Condensation of Acetylenes with Compounds Containing Active Hydrogen (Vinylation)

$$
HC\!\equiv\!CH\ \longrightarrow\
\begin{cases}
\xrightarrow{HC\equiv CH} & H_2C\!=\!CHC\!\equiv\!CH \\[4pt]
\xrightarrow{HCl} & H_2C\!=\!CHCl \\[4pt]
\xrightarrow{ROH} & H_2C\!=\!CHOR \\[4pt]
\xrightarrow{RCO_2H} & H_2C\!=\!CHO_2CR
\end{cases}
$$

Acetylene is condensed to vinylacetylene and divinylacetylene by cuprous chloride and ammonium chloride.[514] Similar additions of other compounds containing an active hydrogen atom occur in the presence of various catalysts. Mercury salts are most effective in the vapor-phase reaction of acetylene with hydrogen chloride to give vinyl chloride (100%).[526] Basic catalysts such as potassium hydroxide, potassium ethoxide, or zinc oxide are used for the vinylation of alcohols, glycols, amines, and acids.[527] Most of these reactions involve the use of acetylene under pressure, and few have been described as simple laboratory procedures. Chloroacetic acid, however, reacts with acetylene at atmospheric pressure in the presence of mercuric oxide to yield vinyl chloroacetate (49%).[528]

36. Aldol Condensation

$$RCH_2CHOHCH(R)CHO \xrightarrow{-H_2O} \begin{cases} RCH_2CH = C(R)CHO \\ RCH = CHCH(R)CHO \end{cases}$$

Olefinic aldehydes and ketones result from the dehydration of the corresponding β-hydroxy compounds. The availability of olefinic compounds by this method is subject to the limitations of the aldol condensation (method 102) and the mode of dehydration. The tendency for dehydration to a conjugated system (α,β-olefinic compounds) is not as pronounced as is generally believed.

Many aldols dehydrate spontaneously at room temperature or upon acidification by acetic acid. Thus, the condensation of benzaldehyde with propionaldehyde or butyraldehyde gives the α-alkylcinnamaldehydes directly (58-67%).[312, 314]

$$C_6H_5CHO + RCH_2CHO \rightarrow C_6H_5CH = CRCHO + H_2O$$

However, direct dehydration of the aldol is inferior to pyrolysis of its benzoate (method 24) in the preparation of α-isopropylacrolein.[167]

The γ-hydrogen atom of crotonaldehyde is involved in its self-condensation and in its condensation with benzaldehyde,[318] acetaldehyde,[317] or cinnamaldehyde.[483] The linear olefinic aldehydes,

$$CH_3CH = CHCH = CHCH = CHCHO, \quad C_6H_5CH = CHCH = CHCHO,$$

$$CH_3CH = CHCH = CHCHO, \text{ and } C_6H_5CH = CHCH = CHCH = CHCHO,$$

are obtained directly in low yields. In the presence of dibutylamine crotonaldehyde condenses to dihydro-o-tolylaldehyde (75%).[481]

β-Hydroxy ketones obtained by the condensation of ketones or by the crossed condensation of aldehydes with ketones are important sources of olefinic ketones. Dehydration is effected by warming the ketols with oxalic acid,[77] dilute sulfuric acid,[72] hydrobromic acid,[71] phosphoric acid,[291] or a trace of iodine.[67, 70, 76] A typical example is the dehydration of di-acetone alcohol obtained from the self-condensation of acetone. The product is an equilibrium mixture of the conjugated and unconjugated isomers, $(CH_3)_2C=CHCOCH_3$ and $CH_2=C(CH_3)CH_2COCH_3$, in a ratio of 91 to 9, respectively.[67, 68]

The condensation of methyl ketones and subsequent dehydration to olefinic ketones is frequently accomplished without isolation of the ketol. The course of the condensation of methyl n-alkyl ketones depends upon the nature of the reagent. The methyl group is involved when a basic catalyst such as aluminum t-butoxide is employed. The unsaturated ketones are obtained in 70–80% yields; branched ketones give somewhat lower yields.[321]

$$2RCH_2COCH_3 \rightarrow RCH_2C(CH_3)=CHCOCH_2R$$

An acidic reagent such as hydrogen chloride causes condensation on the higher alkyl group of the ketone. β-Chloro ketones are formed which are dehydrohalogenated by the action of heat or by treatment with bases.[290, 320, 322] Thus, the condensation of methyl ethyl ketone in acid media leads to $C_2H_5C(CH_3)=C(CH_3)COCH_3$, whereas, with basic catalysts, condensation gives $C_2H_5C(CH_3)=CHCOC_2H_5$. These condensations are further complicated by the equilibria between the conjugated and non-conjugated forms of the olefinic ketones as well as by cis-trans isomerism.[290, 322, 488]

Methyl aryl ketones are converted smoothly to the olefinic ketones by aluminum t-butoxide. This reagent has the added advantage of removing the water formed by the dehydration of the ketols. The condensations are carried out at 60–140°, with the distillation of t-butyl alcohol from the reaction mixture if necessary. An example is the preparation of dypnone, $C_6H_5C(CH_3)=CHCOC_6H_5$, from acetophenone in 82% yield.[321]

The crossed condensation of an aromatic aldehyde with a ketone usually gives a high yield of the unsaturated ketone directly. Acetone is condensed with either one or two molecules of benzaldehyde to give ben-zalacetone (68%)[294] or dibenzalacetone (94%),[293] respectively. Alkyl styryl ketones, $C_6H_5CH=C(R)COR$, have been prepared from benzalde-hyde and higher ketones in the presence of hydrochloric acid[304] or alkali hydroxide.[480, 484] Substituents on the phenyl group include methyl,[302] hydroxyl,[298] methoxyl,[294, 299] and nitro[303] groups. A survey of condensations of substituted benzaldehydes and methyl ethyl ketone has been made.[306] The reaction with acetophenone leads to phenyl styryl ketones, the simplest of which is benzalacetophenone or chalcone, $C_6H_5CH=CHCOC_6H_5$ (85%).[295] Many substituted chalcones have been prepared with substituents on one or both of the phenyl groups.[300, 301, 305] Furfural,[311] 5-methylfurfural,[310] and 2-thiophenealdehyde[482] condense with ketones in good yields. Examples are furfuralacetone (66%),[307] furfural-acetophenone (90%),[308] and furfuralacetofuran (89%)[309] from acetone, acetophenone, and acetylfuran, respectively.

Substituted *cyclopentenones* are formed by internal aldol condensation of γ-diketones in the presence of basic catalysts.

$$RCH_2COCH_2CH_2COCH_3 \xrightarrow{OH^-} \begin{array}{c} CH_3 \\ | \\ C \\ \diagup \ \diagdown\diagdown \\ CH_2 \quad CR \\ | \qquad | \\ CH_2-CO \end{array}$$

The methyl group on the carbonyl carbon atom does not take part in the condensation. The single product is a 1-methyl-2-alkyl-1-cyclopenten-3-one. The yields are excellent except for the simplest γ-diketone, acetonylacetone. A similar condensation of α-acyllevulinates, $CH_3COCH_2CH(COR)CO_2CH_3$, leads to 4-carbomethoxy derivatives which are readily decarboxylated to cyclopentenones.[412]

Certain substituted *cyclohexenones* are made by an analogous internal aldol condensation and decarboxylation of *bis*-esters resulting from condensation of aldehydes with acetoacetic ester.

$$RCH[CH(COCH_3)(CO_2C_2H_5)]_2 \xrightarrow[CH_3CO_2H]{H_2SO_4} \underset{CO_2C_2H_5}{\underset{R}{\bigcirc}} CH_3 \xrightarrow[H_2SO_4]{NaOH;} \underset{R}{\bigcirc} CH_3$$

The R group may be aliphatic or aromatic.[409, 414] The use of formaldehyde in the initial condensation gives compounds without the 5-alkyl group.[413]

Cyclic ketones may be converted to olefinic cyclic ketones containing one additional ring. The sodium enolate of the ketone is treated with a Mannich base such as 1-diethylamino-3-butanone. The last substance is a source of methyl vinyl ketone, which condenses with the cyclic ketone enolate by the usual Michael addition. Subsequent cyclization of this 1,5-diketone yields the new dicyclic ketone.[423]

The reaction has been extended with certain improvements to the synthesis of higher polycyclic olefinic ketones.[422]

37. Condensation of Carbonyl Compounds with Compounds Containing an Active Methylene Group (Knoevenagel) *

The active methylene group of malonic acid readily takes part in condensations with aldehydes. The reaction is catalyzed by ammonia and various amines.[325] Decarboxylation occurs at room temperature or upon heating to 100° to give, in most cases, a mixture of α,β- and β,γ-olefinic

---

* The confusion resulting from the association of the name of a scientist with a reaction is deplorable. The Knoevenagel reaction has been stated to include the condensation of compounds containing an active hydrogen atom with a variety of carbonyl compounds in the presence of nitrogen bases.[335] The Doebner reaction usually signifies the use of pyridine as a catalyst, although this base was first used in this manner by Verley.[325] The Perkin reaction (method 38) is sometimes extended to include these and other named reactions. In this chapter the following arbitrary division has been made. When the active methylene group is part of a simple aldehyde or ketone, the condensation is discussed as an aldol condensation (method 36), and when it is part of a simple anhydride, the condensation is discussed as a Perkin reaction (method 38). All other condensations of this type are treated here (method 37) regardless of the nature of the catalyst.

acids. The use of pyridine as a solvent leads to good yields of α,β-olefinic acids from most low-molecular-weight aliphatic, alicyclic, and aromatic aldehydes. The small amount of β,γ-olefinic acid present is best removed by distillation and crystallization.[324] When acetaldehyde is used, the resulting crotonic acid is the *trans* form.[323] The best examples are found in the preparations of 2-hexenoic acid (64%)[326] and 2-nonenoic acid (85%),[372] although α,β-olefinic acids as high as 2-heptadecenoic acid have been made.[334] Triethanolamine is the best catalyst for the preparation of β,γ-olefinic acids such as 3-hexenoic acid (42%)[327] and β-cyclohexylidenepropionic acid (36%).[331]

Substituted benzaldehydes and malonic acid give cinnamic acids in excellent yields. Among the common nuclear substituents are methyl,[341] halo,[255, 342, 348] hydroxyl,[335, 341] methoxyl,[255, 341, 346, 347] cyano,[257] nitro,[343, 345] and diethylamino[255] groups. Other β-arylacrylic acids have been made by the use of α-naphthaldehyde,[344] phenanthraldehydes,[351] and furfural.[354] Phenyl-substituted aliphatic aldehydes have also been used in this condensation.[340, 349, 350]

Conjugated olefinic acids containing more than one double bond are prepared from olefinic aldehydes. Thus, acrolein and crotonaldehyde with malonic acid yield vinylacrylic acid (60%)[336] and sorbic acid, (32%)[337] respectively. In this manner, the completely conjugated 2,4,6,8,10,12-tetradecahexaenoic acid, $CH_3(CH=CH)_6CO_2H$, has been made.[339]

Olefinic esters may be obtained directly by the Knoevenagel reaction. Alkyl hydrogen malonates are used in place of malonic acid. Decarboxylation then gives the ester directly as in the preparation of ethyl 2-heptenoate (78%)[362] and methyl *m*-nitrocinnamate (87%).[345] Alkyl hydrogen malonates are readily available by partial hydrolysis of dialkyl malonates.[345] The use of malonic ester in the condensation leads to *olefinic diesters,* namely, alkylidenemalonates such as ethyl heptylidenemalonate (68%).[358] A small amount of organic acid is added to the amine catalyst[357] since the salts rather than the free amines have been shown to be the catalysts in condensations of this type.[355, 356] Various catalysts have been studied in the preparation of diethyl methylenemalonate. Increased yields are obtained in the presence of copper salts.[360] Trimethylacetaldehyde and malonic ester are condensed by acetic anhydride and zinc chloride.[404] Acetic anhydride is also used for the condensation of furfural and malonic ester to furfurylidenemalonic ester (82%).[406]

Certain aromatic and heterocyclic olefinic esters are best prepared by condensation of ethyl acetate and aromatic aldehydes by sodium sand (Claisen). Benzaldehyde in this reaction gives ethyl cinnamate, $C_6H_5CH=CHCO_2C_2H_5$ (74%).[394] *p*-Methylbenzaldehyde,[395] furfural,[406] furylacrolein,[406] and 2-thiophenecarboxaldehyde[352] have been condensed in a similar manner.

Ketones do not condense readily with malonic ester. The condensation of acetone and diethyl malonate is brought about by heating for 24 hours with acetic anhydride and zinc chloride. The yield of diethyl isopropylidenemalonate is 52%.[370] Under similar conditions methyl ethyl ketone condenses to the extent of only 19%.[405]

Olefinic dibasic acids with the carboxyl groups farther apart are prepared from aldehyde esters, $C_2H_5 O_2C(CH_2)_nCHO$, malonic acid, and pyridine.[359]

Ketones are condensed with diethyl succinate,

$$C_2H_5 O_2CCH_2CH_2CO_2C_2H_5$$

by a variety of basic reagents (Stobbe condensation).[529] Acetone, sodium ethoxide, and succinic ester give diethyl isopropylidenesuccinate, $(CH_3)_2C = C(CO_2C_2H_5)CH_2CO_2C_2H_5$ (41%).[358] Cyclohexanone has been similarly condensed.[374] Potassium t-butoxide and sodium hydride are excellent catalysts for condensations involving aryl ketones.[373] Here, acid esters are formed which are readily decarbethoxylated to a tautomeric mixture of olefinic acid and lactone. The over-all process combined with reduction of the lactones or olefinic acids is a method of introduction of a propionic acid residue at the site of a carbonyl group of a ketone.

$$R_2CO \rightarrow R_2C = \underset{\underset{CO_2C_2H_5}{|}}{C}CH_2CO_2H \xrightarrow{HBr} R_2\underset{\underset{O}{\lfloor\qquad\rfloor}}{C}CH_2CH_2CO \rightleftharpoons R_2C = CHCH_2CO_2H$$

Various modifications of this process have been used with moderate success to make β,γ-olefinic acids (pyrolysis of paraconic acids).[329, 373]

Acetoacetic ester condenses with aldehydes at 5–10° in the presence of piperidine, piperidine acetate, or acetamide. Several *olefinic β-keto esters* have been made in this way: for example, ethyl butylideneacetoacetate (81%).[371]

The methyl group of pyruvic acid, CH_3COCO_2H, undergoes condensation with aldehydes to give *olefinic α-keto acids*. Directions for improved yields are given for benzalpyruvic acid, $C_6H_5 CH = CHCOCO_2H$ (80%).[377] Aromatic aldehydes containing alkyl[375] and alkoxyl[376] groups, as well as olefinic aliphatic aldehydes[378] and furfural,[406] have been condensed.

The reaction of aliphatic, alicyclic, and aromatic aldehydes and ketones with cyanoacetic ester, $NCCH_2CO_2C_2H_5$, is general. The products are *α,β-olefinic cyanoacetates*. The aldehydes are condensed with the ester in the presence of amines[350, 368, 369] or with sodium cyanoacetate in the presence of sodium hydroxide.[366, 367] Similarly, cyanoacetic ester is condensed with ketones by catalysts such as acetamide or the acetates of ammonia or amines.[357, 364, 365, 530] The reaction is reversible and is carried to completion by removal of water.[363]

Excellent yields of alkylidenemalononitriles, $RR'C = C(CN)_2$, are obtained by condensation of aldehydes and ketones with malononitrile.[380-382] The catalysts are piperidine and benzylamine for aldehydes and ammonium acetate for ketones.

Olefinic cyanides are also produced by condensation of aldehydes or ketones[486, 531] with benzyl cyanide, $C_6H_5CH_2CN$. The yields from aldehydes are in the range of 36-91% when sodium ethoxide is used as the condensing agent.[379, 383, 485] Condensations involving all types of cyano compounds containing active methylene groups were reviewed in 1947.[494]

Olefinic nitro compounds are made by condensation of aldehydes and ketones with nitro compounds containing an active hydrogen atom.

$$RCHO + R'CH_2NO_2 \xrightarrow{\text{Base}} RCH = CR'NO_2$$

Nitro alcohols are usually isolated (method 102) but are sometimes dehydrated directly to olefinic nitro compounds as in the preparation of ω-nitro-2-vinylthiophene from nitromethane, thiophenecarboxaldehyde, and sodium hydroxide (78% yield).[352] Many substituted β-nitrostyrenes have been obtained by condensation of nitromethane or nitroethane[490] with substituted benzaldehydes.[445, 489] A methyl group on the benzene ring is sufficiently activated by nitro groups in the *ortho* or *para* position to cause condensation with aldehydes. A series of nitrostilbenes has been made in this way from substituted benzaldehydes.[491]

38. Condensation of Aromatic Aldehydes with Anhydrides and Acid Salts (Perkin)

$$ArCHO + (RCH_2CO)_2O + RCH_2CO_2Na \rightarrow ArCH = C(R)CO_2Na$$

This condensation is essentially an aldol-type reaction of an aldehyde with the methylene group of an anhydride. The sodium salt may be replaced by other basic catalysts such as potassium carbonate or tertiary amines.[398] If the acid residue in the anhydride is not the same as that in the sodium salt, an equilibrium between these substances may occur before condensation. Thus, a mixture of acetic anhydride and sodium butyrate or a mixture of butyric anhydride and sodium acetate gives cinnamic acid and α-ethylcinnamic acid in the same ratio.[399]

A review of the literature of this reaction to 1941 has been made.[384] The condensation is most valuable for the preparation of substituted cinnamic acids, particularly those containing halo, methyl, and nitro groups.[386, 387, 400] Furfural has been condensed in good yields with acetic anhydride,[390] butyric anhydride,[402] and sodium phenylacetate in the presence of acetic anhydride.[391] Homologs of acetic anhydride give α-substituted cinnamic acids, $ArCH = C(R)CO_2H$, where R is methyl (70%),[384] phenyl, (56%)[388] and vinyl (40%).[389] Sodium salts of arylacetic acids, $ArCH_2CO_2Na$, may be used with acetic anhydride for this purpose, the aryl group appearing on the α-carbon atom of the product.[391, 393]

The reaction is usually carried out be heating equimolar quantities of the aldehyde and salt with excess of the anhydride for 8 hours at 170–180°. Lower temperatures are often employed when potassium acetate[390] or trialkylamines[86, 388, 398] are used as condensing agents. Continuous removal of acetic acid during the reaction was found to have no effect on the yield of cinnamic acid.[385] Substitution of diacetimide for acetic anhydride gives cinnamide (77%).[495]

Highly conjugated diphenylpolyenes, $C_6H_5 (CH = CH)_n C_6H_5$, are obtained directly from the condensation of olefinic aldehydes such as cinnamaldehyde, $C_6H_5 CH = CHCHO$, with sodium salts of phenylacetic or succinic acids in the presence of lead oxide and acetic anhydride.[397, 401] The unsaturated acids first formed are decarboxylated under the conditions of the condensation.

39. Cleavage of Substituted α-Ketolactones

$$\underset{\rule{2.5cm}{0.5pt}\ O\ \rule{1.5cm}{0.5pt}}{RCHCH(COR')COCO} \xrightarrow{Br_2} \underset{\rule{2.5cm}{0.5pt}\ O\ \rule{1.5cm}{0.5pt}}{RCHCBr(COR')COCO} \xrightarrow{KHCO_3}$$

$$RCH = C(Br)COR' + (COOK)_2$$

Several α-bromo-α,β-olefinic ketones and esters have been prepared by an interesting cleavage of β-acyl or β-carbethoxy-α-ketolactones. It is unnecessary to isolate the bromolactone. Bromination and cleavage take place readily at 0–20°; over-all yields are 60–85%.[147] The β-acyl and β-carbethoxy-α-ketolactones are prepared by aldol-type condensations of aldehydes with the active methylene groups of ethyl β-acetylpyruvate, $CH_3COCH_2COCO_2C_2H_5$, and ethyl oxalacetate, $C_2H_5 O_2CCOCH_2CO_2C_2H_5$, respectively.

40. Stilbenes by Pyrolysis of Ethylene Sulfones[522]

$$2ArRC = NNH_2 \xrightarrow{HgO} 2ArRCN_2 \xrightarrow{SO_2} \underset{SO_2}{ArRC \overset{\diagdown\ \diagup}{\underset{}{-}} CRAr} \xrightarrow{Heat} ArRC = CRAr$$

41. Allenes by Reduction of Acetylenic Halides[525]

$$RCHClC \equiv CH \xrightarrow[(H)]{Zn-Cu} RCH = C = CH_2 \quad (71\%)$$

42. Vinylacetylenes from Sulfonates of Acetylenic Alcohols[517]

$$RCHOHCH_2C \equiv CH \xrightarrow{ArSO_2Cl} ArSO_3CHRCH_2C \equiv CH \xrightarrow{Base}$$

$$RCH = CHC \equiv CH \quad (91\%)$$

TABLE 2. OLEFINS

C_n	Compound	Method	Yield (%)	Chapter[ref.]	B.p./mm., n_D^t, (M.p.), Deriv.
			Aliphatic Olefins		
C_2	Ethylene	19	....	2^7	-104 *
C_3	Propene	....	85	2^{524}	
		19	....	2^7	
		19	90	2^{27}	-48/755
C_4	1-Butene	19	....	2^{34}	
		20	....	2^{115}	
		22	....	2^{27}	-6.7/755
		24	....	2^{229}	-7
		29	40	2^{177}	
	cis- and trans-2-Butene	19	80	2^{27}	
	2-Butene	19	48	2^{26}	
	cis-2-Butene	27	65	2^{83}	3/746
	trans-2-Butene	27	84	2^{83}	0.4/744
	Isobutene	19	100	2^{34}	
		19	82	2^{27}	-6.7/770
C_5	1-Pentene	21	65	2^{244}	29-31
		24	84	2^{467}	30/758, 1.3716
		29	54	2^{178}	30, 1.3717[21]
	2-Pentene	19	80	2^{15}	36/760, 1.3839[25]
		19	90	2^{38}	36
		20	90	2^{114}	36/760, 1.3796
		24	71	2^{229}	36, 1.3801
	cis-2-Pentene	22	74	2^{16}	36/744, 1.3828
		27	55	2^{84}	36/760, 1.3817
		30	55	2^{209}	38/760, 1.3822
	trans-2-Pentene	22	74	2^{16}	35.5/744, 1.3798
		27	90	2^{84}	36/760, 1.3799
	2-Methyl-1-butene	19	12	2^{24}	33/740, 1.3788
		19	80	2^{38}	33
		21	74	2^{139}	31/760, 1.3783
	3-Methyl-1-butene	20	11	2^{116}	19/731, 1.3640
		19	66	2^{38}	21
	Trimethylethylene	19	86	2^{24}	39.5/740, 1.3870
		19	36	2^{19}	38/744
C_6	1-Hexene	21	78	2^{138}	64/760, 1.3858
		24	66	2^{229}	64, 1.3887
		24	84	2^{467}	63/755, 1.3882
		29	....	2^{117}	62.5, 1.3891
	2-Hexene	21	75	2^{138}	68/760, 1.3928
	3-Hexene	21	85	2^{138}	67/760, 1.3942
	cis-3-Hexene	30	75	2^{206}	67/741, 1.3934
	trans-3-Hexene	30	40	2^{206}	68/741, 1.3938
	2-Methyl-1-pentene	21	65	2^{138}	62/760, 1.3921
		29	....	2^{117}	61, 1.3924

TABLE 2. OLEFINS 59

TABLE 2. (*continued*)

C_n	Compound	Method	Yield (%)	Chapter[ref.]	B.p./mm., n_D^t, (M.p.), Deriv.
			Aliphatic Olefins (*continued*)		
C_6	3-Methyl-1-pentene	21	72	2^{138}	54/760, 1.3835
	4-Methyl-1-pentene	21	57	2^{138}	54/760, 1.3825
	2-Methyl-2-pentene	21	40	2^{138}	67/760, 1.4005
	4-Methyl-2-pentene	21	70	2^{138}	58/760, 1.3885
		29	57	2^{51}	59, 1.3869[25]
	2-Ethyl-1-butene	20	21	2^{117}	63/728, 1.3967
		21	58	2^{138}	67/760, 1.3990
		24	80	2^{229}	65, 1.3974
		24	53	2^{228}	65/743, 1.3948[24]
	t-Butylethylene	19	54	2^{17}	41.4, 1.3765
		24	72	2^{223}	42/760
		25	58	2^{165}	41/760, 1.3759
		26	50	2^{279}	41, 1.3762
	2,3-Dimethyl-1-butene	19	20	2^{165}	55/748, 1.3899
		21	70	2^{138}	56/760, 1.3995
	Tetramethylethylene	19	80	2^{165}	72.5/747, 1.4115
C_7	1-Heptene	19	60	2^9	94/760, 1.4008
		21	88	2^{246}	95/760, 1.3999
		24	72	2^{229}	94, 1.3999
		29	20	2^{460}	94/760, 1.3996
		30	65	2^{205}	93/740, 1.3978
	2-Heptene	21	77	2^{246}	98/760, 1.4041
	3-Heptene	21	87	2^{246}	96/760, 1.4090
	2-Methyl-1-hexene	21	66	2^{246}	92/760, 1.4040
	3-Methyl-1-hexene	21	75	2^{246}	84/760, 1.3970
	4-Methyl-1-hexene	21	72	2^{246}	88/760, 1.3985
	5-Methyl-1-hexene	21	70	2^{246}	85/760, 1.3954
		29	21	2^{51}	86, 1.3940[25]
	2-Methyl-2-hexene	19	95	2^{37}	96
		21	....	2^{246}	95/760, 1.4075
	3-Methyl-2-hexene	21	75	2^{246}	93/760, 1.4080
	4-Methyl-2-hexene	21	92	2^{246}	86/760, 1.4000
	5-Methyl-2-hexene	21	91	2^{246}	86/760, 1.3995
	2-Methyl-3-hexene	21	78	2^{246}	87/760, 1.3991
	3-Methyl-3-hexene	19	93	2^{37}	96
	2-Ethyl-1-pentene	21	62	2^{246}	94/760, 1.4050
	2,3-Dimethyl-1-pentene	21	66	2^{246}	84/760, 1.4022
	2,4-Dimethyl-1-pentene	21	66	2^{246}	81/760, 1.3970
	3,3-Dimethyl-1-pentene	25	67	2^{165}	76/745, 1.3991
	4,4-Dimethyl-1-pentene	22	91	2^{180}	72/760, 1.3911
	(neopentylethylene)	29	85	2^{180}	71, 1.3918

For explanations and symbols see pp. xi–xii.

TABLE 2. (continued)

C_n	Compound	Method	Yield (%)	Chapter[ref.]	B.p./mm., n_D^t, (M.p.), Deriv.

Aliphatic Olefins (continued)

C_n	Compound	Method	Yield (%)	Chapter[ref.]	B.p./mm., n_D^t, (M.p.), Deriv.
C_7	3-Ethyl-2-pentene	19	96	2^{25}	97/737, 1.4142
		19	95	2^{37}	97
		19	84	2^{36}	96
		21	69	2^{246}	95/760, 1.4120
	2,3-Dimethyl-2-pentene	19	54	2^{37}	95
	2,4-Dimethyl-2-pentene	19	91	2^{37}	83
		19	49	2^2	83/760, 1.4018[22]
		24	88	2^{229}	83, 1.4042
	3,4-Dimethyl-2-pentene	21	60	2^{246}	86/760, 1.4052
	4,4-Dimethyl-2-pentene	24	71	2^{224}	77, 1.3983
		25	73	2^{165}	75/739, 1.3986
	2-Ethyl-3-methyl-1-butene	21	84	2^{246}	89/760, 1.4120
	2,3,3-Trimethyl-1-butene	19	67	2^2	78, 1.4029
		19	95	2^{37}	78
C_8	1-Octene	24	77	2^{229}	121, 1.4094
		24	70	2^{467}	122/760, 1.4087
		29	....	2^4	122/765, 1.4088
		30	90	2^{204}	121/760, 1.4088
	2-Octene (mostly cis)	30	....	2^{204}	126/760, 1.4150
	trans-2-Octene	30	81	2^{204}	125/760, 1.4132
	3-Octene	21	70	2^{245}	122/760, 1.4136
	trans-3-Octene	30	98	2^{204}	123/760, 1.4129
	cis-4-Octene	30	80	2^{205}	72/150, 1.4139
	trans-4-Octene	30	99	2^{204}	122/760, 1.4122
	4-Methyl-2-heptene	29	27	2^{51}	114, 1.4100[25]
	2-Ethyl-1-hexene	24	79	2^{229}	119, 1.4155
	2,2-Dimethyl-3-hexene	25	63	2^{165}	100/760, 1.4068
	4,4-Dimethyl-2-hexene	25	55	2^{165}	104/739, 1.4120
	2,4,4-Trimethyl-1-pentene	19	78	2^{24}	103/742, 1.4086
	2,2,4-Trimethyl-2-pentene	24	75	2^{229}	105, 1.4160
	2,2,3-Trimethyl-3-pentene	19	52	2^2	111, 1.4220
C_9	1-Nonene	24	74	2^{467}	147/760, 1.4157
	4-Methyl-2-octene	29	28	2^{51}	138, 1.4158[25]
	4,6-Dimethyl-2-heptene	29	36	2^{51}	130, 1.4135[25]
C_{10}	3,4-Diethyl-3-hexene	19	85	2^{41}	158/758, 1.4338
C_{11}	4-Methyl-1-decene	29	71	2^{190}	72/12, 1.4241[25]
C_{12}	1-Dodecene	24	70	2^{227}	93/13
C_{13}	1-Tridecene	29	77	2^{182}	103/10, 1.4328[25]

TABLE 2. OLEFINS   61

TABLE 2. (continued)

C_n	Compound	Method	Yield (%)	Chapter[ref.]	B.p./mm., n_D^t, (M.p.), Deriv.
		Aliphatic Olefins (continued)			
C_{16}	1-Hexadecene	21	63	2[243]	122/3, 1.4410
		29	47	2[189]	
C_{20}	3-Ethyloctadecene	19	100	2[21]	147/1.3
		Alicyclic Olefins			
C_3	Cyclopropene	26	45	2[280]	-36/744
C_5	Cyclopentene	19	83	2[49]	44/760, 1.4223
		19	90	2[435]	45
	Methylenecyclobutane	22	70	2[476]	42
C_6	Cyclohexene	19	89	2[13]	82
		19	73	2[40]	83
		19	73	2[29]	
		34	18	2[499]	83/758, 1.4461
	1-Methyl-1-cyclopentene	19	84	2[104]	75, 1.4335[22]
		19	89	2[176]	75, 1.4325
		31	34	2[508]	75, 1.4300[25]
	3-Methylcyclopentene	29	24 †	2[183]	65/760, 1.4207
	1-Methyl-2-cyclopentene	31	14	2[508]	65, 1.4198[25]
	Methylenecyclopentane	27	81	2[470]	74/745, 1.4354
	Isopropenylcyclopropane	19	80	2[170]	70.4/760, 1.4254
C_7	Cycloheptene	19	....	2[20]	115/756, 1.4576
		19	80	2[18]	114/760, 1.4580
	1-Methylcyclohexene	19	80	2[31]	110, 1.4498
	Methylenecyclohexane	24	72	2[232]	102/738
	3-Ethylcyclopentene	29	48 †	2[183]	98/760, 1.4321
	1,2-Dimethyl-1-cyclopentene	19	87	2[28]	105
	1,2-Dimethyl-2-cyclopentene	31	16	2[508]	92, 1.4265[25]
C_8	1-Ethyl-1-cyclohexene	19	58	2[11]	135/747
		19	80	2[31]	136, 1.4583
	1,1-Dimethyl-1-cyclohexene	19	81	2[10]	124/752, 1.4474[16]
	1,2-Dimethylcyclohexene	34	50	2[499]	138/760, 1.4612
	3-n-Propylcyclopentene	29	48 †	2[183]	126/760, 1.4359
	3-Isopropylcyclopentene	29	28 †	2[183]	121/760, 1.4380
	Allylcyclopentane	29	75	2[184]	126/739, 1.4410
C_9	1-n-Propylcyclohexene	19	80	2[31]	157, 1.4578
	1-Isopropylcyclohexene	19	80	2[31]	154, 1.4594
	1-Ethyl-4-methylcyclohexene	19	89	2[429]	149, 1.4526

For explanations and symbols see pp. xi–xii.

TABLE 2. *(continued)*

C_n	Compound	Method	Yield (%)	Chapter[ref.]	B.p./mm., n_D^t, (M.p.), Deriv.
		Alicyclic Olefins *(continued)*			
C_{10}	1-Cyclopentyl-2-cyclopentene	29	73	2[195]	186/760, 1.4760
C_{12}	1-Cyclohexylcyclohexene	....	85	2[513]	104/12, 1.493, 127Di
		Aryl-Substituted Olefins			
C_8	Styrene	19	90	2[434]	
		19	57	2[49]	67/60, 1.5470
		21	89	2[247]	146/760, 1.5463
		27	41	2[252]	45/40
C_9	Allylbenzene	29	82	2[185]	154/725
	1-Phenyl-1-propene	19	60	2[42]	62/11
		30	50	2[207]	167/746, 1.5420
	α-Methylstyrene	19	71	2[433]	
		19	90	2[1]	162/752, 1.5370[22]
		20	77	2[121]	72/30, 1.5350[25]
	p-Methylstyrene	19	83	2[166]	66/18, 1.5402[25]
C_{10}	*cis*-2-Phenyl-2-butene	19	59	2[427]	94/30, 1.5393[25]
	trans-2-Phenyl-2-butene	19	14	2[427]	77/30, 1.5192
	o-Allyltoluene	29	70	2[187]	181/750, 1.5171[24]
	p-Allyltoluene	29	75	2[187]	181/750, 1.5082
	m-Ethylstyrene	19	93	2[166]	74/14, 1.5315[25]
	p-Ethylstyrene	19	83	2[166]	68/16, 1.5350[25]
	2,4-Dimethylstyrene	19	85	2[107]	79/12, 1.539
		19	71	2[22]	90/25, 1.5423
	2,5-Dimethylstyrene	19	88	2[22]	83/23, 1.5395
	3,4-Dimethylstyrene	19	80	2[22]	96/26, 1.5463
	3,5-Dimethylstyrene	19	87	2[22]	58/4, 1.5382
	α,4-Dimethylstyrene	20	60	2[121]	77/19, 15290[25]
	1,4-Dihydronaphthalene	22	67	2[271]	(25)
C_{11}	*m*-Allylethylbenzene	29	65	2[186]	88/18
C_{12}	*m-s*-Butylstyrene	19	61	2[23]	98/15, 1.5246
	m-t-Butylstyrene	19	61	2[23]	100/17, 1.5234
	p-t-Butylstyrene	19	76	2[166]	100/14, 1.5245[25]
	3,5-Diethylstyrene	19	83	2[166]	107/15, 1.5280[25]
	α-Vinylnaphthalene	19	57	2[166]	87/2.0, 1.6436[25]
	β-Vinylnaphthalene	19	75	2[166]	79/2.5, (66)
C_{13}	α-Allylnaphthalene	29	81	2[188]	128/8, 1.6089[25]
C_{14}	1,1-Diphenylethylene	19	70 †	2[14]	113/2
	cis-Stilbene (isostilbene)	27	65	2[254]	134/10
		30	80	2[205]	145/18, 1.6265
	trans-Stilbene	19	57	2[12]	(124)

TABLE 3. DIOLEFINS 63

TABLE 2. (*continued*)

C_n	Compound	Method	Yield (%)	Chapter[ref.]	B.p./mm., n_D^t, (M.p.), Deriv.
		Aryl-Substituted Olefins (*continued*)			
C_{14}	Stilbene	19	55	2^{30}	(124), 238Di
		28	25	2^{273}	(125)
		32	45	2^{287}	(124)
	o-Vinylbiphenyl	19	70	2^{172}	116/1, 1.6168[25]
	m-Vinylbiphenyl	19	55	2^{172}	112/1, 1.6263[25]
	p-Vinylbiphenyl	19	82	2^{172}	137/6, (119)
	1-(β-Naphthyl)-1-butene	20	81 †	2^{446}	(40)
C_{15}	1,1-Diphenyl-1-propene	19	70	2^{35}	
	o-Methylstilbene	28	12	2^{477}	125/0.15, 159Di
	m-Methylstilbene	28	14	2^{477}	(48), 176Di
	p-Methylstilbene	28	32	2^{273}	(120), 188Di *
	2-Vinylfluorene	19	28	2^{166}	(134)
C_{16}	1,3-Diphenyl-1-butene	22	89	2^{474}	167/9, 1.5930
	α, α´-Dimethylstilbene	32	18	2^{288}	(106), 153Di
	cis-α,α´-Dimethylstilbene	33	40	2^{276}	(67)
	1-Vinylacenaphthene	19	32	2^{166}	135/2, 1.6512[25]
C_{20}	Triphenylethylene	19	59	2^{431}	(69)

For explanations and symbols see pp. xi–xii.

TABLE 3. DIOLEFINS

C_n	Compound	Method	Yield (%)	Chapter[ref.]	B.p./mm., n_D^t, (M.p.), Deriv.
		Aliphatic Diolefinic Hydrocarbons			
C_3	Allene	22	....	2^{516}	-34/762
C_4	Methylallene	22	72	2^{263}	10, 1.4205[1]
	1,3-Butadiene	20	30	2^{122}	
		22	90	2^{270}	-4
		34	75	2^{511}	
C_5	1,2-Pentadiene (ethylallene)	22	70	2^{265}	45, 1.4149
	1,3-Pentadiene	19	....	2^6	43, 1.4309
		23	72	2^{49}	42/770, 1.4304
		24	65	2^{230}	44, 1.4314, 114Te
	1,4-Pentadiene	21	75	2^{516}	26/767
		21	53	2^{248}	29/742, 1.3880, 86Te
		24	91	2^{230}	27, 1.3865[26], 86Te
		29	15	2^{199}	26/756, 1.3883

For explanations and symbols see pp. xi–xii.

TABLE 3. (*continued*)

C_n	Compound	Method	Yield (%)	Chapter[ref.]	B.p./mm., n_D^t, (M.p.), Deriv.
		Aliphatic Diolefinic Hydrocarbons (*continued*)			
C_5	2-Methyl-1,3-butadiene	19	....	2^6	34/748, 1.4207
	(isoprene)	19	88	2^{47}	34
		34	58	2^{512}	
C_6	1,2-Hexadiene (*n*-propylallene)	22	70	2^{265}	78, 1.4298[17]
		40	71	2^{525}	75/740, 1.4282
	1,4-Hexadiene	21	67	2^{248}	64/745, 1.4162, 64Te
		24	34	2^{461}	66/761, 1.4167[16]
	1,5-Hexadiene (biallyl)	29	65	2^{194}	60/760, 1.4040
	2,4-Hexadiene	24	66	2^{229}	78–81, 1.4469
	1,3,5-Hexatriene	19	64	2^{175}	80, 1.5035[28]
		33	30	2^{268}	75/748, 1.4770[25]
	4-Methyl-1,2-pentadiene (isopropylallene)	22	70	2^{265}	70, 1.4232[22]
	2-Methyl-1,3-pentadiene	19	....	2^6	76/765, 1.4467
	3-Methyl-1,3-pentadiene	19	64	2^{52}	75–80
		19	....	2^6	78/747, 1.4511
		19	42	2^{54}	78, 1.4561[21]
	4-Methyl-1,3-pentadiene	19	23	2^{45}	76/760
		20	....	2^6	77/758, 1.4525
	2-Ethylbutadiene	24	23	2^{173}	66, 1.4325
	2,3-Dimethyl-1,3-butadiene	19	72	2^{49}	69/765, 1.4390
		19	86	2^{44}	70
		19	60	2^{43}	70
		24	85	2^{231}	69
C_7	1,2-Heptadiene (*n*-butylallene)	22	70	2^{265}	106, 1.4360[21]
	1,4-Heptadiene	21	42	2^{248}	92/755, 1.4202
		24	80	2^{461}	93/772, 1.4273[11]
	1,6-Heptadiene	30	61	2^{204}	90/760, 1.4142
	5-Methyl-1,2-hexadiene (isobutylallene)	22	70	2^{265}	96, 1.4282[19]
	4-Methyl-1,3-hexadiene	19	88	2^{123}	98, 1.4342[25]
	2-Methyl-2,4-hexadiene	20	68	2^{124}	107/760
	2,4-Dimethyl-1,3-pentadiene	19	60 †	2^3	93, 1.4412
	2-Isopropyl-1,3-butadiene	24	54	2^{173}	86, 1.4337
	1,1,3-Trimethyl-1,3-butadiene	19	58 †	2^{46}	95/771
		19	65	2^{48}	93

TABLE 3. DIOLEFINS 65

TABLE 3. (continued)

C_n	Compound	Method	Yield (%)	Chapter ref.	B.p./mm., n_D^t, (M.p.), Deriv.
	Aliphatic Diolefinic Hydrocarbons (continued)				
C_8	1,4-Octadiene	24	57	2[461]	119/746, 1.4322[15]
	2,4-Octadiene	19	33	2[51]	134, 1.4542[25]
	2,4,6-Octatriene	19	43	2[56]	45/11
	4-Methyl-1,5-heptadiene	29	49	2[51]	111, 1.4213[25]
	2,2-Dimethyl-3,4-hexadiene	19	19	2[51]	108, 1.4425[25]
	2,5-Dimethyl-1,5-hexadiene	29	80	2[203]	137/760
	2,5-Dimethylhexatriene	33	27	2[269]	90/200, 1.5150[21]
C_9	trans-trans-2,7-Nonadiene	30	79	2[204]	150/760, 1.4358
	2,5,5-Trimethyl-1,3-hexadiene	19	27 †	2[50]	128/732, 1.4489
	2-n-Amyl-1,3-butadiene	24	43	2[173]	69/65, 1.4450
C_{10}	4,5-Dimethyl-2,6-octadiene	29	38	2[51]	154, 1.4375[25]
	1,1-Dimethyl-3-t-butyl-1,3-butadiene	19	64	2[48]	59/32
	Alicyclic Diolefinic Hydrocarbons				
C_5	Cyclopentadiene	34	70	2[516]	41/772
C_6	1,3-Cyclohexadiene	20	90	2[124]	
	Cyclohexadiene	23	57	2[516]	80/757, 1.4740
	1,4-Dihydrobenzene	4	65 †	2[80]	89
C_7	Cycloheptadiene	26	90	2[18]	121/758
	Cycloheptatriene	20	66	2[18]	115/760, 1.5243
	1-Vinyl-1-cyclopentene	19	88	2[5]	114
C_8	1-Vinyl-1-cyclohexene	30	44	2[212]	145, 1.4911[14]
C_{10}	1-(3-Butenyl)-1-cyclohexene	19	70	2[8]	62/10, 1.4745[18]
	Aromatic Diolefinic Hydrocarbons				
C_{10}	1-Phenyl-1,2-butadiene	22	77	2[264]	77/10, 1.5716[24]
	trans-1-Phenyl-1,3-butadiene	19	75	2[108]	78–81/8, 1.6090
	β-Phenylbutadiene	20	46 †	2[518]	67/13
	p-Divinylbenzene	19	83	2[166]	46/1, (31)
		27	45	2[493]	(31)
C_{12}	1,3,5-Trivinylbenzene	19	75	2[53]	73/0.5, 1.5967
C_{16}	1,4-Diphenylbutadiene (bistyryl)	38	25	2[397]	(153)
	2,3-Diphenylbutadiene	19	80	2[518]	(51)

For explanations and symbols see pp. xi–xii.

REFERENCES FOR CHAPTER 2

[1] Sabetay, *Bull. soc. chim. France*, **47**, 614 (1930).
[2] Wibaut et al., *Rec. trav. chim.*, **58**, 329 (1939).
[3] Waterman and Kok, *Rec. trav. chim.*, **52**, 234 (1933).
[4] Waterman and Kok, *Rec. trav. chim.*, **53**, 725 (1934).
[5] Backer and vander Bij, *Rec. trav. chim.*, **62**, 564 (1943).
[6] Farmer and Warren, *J. Chem. Soc.*, 3221 (1931).
[7] Newth, *J. Chem. Soc.*, **79**, 917 (1901).
[8] Linstead et al., *J. Chem. Soc.*, 1138 (1937).
[9] Griffith, *J. Chem. Soc.*, 715 (1945).
[10] Elliott and Linstead, *J. Chem. Soc.*, 662 (1938); Hibbit and Linstead, *ibid.*, 474 (1936).
[11] Baker and Groves, *J. Chem. Soc.*, 1148 (1939).
[12] Shriner and Berger, *Org. Syntheses*, **23**, 86 (1943); Ballard and Dehn, *J. Am. Chem. Soc.*, **54**, 3969 (1932).
[13] Coleman and Johnstone, *Org. Syntheses*, Coll. Vol. I, 183 (1941); Hershberg and Ruhoff, *ibid.*, 184 (1941).
[14] Allen and Converse, *Org. Syntheses*, Coll. Vol. I, 226 (1941).
[15] Norris, *Org. Syntheses*, Coll. Vol. I, 430 (1941).
[16] Lucas, Schlatter, and Jones, *J. Am. Chem. Soc.*, **63**, 27 (1941).
[17] Cramer and Glasebrook, *J. Am. Chem. Soc.*, **61**, 230 (1939).
[18] Kohler et al., *J. Am. Chem. Soc.*, **61**, 1058 (1939).
[19] Walling, Kharasch, and Mayo, *J. Am. Chem. Soc.*, **61**, 2695 (1939).
[20] Pines, Edeleanu, and Ipatieff, *J. Am. Chem. Soc.*, **67**, 2194 (1945).
[21] Sherk, Augur, and Soffer, *J. Am. Chem. Soc.*, **67**, 2240 (1945).
[22] Marvel, Saunders, and Overberger, *J. Am. Chem. Soc.*, **68**, 1085 (1946).
[23] Marvel, Allen, and Overberger, *J. Am. Chem. Soc.*, **68**, 1088 (1946).
[24] Whitmore et al., *J. Am. Chem. Soc.*, **64**, 2970 (1942).
[25] Church, Whitmore, and McGrew, *J. Am. Chem. Soc.*, **56**, 180 (1934).
[26] Lucas, Prater, and Morris, *J. Am. Chem. Soc.*, **57**, 723 (1935); Young and Lucas, *ibid.*, **52**, 1964 (1930); Wilson and Lucas, *ibid.*, **58**, 2398 (1936).
[27] Kistiakowsky et al., *J. Am. Chem. Soc.*, **57**, 876 (1935).
[28] Bartlett and Bavley, *J. Am. Chem. Soc.*, **60**, 2418 (1938).
[29] Bartlett and Berry, *J. Am. Chem. Soc.*, **56**, 2684 (1934).
[30] Pearl and Dehn, *J. Am. Chem. Soc.*, **60**, 58 (1938).
[31] Signaigo and Cramer, *J. Am. Chem. Soc.*, **55**, 3329 (1933).
[32] Whitmore and Meunier, *J. Am. Chem. Soc.*, **55**, 3721 (1933); Whitmore and Rothrock, *ibid.*, **55**, 1106 (1933).
[33] Whitmore and Stahly, *J. Am. Chem. Soc.*, **55**, 4153 (1933).
[34] Pines, *J. Am. Chem. Soc.*, **55**, 3892 (1933).
[35] Hussey, Marvel, and Hager, *J. Am. Chem. Soc.*, **52**, 1123 (1930).
[36] Lucas, *J. Am. Chem. Soc.*, **51**, 252 (1929).
[37] Edgar, Calingaert, and Marker, *J. Am. Chem. Soc.*, **51**, 1485 (1929).
[38] Norris and Joubert, *J. Am. Chem. Soc.*, **49**, 884 (1927).
[39] Adkins and Perkins, *J. Am. Chem. Soc.*, **47**, 1163 (1925).
[40] Osterberg and Kendall, *J. Am. Chem. Soc.*, **42**, 2620 (1920).
[41] Koch and Hilberath, *Ber.*, **73**, 1171 (1940).
[42] Wittig and Harborth, *Ber.*, **77**, 319 (1944).
[43] Allen and Bell, *Org. Syntheses*, **22**, 39 (1942); Kilby and Kipping, *J. Chem. Soc.*, 437 (1939).

[44] Newton and Coburn, *Org. Syntheses*, 22, 40 (1942).

[45] Bachman and Goebel, *J. Am. Chem. Soc.*, 64, 787 (1942).

[46] Jitkow and Bogert, *J. Am. Chem. Soc.*, 63, 1981 (1941).

[47] Taylor and Shenk, *J. Am. Chem. Soc.*, 63, 2756 (1941).

[48] Fieser and Wieghard, *J. Am. Chem. Soc.*, 62, 154 (1940).

[49] Dolliver et al., *J. Am. Chem. Soc.*, 59, 833 (1937).

[50] Campbell, *J. Am. Chem. Soc.*, 59, 1982 (1937).

[51] Mulliken, Wakeman, and Gerry, *J. Am. Chem. Soc.*, 57, 1607 (1935).

[52] Kyrides, *J. Am. Chem. Soc.*, 55, 3434 (1933).

[53] Mowry and Ringwald, *J. Am. Chem. Soc.*, 72, 2037 (1950).

[54] Fisher and Chittenden, *Ind. Eng. Chem.*, 22, 869 (1930).

[55] Bacon and Farmer, *J. Chem. Soc.*, 1065 (1937).

[56] Kuhn and Grundmann, *Ber.*, 71, 445 (1938).

[57] Kharasch, Rossin, and Fields, *J. Am. Chem. Soc.*, 63, 2560 (1941).

[58] Price and Marshall, *J. Org. Chem.*, 8, 532 (1943).

[59] Hill and Fischer, *J. Am. Chem. Soc.*, 44, 2582 (1922).

[60] Emerson and Agnew, *J. Am. Chem. Soc.*, 67, 518 (1945).

[61] Emerson and Lucas, *J. Am. Chem. Soc.*, 70, 1180 (1948); cf. ref. 437.

[62] Marvel and Moon, *J. Am. Chem. Soc.*, 62, 47 (1940); cf. ref. 437.

[63] Porter and Suter, *J. Am. Chem. Soc.*, 57, 2024 (1935).

[64] Marvel, Allen, and Overberger, *J. Am. Chem. Soc.*, 68, 1089 (1946).

[65] Kamm and Marvel, *Org. Syntheses*, Coll. Vol. I, 42 (1941).

[66] Urion, *Ann. chim.*, (11) 1, 33 (1934).

[67] Conant and Tuttle, *Org. Syntheses*, Coll. Vol. I, 345 (1941).

[68] Stross, Monger, and Finch, *J. Am. Chem. Soc.*, 69, 1627 (1947).

[69] Bourdiol, Calcagni, and Ducasse, *Bull. soc. chim. France*, (5) 8, 380 (1941).

[70] Milas et al., *J. Am. Chem. Soc.*, 70, 1602 (1948).

[71] Kyrides, *J. Am. Chem. Soc.*, 55, 3431 (1933); Powell, *ibid.*, 46, 2514 (1924).

[72] Smith, Chase, and Rhodes, *J. Am. Chem. Soc.*, 66, 1548 (1944).

[73] Powell and Ballard, *J. Am. Chem. Soc.*, 60, 1914 (1938).

[74] Powell and Hagemann, *J. Am. Chem. Soc.*, 66, 372 (1944).

[75] Colonge, *Bull. soc. chim. France*, (5) 3, 415 (1936).

[76] Rapson, *J. Chem. Soc.*, 1626 (1936).

[77] Vavon and Flurer, *Bull. soc. chim. France*, (4) 45, 755 (1929).

[78] Allen, Gates, and VanAllan, *Org. Syntheses*, 27, 30 (1947).

[79] Bartlett and Woods, *J. Am. Chem. Soc.*, 62, 2935 (1940).

[80] Bardhan and Banerji, *J. Chem. Soc.*, 477 (1935).

[81] Bruce, *Org. Syntheses*, Coll. Vol. II, 12 (1943).

[82] Kloetzel, *J. Am. Chem. Soc.*, 62, 1710 (1940).

[83] Young, Dillon, and Lucas, *J. Am. Chem. Soc.*, 51, 2528 (1929).

[84] Lucas and Prater, *J. Am. Chem. Soc.*, 59, 1682 (1937).

[85] Natelson and Gottfried, *J. Am. Chem. Soc.*, 58, 1435 (1936).

[86] Schwenk and Papa, *J. Am. Chem. Soc.*, 67, 1432 (1945).

[87] Shriner in *Organic Reactions*, Vol. I, John Wiley & Sons, New York, 1942, pp. 11–14.

[88] Braun, *J. Am. Chem. Soc.*, 52, 3170 (1930).

[89] Bohnsack, *Ber.*, 74, 1582 (1941); cf. ref. 421.

[90] Linstead and Meade, *J. Chem. Soc.*, 942 (1934).

[91] Cook and Linstead, *J. Chem. Soc.*, 956 (1934).

[92] Cook and Lawrence, *J. Chem. Soc.*, 1637 (1935).

[93] Kon and Nargund, *J. Chem. Soc.*, 2461 (1932).
[94] Huston, Goerner, and György, *J. Am. Chem. Soc.*, 70, 390 (1948).
[95] Linstead, Whetstone, and Levine, *J. Am. Chem. Soc.*, 64, 2019 (1942).
[96] Emerson et al., *J. Am. Chem. Soc.*, 68, 674 (1946).
[97] Emerson et al., *J. Am. Chem. Soc.*, 68, 1665 (1946).
[98] Rapson and Robinson, *J. Chem. Soc.*, 1538 (1935).
[99] Koelsch, *J. Am. Chem. Soc.*, 65, 2462 (1943).
[100] Gotkis and Cloke, *J. Am. Chem. Soc.*, 56, 2711 (1934).
[101] King and Robinson, *J. Chem. Soc.*, 467 (1941).
[102] Kern and Fernow, *J. prakt. Chem.*, 160, 297 (1942).
[103] Jacobs et al., *J. Am. Chem. Soc.*, 68, 1311 (1946).
[104] Piaux, *Ann. chim.*, (11) 4, 209 (1935).
[105] Marvel and Schertz, *J. Am. Chem. Soc.*, 65, 2056 (1943).
[106] Brown and Marvel, *J. Am. Chem. Soc.*, 59, 1177 (1937).
[107] Harispe, *Ann. chim.*, (11) 6, 342 (1936).
[108] Grummitt and Becker, *Org. Syntheses*, 30, 75 (1950).
[109] Prevost, *Bull. soc. chim. France*, (5) 8, 89 (1941).
[110] Milas, MacDonald, and Black, *J. Am. Chem. Soc.*, 70, 1831 (1948).
[111] Thompson, Milas, and Rovno, *J. Am. Chem. Soc.*, 63, 754 (1941).
[112] Bardan, *Bull. soc. chim. France*, (4) 49, 1551 (1931).
[113] Bardan, *Bull. soc. chim. France*, (5) 1, 368 (1934).
[114] Sherrill, Otto, and Pickett, *J. Am. Chem. Soc.*, 51, 3028 (1929).
[115] Olson and Whitacre, *J. Am. Chem. Soc.*, 65, 1019 (1943).
[116] Whitmore et al., *J. Am. Chem. Soc.*, 63, 126 (1941).
[117] Whitmore et al., *J. Am. Chem. Soc.*, 62, 795 (1940).
[118] Asinger, *Ber.*, 75, 1247 (1942).
[119] Ward and Fulweiler, *J. Am. Chem. Soc.*, 56, 1641 (1934).
[120] Loevenich et al., *Ber.*, 62, 3084 (1929).
[121] Bachman and Hellman, *J. Am. Chem. Soc.*, 70, 1772 (1948).
[122] Muskat and Northrup, *J. Am. Chem. Soc.*, 52, 4050 (1930).
[123] Milas and McAlevy, *J. Am. Chem. Soc.*, 57, 580 (1935).
[124] Ziegler et al., *Ann.*, 551, 113 (1942).
[125] Semb and McElvain, *J. Am. Chem. Soc.*, 53, 690 (1931).
[126] Noller and Dinsmore, *J. Am. Chem. Soc.*, 54, 1025 (1932).
[127] French, McShan, and Johler, *J. Am. Chem. Soc.*, 56, 1346 (1934).
[128] French and Wade, *J. Am. Chem. Soc.*, 57, 1574 (1935).
[129] Burkhardt and Cocker, *Rec. trav. chim.*, 50, 843 (1931).
[130] Spence, *J. Am. Chem. Soc.*, 55, 1290 (1933).
[131] Lespieau and Bourguel, *Org. Syntheses*, Coll. Vol. I, 209 (1941).
[132] Hurd and Webb, *J. Am. Chem. Soc.*, 58, 2191 (1936).
[133] Henne and Haeckl, *J. Am. Chem. Soc.*, 63, 2692 (1941).
[134] Prins, *Rec. trav. chim.*, 54, 250 (1935).
[135] Kharasch and Fuchs, *J. Am. Chem. Soc.*, 65, 506 (1943).
[136] Wittig and Harborth, *Ber.*, 77, 311 (1944).
[137] Wittig and Harborth, *Ber.*, 77, 320 (1944).
[138] Schmitt and Boord, *J. Am. Chem. Soc.*, 54, 758 (1932).
[139] Sherrill and Walter, *J. Am. Chem. Soc.*, 58, 742 (1936).
[140] Dolliver et al., *J. Am. Chem. Soc.*, 60, 440 (1938).
[141] Ruigh and Major, *J. Am. Chem. Soc.*, 53, 2662 (1931).
[142] Powell and Adams, *J. Am. Chem. Soc.*, 42, 652 (1920).

[143] McElvain and Fajardo-Pinzón, *J. Am. Chem. Soc.*, 67, 652 (1945).
[144] Hurd and Botteron, *J. Am. Chem. Soc.*, 68, 1200 (1946).
[145] Frank et al., *J. Am. Chem. Soc.*, 68, 1365 (1946).
[146] Quelet, *Bull. soc. chim. France*, (5) 7, 196, 205 (1940).
[147] Nield, *J. Am. Chem. Soc.*, 67, 1145 (1945).
[148] Allen et al., *J. Am. Chem. Soc.*, 62, 663 (1940).
[149] Colonge, *Bull. soc. chim. France*, (5) 3, 2116 (1936).
[150] Colonge and Mostafavi, *Bull. soc. chim. France*, (5) 6, 342 (1939).
[151] Cromwell, Cram, and Harris, *Org. Syntheses*, 27, 9 (1947).
[152] Christ and Fuson, *J. Am. Chem. Soc.*, 59, 895 (1937).
[153] Dey, *J. Chem. Soc.*, 1059 (1937).
[154] Guha and Sankaran, *Org. Syntheses*, 26, 57 (1946).
[155] Gardner and Rydon, *J. Chem. Soc.*, 53 (1938).
[156] Phillips, *J. Chem. Soc.*, 2981 (1926).
[157] v. Braun and Nelles, *Ber.*, 66, 1467 (1933).
[158] Marvel et al., *J. Am. Chem. Soc.*, 62, 3497 (1940).
[159] Philippi, Hendgen, and Hernler, *Monatsch.*, 69, 279 (1936).
[160] Glattfeld and Rietz, *J. Am. Chem. Soc.*, 62, 976 (1940).
[161] Newman and Rosher, *J. Org. Chem.*, 9, 221 (1944).
[162] Marvel and Cowan, *J. Am. Chem. Soc.*, 61, 3158 (1939).
[163] Cason et al., *J. Am. Chem. Soc.*, 66, 1764 (1944).
[164] Murfitt and Roberts, *J. Chem. Soc.*, 372 (1944).
[165] Schurman and Boord, *J. Am. Chem. Soc.*, 55, 4930 (1933).
[166] Mowry, Renoll, and Huber, *J. Am. Chem. Soc.*, 68, 1105 (1946).
[167] Marvel, Myers, and Saunders, *J. Am. Chem. Soc.*, 70, 1694 (1948).
[168] Bergmann and Szmuszkowicz, *J. Am. Chem. Soc.*, 70, 2748 (1948).
[169] Huntress and Sanchez-Nieva, *J. Am. Chem. Soc.*, 70, 2813 (1948).
[170] Volkenburgh et al., *J. Am. Chem. Soc.*, 71, 172 (1949).
[171] Fieser, Leffler et al., *J. Am. Chem. Soc.*, 70, 3209 (1948); cf. ref. 413.
[172] Huber et al., *J. Am. Chem. Soc.*, 68, 1109 (1946).
[173] Marvel and Williams, *J. Am. Chem. Soc.*, 70, 3842 (1948).
[174] Sobotka and Chanley, *J. Am. Chem. Soc.*, 70, 3915 (1948).
[175] Woods and Schwartzman, *J. Am. Chem. Soc.*, 70, 3394 (1948).
[176] Lutz et al., *J. Am. Chem. Soc.*, 70, 4140 (1948).
[177] Lucas and Dillon, *J. Am. Chem. Soc.*, 50, 1461 (1928); Regier and Blue, *J. Org. Chem.*, 14, 507 (1949).
[178] Hurd, Goodyear, and Goldsby, *J. Am. Chem. Soc.*, 58, 235 (1936).
[179] Wilkinson, *J. Chem. Soc.*, 3057 (1931).
[180] Whitmore and Homeyer, *J. Am. Chem. Soc.*, 55, 4556 (1933).
[181] Danehy, Killian, and Nieuwland, *J. Am. Chem. Soc.*, 58, 611 (1936).
[182] Kozacik and Reid, *J. Am. Chem. Soc.*, 60, 2436 (1938).
[183] Crane, Boord, and Henne, *J. Am. Chem. Soc.*, 67, 1237 (1945).
[184] Coleman, Callen, and Dornfeld, *J. Am. Chem. Soc.*, 68, 1101 (1946); Whitmore et al., *ibid.*, 67, 2060 (1945).
[185] Hershberg, *Helv. Chim. Acta*, 17, 352 (1934).
[186] Lewis and Elderfield, *J. Org. Chem.*, 5, 296 (1940).
[187] Hurd and Bollman, *J. Am. Chem. Soc.*, 56, 447 (1934).
[188] Fieser and Hershberg, *J. Am. Chem. Soc.*, 60, 1662 (1938).
[189] Suida and Drahowzal, *Ber.*, 75, 997 (1942).
[190] Letsinger and Traynham, *J. Am. Chem. Soc.*, 70, 3342 (1948); 72, 850 (1950).

[191] Pummerer and Schönamsgruber, *Ber.*, **72**, 1839 (1939).

[192] Palomaa, *Ber.*, **77**, 65 (1944).

[193] Kharasch and Fuchs, *J. Org. Chem.*, **9**, 364 (1944).

[194] Turk and Chanan, *Org. Syntheses*, **27**, 7 (1947); Cortese, *J. Am. Chem. Soc.*, **51**, 2266 (1929).

[195] Goheen, *J. Am. Chem. Soc.*, **63**, 746 (1941).

[196] Lespieau and Bourguel, *Org. Syntheses*, Coll. Vol. I, 186 (1941).

[197] Henne, Chanan, and Turk, *J. Am. Chem. Soc.*, **63**, 3474 (1941).

[198] Young, Roberts, and Wax, *J. Am. Chem. Soc.*, **67**, 841 (1945).

[199] Kogerman, *J. Am. Chem. Soc.*, **52**, 5060 (1930).

[200] Ozanne and Marvel, *J. Am. Chem. Soc.*, **52**, 5269 (1930).

[201] Johnson and McEwen, *J. Am. Chem. Soc.*, **48**, 473 (1926).

[202] Gredy, *Ann. chim.*, (11) **4**, 23 (1935).

[203] Schales, *Ber.*, **70**, 119 (1937); Ott, Marple, and Hearne, *Ind. Eng. Chem.*, **33**, 120 (1941).

[204] Henne and Greenlee, *J. Am. Chem. Soc.*, **65**, 2020 (1943).

[205] Campbell and Young, *J. Am. Chem. Soc.*, **65**, 965 (1943).

[206] Campbell and Eby, *J. Am. Chem. Soc.*, **63**, 216, 2683 (1941).

[207] Campbell and O'Connor, *J. Am. Chem. Soc.*, **61**, 2897 (1939); Dupont, *Bull. soc. chim. France*, (5) **3**, 1030 (1936).

[208] Thompson and Wyatt, *J. Am. Chem. Soc.*, **62**, 2555 (1940).

[209] Sherrill and Matlack, *J. Am. Chem. Soc.*, **59**, 2134 (1937).

[210] McElvain et al., *J. Am. Chem. Soc.*, **62**, 1482 (1940); **64**, 1966, 2525 (1942); **68**, 1922 (1946).

[211] Kharasch, Walling, and Mayo, *J. Am. Chem. Soc.*, **61**, 1559 (1939).

[212] Heilbron, Jones, and Richardson, *J. Chem. Soc.*, 291 (1949).

[213] Taylor and Shenk, *J. Am. Chem. Soc.*, **63**, 2756 (1941).

[214] Johnson, *J. Chem. Soc.*, 1015 (1946); Valette, *Ann. chim.*, (12) **3**, 667 (1948).

[215] Heilbron et al., *J. Chem. Soc.*, 86 (1945).

[216] Golse, *Ann. chim.*, (12) **3**, 538 (1948).

[217] Gredy, *Bull. soc. chim. France*, (5) **3**, 1096 (1936).

[218] Bourguel, *Bull. soc. chim. France*, (4) **45**, 1067 (1929).

[219] Ahmad and Strong, *J. Am. Chem. Soc.*, **70**, 1700 (1948).

[220] Ruggli and Zaeslin, *Helv. Chim. Acta*, **18**, 855 (1935).

[221] Ruggli and Lang, *Helv. Chim. Acta*, **19**, 1002 (1936).

[222] Smith and Rouault, *J. Am. Chem. Soc.*, **65**, 747 (1943).

[223] Whitmore and Rothrock, *J. Am. Chem. Soc.*, **55**, 1106 (1933); Cramer and Mulligan, *ibid.*, **58**, 373 (1936); Wibaut and Gitsels, *Rec. trav. chim.*, **60**, 241 (1941).

[224] Cramer and Miller, *J. Am. Chem. Soc.*, **62**, 1452 (1940).

[225] Dover and Hensley, *Ind. Eng. Chem.*, **27**, 337 (1935).

[226] Asinger and Eckoldt, *Ber.*, **76B**, 589 (1943).

[227] Asinger, *Ber.*, **75B**, 663 (1942); Baumgarten, *ibid.*, **75B**, 980 (1942).

[228] Colonge, *Bull. soc. chim. France*, (5) **9**, 732 (1942).

[229] Wibaut and Van Pelt, *Rec. trav. chim.*, **57**, 1055 (1938); *ibid.*, **60**, 55 (1941).

[230] Schniepp and Geller, *J. Am. Chem. Soc.*, **67**, 54 (1945).

[231] Lebedev and Yakubchik, *J. Chem. Soc.*, 2191 (1928).

[232] Arnold and Dowdall, *J. Am. Chem. Soc.*, **70**, 2590 (1948).

[233] Bergmann, Weizman, and Schapiro, *J. Org. Chem.*, **9**, 408 (1944).

[234] Rehberg and Fisher, *J. Am. Chem. Soc.*, **67**, 56 (1945).

[235] Smith et al., *Ind. Eng. Chem.*, **34**, 473 (1942).

[236] Filachione, Lengel, and Fisher, *J. Am. Chem. Soc.*, **66**, 495 (1944).

[237] Fisher, Rehberg, and Smith, *J. Am. Chem. Soc.*, **65**, 763 (1943).

[238] Snyder, Stewart, and Myers, *J. Am. Chem. Soc.*, **71**, 1055 (1949).

[239] Burns, Jones, and Ritchie, *J. Chem. Soc.*, **405** (1935).

[240] Blomquist, Tapp, and Johnson, *J. Am. Chem. Soc.*, **67**, 1522 (1945); Gold, *ibid.*, **68**, 2544 (1946).

[241] Nightingale and Janes, *J. Am. Chem. Soc.*, **66**, 352 (1944); Parham and Bleasdale, *ibid.*, **72**, 3844 (1950).

[242] Whitmore and Simpson, *J. Am. Chem. Soc.*, **55**, 3809 (1933).

[243] Niemann and Wagner, *J. Org. Chem.*, **7**, 228 (1942).

[244] Dykstra, Lewis, and Boord, *J. Am. Chem. Soc.*, **52**, 3396 (1930).

[245] Wibaut and Gitsels, *Rec. trav. chim.*, **59**, 947 (1940).

[246] Soday and Boord, *J. Am. Chem. Soc.*, **55**, 3293 (1933).

[247] Waterman and de Kok, *Rec. trav. chim.*, **53**, 1133 (1934).

[248] Shoemaker and Boord, *J. Am. Chem. Soc.*, **53**, 1505 (1931).

[249] Anzilotti and Vogt, *J. Am. Chem. Soc.*, **61**, 572 (1939).

[250] Golse, *Ann. chim.* (12) **3**, 542 (1948).

[251] Jacobs, Cramer, and Hanson, *J. Am. Chem. Soc.*, **64**, 223 (1942).

[252] Abbott and Johnson, *Org. Syntheses*, Coll. Vol. I, 440 (1941); cf. ref. 255.

[253] Lauer and Spielman, *J. Am. Chem. Soc.*, **53**, 1533 (1931).

[254] Taylor and Crawford, *J. Chem. Soc.*, 1130 (1934); Kayser, *Ann. chim.*, (11) **6**, 221 (1936).

[255] Walling and Wolfstirn, *J. Am. Chem. Soc.*, **69**, 852 (1947).

[256] Marvel and Hein, *J. Am. Chem. Soc.*, **70**, 1897 (1948).

[257] Wiley and Smith, *J. Am. Chem. Soc.*, **70**, 1560 (1948).

[258] Wiley and Smith, *J. Am. Chem. Soc.*, **70**, 2296 (1948).

[259] Weygand and Gabler, *Ber.*, **71B**, 2476 (1938).

[260] Winstein, Pressman, and Young, *J. Am. Chem. Soc.*, **61**, 1646 (1939).

[261] Farrell and Bachman, *J. Am. Chem. Soc.*, **57**, 1281 (1935); Bachman, *ibid.*, **55**, 4279 (1933).

[262] Bogert and Davidson, *J. Am. Chem. Soc.*, **54**, 334 (1932).

[263] Hurd and Meinert, *J. Am. Chem. Soc.*, **53**, 293 (1931).

[264] Acree and LaForge, *J. Org. Chem.*, **4**, 573 (1939).

[265] Bouis, *Ann. chim.*, (10) **9**, 438 (1928).

[266] Wilson, *J. Chem. Soc.*, 50 (1945).

[267] Summerbell and Umhoefer, *J. Am. Chem. Soc.*, **61**, 3017, 3020 (1939).

[268] Kharasch and Sternfeld, *J. Am. Chem. Soc.*, **61**, 2318 (1939); Howton, *J. Org. Chem.*, **14**, 7 (1949).

[269] Kharasch, Nudenberg, and Sternfeld, *J. Am. Chem. Soc.*, **62**, 2034 (1940).

[270] Hickinbottom, *Reactions of Organic Compounds*, Longmans, Green & Co., New York, 1948, p. 400; Thiele, *Ann.*, **308**, 339 (1899).

[271] Strauss, *Ber.*, **46**, 1054 (1913); cf. ref. 270.

[272] Fuson and Cooke, *J. Am. Chem. Soc.*, **62**, 1180 (1940).

[273] Meerwein, Büchner, and Emster, *J. prakt. Chem.*, **152**, 242, 256 (1939).

[274] Bergmann and Weizman, *J. Org. Chem.*, **9**, 415 (1944).

[275] Koelsch, *J. Am. Chem. Soc.*, **65**, 57 (1943).

[276] Kharasch and Kleiman, *J. Am. Chem. Soc.*, **65**, 14 (1943).

[277] Bergmann and Weinberg, *J. Org. Chem.*, **6**, 134 (1941).

[278] Bergmann, Dimant, and Japhe, *J. Am. Chem. Soc.* **70**, 1618 (1948).

[279] Stevens and Richmond, *J. Am. Chem. Soc.*, 63, 3132 (1941).
[280] Schlatter, *J. Am. Chem. Soc.*, 63, 1733 (1941).
[281] Ingold et al., *J. Chem. Soc.*, 997 (1927); 3125 (1928); 68, 69 (1933).
[282] Hofmann, *Ber.*, 14, 494, 659 (1881).
[283] Blicke in *Organic Reactions*, Vol. 1, John Wiley & Sons, New York, 1942, p. 318.
[284] Blomquist and Shelley, *J. Am. Chem. Soc.*, 70, 147 (1948).
[285] Burckhalter and Fuson, *J. Am. Chem. Soc.*, 70, 4184 (1948).
[286] Mannich and Ritsert, *Ber.*, 57, 1116 (1924).
[287] Wood et al., *J. Am. Chem. Soc.*, 63, 1334 (1941).
[288] Cline, Campaigne, and Spies, *J. Am. Chem. Soc.*, 66, 1136 (1944).
[289] Schönberg, Schütz, and Nickel, *Ber.*, 61, 1383 (1928).
[290] Kon and Leton, *J. Chem. Soc.*, 2496 (1931); Abbott, Kon, and Satchell, *ibid.*, 2514 (1928).
[291] Landau and Irany, *J. Org. Chem.*, 12, 422 (1947); McMahon et al., *J. Am. Chem. Soc.*, 70, 2971 (1948); Wagner, *ibid.*, 71, 3215 (1949).
[292] Campbell, *J. Am. Chem. Soc.*, 59, 1982 (1937).
[293] Conard and Dolliver, *Org. Syntheses*, Coll. Vol. II, 167 (1943).
[294] Drake and Allen, *Org. Syntheses*, Coll. Vol. I, 77 (1941).
[295] Kohler and Chadwell, *Org. Syntheses*, Coll. Vol. I, 78 (1941).
[296] Hill and Bramann, *Org. Syntheses*, Coll. Vol. I, 81 (1941).
[297] Wilds et al., *J. Am. Chem. Soc.*, 69, 1994 (1947).
[298] Dickinson, *J. Chem. Soc.*, 2237 (1926).
[299] Delepine and Sosa, *Bull. soc. chim. France*, (5) 9, 772 (1942); Friedmann, *J. prakt. Chem.* 145, 324 (1936).
[300] Raiford and Tanzer, *J. Org. Chem.*, 6, 722 (1941).
[301] Dippy and Lewis, *Rec. trav. chim.*, 56, 1002 (1937).
[302] Harvey, Heilbron, and Wilkinson, *J. Chem. Soc.*, 429 (1930).
[303] Hinkel and Dippy, *J. Chem. Soc.*, 1388 (1930).
[304] Bogert and Davidson, *J. Am. Chem. Soc.*, 54, 335 (1932).
[305] Tanasescu and Baciu, *Bull. soc. chim. France*, (5) 4, 1742 (1937); Shriner and Kurosawa, *J. Am. Chem. Soc.*, 52, 2538 (1930); Weygand and Mensdorf, *Ber.*, 68, 1832 (1935).
[306] Haeussler and Brugger, *Ber.*, 77, 152 (1944).
[307] Leuck and Cejka, *Org. Syntheses*, Coll. Vol. I, 283 (1941).
[308] Drake and Gilbert, *J. Am. Chem. Soc.*, 52, 4965 (1930).
[309] Alexander and Smith, *J. Am. Chem. Soc.*, 71, 735 (1949).
[310] Alder and Schmidt, *Ber.*, 76, 195, 200 (1943); Hunsdiecker, *ibid.*, 75, 451 (1942).
[311] Maxim and Angelesco, *Bull. soc. chim. France*, (5) 1, 1129 (1934).
[312] Kraft, *J. Am. Chem. Soc.*, 70, 3570 (1948).
[313] Burdick and Adkins, *J. Am. Chem. Soc.*, 56, 438 (1934).
[314] Bernhauer and Skudrzyk, *J. prakt. Chem.*, 155, 310 (1940).
[315] Evans and Gillam, *J. Chem. Soc.*, 571 (1943); cf. ref. 314.
[316] Burton, *J. Chem. Soc.*, 748 (1932).
[317] Kuhn and Hoffer, *Ber.*, 64, 1977 (1931).
[318] Kuhn and Winterstein, *Helv. Chim. Acta*, 12, 496 (1929); cf. ref. 356.
[319] Powell and Secoy, *J. Am. Chem. Soc.*, 53, 765 (1931); cf. refs. 290 and 321.
[320] Price, Knell, and West, *J. Am. Chem. Soc.*, 65, 2469 (1943); Rapson, *J. Chem. Soc.*, 16, (1941); Gault et al., *Bull. soc. chim. France*, (5e) 12, 952 (1945); cf. ref. 321.

[321] Wayne and Adkins, *J. Am. Chem Soc.*, **62**, 3401 (1940).
[322] Colonge, *Bull. soc. chim. France*, (4) **49**, 426, 432, 441 (1931); cf. ref. 290.
[323] Letch and Linstead, *J. Chem. Soc.*, 454 (1932).
[324] Schjanberg, *Ber.*, **70B**, 2386 (1937).
[325] Boxer and Linstead, *J. Chem. Soc.*, 740 (1931).
[326] Niemann and Redemann, *J. Am. Chem. Soc.*, **68**, 1933 (1946); Baker et al., *J. Org. Chem.*, **12**, 144 (1947); cf. ref. 325.
[327] Linstead, Noble, and Boorman, *J. Chem. Soc.*, 559 (1933); cf. ref. 325.
[328] Goldberg and Linstead, *J. Chem. Soc.*, 2353 (1928).
[329] Linstead and Mann, *J. Chem. Soc.*, 2064 (1930).
[330] Anker and Cook, *J. Chem. Soc.*, 312 (1945).
[331] Linstead et al., *J. Chem. Soc.*, 1140 (1937).
[332] Sircar, *J. Chem. Soc.*, 54 (1928); cf. ref. 331.
[333] Fried and Elderfield, *J. Org. Chem.*, **6**, 574 (1941).
[334] Lauer, Gensler, and Miller, *J. Am. Chem. Soc.*, **63**, 1153 (1941).
[335] Johnson in *Organic Reactions*, Vol. 1, John Wiley & Sons, New York, 1942, pp. 226, 227, and 233.
[336] Muskat, Becker, and Lowenstein, *J. Am. Chem. Soc.*, **52**, 329 (1930); Kohler and Butler, *ibid.*, **48**, 1041 (1926); Alder, Schumacher, and Wolff, *Ann.*, **564**, 91 (1949).
[337] Allen and Van Allan, *Org. Syntheses*, **24**, 92 (1944).
[338] Lennartz, *Ber.*, **76B**, 1009 (1943).
[339] Kuhn and Grundmann, *Ber.*, **70B**, 1326 (1937).
[340] Burton and Shoppee, *J. Chem. Soc.*, 548 (1937).
[341] Dippy and Page, *J. Chem. Soc.*, 362 (1938).
[342] Fieser, Leffler, et al., *J. Am. Chem. Soc.*, **70**, 3197 (1948).
[343] Ruggli, Steiger, and Schobel, *Helv. Chim. Acta*, **28**, 335 (1945); Slotta and Szyszka, *Ber.*, **68B**, 187 (1935).
[344] West, *J. Am. Chem. Soc.*, **42**, 1664 (1920).
[345] Galat, *J. Am. Chem. Soc.*, **68**, 377 (1946).
[346] Johnson and Robertson, *J. Chem. Soc.*, 24 (1930); Friedmann, *J. prakt. Chem.*, **145**, 334 (1936).
[347] Robinson and Walker, *J. Chem. Soc.*, 193 (1936).
[348] Bachmann, *J. Org. Chem.*, **3**, 444 (1938).
[349] Borsche, *Ann.*, **526**, 18 (1936).
[350] Linstead and Williams, *J. Chem. Soc.*, 2735 (1926).
[351] Bachmann and Kloetzel, *J. Am. Chem. Soc.*, **59**, 2209 (1937).
[352] King and Nord, *J. Org. Chem.*, **14**, 405 (1949).
[353] Panizzon, *Helv. Chim. Acta*, **24**, 27E (1941).
[354] Rajagopalan and Raman, *Org. Syntheses*, **25**, 51 (1945).
[355] Kroeker and McElvain, *J. Am. Chem. Soc.*, **56**, 1172, 1173 (1934); Allen and Spangler, *Org. Syntheses*, **25**, 42 (1945).
[356] Kuhn, Badstübner, and Grundmann, *Ber.*, **69B**, 98 (1936).
[357] Cope et al., *J. Am. Chem. Soc.*, **63**, 3452 (1941).
[358] Wojcik and Adkins, *J. Am. Chem. Soc.*, **56**, 2424 (1934).
[359] English, *J. Am. Chem. Soc.*, **63**, 942 (1941).
[360] Bachman and Tanner, *J. Org. Chem.*, **4**, 493 (1939).
[361] King, Clifton, and Openshaw, *J. Chem. Soc.*, 424 (1942).
[362] Martin, Schepartz, and Daubert, *J. Am. Chem. Soc.*, **70**, 2601 (1948).
[363] Cope, *J. Am. Chem. Soc.*, **59**, 2327 (1937).
[364] Jackman, Bergman, and Archer, *J. Am. Chem. Soc.*, **70**, 499 (1948).

[365] Vogel, *J. Chem. Soc.*, 2019–2026 (1928); Vogel and Oommen, *ibid.*, 768 (1930).

[366] Lapworth and Baker, *Org. Syntheses*, Coll. Vol. I, 181 (1941); Robinson and Young, *J. Chem. Soc.*, 1415 (1935).

[367] Naps and Johns, *J. Am. Chem. Soc.*, 62, 2451 (1940).

[368] Lohaus, *Ann.*, 514, 137 (1934).

[369] Letch and Linstead, *J. Chem. Soc.*, 450 (1932).

[370] Cope and Hancock, *J. Am. Chem. Soc.*, 60, 2645 (1938).

[371] Cope and Hofmann, *J. Am. Chem. Soc.*, 63, 3456 (1941).

[372] Johnson in *Organic Reactions*, Vol. 1, John Wiley & Sons, New York, 1942, p. 252.

[373] Johnson et al., *J. Am. Chem. Soc.*, 70, 418 (1948); 67, 1357, 1360, 1366 (1945); 69, 74 (1947).

[374] Swain, Todd, and Waring, *J. Chem. Soc.*, 551 (1944).

[375] Reimer and Chase, *J. Am. Chem. Soc.*, 60, 2470 (1938).

[376] Reimer and Howard, *J. Am. Chem. Soc.*, 50, 2507 (1928).

[377] Reimer, *J. Am. Chem. Soc.*, 46, 785 (1924).

[378] Fischer and Wiedemann, *Ann.*, 513, 251 (1934).

[379] Murray and Cloke, *J. Am. Chem. Soc.*, 56, 2751 (1934).

[380] Mowry, *J. Am. Chem. Soc.*, 67, 1050 (1945).

[381] Corson and Stroughton, *J. Am. Chem. Soc.*, 50, 2830 (1928).

[382] Boehm and Grohnwald, *Arch. Pharm.*, 274, 321 (1936); cf. ref. 381.

[383] Knowles and Cloke, *J. Am. Chem. Soc.*, 54, 2036 (1932).

[384] Johnson in *Organic Reactions*, Vol. 1, John Wiley & Sons, New York, 1942, pp. 210, 248–254.

[385] Utermohlen and Wallace, *J. Org. Chem.*, 12, 547 (1947).

[386] Thayer, *Org. Syntheses*, Coll. Vol. I, 398 (1941).

[387] Maxwell and Adams, *J. Am. Chem. Soc.*, 52, 2967 (1930).

[388] Buckles and Hausman, *J. Am. Chem. Soc.*, 70, 415 (1948); cf. ref. 372.

[389] Kuhn and Ishikawa, *Ber.*, 64B, 2349 (1931).

[390] Johnson, *Org. Syntheses*, 20, 55 (1940).

[391] Maxim and Stancovici, *Bull. soc. chim. France*, (5) 2, 600 (1935).

[392] Hinkel, Ayling, and Beynon, *J. Chem. Soc.*, 779 (1937).

[393] McPhee and Erickson, *J. Am. Chem. Soc.*, 68, 625 (1946).

[394] Marvel and King, *Org. Syntheses*, Coll. Vol. I, 252 (1941).

[395] Ramage, *J. Chem. Soc.*, 398 (1938).

[396] Fuson, Parham, and Reed, *J. Org. Chem.*, 11, 194 (1946); Parham and Reed, *Org. Syntheses*, 28, 60 (1948).

[397] Corson, *Org. Syntheses*, Coll. Vol. II, 229 (1943).

[398] Kalnin, *Helv. Chim. Acta*, 11, 977 (1928).

[399] Breslow and Hauser, *J. Am. Chem. Soc.*, 61, 786 (1939).

[400] Böck, Lock, and Schmidt, *Monatsh.*, 64, 399 (1934).

[401] Kuhn and Winterstein, *Helv. Chim. Acta*, 11, 87 (1928).

[402] Carter, *J. Am. Chem. Soc.*, 50, 2301 (1928).

[403] Slotta and Szyszka, *Ber.*, 68B, 189 (1935).

[404] Foreman and McElvain, *J. Am. Chem. Soc.*, 62, 1438 (1940).

[405] Cope and Hancock, *J. Am. Chem. Soc.*, 60, 2901 (1938).

[406] Hinz, Meyer, and Schücking, *Ber.*, 76B, 683 (1943).

[407] Nieuwland and Daly, *J. Am. Chem. Soc.*, 53, 1842 (1931); cf. ref. 93.

[408] Lipkin and Stewart, *J. Am. Chem. Soc.*, 61, 3295 (1939).

[409] Horning, Denekas, and Field, *Org. Syntheses,* **27,** 24 (1947); *J. Org. Chem.,* **9,** 547 (1944); *J. Am. Chem. Soc.,* **68,** 384 (1946).

[410] Burton and Shoppee, *J. Chem. Soc.,* 1160 (1935); Rupe, Steiger, and Fiedler, *Ber.,* **47,** 68 (1914); cf. ref. 87, p. 17.

[411] Woodruff and Pierson, *J. Am. Chem. Soc.,* **60,** 1076 (1938).

[412] Hunsdiecker, *Ber.,* **75B,** 455, 460 (1942).

[413] Bergmann and Weizmann, *J. Org. Chem.,* **4,** 266 (1939).

[414] Henze, Wilson, and Townley, *J. Am. Chem. Soc.,* **65,** 964 (1943).

[415] Kuhn and Hoffer, *Ber.,* **65B,** 655 (1932); Burton and Ingold, *J. Chem., Soc.,* 2028 (1929).

[416] Wagner-Jauregg and Hippchen, *Ber.,* **76B,** 698 (1943).

[417] Kon et al., *J. Chem. Soc.,* 1411 (1931).

[418] Johnson and Kon, *J. Chem. Soc.,* 2748 (1926).

[419] Colonge and Joly, *Ann. chim.,* (11) **18,** 306 (1943); Kon and Linstead, *J. Chem. Soc.,* 620 (1925); Kon, Linstead, and Wright, *ibid.,* 602 (1934).

[420] Huston and Goerner, *J. Am. Chem. Soc.,* **68,** 2504 (1946).

[421] Baker and Holdsworth, *J. Chem. Soc.,* 728 (1945).

[422] Wilds and Shunk, *J. Am. Chem. Soc.,* **65,** 469 (1943).

[423] Rapson and Robinson, *J. Chem. Soc.,* 1285 (1935); du Feu, McQuillin, and Robinson, *J. Chem. Soc.,* 53 (1937).

[424] Owen, *J. Chem. Soc.,* 385 (1945); 236, 3089 (1949).

[425] Bachman and Heisey, *J. Am. Chem. Soc.,* **71,** 1986 (1949).

[426] Dice, Loveless, and Cates, *J. Am. Chem. Soc.,* **71,** 3547 (1949).

[427] Cram, *J. Am. Chem. Soc.,* **71,** 3887 (1949).

[428] Walker, *Ind. Eng. Chem.,* **41,** 2640 (1949).

[429] Ipatieff, Appell, and Pines, *J. Am. Chem. Soc.,* **72,** 4260 (1950).

[430] Whitmore, Whitmore, and Cook, *J. Am. Chem. Soc.,* **72,** 51 (1950).

[431] Adkins and Zartman, *Org. Syntheses,* Coll. Vol. II, 606 (1943).

[432] Whitmore, *Ind. Eng. Chem., News Ed.,* **26,** 668 (1948).

[433] Nickels et al., *Ind. Eng. Chem.,* **41,** 563 (1949).

[434] Mavity, Zetterholm, and Hervert, *Ind. Eng. Chem.,* **38,** 829 (1946); cf. ref. 433.

[435] Kögl and Ultee, *Rec. trav. chim.,* **69,** 1582 (1950).

[436] Heilbron et al., *J. Chem. Soc.,* 1827, 2023, 2028 (1949); cf. ref. 110.

[437] Overberger and Saunders, *Org. Syntheses,* **28,** 31 (1948); cf. refs. 105, 106, and 458.

[438] Kon and Spickett, *J. Chem. Soc.,* 2724 (1949).

[439] Wendler and Slates, *J. Am. Chem. Soc.,* **72,** 5341 (1950).

[440] Price and Pappalardo, *J. Am. Chem. Soc.,* **72,** 2613 (1950).

[441] Doering and Wiberg, *J. Am. Chem. Soc.,* **72,** 2609 (1950).

[442] Hands and Walker, *J. Soc. Chem. Ind.,* **67,** 458 (1948).

[443] Buckley and Scaife, *J. Chem. Soc.,* 1471 (1947).

[444] Fraser and Kon, *J. Chem. Soc.,* 606 (1934).

[445] Emerson, *Chem. Revs.* **45,** 347 (1949).

[446] Pickering and Smith, *Rec. trav. chim.,* **69,** 537 (1950).

[447] Fosdick, Fancher, and Urbach, *J. Am. Chem. Soc.,* **68,** 841 (1946).

[448] Braude and Timmons, *J. Chem. Soc.,* 2004 (1950).

[449] Ecke, Cook, and Whitmore, *J. Am. Chem. Soc.,* **72,** 1511 (1950).

[450] Paul et al., *Bull. soc. chim. France,* (5) **17,** 124 (1950).

[451] Heilbron et al., *J. Chem. Soc.,* 739 (1949).

[452] Rinne et al., *J. Am. Chem. Soc.,* **72,** 5759 (1950).

[453] McElvain and Walters, *J. Am. Chem. Soc.*, 64, 1059 (1942); McElvain and Kundiger, *Org. Syntheses*, 23, 45 (1943).

[454] Kuhn and Grundmann, *Ber.*, 70, 1894 (1937); McElvain, Clarke, and Jones, *J. Am. Chem. Soc.*, 64, 1966 (1942).

[455] Strassburg, Gregg, and Walling, *J. Am. Chem. Soc.*, 69, 2141 (1947).

[456] Emerson and Patrick, *J. Org. Chem.*, 13, 730 (1948).

[457] Iddles, Lang, and Gregg, *J. Am. Chem. Soc.*, 59, 1945 (1937).

[458] Brooks, *J. Am. Chem. Soc.*, 66, 1295 (1944).

[459] Jacobs in *Organic Reactions*, Vol. 5, John Wiley & Sons, New York, 1949, p. 24.

[460] Waterman and De Kok, *Rec. trav. chim.*, 52, 298 (1933); cf. ref. 467.

[461] Riobe, *Ann. chim.*, (12) 4, 634 (1949).

[462] Taylor and Strong, *J. Am. Chem. Soc.*, 72, 4264 (1950).

[463] Crombie and Harper, *J. Chem. Soc.*, 877, 1712 (1950).

[464] Birch, *J. Chem. Soc.*, 812 (1945).

[465] Backer and van der Bij, *Rec. trav. chim.*, 62, 564 (1943).

[466] Brandenberg and Galat, *J. Am. Chem. Soc.*, 72, 3275 (1950).

[467] Geldof and Wibaut, *Rec. trav. chim.*, 67, 110 (1948).

[468] Scaife and Wilder-Smith, *J. Chem. Soc.*, 1477 (1947).

[469] Alexander and Mudrak, *J. Am. Chem. Soc.*, 72, 1810 (1950).

[470] Arnold, Amidon, and Dodson, *J. Am. Chem. Soc.*, 72, 2871 (1950).

[471] St. Pfau et al., *Helv. Chim. Acta*, 18, 946 (1935); Paul and Tchelitcheff, *Bull. soc. chim. France*, (5) 14, 453 (1947).

[472] Arnold, Elmer, and Dodson, *J. Am. Chem. Soc.*, 72, 4359 (1950).

[473] Johnson and Heinz, *J. Am. Chem. Soc.*, 71, 2913 (1949).

[474] Spoerri and Rosen, *J. Am. Chem. Soc.*, 72, 4918 (1950).

[475] Bickel, *J. Am. Chem. Soc.*, 72, 349 (1950).

[476] Roberts and Sauer, *J. Am. Chem. Soc.*, 71, 3927 (1949).

[477] Bergmann and Schapiro, *J. Org. Chem.*, 12, 57 (1947).

[478] Hagemeyer, *J. Am. Chem. Soc.*, 71, 1119 (1949).

[479] Wiley and Behr, *J. Am. Chem. Soc.*, 72, 1822 (1950).

[480] Southwick, Pursglove, and Numerof, *J. Am. Chem. Soc.*, 72, 1605 (1950).

[481] Grundmann, *Ber.*, 81, 516 (1948).

[482] Emerson and Patrick, *J. Org. Chem.*, 14, 795 (1949).

[483] Korach and Bergmann, *J. Org. Chem.*, 14, 1121 (1949).

[484] Metayer, *Ann. chim.*, (12) 4, 201, 202 (1949).

[485] Wawzonek and Smolin, *Org. Syntheses*, 29, 83 (1949); Mattocks and Hutchison, *J. Am. Chem. Soc.*, 70, 3516 (1948).

[486] Buu-Hoi and Lecocq, *J. Chem. Soc.*, 641 (1947).

[487] Wagner, *J. Am. Chem. Soc.*, 71, 3215 (1949).

[488] McMahon et al., *J. Am. Chem. Soc.*, 70, 2971 (1948).

[489] Worrall, *Org. Syntheses*, Coll. Vol. I, 413 (1941).

[490] Hoover and Hass, *J. Org. Chem.*, 12, 504 (1947).

[491] Hargreaves and McGookin, *J. Soc. Chem. Ind.*, 69, 186 (1950).

[492] Overberger and Allen, *J. Am. Chem. Soc.*, 68, 722 (1946).

[493] Wiley and Hobson, *J. Am. Chem. Soc.*, 71, 2429 (1949).

[494] Migrdichian, *Organic Cyanogen Compounds*, Reinhold Publishing Corp., New York, 1947, p. 319.

[495] Polya and Tardrew, *Rec. trav. chim.*, 68, 566 (1949).

[496] Norton, *Chem. Revs.*, **31**, 319 (1942); Alder in *Newer Methods of Preparative Organic Chemistry*, Interscience Publishers, New York, 1948, p. 381; Kloetzel, *Organic Reactions*, Vol. 4, John Wiley & Sons, New York, 1948, p. 1; Holmes, *ibid.*, p. 60.

[497] Roberts, Jeydel, and Armstrong, *J. Am. Chem. Soc.*, **71**, 3248 (1949).

[498] Cope, Kovacic, and Burg, *J. Am. Chem. Soc.*, **71**, 3658 (1949).

[499] Joshel and Butz, *J. Am. Chem. Soc.*, **63**, 3350 (1941).

[500] Kloetzel and Herzog, *J. Am. Chem. Soc.*, **72**, 1991 (1950).

[501] Alder et al., *Ann.*, **565**, 57, 73, 99, 135 (1949).

[502] Alder et al., *Ann.*, **564**, 79, 96, 109, 120 (1949).

[503] Weizmann, Sulzbacher, and Bergmann, *J. Am. Chem. Soc.*, **70**, 1157 (1948).

[504] Sigmund and Uchann, *Monatsh.*, **51**, 234 (1929).

[505] Norris, Verbanc, and Hennion, *J. Am. Chem. Soc.*, **60**, 1160 (1938); Dykstra, *ibid.*, **57**, 2257 (1935).

[506] Killian, Hennion, and Nieuwland, *J. Am. Chem. Soc.*, **57**, 545 (1935).

[507] Scheibler and Baganz, *Ann.*, **565**, 170 (1949).

[508] Adkins and Roebuck, *J. Am. Chem. Soc.*, **70**, 4041 (1948).

[509] Tarbell in *Organic Reactions*, Vol. 2, John Wiley & Sons, New York, 1944, p. 27.

[510] Eccott and Linstead, *J. Chem. Soc.*, 2153 (1929); Kon and Thakur, *ibid.*, 2220 (1930); Goldberg and Linstead, *ibid.*, 2354 (1928).

[511] Johnson, Jobling, and Bodamer, *J. Am. Chem. Soc.*, **63**, 133 (1941); Williams and Hurd, *J. Org. Chem.*, **5**, 122 (1940); Kharasch, Margolis, and Mayo, *ibid.*, **1**, 393 (1936); Hershberg and Ruhoff, *Org. Syntheses*, Coll. Vol. II, 102 (1943); cf. ref. 516.

[512] Boonstra and van Amerongen, *Ind. Eng. Chem.*, **41**, 161 (1949).

[513] Truffault, *Bull. soc. chim. France*, (5) 3, 444 (1936).

[514] Nieuwland, Calcott, Downing, and Carter, *J. Am. Chem. Soc.*, **53**, 4201 (1931); Dunicz, *ibid.*, **63**, 2468 (1941).

[515] Willstatter and Wirth, *Ber.*, **46**, 535 (1913).

[516] Kistiakowsky et al., *J. Am. Chem. Soc.*, **58**, 146 (1936).

[517] Eglinton and Whiting, *J. Chem. Soc.*, 3650 (1950).

[518] Alder and Haydn, *Ann.*, **570**, 208, 212 (1950).

[519] Grob and Tscharner, *Helv. Chim. Acta*, **33**, 1075 (1950).

[520] Lunt and Sondheimer, *J. Chem. Soc.*, 3365 (1950).

[521] Armstrong and Robinson, *J. Chem. Soc.*, 1650 (1934); Goldberg and Müller, *Helv. Chim. Acta*, **21**, 1701 (1938).

[522] Vargha and Kovacs, *Ber.*, **75**, 794 (1942).

[523] Hagemeyer, *Ind. Eng. Chem.*, **41**, 766 (1949).

[524] Nystrom and Brown, *J. Am. Chem. Soc.*, **70**, 3739 (1948).

[525] Hennion and Sheehan, *J. Am. Chem. Soc.*, **71**, 1964 (1949).

[526] Fierz-David and Zollinger, *Helv. Chim. Acta*, **28**, 1130 (1945).

[527] Hanford and Fuller, *Ind. Eng. Chem.*, **40**, 1171 (1948); Schildknecht, Zoss, and McKinley, *ibid.*, **39**, 180 (1947).

[528] Wiley, *Org. Syntheses*, **28**, 94 (1948).

[529] Johnson and Daub in *Organic Reactions*, Vol. 6, John Wiley & Sons, New York, 1951, p. 1.

[530] Cope et al., *Org. Syntheses*, **31**, 25 (1951).

[531] Wawzonek and Smolin, *Org. Syntheses*, **31**, 52 (1951).

3

Acetylenic Compounds

CONTENTS

43. Dehydrohalogenation of Halides

$$RCX = CH_2 \xrightarrow{\text{Base}} RC \equiv CH + (HX)$$

A triple bond may be formed by dehydrohalogenation of dihalides and olefinic halides of the general types $RCX = CH_2$, $RCH = CHX$, $RCH = CXR'$, $RCHXCH_2X$, $RCHXCHXR'$, RCH_2CHX_2, and RCX_2CH_2R'.[35] The choice of a base depends somewhat on the position desired for the triple bond in the product. Sodium amide tends to rearrange the triple bond toward the end of the chain,[58] and potassium hydroxide favors reverse isomerization toward the center of the chain.[35,42,43] Although neither rearrangement is dependable from a synthetic standpoint, it is best to choose the base favoring the desired product.

A suspension of sodium amide in mineral oil[30,40,41,46] or sodium amide in liquid ammonia[28] has been used to prepare 1-alkynes of various types in 45–96% yields. The acetylenes are liberated from their sodium salts by dilute acid. It is important that the sodium amide be of good quality and that moisture be excluded from the reaction mixture.[34]

Suspensions of potassium hydroxide in mineral oil,[35] molten potassium hydroxide,[31] and alcoholic potassium hydroxide[32,36,37,38] give consistently better yields (60–88%) of 1- and 2-alkynes. Most of the 1-alkynes prepared in this way are incapable of isomerization: e.g., propyne, phenylacetylene, and t-butylacetylene. Alcoholic potassium hydroxide dehydrohalogenates stilbene dibromide to diphenylacetylene (tolane), $C_6H_5C \equiv CC_6H_5$ (85%),[29] whereas sodium amide in liquid ammonia causes dehalogenation to stilbene, $C_6H_5CH = CHC_6H_5$ (86%).[34] A series of alkylphenylacetylenes, $C_6H_5C \equiv CR$, has been prepared directly from α-alkylcinnamic acid dibromides, $C_6H_5CHBrCRBrCO_2H$, by dehydrohalogenation and decarboxylation with alcoholic potassium hydroxide.[39]

An interesting rearrangement of an aryl group occurs in the dehydrohalogenation of $unsym$-diarylhaloethylenes to diarylacetylenes.

$$Ar_2C = CHX + KNH_2 \rightarrow ArC \equiv CAr + KX + NH_3$$

The relative positions of groups on the nucleus are not changed during the migration. The yields of tolanes are generally 80–90%.[62]

Many *acetylenic acids* have been made by the dehydrohalogenation of the dibromo derivatives of olefinic acids. Aliphatic α,β-acetylenic acids are often decarboxylated under the conditions of the reaction.[53] However, phenylpropiolic acid,[52] $C_6H_5C \equiv CCO_2H$, and acetylenedicarboxylic acid,[51] $HO_2CC \equiv CCO_2H$, are prepared in this way as well as acids having the triple bond in the $\beta\gamma$-, γ,δ-, and more remote positions in the aliphatic chain.[50,53]

Other functional groups may be present in the molecule during dehydrohalogenation. Dichloroacetylene is obtained by passing trichloroethylene over solid potassium hydroxide at 130°.[49] Aryl halogen atoms are stable during dehydrohalogenation.[61] Aqueous sodium hydroxide removes hydrogen chloride from 3-chloro-2-buten-1-ol to give 2-butyn-1-ol (40%).[44] Powdered potassium hydroxide at 100° is used with bromides of the general type $ROCH = CHBr$ for the preparation of alkoxy- and phenoxyacetylenes (34–80%).[48,57] Ethylene glycol is the solvent for potassium hydroxide in a preparation of methyl propargyl ether, $CH_3OCH_2C \equiv CH$, from 2,3-dibromo-1-methoxypropane.[59] The aldehyde group is protected as the acetal in the preparation of phenylpropargyl aldehyde (81%).[33] Sodium amide in liquid ammonia removes hydrogen bromide from 1-diethylamino-2-bromo-2-propene, $(C_2H_5)_2NCH_2C(Br) = CH_2$, to give 1-diethylamino-2-propyne (82%).[55] o- and p-Nitro groups have been present in a series of diphenylacetylenes prepared from the corresponding stilbene dihalides and alcoholic potassium hydroxide.[56] A modification involves a one-step process of coupling and dehydrohalogenation of a substituted benzal chloride by sodium in alcohol.[56]

$$\text{ArCHCl}_2 \xrightarrow[\text{C}_2\text{H}_5\text{ OH}]{\text{Na}} \text{ArC} \equiv \text{CAr}$$

44. Alkylation of Acetylenic Compounds

$$\text{RCH}_2\text{CH}_2\text{X} + \text{HC} \equiv \text{CNa} \rightarrow \text{RCH}_2\text{CH}_2\text{C} \equiv \text{CH} + \text{NaX}$$

$$\text{RCH}_2\text{CH}_2\text{X} + \text{R}'\text{C} \equiv \text{CNa} \rightarrow \text{RCH}_2\text{CH}_2\text{C} \equiv \text{CR}' + \text{NaX}$$

Mono- and di-alkylacetylenes are prepared from sodium alkydes and primary alkyl halides which lack branching on the second carbon atom. The branched primary halides as well as secondary and tertiary halides undergo dehydrohalogenation to olefins by the basic alkyde. The alkydes are best prepared from the acetylenes and sodium amide in liquid ammonia.[10,60] The yields of 1-alkynes are frequently 70–90% when alkyl bromides are employed as alkylating agents.[8,9,11,26] Dialkylacetylenes are formed in somewhat lower yields (30–70%), which decrease rapidly with increasing chain length of the alkyl bromides above *n*-amyl bromide.[2,8,9,60,74] Alkyl sulfates and alkyl sulfonates are also used as alkylating agents to give mono- and di-alkylacetylenes in yields of 60–83%.[1,3,4,7,15] Symmetrical dialkylacetylenes may be prepared by a one-step process from sodium acetylide, sodium amide, and an alkyl halide or sulfate in liquid ammonia.[2,6,7]

Acetylenic Grignard reagents are less active than sodium alkydes but are readily alkylated by benzyl halides as well as by alkyl sulfates and sulfonates.[1,12,14,18] The Grignard reagents are conveniently prepared from the acetylenes and ethylmagnesium bromide in ether solution.

$$\text{RC} \equiv \text{CH} \xrightarrow{\text{C}_2\text{H}_5 \text{ MgBr}} \text{RC} \equiv \text{CMgBr} \xrightarrow{\text{R}_2'\text{SO}_4} \text{RC} \equiv \text{CR}'$$

Several critical reviews of the alkylation reaction have been made in which the best experimental procedures are indicated.[5,8,10] High-efficiency fractionation is necessary to obtain pure acetylenes free from halides and olefins.[9] 1-Alkynes are sometimes purified through their silver salts.[13]

An additional functional group may be present in one of the reactants. Alkylation of vinylacetylene gives low yields of 1-*alken-3-ynes*.[19] Cuprous halide catalyst is required for alkylations by allyl bromide; the yields of 1-alken-4-ynes are about 88%.[27] Both halogen atoms of dibromides can be induced to take part in alkylation if the halogens are not on the same or adjacent carbon atoms. The yields of *diynes* are 46–85%.[9] Diynes in which the triple bonds are closer together have been made by the action of substituted propargyl bromides, $RC \equiv CCH_2Br$, on sodium alkydes or by the coupling of two propargyl residues by magnesium[25] (method 45). Polymethylene chlorobromides[9,20] and iodochlorides[21,75] when used as alkylating agents lead to ω-chloroacetylenes. The last compounds may also be prepared by alkylation with ω-haloalkyl sulfonates[1,22] (cf. method 10). Alkylations have been effected with both α- and β-halo ethers to give acetylenic ethers.[23,24] The amino acetylene, 2-diethylamino-1-propyne, has been alkylated by the sodium amide procedure with a series of primary halides including allyl bromide. Average yields are better than 60%.[55]

45. Coupling of Grignard Reagents with Haloacetylenes

$$RC \equiv CCXR_2 \xrightarrow{R'MgX} \begin{array}{l} \rightarrow RC \equiv CCR_2R' \\ \rightarrow RR'C = C = CR_2 \end{array}$$

Acetylenic hydrocarbons are prepared in 60-74% yields by the coupling of Grignard reagents and substituted propargyl halides. Allenes are also formed by an allylic-type rearrangement of the halogen atom.[18,25,63] 1,5-Diynes are available by this reaction in 50-60% yields by coupling two molecules of substituted propargyl halide by magnesium.[25]

Organomagnesium compounds react with dichloroacetylene to give 40-70% yields of aryl- and alkyl-1-chloroacetylenes.[69]

46. Diacetylenes by Oxidation of Metallic Acetylides

$$2RC \equiv CCu \xrightarrow{(O)} RC \equiv C - C \equiv CR$$

Oxidation of cuprous acetylides by air or potassium ferricyanide brings about the union of two acetylenic groupings as in the preparation of dimethyldiacetylene (42%).[7,38] The reaction has been applied to the synthesis of diynediols from acetylenic carbinols.[65]

47. Decarboxylation of Acetylenic Acids

$$ArC \equiv CCO_2H \longrightarrow ArC \equiv CH + CO_2$$

Arylpropiolic acids lose carbon dioxide when refluxed with water[71,73] or a solution of sodium bicarbonate and cupric chloride.[72] Yields of phenylacetylenes containing nuclear halo, alkoxyl, and nitro groups are in the range of 40-67%. Alkylphenylacetylenes, $C_6H_5C \equiv CR$, may be made directly from α-alkylcinnamic acid dibromides, $C_6H_5CHBrCRBrCO_2H$, by dehydrohalogenation and decarboxylation.[39]

48. Tolanes by Oxidation of Hydrazones of Diketones[66]

$$\begin{array}{c} ArC=NNH_2 \\ | \\ ArC=NNH_2 \end{array} \xrightarrow{2HgO} ArC\equiv CAr + 2Hg + 2H_2O + 2N_2$$

49. Isomerization of Allenes[68]

$$RCH=C=CH_2 \xrightarrow{NaNH_2} RCH_2C\equiv CNa \xrightarrow[H^+]{H_2O} RCH_2C\equiv CH$$

50. Coupling of Acetylenic Grignard Reagents with Cyanogen Chloride[67]

$$RC\equiv CMgX + ClCN \longrightarrow RC\equiv CCN$$

TABLE 4. ACETYLENES 83

TABLE 4. ACETYLENES

C_n	Compound	Method	Yield (%)	Chapter[ref.]	B.p./mm., n_D^t, (M.p.)
	Aliphatic and Alicyclic Acetylenic Hydrocarbons				
C_3	Propyne (methylacetylene)	43	60	3[38]	−23/760
		43	85	3[38]	−23/760
		44	75	3[4]	
C_4	1-Butyne (ethylacetylene)	43	40	3[46]	11
		44	60	3[3]	8.5
	2-Butyne (dimethylacetylene)	44	41	3[6]	27/754, 1.3920
C_5	1-Pentyne (n-propylacetylene)	44	50	3[26]	40, 1.3850
		44	85	3[9]	40/760, 1.3852
	2-Pentyne (methylethylacetylene)	43	56	3[37]	55, 1.4050
		44	41	3[12]	56/755, 1.4035
C_6	1-Hexyne (n-butylacetylene)	44	89	3[8]	71/760, 1.3990
		44	77	3[26]	72, 1.3987
	3-Hexyne (diethylacetylene)	44	47	3[2]	82/744, 1.4115
	Methylisopropylacetylene	44	36	3[16]	72, 1.4078[19]
	3,3-Dimethyl-1-butyne (t-butylacetylene)	43	81	3[36]	37/768
C_7	1-Heptyne (n-amylacetylene)	43	88	3[35]	
		44	52	3[8]	100/760, 1.4088
		44	75	3[26]	98, 1.4088
	2-Heptyne	44	48	3[74]	111, 1.4192[25]
	5-Methyl-1-hexyne	44	75	3[26]	92, 1.4060
	4,4-Dimethyl-1-pentyne	43	45	3[40]	74, 1.4028
C_8	1-Octyne (n-hexylacetylene)	44	65	3[26]	77/150, 1.4157
		44	72	3[9]	126/760, 1.4159
	2-Octyne (methyl-n-amylacetylene)	44	36	3[8]	131-135/750, 1.4285[25]
	3-Octyne (ethyl-n-butylacetylene)	44	64	3[2]	133/760, 1.4250
		44	70	3[14]	131/745, 1.4261
	4-Octyne (di-n-propylacetylene)	44	66	3[2]	130/744, 1.4248
	1-Cyclopentyl-1-propyne	44	50	3[17]	143, 1.4636[22]
	3-Cyclopentyl-1-propyne	43	65	3[17]	133, 1.4494[25]
C_9	1-Cyclopentyl-2-butyne	44	65	3[17]	165, 1.4621[26]
	3-Cyclohexylpropyne	43	66	3[30]	62/24
C_{10}	Di-t-butylacetylene	9	55	3[70]	112/746, (19), 1.4055
	Aryl-substituted Acetylenes				
C_8	Phenylacetylene	43	67	3[31]	143
		43	52	3[28]	74/80
C_9	Phenylmethylacetylene	44	50	3[60]	113/84, 1.5650
		44	66	3[15]	73/15, 1.565
	Benzylacetylene	43	52	3[41]	48–58/5
	p-Tolylacetylene	43	48	3[32]	81/32

For explanations and symbols see pp. xi–xii.

TABLE 4 (continued)

C_n	Compound	Method	Yield (%)	Chapter[ref.]	B.p./mm., n_D^t, (M.p.)
	Aryl-substituted Acetylenes (continued)				
C_{10}	1-Phenyl-1-butyne	44	77	3[1]	82/5
	4-Phenyl-1-butyne	43	63	3[41]	95-99/17
C_{14}	Diphenylacetylene (tolane)	43	69[†]	3[29]	(61)
		48	75	3[66]	(59)
C_{15}	1,3-Diphenylpropyne	44	72	3[18]	129/2, 1.5946

For explanations and symbols see pp. xi–xii.

TABLE 5. DIACETYLENES

C_n	Compound	Method	Yield (%)	Chapter[ref.]	B.p./mm., n_D^t, (M.p.)
C_4	1,3-Butadiyne (diacetylene)	46	....	3[38]	10/760
C_6	2,4-Hexadiyne (dimethyldiacetylene)	46	42	3[38]	(64)
	1,3,5-Hexatriyne (triacetylene)	43	10[†]	3[64]	
C_7	1,6-Heptadiyne	44	46	3[9]	112/760, 1.4423
C_9	1,8-Nonadiyne	44	85	3[9]	162/760, 1.4490
	2,7-Nonadiyne	44	76	3[9]	180/760, 1.4674

For explanations and symbols see pp. xi–xii.

TABLE 6. OLEFINIC ACETYLENES

C_n	Compound	Method	Yield (%)	Chapter[ref.]	B.p./mm., n_D^t, (M.p.)
C_4	Vinylacetylene	26	28	2[515]	3/729
		35	....	2[514]	5/740
		42	92	2[517]	
C_5	1-Penten-3-yne (methylvinylacetylene)	44	38	3[19]	59/760, 1.4496
	2-Penten-4-yne	42	91	2[517]	47, 1.4356[19]
	2-Methyl-1-buten-3-yne	19	50	2[111]	35-40
C_6	1-Hexen-3-yne (ethylvinylacetylene)	44	31	3[19]	85/758, 1.4522
	Divinylacetylene	35	75	2[514]	84/760, 1.504
	3-Methyl-3-penten-1-yne	19	55	2[111]	71
C_7	1-Hepten-3-yne	21	77	2[249]	45/75, 1.4520[25]
	1-Ethynylcyclopentene	19	42	2[436]	66/125, 1.4880[19]

TABLE 6. OLEFINIC ACETYLENES   85

TABLE 6 (continued)

C_n	Compound	Method	Yield (%)	Chapter ref.	B.p./mm., n_D^t, (M.p.)
C_8	1-Octen-3-yne	21	73	2^{249}	62/60, 1.4505^{25}
	1-Ethynyl-1-cyclohexene	19	34	2^{110}	53/30, 1.4934^{25}
		19	40	2^{174}	39/12, 1.4970
		42	40	2^{517}	34-37/14, 1.4962^{17}
C_9	1-Nonen-3-yne	21	76	2^{249}	28/4, 1.4487^{25}
	1-Nonen-4-yne	29	88	2^{181}	58/22, 1.4413^{25}
	2-Nonen-4-yne	21	70	2^{249}	70/29, 1.4590^{25}
	1-Ethynylcycloheptene	19	52	2^{436}	78/35, 1.4980
	2-Methyl-1-ethynyl-1-cyclohexene	19	54	2^{436}	68/35, 1.4890^{23}
	2-Methyl-1-ethynyl-1-cyclohexene	19	62	2^{436}	72/40, 1.4836^{18}

For explanations and symbols see pp. xi-xii.

REFERENCES FOR CHAPTER 3

[1] Johnson, Schwartz, and Jacobs, *J. Am. Chem. Soc.*, 60, 1882 (1938).
[2] Bried and Hennion, *J. Am. Chem. Soc.*, 59, 1310 (1937); 60, 1717 (1938); cf. ref. 8.
[3] Hurd and Meinert, *J. Am. Chem. Soc.*, 53, 296 (1931); cf. refs. 11 and 12.
[4] Kharasch, McNab, and McNab, *J. Am. Chem. Soc.*, 57, 2465 (1935); Meinert and Hurd, *ibid.*, 52, 4544 (1930); see also refs. 7 and 8.
[5] Nieuwland and Vogt, *The Chemistry of Acetylene*, Reinhold Publishing Corp., New York, 1945, pp. 74–81.
[6] Walling, Kharasch, and Mayo, *J. Am. Chem. Soc.*, 61, 1711 (1939); cf. ref. 7.
[7] Conn, Kistiakowsky, and Smith, *J. Am. Chem. Soc.*, 61, 1868 (1939).
[8] Vaughn et al., *J. Org. Chem.*, 2, 1 (1937); cf. ref. 9.
[9] Henne and Greenlee, *J. Am. Chem. Soc.*, 67, 484 (1945); cf. ref. 10.
[10] Jacobs in *Organic Reactions*, Vol. 5, John Wiley & Sons, New York, 1949, p. 1.
[11] Tchao Yin Lai, *Bull soc. chim. France*, 53, 687 (1933).
[12] Kharasch, Walling, and Mayo, *J. Am. Chem. Soc.*, 61, 1561 (1939).
[13] Young, Vogt, and Nieuwland, *J. Am. Chem. Soc.*, 58, 56 (1936).
[14] Thorn, Hennion, and Nieuwland, *J. Am. Chem. Soc.*, 58, 796 (1936).
[15] Truchet, *Ann. chim.*, (10) 16, 390 (1931).
[16] Gredy, *Bull. soc. chim. France*, (5) 2, 1953 (1935).
[17] Gredy, *Ann. chim.*, (11) 4, 16–31 (1935).
[18] Johnson, Jacobs, and Schwartz, *J. Am. Chem. Soc.*, 60, 1887 (1938).
[19] Jacobson and Carothers, *J. Am. Chem. Soc.*, 55, 1622 (1933).
[20] Newman and Wotiz, *J. Am. Chem. Soc.*, 71, 1292 (1949).
[21] Ahmad and Strong, *J. Am. Chem. Soc.*, 70, 1699 (1948); Ahmad, Bumpus, and Strong, *ibid.*, 70, 3391 (1948).
[22] Gilman and Beaber, *J. Am. Chem. Soc.*, 45, 839 (1923).
[23] McCusker and Kroeger, *J. Am. Chem. Soc.*, 59, 213 (1937).
[24] Golse, *Ann. chim.*, (12) 3, 537, 557 (1948).
[25] Tchao Yin Lai, *Bull. soc. chim. France*, (4) 53, 1537, 1545 (1933).
[26] Campbell and Campbell, *Org. Syntheses*, 30, 15 (1950).
[27] Danehy, Killian, and Nieuwland, *J. Am. Chem. Soc.*, 58, 611 (1936).
[28] Campbell and Campbell, *Org. Syntheses*, 30, 72 (1950); cf. refs. 34 and 47.
[29] Smith and Falkof, *Org. Syntheses*, 22, 50 (1942); cf. refs. 45 and 60.
[30] Lespieau and Bourguel, *Org. Syntheses*, Coll. Vol. I, 191 (1941).
[31] Hessler, *Org. Syntheses*, Coll. Vol. I, 438 (1941).
[32] Smith and Hoehn, *J. Am. Chem. Soc.*, 63, 1175 (1941); cf. ref. 34.
[33] Allen and Edens, *Org. Syntheses*, 25, 92 (1945).
[34] Vaughn, *J. Am. Chem. Soc.*, 56, 2064 (1934); Vaughn, Vogt, and Nieuwland, *ibid.*, 56, 2120 (1934).
[35] Bachman and Hill, *J. Am. Chem. Soc.*, 56, 2730 (1934).
[36] Bartlett and Rosen, *J. Am. Chem. Soc.*, 64, 544 (1942); Ivitzky, *Bull. soc. chim. France*, (4) 35, 357 (1924).
[37] Sherrill and Matlack, *J. Am. Chem. Soc.*, 59, 2137 (1937).
[38] Pauling, Springall, and Palmer, *J. Am. Chem. Soc.*, 61, 927 (1939); Heisig and Davis, *ibid.*, 57, 339 (1935); Chauvelier, *Ann. chim.*, (12) 3, 410 (1948); cf. ref. 7.
[39] Bogert and Davidson, *J. Am. Chem. Soc.*, 54, 337 (1932).

[40] Ozanne and Marvel, *J. Am. Chem. Soc.*, 52, 5269 (1930).
[41] Johnson and McEwen, *J. Am. Chem. Soc.*, 48, 469 (1926).
[42] Hurd, Meinert, and Spence, *J. Am. Chem. Soc.*, 52, 1141 (1930).
[43] Guest, *J. Am. Chem. Soc.*, 50, 1746 (1928).
[44] Hatch and Nesbitt, *J. Am. Chem. Soc.*, 72, 730 (1950).
[45] Paillard and Wieland, *Helv. Chim. Acta*, 21, 1363 (1938).
[46] Stoll and Rouve, *Helv. Chim. Acta*, 21, 1544 (1938).
[47] Golse, *Ann. chim.*, (12) 3, 529 (1948).
[48] Jacobs and Tuttle, *J. Am. Chem. Soc.*, 71, 1318 (1949); Jacobs, Cramer, and Weiss, *ibid.*, 62, 1849 (1940).
[49] Ott, Ottemeyer, and Packendorff, *Ber.*, 63, 1943 (1930).
[50] Adkins and Burks, *Org. Syntheses*, 27, 76 (1947).
[51] Abbott, Arnold, and Thompson, *Org. Syntheses*, Coll. Vol. II, 10 (1943).
[52] Reimer, *J. Am. Chem. Soc.*, 64, 2510 (1942); Abbott, *Org. Syntheses*, Coll. Vol. II, 515 (1943); Gitsels and Wibaut, *Rec. trav. chim.*, 59, 1100 (1940).
[53] Schjanberg, *Ber.*, 71, 569 (1938); cf. Jeffery and Vogel, *J. Chem. Soc.*, 677 (1948).
[54] West, *J. Am. Chem. Soc.*, 42, 1666 (1920).
[55] Parcell and Pollard, *J. Am. Chem. Soc.*, 72, 2385 (1950).
[56] Ruggli et al., *Helv. Chim. Acta*, 18, 855 (1935); 19, 1001 (1936); 20, 257 (1937); 21, 42 (1938).
[57] Jacobs, Cramer, and Hanson, *J. Am. Chem. Soc.*, 64, 225 (1942).
[58] Bourguel, *Ann. chim.*, (10) 3, 191, 325 (1925).
[59] Heilbron, Jones, and Lacey, *J. Chem. Soc.*, 28 (1946).
[60] Campbell and O'Connor, *J. Am. Chem. Soc.*, 61, 2897 (1939).
[61] Dufraisse and Dequesnes, *Bull. soc. chim. France*, (4) 49, 1880 (1931).
[62] Coleman and Maxwell, *J. Am. Chem. Soc.*, 56, 132 (1934); Coleman, Holst, and Maxwell, *ibid.*, 58, 2310 (1936).
[63] Campbell and Eby, *J. Am. Chem. Soc.*, 62, 1798 (1940); Zakharova, *J. Gen. Chem. (U.S.S.R.)* 17, 1277 (1947); *Chem. Abstracts*, 42, 3722 (1948).
[64] Hunsmann, *Chem. Ber.*, 83, 213 (1950).
[65] Bowden, Heilbron, Jones, and Sargent, *J. Chem. Soc.*, 1579 (1947).
[66] Schlenk and Bergmann, *Ann.*, 463, 76 (1928).
[67] Grignard and Perrichon, *Ann. chim.*, (10) 5, 28 (1926).
[68] Bouis, *Ann. chim.*, (10) 9, 459 (1928).
[69] Ott and Bossaller, *Ber.*, 76, 88 (1943).
[70] Hennion and Banigan, *J. Am. Chem. Soc.*, 68, 1202 (1946).
[71] Otto, *J. Am. Chem. Soc.*, 56, 1393 (1934); Gilman, Hewlett, and Wright, *ibid.*, 53, 4192 (1931); Weltzien, Micheel, and Hess, *Ann.*, 433, 257 (1923).
[72] Bergmann and Bondi, *Ber.*, 66, 278 (1933); cf. ref. 71.
[73] Schofield and Simpson, *J. Chem. Soc.*, 517 (1945).
[74] Hennion and Pillar, *J. Am. Chem. Soc.*, 72, 5317 (1950).
[75] Taylor and Strong, *J. Am. Chem. Soc.*, 72, 4263 (1950).

4

Halides

CONTENTS

In this chapter are gathered twenty-eight methods for introducing the halogen atom into organic substances. These methods are grouped in accordance with some general type of reaction such as replacement reactions (methods 51-63), halogenation reactions (methods 64-72), and addition reactions (methods 73-78).

In the tables are collected a number of halogenated compounds, which have been prepared by these methods and, as such, serve as examples.

Special works on summarizing information concerning halogen compounds are noteworthy. Outstanding is the compilation of data on organic chlorine compounds, which presents their preparation, properties, chemical behavior, and identification.[685] The chemistry of fluorine compounds has been reviewed in several excellent works.[686]

51. Action of Hydrogen Halides on Hydroxy Compounds

$$ROH + HBr \rightarrow RBr + H_2O$$

A general method for the preparation of primary alkyl bromides of the type RCH_2CH_2Br consists in the treatment of the alcohol with excess aqueous hydrobromic acid together with sulfuric acid (90-95%).[1] The hydrobromic acid is readily prepared from bromine and sulfur dioxide. The use of sodium bromide, sulfuric acid, and water is satisfactory in the preparation of low-molecular-weight compounds such as n-butyl bromide and trimethylene bromide, but this procedure leads to comparatively low yields of high-molecular-weight bromides. The higher primary bromides are prepared more conveniently by saturating the alcohol at 100-120° with dry hydrogen bromide.[3]

Primary alkyl chlorides are formed by the action of zinc chloride and hydrochloric acid.[18] The original procedure has been modified so that the time of action of the hot reagents has been shortened; the yields are higher (70-90%).[18] Long contact time of the halide with the *hot* reagent causes the formation of isomeric halides.[12] Efforts have been made to avoid possible isomeric changes by using *cold* $ZnCl_2$-HCl reagent and long reaction periods.[8,12,13] Thionyl chloride is a more satisfactory reagent for the preparation of primary alkyl chlorides (method 53).

Highly branched primary halides, $RR'R''CCH_2X$, cannot be made from the corresponding alcohols except in small yields; the main product is a tertiary halide formed by the rearrangement of one of the alkyl groups. Similarly, secondary carbinols ($RR'CHCHOHR''$) having a tertiary hydrogen atom *alpha* to the carbinol group give tertiary halides even under the mildest conditions on treatment with halogen acids.[9] Primary halides of the type $RR'CHCH_2X$ can be obtained best using phosphorus tribromide or thionyl chloride in pyridine; other reagents cause rearrangement.[11]

Secondary chlorides of propane and butane can be made without side reactions from isopropyl alcohol and s-butyl alcohol by treatment with HCl and $ZnCl_2$ in the cold; however, treatment of the next higher homolog 3-pentanol under the same conditions gives a mixture of chloropentanes. The 2- and 3-chloropentanes are best obtained by the $SOCl_2$-pyridine procedure.[12] The corresponding bromo derivatives have been obtained using hydrogen bromide at a low temperature;[7] however, care must be taken to avoid isomerization.

Tertiary halides, RR'R''CX, are formed easily by reaction of the alcohol and aqueous hydrogen halide.[19,21,22] Acetyl chloride or bromide has also been used as the halogenating agent, as illustrated by the synthesis of triphenylchloromethane and its derivatives.[37,562]

Alkyl iodides are obtained from primary, secondary, and tertiary alcohols in 88–95% yields by the action of potassium or sodium iodide and phosphoric acid at reflux temperatures.

$$ROH + KI + H_3PO_4 \xrightarrow{\text{Reflux}} RI + KH_2PO_4 + H_2O$$

Extensive reduction of the sensitive iodide, usually encountered with hydrogen iodide, is avoided. In the conversion of 2-methyl-1-propanol, $(CH_3)_2CHCH_2OH$, apparently no isomerization to the tertiary halide occurs.

The physical properties of alkyl monohalides prepared by various reagents have been compared.[17]

Improved directions for the preparation of *dihalides* by this method have been described.[71] Since ω-acetoxyamyl chloride is readily available by the ring opening of tetrahydropyran with acetyl chloride, an attractive route for making pentamethylene chlorobromide is afforded by reaction of this ester with hydrobromic acid (82%).[566] Other diesters have been cleaved to furnish dihalides, the procedure being particularly valuable for obtaining sterically pure α-dibromides.[43,564]

Other *difunctional compounds* have been made. A few examples are noteworthy. Olefinic carbinols of the types RCH=$CHCH_2OH$ and $RCHOHCH$=CH_2 on treatment with dry hydrogen bromide or chloride undergo allylic rearrangements to yield equilibrium mixtures of isomeric unsaturated halides.[47,49,51] Acetylenic carbinols prepared from sodium acetylide and aldehydes or ketones[55] can be converted to their chlorides by means of anhydrous hydrogen chloride at $-5°C$.[54] However, it should be noted that, in the reaction of dimethylethynylcarbinol, $(CH_3)_2C(OH)C$≡CH, with hydrochloric acid, extensive production of 2-chloro-3-methyl-1,3-butadiene, H_2C=$C(CH_3)C(Cl)$=CH_2, occurs instead of the expected metathesis product.[575] *m*-Methoxybenzyl alcohol has been converted to the corresponding halide in 90% yield without cleavage of the ether linkage.[65] β-Bromoethylamine hydrobromide is synthesized from ethanolamine and hydrobromic acid in 83% yield.[70]

52. Action of Phosphorus Halides on Hydroxy Compounds

$$3\,ROH + PX_3 \xrightarrow{\text{Pyridine}} 3\,RX + H_3PO_3$$

This method is superior to the hydrobromic-sulfruic acid method in the preparation of certain low-molecular-weight alkyl bromides.[74] It has been applied in the preparation of a large number of primary and secondary bromides without any apparent isomerization.[78] Thus, primary bromides of the type $RR'CHCH_2Br$ are best obtained using phosphorus tribromide in pyridine; other reagents cause rearrangements.[11] The presence of pyridine helps to retard isomeric changes. In the preparation of tetrahydrofurfuryl bromide, this combination gives markedly improved yields (61%).[98,99] Alkyl iodides are conveniently prepared by bringing the alcohol in contact with phosphorus and iodine.[72,73] Phosphorus pentachloride has been used for the formation of alkyl chlorides,[86] although thionyl chloride is more satisfactory. Certain phenolic groups are replaced by halogen by the action of phosphorus tribromide[95] or phosphorus pentabromide.[94]

The method has been extended to the preparation of *difunctional compounds*. Dihalides including the mixed variety are formed in 90 to 98% yields.[104,105,109] Primary unsaturated bromides of the type $RCH=CHCH_2Br$ have been formed from the corresponding alcohols by the action of phosphorus tribromide and pyridine at a low temperature without any apparent rearrangement.[47,113] However, the corresponding secondary-carbinol system, $RCHOHCH=CH_2$, is very susceptible to allylic isomerization.[47,51] The formation of α,β-acetylenic bromides from acetylenic alcohols and phosphorus tribromide is common (40-70%).[119-121] An acetylenic-allenic isomerization has been observed,[122,575] viz., $RC\equiv CCH_2X \rightarrow RCX=C=CH_2$. β,γ- and γ,δ-Acetylenic alcohols can be transformed to the halides in better yields by an alternative procedure, which consists in their esterification with p-toluenesulfonyl chloride and subsequent cleavage of the ester by the action of sodium iodide, lithium chloride, or calcium bromide in an appropriate solvent (60-90%).[578] Halo ethers are prepared by the action of phosphorus tribromide on hydroxy ethers, as in the preparation of β-ethoxyethyl bromide (66%).[123] In a similar manner, β-halo esters have been prepared without appreciable dehydration of the β-hydroxy ester (40-60%).[132] The reaction of cyanohydrins leads to α-halo nitriles.[140] Treatment of 2-nitro-1-propanol with phosphorus pentachloride gives 1-chloro-2-nitropropane (47%).[580]

53. Action of Thionyl Chloride on Hydroxy Compounds

$$\text{ROH} + \text{SOCl}_2 \xrightarrow{\text{C}_5\text{H}_5\text{N}} \text{RCl} + \text{SO}_2 + \text{C}_5\text{H}_5\text{N} \cdot \text{HCl}$$

Alcohols on treatment with thionyl chloride in the presence of pyridine are converted in good yields to chlorides. This method has been successful where other methods have given poor results[147] or have led to isomeric products (cf. methods 51 and 52).[11,12]

Only a small amount of pyridine or its hydrochloride is required for the decomposition of the intermediate alkyl chlorosulfinate.[91,141,155] Oftentimes, in the absence of pyridine, the reaction takes other courses.[151] On the other hand, certain aromatic and heterocyclic alcohols react normally without the hydrogen chloride acceptor, as in the preparation of α-naphthylmethyl chloride (79%)[145] and γ-(α-tetrahydrofuryl)-propyl chloride (83%).[147]

The method has been used for the preparation of *dihalides*, e.g., 1,9-dichlorononane (93%);[154] *unsaturated halides*, e.g., 11-undecylenyl chloride (83%);[156] *halo ethers*, e.g., β-ethoxyethyl chloride (80%);[159] *halo ketones*, e.g., desyl chloride (79%);[183] *halo esters*, e.g., methyl α-chloropropionate (71%);[169] *halo cyanides*, e.g., phenylchloroacetonitrile (80%);[179] and *aminoalkyl halides*.[170-178] An interesting isomerization has been observed in liberating 2-diethylamino-1-chloropropane from its hydrochloride salt; 1-diethylamino-2-chloropropane is formed.[172]

54. Cleavage of Ethers

$$\text{C}_6\text{H}_5\text{OR} + \text{HX} \rightarrow \text{RX} + \text{C}_6\text{H}_5\text{OH}$$

The cleavage of alkyl aryl ethers is more important as a preparative method for phenols than for alkyl halides (method 97). The procedure has been employed as the final step in a synthesis proposed as a means for increasing the carbon chain of an alkyl halide, viz.,[365]

$$\text{RX} \xrightarrow{\text{Mg}} \text{RMgX} \xrightarrow{\text{ClCH}_2\text{OCH}_3} \text{RCH}_2\text{OCH}_3 \xrightarrow{\text{HX}} \text{RCH}_2\text{X}$$

It should be mentioned that the formation of methyl iodide by heating methyl ethers with concentrated hydriodic acid is quantitative and is the basis of the Zeisel method for the determination of methoxyl groups.

Gaseous or aqueous hydrogen iodide is the common reagent for cleavage; however, it also leads to extensive reduction of the product. A modification which overcomes this difficulty consists in heating the ether with orthophosphoric acid and potassium iodide, viz.,[603]

$$\text{ROR} + 2\text{KI} + 2\text{H}_3\text{PO}_4 \xrightarrow{\text{Heat}} 2\text{RI} + 2\text{KH}_2\text{PO}_4 + \text{H}_2\text{O}$$

In this manner, dibutyl ether is converted to 1-iodobutane in 81% yield. Certain ethers have been cleaved successfully with boron tribromide.[368] More often, the method is applied in the synthesis of halogenated acids,[373,591,604] ketones,[125] and amines.[376,377] The halo group in the starting material is substituted by the relatively unreactive alkoxyl group before taking steps in which the halogen itself would react; the halo group is then "regenerated" at the appropriate time.

γ-Alkoxybutyryl chlorides are transformed by heat into alkyl γ-chlorobutyrates as a result of an intramolecular rearrangement, viz.,[605]

$$\text{CH}_3\text{OCH}_2\text{CH}_2\text{CH}_2\text{COCl} \rightarrow \text{ClCH}_2\text{CH}_2\text{CH}_2\text{CO}_2\text{CH}_3 \quad (84\%)$$

The cleavage of tetrahydrofuran and its alkylated derivatives with halogen acids is an excellent method for the preparation of 1,4-dihaloalkanes.[410,413] The reaction of tetrahydrofuran with the less-reactive hydrogen chloride stops at the chlorohydrin stage,[606] whereas the reaction in the presence of zinc chloride catalyst leads to the formation of the dichloride.[410] The crude reaction mixture containing the intermediate chlorohydrin may be treated directly with phosphorus tribromide, yielding tetramethylene chlorobromide.[119] The preparation of dibromides can be accomplished easily with hydrogen bromide[411] or phosphorus and bromine[412] and diiodides, by the action of potassium iodide and orthophosphoric acid.[633]

$$\begin{array}{c} \text{H}_2\text{C---CH}_2 \\ |\quad\quad| \\ \text{RHC}\quad\text{CH}_2 \\ \backslash\ / \\ \text{O} \end{array} + 2\text{HBr} \rightarrow \text{BrCH}_2\text{CH}_2\text{CH}_2\text{CHBrR} + \text{H}_2\text{O}$$

Cleavage of tetrahydrofuran and its derivatives with other reagents has been carried out—acid halides lead to 4-halobutyl esters[416] and phosphorus oxychloride to chloro ethers.[415]

Similarly, tetrahydropyrans react to yield the 1,5-dihaloalkanes[416,418] and 5-haloamyl esters.[414,566]

55. Interchange of Halogen

$$\text{RX} + \text{NaI} \rightarrow \text{RI} + \text{NaX}$$

The exchange of chlorine or bromine atoms for iodine is an important method for the preparation of alkyl iodides. In general, the reactivity of the halogen atom is in the order of primary > secondary > tertiary. Vinyl and aryl halogen atoms show little or no reactivity. Bromine is replaced more readily than chlorine. The exchange is effected by heating the halogen compound with a solution of sodium iodide in acetone; sodium chloride or sodium bromide precipitates.[378] Potassium or silver fluoride at high temperatures leads to alkyl fluorides; sodium fluoride is without action.[380,607]

Mixed *dihalides* such as iodochlorides have been prepared by treating a dichloride or bromochloride with one equivalent of sodium iodide (50-90%).[154,270] Mixtures of dichloride, iodochloride, and diiodide may result. 1,2-Dihalides yield only the olefin and iodine (method 22).

This method is adaptable to the preparation of *benzyl iodides,*[288] *unsaturated iodides,*[383] *iodo ethers,*[384] *iodo esters,*[387] and *iodo nitriles.*[390]

56. Replacement of the Diazonium Group by Halogen

$$ArN_2{}^+ \; X^- \xrightarrow[HX]{Cu_2X_2} ArX + N_2$$

The replacement of the diazonium group by halogen constitutes an important method for the preparation of aromatic halides, particularly when the assignment of the halogen to a definite position is desired.

For the preparation of chlorides or bromides, the diazonium salt is decomposed with a solution of cuprous chloride or bromide in the corresponding halogen acid (Sandmeyer reaction). It is possible to prepare the aryl bromide from the diazonium chloride or sulfate.[299] A variation involves the use of copper powder and a mineral acid for the decomposition step (Gattermann reaction). Both procedures are illustrated by the syntheses of the isomeric bromotoluenes[300] and chlorotoluenes.[301] The usual conditions of the Sandmeyer reaction fail in the preparation of the chloro- and bromo-phenanthrenes. However, these compounds can be successfully obtained by the interaction of the diazonium compound with mercuric and potassium halides (Schwechten procedure).[310] Another procedure for formation of aryl bromides involves treatment of the amine hydrobromide with nitrogen trioxide in the presence of excess 40% hydrobromic acid. The intermediate diazonium perbromide is then decomposed by heat.[316]

$$ArNH_2 \cdot HBr \xrightarrow[HBr]{N_2O_3} ArN_2Br_3 \xrightarrow{Heat} ArBr + N_2 + Br_2$$

In a somewhat analogous fashion, pyridine hydrobromide on treatment with sodium nitrite and bromine gives a perbromide which decomposes to 2-bromopyridine (92%).[312]

If the decomposition of the diazonium chloride is carried out in the presence of aqueous potassium iodide, an aryl iodide results.[302] This method furnishes a very satisfactory means for obtaining many aromatic iodo compounds.

The introduction of fluorine into the aromatic nucleus can readily be accomplished by first converting the diazonium chloride with fluoroboric acid to an insoluble borofluoride, which is isolated and then decomposed by heat (Schiemann reaction).

$$ArN_2BF_4 \xrightarrow{\text{Heat}} ArF + N_2 + BF_3$$

A critical discussion of the reaction has been presented along with a table of fluoro compounds.[303] More recently, the reaction has been extended to the preparation of heterocyclic fluorine compounds.[314]

Difunctional compounds, including certain halogenated ethers,[318] aldehydes,[329] ketones,[333] phenols,[324] amines,[336] and nitro compounds,[337] have been prepared by the Sandmeyer reaction. However, fluorophenols and fluoro acids are best obtained from the corresponding ethers and esters, respectively, which have been fluorinated by the Schiemann reaction.[303]

57. Action of Hydrogen Halides on Diazo Ketones

$$RCOCHN_2 + HBr \rightarrow RCOCH_2Br + N_2$$

The action of hydrogen bromide or hydrogen chloride on diazo ketones represents a general preparative method (50–90%) for pure halomethyl alkyl,[519, 524, 635] halomethyl aryl,[520] or halomethyl heterocyclic ketones.[525, 527, 644]

Interaction of hydrogen iodide and diazoketones forms methyl ketones with the liberation of nitrogen and iodine (method 228). If the diazoketone is treated with bromine, then a dibromomethyl ketone, $RCOCHBr_2$, is formed.[645]

The diazo ketones are readily prepared from acyl halides and diazomethane.[521]

58. Replacement of the Sulfonic Acid Group by Halogen

$$4\text{-}HOC_6H_4SO_3H + Br_2 \rightarrow 2,4,6\text{-}Br_3C_6H_2OH$$

The replacement of the sulfonic acid group by halogen is governed largely by groups already present on the nucleus. When there is no other group, as in benzenesulfonic acid, the replacement does not take place. The reaction occurs readily with phenolic sulfonic acids and is accompanied by halogenation to give polyhalogenated phenols. The amino group also accelerates the reaction. On the other hand, a nitro group retards the reaction and alkylated and halogenated sulfonic acids undergo the reaction with difficulty.[354] An aqueous solution of the potassium salt is treated with bromine and sodium bromide for a short time and then extracted with ether, as illustrated by the preparation of 1-methyl-4-bromonaphthalene from 1-methyl-4-naphthalenesulfonic acid (68%).[291]

59. Interaction of Organometallic Compounds and Halogen

$$RHgX + Br_2 \longrightarrow RBr + HgXBr$$

Organometallic compounds of magnesium, mercury, or lithium have been treated with iodine or bromine to form organic halides. The method has been successful for obtaining neopentyl iodide where other methods have failed (92%).[354] It has been found convenient in the synthesis of 9-iodoanthracene (53%)[355] and certain heterocyclic halides.[356]

The method has been of particular value in the preparation of *difunctional compounds*. For example, the action of elemental halogen on sodium acetylides or alkynylmagnesium halides gives 1-halo-1-alkynes (70–90%).[359,360,363] Also, halo esters, phenols, or acids result when the appropriate aromatic mercurial is treated.[361,362,364] Sometimes *p*-toylsulfonyl chloride is substituted for chlorine gas.[363] *p*-Iododimethylaniline is easily made in 42–54% yield by the reaction of *p*-dimethylaminophenyllithium and iodine.[601]

60. Interaction of Grignard Reagents and Haloalkyl Sulfonates

$$RMgX + p\text{-}CH_3C_6H_4SO_2O(CH_2)_nCl \longrightarrow R(CH_2)_nCl + p\text{-}CH_3C_6H_4SO_2OMgX$$

The reaction of various Grignard reagents with excess γ-chloropropyl *p*-toluenesulfonate ($n = 3$) is a satisfactory procedure for lengthening carbon chains by three methylene groups; the yields are about 50–60% when the Grignard reagent has six or more carbon atoms.[352] β-Chloroethyl *p*-toluenesulfonate ($n = 2$) or di-(β-chloroethyl) sulfate[353] can be employed to effect an increase of two carbon atoms in the chain; however, reaction of the Grignard reagent with ethylene oxide is usually superior.

61. Interaction of Organic Silver Salts and Halogen (Simonini)

$$RCO_2Ag + X_2 \longrightarrow RX + CO_2 + AgX$$

Silver salts of carboxylic acids react with bromine or chlorine in an inert solvent to give carbon dioxide, a silver halide, and the halide containing one less carbon atom than the acid. The method has been reviewed.[391] Both low- and high-molecular-weight aliphatic bromides have been prepared.[142,396,613] The degradation of silver salts of aromatic acids is complicated by nuclear halogenation.[611] The procedure is valuable as a step in the synthesis of ω-bromo esters (C_5 to C_{17}) from dicarboxylic acids.[392,393]

The formation of neopentyl bromide by the degradation of silver t-butylacetate is in keeping with a free-radical mechanism and eliminates the possibility of a carbonium-ion mechanism.[610]

62. Reductive Elimination of Halogen from Polyhalides

$$CHBr_3 + Na_3AsO_3 + NaOH \rightarrow CH_2Br_2 + Na_3AsO_4 + NaBr$$

The replacement of halogen by hydrogen has been discussed (method 7). The procedure becomes of practical importance for the stepwise replacement of halogen in polyhalides. For example, methylene bromide has been synthesized from bromoform by the reducing action of sodium arsenite.[404] Similarly, trichloroacetic acid in aqueous solution is converted to dichloroacetic acid by the action of copper.[406] Dihalo ketones have been selectively hydrogenated to monohalo ketones, as illustrated by the conversion of phenyl α,α-dichlorobenzyl ketone to phenyl α-chlorobenzyl ketone (65%).[407] Tetraiodothiophene on reduction with sodium amalgam loses three iodine atoms to give β-iodothiophene (64%).[409]

63. Interaction of Amides and Phosphorus Pentahalides (von Braun)

$$RNHCOC_6H_5 + PCl_5 \rightarrow POCl_3 + C_6H_5CN + RCl + HCl$$

The amine group in primary amines can be replaced by halogen by warming the benzoyl derivative with phosphorus pentachloride or phosphorus pentabromide. Oftentimes, the separation of the halide from the benzonitrile, which is also formed, is troublesome.[397] The process has been applied mostly to high-molecular-weight amines obtained by the Hofmann degradation of acid amides or by reduction of nitriles.[402,403]

Diamines lead to dihalogen derivatives.[400,402] If N-benzoyl piperidines are treated, substituted pentamethylene halides are formed.[397,399] An example is the synthesis of pentamethylene bromide by the action of phosphorus pentabromide on N-benzoyl piperidine (72%).[397]

$$C_5H_{10}NCOC_6H_5 + PBr_5 \rightarrow Br(CH_2)_5Br + C_6H_5CN + POBr_3$$

64. Direct Halogenation of Hydrocarbons

$$RH + X_2 \rightarrow RX + HX$$

Direct halogenation of alkanes has found limited use in the laboratory preparation of aliphatic mono- and di-halides;[211-213,270,591] mixtures are obtained, and other methods are more convenient and satisfactory. The reaction may be carried out in the liquid or vapor phase; slow at room temperature, it is accelerated by heat and light and proceeds rapidly in the vapor phase.[209,210] In general, substitution occurs most readily with tertiary hydrogens and least at primary positions; the relative rates approach equality with higher temperatures. Many paraffins can be chlorinated in the dark using sulfuryl chloride in the presence or organic peroxides.[217] Halogenation of alkenes at elevated temperatures leads to allyl-type monohalides.[241]

Direct halogenation of aromatic hydrocarbons finds more use. In sunlight and in the absence of catalysts, the alkylbenzenes are chlorinated or brominated predominately in the side chain.[214-216] A peroxide-induced reaction with sulfuryl chloride proceeds smoothly and easily, giving no nuclear substitution.[217] In contrast, the thiophene ring undergoes substitution under these conditions.[257] Benzyl bromide has been prepared in 60-75% yield by bromination of toluene with carbon tetrabromide[240] or N-bromosuccinimide.[455] In the presence of benzoyl peroxide, the latter agent causes a predominance of side-chain substitution.[218,255] The side-chain halogenation of 2-methylnaphthalene has been accomplished using chlorine, phosphorus trichloride, and light.[246]

In the presence of halogen carriers, such as certain metal salts or iodine, halogenation of aromatic hydrocarbons occurs in the nucleus; however, these materials are not always needed. General directions for the procedure have been given which include preparation and measurement of the halogenating agent and choice of solvent.[226] Good examples of liquid-phase halogenation are found in the chlorination[231] and bromination[229,230] of the polyalkylbenzenes (60-80%). The course of the bromination in the gaseous phase is markedly influenced by the temperature; at 400° p-dibromobenzene (57%) is formed, whereas at 450° to 630° m-dibromobenzene (60%) is formed.[272] Polybromination substitutes the benzene ring completely with the replacement of any sec- or tert-alkyl groups; however, straight-chain-alkyl groups are not affected.[271]

Bromine,[234] iodine monobromide,[245] and N-bromosuccinimide[235] have been employed as brominating agents in the treatment of certain polycyclic hydrocarbons. The conversion of naphthalene to its α-bromo derivative with one equivalent of bromine occurs rapidly at room temperature (75%); no halogen carrier is needed.[234] In the presence of an iron catalyst and at a temperature of 150° to 165°, β-bromonaphthalene is formed to the extent of 57%. These conditions are favorable for an $\alpha \rightleftharpoons \beta$-bromonaphthalene equilibrium.[587]

Direct iodination of the nucleus can be brought about if the hydrogen iodide is removed as fast as it is formed. Its removal may be accomplished either by oxidation or by reaction with a basic agent. For example, nitric acid as an oxidizing agent is convenient and effective in the preparation of iodobenzene (87%).[236] Sodium persulfate in acetic acid gives good results in the iodination of benzene and its homologs.[237] Mercuric oxide has been used as a basic agent in the iodination of thiophene (75%).[238] Another general method consists in treating the organic compound in ether with a suspension of silver perchlorate, iodine, and calcium carbonate; the last neutralizes the liberated perchloric acid.[298] Iodine monochloride has been used for the iodination of phenols and amines in which the substitution of hydrogen atoms takes place readily.[239] Direct iodination of benzoic acid is performed by the action of iodine and silver sulfate in concentrated sulfuric acid to yield m-iodobenzoic acid (75%).[593]

Various heterocyclic compounds undergo nuclear halogenation.[255-269] In furan and thiophene, the halogen enters the alpha position. The vapor-phase reaction of pyridine and bromine at 500° furnishes 2-bromo- and 2,6-dibromo-pyridines, and at 300°, 3-bromo- and 3,5-dibromo-pyridines.[265] 3-Bromopyridine is more conveniently prepared by pyrolysis of pyridine hydrobromide perbromide (40%). Similarly, quinoline yields 3-bromo-quinoline at 300° and 2-bromoquinoline at 500°.[262] Pyrolysis of iso-quinoline hydrobromide perbromide gives the 4-bromo derivative (53%).[263]

Difunctional compounds have been prepared by the nuclear halogenation of phenols,[282] acids,[285,287] amines,[290] cyanides,[293] and nitro compounds.[295] Aromatic esters containing nuclear halogen atoms are best prepared by halogenating the acid chloride followed by esterification.[288] The direct halogenations of ethers (method 65), aldehydes and ketones (method 66), and acids and esters (method 67) are discussed later.

The process of halogenation has been reviewed; in addition, articles on this subject appear periodically.[594]

65. Halogenation of Ethers

$$C_6H_5OCH_3 + PBr_5 \longrightarrow p\text{-}BrC_6H_4OCH_3 + PBr_3 + HBr$$

Halogens react very vigorously with aliphatic ethers at room temperature to yield complex mixtures. Thus, the products formed by successive substitution in the chlorination of diethyl ether at room temperature are α-chloroethyl, α,β-dichloroethyl, α,β,β-trichloroethyl, and α,β,β,β-tetra-chloroethyl ethyl ether.   The β-chlorine atoms probably arise by the repeated loss of hydrogen chloride followed by addition of chlorine to the resultant double bond, the chlorine atom of the hydrogen chloride coming from the labile alpha position.

On the other hand, if diethyl ether is treated at −20° or below with one equivalent of chlorine, α-chloroethyl ethyl ether is formed in 42% yield.   Further chlorination at this low temperature leads to α,α′-di-chlorodiethyl ether in 57% yield, the second chlorine atom entering a new alpha position in preference to an alpha position already substituted. The extension of this new technique to higher ethers is under way.[633] Other methods are available for the preparation of α- and β-halo ethers (see Chapter 6).

Aryl ethers in the presence of a solvent can be preferentially halo-genated in the nucleus.   Thus, anisole with phosphorus pentabromide or with iodine monochloride yields p-bromoanisole (90%)[479] and p-iodo-anisole (46%),[283] respectively.   Phosphorus pentachloride has also been used for the halogenation of the nucleus as in the preparation of 4-chloro-biphenyl ether (90%).[284]   The action of this reagent with aliphatic and aryl-aliphatic ethers is very complex, giving both cleavage and halo-genation products.[481]

The bromination of α-chloro ethers proceeds readily and represents the second stage in the Boord synthesis of olefins (method 21):

$$RCH_2CHClOR' + Br_2 \longrightarrow RCHBrCHBrOR' + HCl$$

In the conversion, the chlorine atom is replaced by bromine.   Since the yield is nearly quantitative (90–95%), the bromination product is often used without purification to avoid losses by decomposition.[384,480]

66. Halogenation of Aldehydes and Ketones

$$RCH_2COCH_2R + Br_2 \longrightarrow RCHBrCOCH_2R + HBr$$

The direct bromination of aliphatic ketones occurs readily, often giving isomeric mixtures.   Thus, methyl ethyl ketone and an equimolar quantity of bromine yield the α-bromomethyl (17%) and the α-bromoethyl (50%) isomers; polybrominated products are also formed.[484]   On the other hand, only the tertiary hydrogen in methyl isopropyl ketone is substituted upon monobromination.[485]   By varying the conditions for the bromination of acetone, mono- or poly-substitution products may be formed: e.g., bromo-acetone (44%),[483] α,α′-dibromoacetone (60%), and α,α,α′-tribromoacetone (60%).[634]

Oftentimes condensation reactions are promoted by the liberated hydrogen halide (cf. method 36). This difficulty may be overcome by brominating in the presence of calcium carbonate or potassium chlorate.[484]

$$6RCH_2COR + 3Br_2 + KClO_3 \rightarrow 6RCHBrCOR + KCl + 3H_2O$$

The bromine may be added in a stream of nitrogen which also serves to remove the liberated hydrogen halide. In the bromination of pinacolone, aluminum amalgam or aluminum chloride is used as a catalyst.[489] Phosphorus pentabromide,[490] N-bromosuccinimide,[218] and pyridine hydrobromide perbromide[491] have been used as brominating agents.

Chloro ketones have been prepared by direct chlorination[496, 497] or by the action of sulfuryl chloride.[495] Cyclohexanol suspended in water in the presence of calcium carbonate is oxidized and chlorinated in one step to 2-chlorocyclohexanone (57%).[498]

Aliphatic aromatic ketones are halogenated in the side chain exclusively, as in the synthesis of α-bromoacetophenone (96%).[499] The reaction is frequently carried out in cold ether, which can be easily removed.[499, 507] The third chlorine atom is introduced into trichloroacetophenone by passing chlorine into a solution of dichloroacetophenone and fused *sodium acetate* in acetic acid at 95° (95%).[636] The treatment of 2-acetylthiophene with bromine in carbon tetrachloride in the presence of iron filings yields 2-(bromoacetyl)-thiophene (80%).[509]

Direct halogenation of aldehydes is more complicated. Substitution on the aldehyde carbon as well as the α-carbon may take place. Thus, acetaldehyde in aqueous solution yields chloral, whereas, in the absence of water, acetyl chloride is formed. Bromination of cyclohexanealdehyde in chloroform at 0° in the presence of calcium carbonate is straightforward, the 1-bromo compound being formed in 80% yield.[639] Also, the direct bromination of *n*-valeraldehyde in chloroform solution at −15° has been successfully accomplished, α-bromo-*n*-valeraldehyde being formed in 70% yield.[514] Frequently, the reaction mixture containing the α-bromo aldehyde is treated with absolute ethanol and the product is isolated as the diethyl acetal.[641] o-Chlorobenzaldehyde, which lacks an α-hydrogen, undergoes chlorination to give o-chlorobenzoyl chloride.

Bromination of acetals affords satisfactory yields of the α-bromo acetals. The reaction is carried out in cold chloroform solution in the presence of calcium carbonate, which reacts with the liberated hydrogen bromide.[640]

$$RCH_2CH(OC_2H_5)_2 + Br_2 + CaCO_3 \rightarrow RCHBrCH(OC_2H_5)_2 + CaBr_2 + CO_2$$

Acetals may also be converted by the action of phosphorus trichlorodi-
bromide to α-bromoaldehydes (60–75%).[518]

$$RCH_2CH(COR')_2 + 2PCl_3Br_2 \rightarrow RCHBrCHO + 2R'Br + HBr +$$

$$POCl_3 + PCl_3$$

In other instances, aldehyde trimers have been brominated and then heated
to yield the monomolecular derivative.[513, 516, 517]

Bromination of enol acetates of aldehydes with subsequent reaction of
the brominated product with methanol furnishes a novel synthesis of
α-bromoaldehyde acetals.

$$RCH = CHOCOCH_3 \xrightarrow[CCl_4]{Br_2} RCHBrCHBrOCOCH_3 \xrightarrow{CH_3OH} RCHBrCH(OCH_3)_2$$

The yields of enol acetates prepared by boiling the aldehydes with acetic
anhydride and potassium acetate range from 40%–60%, and the α-bromoaldehyde dimethyl acetals are formed in about 80% yield. These products
can be hydrolyzed with varying yields to the α-bromoaldehydes. A
typical example is the synthesis of α-bromoheptaldehyde (40% over-
all).[642]

An analogous change is involved in the conversion of ketones possessing a methylenic hydrogen atom as in methyl n-amyl ketone, propiophenone,
and cyclohexanone. Bromination of the enol acetates with subsequent
hydrolysis in methanol gives α-bromo ketones in 46–90% yields.[643]

67. Halogenation of Acids and Esters

$$RCH_2COOH + Br_2 \xrightarrow{PBr_3} RCHBrCOOH + HBr$$

Direct bromination of an acid yields the α-substituted product when red
phosphorus or phosphorus halides are used as carriers. The procedure
is illustrated by the preparation of α-bromo-n-caproic acid (89%)[530] and
α-bromoisovaleric acid (89%).[528] An excellent laboratory preparation of
bromoacetic acid is furnished by a modification of the reaction in which
acetic anhydride with pyridine is used as the catalyst.[544]

Direct chlorination of acetic acid in the presence of a small quantity
of red phosphorus is a standard procedure for the preparation of chloroacetic acid;[221] however, similar treatment of its straight-chain homologs
gives complex mixtures of halogenated acids.[547] Substitution by chlorine
in a branched-chain acid such as isovaleric acid occurs largely at the
tertiary hydrogen. The peroxide-catalyzed chlorination of aliphatic acids

or acyl chlorides with sulfuryl chloride produces preferentially *beta-* and *gamma-* rather than *alpha-*substitution products. For example, chlorination of *n*-butyryl chloride yields 15% α-, 55% β-, and 30% γ-chlorobutyryl chloride.[647] Oftentimes, it is desirable to halogenate the acyl chloride and then hydrolyze the resulting α-halo acyl chloride or convert it to an ester with alcohol.[545,648–650] Formation of the acyl halide and α-halogenation can be accomplished in a single operation by using two molecular equivalents of bromine (Hell-Volhard-Zelinsky).[546,646] Another successful procedure employs thionyl chloride not only as the reagent for forming the acyl chloride but also as a solvent for the subsequent halogenation, which is accomplished with either bromine or sulfuryl chloride; no red phosphorus is needed.[550] Malonic acid, ethyl malonate, and their monoalkyl derivatives can be readily halogenated in ether solution; subsequent decarboxylation leads to the corresponding α-halogenated acetic acid in 55–80% yield.[537] The reaction of the potassium salts of monoethyl alkylmalonates with bromine provides the α-bromo esters directly, although the yields are relatively low.[552] Halogenation of the higher dicarboxylic acids occurs readily to give α,α'-dibromo acids, for example, α,α'-dibromoadipic acid (70%).[542] In fact, it is difficult to avoid these products when the α-halo dicarboxylic acid is desired. Preparation of the monohalogenated compounds is accomplished by treatment of the ester acyl chloride with bromine or sulfuryl chloride in thionyl chloride solution (88–98%).[550]

68. N-Halogenation of Amides and Imides

$$RCONH_2 + Br_2 + KOH \longrightarrow RCONHBr + KBr + H_2O$$

Amido[690,691] or imido[687,688] hydrogen atoms are easily replaced in the cold by the positive bromine atom of alkali hypobromites. The reaction is the first step in the Hofmann degradation of acid amides (method 446) and, as such, has been extensively studied. The N-bromoamides are sometimes isolated.[690] Excellent directions are given for the preparation of N-bromoacetamide (51%).[695]

69. N-Halogenation of Amines

$$RNH_2 + NaOCl \longrightarrow RNHCl + NaOH$$

N-Halogenated amines can be prepared in excellent yields by treating the amine with sodium hypochlorite in ethereal solution, the mono- or di-chloro derivative being formed depending on the molecular proportion of reactants.[655] A number of dichloroamines have been made by passing chlorine directly into a cold solution of sodium bicarbonate and the free amine, as in the preparation of n-butyldichloroamine (92%).[656] N-Chloro-t-butylamine is formed in a similar way.[657]

70. Haloalkylation

$$ArH + CH_2O + HX \rightarrow ArCH_2X + H_2O$$

A survey of the chloromethylation of aromatic compounds has been made,[338] and a thorough study of the conditions of the reaction for the production of benzyl chloride has been carried out.[339] The reaction is generally applicable to aromatic hydrocarbons. The effect of substituents on the ease of chloromethylation is pronounced; alkyl and alkoxyl groups facilitate the introduction of the chloromethyl group, whereas halogen, carboxyl, and nitro substituents retard or prevent the reaction. Zinc chloride, sulfuric acid, and phosphoric acid[343] have been used as catalysts when needed. A chief by-product is the bis-chloromethyl compound. Indeed, these disubstituted hydrocarbons are readily obtained by employing excess hydrochloric acid and formaldehyde, e.g., bis-(chloromethyl)-durene (67%)[599] and 2,5-bis-(chloromethyl)-p-xylene (55%).[600]

Related reactions such as bromomethylation,[340, 597] chloroethylation, and chloropropylation[341] have been reported.

Thiophene and benzothiophene undergo chloromethylation to furnish the respective 2- and 3-chloromethyl derivatives.[349-351]

A few aliphatic ketones have been condensed with formaldehyde in the presence of hydrochloric acid to yield β-chloro ketones.[348]

$$RCOCH_3 + CH_2O + HCl \rightarrow RCOCH_2CH_2Cl + H_2O$$

The formation of halo ethers by chloroalkylation of alcohols is discussed under Ethers (method 117).

71. Allylic Bromination (Wohl-Ziegler)

$$RCH = CH-CH_2R \xrightarrow{\text{N-Bromosuccinimide}} RCH = CH - CHBrR$$

Bromination of an olefin in the allylic position with N-bromoimides has become a valuable method for the preparation of unsaturated halogenated compounds. In general, it consists in heating the unsaturated compound in anhydrous carbon tetrachloride under reflux with N-bromo-succinimide (or N-bromophthalimide). As the bromination proceeds, succinimide collects at the surface of the mixture. After the completion of the reaction, the insoluble imide is filtered and the solution is processed. The scope, limitation, and experimental details have been elegantly reviewed.[455]

As a result of an extensive study, it has been found that methylene groups are attacked much more readily than a methyl group. For example, 2-methyl-2-butene requires 16 hours for completion of the reaction, whereas, 2-methyl-2-hexene requires 10 minutes. The conversion of cyclohexene to 3-bromocyclohexene is accomplished in 20 minutes in 87% yield.[456] It is noteworthy that the bromination of 1-octene with N-bromosuccinimide yields a mixture of 1-bromo-2-octene and 3-bromo-1-octene and that the proportion of these isomers is in close agreement with the equilibrium mixture formed at 100° by analogous bromides.[625]

More recently, the use of benzoyl peroxide catalyst or light (or both) has extended the scope of the reaction. Thus, previously unsuccessful brominations of conjugated diene systems and terminal methyl groups can now be accomplished.[457,458]

72. Action of Phosphorus Pentachloride on Carbonyl Compounds

$$RCOCH_2R' + PCl_5 \longrightarrow RCCl_2CH_2R' + POCl_3$$

The reaction of phosphorus pentachloride with aliphatic aldehydes or ketones has been used to prepare gem-dihalides. These compounds are important intermediates in the synthesis of acetylenes (method 43). Often, a large quantity of hydrogen chloride is evolved with the formation of monochloroölefins, $RC(Cl) = CHR'$; however, the resulting mixture is suitable for the acetylene synthesis.[444] Small amounts of dichloro compounds of the type $RCHClCHClR'$ are also formed. These side reactions are limited by adding the ketone to the phosphorus pentachloride at 0° C.

Arylacetones are converted mostly to mixtures of chloroölefins, giving very little of the dichlorides. Aromatic methyl ketones yield mixtures of an α-chloro ketone and the monochloroölefin.[452]

Phosphorus pentabromide causes mainly α-halogenation.[450] Even phosphorus pentachloride leads to an α-chloro ketone in the case of ethyl t-butyl ketone.[451]

$$(CH_3)_3CCOCH_2CH_3 + PCl_5 \longrightarrow (CH_3)_3CCOCHClCH_3 + HCl + PCl_3$$

73. Addition of Hydrogen Halides to Olefinic Compounds

$$CH_3CH = CH_2 \xrightarrow[\text{Peroxides}]{HBr} \begin{array}{l} \longrightarrow CH_3CHBrCH_3 \\ \longrightarrow CH_3CH_2CH_2Br \end{array}$$

The addition of hydrogen halides to olefinic linkages is of little preparative importance for simple alkyl halides since these compounds can usually be prepared by more convenient methods; however, addition to an α,β-olefinic system is important for obtaining certain unsaturated halides,[194] and halogenated acids,[199] esters,[202] and cyanides,[206] all having the halogen atom in the beta position. The reaction between isoprene and dry hydrogen chloride is noteworthy. These compounds combine in ether solution at $-15°$ to form 3-chloro-3-methyl-1-butene on addition of a limited quantity of halogen acid (1,2-addition) or 1-chloro-3-methyl-2-butene with excess acid; furthermore, the former rearranges upon heating to the latter under the catalytic influence of hydrochloric acid.[585]

$$H_2C = C -CH =CH_2 \xrightarrow{HCl} H_3C- \underset{\underset{CH_3}{|}}{\overset{\overset{Cl}{|}}{C}} - CH = CH_2 \xrightarrow[\sim]{Heat}$$
$$\underset{CH_3}{|}$$

$$H_3C - \underset{\underset{CH_3}{|}}{C} = CHCH_2Cl$$

Reactions with hydrogen bromide or hydrogen iodide generally occur at room temperature, whereas the addition of hydrogen chloride may require heat. Benzene, pentane, and ether are employed as solvents.

A unique procedure for adding hydrogen iodide to olefins consists in refluxing the olefin with a mixture of sodium iodide and 95% phosphoric acid, as in the preparation of 2,3-dimethyl-2-iodobutane (91%).[603]

Many olefinic compounds are capable of adding hydrogen bromide, but rarely the other halogen acids, to form either or both of the possible bromides. In the absence of oxygen or peroxides, the "normal" reaction takes place, giving halogen addition to the carbon with the fewer hydrogen atoms (Markownikoff's rule). In the presence of peroxides or oxygen, the direction of addition is reversed. A discussion of the peroxide effect has been presented.[195] Examples include the addition of hydrogen bromide to trimethylethylene, $(CH_3)_2C = CHCH_3$, and styrene, $C_6H_5 CH = CH_2$.[198]

From methylene compounds of the type $R_2CHCH = CH_2$, a mixture of isomeric halides may form as a result of an isomerization.[185]

$$(CH_3)_2CHCH = CH_2 \xrightarrow{HCl} (CH_3)_2CClCH_2CH_3 + (CH_3)_2CHCHClCH_3$$

74. Addition of Halogen to Olefinic Compounds

$$RCH = CHR + X_2 \rightarrow RCHXCHXR$$

The addition of halogen to unsaturated carbon compounds occurs readily, and under proper conditions the reaction is a valuable method for preparing compounds with the halogen atoms in adjacent positions. In the laboratory, the dibromides are the most conveniently and easily prepared. The reaction is generally run at low temperatures. ($-20°$ to $20°$) using a solvent, such as chloroform, carbon disulfide, acetic acid, or ether; it is sometimes aided by artificial light or sunlight. Heating is usually not recommended because it promotes substitution and dehydrohalogenation. The procedure is illustrated by the addition of bromine to allyl bromide to yield 1,2,3-tribromopropane (98%).[422]

The dibromides are often used for the purification of olefins since the double bond is easily regenerated by zinc and alcohol treatment.[424,425]

Compounds of the type RR'CHCHBrCHBrR'', where R'' is an alkyl group or a hydrogen atom are prepared directly from the corresponding tertiary alcohols.[423] Under the conditions of bromination, simultaneous dehydration and addition occurs: e.g., t-amyl alcohol to trimethylethylene dibromide (70%).[423]

Additions with more-reactive gaseous chlorine are carried out slowly at low temperatures to avoid substitution reactions. An efficient gas-liquid reaction tower has proved satisfactory for this purpose.[443] The addition to the double bond is *trans*.[420] Sulfuryl chloride[427] and phosphorus pentachloride[186] have been used as chlorinating agents. With sulfuryl chloride, cyclohexene is converted in 90% yield to 1,2-dichlorocyclohexane, which is difficult to obtain in good yields by direct chlorination.[427]

Iodochlorides have been prepared by the action of mercuric chloride and iodine on olefins.[421]

A conjugated double bond system undergoes 1,4-addition (Thiele's rule); for example, butadiene and an equimolar quantity of bromine yield 1,4-dibromo-2-butene (90%).[618] On the other hand, chlorination of butadiene in the liquid or vapor phase furnishes about equal amounts of 1,2- and 1,4-addition products.[619] Other polyfunctional compounds resulting from this method of preparation include *dihalogenated acids,*[432] *esters,*[436] *aldehydes,*[438] and *ketones.*[439,442] The addition of bromine to unsaturated ethers yields *dibromo ethers* which are used as intermediates in the synthesis of olefins (method 21) and olefinic alcohols (method 99).

75. Peroxide-Induced Addition of Halogenated Compounds to Olefins

$$CCl_4 + RCH = CH_2 \xrightarrow{\text{Peroxide}} RCHClCH_2CCl_3$$

In photochemical or peroxide-induced reactions, polyhaloalkanes—carbon tetrachloride, chloroform, dibromodichloromethane or bromotrichloromethane—add to olefins containing a terminal double bond.[557,558]

For example, the addition of carbon tetrachloride to 1-octene yields 1,1,1,3-tetrachlorononane (85%). The reactions are carried out under pressure in the usual hydrogenation equipment when low-boiling reactants are involved. When this free-radical-initiated reaction is applied to a combination of ethylene and a polyhalomethane, products of the general formula $X(CH_2CH_2)_nY$ are obtained, in which X is hydrogen or halogen and Y is the remainder of the polyhalomethane molecule.[652]

Aliphatic olefins and α-bromocarboxylic esters yield γ-bromo esters in good yields, as illustrated by the formation of ethyl γ-bromocapoate from 1-octene and ethyl bromoacetate (57%).[559]

76. Condensation of Hydrocarbons and Halogenated Compounds

$$RX + H_2C = CH_2 \xrightarrow{AlCl_3} RCH_2CH_2X$$

Certain halogenated compounds will condense with paraffinic, olefinic, or aromatic hydrocarbons. Catalysts for these reactions are of the Friedel-Crafts type. Thus, the condensation of alkyl halides with ethylene in the presence of aluminum chloride, zinc chloride, iron chloride, etc., furnishes higher alkyl halides. An example is the reaction of t-butyl chloride and ethylene to form 1-chloro-3,3-dimethylbutane (75%).[654] Although the yields are good with tertiary halides, the combination of primary and secondary alkyl halides with ethylene is slow and complicated by isomerization.

The condensation of saturated hydrocarbons with haloölefins in the presence of anhydrous aluminum chloride also results in the formation of alkyl halides, as in the preparation of 1-chloro-3,4-dimethylpentane from isobutane and allyl chloride (40%).[555] Under the same conditions, alkyl halides react with olefinic halides to give dihaloalkanes.[556] unsym-Heptachloropropane is synthesized from tetrachloroethylene and chloroform (93%).[659]

α-Chloro ethers have been added to butadiene in the presence of zinc chloride to give a mixture of unsaturated halo ethers in 61-86% yields.[653]

$$ROCHClR' \xrightarrow[\text{ZnCl}_2]{H_2C=CHCH=CH_2} \begin{cases} \to R'CHORCH_2CHClCH=CH_2 \\ \to R'CHORCH_2CH=CHCH_2Cl \end{cases}$$

These isomers can be separated by fractional distillation at reduced pressure and represent valuable intermediates for synthetic work.

Aromatic compounds have been alkylated with unsaturated halides to aryl-aliphatic halides. Hydrofluoric acid is an effective condensing agent for this purpose, as illustrated by the preparation of β-chloro-t-butyl-benzene (60%).[660] Benzene and allyl bromide are converted to β-bromo-isopropylbenzene by means of concentrated sulfuric acid in 58% yield.[661] A large number of alkyl-substituted aryl halides have been made by alkylating halogenated benzenes. An example is the treatment of bromo-benzene with isopropyl chloride in the presence of aluminum chloride, 4-bromocumene being formed in 67% yield.[662] Similarly, o-dichlorobenzene and ethyl bromide give 3,4-dichloroethylbenzene (53%).[663] Alkylation of chlorobenzene with alcohols and aluminum chloride at 90° yields mainly the *para* isomers with some *meta*, but with ethylene at 100° the principal products are the *meta* isomers (80%).[664] Boron trifluoride in the presence of a strong dehydrating agent like phosphoric anhydride is an excellent catalyst for the alkylation of monohalobenzenes with alcohols, p-s-alkyl-halobenzenes being formed in 30-66% yields. Its chief advantages are lack of *meta*-isomer formation and halogen migration, both of which may occur with aluminum chloride as catalyst.[665]

Triphenylchloromethane is synthesized in 86% yield by the reaction of carbon tetrachloride and benzene in the presence of aluminum chloride.[666]

77. Addition of Hypohalous Acids to Olefins

$$RCH = CHR' + HOX \longrightarrow RCHOHCHXR'$$

Halohydrins are prepared by vigorously stirring a cold mixture of an olefinic compound and a dilute hypohalous acid solution until the re-action is complete. Solutions of hypohalous acid for this purpose may be conveniently prepared from an aqueous suspension of freshly precipi-tated mercurous oxide and the appropriate halogen;[464] also a solution of halogen in water has been used.[459] In other instances, t-butyl hypochlorite in dilute acetic acid,[470] aqueous calcium hypochlorite,[470] monochlorourea and acetic acid,[464] benzenesulfondibromamide,[692] or N-bromoacetamide and water[471] have been used successfully as a source of the hypohalous acid. An emulsifying agent with efficient stirring gives improved yields.[470,472] The hydroxyl group joins the carbon having the smaller number of hydrogen atoms. Typical examples of the synthesis of halo-hydrins are found in the preparation of *trans*-2-chlorocyclohexanol (73%),[464] styrene chlorohydrin (76%),[470] and *trans*-2-bromocyclohexanol (79%).[471]

The reaction has been carried out with diolefins,[474] unsaturated ketones,[627] and unsaturated acids.[475]

When the above reagents are combined with olefins in the presence of a reactive solvent like an alcohol or acid, the corresponding halohydrin ether or ester is formed.[628-630] For example, propylene and *t*-butyl hypochlorite react in the presence of either methanol or acetic acid to give 1-chloro-2-methoxypropane (56%) or 1-chloro-2-acetoxypropane, (72%) respectively. The addition of small amounts of *p*-toluenesulfonic acid increases the yields.

Chlorohydrins are also formed in 35–50% yields by the interaction of 1-olefins (C_3 to C_6) and chromyl chloride, CrO_2Cl_2, with subsequent hydrolysis. In each instance, the hydroxyl group takes a primary position as in $RCHClCH_2OH$, opposite to that given by hypochlorous acid.[631]

78. Addition of Hydrogen Halides to Oxides

$$\overset{\displaystyle O}{\overset{\displaystyle \diagup\!\diagdown}{RCH\!\!-\!\!CHR'}} + HX \longrightarrow RCHOHCHXR'$$

The opening of oxide rings with halogen acids furnishes an excellent method for preparing halohydrins of known stereoconfiguration. Thus, the isomeric 2,3-epoxybutanes are first prepared from a mixture of the isomeric bromohydrins, separated by fractional distillation, and then converted to the pure *erythro*- or *threo*-halohydrins with hydrogen halide.[478] In each instance, the bromohydrin is regenerated by a *trans* opening of the oxide. Also cyclohexene oxide gives the *trans*-halohydrin with hydrogen bromide or hydrogen iodide.[476, 477] When an oxide is not symmetrical, the ring opening leads to an isomeric mixture, the composition of which depends on the structure of the oxide. Extensive studies of the mechanism of the reaction have been made and have been reviewed.[632]

TABLE 7. HALIDES　　　　111

TABLE 7. HALIDES

C_n	Compound	Method	Yield %	Chapter[ref.]	B.p./mm., n_D^t, (M.p.), Deriv.
		Aliphatic Halides			
C_1	Methyl iodide	52	95	4[72]	42.5
C_2	Ethyl bromide	51	95	4[1]	39.5
C_3	n-Propyl chloride	51	70	4[18]	47*
	n-Propyl bromide	51	87	4[565]	71, 1.4330
		52	95	4[74]	73
	n-Propyl iodide	51	91	4[603]	
		52	90	4[73]	102
	Isopropyl bromide	51	74	4[20]	61
		51	60	4[23]	60/720
		52	68	4[74]	63
	Isopropyl iodide	52	92	4[73]	89
		55	63	4[378]	
C_4	n-Butyl chloride	51	78	4[18]	77.5
	n-Butyl bromide	51	95	4[1]	104, 1.4392*
	n-Butyl iodide	52	94	4[73]	129
		54	78	4[603]	130, 1.504
	s-Butyl chloride	51	88	4[18]	68*
	s-Butyl bromide	52	80	4[74]	93
	Isobutyl bromide	52	60	4[74]	93/760, 43/135
	Isobutyl iodide	51	88	4[603]	
		52	80	4[73]	122
	t-Butyl chloride	51	88	4[19]	52
	t-Butyl iodide	51	90	4[603]	100d*
C_5	n-Amyl fluoride	55	50	4[607]	64/766, 1.3569[25]
	n-Amyl chloride	53	80	4[15]	106/725, 1.4128
	n-Amyl bromide	51	78	4[565]	127, 1.4443[22]
		54	88	4[365]	124/760, 1.4290[25]
		55	85	4[378]	
	2-Chloropentane	53	28	4[12]	95/729, 1.4068
	2-Bromopentane	51	90	4[7]	118/745, 1.4415
	3-Chloropentane	53	46	4[12]	96, 1.4104
	3-Bromopentane	51	85	4[7]	118/760, 1.4443
	(+)-2-Methylbutyl bromide	52	66	4[574]	120, 1.4552
	Isoamyl bromide	51	90	4[1]	120
	Isoamyl iodide	52	85	4[73]	148
	t-Amyl chloride	51	65	4[22]	86
	Neopentyl bromide	59	82	4[354]	105/732, 1.4370
		61	62†	4[610]	104–109, 1.4369
	Neopentyl iodide	59	92	4[354]	70/100, 1.4890
C_6	n-Hexyl bromide	51	82	4[2]	156
	3-Bromohexane	73	76	4[186]	68/50, 1.4450
	1-Bromo-2-methyl-pentane	52	65	4[77]	44/17, 1.4495
	2-Chloro-4-methyl-pentane	51	82	4[10]	112/733, 1.4113

For explanations and symbols see pp. xi–xii.

TABLE 7 (*continued*)

C_n	Compound	Method	Yield %	Chapter[ref.]	B.p./mm., n_D^t, (M.p.), Deriv.
		Aliphatic Halides (*continued*)			
C_6	3-Chloro-3-methyl-pentane	51	59[†]	4[21]	69/160, 1.4208
	1-Chloro-2-ethylbutane	53	82	4[11]	88/225, 1.4230
	1-Bromo-2-ethylbutane	52	48	4[114]	74.7/70
	4-Bromo-2,2-dimethyl-butane	52	63	4[79]	59/51
	1-Chloro-3,3-dimethyl-butane	75	75	4[654]	41/50, 115, 1.4160
	2,3-Dimethyl-2-iodo-butane	73	91	4[603]	1.495
C_7	1-Bromoheptane	51	75	4[8]	71/19
		51	90	4[3]	
		52	90	4[75]	178
	2-Bromoheptane	51	75	4[8]	66/24, 1.4476
	3-Bromoheptane	51	75	4[8]	62/18, 1.4503
	4-Bromoheptane	51	75	4[8]	60/18, 1.4495
	2-Chloro-2-methylhexane	51	75	4[21]	35/15.5, 1.4205
	2-Chloro-5-methylhexane	51	90	4[10]	138d/735
	3-Chloro-3-methylhexane	51	90	4[21]	63/52, 1.4250
	3-Chloro-3-ethylpentane	51	94	4[13]	83.5, 1.4311
		51	88	4[21]	65/52, 1.4329
	1-Iodo-2,4-dimethyl-pentane	52	83	4[80]	55/9
	1-Chloro-3,4-dimethyl-pentane	75	40	4[555]	53/20, 1.4299
	2-Chloro-4,4-dimethyl-pentane	51	90	4[10]	93/250, 1.4180′
	1-Bromo-4,4-dimethyl-pentane	73	88	4[187]	71/35, 1.4484
	1-Iodo-2-ethyl-3-methyl-butane	52	79	4[80]	70/14
C_8	1-Bromoöctane	51	90	4[4]	106/39, 1.4527
		51	91	4[1]	93/22, 200
	2-Bromoöctane	52	88	4[76]	70/10, 1.4500
	2-Chloro-2-methylheptane	51	73	4[21]	1.4257
	2-Iodo-6-methylheptane	52	80	4[81]	83/14, 1.4870[17]
	1-Bromo-4-ethylhexane	51	83	4[114]	84/17
	Chlorohexamethylethane	64	33	4[212]	81/40, (53)
C_9	n-Nonyl chloride	60	52	4[352]	79/4, 1.4400[25]
	n-Nonyl bromide	51	82	4[16]	107.5/17.5
		52	85	4[75]	112/21, 1.4578[13,5]
		63	70	4[402]	91/9
	Isononyl bromide	51	91	4[5]	93/13
C_{10}	n-Decyl chloride	60	50	4[352]	142/24, 1.4400[25]
	n-Decyl bromide	51	73	4[6]	124/20, 1.4558

TABLE 7. HALIDES   113

TABLE 7 *(continued)*

C_n	Compound	Method	Yield %	Chapter[ref.]	B.p./mm., n_D^t, (M.p.), Deriv.
		Aliphatic Halides *(continued)*			
C_{11}	n-Undecyl chloride	53	94	4[142]	166/2, (23.5)
	n-Undecyl bromide	61	67	4[394]	134/15
C_{12}	n-Dodecyl bromide	51	91	4[1]	180/45
	(lauryl bromide)	51	88	4[3]	202/100, 136/6, 1.4586
C_{14}	n-Tetradecyl bromide	51	71	4[14]	147/5, (5.5), 1 4608
		51	98	4[3]	
C_{16}	n-Hexadecyl bromide	51	75	4[14]	154/1.5, (17.8), 1.4627
	n-Hexadecyl iodide (cetyl)	52	78	4[82]	225/22, 205/9, (22)
C_{18}	n-Octadecyl bromide	51	74	4[14]	169/1.5, (27.4)
		51	91	4[3]	175/2, (27.6), 1.4594[30]
	n-Octadecyl iodide	52	94	4[83]	(32.9)
		Alicyclic Halides			
C_4	Cyclobutyl bromide	61	50	4[396]	108/760, 1.4801
	Cyclopropylmethyl bromide	63	48	4[398]	110
C_5	Cyclopentyl chloride	51	60	4[102]	115/777
		51	80	4[24]	114/752
	Cyclopentyl bromide	51	70	4[6]	137/737, 1.4890
		52	84	4[84]	136, 56/45, 1.4882
	Cyclopentyl iodide	51	80	4[102]	58/22
C_6	Cyclohexyl fluoride	73	70	4[189]	63/200, (13), 1.4130[25]
	Cyclohexyl chloride	51	70	4[26]	48/26, 1.4600
		51	70	4[102]	142/755
		64	72	4[217]	68/62, 1.462
	Cyclohexyl bromide	51	75	4[3]	
		51	90	4[25]	64/21
		52	77	4[40]	71/30, 1.4917[25]
	Cyclohexyl iodide	51	80	4[603]	
		52	80	4[102]	83/20
	Cyclopentylmethyl chloride	52	80	4[87]	60/50, 1.4611
	Cyclopentylmethyl bromide	52	50	4[84]	57/17
	1-Chloro-1-methyl-cyclopentane	51	56	4[560]	64–74/152–162
		73	100	4[86]	67/125, 1.4477
	1-Chloro-2-methyl-cyclopentane	52	34	4[86]	72/125, 1.4477
	1-Chloro-3-methyl-cyclopentane	52	60	4[86]	76/125, 1.4469
C_7	Cyclohexylmethyl bromide	51	78	4[26]	83/26, 1.4906[25]
		52	60	4[40]	77/26, 1.4889[25]
	β-Cyclopentylethyl bromide	51	65	4[85]	77/19, 1.4863

For explanations and symbols see pp. xi–xii.

TABLE 7 (*continued*)

C_n	Compound	Method	Yield %	Chapter[ref.]	B.p./mm., n_D^t, (M.p.), Deriv.
		Alicyclic Halides (*continued*)			
C_7	1-Chloro-1,3-dimethyl-cyclopentane	51	84	4 [28]	33/15, 1.4406
C_8	α-Cyclohexylethyl bromide	51	59	4 [89]	96/26
	β-Cyclohexylethyl bromide	51	65	4 [27]	71/6, 1.4888 [25]
	γ-Bromopropylcyclopentane	73	75	4 [188]	145/124, 1.4841
	γ-Chloropropylcyclopentane	60	19	4 [188]	87/22.5, 1.4582 [25]
C_9	γ-Cyclohexylpropyl chloride	60	62	4 [352]	79/5, 1.4660 [25]
	γ-Cyclohexylpropyl bromide	51	77	4 [40]	79/4, 1.4848 [25]
	δ-Cyclopentylbutyl bromide	51	65	4 [85]	111/17, 1.4820
C_{10}	δ-Cyclohexylbutyl bromide	52	74	4 [40]	92/4, 1.4832 [25]
	β-Chlorodecalin (*cis* or *trans*)	64	49	4 [242]	115/13
C_{11}	ε-Cyclohexylpentyl bromide	52	74	4 [40]	114/5, 1.4814 [25]
		52	87	4 [88]	90.5/1, 1.4784 [24]
		Aromatic Halides			
C_6	Fluorobenzene	56	57	4 [304]	85
	Chlorobenzene	64	90	4 [219]	132*
	Bromobenzene	64	59	4 [221]	155
	Iodobenzene	56	76	4 [302]	78/20, 64/8
		64	70	4 [237]	186
		64	87	4 [236]	186
C_7	Benzyl fluoride	55	60	4 [381]	40/14, 140/760
	Benzyl chloride	64	70	4 [221]	64/12
		64	80	4 [217]	99/62, 1.5390
		70	79	4 [339]	70/15
	Benzyl bromide	64	64	4 [218]	198/760
		70	87	4 [597]	
	o-Chlorotoluene	56	79	4 [301]	158
		64	90 †	4 [220]	159
	o-Bromotoluene	56	47	4 [300]	181
	o-Iodotoluene	64	65	4 [298]	210
		64	86	4 [237]	204
	m-Fluorotoluene	56	89	4 [303]	115

TABLE 7. HALIDES 115

TABLE 7 (*continued*)

C_n	Compound	Method	Yield %	Chapter[ref.]	B.p./mm., n_D^t, (M.p.). Deriv.
		Aromatic Halides (*continued*)			
C_7	m-Bromotoluene	14	59	4[679]	183/760
	p-Chlorotoluene	56	79	4[301]	162, (7)
	p-Bromotoluene	56	73	4[300]	185, (26)
		64	40	4[226]	(28)
	p-Iodotoluene	56	90	4[305]	212, (35)
C_8	α-Chloroethylbenzene	64	85	4[217]	93/30
		73	90	4[191]	73/11
	α-Bromoethylbenzene	73	85	4[198]	66/3*
		51	74	4[30]	94/8
	β-Phenylethyl chloride	51	82	4[31]	92/16
		52	80	4[90]	86/12
	β-Phenylethyl bromide	51	92	4[4]	99/15, 1.5572
		51	76	4[26]	97/14, 1.5543[25]
		51	97	4[29]	95/13
		52	80	4[90]	93/11
	o-Bromoethylbenzene	5	42[†]	4[674]	88/18
	m-Chloroethylbenzene	76	80	4[664]	72/14, 1.5171[25]
	m-Bromoethylbenzene	3	80	4[669]	102/30, 1.5407[25]
		5	86	4[672]	86/20, 1.5470
	o-Methylbenzyl chloride	51	91	4[33]	100/28
		53	89	4[91]	84/14
	o-Methylbenzyl bromide	64	80	4[216]	218
	m-Methylbenzyl chloride	64	80	4[217]	102/30, 1.5345
	p-Methylbenzyl bromide	70	87	4[597]	(39)
	4-Bromo-o-xylene	64	97	4[223]	94/15, 1.5558[22]
	4-Bromo-m-xylene	64	70	4[222]	205
	Chloro-p-xylene	64	83	4[224]	184, (13)
C_9	α-Chloropropylbenzene	51	55	4[34]	87/15
	1-Phenyl-2-bromopropane	52	63	4[91]	114/21, 1.5416[30]
	3-Phenylpropyl chloride	60	62	4[352]	93/6, 1.5160[25]
		53	50	4[143]	97/12
	3-Phenylpropyl bromide	51	82	4[561]	110/9
		51	68	4[26]	109/10, 1.5540
	2-Phenyl-1-bromopropane	51	75	4[32]	118/20
		76	58	4[661]	111/16, 1.5462[25]
	2-Phenyl-2-chloropropane	64	90	4[217]	99/21
	m-Bromo-n-propylbenzene	5	85	4[673]	100/17, 1.5354
	p-Bromo-n-propylbenzene	3	45	4[670]	226
	3-Bromo-1-isopropyl-benzene	14	58	4[680]	96/20
	4-Chloro-1-isopropyl-benzene	76	63	4[665]	66–72/11, 1.5109
	4-Bromo-1-isopropyl-benzene	76	67	4[662]	89/9, 216/744
	p-Ethylbenzyl chloride	70	71	4[342]	100/11, 1.5293[25]

For explanations and symbols see pp. xi–xii.

TABLE 7 (continued)

C_n	Compound	Method	Yield %	Chapter[ref.]	B.p./mm., n_D^t, (M.p.), Deriv.
			Aromatic Halides (continued)		
C₉	2,4-Dimethylbenzyl chloride	70	61	4[344]	118/16
	2,5-Dimethylbenzyl chloride	70	90	4[344]	101/15
	3-Chloropseudocumene	16	79	4[667]	127/61
	Chloromesitylene	64	75	4[231]	91/20
	Bromomesitylene	64	82	4[229]	107/17, 139/70
	2-Bromoindene	19	55	2[63]	124/22, (39)
C₁₀	2-Phenyl-1-bromobutane	51	80	4[32]	132/28
		52	70	4[92]	60/1, 1.5385[25]
	3-Phenylbutyl bromide	52	85	4[93]	112/11
	4-Phenylbutyl chloride	53	98	4[144]	123/17
		60	50	4[352]	102/6, 1.5183[25]
	m-Bromo-n-butylbenzene	5	83	4[673]	116/18, 1.5330
	p-Chloro-n-butylbenzene	64	72	4[225]	224/748
	m-Bromo-s-butylbenzene	5	92	4[675]	107/15, 1.5338
	β-Chloro-t-butylbenzene	64	70	4[217]	120/30, 1.5253
		76	66	4[660]	111/90
	m-Bromo-t-butylbenzene	14	56	4[675]	106/17, 1.5337
	p-Bromo-t-butylbenzene	64	75	4[227]	81/2
	p-Isopropylbenzyl chloride	70	21	4[598]	124/26
	Isopropylphenylbromomethane	51	64	4[30]	119/17
	3-Bromo-p-cymene	52	60	4[94]	233
	Chloroprehnitene	64	59	4[231]	132/24, (24), 1.5422[28]
	Bromoprehnitene	64	76	4[230]	141/30, 1.5650[22], (30)
	Chlorodurene	64	57	4[231]	(48)
	Bromodurene	64	80	4[230]	(60.5)
	Chloroisodurene	64	37	4[231]	139/41, 1.5382[28]
	Bromoisodurene	64	88	4[230]	142/22, 1.5614[28], (8.5)
	α-Fluoronaphthalene	56	90	4[307]	98/17
	α-Chloronaphthalene	64	90	4[244]	263*
	α-Bromonaphthalene	64	75	4[234]	135/12, 148/20
	β-Fluoronaphthalene	56	81	4[303]	(60)
	β-Chloronaphthalene	56	80	4[306]	(61)
	β-Bromonaphthalene	52	50	4[95]	282, (59)
		56	45	4[95]	(59)
	α-Bromotetralin	56	55	4[311]	130/2
C₁₁	5-Phenyl-1-chloropentane	63	73	4[402]	123/17
	n-Butylphenylbromomethane	51	70	4[30]	123/10
	p-Bromo-n-amylbenzene	6	60	4[672]	115/5, 1.5545
	p-Bromo-t-amylbenzene	64	70	4[228]	125/20, 1.5321

TABLE 7. HALIDES 117

TABLE 7 (*continued*)

C_n	Compound	Method	Yield %	Chapter[ref.]	B.p./mm., n_D^t, (M.p.), Deriv.
		Aromatic Halides (*continued*)			
C_{11}	p-Butylbenzyl chloride	70	67	4[343]	146/27, 1.5159[25]
	t-Butylphenylbromo-	51	55	4[30]	112/9
	methane	51	75	4[36]	104/7.4, 112/9
	Chloromethyldurene	70	73	4[596]	141/15, (66)
	1-Chloromethyl-	53	79	4[145]	139/6
	naphthalene	70	77	4[345]	133/5, 153/14, 1.635*
	1-Bromomethyl-	64	56	4[235]	(56)
	naphthalene	70	81	4[597]	(53)
	2-Chloromethyl-	64	53	4[246]	(49)
	naphthalene				
	2-Bromomethyl-	64	22	4[250]	214/100, (54)
	naphthalene				
C_{12}	2,4,6-Triethylbromo-	64	70	4[232]	99/3, 1.5366
	benzene				
	β-(1-Naphthyl)-ethyl	51	91	4[38]	137/1.5
	bromide				
	5-Chloroacenaphthene	64	70	4[254]	163/13, (69.5)
	7-Bromoacenaphthene	52	89	4[96]	(72)
	o-Chlorobiphenyl	64	32	4[243]	274/738, (32)
	o-Iodobiphenyl	12	52	4[677]	158/6
		56	52	4[308]	158/6
	m-Bromobiphenyl	12	16	4[678]	173/17, 1.6411
		14	58	4[682]	158–167/11, 1.6390[25]
	m-Iodobiphenyl	56	48	4[309]	152/1
	p-Chlorobiphenyl	64	25	4[243]	291/745, (77)
	p-Bromobiphenyl	12	35	4[676]	(90)
C_{13}	Diphenylchloro-	51	82	4[35]	116/1, 120/2.5
	methane				
	o-Chlorodiphenyl-	6	81	4[671]	144/5
	methane				
	p-Bromodiphenyl-	3	92	4[668]	162/13, 128/3
	methane				
	2-Bromofluorene	64	65	4[251]	239/48, (110)
	9-Bromofluorene	51	80	4[37]	
		64	64	4[252]	(105)
C_{14}	3-Bromo-1,2,4,5-tetra-	64	96	4[233]	151/10, 1.5425, (9)
	ethylbenzene				
	1-Chlorophenanthrene	56	41	4[310]	(120)
	1-Bromophenanthrene	56	72	4[310]	(110)
	1-Iodophenanthrene	56	53	4[310]	(113)
	2-Chlorophenanthrene	56	42	4[310]	(86)
	2-Bromophenanthrene	56	70	4[310]	(96)
	2-Iodophenanthrene	56	47	4[310]	(116)
	3-Chlorophenanthrene	56	48	4[310]	(81.5)

For explanations and symbols see pp. xi–xii.

TABLE 7 (*continued*)

C_n	Compound	Method	Yield %	Chapter[ref.]	B.p./mm., n_D^t, (M.p.), Deriv.
		Aromatic Halides (*continued*)			
C_{14}	3-Bromophenanthrene	56	70	4[310]	(84)
	3-Iodophenanthrene	56	47	4[310]	(84)
	9-Fluorophenanthrene	56	30	4[248]	(52), 107Pi
	9-Chlorophenanthrene	64	85	4[247]	(51.5)
	9-Bromophenanthrene	64	94	4[249]	(56)
	9-Iodophenanthrene	56	45	4[248]	(92), 141Pi
	9-Bromoanthracene	64	55	4[253]	(101)
		....	48	4[684]	(102)
	9-Iodoanthracene	59	53	4[355]	(83)
C_{15}	9-Chloromethyl-phenanthrene	70	21	4[346]	(102), 102Pi
C_{16}	β-(9-Phenanthryl)-ethyl chloride	53	77	4[146]	(84)
C_{19}	Triphenylchloromethane	51	95	4[37]	(112)
		76	86	4[666]	(112)
		Heterocyclic Halides			
C_4	2-Chlorofuran	559	91	39[184]	77/744, 1.4569
	3-Chlorofuran	559	79	39[184]	79/742, 1.4600
	2-Bromofuran	64	49	4[259]	103/744, 1.4980
		559	75	39[184]	102/744, 1.4981
	3-Bromofuran	559	48	39[184]	103/745, 1.4958
	2-Iodofuran	559	20	39[183]	44/15, 1.5661
	β-Bromotetrahydrofuran	560	77	39[41]	61/29, 1.4912[25]
	2-Chlorothiophene	64	50	4[257]	129/742, 56/56, 1.5490
	2-Bromothiophene	64	55	4[256]	154
	2-Iodothiophene	64	75	4[238]	73/15, 81/20
		64	72	4[588]	89-93/36, 1.6465[25]
	3-Iodothiophene	62	64	4[409]	80/11
C_5	2-Furfuryl chloride	53	63	4[149]	50/27, 1.4941
	2-Furfuryl bromide	52	50	4[97]	34.5/2
	3-Chloromethylfuran	53	55	4[581]	43/17, 52/27, 1.4863
	Tetrahydrofurfuryl chloride	53	75	4[148]	42/11
	Tetrahydrofurfuryl bromide	52	61	4[98]	70/22, 50/4
	2-Chloromethylthiophene	70	41	4[351]	75/17
	3-Thenyl bromide	64	....	4[255]	78/1, 1.604
	2-Chloropyridine	64	31	4[266]	67/17, 1.5325
	2-Bromopyridine	56	92	4[312]	75/13
		64	46	4[265]	92/25
	2-Iodopyridine	56	32	4[313]	93/13
	3-Fluoropyridine	56	50	4[303]	107/752

TABLE 7. HALIDES 119

TABLE 7 (*continued*)

C_n	Compound	Method	Yield %	Chapter[ref.]	B.p./mm., n_D^t, (M.p.), Deriv.
		Heterocyclic Halides (*continued*)			
C_5	3-Bromopyridine	64	37	4[265]	63/15, 159HCl
	3-Iodopyridine	64	19	4[267]	(53), 154Pi
	4-Chloropyridine	52	75	4[100]	148*
	4-Bromopyridine	52	47	4[100]	26.5/0.3, (9.5)
	N-Chloropiperidine	69	90	4[658]	
	4-Bromopiperidine	51	80	4[39]	193
C_6	2-α-Furylethyl chloride	53	61	4[150]	71/42, 63/26, 1.4788[25]
	2,2-Dimethyl-4-bromo-tetrahydrofuran	560	44	39[40]	51/11, 1.4686[15]
	β-(2-Thienyl)-ethyl chloride	60	71	4[351]	92/20
	2,5-*bis*-(Chloromethyl)-thiophene	70	79	4[349]	108/5, (37)
	2-Piperidylmethyl chloride hydrochloride	53	60	4[152]	(178)
	ω-Trichloropicoline	64	25	4[268]	115/15
C_7	γ-(α-Tetrahydrofuryl)-propyl chloride	53	83	4[147]	75/4, 1.4540
	γ-(α-Tetrahydrofuryl)-propyl bromide	52	66	4[99]	101/16
	2-(2-Piperidyl)-1-chloroethane	53	85	4[152]	150HCl
C_8	2-Chloro-t-butyl-thiophene	558	50	39[196]	57/1.5, 1.5315
	2-Bromobenzofuran	....	55	39[215]	
	3-Bromobenzofuran	....	77	39[215]	220, (39)
	3-Bromothionaphthene	64	90	4[258]	140/18
C_9	2-Bromomethyl-2,3-dihydrobenzofuran	560	63	39[50]	145/20, 1.575
	2-Chloromethylthio-naphthene	53	79	4[582]	126/2, (56)
	3-Chloromethylthio-naphthene	70	56	4[350]	131/5, (45)
	2-Chloroquinoline	72	90	4[453]	268/744, (38)
	2-Bromoquinoline	64	25	4[262]	95/0.5, (12.5)
	3-Bromoquinoline	64	50	4[261]	162/24
	5-Chloroquinoline	56	59	39[146]	257/756, (43)
	5-Bromoquinoline	56	47	4[315]	(48)
		56	48	39[146]	280/756, (48)
	6-Chloroquinoline	575	88	39[176]	159/45, (42)
	7-Chloroquinoline	56	59	39[146]	268, (30)
	7-Bromoquinoline	56	45	39[146]	288/753, (35)
	8-Chloroquinoline	575	55	39[176]	163/20
	8-Bromoquinoline	56	74	4[315]	166/18

For explanations and symbols see pp. xi–xii.

TABLE 7 (continued)

C_n	Compound	Method	Yield %	Chapter[ref.]	B.p./mm., n_D^t, (M.p.), Deriv.
		Heterocyclic Halides (continued)			
C₉	1-Chloroisoquinoline	64	91	4 [264]	165/30
		72	66	4 [454]	278/759, (24)
		72	91	39 [220]	278/759, (38)*
	4-Bromoisoquinoline	64	45	4 [263]	152/13, (40)
C₁₀	4-Bromo-2-methyl-quinoline	52	25	39 [142]	89/1
	2-Chloro-4-methyl-quinoline	52	95	4 [101]	(58)
	2-Bromo-4-methyl-quinoline	52	91	39 [142]	126/1, (81)
C₁₂	1-Bromodibenzofuran	14	78	4 [681]	(67)
	2-Bromodibenzofuran	64	51	4 [260]	(109)
	4-Bromodibenzofuran	59	41	4 [356]	(71)
	4-Iododibenzofuran	59	42	4 [358]	(73)
	4-Iododibenzothiophene	59	22	4 [357]	(102)
	1-Chlorocarbazole	557	90	39 [158]	(110)
	3-Bromocarbazole	64	55	4 [218]	(199)
	3-Iodocarbazole	64	40	4 [269]	(194)
C₁₃	9-Chloroacridine	....	100	39 [217]	(120)

For explanations and symbols see pp. xi–xii.

TABLE 8. DIHALIDES

C_n	Compound	Method	Yield (%)	Chapter[ref.]	B.p./mm., n_D^t, (M.p.)
		Aliphatic and Alicyclic Di- and Poly-halides			
C₁	Methylene bromide	62	90	4 [404]	100
	Methylene iodide	62	97	4 [405]	107/70
	Trifluoroiodomethane	61	80	4 [612]	−22
	Bromodichloromethane	....	87	4 [558]	88, 1.4962
C₂	Ethylidene dibromide	72	20	4 [445]	106–114
	1-Chloro-2-fluoroethane	53	69	4 [607]	51–55, 1.3727[25]
	1-Bromo-2-fluoroethane	52	57	4 [607]	74
	sym-Tetrachloroethane	74	85	4 [427]	145, 1.4942
C₃	Propylidene dichloride	72	30	4 [446]	88
	Trimethylene bromide	51	95	4 [1]	165
	Trimethylene iodide	55	84	4 [378]	78/5*
	Trimethylene chloro-bromide	52	94	4 [104]	143

TABLE 8. DIHALIDES 121

TABLE 8 (*continued*)

C_n	Compound	Method	Yield (%)	Chapter[ref.]	B.p./mm., n_D^t, (M.p.)
	Aliphatic and Alicyclic Di- and Poly-halides (*continued*)				
C_3	Trimethylene fluoro-bromide	55	71	4[607]	101/756
	Trimethylene iodo-chloride	55	53	4[270]	60/15
		52	58	4[103]	173
	1,2,3-Trichloropropane	52	57	4[106]	158
		74	90	4[427]	
	1,2,3-Tribromopropane	74	98	4[422]	103/18
	unsym-Heptachloropropane	76	93	4[659]	113/10, 140/32, (30)
C_4	1,3-Dichlorobutane	53	44	4[153]	133
	2,2-Dichlorobutane	72	50	4[447]	102/728
	dl-2,3-Dichlorobutane	74	81	4[420]	53.2/80, 1.4409
	meso-2,3-dichloro-butane	74	63	4[420]	49.5/80, 1.4386[25]
	1,4-Dibromobutane	51	85	4[41]	97/30, 110/30
		54	47	4[367]	85/18
		54	63	4[411]	63/3
		61	58	4[395]	81/11
		63	49	4[400]	78/10
	1,4-Diiodobutane	54	96	4[419]	110/10, 1.615
		54	70	4[367]	152/26
	1-Bromo-4-chlorobutane	64	35	4[591]	112/100
		52	62	4[119]	82/30
		52	98	4[105]	176, 1.4885
	1-Iodo-3-chlorobutane	55	78	4[270]	51/6.5, 1.5267
	1-Iodo-4-chlorobutane	55	71	4[379]	94/17
	erythro-2-Chloro-3-iodobutane	51	63	4[563]	35/5, 1.5313[25]
	1,2-Dibromo-2-methyl-propane	74	75	4[423]	150/735, 62/45, 1.5068*
	Isobutylene iodochloride	74	67	4[421]	56/22, 1.5237[23]
C_5	1,3-Dichloropentane	64	30	4[270]	80/60, 1.4485
	1,4-Dichloropentane	64	31	4[270]	88/60, 1.4503
	1,5-Dichloropentane	64	19	4[270]	102/60, 1.4563
	1,5-Dibromopentane	54	82	4[417]	106/19
		63	72	4[397]	110/20
	2,3-Dibromopentane	51	94	4[43]	91/50, 1.5087
		74	87	4[43]	91/50, 1.5087
	1-Bromo-5-chloro-pentane	51	82	4[566]	102/30, 1.4838[23]
		52	88	4[119]	93/20, 1.4815[25]
	1-Iodo-3-chloro-pentane	55	90	4[270]	51/2.5, 1.5229
	1-Iodo-4-chloro-pentane	55	90	4[270]	61/3.5, 1.5248
	1-Iodo-5-chloro-pentane	55	62	4[270]	76/4, 1.5304

For explanations and symbols see pp. xi–xii.

TABLE 8 (*continued*)

C_n	Compound	Method	Yield (%)	Chapter[ref.]	B.p./mm., n_D^t, (M.p.)
		Aliphatic and Alicyclic Di- and Poly-halides (*continued*)			
C_5	1,1-Dichloro-3-methyl-butane	75	34	4[556]	59/70, 1.4344
	1,2-Dibromo-2-methyl-butane	74	80	4[423]	62/15
	2,3-Dibromo-2-methyl-butane	74	70	4[423]	51/11
	1,3-Dibromo-2,2-dimethyl-propane	52	46	4[108]	68/9, 1.5050
	Pentaerythrityl bromide	52	76	4[107]	(163)
		....	78	4[694]	(158)
	Pentaerythrityl iodide	55	98	4[107]	(233)
	1,2,4,5-Tetrabromopentane	74	90	4[429]	(86)
		74	65	4[480]	(86)
C_6	1,2-Dibromohexane	73	85	4[192]	90/18, 1.5023
		74	100	4[424]	90/18, 1.5024
	1,4-Dibromohexane	54	60	4[410]	100/15, (30)
	1,4-Diiodohexane	54	75	4[410]	119/12
	1,6-Dibromohexane	51	75	4[52]	80/3
		51	90	4[71]	108–112/8
	1,6-Diiodohexane	51	95	4[603]	113/3, (9), 1.585
	2,3-Dibromohexane	74	100	4[424]	90/16, 1.5025
	2,5-Dibromohexane	52	96	4[182]	89/13
		51	70	4[567]	106/25
	3,4-Dichlorohexane	74	67	4[186]	70/30, 1.4490
	3,4-Dibromohexane	74	100	4[424]	81/13, 1.5045
		51	80 †	4[564]	72/9, 1.5050
	1,2-Dichlorocyclo-hexane	74	90	4[427]	80/22, 1.4903
	1,2-Dibromocyclo-hexane	74	95	4[426]	103/16, 112/25
	1,3-Dibromo-2-methyl-pentane	52	75	4[110]	82/12
		74	100	4[424]	88/20, 1.5015
	2,3-Dibromo-2-methyl-pentane	74	64	4[423]	68/15, 1.4975
		74	100	4[424]	72/18, 1.5063
	2,4-Dibromo-2-methyl-pentane	52	90	4[109]	62/4, 1.4980
	1,2-Dibromo-3-methyl-pentane	74	100	4[424]	99/30, 1.5060
	1,5-Dibromo-3-methyl-pentane	63	65	4[399]	98/10, 1.5073
	2,3-Dibromo-3-methyl-pentane	74	50	4[423]	50/5, 1.5085
	1,2-Dibromo-4-methyl-pentane	74	100	4[424]	87/21, 1.4980

TABLE 8. DIHALIDES   123

TABLE 8 (*continued*)

C_n	Compound	Method	Yield (%)	Chapter[ref.]	B.p./mm., n_D^t, (M.p.)
	Aliphatic and Alicyclic Di- and Poly-halides (*continued*)				
C_6	1,2-Dibromo-2-ethyl-butane	74	100	4[424]	87/21, 1.5112
	1,2-Dibromo-2,3-dimethyl-butane	74	100	4[424]	80/17, 1.5105
	1,1-Dichloro-3,3-di-methylbutane	75	77	4[556]	57/31, 1.4389
	1,2-Dichloro-3,3-di-methylbutane	74	53	4[614]	52/11, 1.4553
	2,2-Dichloro-3,3-di-methylbutane	72	50	4[448]	(152)
C_7	1,1-Dichloroheptane	72	70	4[449]	82/20, 1.4440
	2,2-Dichloroheptane	72	23	4[449]	77/25, 1.4440
	1,4-Dibromoheptane	54	79	4[413]	112/11, 1.5004[11]
	1,7-Dibromoheptane	63	65	4[402]	127/9
	2,3-Dibromo-2-methyl-hexane	74	71	4[423]	78/6, 1.5024
	3-Methyl-2,4-dibromo-hexane	52	90	4[109]	72.5/1, 1.4967
	2,3-Dibromo-3-ethyl-pentane	74	63	4[423]	77/4, 1.5098
	1,2-Dichloro-3,4-di-methylpentane	75	48	4[556]	59/12, 1.4489
	2,2-Dichloro-4,4-di-methylpentane	75	49	4[556]	60/20, 1.4470
	1,3-Dibromo-2,2-di-ethylpropane	52	40	4[108]	97/10, (40.6)
C_8	1,4-Dibromoöctane	54	82	4[413]	126/11, 1.5003[11]
	1,8-Dibromoöctane	51	75	4[42]	120/2
		61	60	4[394]	93/0.45
		63	74	4[401]	142/13
	1,1-*bis*-(Bromomethyl)-cyclohexane	52	27	4[108]	117/6, 1.5390
	3-Isopropyl-1,5-di-bromopentane	54	83	4[418]	130/10
C_9	1,9-Dichlorononane	53	93	4[154]	92/0.1, 1.4591
	1,9-Dibromononane	51	93	4[71]	130/2
	1-Chloro-9-iodononane	55	59	4[154]	124/2.9, 1.5060[25]
	1,1,1,3-Tetrachloro-nonane	75	85	4[557]	79/0.1, 1.4770
	1,3-Dibromo-2-ethyl-2-butylpropane	52	49	4[108]	133/16, 1.5018
C_{10}	Decamethylene bromide	51	90	4[71]	142/2
C_{14}	Tetradecamethylene bromide	51	65	4[44]	175/3

For explanations and symbols see pp. xi–xii.

TABLE 8 (*continued*)

C_n	Compound	Method	Yield (%)	Chapter[ref.]	B.p./mm., n_D^t, (M.p.)
		Aromatic Di- and Poly-halides			
C_6	o-Chlorobromobenzene	56	95	4[318]	201/742
	o-Chloroiodobenzene	56	78	4[320]	(0.7)
	m-Dibromobenzene	56	87	4[318]	217
	m-Chlorobromobenzene	56	94	4[318]	194
	p-Fluorochlorobenzene	56	66	4[319]	130
	p-Bromofluorobenzene	56	77	4[303]	151
	p-Chloroiodobenzene	64	95	4[298]	(55)
	sym-Tribromobenzene	14	71	4[683]	(122.5)
	Hexachlorobenzene	64	79	4[273]	(227)
C_7	Benzal chloride	64	90	4[217]	105/30, 1.5503
	o-Chlorobenzyl chloride	64	76	4[289]	84/9
	o-Chlorobenzyl bromide	64	98	4[289]	107/12
	o-Iodobenzyl bromide	64	65	4[278]	125/4
	m-Chlorobenzyl bromide	64	55	4[277]	105/8, (15.5)
	m-Bromobenzotrifluoride	64	52	4[274]	(152)
	p-Fluorobenzyl bromide	64	65	4[589]	202, 95/20, 1.5480[22]
	p-Chlorobenzyl chloride	64	70	4[217]	117/30, (29)
	p-Bromobenzyl chloride	64	60	4[275]	238, (50)
	p-Bromobenzyl bromide	64	66	4[276]	(61)
		70	35	4[597]	(63)
	p-Iodobenzyl bromide	64	60	4[590]	(79)
C_8	Styrene dibromide	74	98	4[616]	140/15, (74)*
	Styrene iodochloride	74	47	4[421]	(40)
	α,m-Dichloroethylbenzene	64	91	4[664]	63-70/2, 1.5401-23[25]
	3,4-Dichloroethylbenzene	76	53	4[663]	65/3, 1.5411
	p-Chloromethylbenzyl chloride	70	40	4[347]	135/16, (100)
	ω,ω-Dibromo-m-xylene	64	35	4[279]	(76)
	ω,ω-Dibromo-p-xylene	64	43	4[279]	(144)
	α,α,α′,α′-Tetrabromo-p-xylene	64	55	4[280]	(170)

TABLE 9. OLEFINIC HALIDES   125

TABLE 8 (*continued*)

C_n	Compound	Method	Yield (%)	Chapter[ref.]	B.p./mm., n_D^t, (M.p.)
	Aromatic Di- and Poly-halides (*continued*)				
C_9	o-β-Bromoethylbenzyl bromide	51	90	4[46]	(53)
	1,1,1,3-Tetrabromo-3-phenylpropane	75	96	4[557]	(59)
C_{10}	2-Phenyl-1,4-dibromobutane	51	80	4[45]	175/16
	2,5-*bis*-(Chloromethyl)-*p*-xylene	70	55	4[600]	(134)
C_{11}	3-Phenyl-1,5-dibromopentane	51	80	4[45]	182/16, (72)
	bis-(Chloromethyl)-mesitylene	70	80	4[599]	(106)
C_{12}	*bis*-(Chloromethyl)-durene	70	67	4[599]	(194)
	bis-(Chloromethyl)-isodurene	70	80	4[599]	(107)
	4,4'-Difluorobiphenyl	56	56	4[321]	(90)
	4,4'-Dibromobiphenyl	64	77	4[693]	(163)
C_{14}	a,a'-Dichlorobibenzyl				
	(*dl*)	74	55	4[615]	(91)
	(*meso*)				(191)
	Stilbene dibromide	74	78	4[428]	(244)
		74	83	4[615]	(111)

For explanations and symbols see pp. xi–xii.

TABLE 9. OLEFINIC HALIDES

Cn	Compound	Method	Yield (%)	Chapter[ref]	B.p./mm., n_D^t, (M.p.), Deriv.
	Aliphatic Olefinic Halides				
C_2	Vinyl chloride	35	100	2[526]	15/724
	Vinyl bromide	20	50	2[129]	16*
	Vinyl iodide	20	32	2[130]	56
	Tetrachloroethylene	20	95	2[134]	121*
	unsym-Dibromoethylene	27	30	2[261]	92
C_3	Allyl bromide	51	96	4[1]	72, 1.4689*
	Allyl iodide	55	77	4[382]	102, 1.5542[22]
	2-Bromopropene	27	32	2[261]	49, 1.4426
	1- and 2-Bromo-1-propenes	20	....	2[135]	48–60*
	β-Chloroallyl chloride	19	75	2[59]	108

For explanations and symbols see pp. xi–xii.

TABLE 9 (continued)

C_n	Compound	Method	Yield (%)	Chapter[ref.]	B.p./mm., n_D^t, (M.p.), Deriv.
	Aliphatic Olefinic Halides (continued)				
C_3	1,2-Dichloro-1-propene	20	58	2^{169}	77/757, 1.4451[25]
	1,1-Dibromo-1-propene	27	88	2^{261}	127/750, 1.5260
	2,3-Dichloropropene	20	80	2^{132}	94, 1.4600[21]
		20	87	2^{133}	93
	2,3-Dibromopropene	20	84	2^{131}	74/75
	3,3,3-Trichloropropene	19	84	2^{57}	57/103, 1.4827
C_4	1-Bromo-1-butene	27	28	2^{261}	88, 1.4536
	3-Chloro-1-butene	51	35	4^{568}	64/748, 1.4151
		73	26	4^{193}	63, 1.4153
	3-Bromo-1-butene	52	....	4^{47}	31/93, 1.4602[25]
	1,1-Dibromo-1-butene	27	83	2^{261}	54/22, 1.5168
	trans-Crotyl chloride	51	65	4^{568}	84/748, 1.4350
		73	49	4^{193}	83, 1.4352
	1-Bromo-2-butene	52	96	4^{47}	49/93, 1.4795[25]
	2-Bromo-2-butene	27	71	2^{261}	109, 1.4580
	1,4-Dibromo-2-butene	74	90	4^{618}	(54)
	1,4-Dibromo-2-butene	74	70	4^{159}	(52)
	1-Chloro-2-methyl-1-propene	....	85	4^{553}	68, 1.4221
	1-Bromo-2-methyl-1-propene	27	81	2^{261}	91, 1.4625
		20	27	2^{448}	91, 1.4603[21]
	1,1-Dibromo-2-methyl-1-propene	27	81	2^{261}	157, 1.5300
	1,1,1-Trichloro-2-methyl-2-propene	19	43	2^{58}	43/30
C_5	1-Bromo-1-pentene	27	32	2^{261}	114, 1.4572
	1,1-Dibromo-1-pentene	27	79	2^{261}	73/22, 1.5097
	5-Bromo-1-pentene	22	71	2^{266}	128/770
		52	82	4^{111}	130, 1.4610[28]
	1-Chloro-2-pentene	51	33	4^{49}	63/146
	3-Chloro-1-pentene		33		50/150
	1-Bromo-2-pentene	51	90	4^{51}	43.5/30, 1.4777[25]
	3-Bromo-1-pentene				30.5/30, 1.4626[25]
	1-Bromo-2-pentene	52	73	4^{112}	38/20
	2-Bromo-2-pentene	27	75	2^{261}	109, 1.4580
	3-Bromo-2-pentene	27	73	2^{261}	111, 1.4628
	4-Bromo-2-pentene	51	54	4^{48}	72/145
	5-Bromo-2-pentene	52	60	4^{113}	121/621, 1.4695
	1-Bromo-3-methyl-1-butene	27	28	2^{261}	100, 1.4482
	3-Chloro-3-methyl-1-butene	73	66	4^{585}	32/120, 1.4190
	1,1-Dibromo-3-methyl-1-butene	27	70	2^{261}	160, 1.5037

TABLE 9. OLEFINIC HALIDES   127

TABLE 9 (*continued*)

C_n	Compound	Method	Yield (%)	Chapter[ref.]	B.p./mm., n_D^t, (M.p.), Deriv.
		Aliphatic Olefinic Halides (*continued*)			
C_5	1-Chloro-3-methyl-2-butene	73	65	4[585]	113/760
	2-Bromo-3-methyl-2-butene	27	84	2[261]	119, 1.4738
	1,4-Dibromo-2-methyl-2-butene	74	31	4[430]	96/12
C_6	1-Bromo-1-hexene	27	27	2[261]	139, 1.4584
		73	72	4[192]	141/751, 1.4596
	1,1-Dibromo-1-hexene	27	75	2[261]	91/22, 1.5050
	3-Bromo-1,5-hexadiene	71	45	4[458]	47/11
	1-Bromo-2-hexene }	51	90	4[51]	32/3, 1.4745[25]
	3-Bromo-1-hexene }				22/9, 1.4627[25]
	4-Chloro-2-hexene	51	70	4[50]	67/110, 1.4385
	1-Bromo-3-hexene	52	68	4[112]	54/17
	2-Chloro-2-methyl-4-pentene	51	63	4[569]	44/90, 1.4284[14]
	1-Chloro-3,3-dimethyl-1-butene	20	32	2[449]	105/730, 1.4276
	2-Chloro-3,3-dimethyl-1-butene	20	68	2[449]	96/730, 1.4247
	1-Bromo-2,3-dimethyl-2-butene	73	73	4[194]	66/40, 1.4948
C_7	1-Bromo-1-heptene	27	35	2[261]	162/747, 1.4594
	1,1-Dibromo-1-heptene	27	74	2[261]	106/22, 1.5009
	2-Chloro-1-heptene	72	40	4[449]	71/75, 1.4349
	4-Bromo-4-methyl-1-hexene	52	44	4[115]	59.8/27
	4,4-Dimethyl-2-bromo-1-pentene	29	62	2[200]	137, 1.4630
C_8	1-Bromo-1-octene	27	26	2[261]	179/750, 1.4602
	1,1-Dibromo-1-octene	27	70	2[261]	121/22, 1.4978
C_{10}	2-Bromo-1-decene	29	60	2[201]	116/22, 1.4629
		29	65	2[196]	77/3
C_{11}	11-Undecylenyl chloride	53	83	4[156]	115/12, 1.4487[25]
		53	76	4[142]	122/16, 1.4510[18]
	11-Undecylenyl iodide	55	91	4[383]	104/2, 1.4937[25]
C_{18}	9,10-Octadecenyl chloride	53	82	4[141]	165/3, 1.4586[25]
		Alicyclic Olefinic Halides			
C_5	2-Cyclopentenyl chloride	73	89	4[196]	31/30
C_6	3-Bromocyclohexene	71	87	4[456]	

For explanations and symbols see pp. xi–xii.

TABLE 9 (*continued*)

C_n	Compound	Method	Yield (%)	Chapter[ref.]	B.p./mm., n_D^t (M.p.), Deriv.
			Alicyclic Olefinic Halides (*continued*)		
C_6	1-Chloro-1-cyclo-	20	40	2[136]	143
	hexene	72	60	4[623]	95/160, 1.4798
	1-Cyclopentenyl-	52	30	4[118]	59/15, 1.5170
	methyl bromide				
C_7	2-Cyclopentenyl-	52	53	4[116]	72/16, 1.4995
	ethyl bromide				
C_8	1-Cyclohexenyl-	52	50	4[117]	90/7
	ethyl bromide				
	3-Cyclopentyl-2-	29	82	2[202]	75/13, 1.4930[23]
	bromopropene				
C_9	2-Cyclopentenylbutyl	52	47	4[116]	86/5, 1.4942
	bromide				
	3-Cyclohexyl-2-bromo-	29	64	2[196]	89/14
	propene				
			Aromatic Olefinic Halides		
C_8	β-Chlorostyrene	19	63	2[60]	88-100/18
	o-Fluorostyrene	19	76	2[458]	33/3, 1.5197
		27	66	2[256]	46/32, 1.5201
	o-Chlorostyrene	19	70	2[458]	61/4, 1.5648
		27	50	2[255]	59/7, 1.5641
	o-Bromostyrene	19	33	2[62]	65/4, 1.5893[25]
	m-Fluorostyrene	19	80	2[458]	31/4, 1.5173
	m-Chlorostyrene	19	84	2[61]	63/6, 1.5612[25]
		20	93	2[61]	63/6, 1.5616[25]
		27	65	2[255]	58/10, 1.5630
	m-Bromostyrene	19	56	2[437]	75/3, 1.5855
		27	47	2[255]	48/0.5, 1.5900
	p-Fluorostyrene	19	81	2[458]	30/4, 1.5158
		20	72	2[447]	59/25, 75Di
	p-Chlorostyrene	19	57	2[437]	65/4, 1.5648
		27	51	2[255]	61/6, 1.5650
	p-Bromostyrene	19	50	2[437]	88/12
	p-Iodostyrene	19	60	2[455]	(44)
C_9	1-Phenyl-2-chloro-	20	70	2[137]	83-87/11
	1-propene				
	1-Bromo-1-phenyl-	71	50	4[624]	120/6
	2-propene				
	Cinnamyl chloride	51	85	4[53]	119/17, 1.5830
		53	83	4[158]	87/2, 103/5, (8)
	Cinnamyl bromide	71	75	4[456]	85/0.8, (34)
	4-Chloro-α-methyl-	20	16	2[121]	82/10, 1.5529[25]
	styrene				

TABLE 10. ACETYLENIC HALIDES   129

TABLE 9 (*continued*)

C_n	Compound	Method	Yield (%)	Chapter[ref.]	B.p./mm., n_D^t, (M.p.), Deriv.
		Aromatic Olefinic Halides (*continued*)			
C_{10}	4-Phenyl-2-bromo-1-butene	29	45	2[196]	119/20
	β-Ethyl-β-bromostyrene	27	85	2[262]	127/23
	1-(*m*-Bromophenyl)-1,2-dimethylethylene	19	70	2[64]	111/17, 1.5620
C_{11}	β-*n*-Propyl-β-bromostyrene	27	85	2[262]	139/22
C_{14}	α-Chlorostilbene	72	38	4[615]	(51)
	o-Chlorostilbene	24	80	2[233]	209
	m-Chlorostilbene	28	16	2[233]	(74), 166Di
	m-Bromostilbene	28	17	2[233]	(90), 166Di
	p-Chlorostilbene	28	40	2[233]	(129), 190Di
	p-Bromostilbene	28	23	2[233]	(139), 202Di
C_{15}	2,3-Diphenylallyl bromide	71	75	4[457]	133/0.01
	3,3-Diphenylallyl bromide	71	86	4[456]	98/0.05
	o-Chloromethylstilbene	53	74	4[157]	185/15
C_{20}	Triphenylvinyl bromide	74	98	4[431]	(115.5)

For explanations and symbols see pp. xi–xii.

TABLE 10. ACETYLENIC HALIDES

C_n	Compound	Method	Yield (%)	Chapter[ref.]	B.p./mm., n_D^t, (M.p.)
		Aliphatic and Alicyclic Acetylenic Halides			
C_2	Dichloroacetylene	43	65	3[49]	29/743
	Diiodoacetylene	59	87	4[366]	(79)
C_4	4-Chloro-1-butyne	52	90	4[578]	86/762, 1.4383[22]
	4-Bromo-1-butyne	52	82	4[578]	107/740, 1.4817
	4-Iodo-1-butyne	52	64	4[578]	61/80, 1.5504[19]
C_5	5-Chloro-1-pentyne	44	57	3[9]	68/145, 1.445
	5-Iodo-1-pentyne	52	70	4[578]	84–89/43, 1.5351[17]
	1-Bromo-2-pentyne	52	65	4[121]	148/754, 1.4983[24]
C_6	1-Bromo-1-hexyne	59	78	4[360]	46/54, 1.4579[13]
	1-Iodo-1-hexyne	59	76	4[360]	54/23, 1.5148[19]
	3-Chloro-1-hexyne	53	72	4[160]	64/100, 1.4375[25]
	3-Bromo-1-hexyne	52	48	4[577]	83/110, 1.4731[21]
	1-Bromo-2-hexyne	52	63	4[119]	98/80, 1.4884[25]
	1-Chloro-5-hexyne	44	80	3[75]	48/17, 1.4480[25]
		44	74	3[20]	144
	1-Iodo-5-hexyne	55	82	4[119]	95/35, 1.5286[25]

For explanations and symbols see pp. xi–xii.

TABLE 10 (*continued*)

C_n	Compound	Method	Yield (%)	Chapter[ref.]	B.p./mm., n_D^t, (M.p.)
	Aliphatic and Alicyclic Acetylenic Halides (*continued*)				
C_6	3-Chloro-3-methyl-4-	51	60	4[54]	55/130, 1.4330
	pentyne	51	50	4[55]	52/135, 1.4331
C_7	1-Chloro-1-heptyne	59	70	4[359]	65/45, 1.4411[24]
	1-Bromo-1-heptyne	59	70	4[359]	69/25, 1.4678[22]
		59	50	4[602]	57/13, 165/758
	1-Iodo-1-heptyne	59	68	4[359]	93/21, 1.5105[26]
	1-Bromo-2-heptyne	52	72	4[119]	105/56, 1.4878[25]
	1-Bromo-3-heptyne	52	41	4[119]	100/65, 1.4785[25]
	1-Chloro-5-heptyne	44	73	3[20]	175, 1.4599[25]
	1-Chloro-6-heptyne	44	70	3[20]	166, 1.4507[25]
		44	85	3[75]	79/33, 1.4490[25]
	1-Bromo-6-heptyne	44	27	3[20]	92/20, 1.4750[25]
	1-Bromo-4,4-dimethyl-2-pentyne	52	41	4[120]	52.5/20, 1.4751
C_8	1-Chloro-1-octyne	59	65	4[363]	62/17, 1.445
	3-Chloro-3-methyl-4-heptyne	51	66	4[54]	64/25, 1.4514
	Cyclohexylchloroacetylene	45	48	3[69]	115/15
	Cyclohexylbromoacetylene	59	78	4[360]	84/20, 1.5124[12]
	Cyclohexyliodoacetylene	59	76	4[360]	86/5, 1.559[11]
C_9	n-Heptylchloroacetylene	59	55	4[363]	77/15, 1.450
	2-Chloro-2-methyl-3-octyne	51	85	4[54]	68/15, 1.4480
	t-Butylethynyldimethylcarbinyl chloride	51	80	4[56]	81/100, (15), 1.4343
	Aromatic Acetylenic Halides				
C_8	Phenylchloroacetylene	45	70	3[69]	72/15
		59	60	4[363]	71/16, 1.576[18]
	Phenylbromoacetylene	59	88	4[602]	89/13
	Phenyliodoacetylene	59	92	4[359]	1.6591[25]
	o-Chlorophenylacetylene	47	67	3[72]	71/18, 1.5690[25]
	p-Bromophenylacetylene	43	53	3[61]	89/16, (65)
C_9	1-Bromo-3-phenyl-1-propyne	59	68	4[360]	107/15, 1.5693[12]
	1-Bromo-3-phenyl-2-propyne	52	70	4[121]	108/6, 1.625[19]
C_{10}	4-Chloro-1-phenyl-1	44	75	3[22]	
	butyne	44	46	3[1]	95/3, 1.5724

TABLE 10. ACETYLENIC HALIDES   131

TABLE 10 (*continued*)

C_n	Compound	Method	Yield (%)	Chapter[ref.]	B.p./mm., n_D^t, (M.p.)
		Aromatic Acetylenic Halides (*continued*)			
C_{10}	3-Bromo-1-phenyl-1-butyne	52	60	4[579]	133/20, 1.6050
	4-Bromo-1-phenyl-1-butyne	52	40	4[579]	145/18, 1.5951
	1-Bromo-4-phenyl-1-butyne	59	68	4[360]	111/7, 1.5636[12]
C_{11}	1-Phenyl-5-chloro-1-pentyne	44	75	3[1]	126/4, 1.5615

For explanations and symbols see pp. xi–xii.

REFERENCES FOR CHAPTER 4

[1] Kamm and Marvel, *Org. Syntheses*, Coll. Vol. I, 25 (1941).

[2] Dox, *J. Am. Chem. Soc.*, 46, 1707 (1924).

[3] Reid, Ruhoff, and Burnett, *Org. Syntheses*, Coll. Vol. II, 246 (1943); Whitmore et al., *J. Am. Chem. Soc.*, 69, 235 (1947); 70, 529 (1948); 67, 2059 (1945).

[4] Whitmore et al., *J. Am. Chem. Soc.*, 67, 2059 (1945).

[5] Cason, *J. Am. Chem. Soc.*, 64, 1109 (1942).

[6] Whitmore et al., *J. Am. Chem. Soc.*, 64, 1802 (1942).

[7] Sherrill, Otto, and Pickett, *J. Am. Chem. Soc.*, 51, 3023 (1929); Kharasch, Walling, and Mayo, *ibid.*, 61, 1559 (1939); Lucas, Simpson, and Carter, *ibid.*, 47, 1462 (1925); Shonle, Keltch, and Swanson, *ibid.*, 52, 2442 (1930).

[8] Sherrill, *J. Am. Chem. Soc.*, 52, 1982 (1930).

[9] Whitmore et al., *J. Am. Chem. Soc.*, 54, 3431 (1932); 55, 1106 (1933); 60, 2265, 2533 (1938).

[10] Whitmore and Johnson, *J. Am. Chem. Soc.*, 60, 2265 (1938).

[11] Whitmore and Karnatz, *J. Am. Chem. Soc.*, 60, 2533 (1938); cf. ref. 114.

[12] Whitmore and Karnatz, *J. Am. Chem. Soc.*, 60, 2536 (1938).

[13] Lucas, *J. Am. Chem. Soc.*, 51, 252 (1929).

[14] Niemann and Wagner, *J. Org. Chem.*, 7, 227 (1942).

[15] Whitmore, Karnatz, and Popkin, *J. Am. Chem. Soc.*, 60, 2540 (1938).

[16] Strating and Backer, *Rec. trav. chim.*, 55, 913 (1935).

[17] Vogel, *J. Chem. Soc.*, 636 (1943).

[18] Copenhaver and Whaley, *Org. Syntheses*, Coll. Vol. I, 142 (1941); *J. Am. Chem. Soc.*, 60, 2497 (1938).

[19] Norris and Olmsted, *Org. Syntheses*, Coll. Vol. I, 144 (1941).

[20] Werner, *J. Soc. Chem. Ind.*, 52, 285 (1933).

[21] Whitmore et al., *J. Am. Chem. Soc.*, 55, 361, 406, 1559 (1933).

[22] Corson, Thomas, and Waugh, *J. Am. Chem. Soc.*, 51, 1950 (1929).

[23] Klages et al., *Ann. chim.*, 547, 33 (1941).

[24] Neunhoeffer and Schlüter, *Ann. chim.*, 526, 70 (1936); Yarnall and Wallis, *J. Org. Chem.*, 4, 287 (1939).

[25] King, *J. Chem. Soc.*, 982 (1935).

[26] Perlman, Davidson, and Bogert, *J. Org. Chem.*, 1, 288 (1936).

[27] Hiers and Adams, *J. Am. Chem. Soc.*, 48, 1091 (1926).

[28] McKinley, Stevens, and Baldwin, *J. Am. Chem. Soc.*, 67, 1458 (1945).

[29] Slotta and Altner, *Ber.*, 64, 1515 (1931); Ashley et al., *J. Chem. Soc.*, 115 (1942).

[30] Conant and Blatt, *J. Am. Chem. Soc.*, 50, 554 (1928).

[31] Norris and Taylor, *J. Am. Chem. Soc.*, 46, 753 (1924).

[32] Amagat, *Bull. soc. chim. France*, (4) 49, 1410 (1931).

[33] Smith and Spillane, *J. Am. Chem. Soc.*, 62, 2640 (1940); Reichstein et al., *Helv. Chim. Acta*, 19, 412 (1936).

[34] Kharasch and Kleiman, *J. Am. Chem. Soc.*, 65, 14 (1943).

[35] Nauta and Mulder, *Rec. trav. chim.*, 58, 1075 (1939).

[36] Skell and Hauser, *J. Am. Chem. Soc.*, 64, 2633 (1942).

[37] Bachmann, *Org. Syntheses*, 23, 100 (1943); cf. Bachmann, *J. Am. Chem. Soc.*, 55, 2135 (1933).

[38] Newman, *J. Org. Chem.*, 9, 518 (1944).

[39] Renshaw and Conn, *J. Am. Chem. Soc.*, **60**, 745 (1938); Koenigs and Neumann, *Ber.*, **48**, 961 (1915).

[40] Hiers and Adams, *J. Am. Chem. Soc.*, **48**, 2385 (1926).

[41] Steele, *J. Am. Chem. Soc.*, **53**, 285 (1931); Nenitzescu and Necsoiu, *ibid.*, **72**, 3483 (1950); Goldsworthy, *J. Chem. Soc.*, 484 (1931).

[42] Adams and Kornblum, *J. Am. Chem. Soc.*, **63**, 199 (1941).

[43] Lucas, Schlatter, and Jones, *J. Am. Chem. Soc.*, **63**, 22 (1941).

[44] Stone, *J. Am. Chem. Soc.*, **62**, 571 (1940).

[45] Manske, *J. Am. Chem. Soc.*, **53**, 1104 (1931).

[46] Holliman and Mann, *J. Chem. Soc.*, 737 (1942).

[47] Young et al., *J. Am. Chem. Soc.*, **58**, 104 (1936); **59**, 2051 (1937).

[48] Mulliken, Wakeman, and Gerry, *J. Am. Chem. Soc.*, **57**, 1605 (1935).

[49] Lauer and Filbert, *J. Am. Chem. Soc.*, **58**, 1388 (1936).

[50] Smith et al., *J. Am. Chem. Soc.*, **61**, 3080 (1939).

[51] Young, Richards, and Azorlosa, *J. Am. Chem. Soc.*, **61**, 3070 (1939).

[52] Baudart, *Bull. soc. chim. France*, (5) **11**, 337 (1944).

[53] Carroll, *J. Chem. Soc.*, 1266 (1940); Meisenheimer and Link, *Ann.*, **479**, 240 (1930).

[54] Campbell and Eby, *J. Am. Chem. Soc.*, **62**, 1789 (1940).

[55] Campbell, Campbell, and Eby, *J. Am. Chem. Soc.*, **60**, 2882, (1938).

[56] Hennion and Banigan, Jr., *J. Am. Chem. Soc.*, **68**, 1202 (1946).

[57] Marvel and Calvery, *Org. Syntheses*, Coll. Vol. I, 533 (1941); also, Hultman, Davis, and Clarke, *J. Am. Chem. Soc.*, **43**, 369 (1921).

[58] McElvain and Carney, *J. Am. Chem. Soc.*, **68**, 2596 (1946).

[59] Campbell et al., *J. Am. Chem. Soc.*, **68**, 1556 (1946); *Org. Syntheses*, **28**, 65 (1948).

[60] Conant and Quayle, *Org. Syntheses*, Coll. Vol. I, 292 (1941).

[61] Conant and Quayle, *Org. Syntheses*, Coll. Vol. I, 294 (1941).

[62] Bogert and Slocum, *J. Am. Chem. Soc.*, **46**, 763 (1924); Kamm and Newcomb, *ibid.*, **43**, 2228 (1921).

[63] Ayers, Jr., *J. Am. Chem. Soc.*, **60**, 2959 (1938).

[64] Leffler and Volwiler, *J. Am. Chem. Soc.*, **60**, 898 (1938).

[65] Silverman and Bogert, *J. Org. Chem.*, **11**, 43 (1946).

[66] Sosa, *Ann. chim.*, (11) **14**, 88 (1940).

[67] Franke and Kroupa, *Monatsh.*, **69**, 202 (1936).

[68] Fling, Minard, and Fox, *J. Am. Chem. Soc.*, **69**, 2466 (1947).

[69] Beilenson and Hamer, *J. Chem. Soc.*, 101 (1942).

[70] Cortese, *Org. Syntheses*, Coll. Vol. II, 91 (1943).

[71] McEwen, *Org. Syntheses*, **20**, 24 (1940).

[72] King, *Org. Syntheses*, Coll. Vol. II, 399 (1943).

[73] Bogert and Slocum, *J. Am. Chem. Soc.*, **46**, 763 (1924); cf. ref. 72.

[74] Noller and Dinsmore, *Org. Syntheses*, Coll. Vol. II, 358 (1943); Whitmore and Lux, *J. Am. Chem. Soc.*, **54**, 3450 (1932).

[75] Delaby, *Bull. soc. chim. France*, (5) **3**, 2375 (1936).

[76] Kornblum et al., *J. Am. Chem. Soc.*, **69**, 309 (1947).

[77] Rehberg and Henze, *J. Am. Chem. Soc.*, **63**, 2789 (1941).

[78] Shonle et al., *J. Am. Chem. Soc.*, **58**, 585 (1936).

[79] Strating and Backer, *Rec. trav. chim.*, **55**, 911 (1936).

[80] Dirscherl and Nahm, *Ber.*, **76**, 640, 710 (1943).

[81] Peak and Robinson, *J. Chem. Soc.*, 1590 (1937).

[82] Hartman, Byers, and Dickey, *Org. Syntheses,* Coll. Vol. II, 322 (1943).
[83] Smith, *J. Chem. Soc.,* 737 (1932).
[84] Noller and Adams, *J. Am. Chem. Soc.,* **48**, 1080 (1926).
[85] Yohe and Adams, *J. Am. Chem. Soc.,* **50**, 1503 (1928).
[86] Lutz et al., *J. Am. Chem. Soc.,* 70, 4135 (1948).
[87] Turkiewicz, *Ber.,* 7 2, 1062 (1939).
[88] Clemence and Leffler, *J. Am. Chem. Soc.,* **70**, 2439 (1948).
[89] Blicke and Zienty, *J. Am. Chem. Soc.,* **61**, 772 (1939).
[90] Bergs, *Ber.,* **67**, 244 (1934).
[91] Newman, *J. Am. Chem. Soc.,* **62**, 2295 (1940).
[92] Hauser et al., *J. Am. Chem. Soc.,* **69**, 589 (1947).
[93] Rupe and van Walraven, *Helv. Chim. Acta,* **13**, 369 (1930).
[94] Bogert and Tuttle, *J. Am. Chem. Soc.,* **38**, 1361 (1916); Lester and Bailey, *ibid.,* **68**, 375 (1946).
[95] Sah, *Rec. trav. chim.,* **59**, 1022 (1940).
[96] Bachmann and Sheehan, *J. Am. Chem. Soc.,* **63**, 204 (1941).
[97] Zanetti and Bashour, *J. Am. Chem. Soc.,* **61**, 2249 (1939); Woodward, *ibid.,* **62**, 1481 (1940).
[98] Smith, *Org. Syntheses,* **23**, 88 (1943).
[99] Barger, Robinson, and Smith, *J. Chem. Soc.,* 720 (1937).
[100] Wibaut and Broekman, *Rec. trav. chim.,* **58**, 885 (1939).
[101] Krahler and Burger, *J. Am. Chem. Soc.,* **63**, 2368 (1941).
[102] Vogel, *J. Chem. Soc.,* 1809 (1948).
[103] Case, *J. Am. Chem. Soc.,* **55**, 2927 (1933).
[104] Cloke et al., *J. Am. Chem. Soc.,* **53**, 2794 (1931).
[105] Starr and Hixon, *J. Am. Chem. Soc.,* **56**, 1595 (1934); cf. ref. 119.
[106] Hurd and Webb, *J. Am. Chem. Soc.,* **58**, 2190 (1936).
[107] Schurink, *Org. Syntheses,* Coll. Vol. II, 476 (1943).
[108] Shortridge et al., *J. Am. Chem. Soc.,* 70, 946 (1948).
[109] Bartleson, Burk, and Lankelma, *J. Am. Chem. Soc.,* **68**, 2513 (1946).
[110] Montmollin and Martenet, *Helv. Chim. Acta,* 12, 604 (1929).
[111] LaForge, Green, and Gersdorff, *J. Am. Chem. Soc.,* **70**, 3707 (1948).
[112] Hunsdiecker, *Ber.,* **75**, 460 (1942).
[113] Goering, Cristol, and Dittmer, *J. Am. Chem. Soc.,* 70, 3314 (1948).
[114] Prout and Cason, *J. Org. Chem.,* **14**, 132 (1949).
[115] Milas and McAlevy, *J. Am. Chem. Soc.,* **57**, 580 (1935).
[116] Arvin and Adams, *J. Am. Chem. Soc.,* **50**, 1790 (1928).
[117] Cook and Dansi, *J. Chem. Soc.,* 500 (1935).
[118] Piaux, *Ann. chim.,* (11) **4**, 211 (1935).
[119] Newman and Wotiz, *J. Am. Chem. Soc.,* **71**, 1292 (1949).
[120] Bartlett and Rosen, *J. Am. Chem. Soc.,* **64**, 543 (1942).
[121] Lai, *Bull. soc. chim. France,* **53**, 1533 (1933).
[122] Johnson, *Acetylenic Compounds,* Edward Arnold & Co., London, 1946, Vol. I, p 63.
[123] Harrison and Diehl, *Org. Syntheses,* **23**, 32 (1943).
[124] Smith and Sprung, *J. Am. Chem. Soc.,* **65**, 1276 (1943).
[125] Anderson, Crawford, and Sherrill, *J. Am. Chem. Soc.,* **68**, 1294 (1946).
[126] Pummerer and Schönamsgruber, *Ber.,* **72**, 1838 (1939).
[127] Prelog and Seiwerth, *Ber.,* **72**, 1640 (1939).
[128] Elderfield et al., *J. Am. Chem. Soc.,* **68**, 1579 (1946).

[129] Marvel and Tanenbaum, *J. Am. Chem. Soc.*, **44**, 2645 (1922).
[13c] Braun, *Org. Syntheses*, Coll. Vol. II, 308 (1943).
[131] Cowdrey, Hughes, and Ingold, *J. Chem. Soc.*, 1227 (1937); cf. Gerrard, Kenyon, and Phillips, *ibid.*, 155 (1937).
[132] Philippi, Hendgen, and Hernler, *Monatsh.*, **69**, 278 (1936).
[133] Meincke and McElvain, *J. Am. Chem. Soc.*, **57**, 1443 (1935).
[134] Glattfeld and Lee, *J. Am. Chem. Soc.*, **62**, 354 (1940).
[135] Foreman and McElvain, *J. Am. Chem. Soc.*, **62**, 1438 (1940).
[136] Wagner-Jauregg, *Helv. Chim. Acta*, **12**, 63 (1929).
[137] Osterberg and Kendall, *J. Am. Chem. Soc.*, **42**, 2616 (1920).
[138] Leffler and Adams, *J. Am. Chem. Soc.*, **59**, 2252 (1937).
[139] Foreman and McElvain, *J. Am. Chem. Soc.*, **62**, 1435 (1940).
[140] McElvain and Fajardo-Pinzon, *J. Am. Chem. Soc.*, **67**, 690 (1945).
[141] Noller and Bannerot, *J. Am. Chem. Soc.*, **56**, 1563 (1934).
[142] Barkovsky, *Ann. chim.*, (11) **19**, 491 (1944).
[143] Cohen, *J. Chem. Soc.*, 433 (1935).
[144] Scheer, *J. Am. Chem. Soc.*, **56**, 744 (1934).
[145] Gilman and Kirby, *J. Am. Chem. Soc.*, **51**, 3476 (1929).
[146] Bergmann and Blum-Bergmann, *J. Am. Chem. Soc.*, **58**, 1678 (1936).
[147] Gilman and Hewlett, *Rec. trav. chim.*, **51**, 93 (1932).
[148] Kirner, *J. Am. Chem. Soc.*, **52**, 3254 (1930); Wilson, *J. Chem. Soc.*, 51 (1945).
[149] Kirner, *J. Am. Chem. Soc.*, **50**, 1955 (1928).
[150] Amstutz and Plucker, *J. Am. Chem. Soc.*, **63**, 206 (1941).
[151] Bissinger and Kung, *J. Am. Chem. Soc.*, **69**, 2158 (1947).
[152] Norton et al., *J. Am. Chem. Soc.*, **68**, 1572 (1946).
[153] Sisido and Nozaki, *J. Am. Chem. Soc.*, **69**, 961 (1947).
[154] Ahmad, Bumpus, and Strong, *J. Am. Chem. Soc.*, **70**, 3391 (1948).
[155] Gerrard, *J. Chem. Soc.*, 99 (1939).
[156] Brody and Bogert, *J. Am. Chem. Soc.*, **65**, 1075 (1943).
[157] Natelson and Gottfried, *J. Am. Chem. Soc.*, **64**, 2962 (1942).
[158] Gilman and Harris, *Rec. trav. chim.*, **50**, 1052 (1931).
[159] Hurd and Fowler, *J. Am. Chem. Soc.*, **61**, 249 (1939).
[160] Hennion and Sheehan, *J. Am. Chem. Soc.*, **71**, 1964 (1949).
[161] Lauer and Spielman, *J. Am. Chem. Soc.*, **55**, 1572 (1933).
[162] Palomaa, *Ber.*, **74**, 298 (1941).
[163] Hardegger, Redlich, and Gal, *Helv. Chim. Acta*, **28**, 628 (1945); Hill, Short, and Strong, *J. Chem. Soc.*, 1620 (1937).
[164] Cornforth and Robinson, *J. Chem. Soc.*, 686 (1942).
[165] Kindler and Gehlhaar, *Arch. Pharm.*, **274**, 385 (1936).
[166] Kirner and Richter, *J. Am. Chem. Soc.*, **51**, 2505 (1929).
[167] Thayer and McElvain, *J. Am. Chem. Soc.*, **50**, 3353 (1928).
[168] Barger, Robinson, and Smith, *J. Chem. Soc.*, 718 (1937).
[169] Niemann, Benson, and Mead, *J. Org. Chem.*, **8**, 397 (1943).
[170] Breslow et al., *J. Am. Chem. Soc.*, **66**, 1921 (1944).
[171] Schultz and Sprague, *J. Am. Chem. Soc.*, **70**, 48 (1948); cf. Shapiro, *J. Org. Chem.*, **14**, 844 (1949).
[172] Kerwin et al., *J. Am. Chem. Soc.*, **69**, 2961 (1947).
[173] Magidson and Strukow, *Arch. Pharm.*, **271**, 572 (1933).
[174] Elderfield et al., *J. Am. Chem. Soc.*, **68**, 1516 (1946).

[175] Mannich and Margotte, *Ber.*, **68**, 274 (1935).

[176] Lasselle and Sundet, *J. Am. Chem. Soc.*, **63**, 2374 (1941).

[177] Mann, *J. Chem. Soc.*, 461 (1934); Ward, *J. Am. Chem. Soc.*, **57**, 914 (1935).

[178] Alphen, *Rec. trav. chim.*, **56**, 1008 (1937); Ward, ref. 177.

[179] Hignett and Kay, *J. Soc. Chem. Ind.*, **54**, 98 (1935).

[180] Knowles and Cloke, *J. Am. Chem. Soc.*, **54**, 2034 (1932).

[181] Kornblum and Iffland, *J. Am. Chem. Soc.*, **71**, 2137 (1949).

[182] Kornblum and Eicher, *J. Am. Chem. Soc.*, **71**, 2259 (1949).

[183] Ward, *Org. Syntheses*, Coll. Vol. II, 159 (1943).

[184] Kharasch et al., *J. Org. Chem.*, **2**, 288 (1937); **4**, 428 (1939).

[185] Whitmore and Johnston, *J. Am. Chem. Soc.*, **55**, 5020 (1933).

[186] Spiegler and Tinker, *J. Am. Chem. Soc.*, **61**, 940 (1939).

[187] Whitmore and Homeyer, *J. Am. Chem. Soc.*, **55**, 4555 (1933); Kharasch, Hannum, and Gladstone, *ibid,*, **56**, 244 (1934).

[188] Coleman, Callen, and Dornfeld, *J. Am. Chem. Soc.*, **68**, 1101 (1946); ref. 4.

[189] McElvain and Langston, *J. Am. Chem. Soc.*, **66**, 1762 (1944).

[190] Kharasch and Kleiman, *J. Am. Chem. Soc.*, **65**, 11 (1943).

[191] Goerner and Hines, *J. Am. Chem. Soc.*, **70**, 3511 (1948); ref. 190.

[192] Young, Vogt, and Nieuwland, *J. Am. Chem. Soc.*, **58**, 1806 (1936).

[193] Henne, Chanan, and Turk, *J. Am. Chem. Soc.*, **63**, 3474 (1941).

[194] Naves, Grampoloff, and Bachmann, *Helv. Chim. Acta*, **30**, 1604 (1947).

[195] Mayo and Walling, *Chem. Revs.*, **27**, 351 (1940).

[196] Noller and Adams, *J. Am. Chem. Soc.*, **48**, 2446 (1926).

[197] Jacobs et al., *J. Org. Chem.*, **11**, 225 (1946).

[198] Walling, Kharasch, and Mayo, *J. Am. Chem. Soc.*, **61**, 2693 (1939).

[199] Guest, *J. Am. Chem. Soc.*, **69**, 300 (1947).

[200] Sherrill and Matlack, *J. Am. Chem. Soc.*, **59**, 2137 (1937).

[201] Jones, *J. Am. Chem. Soc.*, **69**, 2352 (1947); Ashton and Smith, *J. Chem. Soc.*, 435 (1934).

[202] Mozingo and Patterson, *Org. Syntheses*, **20**, 64 (1940); including note 5.

[203] Price and Coyner, *J. Am. Chem. Soc.*, **62**, 1306 (1940); also, Clemo and Melrose, *J. Chem. Soc.*, 424 (1942).

[204] Kharasch and Fuchs, *J. Org. Chem.*, **9**, 365 (1944).

[205] Stevens, *J. Am. Chem. Soc.*, **70**, 165 (1948).

[206] Stewart and Clark, *J. Am. Chem. Soc.*, **69**, 713 (1947).

[207] Büchi and Jeger, *Helv. Chim. Acta*, **32**, 538 (1949).

[208] Sorkin and Hinden, *Helv. Chim. Acta*, **32**, 65 (1949).

[209] Groggins, *Unit Processes in Organic Synthesis*, McGraw-Hill Book Co., New York, 1947, pp. 168–259.

[210] McBee and Haas, *Ind. Eng. Chem.*, **33**, 137 (1941).

[211] Whitmore et al., *J. Am. Chem. Soc.*, **55**, 4161 (1933); **60**, 2539 (1938).

[212] Whitmore, Marker, and Plambeck, Jr., *J. Am. Chem. Soc.*, **63**, 1626 (1941).

[213] Stevens, *J. Am. Chem. Soc.*, **68**, 620 (1946).

[214] Sampey, Fawcett, and Morehead, *J. Am. Chem. Soc.*, **62**, 1839 (1940).

[215] Mason et al., *J. Chem. Soc.*, 3150 (1931).

[216] Atkinson and Thorpe, *J. Chem. Soc.*, 1695 (1907).

[217] Kharasch and Brown, *J. Am. Chem. Soc.*, **61**, 2142 (1939).

[218] Schmid and Karrer, *Helv. Chim. Acta*, **29**, 573 (1946).

[219] Gindraux, *Helv. Chim. Acta*, **12**, 921 (1929).

[220] McMaster and Carol, *Ind. Eng. Chem.*, **23**, 218 (1931).

[221] Gatterman and Wieland, *Laboratory Methods of Organic Chemistry,* The Macmillan Co., New York, 1938.
[222] Maxwell and Adams, *J. Am. Chem. Soc.,* 52, 2962 (1930).
[223] Wisansky and Ansbacher, *Org. Syntheses,* 28, 22 (1948).
[224] Wahl, *Ann. chim.,* (11) 5, 12 (1936).
[225] Jenkins et al., *J. Org. Chem.,* 13, 865 (1948).
[226] Weygand, *Organic Preparations,* Interscience Publishers, New York, 1945, p. 76.
[227] Marvel et al., *J. Am. Chem. Soc.,* 66, 916 (1944).
[228] Marvel, Kaplan, and Himel, *J. Am. Chem. Soc.,* 63, 1894 (1941).
[229] Smith, *Org. Syntheses,* Coll. Vol. II, 95 (1943).
[230] Smith and Moyle, *J. Am. Chem. Soc.,* 55, 1676 (1933).
[231] Smith and Moyle, *J. Am. Chem. Soc.,* 58, 1 (1936).
[232] Fuson and Corse, *J. Am. Chem. Soc.,* 60, 2065 (1938).
[233] Smith and Guss, *J. Am. Chem. Soc.,* 62, 2635 (1940).
[234] Clarke and Brethen, *Org. Syntheses,* Coll. Vol. I, 121 (1941).
[235] Buu-Hoï, *Ann.,* 556, 6 (1944); Lecocq, *Ann. chim.,* (12) 3, 79 (1948).
[236] Dains and Brewster, *Org. Syntheses,* Coll. Vol. I, 323 (1941).
[237] Elbs and Jaroslawzew, *J. prakt. Chem.,* 88, 92 (1913).
[238] Minnis, *Org. Syntheses,* Coll. Vol. II, 357 (1943).
[239] Sandin, Drake, and Leger, *Org. Syntheses,* Coll. Vol. II, 196 (1943); Woollett and Johnson, *ibid.,* Coll. Vol. II, 343 (1943).
[240] Hunter and Edgar, *J. Am. Chem. Soc.,* 54, 2025 (1932).
[241] Groll and Hearne, *Ind. Eng. Chem.,* 31, 1239, 1413, 1530 (1939).
[242] Tsatsas, *Ann. chim.,* (11) 19, 224 (1944).
[243] Jenkins, McCullough, and Booth, *Ind. Eng. Chem.,* 22, 31 (1930).
[244] Ferrero and Corbaz, *Helv. Chim. Acta,* 13, 1009 (1930).
[245] Militzer, *J. Am. Chem. Soc.,* 60, 256 (1938).
[246] Tarbell, Fukushima, and Dam. *J. Am. Chem. Soc.,* 67, 197 (1945).
[247] Schultz et al., *J. Org. Chem.,* 11, 320 (1946).
[248] Goldberg, Ordas, and Carsch, *J. Am. Chem. Soc.,* 69, 260 (1947).
[249] Dornfeld, Callen, and Coleman, *Org. Syntheses,* 28, 19 (1948); cf. ref. 246.
[250] Campbell, Anderson, and Gilmore, *J. Chem. Soc.,* 819 (1940); cf. ref. 246.
[251] Clarkson and Gomberg, *J. Am. Chem. Soc.,* 52, 2886 (1930); Thurston and Shriner, *ibid.,* 57, 2164 (1935).
[252] Fuson and Porter, *J. Am. Chem. Soc.,* 70, 896 (1948); Sampey and Reid, *ibid.,* 69, 234 (1947); Wittig and Felletschun, *Ann.,* 555, 138 (1944).
[253] Bachmann and Kloetzel, *J. Org. Chem.,* 3, 58 (1938).
[254] Paillard and Farvarger, *Helv. Chim. Acta,* 16, 614 (1933).
[255] Campaigne and LeSuer, *J. Am. Chem. Soc.,* 70, 1555 (1948); Dittmer et al., *ibid.,* 71, 1201 (1949).
[256] Blicke and Burckhalter, *J. Am. Chem. Soc.,* 64, 477 (1942).
[257] Truitt, Mattison, and Richardson, *J. Am. Chem. Soc.,* 70, 79 (1948); Campaigne and LeSuer, *ibid.,* 70, 415 (1948).
[258] Crook and Davies, *J. Chem. Soc.,* 1697 (1937).
[259] Klopp and Wright, *J. Org. Chem.,* 4, 142 (1939).
[260] Gilman and Avakian, *J. Am. Chem. Soc.,* 68, 580 (1946).
[261] Renshaw and Friedman, *J. Am. Chem. Soc.,* 61, 3320 (1939); cf. ref. 262.
[262] Jansen and Wibaut, *Rec. trav. chim.,* 56, 699 (1937).
[263] Bergstrom and Rodda, *J. Am. Chem. Soc.,* 62, 3030 (1950); Craig and Cass, *ibid.,* 64, 783 (1942).

[264] Elpern and Hamilton, *J. Am. Chem. Soc.*, **68**, 1436 (1946).

[265] McElvain and Goese, *J. Am. Chem. Soc.*, **65**, 2227 (1943); Wibaut and Den Hertog, *Rec. trav. chim.*, **64**, 55 (1945).

[266] Wibaut and Nicolai, *Rec. trav. chim.*, **58**, 709 (1939).

[267] Rodewald and Plazek, *Ber.*, **70**, 1159 (1937).

[268] Dyson and Hammick, *J. Chem. Soc.*, 781 (1939).

[269] Tucker, *J. Chem. Soc.*, 546 (1926).

[270] Hass and Huffman, *J. Am. Chem. Soc.*, **63**, 1233 (1941).

[271] Hennion and Anderson, *J. Am. Chem. Soc.*, **68**, 424 (1946).

[272] Wibaut, Van De Lande, and Wallagh, *Rec. trav. chim.*, **52**, 794 (1933).

[273] Dvornikoff, Sheets, and Zienty, *J. Am. Chem. Soc.*, **68**, 142 (1946).

[274] Simons and Ramler, *J. Am. Chem. Soc.*, **65**, 389 (1943).

[275] Dippy and Williams, *J. Chem. Soc.*, 164 (1934).

[276] Weizmann and Patai, *J. Am. Chem. Soc.*, **68**, 150 (1946).

[277] Jenkins, *J. Am. Chem. Soc.*, **55**, 2896 (1933).

[278] Rapson and Shuttleworth, *J. Chem. Soc.*, 489 (1941); cf. ref. 590.

[279] Ruggli and Theilheimer, *Helv. Chim. Acta*, **24**, 906 (1941); Titley, *J. Chem. Soc.*, 513 (1926); Atkinson and Thorpe, *ibid.*, 1698 (1907).

[280] Snell and Weissberger, *Org. Syntheses*, **20**, 92 (1940).

[281] Koelsch, *Org. Syntheses*, **20**, 18 (1940).

[282] Adams and Marvel, *Org. Syntheses*, Coll. Vol. I, 128 (1941).

[283] Blicke and Smith, *J. Am. Chem. Soc.*, **50**, 1229 (1928); Frank, Fanta, and Tarbell, *ibid.*, **70**, 2317 (1948).

[284] Brewster and Stevenson, *J. Am. Chem. Soc.*, **62**, 3144 (1940).

[285] Plati, Strain, and Warren, *J. Am. Chem. Soc.*, **65**, 1273 (1943).

[286] Dippy and Williams, *J. Chem. Soc.*, 1891 (1934).

[287] Wallingford and Krueger, *Org. Syntheses*, Coll. Vol. II, 349 (1943).

[288] Fuson and Cooke, Jr., *J. Am. Chem. Soc.*, **62**, 1180 (1940).

[289] Barnes and Gordon, *J. Am. Chem. Soc.*, **71**, 2644 (1949).

[290] Brewster, *Org. Syntheses*, Coll. Vol. II, 347 (1943).

[291] Fieser and Bowen, *J. Am. Chem. Soc.*, **62**, 2103 (1940).

[292] Fuson, *J. Am. Chem. Soc.*, **48**, 830 (1926).

[293] Case, *J. Am. Chem. Soc.*, **47**, 1143 (1925).

[294] Blicke and Patelski, *J. Am. Chem. Soc.*, **58**, 559 (1936).

[295] Johnson and Gauerke, *Org. Syntheses*, Coll. Vol. I, 123 (1941).

[296] Coleman and Honeywell, *Org. Syntheses*, Coll. Vol. II, 443 (1943); cf. Cavill, *J. Soc. Chem. Ind.*, **65**, 124 (1946).

[297] van Tamelen and Van Zyl, *J. Am. Chem. Soc.*, **71**, 835 (1949).

[298] Birckenbach and Goubeau, *Ber.*, **65**, 395 (1932).

[299] Hodgson, *Chem. Revs.*, **40**, 251 (1947).

[300] Bigelow, *Org. Syntheses*, Coll. Vol. I, 133-126 (1941).

[301] Marvel and McElvain, *Org. Syntheses*, Coll. Vol. I, 170 (1941).

[302] Lucas and Kennedy, *Org. Syntheses*, Coll. Vol. II, 351 (1943).

[303] Roe in *Organic Reactions*, Vol. 5, John Wiley & Sons, New York, 1949, pp. 193.

[304] Flood, *Org. Syntheses*, Coll. Vol. II, 295 (1943).

[305] Sah and Hsü, *Rec. trav. chim.*, **59**, 351 (1940); Lucas, Kennedy, and Wilmot, *J. Am. Chem. Soc.*, **58**, 157 (1936).

[306] Chattaway et al., *J. Chem. Soc.*, **65**, 875 (1894).

[307] Vogel, *J. Chem. Soc.*, 650 (1948).

[308] Gilman, Kirby, and Kinney, *J. Am. Chem. Soc.*, **51**, 2260 (1929).
[309] Campaigne and Reid, Jr., *J. Am. Chem. Soc.*, **68**, 1663 (1946).
[310] Bachmann and Boatner, *J. Am. Chem. Soc.*, **58**, 2194 (1936).
[311] Fieser and Seligman, *J. Am. Chem. Soc.*, **58**, 478 (1936).
[312] Allen and Thirtle, *Org. Syntheses*, **26**, 16 (1946).
[313] Wibaut and Bastide, *Rec. trav. chim.*, **52**, 495 (1933).
[314] Roe and Hawkins, *J. Am. Chem. Soc.*, **69**, 2443 (1947); **71**, 1785 (1949).
[315] Dikshoorn, *Rec. trav. chim.*, **48**, 550 (1929).
[316] Newman and Fones, *J. Am. Chem. Soc.*, **69**, 1221 (1947).
[317] Fry and Grote, *J. Am. Chem. Soc.*, **48**, 710 (1926).
[318] Hartwell, *Org. Syntheses*, **24**, 22 (1944).
[319] Ingold and Vass, *J. Chem. Soc.*, 2265 (1928).
[320] Wallagh and Wibaut, *Rec. trav. chim.*, **55**, 1072 (1936).
[321] Schiemann and Winkelmüller, *Org. Syntheses*, Coll. Vol. II, 188 (1943).
[322] Leslie and Turner, *J. Chem. Soc.*, 282 (1932).
[323] Li and Adams, *J. Am. Chem. Soc.*, **57**, 1568 (1935).
[324] Dains and Eberly, *Org. Syntheses*, Coll. Vol. II, 355 (1943).
[325] Bradlow and Vanderwerf, *J. Am. Chem. Soc.*, **70**, 656 (1948).
[326] Weygand, *Organic Preparations*, Interscience Publishers, New York, 1945, p. 117.
[327] Searle and Adams, *J. Am. Chem. Soc.*, **55**, 1652 (1933).
[328] Schiemann and Winkelmüller, *Org. Syntheses*, Coll. Vol. II, 299 (1943).
[329] Buck and Ide, *Org. Syntheses*, Coll. Vol. II, 130 (1943).
[330] Schoutissen, *Rec. trav. chim.*, **54**, 98 (1935).
[331] Marvel, Allen, and Overberger, *J. Am. Chem. Soc.*, **68**, 1089 (1946).
[332] Elson, Gibson, and Johnson, *J. Chem. Soc.*, 1128 (1930).
[333] Zenitz and Hartung, *J. Org. Chem.*, **11**, 444 (1946), cf. ref. 332.
[334] Evans, Morgan, and Watson, *J. Chem. Soc.*, 1172 (1935); Leonard and Boyd, *J. Org. Chem.*, **11**, 412 (1946).
[335] Strassburg, Gregg, and Walling, *J. Am. Chem. Soc.*, **69**, 2141 (1947).
[336] Ayling, Gorvin, and Hinkel, *J. Chem. Soc.*, 618 (1941).
[337] Hartman and Brethen, *Org. Syntheses*, Coll. Vol. I, 162 (1941).
[338] Fuson and McKeever in *Organic Reactions*, Vol. I, John Wiley & Sons, New York, 1942, p. 63.
[339] Whitmore et al., *Ind. Eng. Chem.*, **38**, 478 (1946); cf. ref. 338.
[340] Darzens, *Compt. rend.*, **208**, 818 (1939).
[341] Quelet, *Bull. soc. chim. France*, (5e) 7, 196, 205 (1940).
[342] Emerson et al., *J. Am. Chem. Soc.*, **69**, 1905 (1947); cf. ref. 343.
[343] Kosolapoff, *J. Am. Chem. Soc.*, **68**, 1670 (1946).
[344] Akin, Stamatoff, and Bogert, *J. Am. Chem. Soc.*, **59**, 1271 (1937); cf. ref. 338.
[345] Grummitt and Buck, *Org. Syntheses*, **24**, 30 (1944).
[346] Tarbell and Wystrach, *J. Am. Chem. Soc.*, **65**, 2151 (1943).
[347] Quelet, *Bull. soc. chim. France*, **53**, 222 (1933).
[348] Colonge, *Bull. soc. chim. France*, (5e) 3, 2116 (1936).
[349] Griffling and Salisbury, *J. Am. Chem. Soc.*, **70**, 3416 (1948).
[350] Avakian, Moss, and Martin, *J. Am. Chem. Soc.*, **70**, 3075 (1948); Blicke and Sheets, *ibid.*, **70**, 3768 (1948).
[351] Wiberg and McShane, *Org. Syntheses*, **29**, 31 (1949); cf. ref. 256.
[352] Rossander and Marvel, *J. Am. Chem. Soc.*, **50**, 1491 (1928); Harmon and Marvel, *ibid.*, **54**, 2515 (1932).

[353] Suter and Evans, *J. Am. Chem. Soc.*, **60**, 536 (1938).

[354] Whitmore, Wittle, and Harriman, *J. Am. Chem. Soc.*, **61**, 1585 (1939).

[355] Bachmann and Kloetzel, *J. Org. Chem.*, **3**, 55 (1938).

[356] Gilman et al., *J. Am. Chem. Soc.*, **61**, 2836 (1939).

[357] Gilman and Norris, *J. Am. Chem. Soc.*, **67**, 1479 (1945).

[358] Gilman and Avakian, *J. Am. Chem. Soc.*, **67**, 349 (1945).

[359] Vaughn and Nieuwland, *J. Am. Chem. Soc.*, **55**, 2150 (1933); McCusker and Vogt, *ibid.*, **59**, 1307 (1937); cf. ref. 360.

[360] Grignard and Perrichon, *Ann. chim.*, (10) **5**, 5 (1926); cf. ref. 359.

[361] Whitmore and Woodward, *Org. Syntheses*, Coll. Vol. I, 325 (1941).

[362] Whitmore and Hanson, *Org. Syntheses*, Coll. Vol. I, 326 (1941).

[363] Truchet, *Ann. chim.*, (10) **16**, 334 (1931).

[364] Carter and West, *Org. Syntheses*, **20**, 81, 101 (1940).

[365] Gredy, *Bull. soc. chim. France*, (5e) **3**, 1094 (1936).

[366] Dehn, *J. Am. Chem. Soc.*, **33**, 1598 (1911); Vaughn and Nieuwland, *ibid.*, **54**, 788 (1932).

[367] Marvel and Tanenbaum, *J. Am. Chem. Soc.*, **44**, 2645 (1922).

[368] Benton and Dillon, *J. Am. Chem. Soc.*, **64**, 1128 (1942).

[369] Hass and Bender, *J. Am. Chem. Soc.*, **71**, 1767 (1949).

[370] Finkelstein and Elderfield, *J. Org. Chem.*, **4**, 372 (1939).

[371] Marvel and Birkhimer, *J. Am. Chem. Soc.*, **51**, 260 (1929).

[372] Merchant, Wickert, and Marvel, *J. Am. Chem. Soc.*, **49**, 1828 (1927).

[373] Marvel et al., *J. Am. Chem. Soc.*, **46**, 2838 (1924); Sayles and Degering, *ibid.*, **71**, 3161 (1949); cf. ref. 372.

[374] Carter, *J. Am. Chem. Soc.*, **50**, 1967 (1928).

[375] Marvel, Zartman, and Bluthardt, *J. Am. Chem. Soc.*, **49**, 2299 (1927).

[376] Gibbs, Littmann, and Marvel, *J. Am. Chem. Soc.*, **55**, 753 (1933).

[377] Drake et al., *J. Am. Chem. Soc.*, **68**, 1536 (1946).

[378] Finkelstein, *Ber.*, **43**, 1528 (1910).

[379] Ahmad and Strong, *J. Am. Chem. Soc.*, **70**, 1699 (1948).

[380] Gryszkiewicz-Trochimowski, *Rec. trav. chim.*, **66**, 415 (1947); Saunders and Stacey, *J. Chem. Soc.*, 1773 (1948).

[381] Ingold and Ingold, *J. Chem. Soc.*, 2249 (1928).

[382] Letsinger and Traynham, *J. Am. Chem. Soc.*, **70**, 2818 (1948).

[383] Brody and Bogert, *J. Am. Chem. Soc.*, **65**, 1080 (1943).

[384] Swallen and Boord, *J. Am. Chem. Soc.*, **52**, 651 (1930).

[385] Gibson and Johnson, *J. Chem. Soc.*, 2525 (1930).

[386] Bennett and Hock, *J. Chem. Soc.*, 472 (1927).

[387] King and L'Ecuyer, *J. Chem. Soc.*, 1901 (1934); Baker, *ibid.*, 216 (1933).

[388] Adickes, *J. prakt. Chem.*, **161**, 277 (1943).

[389] Borsche, *Ann.*, **526**, 14 (1936).

[390] Newman and Closson, *J. Am. Chem. Soc.*, **66**, 1553 (1944).

[391] Kleinberg, *Chem. Revs.*, **40**, 381 (1947).

[392] Hunsdiecker and Hunsdiecker, *Ber.*, **75**, 291 (1942); U. S. patent 2,176,181 (1939).

[393] Allen and Wilson, *Org. Syntheses*, **26**, 52 (1946).

[394] Luttringhaus and Schade, *Ber.*, **74**, 1565 (1941); cf. ref. 392.

[395] Schmid, *Helv. Chim. Acta*, **27**, 134 (1944).

[396] Cason and Way, *J. Org. Chem.*, **14**, 31 (1949).

[397] von Braun, *Org. Syntheses*, Coll. Vol. I, 428 (1941).

[398] Arvin and Adams, *J. Am. Chem. Soc.*, **50**, 1984 (1928).

[399] Leonard and Wicks, *J. Am. Chem. Soc.*, **68**, 2402 (1946).

[400] Stone, *J. Am. Chem. Soc.*, **58**, 488 (1936).

[401] Müller and Kindlmann, *Ber.*, **74**, 416 (1941).

[402] Braun and Sobecki, *Ber.*, **44**, 1464 (1911).

[403] Suida and Drahowzal, *Ber.*, **75**, 991 (1942).

[404] Hartman and Dreger, *Org. Syntheses*, Coll. Vol. I, 357 (1941).

[405] Adams and Marvel, *Org. Syntheses*, Coll. Vol. I, 358 (1941).

[406] Doughty and Derge, *J. Am. Chem. Soc.*, **53**, 1594 (1931).

[407] Buck and Ide, *J. Am. Chem. Soc.*, **54**, 4359 (1932).

[408] Glattfeld and Schneider, *J. Am. Chem. Soc.*, **60**, 415 (1938).

[409] Rinkes, *Rec. trav. chim.*, **55**, 991 (1936); Steinkopf et al., *Ann.*, **527**, 237 (1936).

[410] Fried and Kleene, *J. Am. Chem. Soc.*, **63**, 2691 (1941); **62**, 3258 (1940).

[411] Tarbell and Weaver, *J. Am. Chem. Soc.*, **63**, 2939 (1941); cf. refs. 410 and 412.

[412] Cloke and Ayers, *J. Am. Chem. Soc.*, **56**, 2144 (1934).

[413] Paul, *Bull. soc. chim. France*, (5) **5**, 1053 (1938).

[414] Synerholm, *J. Am. Chem. Soc.*, **69**, 2581 (1947).

[415] Alexander and Schniepp, *J. Am. Chem. Soc.*, **70**, 1839 (1948); *Org. Syntheses*, **30**, 27 (1950).

[416] Cloke and Pilgrim, *J. Am. Chem. Soc.*, **61**, 2667 (1939); Synerholm, *Org. Syntheses*, **29**, 30 (1949).

[417] Andrus, *Org. Syntheses,* **23**, 67 (1943).

[418] Piantanida, *J. prakt. Chem.*, **153**, 257 (1939).

[419] Stone and Schechter, *Org. Syntheses*, **30**, 33 (1950).

[420] Lucas and Gould, Jr., *J. Am. Chem. Soc.*, **63**, 2541 (1941).

[421] Winstein and Grunwald, *J. Am. Chem. Soc.*, **70**, 836 (1948).

[422] Johnson and McEwen, *Org. Syntheses*, Coll. Vol. I, 521 (1941).

[423] Evers et al., *J. Am. Chem. Soc.*, **55**, 1136 (1933); Whitmore, Evers, and Rothrock, *Org. Syntheses*, Coll. Vol. II, 408 (1943).

[424] Schmitt and Boord, *J. Am. Chem. Soc.*, **54**, 751 (1932).

[425] Soday and Boord, *J. Am. Chem. Soc.*, **55**, 3293 (1933).

[426] Snyder and Brooks, *Org. Syntheses*, Coll. Vol. II, 171 (1943).

[427] Kharasch and Brown, *J. Am. Chem. Soc.*, **61**, 3432 (1939).

[428] Smith and Hoehn, *J. Am. Chem. Soc.*, **63**, 1180 (1941).

[429] Paul and Normant, *Bull. soc. chim. France*, (5) **11**, 365 (1944).

[430] Shepard and Johnson, *J. Am. Chem. Soc.*, **54**, 4385 (1932).

[431] Koelsch, *J. Am. Chem. Soc.*, **54**, 2045 (1932).

[432] Farrell and Bachman, *J. Am. Chem. Soc.*, **57**, 1281 (1935).

[433] Jackson and Pasiut, *J. Am. Chem. Soc.*, **50**, 2249 (1928).

[434] Rhinesmith, *Org. Syntheses*, Coll. Vol. II, 177 (1943).

[435] Marvel et al., *J. Am. Chem. Soc.*, **62**, 3495 (1940).

[436] Abbott and Althousen, *Org. Syntheses*, Coll. Vol. II, 270 (1943).

[437] Carter and Ney, *J. Am. Chem. Soc.*, **64**, 1223 (1942).

[438] Lichtenberger and Naftali, *Bull. soc. chim. France*, (5) **4**, 325 (1937).

[439] Cromwell and Benson, *Org. Syntheses*, **27**, 5 (1947).

[440] Cromwell and Wankel, *J. Am. Chem. Soc.*, **70**, 1320 (1948).

[441] Auwers and Hügel, *J. prakt. Chem.*, **143**, 157 (1934); cf. ref. 440.

[442] Wagner, *J. Am. Chem. Soc.*, **71**, 3214 (1949).

[443] Degering, *Ind. Eng. Chem.*, **24**, 181 (1932).

[444] Jacobs in *Organic Reactions*, Vol. 5, John Wiley & Sons, New York, 1949, p. 20.

[445] Burkhardt and Cocker, *Rec. trav. chim.*, **50**, 843 (1931).

[446] Hurd, Meinert, and Spence, *J. Am. Chem. Soc.*, **52**, 1138 (1930).

[447] Stoll and Rouvé, *Helv. Chim. Acta*, **21**, 1542 (1938).

[448] Bartlett and Rosen, *J. Am. Chem. Soc.*, **64**, 543 (1942).

[449] Bachman and Hill, *J. Am. Chem. Soc.*, **56**, 2730 (1934).

[450] Favorski, *J. prakt. Chem.*, (2) **88**, 641 (1913).

[451] Vassliev, *Bull. soc. chim. France*, (4) **43**, 563 (1928).

[452] Smith and Hoehn, *J. Am. Chem. Soc.*, **63**, 1175 (1941); Adams and Theobald, *ibid.*, **65**, 2208 (1943).

[453] Perkin and Robinson, *J. Chem. Soc.*, **103**, 1977 (1913).

[454] Fisher and Hamer, *J. Chem. Soc.*, 1907 (1934).

[455] Djerassi, *Chem. Revs.*, **43**, 271 (1948).

[456] Ziegler et al., *Ann.*, **551**, 80 (1942).

[457] Lüttringhaus, König, and Böttcher, *Ann.*, **560**, 213 (1948).

[458] Karrer and Ringli, *Helv. Chim. Acta*, **30**, 863, 1771 (1947).

[459] Gomberg, *J. Am. Chem. Soc.*, **41**, 1414 (1919); Frahm, *Rec. trav. chim.*, **50**, 261 (1931).

[460] Olson and Whitacre, *J. Am. Chem. Soc.*, **65**, 1019 (1943); Montmollin and Matile, *Helv. Chim. Acta*, **7**, 106 (1924).

[461] Lucas and Gould, *J. Am. Chem. Soc.*, **63**, 2541 (1941).

[462] Glavis, Ryden, and Marvel, *J. Am. Chem. Soc.*, **59**, 707 (1937).

[463] Hurd and Abernethy, *J. Am. Chem. Soc.*, **63**, 976 (1941).

[464] Coleman and Johnstone, *Org. Syntheses*, Coll. Vol. I, 158 (1941); cf. Newman and Venderwerf, *J. Am. Chem. Soc.*, **67**, 233 (1945).

[465] Magidson et al., *Arch. Pharm.*, **272**, 79 (1934).

[466] Rothstein, *Bull. soc. chim. France*, (5) **2**, 1936 (1935).

[467] Detoeuf, *Bull. soc. chim. France*, (4) **31**, 169 (1922).

[468] Read and Williams, *J. Chem. Soc.*, 359, 1214 (1920).

[469] Read and Reid, *J. Chem. Soc.*, 1487 (1928); cf. ref. 473.

[470] Emerson, *J. Am. Chem. Soc.*, **67**, 516 (1945); Hanby and Rydon, *J. Chem. Soc.*, 114 (1946).

[471] Winstein and Buckles, *J. Am. Chem. Soc.*, **64**, 2780 (1942); cf. ref. 476.

[472] Suter and Milne, *J. Am. Chem. Soc.*, **62**, 3476 (1940).

[473] Suter and Zook, *J. Am. Chem. Soc.*, **66**, 738 (1944).

[474] Evans and Owen, *J. Chem. Soc.*, 239 (1949); cf. Kadesch, *J. Am. Chem. Soc.*, **68**, 46 (1946).

[475] Ruggli and Hegedüs, *Helv. Chim. Acta*, **25**, 1285 (1942); Bloomfield and Farmer, *J. Chem. Soc.*, 2062 (1932); Abderhalden and Heyns, *Ber.*, **67**, 530 (1934); Braun, *J. Am. Chem. Soc.*, **52**, 3185 (1930).

[476] Winstein, *J. Am. Chem. Soc.*, **64**, 2792 (1942).

[477] Winstein et al., *J. Am. Chem. Soc.*, **70**, 816 (1948).

[478] Thayer, Marvel, and Hiers, *Org. Syntheses*, Coll. Vol. I, 117 (1941).

[479] Autenrieth and Mühlinghaus, *Ber.*, **39**, 4098 (1906).

[480] Shoemaker and Boord, *J. Am. Chem. Soc.*, **53**, 1505 (1931).

[481] Whitmore and Langlois, *J. Am. Chem. Soc.*, **55**, 1518 (1933).

[482] Dykstra, Lewis, and Boord, *J. Am. Chem. Soc.*, **52**, 3396 (1930).

[483] Levene, *Org. Syntheses*, Coll. Vol. II, 88 (1943).

[484] Catch et al., *J. Chem. Soc.*, 272 (1948); Janetzky and Verkade, *Rec. trav. chim.*, **65**, 691 (1946).

[485] Catch et al., *J. Chem. Soc.*, 276 (1948); Janetzky and Verkade, *Rec. trav. chim.*, **65**, 905 (1946).

[486] Aston et al., *J. Am. Chem. Soc.*, **64**, 300 (1942).

[487] Bachman and Hill, *J. Am. Chem. Soc.*, **56**, 2730 (1934).

[488] Borrows, Holland, and Kenyon, *J. Chem. Soc.*, 1083 (1946).

[489] Hill and Kropa, *J. Am. Chem. Soc.*, **55**, 2509 (1933); Jackman et al., *ibid.*, **70**, 2884 (1948).

[490] Favorski, *J. prakt. Chem.*, **88**, 641 (1913).

[491] Djerassi and Scholz, *J. Am. Chem. Soc.*, **70**, 417 (1948).

[492] Bedoukian, *J. Am. Chem. Soc.*, **67**, 1430 (1945).

[493] Ruggli et al., *Helv. Chim. Acta*, **29**, 95 (1946).

[494] Buchman and Richardson, *J. Am. Chem. Soc.*, **67**, 395 (1945).

[495] Buchman and Sargent, *J. Am. Chem. Soc.*, **67**, 400 (1945).

[496] Rabjohn and Rogier, *J. Org. Chem.*, **11**, 781 (1946).

[497] Newman, Farbman, and Hipsher, *Org. Syntheses*, **25**, 22 (1945).

[498] Meyer, *Helv. Chim. Acta*, **16**, 1291 (1933); Ebel, *ibid.*, **12**, 9 (1929).

[499] Cowper and Davidson, *Org. Syntheses*, Coll. Vol. II, 480 (1943).

[500] Langley, *Org. Syntheses*, Coll. Vol. I, 127 (1941).

[501] Kindler and Blaas, *Ber,*, **77**, 585 (1944).

[502] Taylor, J. *Chem. Soc.*, 304 (1937).

[503] Fourneau and Barrelet, *Bull. soc. chim. France*, **47**, 72 (1930).

[504] Schultz and Mickey, *Org. Syntheses*, **29**, 38 (1949); Verkade and Janetzky, *Rec. trav. chim.*, **62**, 780 (1943); von Wacek et al., *Ber.*, **75**, 1352 (1942).

[505] Machlis and Blanchard, *J. Am. Chem. Soc.*, **57**, 176 (1935).

[506] Maeder, *Helv. Chim. Acta*, **29**, 124 (1946).

[507] Jacobs et al., *J. Org. Chem.*, **11**, 21 (1946).

[508] May and Mosettig, *J. Am. Chem. Soc.*, **70**, 686 (1948).

[509] Kipnis, Soloway, and Ornfelt, *J. Am. Chem. Soc.*, **71**, 10 (1949).

[510] McPhee and Klingsberg, *J. Am. Chem. Soc.*, **66**, 1132 (1944).

[511] Prevost and Sommiere, *Bull. soc. chim. France*, (5) **2**, 1157 (1935).

[512] Emerson and Patrick, Jr., *J. Org. Chem.*, **13**, 722 (1948).

[513] Long and Howard, *Org. Syntheses*, Coll. Vol. II, 87 (1943).

[514] Erlenmeyer and Jung, *Helv. Chim. Acta*, **32**, 37 (1949).

[515] Danilow and Venus-Danilowa, *Ber.*, **63**, 2765 (1930).

[516] Hibbert and Hill, *J. Am. Chem. Soc.*, **45**, 734 (1923).

[517] Danilow and Venus-Danilowa, *Ber.*, **67**, 24 (1934).

[518] Kirrmann, *Ann. chim.*, (10) **11**, 223 (1929); Chancel, *Bull. soc. chim. France*, (5) **17**, 714 (1950).

[519] Catch et al., *J. Chem. Soc.*, 278 (1948).

[520] McPhee and Klingsberg, *Org. Syntheses*, **26**, 13 (1946).

[521] Bachmann in *Organic Reactions*, Vol. 1, John Wiley & Sons, New York, 1942, p. 47.

[522] Ritter and Sokol, *J. Am. Chem. Soc.*, **70**, 3419 (1948).

[523] Karrer and Schmid, *Helv. Chim. Acta*, **27**, 119 (1944).

[524] Lutz and Wilson, *J. Org. Chem.*, **12**, 767 (1947).

[525] King and Work, *J. Chem. Soc.*, 1307 (1940).

[526] Ruggli and Knecht, *Helv. Chim. Acta*, **27**, 1108 (1944).

[527] Burger and Harnest, *J. Am. Chem. Soc.*, **65**, 2382 (1943).

[528] Marvel, *Org. Syntheses*, **20**, 106 (1940).

[529] Marvel, *Org. Syntheses*, 21, 74 (1941); cf. ref. 537.

[530] Clarke and Taylor, *Org. Syntheses,* Coll. Vol. I, 115 (1941); cf. ref. 537.

[531] Ahlberg, *J. prakt. Chem.,* **135,** 282 (1932).

[532] Hurd and Cashion, *J. Am. Chem. Soc.,* **65,** 2037 (1943); cf. ref. 537.

[533] Bernhard and Lincke, *Helv. Chim. Acta,* **29,** 1462 (1946).

[534] Homeyer, Whitmore, and Wallingford, *J. Am. Chem. Soc.,* **55,** 4209 (1933).

[535] Berger, *J. prakt. Chem.,* **152,** 315 (1939).

[536] Grewe, *Ber.,* **76,** 1081 (1943).

[537] Marvel and Du Vigneaud, *Org. Syntheses,* Coll. Vol. II, 93 (1943).

[538] Kandiah, *J. Chem. Soc.,* 1215 (1932).

[539] Bergs, *Ber.,* **63,** 1291 (1930).

[540] Fling, Minard, and Fox, *J. Am. Chem. Soc.,* **69,** 2466 (1947); cf. ref. 372.

[541] Zanden, *Rec. trav. chim.,* **53,** 477 (1934).

[542] Zanden, *Rec. trav. chim.,* **63,** 113 (1944).

[543] Goss and Ingold, *J. Chem. Soc.,* 1471 (1926).

[544] Natelson and Gottfried, *Org. Syntheses,* **23,** 37 (1943).

[545] Vogel, *J. Chem. Soc.,* 648 (1948).

[546] Saunders and Stacey, *J. Chem. Soc.,* 1773 (1948).

[547] Guest and Goddard, Jr., *J. Am. Chem. Soc.,* **66,** 2074 (1944).

[548] Brockmann, *Ann.,* **521,** 42 (1935).

[549] Buchman et al., *J. Am. Chem. Soc.,* **64,** 2696 (1942).

[550] Schwenk and Papa, *J. Am. Chem. Soc.,* **70,** 3626 (1948).

[551] Palmer and McWheterr, *Org. Syntheses,* Coll. Vol. I, 245 (1941).

[552] Dice and Bowden, *J. Am. Chem. Soc.,* **71,** 3107 (1949).

[553] Burgin, Hearne, and Rust, *Ind. Eng. Chem.,* **33,** 385 (1941).

[554] Datta and Bhoumik, *J. Am. Chem. Soc.,* **43,** 303 (1921).

[555] Schmerling, *J. Am. Chem. Soc.,* **67,** 1438 (1945).

[556] Schmerling, *J. Am. Chem. Soc.,* **68,** 1650 (1946).

[557] Kharasch, Jensen, and Urry, *J. Am. Chem. Soc.,* **69,** 1100 (1947).

[558] Kharasch, Kuderna, and Urry, *J. Org. Chem.,* **13,** 895 (1948); Kharasch and Sage, *ibid.,* **14,** 537 (1949).

[559] Kharasch, Skell, and Fisher, *J. Am. Chem. Soc.,* **70,** 1055 (1948).

[560] Hey and Musgrave, *J. Chem. Soc.,* 3156 (1949).

[561] Aspinall and Baker, *J. Chem. Soc.,* 743 (1950).

[562] Marvel et al., *J. Am. Chem. Soc.,* **63,** 1892 (1941); **66,** 914 (1944).

[563] Lucas and Garner, *J. Am. Chem. Soc.,* **72,** 2145 (1950).

[564] Young, Cristol, and Skei, *J. Am. Chem. Soc.,* **65,** 2099 (1943).

[565] Joseph, Ross, and Vulliet, *J. Chem. Education,* **26,** 329 (1949).

[566] Cason, Wallcave, and Whiteside, *J. Org. Chem.,* **14,** 37 (1949).

[567] Jacobs and Florsheim, *J. Am. Chem. Soc.,* **72,** 256 (1950).

[568] Hatch and Nesbitt, *J. Am. Chem. Soc.,* **72,** 727 (1950).

[569] Colonge and Garnier, *Bull. soc. chim. France,* (5) **15,** 436 (1948).

[570] Degering and Boatright, *J. Am. Chem. Soc.,* **72,** 5137 (1950).

[571] Owen and Roberts, *J. Chem. Soc.,* 325 (1949).

[572] Ames, Bowman, and Mason, *J. Chem. Soc.,* 174 (1950).

[573] Katchalski and Ishai, *J. Org. Chem.,* **15,** 1070 (1950).

[574] Crombie and Harper, *J. Chem. Soc.,* 2688 (1950).

[575] Hurd and McPhee, *J. Am. Chem. Soc.,* **71,** 398 (1949).

[576] Prelog, El-Neweihy, and Häfliger, *Helv. Chim. Acta,* **33,** 1937 (1950).

[577] Henbest, Jones, and Walls, *J. Chem. Soc.,* 2699 (1949).

[578] Eglinton and Whiting, *J. Chem. Soc.,* 3650 (1950).

[579] Golse, *Ann. chim.*, (2) **548**, 554 (1948).
[580] Theilacker and Wendtland, *Ann.*, **570**, 49 (1950).
[581] Sherman and Amstutz, *J. Am. Chem. Soc.*, 72, 2195 (1950).
[582] Blicke and Sheets, *J. Am. Chem. Soc.*, 71, 2856 (1949).
[583] Elderfield, Pitt, and Wempen, *J. Am. Chem. Soc.*, 72, 1342 (1950).
[584] Kyrides et al., *J. Am. Chem. Soc.*, 72, 747 (1950).
[585] Ultee, *Rec. trav. chim.*, **68**, 125 (1949).
[586] Walborsky, *J. Am. Chem. Soc.*, 71, 2941 (1949).
[587] Wibaut, Sixma, and Suyver, *Rec. trav. chim.*, **68**, 525, 915 (1949).
[588] Lew and Noller, *Org. Syntheses*, **30**, 53 (1950).
[589] Vaughan et al., *J. Org. Chem.*, **14**, 230 (1949).
[590] Sloviter, *J. Am. Chem. Soc.*, 71, 3360 (1949).
[591] Sayles and Degering, *J. Am. Chem. Soc.*, 71, 3161 (1949).
[592] Hussey and Wilk, *J. Am. Chem. Soc.*, 72, 830 (1950).
[593] Derbyshire and Waters, *J. Chem. Soc.*, 3694 (1950).
[594] Groggins, *Unit Processes in Organic Chemistry*, McGraw-Hill Book Co., New York, 1947, pp. 168–259; McBee and Pierce, *Ind. Eng. Chem.*, **42**, 1694 (1950).
[595] Sandin and Cairns, *Org. Syntheses*, Coll. Vol. II, 604 (1943).
[596] Aitken, Badger, and Cook, *J. Chem. Soc.*, 331 (1950).
[597] Kubiczek and Neugebauer, *Monatsh.*, **81**, 917 (1950).
[598] Horning, Horning, and Platt, *J. Am. Chem. Soc.*, 72, 2731 (1950).
[599] Rhoad and Flory, *J. Am. Chem. Soc.*, 72, 2216 (1950).
[600] Wood, Perry, and Tung, *J. Am. Chem. Soc.*, 72, 2989 (1950).
[601] Gilman and Summers, *J. Am. Chem. Soc.*, 72, 2767 (1950).
[602] Straus, Kollek, and Heyn, *Ber.*, **63**, 1868 (1930).
[603] Stone and Shechter, *J. Org. Chem.*, **15**, 491 (1950); *Org. Syntheses*, **31**, 31, 66 (1951).
[604] Buckle, Pattison, and Saunders, *J. Chem. Soc.*, 1476 (1949).
[605] Blicke, Wright, and Zienty, *J. Am. Chem. Soc.*, **63**, 2488 (1941).
[606] Starr and Hixon, *Org. Syntheses*, Coll. Vol. II, 571 (1943).
[607] Saunders, Stacey, and Wilding, *J. Chem. Soc.*, 773 (1949); Hoffmann, *J. Org. Chem.*, **15**, 430 (1950).
[608] Ford-Moore, *Org. Syntheses*, **30**, 11 (1950).
[609] Leonard and Goode, *J. Am. Chem. Soc.*, 72, 5404 (1950).
[610] Smith and Hull, *J. Am. Chem. Soc.*, 72, 3309 (1950).
[611] Dauben and Tilles, *J. Am. Chem. Soc.*, 72, 3185 (1950); Barnes and Prochaska, *ibid.*, 72, 3188 (1950).
[612] Henne and Finnegan, *J. Am. Chem. Soc.*, 72, 3806 (1950).
[613] Oldham, *J. Chem. Soc.*, 100 (1950).
[614] Ecke, Cook, and Whitmore, *J. Am. Chem. Soc.*, 72, 1511 (1950).
[615] Buckles, Steinmetz, and Wheeler, *J. Am. Chem. Soc.*, 72, 2496 (1950).
[616] Evans and Morgan, *J. Am. Chem. Soc.*, **35**, 54 (1913).
[617] Ames and Bowman, *J. Chem. Soc.*, 406 (1950); cf. ref. 159.
[618] Skinner, Limperos, and Pettebone, *J. Am. Chem. Soc.*, 72, 1648 (1950).
[619] Taylor and Morey, *Ind. Eng. Chem.*, **40**, 432 (1948).
[620] Jacobson, *J. Am. Chem. Soc.*, 72, 1489 (1950).
[621] Brandon, Derfer, and Boord, *J. Am. Chem. Soc.*, 72, 2120 (1950).
[622] Seifert et al., *Helv. Chim. Acta*, 33, 732 (1950).
[623] Braude and Coles, *J. Chem. Soc.*, 2014 (1950).
[624] Lora-Tamayo et al., *J. Chem. Soc.*, 1418 (1950).

[625] Bateman et al., *J. Chem. Soc.*, 936, 941 (1950).
[626] Donahoe and Vanderwerf, *Org. Syntheses*, 30, 24 (1950).
[627] Colonge and Cumet, *Bull. soc. chim. France*, (5) 14, 838 (1947).
[628] Dolliver et al., *J. Am. Chem. Soc.*, 60, 440 (1938).
[629] Irwin and Hennion, *J. Am. Chem. Soc.*, 63, 858 (1941).
[630] Winstein and Henderson, *J. Am. Chem. Soc.*, 65, 2196 (1943).
[631] Cristol and Eilar, *J. Am. Chem. Soc.*, 72, 4353 (1950).
[632] Winstein and Henderson in Elderfield's *Heterocyclic Compounds*, John Wiley & Sons, New York, 1950, Vol. I, pp. 22–42.
[633] Hall and Ubertini, *J. Org. Chem.*, 15, 715 (1950).
[634] Weygand and Schmied-Kowarzik, *Chem. Ber.*, 82, 333 (1949).
[635] Wagner and Moore, *J. Am. Chem. Soc.*, 72, 2884 (1950).
[636] Cohen, Wolosinski, and Scheuer, *J. Am. Chem. Soc.*, 72, 3952 (1950).
[637] Aston et al., *Org. Syntheses*, 23, 48 (1943).
[638] Mentzer and Pillon, *Bull. soc. chim. France*, (5) 17, 809 (1950).
[639] Heilbron et al., *J. Chem. Soc.*, 737 (1949).
[640] Hartung and Adkins, *J. Am. Chem. Soc.*, 49, 2517 (1927); McElvain, Clarke, and Jones, *ibid.*, 64, 1966 (1942).
[641] Kuhn and Grundmann, *Ber.*, 70, 1894 (1937); Fisher, Ertel, and Lowenberg, *ibid.*, 64, 30 (1931).
[642] Bedoukian, *J. Am. Chem. Soc.*, 66, 1325 (1944); *Org. Syntheses*, 29, 14 (1949).
[643] Bedoukian, *J. Am. Chem. Soc.*, 67, 1430 (1945).
[644] Wagner and Tome, *J. Am. Chem. Soc.*, 72, 3477 (1950).
[645] Wagner and Moore, *J. Am. Chem. Soc.*, 72, 3655 (1950).
[646] Arens and van Dorp, *Rec. trav. chim.*, 66, 409 (1947).
[647] Kharasch and Brown, *J. Am. Chem. Soc.*, 62, 925 (1940).
[648] Wagner and Moore, *J. Am. Chem. Soc.*, 72, 974 (1950).
[649] Shriner and Damschroder, *J. Am. Chem. Soc.*, 60, 894 (1938).
[650] Phillips, *J. Chem. Soc.*, 222 (1942).
[651] Levine and Stephens, *J. Am. Chem. Soc.*, 72, 1642 (1950).
[652] Harmon et al., *J. Am. Chem. Soc.*, 72, 2213 (1950).
[653] Emerson, Deebel, and Longley, *J. Org. Chem.*, 14, 696 (1949).
[654] Schmerling, *J. Am. Chem. Soc.*, 67, 1152 (1945).
[655] Coleman, *J. Am. Chem. Soc.*, 55, 3001 (1933).
[656] Jackson, Smart and Wright, *J. Am. Chem. Soc.*, 69, 1539 (1947).
[657] Klages et al., *Ann.*, 547, 25 (1941).
[658] Schöpf et al., *Ann.*, 559, 22 (1947).
[659] Farlow, *Org. Syntheses*, Coll. Vol. II, 312 (1943).
[660] Calcott, Tinker, and Weinmayr, *J. Am. Chem. Soc.*, 61, 1010 (1939).
[661] Adams and Garber, *J. Am. Chem. Soc.*, 71, 525 (1949).
[662] Bruce and Todd, *J. Am. Chem. Soc.*, 61, 157 (1939).
[663] Marvel et al., *J. Am. Chem. Soc.*, 68, 863 (1946).
[664] Emerson and Lucas, *J. Am. Chem. Soc.*, 70, 1180 (1948).
[665] Hennion and Pieronek, *J. Am. Chem. Soc.*, 64, 2751 (1942).
[666] Hauser and Hudson, *Org. Syntheses*, 23, 102 (1943).
[667] Smith in *Organic Reactions*, Vol. 1, John Wiley & Sons, New York, 1942, p. 383.
[668] Speer and Hill, *J. Org. Chem.*, 2, 143 (1937).
[669] Pope and Bogert, *J. Org. Chem.*, 2, 280 (1937).

[670] Mann and Watson, *J. Chem. Soc.*, 508 (1947).

[671] Bradsher, *J. Am. Chem. Soc.*, **62**, 486 (1940).

[672] Brown and Marvel, *J. Am. Chem. Soc.*, **59**, 1176 (1937).

[673] Marvel and Botteron, *J. Am. Chem. Soc.*, **63**, 1482 (1941).

[674] Marvel, Kaplan, and Himel, *J. Am. Chem. Soc.*, **63**, 1894 (1941).

[675] Marvel, Allan, and Overberger, *J. Am. Chem. Soc.*, **68**, 1088 (1946).

[676] Gomberg and Bachman, *Org. Syntheses*, Coll. Vol. I, 113 (1941).

[677] Gilman, Kirby, and Kinney, *J. Am. Chem. Soc.*, **51**, 2260 (1929).

[678] Marvel, Ginsberg, and Mueller, *J. Am. Chem. Soc.*, **61**, 77 (1939).

[679] Bigelow, Johnson, and Sandborn, *Org. Syntheses*, Coll. Vol. I, 133 (1941).

[680] Haworth and Barker, *J. Chem. Soc.*, 1302 (1939).

[681] Gilman and Van Ess, *J. Am. Chem. Soc.*, **61**, 1369 (1939).

[682] Huber et al., *J. Am. Chem. Soc.*, **68**, 1109 (1946).

[683] Coleman and Talbot, *Org. Syntheses*, Coll. Vol. II, 592 (1943).

[684] Bartlett et al., *J. Am. Chem. Soc.*, **72**, 1003 (1950).

[685] Huntress, *Organic Chlorine Compounds*, John Wiley & Sons, New York, 1948.

[686] Simons, *Fluorine Chemistry*, Vol. I, Academic Press, New York, 1950; Bockemüller and Wiechert in *New Methods of Preparative Organic Chemistry*, Interscience Publishers, New York, 1948, pp. 229–245, 315–362; Henne in Gilman's *Organic Chemistry*, Vol. I, John Wiley & Sons, New York, 1948, pp. 944–964.

[687] Lecocq, *Ann. chim.*, (12) **3**, 79 (1948); Zeigler et al., *Ann.*, **551**, 109 (1942).

[688] Meinel, *Ann.*, **516**, 242 (1935).

[689] Hodges, *J. Chem. Soc.*, 241 (1933).

[690] Hauser and Renfrow, *J. Am. Chem. Soc.*, **59**, 122 (1937).

[691] Winstein and Henderson, *J. Am. Chem. Soc.*, **65**, 2198 (1943).

[692] Holmes and Mann, *J. Am. Chem. Soc.*, **69**, 2001 (1947).

[693] Buckles and Wheeler, *Org. Syntheses*, **31**, 29 (1951).

[694] Herzog, *Org. Syntheses*, **31**, 82 (1951).

[695] Oliveto and Gerold, *Org. Syntheses*, **31**, 17 (1951).

[696] Hall, Stephens, and Burckhalter, *Org. Syntheses*, **31**, 37 (1951).

5

Hydroxy Compounds

CONTENTS

79. Reduction of Aldehydes and Ketones

$$RCHO \xrightarrow{(H)} RCH_2OH$$
$$RCOR' \xrightarrow{(H)} RCHOHR'$$

This method is widely used for the preparation of secondary alcohols from ketones. The reduction of aldehydes is important only when these substances are readily available, e.g., heptanal and furfural.

Catalytic reduction procedures give excellent yields. Special apparatus for hydrogenation has been described.[30,87] Platinum oxide catalyst is generally useful for the reduction of carbonyl compounds[89,97,108] but is unsatisfactory for certain ketones.[113] Nickel catalysts have been used extensively.[91,122,137,138,568,676] The most promising of these is the highly active W-6 Raney nickel, which permits hydrogenation in glass apparatus at low temperatures and pressures.[111,140] The rate of hydrogenation with this catalyst is increased markedly by the addition of a small amount of triethylamine.[111] Other catalysts include copper-chromium oxide,[99,674] sometimes fortified with barium,[134,139] and a copper-alumina catalyst used successfully for the preparation of a series of alkylphenylcarbinols.[114] Great selectivity is possible by varying the catalyst and conditions. In this respect, hydrogenation of β-furylacrolein is interesting. The furan ring is not reduced over copper-chromium oxide in the preparation of 3-(α-furyl)-1-propanol (72%).[95] With Raney nickel the double bond may be reduced first (46%),[95] then the aldehyde group (80%),[100] and finally the nucleus to give 3-(tetrahydrofuryl)-1-propanol (80%).[95]

The new metallic hydrides are excellent reducing agents for carbonyl compounds. These hydrides now include lithium aluminum hydride,[4,800] lithium borohydride,[3] and sodium borohydride.[2] The last reagent may be used in either aqueous or methanolic solutions. It does not reduce esters, acids, or nitriles and, for this reason, is superior for certain selective reductions. Other groups which are unaffected by this reagent include α,β-double bonds and hydroxyl, methoxyl, nitro, and dimethylamino groups.[2]

A convenient procedure for the reduction of small amounts of ketones involves the periodic addition of small pieces of sodium to a slowly stirred mixture of an ethereal[121] or benzene[113] solution of the ketone and water or a concentrated solution of sodium carbonate. Sodium and alcohol are used for the conversion of methyl n-amyl ketone to 2-heptanol (65%).[115] These reagents are used to prepare secondary alcohols from olefinic ketones obtained by the aldol condensation.[212,218] Benzophenone and related compounds are reduced by zinc dust and sodium hydroxide,[118] magnesium and methanol,[120] and sodium amalgam.[119] With the last reagent the reaction has been shown to take place through the intermediate sodium ketyl, $(C_6H_5)_2$CONa.

Less basic reagents which are more suitable for the reduction of aldehydes include iron and acetic acid[88,94] and aluminum amalgam in alcohol.[90,103]

A review of electrolytic reduction of carbonyl compounds was made in 1948.[677]

Both exo- and endo-cyclic alicyclic and heterocyclic ketones have been reduced. Important examples are found in the preparations of cyclopentanol (95%),[128] cycloheptanol (92%),[122] β-pyridylmethylcarbinol (85%),[136] and 1-alkyl-4-piperidinols (90%).[133] A comparison of four reagents—sodium and alcohol, lithium aluminum hydride, hydrogen and Raney nickel, and hydrogen and copper-chromium oxide—has been made in the preparation of methyl cyclopropylcarbinol. The last method is superior for the preparation of this compound (90%).[117]

The reduction of aldols and ketols from the aldol condensation (method 102) is often a convenient route to branched 1,3-*diols*. Catalytic hydrogenation over platinum oxide,[142] nickel-on-kieselguhr,[138,145] and copper-chromium oxide[99] has been used. Other procedures include electrolytic reduction[209]and reduction by aluminum amalgam.[103] 1,3-Diols may also be prepared by catalytic reduction of 1,3-diketones. Cleavage of the carbon-to-carbon and carbon-to-oxygen bonds accompanies this conversion. The effect of structure on the course of the reaction has been studied.[144]

1,2-Diols may be prepared by reduction of α-diketones or α-hydroxy ketones such as biacetyl,[2,146] benzoin, and benzil.[2,138] Substituted benzoins containing methoxyl and p-dimethylamino groups have been reduced catalytically over platinum oxide and by sodium amalgam and alcohol.[147] Levorotatory propylene glycol is made from acetol, CH_3COCH_2OH, by an enzymatic reduction with yeast.[141]

Glycols in which the hydroxyl groups are farther apart have also been prepared by this method from a γ-diketone[2] and a δ-hydroxy aldehyde.[102]

The reduction of a carbonyl compound containing an additional functional group is a common practice. If the other group is easily reduced, best results are frequently obtained by the Meerwein-Ponndorf-Verley reaction (method 80). The following paragraphs, however, describe certain useful selective reductions.

The best reagents for reduction of olefinic aldehydes to *olefinic alcohols* are lithium aluminum hydride and sodium borohydride. Crotyl alcohol, $CH_3CH=CHCH_2OH$, and cinnamyl alcohol, $C_6H_5CH=CHCH_2OH$, have been prepared in excellent yields.[2,4] Cinnamyl alcohol is further reduced at higher temperatures to hydrocinnamyl alcohol.[105] Citral, $(CH_3)_2C=CHCH_2CH_2C(CH_3)=CHCHO$, may be selectively reduced to the corresponding dienol by catalytic hydrogenation over platinum catalyst.[92] A new method for the preparation of enediol esters of the type

$$RO_2CC(OH)=C(OH)CO_2R$$

involves the partial reduction of diketosuccinic esters with sodium hydrosulfite.[149]

Halo alcohols in which the halogen atom is on an aliphatic chain[73,150] or an aromatic nucleus[151,152] are prepared from the corresponding halo ketones by catalytic hydrogenation. Sodium borohydride effects the conversion of ω-bromoacetophenone to styrene bromohydrin (71%).[2] Other halohydrins have been made from α-halo ketones and lithium aluminum hydride.[680]

The ether linkage is stable during the reduction of an aldehyde or ketone group by most reagents. A number of *alkoxy* and *aryloxy alcohols* are prepared in excellent yields by this method. Catalytic hydrogenation,[91,107,108,110,155] sodium and wet ether,[153] and sodium with alcohol[154] have been used.

Hydroxy ketones of the type $RCOCH_2CHOHCH_3$ are formed in 35–66% yields by partial catalytic hydrogenation of the corresponding β-diketones over Raney nickel at 100°.[158] Aromatic α-hydroxy ketones (benzoins) are prepared from the corresponding α-diketones (benzils) by catalytic reduction[156] or by reduction with magnesium-magnesium iodide mixture.[157]

The keto group of a keto ester may be preferentially reduced by catalytic hydrogenation. Excellent yields of *hydroxy esters* are obtained. Copper-chromium oxide catalyst has been employed in the preparation of methyl p-(α-hydroxyethyl)-benzoate[160] and several aliphatic β-hydroxy esters.[99] The last compounds have also been made by hydrogenation over nickel catalysts.[161,165] Substituted mandelic esters are prepared by catalytic reduction of aromatic α-keto esters over a palladium catalyst.[159,162] Similarly, platinum oxide and copper-chromium oxide have been used in the aliphatic series for the preparation of the α-hydroxy diester, diethyl

β-methylmalate (92%).[163] The keto group may also be in the *gamma* position to the ester group, which may be in the form of acetoxy, $CH_3COO—$, or carbethoxy, $—CO_2C_2H_5$, γ-hydroxy esters being formed by hydrogenation over nickel catalysts.[137,164]

Certain aryl-substituted α- and β-amino ketones have been successfully reduced to *amino alcohols* by catalytic hydrogenation over palladium,[166,183] platinum,[167,169] or nickel[170] catalysts. Cleavage of the carbon chain sometimes occurs during catalytic hydrogenation of β-amino ketones. Fair yields of the amino alcohols are obtained in these cases by reduction with sodium amalgam in dilute acid[171,182,185] or aluminum amalgam and water.[168,184] β-Amino aldehydes from the Mannich reaction (method 444) are reduced in excellent yields to amino alcohols by lithium aluminum hydride or by catalytic hydrogenation over Raney nickel.[675] Lithium aluminum hydride reduces diazo ketones to 1-amino-2-alkanols (93–99%).[672]

80. Reduction of Carbonyl Compounds by Alcohols (Meerwein-Ponndorf-Verley)

$$RCHO + (CH_3)_2CHOH \underset{}{\overset{Al[OCH(CH_3)_2]_3}{\rightleftharpoons}} RCH_2OH + CH_3COCH_3$$

The reduction of an aldehyde or ketone by this equilibrium reaction is readily accomplished by removal of the acetone as it is formed. In a review of the literature to 1943, experimental conditions and limitations of the reaction have been discussed.[173] Aluminum isopropoxide is superior to other metallic alkoxides that have been used. Yields are better, and the technique for determining the completion of the reaction is simpler. Procedures for the preparation of the reagent are described.[173,175,177] A solution made by dissolving amalgamated aluminum in isopropyl alcohol is used directly, or the aluminum isopropoxide is purified by distillation. Best results are obtained when molecular amounts of the alkoxide are used.

A modification of the procedure has been described in which improved yields of alcohols are obtained from aldehydes and unstable ketones.[686]

The reaction is most useful for the preparation of *olefinic, halo,* and *nitro* alcohols from the corresponding substituted aldehydes and ketones. These substituents are very often affected by other reduction procedures. Excellent directions are found in the preparations of crotyl alcohol (60%),[175] 1-bromo-5-hexanol (64%),[192] 1-chloro-4-pentanol (76%),[164] β,β,β-trichloroethyl alcohol (84%),[253] methyl-p-chlorophenylcarbinol (81%),[193] and o-nitrobenzyl alcohol (90%).[195] The reaction has also been used in the preparation of certain tetralols[178] and decalols[177] as well as 9-fluorenylcarbinol (50%).[181] The thiophene[134,180] and furan[251] nuclei are not reduced.

81. Intramolecular Oxidation-Reduction of Aldehydes (Cannizzaro)

$$2R_3CCHO + NaOH \rightarrow R_3CCO_2Na + R_3CCH_2OH$$

Aldehydes that have no α-hydrogen atom react with concentrated aqueous or alcoholic alkali to give alcohols and salts of acids. The literature of this reaction has been reviewed to 1944.[504] The preparation of carboxylic acids by this procedure is discussed elsewhere (method 261), and a similar reaction of aldehydes that have an α-hydrogen atom is treated separately (method 306).

The reaction is most important for the preparation of carbinols from certain aromatic and heterocyclic[504,508] aldehydes and for the preparation of several aliphatic polyhydroxy compounds. In the normal Cannizzaro reaction the theoretical yield of alcohol is only 50% because half of the aldehyde is converted to the acid. A mixture of an aldehyde with excess formaldehyde, however, results in a dismutation in which most of the higher aldehyde is reduced; formaldehyde is oxidized to sodium formate, viz.,[510]

$$RCHO + HCHO + NaOH \rightarrow RCH_2OH + HCO_2Na$$

Excellent directions are given for the preparation of p-tolylcarbinol (72%).[513] The aryl radical may contain alkyl, halo, hydroxyl, methoxyl, and nitro groups.[504]

The crossed aldol condensation of formaldehyde with aldehydes that have α-hydrogen atoms results in the replacement of these hydrogen atoms by hydroxymethyl groups. The β-hydroxyaldehydes are then reduced to polyhydric alcohols by excess formaldehyde.

$$RCH_2CHO \xrightarrow[\text{Ca(OH)}_2]{\text{2HCHO}} RC(CH_2OH)_2CHO \xrightarrow[\text{Ca(OH)}_2]{\text{HCHO}} RC(CH_2OH)_3$$

Pentaerythritol, $C(CH_2OH)_4$, is obtained in this way from acetaldehyde and formaldehyde (74%).[509] Higher aldehydes give trimethylol compounds,[507,762] and aldehydes with branching on the α-carbon atom give dimethylol compounds or β,β-disubstituted trimethylene glycols,

$$RR'C(CH_2OH)_2.^{506,512}$$

Cyclohexanone gives a tetramethylolcyclohexanol.[798]

82. Bimolecular Reduction of Carbonyl Compounds to Glycols

$$2RCOR' \xrightarrow[\text{H}_2\text{O}]{\text{Mg(Hg)}x;} RR'COHCOHRR'$$

Tetraalkyl- and tetraaryl-ethylene glycols (pinacols) are made by reduction of ketones with active metals such as sodium, magnesium, and aluminum. The reaction is only fair for aliphatic and alicyclic ketones. Acetone,[587] methyl ethyl ketone,[592] cyclopentanone, and cyclohexanone[593] all give less than 50% yields of pinacols. Mixtures of ketones are reduced to unsymmetrical pinacols.[727] An active zinc-copper couple has been employed in the reduction of several simple olefinic aldehydes to diendiols, e.g., crotonaldehyde to dipropenyl glycol,

$$CH_3CH = CHCHOHCHOHCH = CHCH_3 \ (67\%).[728]$$

Diaryl ketones are reduced by a mixture of magnesium and magnesium iodide[590] and by alkali metal amalgams.[588,589] Metal ketyls, $Ar_2C\text{—}OMgX$, are intermediates which associate to pinacolates, $Ar_2C(OMgX)C(OMgX)Ar_2$, from which the pinacols are obtained by hydrolysis. The association of the ketyl radicals is reversible,[589,590] as is shown by reaction of benzopinacolate with benzaldehyde to give triphenylethylene glycol and benzophenone.[594]

$$(C_6H_5)_2C(OMgX)C(OMgX)(C_6H_5)_2 \xrightarrow[H_2O]{C_6H_5CHO;} (C_6H_5)_2CO$$
$$+ \ (C_6H_5)_2COHCHOHC_6H_5$$

A novel preparation of benzopinacol, $(C_6H_5)_2COHCOH(C_6H_5)_2$, is by reduction of benzophenone with isopropyl alcohol in the presence of sunlight (95%).[591]

Aromatic aldehydes and ketones may also be reduced electrolytically to glycols.[104,677,726]

83. Reduction of Quinones

o- and p-Benzoquinones are reduced to dihydroxybenzenes by cold aqueous solutions of sulfur dioxide. The reaction is accompanied, however, by appreciable sulfonation of the benzene ring in the case of p-benzo-

quinone.[635] The reduction has its greatest value in the preparation of dihydroxy derivatives of alkylated benzenes and naphthalenes from the
corresponding quinones. Reduction by zinc in refluxing acetic acid converts o-xyloquinone to o-xylohydroquinone (95%).[631] A saturated solution
of sodium hydrosulfite gives better yields in the preparation of the *para*
isomer.[630] Reductions by stannous chloride and by sodium hydrosulfite
are compared in the preparation of 2-methyl-1,4-naphthohydroquinone.
The product obtained by sodium hydrosulfite darkens more rapidly in
storage.[632] Sodium hydrosulfite is better than sulfur dioxide in the reduction of β-naphthoquinone [633] and is also used in the preparation of
2,3,5-trimethylhydroquinone.[634] Several o-quinones have been reduced by
lithium aluminum hydride to give *trans*-dihydroxydihydro derivatives of
the hydrocarbons.[729] p-Benzoquinone is reduced by this reagent to hydroquinone (70%).[44]

84. Reduction of Carboxylic Acids and Esters

$$RCO_2C_2H_5 \xrightarrow{(H)} RCH_2OH$$

The discovery of lithium aluminum hydride and similar compounds[2,3]
has made possible the direct reduction of the carboxyl group.[75,77] Acid
chlorides, esters, and anhydrides are similarly reduced to primary alcohols.[4] Lactones are converted to diols.[44] The reaction takes place
readily at room temperature. The compound to be reduced is added to an
ethereal solution of the reagent, and the resulting alcoholate is hydrolyzed
by acid.

$$2RCO_2C_2H_5 \xrightarrow{LiAlH_4} LiAl(OC_2H_5)_2(OCH_2R)_2 \xrightarrow{H^+} 2RCH_2OH$$

Alcohols containing heterocyclic nuclei,[57,63] halo,[74,75] and alkoxyl [76–78]
groups as well as double bonds [71,72] may be prepared. Without doubt, this
is the best general procedure for the formation of the primary alcohol
grouping from compounds at the oxidation level of a carboxylic acid. Reductions by this reagent were reviewed in 1951.[800]

The reduction of esters by sodium and alcohol (Bouveault-Blanc) is
widely used. An alcoholic solution of the ester is added to a large excess of sodium under benzene [13] or toluene.[5] The use of absolute alcohol
is essential; otherwise an appreciable quantity of acid is produced by
saponification.[1] Straight-chain primary alcohols containing up to thirty-
five carbon atoms have been made by the reduction of the corresponding
esters with sodium sand and n-butyl alcohol.[26] An improved technique
based on the mechanism of the reaction is described.[12] By this procedure
a xylene solution of the ester and the reducing alcohol is added to molten

sodium in refluxing xylene. Secondary alcohols are best since they are active enough to decompose the intermediate sodium ketyls but do not react rapidly with sodium to produce molecular hydrogen.

Most esters can be converted to primary alcohols in exceptionally high yields by catalytic hydrogenation over copper-chromium oxide at 200-250° (Adkins). This is an equilibrium reaction which is forced to completion by the high pressure of hydrogen gas.[51] The special apparatus, catalysts, and factors influencing yield have been discussed.[30,33] In the hydrogenation of ethyl phenylacetate, $C_6H_5CH_2CO_2C_2H_5$, to β-phenylethanol, some ethylbenzene is produced. Best yields are obtained if hydrogenation is stopped while 5-10% of the ester is still present.[20] Hydrogenation of ethyl benzoate under the usual conditions gives toluene. With relatively large amounts of catalyst, however, hydrogenation proceeds at lower temperatures to give benzyl alcohol (63%).[23] Substituted benzyl alcohols[23] and naphthylcarbinols[28] are obtained in a similar manner. Esters of phenol give cyclohexanol and primary alcohols.[14] Nickel catalysts have also been used for the reduction of higher-molecular-weight esters.[32] The free fatty acids have been reduced over copper catalysts.[35]

Optically active esters in which the activity is due to asymmetry of the α-carbon atom are racemized by the Bouveault-Blanc and catalytic hydrogenation procedures.[31] The optically active alcohols may be prepared by the addition of small pieces of sodium to a stirred mixture of an ethereal solution of the ester and aqueous sodium acetate at 0°. A slight acidity is maintained by periodic additions of acetic acid (Prin's method).[6,11] An asymmetric center in the *alpha* position to a carboxyl group is not racemized by lithium aluminum hydride.[656]

Under certain conditions the reduction of amides leads to primary alcohols (cf. method 428). Thus, phenylethylacetamide is reduced by sodium and absolute ethanol to 2-phenyl-1-butanol (75%).[22] α-Naphthylacetamide is reduced by sodium amalgam and hydrochloric acid to α-naphthylcarbinol (63%).[29] Trifluoroethanol is obtained by catalytic hydrogenation of trifluoroacetamide over a platinum catalyst. Hydrogenation of the corresponding ester over copper-chromium oxide failed.[73]

Certain heterocyclic carbinols are readily prepared from the corresponding esters. The furan nucleus is not reduced by the Bouveault-Blanc procedure.[54,56] However, the pyridine nucleus as well as the carbethoxyl group in the ethyl ester of nicotinic or picolinic acid is reduced by sodium and ethanol.[58,59] Catalytic hydrogenation of several carbethoxypyrroles over copper-chromium oxide gives methyl pyrroles and pyrrolidines rather than the carbinols.[30] The same catalyst has been used in the hydrogenation of piperidino esters of the type $C_5H_{10}N(CH_2)_nCO_2C_2H_5$. Yields are poor when n is 2 or 3. When n is 2, cleavage occurs to give piperidine and ethyl propionate.[15,61] The lactam linkage in carbethoxypyrrolidones and carbethoxypiperidones is stable during catalytic hydrogenation of the ester group to the carbinol group.[62] Lithium aluminum hydride has been used to reduce ethyl indole-2-carboxylate to 2-hydroxymethylindole (68%),[57] thianaphthene-2-carboxylic acid to 2-hydroxymethylthianaphthene (99%),[63] and 3-furoic acid to 3-furylcarbinol (91%).[659]

Both the Bouveault-Blanc[39,41] and catalytic hydrogenation procedures[38,40] are popular methods for the preparation of *diols* from esters of dibasic acids. The reduction of malonic esters, β-keto esters, and β-hydroxy esters by the usual catalytic hydrogenation procedure results in extensive hydrogenolysis of the carbon chain to give lower-molecular-weight alcohols.[30,46] However, with relatively large amounts of catalyst 1,3-glycols are obtained in fair yields.[15,50] Decarboxylation of 1,1-dicarbethoxycyclobutane during its reduction by sodium and alcohol gives cyclobutylcarbinol in 49% yield rather than the diol.[25] Lactones are reduced to diols by lithium aluminum hydride as in the preparation of 1,4-pentanediol (85%) from γ-valerolactone.[43] The tertiary lactones prepared from Grignard reagents and levulinic ester are reduced by the Bouveault-Blanc procedure to glycols of the type $R(CH_3)C(OH)(CH_2)_3OH$. However, catalytic hydrogenation gives branched alcohols of the type $R(CH_3)CH(CH_2)_3OH$.[45] Esters of dibasic acids are reduced to diols in good yields by lithium aluminum hydride.[655,662]

Olefinic alcohols are best prepared by the action of lithium aluminum hydride on the corresponding acid[666] or ester as in the preparation of 3-penten-1-ol (75%).[71] The double bond may be in the α,β-position to the ester group.[72,657] The Bouveault-Blanc procedure has also been used with success for reduction of nonconjugated olefinic esters.[64,66] The addition of the sodium to an alcoholic solution of the ester is superior to the reverse addition of the ester to sodium in toluene for the preparation of 2,2-dimethyl-3-buten-1-ol (62%).[70] Selective catalytic hydrogenation is inferior. Large amounts of catalyst are required, and the products contain saturated alcohols.[69]

Lithium aluminum hydride shows much promise for the preparation of *halo*[74,75] and *alkoxy*[76–78] *alcohols*, although the Bouveault-Blanc method is satisfactory for the latter.

The *keto* group of acetoacetic ester is protected as the ethylene ketal during the reduction of the ester by sodium and alcohol. Hydrolysis of the ketal by acid then gives 1-hydroxy-3-butanone in 44% over-all yield.[669]

Many *amino alcohols* have been made from esters of amino acids by catalytic reductions over Raney nickel[15,84] and copper chromite[83] catalysts. The yields are generally better than those obtained by reduction with sodium and alcohol.[82,86] The action of ammonia or amines on β-keto esters leads to substituted β-aminoacrylates, $RC(NR_2)=CHCO_2C_2H_5$, which are reduced directly by sodium and alcohol to γ-amino alcohols.[85] Electrolytic reduction of anthranilic acid is used to prepare o-aminobenzyl alcohol (78%).[81] Some hydrogenolysis to o-toluidine accompanies the reduction of this acid by lithium aluminum hydride.[661]

85. Reduction of Unsaturated Hydroxy Compounds

$$RCH = CHCHOHR \xrightarrow[\text{Pt}]{H_2} RCH_2CH_2CHOHR$$

Olefinic alcohols react smoothly with hydrogen over platinum oxide catalyst at room temperature.[306] The procedure is illustrated by the preparation of dihydrocholesterol from cholesterol.[652] Cinnamyl alcohol, $C_6H_5CH=CHCH_2OH$, is reduced to dihydrocinnamyl alcohol by lithium aluminum hydride. The reduction of allyl alcohol to n-propyl alcohol by the reagent, however, is unsatisfactory.[105]

Several aliphatic diols and hydroxy ethers have been made by catalytic hydrogenation of the triple bond in the corresponding acetylenic compounds. Both platinum[377] and nickel[653,654] catalysts are used.

86. Reduction of the Aromatic Nucleus

$$C_6H_5OH \xrightarrow[\text{Ni}]{H_2} C_6H_{11}OH$$

This general method for the synthesis of alkyl-[561,568,570,722] and aryl-[573,574] cyclohexanols is limited only by the availability of the phenols. Hydrogenation proceeds smoothly over Raney nickel catalyst at about 150–200° except when both *ortho* positions are substituted by alkyl groups. When these *ortho* substituents are ethyl or n-propyl radicals, reduction is accomplished in the presence of a small amount of aqueous sodium hydroxide.[568] The sodium phenolates are promoters in most hydrogenations of this type.[569] High-pressure hydrogenation at room temperature over platinum oxide catalyst effects nuclear reduction of a number of phenols.[724] Alkylcyclohexanols exhibit geometrical isomerism. Usually only one of the possible geometrical isomers predominates in the product.[568,723]

Hydroquinone is reduced by a nickel-on-kieselguhr catalyst to cis- and trans-1,4-cyclohexanediols.[576] Other cyclohexanediols[577,580,725] and methoxycyclohexanols[575,578] are formed from dihydric phenols and their monomethyl ethers. β-Naphthol may be reduced in either ring, depending upon the catalyst and conditions.[572]

87. Interaction of Organometallic Compounds and Oxygen

$$RMgX \xrightarrow{O_2} ROMgX \xrightarrow[H^+]{H_2O} ROH$$

The oxidation of a Grignard reagent to an alcoholate affords a general method for converting alkyl halides to alcohols. It is particularly useful where direct hydrolysis is difficult or is complicated by elimination of hydrogen halide. Oxidation of the organometallic reagent by air or oxygen is rapid in ether solution at $0°$.[196] Typical examples are found in the preparation of 4,4-dimethyl-1-pentanol (90%)[197] and 2,2,3,3-tetramethyl-1-butanol (53%).[198] The yield of phenol from phenylmagnesium bromide is only 25%.[249] The main by-product is biphenyl, which is formed to the extent of 65% when phenyllithium is used in place of the Grignard compound.[242] The yield of phenol is increased to 64% by the presence of an aliphatic organometallic compound in the reaction mixture.[250] By this technique the first successful preparation of 2-thienol has been achieved,[683] and a number of hydroxydibenzofurans[243-245] and 4-hydroxydibenzothiophene[246] have been prepared in fair yields from the organosodium or lithium compounds.

88. Interaction of Organometallic Compounds and Aldehydes

$$RMgX \xrightarrow{HCHO} RCH_2OMgX \xrightarrow[H^+]{H_2O} RCH_2OH$$

$$RMgX \xrightarrow{R'CHO} RR'CHOMgX \xrightarrow[H^+]{H_2O} RR'CHOH$$

Alkyl- and aryl-magnesium halides react with aldehydes to give halomagnesium alkoxides which are decomposed by dilute acid to yield alcohols. Primary alcohols are formed in 50-70% yields by treatment of primary or secondary Grignard compounds with formaldehyde, and in 30-40% yield in the case of tertiary Grignard reagents.[258] Either gaseous formaldehyde[128,255,268,309] or trioxymethylene[270,285] may be used; the latter reagent is more convenient but usually gives somewhat lower yields. A common by-product is the formal of the alcohol, $CH_2(OR)_2$.[270,285] Most of this by-product can be hydrolyzed if excess dilute acid is added to the Grignard complex before steam distillation of the alcohol.[268]

Benzylmagnesium halides, $C_6H_5CH_2MgX$, react abnormally with formaldehyde to yield o-methylbenzyl alcohol (55%).[281,283] When one *ortho* position is blocked by a methyl group, the rearrangement takes place to the other *ortho* position.[282,283] The influence of structure on this rearrangement has been extensively studied.[689]

Many straight-chain[284] and branched[256,262,267] *secondary* alcohols have been made by the action of organomagnesium compounds on higher aldehydes. The method is popular for the preparation of arylalkylcarbinols from either the aromatic aldehyde or the aromatic Grignard reagent.[265,271,280] Other organometallic compounds have been used with less success. Zinc, aluminum, and boron alkyls give considerable reduction of the aldehyde to the primary alcohol.[317]

Few *diols* have been obtained by this method. An example is the preparation of 2-isopropyl-1,3-butanediol from excess methylmagnesium iodide and 2-isopropyl-3-hydroxypropionaldehyde (72%).[201]

Olefinic primary alcohols are obtained in fair yields by the action of formaldehyde on unsaturated Grignard reagents.[305,306] Crotyl- and cinnamyl-magnesium halides give carbinols derived from the secondary organomagnesium compounds resulting from allylic isomerization.[306,315] Thus, 2-methyl-3-buten-1-ol, $CH_2 = CHCH(CH_3)CH_2OH$, is the sole product from the action of formaldehyde on the butenyl Grignard reagent prepared from a mixture of crotyl and methylvinylcarbinyl bromides.

Olefinic secondary alcohols may be prepared from a Grignard reagent and an olefinic aldehyde or from an olefinic Grignard reagent and a saturated aldehyde. The former method is recommended,[300] although the latter has been used with moderate success for allylmagnesium halides[302,308,692] and vinyllithium compounds.[698] Higher yields have been obtained by adding a mixture of allyl chloride and the aldehyde to a well-stirred suspension of magnesium and ether.[309] Reactions of saturated Grignard compounds with olefinic aldehydes are numerous. Yields vary from 50% to 75%. Acrolein has been treated with methyl-,[293] ethyl-,[301] n-propyl-,[292] n-amyl-,[297] and higher alkyl-magnesium halides.[294] Similar additions have been made to crotonaldehyde[291,295,296,696] and higher homologs.[201,304] Excellent yields of dienols have been obtained by the action of Grignard reagents on pentadienal[311] and sorbic aldehyde.[310] When the Grignard reagent is highly branched, a competing reaction is 1,4-addition to the conjugated system. For example, major products of the reactions of t-butyl and t-amyl Grignard reagents with crotonaldehyde are the saturated aldehydes formed in this manner.[291,328] Aromatic olefinic alcohols have been made from aromatic Grignard reagents or from cinnamaldehyde.[312,313]

Acetylenic carbinols are prepared by the interaction of sodium acetylides or acetylenic Grignard reagents with aldehydes. The formation and reaction of the metallic acetylide may be combined into a single operation. For example, an alkylacetylene in ether solution is treated successively with ethylmagnesium bromide and formaldehyde to give the acetylenic alcohol such as 2-heptyn-1-ol (82%).[320,323]

$$RC \equiv CH \xrightarrow{C_2H_5MgX} RC \equiv CMgX \xrightarrow[H_2O]{HCHO;} RC \equiv CCH_2OH$$

Higher aldehydes give secondary alcohols.[326] In another procedure, sodium is dissolved in liquid ammonia and treated successively with acetylene and an aldehyde to give alkyl-[319,324] and aryl-[321,322] ethynylcarbinols.

$$HC \equiv CH \xrightarrow[NH_3]{Na} HC \equiv CNa \xrightarrow[H_2O]{RCHO;} HC \equiv CCHOHR$$

Sodium acetylide adds to the carbonyl group of conjugated olefinic aldehydes to give olefinic acetylenic alcohols.[318,321,697] Direct addition of acetylene to aldehydes and ketones is catalyzed by copper acetylide (ethynylation).[691]

Aromatic halogen atoms either in the Grignard reagent[271,329] or in the aldehyde[271,330,331,336] are stable during the reaction to give halo alcohols. Similarly, ether groups may be present in the Grignard reagent as in the preparation of 7-methoxy-1-heptanol (35%)[164] and 4-methoxy-1-butanol (37%),[322] or in the aldehyde as in the preparation of 1-phenoxy-2-butanol (86%).[333]

The aldehyde group of aldehyde esters is preferentially attacked by Grignard reagents to give fair yields of hydroxy esters.[334] The method is important in the preparation of compounds in which the hydroxyl group is further removed from the ester group than the gamma position. A hydroxy acid is established indirectly by hydrolysis of the trichloro alcohol resulting from the interaction of chloral and α-naphthylmagnesium bromide. The α-naphthylglycollic acid is obtained in 50% yield.[335]

Dialkylamino aldehydes condense with Grignard reagents to give dialkylamino alcohols.[336]

89. Interaction of Organometallic Compounds and Ketones

$$RCOR' \xrightarrow{R''MgX} RR'R''COMgX \xrightarrow{H_2O} RR'R''COH$$

The addition of Grignard compounds to ketones is the most general method for the preparation of tertiary alcohols. The three radicals may be the same or different alkyl or aryl groups.[278] Yields are in the range of 60–85% if the reactants are not too highly branched. Best procedures involve decomposition of the halomagnesium alcoholates with ice followed by steam distillation of the resulting carbinols.[264,340,344] Mineral acids should be avoided because the last traces are difficult to remove by washing and cause dehydration of the tertiary carbinol. A solution of ammonium chloride is sometimes used to dissolve the magnesium hydroxide, although a large excess of this reagent may be detrimental, as is claimed in the preparation of dimethylcyclopropylcarbinol (68%).[355] Distillation of the tertiary carbinol is carried out at temperatures as low as possible in order to prevent dehydration.

Common side reactions are reduction of the ketone by the Grignard reagent to the corresponding secondary alcohol and enolization and condensation of the ketone. These reactions take place almost to the exclusion of ordinary addition when sterically hindered ketones are treated with highly branched Grignard reagents.[262,340,350] Reduction of the ketone has been related to the presence of β-hydrogen atoms in the organometallic compound. Better yields of the highly branched tertiary alcohols can sometimes be obtained by the action of organolithium compounds and ketones.[347] Many highly branched tertiary alcohols have been prepared, however, from Grignard reagents.[352,353]

Mono- and di-alkylcyclopentanols[356-358] and cyclohexanols are made from the corresponding cyclic ketones.

Low yields of phenyl-substituted 1,2-*diols* are obtained by the action of various Grignard reagents on α-hydroxy ketones.[112] Better results are obtained when the acetate of the hydroxy ketone is used.[363]

Olefinic tertiary alcohols have been prepared from olefinic organometallic compounds or from olefinic ketones. In the former method allyl-[365,367,368] 3-butenyl-,[369] methylvinylcarbinyl-,[366] and 4-pentenyl-[370] magnesium halides have been used. The coupling of two allyl radicals is minimized by adding a mixture of the allyl halide and the ketone to magnesium in ether. α,β-Olefinic ketones react with Grignard reagents by 1,2-addition to give olefinic tertiary alcohols and by 1,4-addition to give saturated ketones. The tendency for 1,4-addition is greater with α,β-olefinic ketones than with α,β-olefinic aldehydes (cf. method 88). The mode of addition depends upon the substituents present in the Grignard reagent and carbonyl compound. Mesityl oxide, $(CH_3)_2C = CHCOCH_3$, and ethylideneacetone, $CH_3CH = CHCOCH_3$, add methyl Grignard reagent to give the olefinic tertiary alcohols.[364,371] With t-butyl Grignard reagent the yield of tertiary alcohol from mesityl oxide is only 37%.[364] A comparison of the mode of addition of four Grignard reagents to 2-cyclohexenone has been made.[373] The amounts of 1,4-addition are as follows: methyl 15%, ethyl 24%, isopropyl 44%, and t-butyl 70%. In a comparison of eight phenyl-substituted ketones with ethyl- and phenyl-magnesium bromides, it has been noted that 1,4-addition increases with decreasing activity of the carbonyl group.[374]

Acetylenic tertiary alcohols are prepared from sodium acetylides or acetylenic Grignard reagents and ketones in the same manner as described for primary and secondary alcohols (method 88). Dimethylethynylcarbinol is prepared from acetone, aqueous potassium hydroxide, and acetylene in an autoclave at 100° and 300 p.s.i.[386] Ketones are sometimes treated with an acetylide prepared from acetylene and a solution of sodium or potassium alkoxide in t-amyl alcohol.[378,388,394] Another procedure utilizes an acetylenic Grignard reagent prepared from the acetylene and ethyl-magnesium bromide.[384,387,391] Better yields of dialkylhexynylcarbinols are obtained by this method than by the preceding one involving the tertiary alkoxide.[388] The most widely used procedure involves the preparation of the sodium acetylide from the acetylene and sodium amide in liquid ammonia.[377,382,383,393] In one modification, the ketone is first converted to its enolate by sodium amide in ether. The enolate is then treated with acetylene at $-10°$.[361] Strictly anhydrous conditions are essential for the production of the carbinols in maximum yield. As little as 0.01% water decreases the yields markedly.[385]

The lithium derivative of phenylacetylene, $C_6H_5C \equiv CLi$, reacts with benzophenone to give diphenylphenylethynylcarbinol,

$$(C_6H_5)_2COHC \equiv CC_6H_5 \ (95\%).[390]$$

The corresponding Grignard reagent has been similarly employed to make phenylethynyldialkylcarbinols.[325,391] Sodium acetylide and acetylenic Grignard reagents exhibit 1,2-addition with α,β-olefinic ketones to give olefinic acetylenic carbinols.[318,376] The sodio derivatives of propiolic esters, $NaC \equiv CCO_2R$, add to certain ketones. This reaction presents a method for introducing a three-carbon chain at the site of a carbonyl group.[701]

A by-product from the reaction of acetone and sodium acetylide is the acetylenic diol, $(CH_3)_2C(OH)C \equiv C(OH)(CH_3)_2$, formed by condensation of two molecules of acetone with one molecule of sodium acetylide.[382] A general method for the preparation of acetylenic diols of this type is from calcium carbide, potassium hydroxide, and ketones.[392] Diethynyl glycols in which the triple bonds are separated by two or four carbon atoms are made from sodium acetylide and α- or β-diketones.[379]

Grignard reagents add to the carbonyl group of α-halo ketones to give low yields of *α-halo alcohols*.[380,381,395,396] The reaction is complicated by further action of the organometallic reagent with the halohydrin.

Fair yields of *alkoxy alcohols* are obtained from α-alkoxy ketones and Grignard reagents.[396] Methylmagnesium iodide and phenoxyacetone give phenoxy-*t*-butyl alcohol (88%).[397]

Aliphatic and aromatic *keto alcohols* of the general formula

$$RC(OH)(CH_3)COCH_3$$

have been made by the action of Grignard reagents on methyl isonitroso-ethyl ketone followed by hydrolysis with 10% oxalic acid.

$$CH_3COC(CH_3) = NOH \xrightarrow[\text{H}^+]{RMgX \quad H_2O} R(CH_3)COHC(CH_3) = NOH$$

$$\xrightarrow{H_2O} R(CH_3)CCHCOCH_3$$

Oximes of α-*hydroxyaldehydes* result when isonitrosoacetone is used.
The free monomeric hydroxy aldehydes are difficult to obtain by hydrolysis
of the oximes.[398] Bromomagnesium enolates prepared from Grignard reagents and sterically hindered ketones act as true Grignard reagents.
β-keto alcohols are formed by their reaction with aldehydes or ketones.[399]

$$(RCOCH_2)MgX \xrightarrow[H_2O]{R'_2CO;} R'_2C(OH)CH_2COR$$

Selective addition of a Grignard reagent to the keto group of a keto
acid or keto ester is possible. Several α-*hydroxy acids* have been prepared in this manner from α-keto acids by the use of an excess of Grignard
reagent, which first replaces the active hydrogen atom of the carboxyl
group.[159,400] Methyl β-benzoylpropionate adds methylmagnesium iodide to
the keto group to the extent of 75% when the molar ratio of keto ester to
Grignard reagent is 1:1.38. Smaller or larger ratios give lower yields.[401]

Amino alcohols have been prepared by this method in two ways: by the
action of a ketone on a Grignard reagent containing a dialkylamino
group,[402] and by the action of organometallic compounds on α-amino[403]
and β-amino[404] ketones.

90. Interaction of Organometallic Compounds and Oxides

$$CH_2 \!-\! CH_2 \xrightarrow[H_2O]{RMgX;} RCH_2CH_2OH$$
$$\diagdown\!_O\!\diagup$$

The reaction of Grignard reagents with ethylene oxide is valuable for
lengthening the carbon chain by two carbon atoms in a one-step process.
A cooled solution of ethylene oxide in ether is added with stirring to a
precooled solution of the Grignard compound. The mixture is then allowed
to stand for a time or is heated before hydrolysis. Benzene is added as
a diluent to prevent violent reaction during heating in the preparation of
n-hexyl alcohol (62%)[442] from n-butyl Grignard reagent. Some 2-hexanol is
also formed in this preparation.[704]

Ethylene halohydrins, XCH_2CH_2OH, are by-products which are formed in
increasing amount as the Grignard reagent is varied from primary to tertiary. The yield of primary alcohol decreases from 50–70% with primary
organomagnesium compounds to 0–15% with tertiary Grignard reagents.[444]
Highest yields are obtained when the molar ratio of ethylene oxide to
Grignard reagent is 2:1. A study of the intermediate compounds and
modes of formation of the products has been made.[446,704]

The Grignard reagent may be aliphatic,[442,446] alicyclic,[448,451] or aromatic.
Many β-arylethanols have been made by this method.[447,453–455]

Oxides other than ethylene oxide have been used. Cyclohexene oxide and diethylmagnesium give *trans*-2-ethylcyclohexanol (42%).[450] 1-Phenyl-2-propanol is obtained from either styrene oxide and methylmagnesium iodide or propylene oxide and phenylmagnesium bromide.[281,452,466] Propylene oxide reacts with alkylmagnesium bromides to give chiefly propylene bromohydrin, $CH_3CHOHCH_2Br$, when the ratio of reactants is 1:1. A ratio of two moles of oxide to one mole of Grignard reagent gives secondary alcohols of the type $CH_3CHOHCH_2R$ in 15-54% yields accompanied by large amounts of the bromohydrins.[466] Addition of the Grignard reagent to the oxides of *cis*- and *trans*-stilbenes has been studied.[457]

Organosodium compounds behave similarly to the Grignard reagent with ethylene oxide. 2-(α-Thienyl)-1-ethanol[459] and γ,γ,γ-triphenylpropyl alcohol[458] are prepared from 2-chlorothiophene and trityl chloride, respectively, through the sodium compounds.

The *diol*, tetradecamethylene glycol, has been synthesized from decamethylene bromide by an adaptation of this method.[460]

The best example of a preparation of an *olefinic alcohol* by this method is that of 1-penten-5-ol from allylmagnesium chloride and ethylene oxide (60%).[461] *Acetylenic alcohols* are made in fair yields from sodium acetylides or acetylenic Grignard compounds and ethylene oxide.[320,463,690]

Halo alcohols available by this method are of two types: those containing aryl halogen formed from halo aryl Grignard reagents,[464,465] and 1-chloro-2-alkanols, $ClCH_2CH(OH)CH_2R$.[467,469] The latter compounds are made by the action of Grignard reagents on epichlorohydrin,

$$ClCH_2CH \underset{\underset{O}{\diagdown \diagup}}{} CH_2.$$

The effect of the structure of the Grignard reagent on the course of this reaction has been studied.[468] Best results are obtained from primary organomagnesium compounds.

Hydroxy ethers in which the alkoxyl group is on an aromatic nucleus[470,471] or an aliphatic chain[472] have been made from alkoxy Grignard reagents in about 50% yields.

91. Action of Organometallic Reagents on Esters or Related Compounds

$$RCO_2C_2H_5 \xrightarrow{R'MgX} RR'C(OMgX)(OC_2H_5) \xrightarrow{R'MgX} RR'_2COMgX \xrightarrow{H_2O} RR'_2COH$$

Symmetrical secondary alcohols are prepared by this method from ethyl formate and organomagnesium halides. Excellent directions are available for 3-pentanol (70%)[407] and 5-nonanol (85%).[408] An ester exchange reaction sometimes gives the formate of the alcohol as an impurity in the product. The pure secondary alcohol is obtained by saponification and steam distillation.

Tertiary alcohols in which two alkyl or aryl groups are identical are formed from higher esters or the corresponding acyl chlorides. Ethyl isobutyrate and methylmagnesium iodide give 2,3-dimethyl-2-butanol (92%).[264] Yields of 40–83% are listed for eighteen aliphatic tertiary alcohols.[348] Ethyl esters of furoic and tetrahydrofuroic acids give tertiary carbinols in good yields with ethyl-, n-butyl-, and phenyl-magnesium bromides.[412] Triphenylcarbinol is made from ethyl benzoate and phenylmagnesium bromide.[420]

By-products formed by condensation, reduction, and fission reactions become appreciable as branching of the organometallic reagent, ester, or acyl halide is increased. β-Keto esters are formed by condensation of esters by the Grignard reagent[262,440] (cf. method 211). Reduction products include the aldehyde and primary alcohol corresponding to the ester or acyl halide and the secondary alcohol resulting either from the addition of the Grignard reagent to the aldehyde or from the reduction of the ketone formed from the Grignard reagent and the acyl halide.[413,416,417]

$$\text{RCOCl} \xrightarrow{\text{R}'\text{MgX}} \text{RCHO} \xrightarrow[\text{H}_2\text{O}]{\text{R}'\text{MgX};} \text{RCH}_2\text{OH}$$

$$\downarrow \text{R}'\text{MgX} \qquad\qquad \downarrow \text{R}'\text{MgX}$$

$$\text{RCOR}' \xrightarrow[\text{H}_2\text{O}]{\text{R}'\text{MgX};} \text{RCHOHR}'$$

In these reductions the organometallic reagent is oxidized to an olefin. Esters give less reduction than acyl chlorides.[415] Relatively simple reagents react in this manner. For example, reduction products are formed exclusively in the reaction of t-butylmagnesium chloride with n-butyryl, isobutyryl, and lauroyl chlorides.[413] Cleavage of allyl esters by the Grignard reagent to give acid salts and hydrocarbons takes place when the carbonyl group is sterically hindered.[414]

$$\text{RCO}_2\text{CH}_2\text{CH}=\text{CH}_2 \xrightarrow{\text{R}'\text{MgX}} \text{RCO}_2\text{MgX} + \text{R}'\text{CH}_2\text{CH}=\text{CH}_2$$

Tertiary alcohols are also made by carbonation of Grignard reagents and treatment of the resulting halomagnesium salts with an excess of the same or different organometallic compound.[406,421] Sixteen aliphatic tertiary alcohols are formed in 40–60% yields from primary Grignard reagents and aliphatic acids. Yields are higher when the reactions are carried out at 83° in benzene solution.[405] Ketones are obtained as by-products.

Symmetrical tertiary alcohols are best prepared from organometallic reagents and ethyl carbonate, $(C_2H_5O)_2CO$ (cf. method 312).[422,424]

Esters react with certain di-Grignard reagents to give tertiary alicyclic alcohols in 20-67% yields.[703]

$$
\begin{array}{c}
CH_2MgBr \\
| \\
(CH_2)_n \\
| \\
CH_2MgBr
\end{array}
\xrightarrow[\text{H}_2\text{O}]{\text{RCO}_2\text{C}_2\text{H}_5;}
(CH_2)_n
\begin{array}{c}
CH_2 \\
\diagup \qquad \diagdown \\
\diagup \qquad \qquad \diagup R \\
\qquad \qquad C \\
\diagdown \qquad \qquad \diagup \diagdown \\
CH_2 \qquad OH
\end{array}
$$

where $n = 2$ or 3.

A number of *other functional groups* may be present in the reacting ester molecule. The method has been applied to the preparation of glycols,[363] pinacols,[427] and olefinic [428,429] and acetylenic [430,431] tertiary alcohols. Esters containing halogen in the *alpha* and *beta* positions have been converted to halo alcohols of questionable purity.[434,435,437] Halogen atoms on the aromatic nucleus are stable.[432] α-Alkoxy esters give good yields of α-alkoxy tertiary alcohols [436,702] (cf. methods 167 and 202). Amino alcohols may be prepared by the addition of excess Grignard reagent to esters of amino acids.[438,439,441]

92. Replacement of the Sulfonic Acid Group by the Hydroxyl Group

$$ ArSO_3Na \xrightarrow[\text{Fuse}]{\text{NaOH + KOH}} ArONa \xrightarrow[\text{H}^+]{\text{H}_2\text{O}} ArOH $$

The preparation of phenols by this method is limited to compounds having substituents which are not attacked by alkali at the fusion temperature. A molten mixture of the hydroxide and a little water in a copper, nickel, or iron crucible is treated with small portions of the sodium salt of a sulfonic acid. The reaction occurs at 300-320°. Fusion of sodium p-toluenesulfonate with sodium hydroxide gives no cresol; potassium hydroxide or a mixture of sodium and potassium hydroxides containing at least 28% of the latter compound is required. Similar results are found in the preparations of m-hydroxybenzoic acid (91%)[720] and 6-methyl-2-naphthol.[721] Several factors affecting the conversion are studied in the preparation of the naphthol. Excellent directions are given for the preparation of p-cresol (72%)[563] and β-naphthol (80%).[562] m-Benzenedisulfonic acid gives m-hydroxybenzenesulfonic acid [567] or resorcinol,[564] depending upon the concentration of alkali used. 5- and 8-Hydroxyisoquinolines are made by this method with the reaction occurring at 210-220°.[566]

93. Replacement of the Diazonium Group by the Hydroxyl Group

$$ ArN_2^+HSO_4^- + H_2O \rightarrow ArOH + H_2SO_4 + N_2 $$

This reaction is of little value for the preparation of aliphatic alcohols. Methyl alcohol cannot be obtained from methylamine and nitrous acid. n-Propylamine gives a mixture of n-propyl alcohol, isopropyl alcohol, and propene.[473]

Many phenols are best prepared by boiling aryldiazonium compounds with water. Excess nitrous acid from the diazotization is first destroyed by addition of solid urea.[475,476,481] Some substituted diazonium compounds are hydrolyzed with difficulty. Refluxing with aqueous sulfuric acid,[476,490] copper sulfate,[474,478] or sodium sulfate[488,494] solutions is usually recommended.

The diazonium sulfates are preferred to the nitrates or chlorides. Aryl chlorides and nitro compounds are sometimes formed as by-products in the decomposition of diazonium chlorides and nitrates. For example, o-nitro-p-cresol is formed in 69% yield by the hydrolysis of the diazonium nitrate from p-toluidine.[501]

A modification of this reaction involves conversion of the diazonium salt to the diazonium fluoroboride with fluoroboric acid. Treatment with glacial acetic acid then gives the aryl acetate, from which the free phenol is obtained by hydrolysis.[244,497]

$$ArN_2{}^+Cl^- \xrightarrow{HBF_4} ArN_2{}^+BF_4{}^- \xrightarrow{CH_3CO_2H} ArOCOCH_3 \xrightarrow{H_2O} ArOH$$

The aryl group may contain halogen,[485,488] phenoxyl,[707] aldehyde,[489] keto,[493] carboxyl,[495,496] carbomethoxyl,[494] cyano,[492] or nitro[490,491] groups. Certain activated methyl groups in the ortho position to the diazonium group cause complications owing to ring closure with the formation of indazoles.[498] Coupling of the phenol with the diazonium compound may also occur (method 494). This reaction may be minimized for phenols which are volatile with steam by employing a dilute solution of the diazonium salt and removing the phenol as it is formed.[705] Amino groups on heterocyclic nuclei such as pyridine,[484,486] thianaphthene,[483] dibenzofuran,[244] and pyrazine[487] are replaced by hydroxyl groups by this method.

94. Replacement of the Amino Group by the Hydroxyl Group

$$C_{10}H_7NH_2 + H_2O \underset{\xrightarrow{NaHSO_3}}{\rightleftharpoons} C_{10}H_7OH + NH_3$$

This equilibrium reaction in the presence of sulfites is used for the preparation of naphthols and naphthylamines (Bucherer reaction) (cf. method 438). A review of the literature to 1942 has been made.[499] The substituted naphthalenes are heated with aqueous sodium bisulfite at 90–150°. Nearly quantitative yields of α- and β-naphthols are obtained from the corresponding naphthylamines. Many substituted naphthols have been prepared by this procedure.

The direct removal of an acetylamino group ($NHCOCH_3$) on naphthalene by boiling with sodium hydroxide is used in the preparation of 1-nitro-2-naphthol (89%).[503]

An amino group on the benzene ring is directly hydrolyzable only when it is in the *meta* position to hydroxyl or other amino groups. *m*-Dihydroxybenzene (resorcinol) has been made by the Bucherer reaction, and 1,3,5-trihydroxybenzene (phloroglucinol) is obtained by direct hydrolysis and decarboxylation of 2,4,6-triaminobenzoic acid.[500]

In the heterocyclic series 5-aminoquinoline has been converted by the Bucherer reaction to 5-hydroxyquinoline (47%).[502]

95. Hydrolysis of Esters

$$RCO_2R' + NaOH \longrightarrow R'OH + RCO_2Na$$

Few alcohols are made by this method because the corresponding esters are usually available only from the alcohols. Several esters of important alcohols are formed by other means and are hydrolyzed to the alcohols. For example, oxidation of acenaphthene by red lead in acetic acid gives 7-acenaphthenol acetate, from which 7-acenaphthenol is obtained by saponification with methanolic sodium hydroxide.[520] Phenols may be prepared indirectly from aromatic aldehydes by oxidation with peracetic acid followed by hydrolysis of the resulting aryl formate.[687]

$$ArCHO \xrightarrow{CH_3CO_3H} ArOCHO \xrightarrow[H^+]{KOH;} ArOH$$

Most esters are cleaved by saponification rather than by acid-catalyzed hydrolysis. The hydrolysis by acid is reversible and requires removal of one of the products for its completion. The procedure employed varies somewhat, depending upon whether the acid or alcohol is desired (cf. method 249). In the preparation of cetyl alcohol, $n\text{-}C_{16}H_{33}OH$, from the natural wax spermaceti, the acid fraction is precipitated as the calcium salt to eliminate troublesome emulsions during the extraction process.[26]

The conversion of dihalides to *diols* through the diacetates is sometimes more convenient than direct hydrolysis (method 96). The diesters are prepared by heating dihalides with sodium or potassium acetate in acetic acid or ethyl alcohol.[515-517] Glycols are distilled directly from mixtures of the diacetates and powdered potassium hydroxide or calcium hydroxide.[517] Ethylene glycol is obtained from the diacetate by "transesterification" with methanolic hydrogen chloride.[515] This modification has also been used for the preparation of several α-hydroxy acids.[526]

A similar conversion of olefins to glycols involves reaction with iodine and silver benzoate followed by saponification of the resulting crude dibenzoate. Over-all yields of more than 70% are obtained for 1,2-octa-decanediol from 1-octadecene,[36] γ-phenylpropylene glycol from allyl-benzene,[518] and 9,10-dihydroxystearic acid from methyl oleate.[710]

The conversion of a halogen compound to a carbinol through its acetate or formate[522] has been used for the preparation of olefinic alcohols,[303,521] halo alcohols,[465,524] α-hydroxy ketones,[522,523,711] α-hydroxy acids,[526] amino alcohols,[709] and p-nitrobenzyl alcohol.[524] Allyl-type halides undergo allylic isomerization during conversion to the acetate. Both phenylvinyl-carbinol, $C_6H_5CHOHCH = CH_2$, and cinnamyl alcohol, $C_6H_5CH = CHCH_2OH$, are obtained from cinnamyl chloride.[521] The replacement of an α-halogen atom on a ketone is not always straightforward. Thus, the α-ketol obtained through the acetate from α-bromopropiophenone, $C_6H_5COCHBrCH_3$, is phenylacetylcarbinol, $C_6H_5CHOHCOCH_3$, whereas that obtained through the formate is methylbenzoylcarbinol, $C_6H_5COCHOHCH_3$.[523] Isomerizations of ketols of this type have been shown to be base-catalyzed equilibria. Lead oxide and acetic acid are used to convert p-bromobenzyl bromide to p-bromobenzyl acetate. The crude acetate is saponified with methanolic potassium hydroxide. The over-all yield of p-bromobenzyl alcohol is 61%.[465] Certain aryl halides are converted to phenols with the aid of higher temperatures and copper acetate.[546]

96. Hydrolysis of Halogen Compounds

$$RX + H_2O \longrightarrow ROH + HX$$

Alkyl halides are hydrolyzed to alcohols by water or dilute bases, the order of reactivity of the halogen atoms being tertiary > secondary > primary and iodine > bromine > chlorine. By heating 1,2-dichloro-2-methyl-propane, $(CH_3)_2CCICH_2Cl$, with an aqueous suspension of calcium carbonate, the tertiary chlorine atom is replaced to give 1-chloro-2-methyl-2-propanol (48%).[553]

A suspension of lead oxide in water is used in the preparation of 2,3-butanediol from the corresponding dibromide.[550] Glycols are usually obtained from dihalides through the acetates (method 95).

Allyl-type halides are hydrolyzed readily to olefinic alcohols.[307] The difference in reactivity between allyl and vinyl halogen atoms is well illustrated by the hydrolysis of 1,3-dichloropropene, $ClCH = CHCH_2Cl$, to 3-chloro-2-propen-1-ol, $ClCH = CHCH_2OH$ (76–81%).[551]

Bromine atoms in the *alpha* position to carbonyl or carboxyl groups may be successfully hydrolyzed in certain cases by exercising proper precautions. α-Hydroxy carbonyl compounds are sensitive to alkali (cf. method 95). Benzylglycolic aldehyde,[555] $C_6H_5CH_2CH(OH)CHO$, and gly-colic acid,[556] CH_2OHCO_2H, are obtained by refluxing the corresponding halo compounds with water and barium carbonate. Higher-molecular-weight α-hydroxy acids may be obtained from α-bromo acids and aqueous alkali hydroxides or carbonates.[545,554]

Halogen atoms attached to an aromatic nucleus are not easily hydrolyzed unless they are activated by electron-attracting groups in the *ortho* or *para* positions. Under the influence of copper catalysts, however, aryl bromides react with aqueous sodium hydroxide at 200–275° to give phenols. This conversion is illustrated by the preparation of 3-pseudocumenol (82%)[548] and 2-hydroxydibenzofuran (75%).[248]

Halogen atoms in the *alpha* position to an aromatic nucleus (benzyl-type) are very readily hydrolyzed. With proper precautions hydrolysis of the halogen atom of *p*-cyanobenzyl chloride is possible without affecting the cyanide group; *p*-cyanobenzyl alcohol is obtained in 85% yield.[549]

97. Cleavage of Ethers

$$ArOR + HI \longrightarrow ArOH + RI$$

This reaction is an important step in the synthesis of many phenols. The phenolic grouping is unstable in numerous chemical transformations but may be "protected" in the form of its ethers. No good general reagent has been found for the cleavage of the ether linkages. By refluxing the alkoxy compounds with hydrogen bromide or hydrogen iodide in water or acetic acid solution, successful conversions to hydroxy compounds have been accomplished for *n*-propylphenol,[528] *o*-dihydroxybenzene,[766] *o*- and *m*-hydroxyphenylacetic acids,[539,540] 4,4'-dihydroxybenzil,[541] several hydroxyquinolines,[502,532] and hydroxy amino acids.[542,543] Yields are in the range of 72–93%. A modification of this procedure involves heating the ether with pyridine hydrochloride or hydrobromide at 200°. Anisole is cleaved to phenol in 82% yield, but diphenyl ether is not attacked. *o*- and *m*-Dimethoxybenzenes may be cleaved to dihydric phenols or to phenolic ethers.[529]

Aluminum and boron halides are sometimes used to dealkylate alkyl aryl ethers to phenols. Boron tribromide cleaves aliphatic ethers to alcohols and alkyl halides, but the reaction has no preparative value in the aliphatic series.[527] Aluminum halide and the ether first form a complex from which a molecule of alkyl halide is eliminated upon heating.

$$ArOR \xrightarrow{AlX_3} ArOR \cdot AlX_3 \xrightarrow{Heat} ArOAlX_2 \xrightarrow{H_2O} ArOH$$

The reaction has been successfully employed to prepare fluorophenols[534,535] and hydroxybenzophenones.[536] Diaryl ethers and alkyl aryl ethers are also cleaved by sodium amide,[533] sodium hydroxide,[716] and by sodium in liquid ammonia[530] or pyridine.[544] Anisole, phenetole, phenyl benzyl ether, and diphenyl ether are converted to phenol in yields above 90% by refluxing with sodium or potassium in pyridine solution. Ethers of benzyl alcohol may be cleaved by catalytic hydrogenation.

An excellent means of protecting phenolic hydroxyl groups for reactions in alkaline media is by the formation of the methoxymethyl ether from the sodium salt of the phenol and chloromethyl ether, viz.,

$$ArONa + ClCH_2OCH_3 \rightarrow ArOCH_2OCH_3.$$

This mixed acetal is stable to alkali but easily hydrolyzed to the phenol by warming with dilute acid.[537]

98. Cleavage of Oxides

$$RCH\!-\!CHR + H_2O \xrightarrow{H^+} RCHOHCHOHR$$
$$\diagdown\!\!\diagup$$
$$O$$

This reaction is the last step in the hydroxylation of the double bond by peracids (cf. method 107). Oxides available by other methods (Chapter 7) may also be converted to diols in good yields. Hydrolysis proceeds readily at room temperature in the presence of a small amount of sulfuric[615,616] or perchloric[614,617] acids. Inversion of the configuration of a carbon atom occurs. Thus, *cis*-2,3-epoxypentane gives *threo*-2,3-pentanediol, and the *trans* oxide gives the *erythro* diol.[615] *Chloro*[618] and *keto*[619] groups in the *alpha* position to the epoxide linkage are unaffected by the ring opening.

Alkene oxides may also be cleaved by reduction with lithium aluminum hydride as in the preparation of α-phenylethyl alcohol from styrene oxide (94%).[44]

99. Cleavage of Furans and Pyrans

$$CH_2\!-\!CH_2$$
$$|\qquad|$$
$$CH_2\quad CHCH_2OH \xrightarrow[CuCrO]{H_2} HO(CH_2)_5OH$$
$$\diagdown\!\!\diagup$$
$$O$$

Various derivatives of furan and pyran are cleaved to give open-chain di- and poly-functional compounds. Fission to give dihalides, halo alcohols, and halo esters is described elsewhere (method 54). Hydrogenation and hydrogenolysis reactions lead to hydroxy compounds, as in the preparation of 5-hydroxy-2-pentanone and 1,4-pentanediol from methyl-

furan[623] and 1,5-pentanediol from tetrahydrofurfuryl alcohol.[621] Tetrahydrofurfuryl alcohol is also cleaved by acetic anhydride and zinc chloride
to give the triacetate of 1,2,5-trihydroxypentane.[622,626]

Hydrolysis of 2,3-dihydropyran by dilute hydrochloric acid gives 5-hy-
droxypentanal (79%),[625] which is readily reduced to 1,5-pentanediol. The
2,3-dihydropyran is prepared by dehydration and rearrangement of tetrahydrofurfuryl alcohol over aluminum oxide.[628]

Dehydrohalogenation and ether cleavage of tetrahydrofurfuryl chloride
by sodium sand produces 4-penten-1-ol in 82% yield.[629] Likewise, 4-octen-
1-ol is obtained from 3-chloro-2-n-propyltetrahydropyran.[731] This synthesis is general for 4-alken-1-ols from the commercially available dihydropyran (cf. method 21).[731]

A similar synthesis of 3-alken-1-ols from 2,3-dichlorotetrahydrofuran has
been devised, and the stereochemical relationships of both syntheses
have been investigated.[733] Many cleavages of furan and pyran rings have
been reviewed.[730]

Dibenzofuran is cleaved by a mixture of sodium and potassium hydroxides at 410° to 2,2'-dihydroxybiphenyl (29%).[627]

100. Rearrangement of Allyl Ethers (Claisen)

$$C_6H_5OCH_2CH = CHR \rightarrow o\text{-}HOC_6H_4CH(R)CH = CH_2$$

This interesting nuclear alkylation by the allyl group of an allyl aryl
ether gives unsaturated phenols. Migration takes place to the *ortho* position of the ring with tautomeric isomerization within the allyl group. If
both *ortho* positions are blocked, migration occurs to the *para* position
either with or without tautomeric change within the allyl group. A large
variety of substituents may be present in the side chain and the aromatic
nucleus. The furfuryl radical contains the necessary allylic structure for
the side chain; rearrangement affords a preparation for o-furfurylphenol
(38%).[560]

The reaction occurs below 200° without catalysts by refluxing the ether
at atmospheric or reduced pressures either with or without solvents. The
yield of o-allylphenol from allyl phenyl ether is 73%.[559]

Excellent literature reviews complete with experimental conditions
have been made.[559]

101. Hydration of Olefinic Compounds

$$RCH = CHR \xrightarrow{H_2SO_4} RCH_2CH(OSO_3H)R \xrightarrow{H_2O} RCH_2CH(OH)R$$

Hydration of olefins is accomplished by dissolving them in aqueous sulfuric acid and hydrolyzing the resulting alkyl hydrogen sulfate. The yields of alcohols are fair for the simple olefins. The hydroxyl group adds to the carbon atom of the double bond which contains the least number of hydrogen atoms. Olefins from t-alcohols are hydrated by 50–65% sulfuric acid, whereas those from primary and secondary alcohols require higher concentration of acid. Details have been worked out for a satisfactory laboratory preparation of t-butyl alcohol from gaseous isobutylene.[581] Kerosene is used as a solvent to lower the vapor pressure of the isobutylene, which is then absorbed by 50% sulfuric acid. The concentration of the sulfuric acid is critical; polymerization of the olefin occurs when the acid is too concentrated.

Other functional groups may be present in the molecule containing the double bond. Methallyl alcohol, $H_2C = C(CH_3)CH_2OH$, is hydrated by a mixture of 25% sulfuric acid in the presence of isobutyraldehyde to give the cyclic acetal of isobutylene glycol with the aldehyde. Hydrolysis of the acetal by dilute mineral acid gives isobutylene glycol (94%).[584] Hydration of the double bond by aqueous sulfuric acid has been used to make chloro-t-butyl alcohol from methallyl chloride[585] and β-hydroxybutyric acid from crotonic acid.[586]

102. Condensation of Aldehydes and Ketones (Aldol Condensation)

$$2RCH_2CHO \xrightarrow{OH} RCH_2CH(OH)CH(R)CHO$$

This is a general reaction exhibited by aldehydes and ketones having labile (usually α) hydrogen atoms. The hydrogen atom of one molecule of the carbonyl compound adds to the carbonyl group of another molecule of the same or different compound to form an aldol (hydroxy aldehyde) or a ketol (hydroxy ketone). The condensation is reversible and is usually promoted by basic catalysts. The products are distilled at temperatures as low as possible to prevent not only the reverse reaction[203] but also the dehydration to olefinic compounds (method 36).

The condensation of an aldehyde or a mixture of two aldehydes is best effected by aqueous sodium or potassium carbonate or aqueous alcoholic hydroxides at 0–30°. From a preparative standpoint, best results from a mixture of two aldehydes are achieved when one of the aldehydes does not contain an α-hydrogen atom. Otherwise, a mixture of products is obtained. Crossed condensations of formaldehyde with isobutyraldehyde and isovaleraldehyde give the aldols, $CH_2OHC(CH_3)_2CHO$, and $(CH_3)_2CHCH(CH_2OH)CHO$, respectively.[200,201] Certain aldols dehydrate spontaneously or upon distillation. This is especially true of those resulting from the crossed condensation of benzaldehyde with another aldehyde (method 36). Self-condensation of aldehydes is sometimes complicated by the formation of trimers believed to be substituted 1,3-dioxanes.[202] The aldol of propionaldehyde may be prepared by distilling the trimer from a small amount of adipic acid.[206]

Self-condensation of methyl ketones to ketols is best accomplished by basic catalysts. Only methyl ketones have been satisfactorily condensed. Diacetone alcohol is prepared by refluxing acetone with barium hydroxide in a Soxhlet extractor.[204] Condensation of higher methyl ketones by basic reagents involves a hydrogen atom on the methyl group rather than one on the higher alkyl group. Most of these condensations lead directly to olefinic ketones (method 36). However, the ketols are prepared in fair yields when bromomagnesium amines are used as catalysts. For example, methyl ethyl ketone gives the ketol, $C_2H_5C(CH_3)(OH)CH_2COCH_2CH_3$, in 67% yield with $C_6H_5N(CH_3)MgBr$ prepared from ethylmagnesium bromide and methylaniline. Eight higher ketols prepared by this procedure are described. Yields are in the range of 55–70%. Pinacolone, which is condensed in poor yields by other basic reagents, gives a 68% yield of the corresponding ketol when the anilinomagnesium bromide is used.[205] The acid-catalyzed condensation of methyl ketones follows a completely different course (method 36).

The crossed condensation of an aldehyde and a ketone is possible under proper conditions. The tendency for self-condensation is much less for ketones than for aldehydes. Advantage is taken of this fact by adding the aldehyde diluted with part of the ketone to a cooled, well-stirred mixture of the ketone and basic catalyst.[210] The carbonyl group of the aldehyde and an α-hydrogen atom of the ketone are involved in the condensation. A study of solvents, pH, catalyst concentration, and mole ratio of reactants has been made for the condensations of paraformaldehyde[208] and acetaldehyde[739] with methyl ethyl ketone. The various by-products formed in the condensations with formaldehyde have been discussed.[741] Base-catalyzed condensation of methyl alkyl ketones with straight-chain aldehydes involves a hydrogen atom on the methylene group of the ketone (3-condensation).[209,211,212,740] It was formerly believed that condensation with α-alkyl-branched aldehydes takes place on the methyl group of the ketone (1-condensation).[217,218] However, the condensation has been shown to depend markedly on the catalyst. For example, the condensation of isobutyraldehyde and methyl ethyl ketone with aqueous base gives both 1- and 3-condensation in the ratio of 55 to 45. With sodium ethylate the ratio is 90 to 10, and with hydrochloric acid only 3-condensation is observed.[213] Cyclopentanone and cyclohexanone have been used in crossed condensations.[215,216] Condensation of higher-molecular-weight ketones gives very poor results.[214] The condensation of aromatic and heterocyclic aldehydes with ketones usually leads directly to unsaturated ketones (method 36).

Many other compounds containing labile hydrogen atoms may be condensed with carbonyl compounds in basic media. The introduction of a trichloromethyl group is achieved by condensation of chloroform with ketones, α-branched aldehydes, or substituted benzaldehydes. Straight-chain aldehydes undergo self-condensation. The condensations are best effected by powdered potassium hydroxide in an acetal solvent. The yield of trichloro-t-butyl alcohol from acetone and chloroform is 80%. The yields of higher homologs vary over a wide range but, in general, are exceptionally good.[736] Condensations with bromoform or iodoform are less successful.[737]

Aliphatic esters have been condensed with benzaldehyde by means of sodium triphenylmethide. The reaction has been stopped at the "aldol" stage to give low yields (26–30%) of β-hydroxy esters.[784]

Either or both active hydrogen atoms of malonic or acetoacetic esters enter into condensation with formaldehyde or acetaldehyde.[754] Acetoacetic ester is readily converted to the dimethylol or diethylol derivatives by condensation with formaldehyde or acetaldehyde, respectively, in the presence of potassium carbonate.[755] α-Methylacetoacetates are similarly condensed with one molecule of aldehyde.[756]

Aliphatic and aryl-substituted aliphatic nitro compounds contain active methylene groups which take part in condensation with carbonyl compounds.

$$RCHO + R'CH_2NO_2 \xrightarrow{\text{Base}} RCHOHCHR'NO_2$$

The yields of nitro alcohols from simple nitroparaffins and aliphatic aldehydes or benzaldehyde are usually above 60%.[742-750] The condensations are generally carried out with aqueous ethanolic sodium hydroxide, although weaker bases are sometimes desirable to prevent polymerization of the aldehyde.[745,749] Sodium bisulfite addition compounds of the aldehydes are sometimes used.[744,749] Better results are obtained with sodium methoxide than with alkali hydroxides in the condensation of nitroethane with formaldehyde.[748] Sodium alkoxides are also used to effect the condensation of nitroethane with acetone[751] and cyclohexanone.[752] Condensation proceeds to the nitroalkanediol stage in certain cases with both nitromethane[753] and with formaldehyde.[745]

103. Condensation of Carbonyl Compounds with Halogenated Compounds
     (Reformatsky)

$$RRCO + R'CHBrCO_2C_2H_5 \xrightarrow[H_2O]{Zn \ or \ Mg;} RRC(OH)CHR'CO_2C_2H_5$$

In this reaction organometallic compounds incapable of existence in high concentration are formed and utilized immediately. When an aldehyde or ketone is condensed with a halo ester the product is a β-hydroxy ester. Sometimes dehydration occurs to give olefinic esters directly (method 19). The use of an ester as the carbonyl compound leads to β-keto esters (method 234). The halo esters most commonly employed are of three types: $XCH_2CO_2C_2H_5$, $RCHXCO_2C_2H_5$, and $R_2CXCO_2C_2H_5$. Vinylogous halo esters, such as γ-bromocrotonate,[234] and certain benzyl halides[238] have been used with variable success.

A review of the literature to 1942 lists 157 condensations involving aldehydes and ketones.[219] Trioxymethylene serves as a source of formaldehyde.[235] In addition to the compounds listed, condensations of 2-pentenal,[240] o-tolualdehyde,[230] methyl ethyl ketone,[227,231,232] diethyl ketone,[228] methyl hexyl ketone,[222] cyclopentanone,[232] and phenyl t-butyl ketone[229] are noteworthy.

The best experimental conditions for the reaction have been discussed.[219] An optimum temperature of 90–105° is easily maintained by the use of a refluxing mixture of benzene and toluene as solvent.[225] Granulated zinc which has been washed with hydrochloric acid can be substituted for the sandpaper-cleaned zinc foil that is sometimes recommended.[224] Magnesium has been used successfully for several condensations.[228,233,759]

Many competing reactions are responsible for the low yields occasionally obtained in the Reformatsky reaction. Zinc salts bring about the aldol condensation of certain aldehydes. Coupling of two molecules of bromo ester by zinc to give a succinic ester sometimes occurs. The extent of this reaction is reduced by adding the bromo ester to a refluxing mixture of benzene, ketone, and zinc.[237] A portion of the bromo ester is sometimes reduced by reaction of the zinc derivative with an active hydrogen atom of the ketone; the ketone is regenerated from its enol salt by

$$R_2CHCOR + BrZnCH_2CO_2R \longrightarrow CH_3CO_2R + (R_2CCOR^-)Zn^+Br$$

hydrolysis. This side reaction occurs to the extent of 90% with acetomesitylene.[220] The reduced ester may also be condensed by the organozinc compound to yield a β-keto ester.[221]

Propargyl bromide, $HC \equiv CCH_2Br$, undergoes a Reformatsky-type reaction with a variety of carbonyl compounds to give β,γ-*acetylenic carbinols* in fair yields.[758]

104. Condensation of Carbonyl Compounds (Acyloin and Benzoin Condensations)

$$RCO_2C_2H_5 \xrightarrow{Na} \begin{matrix} RC-ONa \\ \| \\ RC-ONa \end{matrix} \xrightarrow{H^+} \begin{matrix} RCHOH \\ | \\ RCO \end{matrix}$$

Aliphatic acyloins (α-hydroxy ketones) are formed by the action of sodium sand on ethereal or benzene solutions of aliphatic esters.[636,637] Improved techniques involving highly dispersed sodium preparations are invaluable in this condensation.[801] Straight-chain and branched esters are condensed in 55–75% yields.[636] Contrary to earlier reports, higher-molecular-weight aliphatic esters give acyloins in excellent yields. The reaction has been extended to include esters containing eight to eighteen carbon atoms.[639] The mechanism of the condensation by sodium in liquid ammonia has been studied.[638] Evidence is presented for the existence of intermediate free radicals, $RC(ONa)(OC_2H_5)$, and acyl sodium compounds, $RCONa$. Esters of glutaric and adipic acids give α-hydroxy alicyclic ketones.[761] Several aromatic aldehydes, acids, and esters have been condensed by metals in a similar manner.[638,645]

Aromatic α-hydroxy ketones (benzoins) are best obtained by the condensation of aromatic aldehydes by alkali cyanides. An aqueous-alcoholic solution of the aldehyde and sodium cyanide is refluxed for a short time.[640,642]

$$2ArCHO \xrightarrow{NaCN} ArCH(OH)COAr$$

Crossed condensation of two aldehydes has been accomplished as in the preparation of p-methoxybenzoin.[644] The condensation is reversible, as has been demonstrated by the preparation of mixed benzoins from benzoin and an aromatic aldehyde.[641]

The mechanism and experimental conditions for these reactions have been discussed in two reviews of all methods for the synthesis of benzoins[760] and acyloins.[779]

105. α-Hydroxy Ketones by Interaction of Dicarbonyl Compounds and Aromatic Hydrocarbons

$$ArCOCHO + Ar'H \xrightarrow{AlCl_3} ArCOCH(OH)Ar$$

This reaction was first described as a new synthesis for mixed benzoins.[648] A solution of the aryl glyoxal in the aromatic hydrocarbon is stirred at 0° for 5–20 hours with aluminum chloride. Carbon disulfide may be used as a solvent if necessary. The yields vary from 35% to 90%. The reaction has been extended to the preparation of α-hydroxy ketones of the types RCOCHOHAr[649] and CH₃COCOH(CH₃)Ar[650] by substituting t-butylglyoxal and biacetyl, respectively, for the aryl glyoxal.

106. Alkylation of Phenols

$$C_6H_5OH + (CH_3)_3COH \xrightarrow{AlCl_3} p\text{-}(CH_3)_3CC_6H_4OH$$

Alkylation of the aromatic nucleus has been discussed previously (method 1). Phenols are alkylated chiefly in the *para* position by tertiary alcohols[773,775] or olefins.[778,796] The yields of product range from 24% to 64%. Primary alkyl radicals isomerize to secondary alkyl groups.[774] The best method for the preparation of n-alkylphenols is by reduction of the corresponding acyl derivatives (method 3).[528,651,795,797]

Boron trifluoride catalyzes the condensation of phenol and propylene to isopropyl phenyl ether and the subsequent rearrangement of this compound to o-isopropyl phenol.[772] This rearrangement of an aryl alkyl ether is similar to the Fries reaction of phenolic esters (method 209).

Indirect methylation of reactive phenols is sometimes accomplished by condensation of two molecules of the phenol with one molecule of formaldehyde. The resulting diphenylmethane derivative may be reduced with zinc and sodium hydroxide or cleaved by alkali to the methylated phenol.[776,777] A modification of this procedure involves dimethylaminomethylation of the phenol followed by hydrogenolysis of the dimethylaminomethyl group.[634]

107. Oxidation of Olefinic Compounds to Glycols

$$RCH=CHR + H_2O_2 \xrightarrow[H_2O]{HCO_2H} RCH(OH)CH(OH)R$$

This method has been employed extensively for the conversion of olefins to *glycols* and olefinic acids to *dihydroxy acids*. The best general reagent is performic acid. The olefinic compound is stirred at 40° with a solution of 30% hydrogen peroxide in aqueous formic acid. Only a slight excess of hydrogen peroxide is required. The yields of dihydroxy compounds are 40–99% from 1-olefins,[600] olefinic alicyclic hydrocarbons,[597,601] and olefinic acids.[598] The double bond in the α,β-position of several acids and esters has been hydroxylated by 90% hydrogen peroxide at 55–95°.[599] Epoxides are first formed in the reaction (cf. method 126). These compounds react with formic acid to give hydroxy formoxy compounds, which are then hydrolyzed to the dihydroxy compounds. Inversion of a carbon atom occurs during cleavage of the epoxide in acid solution. The reaction has been reviewed.[735]

Hydroxylation by hydrogen peroxide in t-butyl alcohol solution is catalyzed by osmium tetroxide.[603–605] The catalyst is volatile and dangerous to handle[610] but is conveniently used in a solution of the tertiary alcohol. The yields of diols are usually low (30–60%), and the process has not been adapted to large-scale preparations. In contrast to hydroxylation by performic acid, this procedure leads to cis addition of the two hydroxyl groups to the double bond. An extensive study of other catalysts has been made.[734] Some catalysts, e.g., selenium dioxide and pertungstic acid, catalyze addition in the trans direction. Hydroxylation of cyclopentadiene takes place in the 1,4-positions to give 2-cyclopenten-1,4-diol.[612]

Osmium tetroxide is also a catalyst in the oxidation of the double bond by chlorates. Cis addition of hydroxyl groups takes place as is shown by the preparation of cis-1,2-cyclohexanediol from cyclohexene[607] and the formation of the proper diastereoisomeric dihydroxy derivatives of maleic, fumaric,[610] and 4-halocrotonic acids.[608,609] Silver chlorate is preferred to potassium chlorate in the hydroxylation of crotonic acid.[602]

Perbenzoic acid is an important reagent for the preparation of epoxides from olefinic compounds (method 126). When the epoxides are unstable in aqueous solution, glycols are formed directly. The over-all reaction results in trans addition of hydroxy groups to the double bond for crotonic and isocrotonic acids.[602]

Other reagents used for hydroxylations of this type are peracetic acid[613] and a neutral solution of potassium permanganate.[611,620]

108. Phenols by Dehydrogenation of Cyclic Ketones

The dehydrogenation of alicyclic 6-membered rings to aromatic hydrocarbons is discussed elsewhere (method 2). When a carbonyl group is present in the ring, fair yields of phenols can sometimes be obtained. Dehydrogenation by sulfur or selenium[771] has largely been replaced by catalytic dehydrogenation over nickel[769] or palladium[768,770] catalysts.

109. Unsaturated Alcohols by Oxidation of Olefins or Acetylenes[793]

$$RCH = CHCH_2R \xrightarrow{SeO_2} RCH = CHCHOHR$$

110. Oxidation of Phenols (Elbs)

where Z = H, Cl, CHO, or NO$_2$ (20-48%).[783,791,799]

111. Condensation of Alcohols by Sodium (Guerbet)[767]

$$3RCH_2CH_2OH \xrightarrow[H_2O]{Na,\ Cu\ bronze,\ 300°;} RCH_2CH_2CHRCH_2OH + RCH_2CO_2H$$

112. Condensation of Aromatic Compounds with Ethylene Oxide[788]

$$ArH \xrightarrow[AlCl_3]{Ethylene\ oxide} ArCH_2CH_2OH$$

113. Condensation of Pyridine or Quinoline with Ketones[786]

$$C_5H_5N + R_2CO \xrightarrow[H_2O]{Mg,HgCl_2;} \alpha\text{-}C_5H_4NC(OH)R_2$$

114. Hydrolysis of α-Diazo Ketones[764,765]

$$RCOCl \xrightarrow{CH_2N_2} RCOCHN_2 \xrightarrow[H^+]{H_2O} RCOCH_2OH$$

TABLE 11. HYDROXY COMPOUNDS

C_n	Compound	Method	Yield (%)	Chapter[ref.]	B.p./mm., n_D^t, (M.p.), Deriv.
		Aliphatic Alcohols			
C_3	2-Propanol	79	100	5[99]	82*
		79	100	5[111]	
C_4	1-Butanol	79	85	5[2]	1.3977[25]
		90	80	5[446]	117/740, 1.3993[23], 71Nu
	2-Butanol	79	87	5[2]	1.3956[25]
		101	77	5[582]	98
	2-Methyl-2-propanol	101	40	5[581]	82
C_5	1-Pentanol	84	61	5[1]	137/740*, 1.4101*, 46Pu*
		84	94	5[34]	136
		88	68	5[255]	136/733, 1.4099
		90	76	5[446]	136/740, 1.4100[23], 66Nu
	2-Pentanol	90	54	5[466]	119/745, 1.4801, 61Db
	3-Pentanol	80	60	5[177]	
		91	70	5[407]	115, 1.4078
	2-Methyl-1-butanol	84	78	5[33]	120–124
		88	66	5[285]	128/749
	3-Methyl-1-butanol	90	74	5[446]	130/740, 1.4081[23], 67Nu
		90	60	5[445]	131
	Methylisopropylcarbinol	88	56	5[256]	111/727, 1.4090
		88	54	5[267]	111
	t-Amyl alcohol	101	74	5[583]	100–103
	t-Butylcarbinol	84	88	5[34]	111/738
C_6	1-Hexanol	79	100	5[111]	69/20, 1.4134[25], 42Pu
		84	92	5[33]	153
		90	71	5[446]	154/740, 1.4131[23], 59Nu
		90	62	5[442]	154–157
	2-Hexanol	88	66	5[266]	136
		90	51	5[466]	140/740, 1.4155, 37Db
	2-Methyl-1-pentanol	84	66	5[10]	148/766
		111	72	5[767]	148
	3-Methyl-1-pentanol	90	65	5[446]	152/740, 1.4112[23], 58Nu
	4-Methyl-1-pentanol	90	69	5[446]	151/740, 1.4132[23], 60Nu
	Dimethyl-n-propylcarbinol	89	50	5[351]	123/762, 1.4125[16]
	3-Methyl-2-pentanol	85	75	5[306]	131, 1.4198, 47Db
	4-Methyl-2-pentanol	79	95	5[137]	131/740
		88	49	5[260]	130
		88	42	5[256]	130/734, 1.4111, 97Nu
		90	38	5[466]	68/52, 1.4120, 62Db
	Methyldiethylcarbinol	89	67	5[264]	117–121
		89	71	5[264]	122
	3,3-Dimethyl-1-butanol (neopentylcarbinol)	90	15	5[444]	142, 84Db
	2-Ethyl-1-butanol	84	63	5[19]	147/743, 1.4234[17]
	Ethylisopropylcarbinol	88	52	5[256]	126/742, 1.4170

TABLE 11. HYDROXY COMPOUNDS   183

TABLE 11 *(continued)*

C_n	Compound	Method	Yield (%)	Chapter[ref.]	B.p./mm., n_D^t, (M.p.), Deriv.
				Aliphatic Alcohols *(continued)*	
C_6	2,3-Dimethyl-2-butanol	91	92	5[264]	119/759, 1.4169
	Methyl-*t*-butylcarbinol	79	75	5[121]	120
		79	100	5[138]	117/740
		88	28	5[261]	117–121, 76Pu
C_7	1-Heptanol	79	86	5[4]	175/750
		79	81	5[88]	174, 72/12
		90	69	5[446]	174/740, 1.4231[23], 62Nu
	2-Heptanol	79	65	5[115]	156
		90	56	5[466]	77/24, 1.4214, 48Db
	3-Heptanol	88	40	5[284]	155/745, 1.4197
	4-Heptanol (di-*n*-propyl-carbinol)	80	92	5[177]	155*
		88	63	5[284]	154/745, 1.4199
	3-Methyl-1-hexanol	90	63	5[446]	162/740, 1.4213[23], 45Nu
	4-Methyl-1-hexanol	84	83	5[45]	84/24, 1.4223[27]
		90	58	5[446]	169/740, 1.4233[23], 50Nu
	5-Methyl-1-hexanol	90	59	5[446]	169/740, 1.4251[23], 55Db
		90	53	5[9]	100/45, 82Pu
	2-Methyl-2-hexanol	89	68	5[337]	142/730, 1.4186
		89	92	5[349]	137–141
		89	60	5[343]	60/25, 1.4176
	4-Methyl-2-hexanol	90	31	5[466]	86/44, 1.4223, 63Db
	5-Methyl-2-hexanol	90	15	5[466]	73/32, 1.4227, 36Db
		88	65	5[256]	151/742, 1.4180, 85Nu
	2-Methyl-3-hexanol	88	62	5[256]	145/734, 1.4213
	3-Methyl-3-hexanol	89	64	5[349]	138
	2,4-Dimethyl-1-pentanol	84	77	5[18]	54/7
		88	30	5[260]	66/18, 1.427
	3,4-Dimethyl-1-pentanol	90	46	5[446]	161/740, 1.4261[23]
	4,4-Dimethyl-1-pentanol	87	90	5[197]	96/62, 1.4202, 81Nu
	3-Ethyl-2-pentanol	79	70	5[116]	151/743
	2,3-Dimethyl-2-pentanol	85	80	5[306]	137, 1.4262
		89	35	5[349]	130
	2,4-Dimethyl-2-pentanol	89	54	5[349]	128
		91	82	5[264]	132/760, 1.4162
	4,4-Dimethyl-2-pentanol	79	72	5[113]	137/736, 1.4188, 87Nu
		90	15	5[466]	65/40, 1.4248, 50Db
	3-Ethyl-3-pentanol	89	63	5[116]	73/50, 1.4305
	2,2-Dimethyl-3-pentanol	88	62	5[263]	135–138
		91	88	5[424]	140
	2,3-Dimethyl-3-pentanol	89	59	5[343]	45/14, 1.4287
		89	50	5[338]	51/20, 1.4283
	2,4-Dimethyl-3-pentanol	88	78	5[262]	134–138, 99Pu
		91	100	5[409]	132
	3-Methyl-2-ethyl-1-butanol	84	70	5[17]	66/14, 49 Db

For explanations and symbols see pp. xi-xii.

TABLE 11 *(continued)*

C_n	Compound	Method	Yield (%)	Chapter[ref.]	B.p./mm., n_D^t, (M.p.), Deriv.
				Aliphatic Alcohols *(continued)*	
C_7	2,3,3-Trimethyl-2-butanol	89	75	5[345]	50/20
		89	28	5[349]	130
	Pentamethylethanol hydrate	89	62	5[346]	(83)
C_8	1-Octanol	84	94	5[33]	190
		84	75	5[7]	104/16
		90	49	5[446]	192/740, 1.4303[23], 66Nu
	2-Octanol	....	42	5[792]	77/15, 1.4264
	3-Methyl-1-heptanol	90	43	5[446]	101/26, 1.4293[23]
	3-Methyl-2-heptanol	79	77	5[212]	173/760, 1.436[13]
	6-Methyl-2-heptanol	80	96	5[176]	80/16, 1.4273[19]
	3-Methyl-3-heptanol	89	71	5[343]	66/15, 1.4279
	3-Methyl-4-heptanol	88	62	5[273]	70/15
	2-Ethyl-1-hexanol	84	58	5[6]	90/18, 1.4328
		111	91	5[767]	
	4-Ethyl-1-hexanol	90	38	5[443]	96/20
	2,2-Dimethyl-1-hexanol	88	63	5[343]	81/14, 1.4304
	2,3-Dimethyl-2-hexanol	89	80	5[354]	151/760
	5,5-Dimethyl-2-hexanol	88	60	5[693]	166, 1.4229
	2,3-Dimethyl-3-hexanol	89	32	5[264]	62/14, 1.4309
		89	35	5[343]	43/6, 1.4300
	2,4-Dimethyl-3-hexanol	88	30	5[693]	160, 1.4316
	3,4-Dimethyl-3-hexanol	89	25	5[264]	68/16, 1.4313
	2,4-Dimethyl-4-hexanol	89	56	5[699]	153, 1.4277[18]
	2-Propyl-1-pentanol	84	50	5[8]	179
	2-Methyl-2-ethyl-1-pentanol	88	30	5[258]	76/15, 1.4353
	2,3,3-Trimethyl-2-pentanol	89	65	5[339]	84/58, 1.4280
	2,3,4-Trimethyl-2-pentanol	89	58	5[341]	156/752, 1.4400[13]
		91	40 †	5[410]	50/7, 1.4350
	2,4,4-Trimethyl-2-pentanol	89	78	5[344]	38/8, 1.4272
		....	60	5[782]	146, 1.4301[23]
	2,2,3-Trimethyl-3-pentanol	89	60	5[339]	76/40, 1.4353
	2,2,4-Trimethyl-3-pentanol	88	44	5[262]	148-152, 89Pu
	2,3,4-Trimethyl-3-pentanol	89	95	5[340]	101/125, 1.4350
	2,2,3,3-Tetramethyl-1-butanol	87	53 †	5[198]	(150), 66Pu
C_9	5-Nonanol (di-*n*-butylcarbinol)	91	85	5[408]	97/20
	4-Methyl-1-octanol	84	81	5[45]	105/18, 1.4320[27]
	5-Methyl-1-octanol	84	58	5[16]	123/37
	7-Methyl-1-octanol (isononyl alcohol)	84	57	5[9]	100/13, 65Pu
		90	49	5[9]	118/25, 65Pu
	Dimethyl-*n*-hexylcarbinol	89	85	5[342]	84/20, 1.427
	Methylethyl-*n*-amylcarbinol	89	24	5[272]	98/50, 1.4257[25]
		89	76	5[343]	81/15, 1.4315

TABLE 11. HYDROXY COMPOUNDS 185

TABLE 11 (continued)

C_n	Compound	Method	Yield (%)	Chapter[ref.]	B.p./mm., n_D^t, (M.p.), Deriv.
		Aliphatic Alcohols (continued)			
C_9	Methyl-n-propyl-n-butylcarbinol	89	68	5[343]	79/15, 1.4327
	2,2-Dimethyl-1-heptanol	88	41	5[258]	89/15, 1.4339
	Diethyl-n-butylcarbinol	89	67	5[342]	96/36, 1.4362
	n-Butyl-t-butylcarbinol	91	69	5[416]	71/15, 1.4320, 65Pu
	Methyl-n-butylisopropylcarbinol	89	61	5[343]	57/5, 1.4365
		89	65	5[342]	77/16, 1.4355
	2-Methyl-2-ethyl-1-hexanol	88	31	5[258]	86/11, 1.4401
	Diethyl-t-butylcarbinol	91	77	5[415]	84/40, 1.4418
	Methylisopropyl-t-butylcarbinol	89	71	5[353]	172–176, 1.4495[17]
C_{12}	Dodecyl alcohol (lauryl alcohol)	84	75	5[5]	145/18
		84	80	5[15]	117/4, (24), 74Pu
C_{14}	1-Tetradecanol (myristyl alcohol)	84	60	5[36]	130/3, (38.5)
C_{15}	1-Pentadecanol	84	85	5[259]	113/0.2
C_{18}	1-Octadecanol	84	90	5[37]	(59)
		Alicyclic Alcohols			
C_4	Cyclobutanol	79	90	5[605]	125, 1.4347[25], 131Pu
	Cyclopropylcarbinol	84	27	5[53]	121/730, 1.4273[23]
		84	58	5[664]	123, 1.426, 76Pu
C_5	Cyclopentanol	79	95	5[128]	139, 1.4530
		79	90	5[2]	1.4520[25]
		79	100	5[138]	137
	Cyclobutylcarbinol	84	49	5[25]	142, 1.4449[25]
	Methylcyclopropylcarbinol	79	60	5[678]	124/760, 1.4316, 70Pu
		79	90	5[117]	122/760, 1.4316
	1-Methylcyclopropanemethanol	84	56	5[663]	128/750, 1.4308, 85Db
C_6	Cyclohexanol	80	95	5[177]	
		86	100	5[569]	159, 1.4642, 83Pu
	1-Methylcyclopentanol	89	....	5[358]	81/100, (36), 83NBz
	2-Methylcyclopentanol	79	100	5[125]	148, 1.4510
	3-Methylcyclopentanol	79	100	5[127]	150/750
	Cyclopentylcarbinol	88	40	5[270]	162, 1.4552
	Dimethylcyclopropylcarbinol	91	85	5[411]	124/760
		89	68	5[355]	123/760, 1.4337
C_7	Cycloheptanol	79	92	5[122]	187, 1.4760
	1-Methylcyclohexanol	89	64	5[357]	74/7, 1.4610
	2-Methylcyclohexanol	84	61	5[33]	162
	cis-2-Methylcyclohexanol	79	70	5[673]	45/2, 1.4620[25]
		86	....	5[723]	51/3, 1.4649, 93Pu

For explanations and symbols see pp. xi–xii.

TABLE 11 *(continued)*

C_n	Compound	Method	Yield (%)	Chapter[ref.]	B.p./mm., n_D^t, (M.p.), Deriv.
				Alicyclic Alcohols *(continued)*	
C_7	*trans*-2-Methylcyclohexanol	86	100	5[569]	164, 1.4602, 106Pu
		86	....	5[723]	53/3.5, 1.4616, 105Pu
		95	85	5[673]	61/10, 1.4596[25]
	3-Methylcyclohexanol	86	92	5[722]	82/20, 1.4570
	trans-3-Methylcyclohexanol	86	100	5[569]	169, 1.4545, 92Pu
	cis-4-Methylcyclohexanol	86	....	5[723]	52/2, 1.4614, 104Pu
	trans-4-Methylcyclohexanol	86	92	5[568]	170, 1.4551, 124Pu
		86	....	5[723]	1.4561, 124Pu
	cis- and *trans*-2-, 3-, and 4-Methylcyclohexanols	79		5[131]	
	Cyclohexylcarbinol	84	98	5[33]	181
		88	69	5[268]	91/18, 1.4640[25]
	β-Cyclopentylethanol	90	45	5[451]	85/11, 1.4577
	1-Ethylcyclopentanol	89	....	5[358]	75/20, 1.4494[25], 53NBz
	trans-2-Ethylcyclopentanol	79	90	5[132]	166, 70Pu
	3,3-Dimethylcyclopentanol	79	89	5[123]	155/738, 1.4468[15]
C_8	Cyclooctanol	79	98	5[122]	112/25, (25)
	β-Cyclohexylethyl alcohol	84	94	5[20]	102/12
		90	51	5[448]	89/7, 1.4693[23], 71Db
	1-Ethylcyclohexanol	89	62	5[357]	62/7, 1.4633
	2-Ethylcyclohexanol	86	93	5[722]	89/20, 1.4660
		86	80	5[579]	76–79/12
	trans-2-Ethylcyclohexanol	90	42	5[450]	89/25
	3-Ethylcyclohexanol	86	94	5[568]	192, 1.4600[25], 99Nu
	4-Ethylcyclohexanol	86	88	5[568]	192, 115Pu
	trans, cis, trans-2,5-Dimethylcyclohexanol	86	94	5[568]	180, 1.4555, 117Pu
	trans, cis, cis-3,5-Dimethylcyclohexanol	86	91	5[568]	182, 107Pu
	2,4-Dimethylcyclohexanol	86	91	5[568]	177, 1.4544, 96Pu
	2,6-Dimethylcyclohexanol	86	73	5[570]	172, 1.4625, 132Pu
	3,3-Dimethylcyclohexanol	79	75	5[123]	78/10
	3,4-Dimethylcyclohexanol	86	98	5[568]	189, 1.4570, 97Pu
	3,5-Dimethylcyclohexanol	86	93	5[571]	91/20, 1.4550
	1-*n*-Propylcyclopentanol	91	65	5[703]	171/760, 1.4504
		89	....	5[358]	71/9, 1.4502[25], 60NBz
C_9	3-Cyclohexyl-1-propanol	88	79	5[257]	92/5, 1.4624[25]
	1-*n*-Propyl-1-cyclohexanol	91	41	5[703]	180/760, 1.4634
		89	57	5[357]	86/15, 1.4635
	cis-2-*n*-Propylcyclohexanol	86	94	5[568]	202, 95Pu
	4-*n*-Propylcyclohexanol	79	71	5[126]	211/745, 1.4506[25], 135Nu
	1-Isopropylcyclohexanol	89	41	5[357]	68/7, 1.4648

TABLE 11. HYDROXY COMPOUNDS 187

TABLE 11 *(continued)*

C_n	Compound	Method	Yield (%)	Chapter[ref.]	B.p./mm., n_D^t, (M.p.), Deriv.
	Alicyclic Alcohols (continued)				
C_9	*cis*-4-Isopropylcyclo-hexanol	79	100	5[124]	68/0.6, 1.4671, 89Pu
	trans-4-Isopropylcyclo-hexanol		90	5[124]	1.4658, 114Pu
	4-Isopropylcyclohexanol	86	96	5[561]	124/40, 1.4660
	2,4,6-Trimethylcyclo-hexanol	86	90	5[568]	183
	2,3,5-Trimethylcyclo-hexanol	86	90	5[568]	197, 1.4572[25], 149Nu
	4-Cyclopentyl-1-butanol	90	75	5[451]	90/2, 1.4613
C_{10}	α-Decalol	80	95	5[177]	
	cis-2-Decalol	87	48	5[199]	124–130/16
	trans-2-Decalol	87	53	5[199]	120–126/13
C_{12}	*cis*-2-Cyclohexylcyclo-hexanol	79	....	5[148]	265/748, (63), 153Pu
	trans-4-Cyclohexylcyclo-hexanol	79	86	5[574]	(104), 157Pu
C_{13}	Dicyclohexylcarbinol	79	88	5[2]	(62)
	Aromatic Alcohols and Phenols				
C_7	Benzyl alcohol	79	85	5[4]	
		79	100	5[111]	105/20, 1.5340[25], 76Pu
		80	89	5[173]	90/7
		81	80	5[513]	
		84	90	5[4]	
		84	63	5[23]	104/23, 85NBz
	o-Cresol (*o*-methylphenol)	3	86	5[797]	
		93	40	5[476]	70/6
		93	89	5[705]	190/746, (34)
	m-Cresol (*m*-methylphenol)	93	41	5[476]	81/6
	p-Cresol (*p*-methylphenol)	92	72	5[563]	96/15, (31)
		93	46	5[476]	195–200
C_8	Phenylmethylcarbinol	79	97	5[679]	93/16, 1.5251[25], 94Pu
		80	93	5[177]	
		84	95	5[274]	93/16
		88	80	5[265]	111/28
	β-Phenylethanol	90	70	5[447]	94/5, 1.5351, 119Nu
		84	47	5[21]	117/25
		112	45	5[788]	
	p-Ethylphenol	3	100	5[651]	217/750, (46)
		79	86	5[568]	215/739
		92	58	5[565]	219

For explanations and symbols see pp. xi–xii.

TABLE 11 *(continued)*

C_n	Compound	Method	Yield (%)	Chapter[ref.]	B.p./mm., n_D^t, (M.p.), Deriv.
				Aromatic Alcohols and Phenols (continued)	
C_8	o-Methylbenzyl alcohol	84	70	5[23]	121/23, 101NBz
		88	42	5[281]	109/12, (35), 79Pu
	p-Methylbenzyl alcohol	81	72	5[513]	117/20, (61)
		84	70	5[23]	(58), 118Db
	p-Xylenol	93	70	5[474]	212/760, (74)
C_9	Ethylphenylcarbinol	79	99	5[114]	93/4, 1.5208
		79	100	5[138]	214/740
	3-Phenyl-1-propanol	79	100	5[111]	84/1, 1.5354[25]
		84	93	5[33]	124/19
		84	80	5[15]	87/2, 1.5218[25], 48Pu
		84	83	5[34]	112/8
		85	93	5[105]	132/21, 1.5278
		90	79	5[446]	234/740, 1.5351[23], 47Pu
		97	85	5[713]	116/13, 1.5242[25]
	1-Phenyl-2-propanol	90	53	5[452]	93/8, 1.5210[25], 87Pu
		90	60	5[281]	107/15, 1.5196[26], 89Pu
		90	67	5[466]	95/7, 1.5221, 90Nu
	o-n-Propylphenol	79	83	5[568]	215/740, 110Pu
	p-n-Propylphenol	97	93	5[528]	80/1
	o-Isopropylphenol	106	41	5[772]	
	p-Isopropylphenol	92	35†	5[561]	(59)
		93	74	5[475]	(60)
	m-Methylphenylmethyl-carbinol	88	71	5[271]	104/6, 1.5240
	2,3,6-Trimethylphenol (3-pseudocumenol)	96	82	5[548]	(56)
	5-Hydroxyhydrindene	93	69	5[478]	(54)
C_{10}	2-Phenyl-1-butanol	84	75	5[22]	122/18
		84	64	5[33]	235
	3-Phenyl-1-butanol	84	66	5[27]	120/11
		97	68	5[713]	122/13, 1.5165[25]
	4-Phenyl-1-butanol	84	94	5[20]	126/9
		88	60	5[362]	137/14
		90	60	5[362]	137/14
	2-Phenyl-2-butanol	89	88	5[360]	88/3, 107/15
	4-Phenyl-2-butanol	79	77	5[120]	124/15
	Phenylisopropylcarbinol	88	83	5[265]	103/7
	p-Isopropylbenzyl alcohol	79	70	5[93]	91/0.7, 1.5181, 62Pu
	(Cumyl alcohol)	84	81	5[23]	136/26, 92 Db
	o-t-Butylphenol	7	91	5[796]	218, 1.5160
	p-t-Butylphenol	106	60	5[773]	237/740, (100), 82Bz
	β-Naphthol	92	80	5[562]	286, (123)

TABLE 11. HYDROXY COMPOUNDS 189

TABLE 11 (continued)

C_n	Compound	Method	Yield (%)	Chapter ref.	B.p./mm., n_D^t, (M.p.), Deriv.
		Aromatic Alcohols and Phenols (continued)			
C_{11}	1-Phenyl-1-pentanol	79	99	5^{114}	115/6, 1.5078
		88	62	5^{362}	137/21
		88	85	5^{265}	130/13
	5-Phenyl-1-pentanol	88	68	5^{362}	151/13
		90	68	5^{362}	151/13
		99	72	5^{624}	141/16*
	1-Phenyl-2-pentanol	88	28	5^{362}	127/15
	4-Phenyl-2-pentanol	79	89	5^{135}	124/15
	1-Phenyl-3-pentanol	88	50	5^{362}	130/15
	1-Phenyl-1-cyclopentanol	91	66	5^{703}	136/12, 1.5473
	Phenyl-t-butylcarbinol	88	56	5^{279}	110/15, (45)
	p-n-Amylphenol	3	85	5^{528}	107/2
	p-t-Amylphenol	106	60	5^{773}	249/740, (95), 61Bz
	α-Naphthylcarbinol	84	63	5^{29}	(60)
		88	58	5^{309}	163/11, (60)
	β-Naphthylcarbinol	79	80	5^{101}	(80)
		84	35	5^{28}	(81)
	1-Methyl-1-tetralol	89	94	5^{359}	(87)
C_{12}	1-Phenyl-1-cyclohexanol	91	51	5^{703}	144/12, (60)
	cis-2-Phenylcyclohexanol	86	75	5^{573}	141/16, (42), 128Pu
	trans-2-Phenylcyclohexanol	79	36	5^{682}	(57), 137Pu
		79	60	5^{573}	154/16, (57), 137Pu
	cis-4-Phenylcyclohexanol	79	29	5^{574}	(77), 141Pu
	trans-4-Phenylcyclohexanol	79	60	5^{574}	(118), 140Pu
	β-(1-Naphthyl)-ethyl alcohol	90	76	5^{454}	176/13
	β-(2-Naphthyl)-ethyl alcohol	90	45	5^{456}	(67)
	Methyl-α-naphthylcarbinol	79	85	5^{134}	121/1, 1.6188^{25}
		80	95	5^{177}	
	Methyl-β-naphthylcarbinol	79	100	5^{111}	126/2, (68), 144Pu
		79	75	5^{134}	(73)
		80	90	5^{177}	
	2-Acenaphthenol	93	80	5^{477}	(151)
	7-Acenaphthenol	95	74	5^{520}	(146)
C_{13}	o-n-Heptylphenol	3	86	5^{795}	118–123/1
	Diphenylcarbinol	79	81	5^{3}	
	(benzhydrol)	79	100	5^{111}	(69), 140Pu
		79	87	5^{138}	(65)
		79	97	5^{118}	(68)
		80	99	5^{173}	(69)
		88	70	5^{277}	(68)
	2-Phenylbenzyl alcohol	84	85	5^{668}	177/17
		88	66	5^{694}	146–152/4
		93	96	5^{482}	174/13
	2-(α-Naphthyl)-1-propanol	79	79	5^{94}	145/3, 126Db

For explanations and symbols see pp. xi–xii.

TABLE 11 *(continued)*

C_n	Compound	Method	Yield (%)	Chapter ref.	B.p./mm., n_D^t, (M.p.), Deriv.
				Aromatic Alcohols and Phenols *(continued)*	
C_{13}	1-(α-Naphthyl)-2-propanol	80	83	5 [684]	173/17, 1.604 [22], 108Pu
	2-Hydroxyfluorene	93	57	5 [480]	(169)
		95	38	5 [547]	(138)
	9-Hydroxyfluorene	96	69	5 [547]	(158)
C_{14}	2,2-Diphenylethanol	84	93	5 [24]	145/1, (55), 92Bz
	1,2-Diphenylethanol	88	78	5 [275]	177/15, (67)
	Benzylcyclohexylcarbinol	88	42	5 [269]	174/12
	1-(2-Biphenyl)-1-ethanol	88	56	5 [449]	(112)
	1-Phenanthrol	93	11	5 [479]	(156)*
	2-Phenanthrol	92	50	5 [481]	(167)
		93	40	5 [479]	
	3-Phenanthrol	93	39	5 [479]	(122)*
	9-Phenanthrol	97	30	5 [531]	(154)
	2-Hydroxy-9,10-dihydro-phenanthrene	93	69	5 [481]	(113)
	9-Hydroxyperhydro-phenanthrene	80	83	5 [685]	132/0.5
	9-Fluorenylcarbinol	80	50	5 [181]	(100), 212Db
	1-Acenaphthenylmethyl-carbinol	79	83	5 [134]	(83)
C_{15}	1,2-Diphenyl-1-propanol	79	75	5 [112]	(53), 122Pu
		88	65	5 [112]	182/18, 116Pu
	Dibenzylcarbinol	79	89	5 [120]	199/15
	2-Fluorenylmethylcarbinol	79	65	5 [134]	(140)
C_{16}	1-Phenanthrylmethylcarbinol	88	90	5 [280]	(110)
	β-(9-Phenanthryl)-ethyl alcohol	90	50	5 [453]	(92)
C_{17}	Diphenyl-*t*-butylcarbinol	91	63	5 [419]	149/2.5, 1.5748
C_{19}	Triphenylcarbinol	91	93	5 [420]	(162)
C_{20}	α,β,β-Triphenylethanol	91	32	5 [425]	(88)
C_{21}	Di-α-naphthylcarbinol	91	80	5 [418]	(144)
C_{27}	Di-α-naphthylphenylcarbinol	91	35	5 [423]	(167)
C_{37}	Tribiphenylcarbinol	91	40	5 [422]	(208)
				Heterocyclic Alcohols	
C_4	3-Hydroxytetrahydrofuran	....	30 †	39 [52]	48/0.5
	2-Thienol	87	25	5 [683]	75/5, 1.5644
C_5	2-Furylcarbinol (furfuryl alcohol)	79	90	5 [97]	169/754, 1.4828
		80	88	5 [251]	173
		81	63	5 [508]	76/15
	3-Furylcarbinol	84	91	5 [659]	55/2, 1.4842, 105Pu
	Tetrahydrofurfuryl alcohol	84	55	5 [84]	61Pu
		554	85	39 [97]	178/743, 1.4502 [19]

TABLE 11. HYDROXY COMPOUNDS 191

TABLE 11 (continued)

C_n	Compound	Method	Yield (%)	Chapter[ref.]	B.p./mm., n_D^t, (M.p.), Deriv.
		Heterocyclic Alcohols (continued)			
C_5	2-Thenyl alcohol	95	49	5[708]	96/12, 1.5630[25]
	5-Hydroxy-2-methyl-thiophene	561	19	39[28]	96/15
	Sodium 2-pyridolate	93	95	5[484]	
	3-Hydroxypyridine	96	28	5[552]	(127)
	4-Hydroxypiperidine	554	30	39[119]	213/748, (87), 148HCl
C_6	2-(α-Furyl)-1-ethanol	84	32	5[54]	87/21, 1.4788[25], 86Nu
	α-Furylmethylcarbinol	88	56	5[287]	70/15, 1.4827[15]
	5-Methylfurfuryl alcohol	79	70	5[96]	98/36, 1.4853
	2-(α-Tetrahydrofuryl)-2-ethanol	554	90	39[99]	71/16, 1.4500[17], 84Pu
	2-(α-Thienyl)-ethanol	90	47	5[459]	100/7, 1.5478, 53Pu
	α-Thienylmethylcarbinol	80	87	5[134]	92/11, 1.5422[25]
		88	79	5[289]	91/11
	β-(1-Pyrryl)-ethyl alcohol	95	100	5[514]	112/12
	2-Pyridylmethanol	87	21	5[248]	111–115/16, 150Pi
	3-Pyridylmethanol	79	90	5[98]	145/16, 158Pi
	4-Pyridylcarbinol	93	65	5[706]	141/12, (41), 166Pi
	α-Piperidylcarbinol	84	29	5[58]	82/1
		84	92	5[84]	88/5, (70), 135Pi
	β-Piperidylcarbinol	84	43	5[59]	107/3.5, 1.4964
	1-Methyl-4-piperidinol	79	90	5[133]	97/16
	1-Methyl-3-hydroxy-piperidine	574	39	5[785]	79/15, 1.4695[16], 194Bz
C_7	3-(α-Furyl)-1-propanol	79	80	5[100]	105–115/21, 1.4764[27], 59Nu
	3-(α-Tetrahydrofuryl)-1-propanol	79	65	5[95]	106/10, 1.4560[25]
		84	75	5[55]	112/11, 1.4597[13]
		554	92	39[98]	112/10
	3-(α-Tetrahydrofuryl)-3-propanol	554	88	39[99]	84/15, 1.4527[1]
	α-Furylethylcarbinol	88	82	5[288]	90/23, 1.4759
	2-Furylethynylcarbinol	88	65	5[321]	84/2
	2-(1-Pyrrolidyl)-1-propanol	84	79	5[665]	80/11, 1.4758[25]
	1-(1-Pyrrolidyl)-2-propanol	558	77	39[109]	117/110
	β-(2-Pyridyl)-ethyl alcohol	88	50	5[286]	89/2
		102	32	5[787]	107/7
	β-Pyridylmethylcarbinol	79	85	5[136]	124/5
	1-(α-Piperidyl)-2-ethanol	554	82	39[124]	86/1.5
	2-(β-Piperidyl)-1-ethanol	84	63	5[60]	122/6, 1.4888[25]
	β-Piperidinoethanol	554	100	39[116]	196/746
	3-Piperidylmethylcarbinol	554	61	39[95]	104/4
	N-(2-Hydroxyethyl)-piperidine	84	80	5[61]	

For explanations and symbols see pp. xi–xii.

TABLE 11 *(continued)*

C_n	Compound	Method	Yield (%)	Chapter[ref.]	B.p./mm., n_D^t, (M.p.), Deriv.
		Heterocyclic Alcohols *(continued)*			
C_8	α-Furyl-*n*-propylcarbinol	88	55	5[288]	92/12, 1.4768[25]
	1-(α-Tetrahydrofuryl)-3-butanol	554	76	39[97]	94/2, 1.4546[19]
	4-(α-Tetrahydrofuryl)-4-butanol	554	90	39[99]	95/14, 1.4536[14]
	α-Thienyl-*n*-propylcarbinol	88	84	5[289]	85/3
	4-(1-Pyrrolidyl)-butanol	436	72	24[169]	113/12, 1.4705[25]
	2-(1-Pyrrolidyl)-2-methyl-propanol	436	76	24[169]	87/12, (30), 1.4720[30]
	1-(α-Pyridyl)-2-propanol	88	50	5[290]	117/17
	α-Pyridyldimethylcarbinol	113	12	5[786]	89/12, (50)
	1-(γ-Piperidyl)-2-propanol	554	59	39[124]	125/0.8, (47)
	1-(α-Piperidyl)-3-propanol	554	89	39[124]	95/0.6, 1.4863[25]
	1-(γ-Piperidyl)-3-propanol	554	83	39[124]	131/1.5, (65), 155HCl
	3-Hydroxythianaphthene	87	8	5[247]	(70), 225Se
	5-Hydroxythianaphthene	93	51	5[483]	(104)
C_9	5-(α-Furyl)-1-pentanol	84	85	5[56]	128/16, 58Nu
	α-Furyldiethylcarbinol	91	77	5[412]	95/14
	5-(α-Tetrahydrofuryl)-1-pentanol	554	90	39[98]	142/10
	Tetrahydrofuryldiethyl-carbinol	91	76	5[412]	202/740, 1.4552[25]
	3-Piperidino-1-butanol	79	40	5[185]	110/15, 159BzHCl
	2-Hydroxymethyl-thianaphthene	84	99	5[63]	124/1.5 (100)
	2-Hydroxymethylindole	84	68	5[57]	(77)
	4-Hydroxyquinoline	575	53†	39[144]	(200)
	5-Hydroxyquinoline	94	47	5[502]	(224)
	6-Hydroxyquinoline	97	90	5[502]	(193)
	7-Hydroxyquinoline	97	90	5[502]	(238)
	8-Hydroxyquinoline	97	90	5[532]	122/0.1, (77), 204Pi
	5-Hydroxyisoquinoline	92	48	5[566]	(230)
	8-Hydroxyisoquinoline	92	15†	5[566]	(213), 285Pi
C_{10}	2-Methyl-4-hydroxy-quinoline	575	90	39[132]	(236)
		575	90	39[142]	(228)
	4-Methyl-8-hydroxy-quinoline	575	20	39[172]	(141)
C_{11}	o-Furfurylphenol	100	38	5[560]	152/14, 1.5689[17]
C_{12}	1-Ethyl-4-methyl-2-hydroxy-quinoline	575	83	39[173]	136/0.5
	1-Hydroxydibenzofuran	87	31	5[243]	(141)
	2-Hydroxydibenzofuran	87	37	5[244]	(134)
		96	50	5[243]	(134)
	3-Hydroxydibenzofuran	93	24	5[244]	(139)

TABLE 12. DIHYDROXY COMPOUNDS   193

TABLE 11 (continued)

C_n	Compound	Method	Yield (%)	Chapter[ref.]	B.p./mm., n_D^t, (M.p.), Deriv.
		Heterocyclic Alcohols (continued)			
C_{12}	4-Hydroxydibenzofuran	87	35	5[245]	(102)
	4-Hydroxydibenzothiophene	87	33	5[246]	(167)
C_{14}	N-(β-Hydroxyethyl)-carbazole	558	40	39[180]	(83.5)
C_{15}	N-(β-Hydroxypropyl)-carbazole	558	90	39[180]	(121)

For explanations and symbols see pp. xi-xii.

TABLE 12. DIHYDROXY COMPOUNDS

C_n	Compound	Method	Yield (%)	Chapter[ref.]	B.p./mm., n_D^t, (M.p.), Deriv.
		Aliphatic Diols			
C_2	Ethylene glycol	95	90	5[515]	195
C_3	1,2-Propanediol	84	80	5[15]	97/20, 1.4305, 150Pu
		84	91	5[33]	187
		98	95	5[616]	1.4334[17]
	(−)-1,2-Propanediol	79	58	5[141]	89/12
C_4	1,2-Butanediol	98	95	5[616]	1.4388[17]
	1,3-Butanediol	79	86	5[89]	104/8
		84	30	5[50]	115-120/21, 102NBz
		84	80	5[15]	107/14, 1.4381[25], 116Pu
	1,4-Butanediol	84	81	5[34]	106/4
		84	62	5[41]	134/18, 1.4445[25], 183Pu
		95	61	5[517]	127/20, 198Nu
		97	69	5[538]	108/4, (19), 1.4467, 180Pu
	2,3-Butanediol	79	75	5[146]	58/2
		79	62	5[2]	1.4336[25]
		96	50	5[550]	183/760, 1.4364[25]
		98	95	5[614]	(8), (34)
	1,2,4-Butanetriol	84	67	5[15]	133/1, 1.4688
	1,2,3,4-Butanetetrol (erythritol)	84	80	5[15]	(89)
	2-Methyl-1,2-propanediol	84	80	5[15]	80/12, 1.4340[25], 137Pu
		101	94	5[584]	178, 1.4350
		107	38	5[603]	177
C_5	1,4-Pentanediol	84	83	5[43]	123/15
		99	62	5[623]	115/14, 1.4452[25]

For explanations and symbols see pp. xi-xii.

TABLE 12 *(continued)*

C_n	Compound	Method	Yield (%)	Chapter[ref.]	B.p./mm., n_D^t, (M.p.), Deriv.
		Aliphatic Diols *(continued)*			
C_5	1,5-Pentanediol	79	96	5[102]	105/4, 1.4498, 174Du
		84	92	5[33]	109/2.5
		84	80	5[15]	124/7, 1.4490[25], 172Pu
		95	90	5[517]	174Pu
		99	47	5[621]	119/6
	threo-2,3-Pentanediol	98	81	5[615]	83/10, 1.4320, 161Db
	erythro-2,3-Pentanediol	98	81	5[615]	89/10, 1.4431, 207Db
	2,4-Pentanediol	79	80	5[144]	195-199
	1,2,5-Pentanetriol	99	71	5[622]	170/1, 1.4730[25]
	1,3,5-Pentanetriol	84	60	5[15]	139/1, 1.4594[25], 152Pu
	2-Methyl-1,4-butanediol	84	72	5[46]	127/14
	2-Methyl-2,3-butanediol	107	39	5[603]	175
	2-Ethyl-1,3-propanediol	84	80	5[15]	86/2, 1.4480, 123Pu
		84	49	5[50]	87/0.5, 89NBz
	2,2-Dimethyl-1,3-propanediol	81	76	5[506]	200, (130)
	1,1,1-*tris*-(Hydroxymethyl)-ethane	81	51	5[507]	(198)
	Pentaerythritol	81	74	5[509]	(260)
C_6	1,3-Hexanediol	95	....	5[516]	123/13, 1.4461[22], 99Pu
	1,4-Hexanediol	99	90	5[516]	123/9, 1.4530[17], 71Pu
	1,6-Hexanediol	84	90	5[38]	144/4, (42)
		84	83	5[4]	
	2,5-Hexanediol	79	86	5[2]	1.4453[25]
	2-Methyl-1,3-pentanediol	79	75	5[103]	112-115/12
	4-Methyl-1,4-pentanediol	85	83	5[377]	107/6, 158NBz
	3-Methyl-1,5-pentanediol	84	50	5[47]	136/6
	2-Methyl-2,4-pentanediol	79	100	5[138]	111/22
	3-Methyl-2,4-pentanediol	79	63	5[142]	82-90/1
		79	66	5[209]	125/36
	3-Methyl-2,5-pentanediol	84	86	5[48]	134/20
	2-Ethyl-1,3-butanediol	84	80	5[15]	87/2, 1.4473[25], 135Pu
	Pinacol (anhydrous)	82	30	5[596]	172, (38)
	Pinacol hydrate	82	50	5[587]	(47)
	2-(*n*-Propyl)-1,3-propanediol	84	80	5[15]	97/3, 1.4480[25], 125Pu
	2-Methyl-2-ethyl-1,3-propanediol	81	61	5[512]	120/19, (42)
C_7	1,4-Heptanediol	99	29	5[95]	128/6, 1.4520[25]
	1,7-Heptanediol	84	88	5[39]	145/8
	2,4-Heptanediol	79	94	5[158]	108/8, 1.4386[25], 101Pu
	3-Methyl-2,4-hexanediol	79	54	5[145]	109/9, 1.4450
	2-Methyl-3,5-hexanediol	79	73	5[144]	124/24
	3-Ethyl-2,4-pentanediol	79	64	5[144]	205-210

TABLE 12. DIHYDROXY COMPOUNDS 195

TABLE 12 (continued)

C_n	Compound	Method	Yield (%)	Chapter[ref.]	B.p./mm., n_D^t, (M.p.), Deriv.
		Aliphatic Diols (continued)			
C_7	2-Isopropyl-1,3-butanediol	88	72	5[201]	106/4, 1.4528
	2-Isopropyl-1,4-butanediol	84	96	5[655]	129/6, 1.4515[25]
	2-(n-Butyl)-1,3-propanediol	84	80	5[15]	99/2, 1.4492[25], 131Pu
	2,2-Diethyl-1,3-propanediol	81	91	5[506]	131/13, (62)
		84	50	5[662]	112/5, (57)
	1,1,1-tris-(Hydroxymethyl)-2-methylpropane	81	53	5[507]	170–175/6, (82)
C_8	1,2-Octanediol	107	58	5[600]	(30)
	1,8-Octanediol	84	90	5[42]	155/12, (63)
		84	55	5[525]	168/15, (63)
	2,4-Octanediol	79	94	5[158]	118/8, 1.4422[25], 127Pu
	5-Methyl-2,4-heptanediol	79	80	5[158]	112/8, 1.4449[25], 130Pu
	2-Methyl-4,6-heptanediol	79	77	5[144]	125/14
	2,5-Dimethyl-2,5-hexanediol	85	99	5[653]	(89)
	3,4-Dimethyl-3,4-hexanediol	82	40	5[592]	105/21
	2,2-Dimethyl-3,5-hexanediol	79	17	5[144]	105–110/10
	2-Isobutyl-1,3-butanediol	84	17	5[50]	143/22, 130NBz
	2-Methyl-2-butyl-1,3-propanediol	81	82	5[512]	131/15, (48)
C_9	1,9-Nonanediol	84	84	5[40]	148/1
	4-Methyl-1,4-octanediol	84	61	5[45]	126/4, 1.4540[27]
	2-Ethyl-2-butyl-1,3-propanediol	81	70	5[506]	152/10, (42)
		84	45	5[15]	110/2, (39)
C_{10}	1,10-Decanediol	84	74	5[39]	(74)
		84	94	5[33]	151/3, (71)
C_{18}	1,2-Octadecanediol	95	73	5[36]	(79)
		Alicyclic Diols			
C_5	1-(Hydroxymethyl)-1-cyclobutanol	107	39	5[605]	78–85/2
C_6	cis-1,2-Cyclohexanediol	107	46	5[607]	(98)
	trans-1,2-Cyclohexanediol	98	80	5[617]	(104)
		107	73	5[597]	123/4, (103), 92Bz
	cis and trans-1,2-Cyclohexanediols	86	....	5[577]	(98)(104)
	cis-1,3-Cyclohexanediol	86	24	5[725]	137/13, (85), 66Bz
	trans-1,3-Cyclohexanediol	86	16	5[725]	135/13, (118), 124Bz
	cis-1,4-Cyclohexanediol	79	88	5[138]	(102)
		86	38	5[576]	(107)
	trans-1,4-Cyclohexanediol	86	62	5[576]	(142)
	1-Methyl-1,2-cyclopentanediol	107	58	5[601]	89/1, (65), 92Db

For explanations and symbols see pp. xi–xii.

TABLE 12 (continued)

C_n	Compound	Method	Yield (%)	Chapter[ref.]	B.p./mm., n_D^t, (M.p.), Deriv.
		Alicyclic Diols (continued)			
C_6	1-Methyl-2,3-cyclopentanediol	107	65	5 [601]	96/1, 1.4760 [25], 93Db
C_7	1-Methyl-1,2-cyclohexanediol	107	73	5 [601]	107/2, (84), 71Bz
	1-Methyl-2,3-cyclohexanediol	107	80	5 [601]	98/1
	1-Methyl-3,4-cyclohexanediol	107	81	5 [601]	104/1, (68), 121Db
	2-Hydroxymethylcyclohexanol	79	88	5 [143]	136/9, 134NBz
	3-Hydroxymethylcyclohexanol	84	84	5 [667]	166/27, 1.4900, 181Db
	cis-4-Hydroxymethylcyclohexanol	84	....	5 [52]	135–147/3, 181Pu
	trans-4-Hydroxymethylcyclohexanol			5 [52]	(103)
	1,2-Dimethyl-2,3-cyclopentanediol	107	59	5 [601]	86/1, 1.4755 [25]
C_8	cis-1,2-Dimethyl-1,2-cyclohexanediol	107	27	5 [611]	103/10, (50)
C_{10}	1,1'-Dihydroxy-1,1'-dicyclopentyl	82	31	5 [593]	(109)
C_{12}	1,1'-Dihydroxy-1,1'-dicyclohexyl	82	30	5 [593]	(130)
		Aromatic Dihydroxy Compounds			
C_6	o-Dihydroxybenzene (catechol)	97	87	5 [766]	125/12, (105)
	m-Dihydroxybenzene (resorcinol)	92	77	5 [564]	110/25
	p-Dihydroxybenzene (hydroquinone)	110	18	5 [783]	(173)*
	1,2,4-Trihydroxybenzene	95	80	5 [519]	(140)*
	1,3,5-Trihydroxybenzene (phloroglucinol)	94	53	5 [500]	(219)*
C_7	o-Hydroxybenzyl alcohol	79	41	5 [138]	(84)
		79	57	5 [137]	(86)
	m-Hydroxybenzyl alcohol	79	93	5 [2]	(64)
	p-Hydroxybenzyl alcohol	84	60	5 [23]	(125)
C_8	1-Phenyl-1,2-ethanediol	84	80	5 [15]	(68), 150Pu
	Phthalyl alcohol	84	87	5 [4]	(64), 35Ac
	p-Di-(hydroxymethyl)-benzene	96	40	5 [717]	(118)
C_9	γ-Phenylpropylene glycol	95	84	5 [518]	164/15
	1-Phenyl-1,3-propanediol	95	75	5 [794]	180/18, (45)

TABLE 13. HYDROXY OLEFINS 197

TABLE 12 *(continued)*

C_n	Compound	Method	Yield (%)	Chapter[ref.]	B.p./mm., n_D^t, (M.p.), Deriv.
	Aromatic Dihydroxy Compounds *(continued)*				
C_9	2-Phenyl-1,3-propanediol	84	50	5^{15}	137/2, 1.5348[25], (49), 137Pu
C_{10}	2-Phenyl-1,2-butanediol	89	50	5^{363}	165/23, (56)
	1-Phenyl-1,3-butanediol	79	50	5^{144}	176/21
		79	95	5^{138}	168/13
	2-Phenyl-1,4-butanediol	84	50	5^{49}	165/4, 113Pu
	2-Benzyl-1,3-propanediol	84	80	5^{15}	156/3, (68), 70Pu
	2-Methyl-2-phenyl-1,3-propanediol	81	83	5^{512}	185/15, (87)
C_{12}	2,2'-Dihydroxybiphenyl	99	29	5^{627}	(109)
C_{14}	1,2-Diphenyl-1,2-ethanediol	79	90	5^{138}	(136)
		79	89	5^{2}	(124-131)
		80	90	5^{177}	
C_{15}	1,1-Diphenyl-1,2-propanediol	91	40	5^{426}	(95)
	1,3-Diphenyl-1,3-propanediol	79	51	5^{144}	(93-97)
C_{16}	2,3-Diphenyl-2,3-butanediol	82	13	5^{595}	(122)
C_{20}	Triphenylethylene glycol	82	94	5^{594}	(166)
C_{26}	Benzopinacol (tetraphenylethylene glycol)	82	94	5^{591}	(190)

For explanations and symbols see pp. xi–xii.

TABLE 13. HYDROXY OLEFINS

C_n	Compound	Method	Yield (%)	Chapter[ref.]	B.p./mm., n_D^t, (M.p.), Deriv.
	Aliphatic Olefinic Alcohols				
C_3	Allyl alcohol	19	47	2^{65}	97
C_4	cis-Crotyl alcohol	30	76	5^{657}	121/752, 1.4342, 51Db
	Crotyl alcohol	79	85	5^{2}	1.4249[25]
		80	60	5^{175}	121/760
	Methylvinylcarbinol	88	60	5^{293}	97, 1.4119[25]
	1-Buten-4-ol (allylcarbinol)	88	64	5^{305}	113, 1.4189[25]
	cis-2-Buten-1,4-diol	30	77	2^{214}	135/15, 1.4716[25], 70Bz
	3,4-Dihydroxy-1-butene	19	35	2^{66}	95/12
	Methallyl alcohol	96	90	5^{307}	114, 1.4255
C_5	3-Penten-1-ol	84	75	5^{71}	130/628, 1.4327
		99	83	5^{733}	138, 1.4356
	cis-3-Penten-1-ol	30	75	2^{463}	140, 1.4387, 89Nu
	trans-3-Penten-1-ol	30	60	2^{463}	137, 1.4340, 93Nu
	4-Penten-1-ol	84	55	5^{67}	139/766, 1.4305[15]
		99	82	5^{629}	136/751

For explanations and symbols see pp. xi–xii.

TABLE 13 *(continued)*

C_n	Compound	Method	Yield (%)	Chapter[ref.]	B.p./mm., n_D^t, (M.p.), Deriv.
		Aliphatic Olefinic Alcohols *(continued)*			
C_5	3-Penten-2-ol	88	86	5[291]	120/740
	4-Penten-2-ol	88	65	5[308]	114/740
	1-Penten-3-ol (ethylvinyl-carbinol)	88	55	5[301]	36/20
	1-Penten-5-ol	90	60	5[461]	76/60, 1.4299
	2-Methyl-3-buten-1-ol	88	50	5[306]	121/756, 1.4262, 58Db
	3-Methyl-1-buten-3-ol	30	84	2[213]	97/757
	Divinylcarbinol	30	67	2[215]	65/100, 1.4400[17]
C_6	*trans*-3-Hexen-1-ol	99	53	5[733]	64/16, 1.4385, 69Nu
	4-Hexen-1-ol	99	45	5[731]	159/760, 1.4407
	cis-4-Hexen-1-ol	30	75	2[463]	159, 1.4420, 75Nu
	trans-4-Hexen-1-ol	30	72	2[463]	158, 1.4402, 72Nu
	2,4-Hexadien-1-ol	80	64	5[252]	77/12, (32), 85Db
	5-Hexen-2-ol	79	78	5[670]	139/752, 1.4286[24]
	1-Hexen-3-ol	88	55	5[292]	92/150
	4-Hexen-3-ol (ethylpropenyl-carbinol)	88	50	5[296]	45/13, 1.4325[23]
	1,4-Hexadien-3-ol	30	91	5[215]	87/100, 1.4501[19], 94Nu
	1,5-Hexadien-3-ol	88	59	5[302]	61/40, 1.4471
	1,3-Hexadien-5-ol	88	75	5[311]	65/20, 1.4829[30], 86Nu
	1,5-Hexadien-3,4-diol	82	45	5[728]	100/10
	2-Methyl-3-penten-2-ol	89	70	5[371]	37/13, 1.4285[17]
	4-Methyl-3-penten-2-ol	79	77	5[2]	1.4310[25]
		79	77	5[2]	139, 1.4310[25]
		88	50	5[371]	55/20, 1.4318[17]
	2-Methyl-4-penten-2-ol	88	53	5[302]	46/30, 1.4263
		89	75	5[368]	118, 1.4302
	4-Methyl-4-penten-2-ol	88	65	5[307]	
	2-Methyl-4-penten-3-ol	88	20	5[371]	43/21, 1.4316[16]
	Isopropenylvinylcarbinol	30	81	2[215]	66/50, 1.4530[16]
	2,2-Dimethyl-3-buten-1-ol	84	62	5[70]	130
C_7	2-Hepten-1-ol	84	79	5[72]	75/15
	4-Hepten-1-ol	99	29	5[731]	176/760, 1.4433
	6-Hepten-1-ol	84	72	5[629]	105/20, 1.4403
	3-Hepten-2-ol	80	25	5[254]	67/16, 1.4391[18], 30NBz
	4-Hepten-3-ol	88	74	5[304]	155/760, 1.4384[12]
	1-Hepten-4-ol	88	57	5[302]	66/20, 1.4342
	2-Hepten-4-ol (*n*-propyl-propenylcarbinol)	88	74	5[295]	64/14, 1.4380[18]
	1,5-Heptadien-4-ol	88	83	5[302]	62/15, 1.4533
		88	66	5[316]	64/18, 1.4556[19]
	2-Methyl-4-hexen-3-ol	88	50	5[371]	56/18, 1.4377[21]
	3-Methyl-5-hexen-3-ol	88	84	5[302]	61/35, 1.4370
		89	52	5[367]	70/60, 1.4309[25]

TABLE 13. HYDROXY OLEFINS 199

TABLE 13 *(continued)*

C_n	Compound	Method	Yield (%)	Chapter[ref.]	B.p./mm., n_D^t, (M.p.), Deriv.
			Aliphatic Olefinic Alcohols *(continued)*		
C_7	5-Methyl-1-hexen-5-ol	91	82	5[428]	143
	Vinylisobutenylcarbinol	88	36	5[698]	57/8, 1.4614[18]
	2,4-Dimethyl-3-penten-2-ol	89	86	5[364]	46/14
	2-Isopropyl-3-hydroxy-1-butene	88	75	5[201]	84/75, 1.4361
C_8	cis-2-Octen-1-ol	30	60	5[303]	89/11, 1.4450[22]
	trans-2-Octen-1-ol	95	90	5[303]	98/21, 1.4437[21]
	4-Octen-1-ol	99	86	5[731]	88/12, 1.4435[25]
	1-Octen-3-ol (n-amylvinylcarbinol)	88	49	5[297]	80/20, 1.4379[23]
	1-Octen-4-ol	88	65	5[302]	69/10, 1.4383
	2-Octen-4-ol (n-butylpropenylcarbinol)	88	66	5[696]	83/20, 1.4395, 54Db
	2,4-Octadien-6-ol	88	79	5[310]	75/12, 1.4892[18]
	2,4,6-Octatrien-1-ol	80	70	5[252]	(100)
	2-Methyl-6-hepten-2-ol	89	80	5[370]	61–66/13, 1.4387[14]
		91	89	5[428]	66/15, 1.4393[17], 68Pu
	6-Methyl-2-hepten-6-ol	91	91	5[428]	70/17, 1.4429[15], 89Pu
	6-Methyl-3-hepten-6-ol	91	83	5[428]	64/20, 1.4407[14]
	3-Ethyl-5-hexen-2-ol	79	80	5[670]	164/738, 1.4421[16]
	cis-2,5-Dimethyl-3-hexen-2,5-diol	91	35	5[429]	(70)
C_9	4-Nonen-1-ol	99	60	5[731]	212/760, 1.4478
	8-Nonen-1-ol	84	51	5[629]	135/20, 1.4450[23]
	4,6-Dimethyl-1-hepten-4-ol	88	83	5[302]	75/26, 1.4402
	4,6-Dimethyl-1,5-heptadien-4-ol	89	91	5[302]	72/18, 1.4598
C_{11}	ω-Undecylenyl alcohol	84	70	5[5]	124/6
C_{18}	Oleyl alcohol	84	51	5[64]	152/1, 1.4590[25]
	Linoleyl alcohol	84	45	5[65]	154/3, 1.4698[23], 88Te
			Alicyclic Olefinic Alcohols		
C_5	2-Cyclopentenol	96	26 †	5[719]	52/12, 1.4778[17], 128Pu
C_6	2-Cyclohexenol	80	49	5[187]	85/25, 1.4861, 107Pu
C_7	1-Methyl-2-cyclohexenol	89	38	5[373]	64/20, 1.4736
	2-(1-Cyclopentenyl)-ethanol	84	89	5[660]	77/9, 1.4765[25], 85Db
	1-Vinyl-1-cyclopentanol	30	68	2[465]	57/13
	1-Methyl-2-cyclopentenyl-1-carbinol	84	68	5[109]	164/760, 67NBz
	Methyl-1-cyclopentenyl-carbinol	88	85	5[314]	166/749, 1.4710[24]

For explanations and symbols see pp. xi–xii.

TABLE 13 (continued)

C_n	Compound	Method	Yield (%)	Chapter ref.	B.p./mm., n_D^t, (M.p.), Deriv.
	Alicyclic Olefinic Alcohols (continued)				
C8	β-(1-Cyclohexenyl)-ethyl alcohol	84	72	5[68]	88/8, 80Db
	1-Vinyl-1-cyclohexanol	30	70	2[464]	75/15
	β-(1-Cyclohexenyl)-ethanol	....	77	5[789]	67/2, 81Db
	1-Allylcyclopentanol	89	54	5[365]	63/10, 1.4683
	Ethyl-1-cyclopentenyl-carbinol	88	85	5[314]	79/10, 1.4750[19]
C9	4-n-Propyl-2-cyclohexenol (cryptol)	80	88	5[188]	77NBz
	4-(2'-Cyclopentenyl)-1-butanol	90	38	5[462]	118–123/24, 1.4723
	1-Methallylcyclopentanol	89	25	5[365]	99/40, 1.4720
C12	trans-2-Cyclohexenyl-cyclohexanol	79	93	5[148]	139/15, (42), 117Pu
	Aromatic Olefinic Alcohols and Phenols				
C8	o-Vinylphenol	....	65	5[790]	56/4, (29)
C9	Cinnamyl alcohol	79	97	5[2]	(33)
		79	90	5[105]	(34)
		80	80	5[251]	126–130
	Phenylvinylcarbinol	88	60	5[313]	54/0.2, 1.5464[15]
		88	72	5[312]	107/17, 1.5404[15], 45NBz
		95	30	5[521]	90–95/2, 1.5431
	o-Allylphenol	100	73	5[559]	104/19, 1.5445[24]
	o-Propenylphenol	31	75	2[509]	114/16, (37)
C10	Phenylpropenylcarbinol	88	88	5[313]	77/0.4, 1.5389[18]
	Methyl-α-styrylcarbinol	88	53	5[688]	124/13
	Methyl-β-styrylcarbinol	88	70	5[313]	104/1, (31)
C11	Phenylisobutenylcarbinol	88	33	5[698]	79/0.01, 1.5373[18]
C14	1-(α-Naphthyl)-3-buten-1-ol	88	94	5[692]	143/0.8, 1.6099[25], 117Nu
	o-Cinnamylphenol	100	60	5[559]	209/11, (56), 132Pu
	2-Hydroxymethylstilbene	80	97	5[189]	(93)

For explanations and symbols see pp. xi–xii.

TABLE 14. HYDROXY ACETYLENES 201

TABLE 14. HYDROXY ACETYLENES

C_n	Compound	Method	Yield (%)	Chapter[ref.]	B.p./mm., n_D^t, (M.p.), Deriv.
		Aliphatic Acetylenic Alcohols			
C_3	Propargyl alcohol	88	30	5[389]	117/760, 1.4320
C_4	2-Butyn-1-ol	43	40	3[44]	140/758, 1.4520[25], 71Db
	1,4-Butynediol	88	90	5[691]	145/18, (58)
C_5	2-Pentyn-1-ol	88	70	5[327]	82/54
	1-Pentyn-3-ol (ethylethynyl-carbinol)	88	50	5[324]	123/750, 91Db
	1-Pentyn-4-ol	90	36	5[463]	75/100, 1.4406[16]
	Dimethylethynylcarbinol	89	67	5[377]	103/750
		89	93	5[385]	98-105, 1.4193
		89	85	5[386]	56/97, 1.4211
		89	46	5[361]	103-107
C_6	2-Hexyn-1-ol	88	71	5[320]	88/58, 65Db
	3-Hexyn-1-ol	90	48	5[320]	161, 73Db
	n-Propylethynylcarbinol	88	53	5[319]	64/30, 1.4344[25]
	2-Methyl-4-pentyn-2-ol	103	40	5[758]	126/756, 1.4381[21]
	Methylethylethynyl-carbinol	89	78	5[388]	120/760, 1.4220[22]
		89	72	5[383]	78/150, 1.4310
		89	94	5[385]	116-120, 1.4305
		89	33	5[361]	119-123
	4-Methyl-2-pentyn-1,4-diol	88	61	5[377]	103/2, 1.4702
C_7	2-Heptyn-1-ol	88	82	5[320]	115/56
	3-Heptyn-1-ol	90	30	5[320]	111/70, 1.4530[25], 61Db
	5-Methyl-3-hexyn-2-ol	88	60	5[326]	156, 1.4418
	Methyl-n-propylethynyl-carbinol	89	50	5[383]	58/26, 1.4338
		89	77	5[388]	139/760, 1.4282[22]
	4,4-Dimethyl-2-pentyn-1-ol	88	71	5[323]	163/768, 1.4427[22]
	Diethylethynylcarbinol	89	90	5[389]	138/760, 1.4383
		89	88	5[388]	139/760, 1.4366[22]
	Methylethylpropynyl-carbinol	89	70	5[387]	134/760, 1.4308[25]
	2,5-Heptadiyn-4-ol (di-propynylcarbinol)	91	90	5[431]	(107)
C_8	2-Octyn-1-ol	88	57	5[695]	77/2, 1.4550
	3-Octyn-1-ol	88	21	5[320]	106/25
	3-Octyn-2-ol	89	21	5[383]	88/40, 1.4347
	3,5-Octadiyne-2,7-diol	46	84	3[65]	120/10^{-4}
	Methyl-t-butylethynyl-carbinol	89	87	5[361]	144
	2,5-Dimethyl-3-hexyn-2,5-diol	89	98	5[392]	(95)

For explanations and symbols see pp. xi-xii.

TABLE 14 *(continued)*

C_n	Compound	Method	Yield (%)	Chapter[ref.]	B.p./mm., n_D^t, (M.p.), Deriv.
		Aliphatic Acetylenic Alcohols *(continued)*			
C_9	3-Nonyn-2-ol	88	82	5[325]	100/16, 1.4500[23]
	Methyl-*n*-amylethynyl-	89	74	5[388]	175/760, 1.4362[22]
	carbinol	89	40	5[383]	88/26, 1.4396
	Diisopropylethynyl-	89	78	5[388]	163/760, 1.4492[22]
	carbinol				
		Alicyclic and Aromatic Acetylenic Alcohols			
C_7	1-Ethynylcyclopentanol	89	40	5[375]	66/16, (21)
C_8	1-Ethynylcyclohexanol	89	82	5[393]	76/15, (32)
		89	75	5[700]	74/14, 1.4822, (30)
C_9	1-Ethynylcycloheptanol	89	60	5[375]	91/12, (14)
	4-Cyclopentyl-2-butyn-1-ol	88	35	5[325]	117/14, 1.4885[23]
	Phenylethynylcarbinol	88	65	5[321]	116/16, (28), 82Pu
C_{10}	1-Phenyl-1-butyn-3-ol	88	52	5[690]	124/9
	1-Phenyl-1-butyn-4-ol	90	40	5[690]	147/16, 1.573
C_{15}	Diphenylethynylcarbinol	89	50	5[383]	(49)

For explanations and symbols see pp. xi–xii.

TABLE 15. HYDROXY HALIDES

C_n	Compound	Method	Yield (%)	Chapter[ref.]	B.p./mm., n_D^t, (M.p.), Deriv.
		Aliphatic Halo Alcohols			
C_2	2-Fluoroethanol	55	42	4[607]	105, 1.3633[25], 128Nu
		95	75	5[433]	101
	Ethylene chlorohydrin	77	86	4[459]	129*
		84	62	5[75]	
	Ethylene bromohydrin	77	33	4[468]	55/14
		78	92	4[478]	59/22
	2,2-Dichloroethanol	84	63	5[75]	145/739
	2,2,2-Trifluoroethanol	84	77	5[73]	76/740
	2,2,2-Trichloroethanol	79	61	5[2]	
		80	84	5[253]	94–97/125, (19)
		84	65	5[75]	
	β,β,β-Tribromoethanol	80	77	5[177]	(80)
C_3	2-Chloro-1-propanol	77	43	4[631]	124/613, 1.4377, 77Db
	Trimethylene fluorohydrin	55	50	4[607]	128, 1.3771[25]
		95	80	5[433]	128
	Trimethylene chlorohydrin	51	60	4[57]	64/10
	Trimethylene bromohydrin	51	74	4[62]	82/22

TABLE 15. HYDROXY HALIDES 203

TABLE 15 (continued)

C_n	Compound	Method	Yield (%)	Chapter[ref.]	B.p./mm., n_D^t, (M.p.), Deriv.
		Aliphatic Halo Alcohols (continued)			
C_3	Trimethylene iodohydrin	51	68	4[62]	113/15
	Glycerol α-monochloro-hydrin	51	66	4[61]	120/14
	Glycerol α,γ-dichloro-hydrin	51	70	4[60]	73/14
	Glycerol α,γ-dibromo-hydrin	52	54	4[130]	112/20
	3,3,3-Trifluoropropanol	87	39	5[241]	100, 1.3200[28]
	Trifluoroisopropanol	79	90	5[73]	78
C_4	2-Chloro-1-butanol	77	49	4[631]	53/13, 1.4428, 76Db
	Tetramethylene chloro-hydrin	51	16	4[58]	87/10, 1.4502
		53	47	4[166]	85/16, 1.4518
		54	56	4[105]	82/14
		54	57	4[606]	82/14
	β,β,γ-Trichlorobutyl alcohol	80	92	5[251]	(62)
	1-Chloro-2-butanol	77	50	4[460]	55/17
	threo-3-Chloro-2-butanol	77	61	4[461]	52/30, 1.4386[25]
	erythro-3-Chloro-2-butanol	78	83	4[461]	56/30, 1.4397[25]
	3-Bromo-2-butanol	77	82	4[471]	50–54/13, 1.4762[25]
	erythro-3-Bromo-2-butanol	78	73	4[563]	49/10, 1.4758[25]
	erythro-3-Iodo-2-butanol	78	75	4[563]	(18.9), 1.5371[25]
	1,1,1-Trifluoro-2-butanol	84	31	5[73]	91/752, 1.3403
	2-Methyl-2-chloro-1-propanol	89	15	5[381]	127
	1-Chloro-2-methyl-2-propanol	96	48	5[553]	71/100
		101	63	5[585]	127
	1-Bromo-2-methyl-2-propanol	77	73	4[473]	49.5/16, 1.4710[25]
	1,1-Dichloro-2-methyl-2-propanol	91	74	5[437]	38/5, 1.4598[19]
	1,3-Dichloro-2-methyl-2-propanol	77	30	4[463]	73/23
	1-Chloro-3-bromo-2-methyl-2-propanol	77	98	4[463]	85/20, 1.5171
	3,3,3-Trifluoro-2-methyl-2-propanol	91	80	5[433]	(19)
	Trichloromethyldimethyl-carbinol	102	80	5[736]	
	3-Chloro-2-methyl-1,2-propanediol	98	95	5[618]	80/1.6, 1.4748
C_5	2-Chloro-1-pentanol	77	43	4[631]	59–64/13, 1.4457, 71Db
	Pentamethylene chlorohydrin	51	23	4[58]	103/8, 1.4518
	1-Chloro-2-pentanol	77	43	4[462]	75/30, 1.4520
		90	80	5[467]	80/28, 1.4425, 84Db

For explanations and symbols see pp. xi–xii.

TABLE 15 *(continued)*

C_n	Compound	Method	Yield (%)	Chapter[ref.]	B.p./mm., n_D^t, (M.p.), Deriv.
		Aliphatic Halo Alcohols *(continued)*			
C_5	3-Bromo-2-pentanol	78	90	4[43]	53–59/10, 1.4758–1.4717
	2-Chloro-3-pentanol	77	48	4[43]	64–71/30
	1-Chloro-4-pentanol	80	76	5[164]	67/3
	3-Chloro-2-methyl-2-butanol	77	70	4[467]	141
	3-Bromo-2-methyl-2-butanol	77	50	4[469]	46/12
	1-Chloro-3-methyl-2-butanol	77	35	4[465]	145
	Trichloromethylmethylethyl-carbinol	102	89	5[736]	99/29
C_6	2-Chloro-1-hexanol	77	36	4[631]	1.4486
	Hexamethylene chlorohydrin	51	55	4[59]	89/4, 1.4544
		51	31	4[58]	112/12, 1.4541
	Hexamethylene bromohydrin	51	81	4[570]	106/5, 1.4845[24]
	1-Chloro-2-hexanol	77	60	4[466]	75/12, 1.4478
	2-Chloro-3-hexanol	77	60	4[467]	70/15, 171/753
	1-Bromo-5-hexanol	80	64	5[192]	89/4, 1.4808[25]
	1,1-Dichloro-2-ethyl-2-butanol	91	70	5[437]	76/14, 1.4710[21]
	3-Chloro-2,3-dimethyl-2-butanol	77	67	4[467]	152, (65)
	Tetramethylethylene bromo-hydrin	51	27	4[63]	(71)
C_7	1-Chloro-2-heptanol	77	60	4[466]	92/14, 1.4489
		90	16	5[468]	93/13, 59Db
	1-Chloro-5-methyl-2-hexanol	77	60	4[466]	87/15, 1.4475
C_8	1-Chloro-2-octanol	90	30	5[468]	106/13, 55Db
	2-Chloro-3-octanol	77	50	4[467]	110/14, 1.4523[19]
	1-Chloro-6-methyl-2-heptanol	77	60	4[466]	100/12, 1.4508
	2-Ethyl-3-chlorohexanol	51	30	4[58]	121/30, 1.4559
	1-Chloro-4-ethyl-2-hexanol	90	11	5[468]	104/15
		Alicyclic Halo Alcohols			
C_5	*trans*-2-Chlorocyclopentanol	77	56	4[626]	82/15, 1.4770[25]
C_6	2-Chlorocyclohexanol	77	73	4[464]	90/20, 106/45
	2-Bromocyclohexanol	77	79	4[471]	88/10, 1.5184[25]
		78	73	4[476]	86/10, 1.5178[25]
		80	30	5[194]	86/10, 1.5164[25]
	trans-2-Iodocyclohexanol	78	66	4[477]	(40.4)
	4-Chlorocyclohexanol	51	56	4[571]	85/5, 1.4964[16]
C_7	1-Methyl-2-chlorocyclo-hexanol	89	82	5[380]	74/15, 1.4775[25]
	1-Trichloromethyl-1-cyclohexanol	102	85	5[736]	122/20, (52)

TABLE 15. HYDROXY HALIDES 205

TABLE 15 (continued)

C_n	Compound	Method	Yield (%)	Chapter[ref.]	B.p./mm., n_D^t, (M.p.), Deriv.

Alicyclic Halo Alcohols (continued)

| C_9 | 1-Chloro-3-cyclohexyl-2-propanol | 90 | 15 | 5[468] | 123/11, 96Db |

Aromatic Halo Alcohols and Halo Phenols

C_6	o-Fluorophenol	56	55†	4[326]	46/10
		97	75	5[535]	50/14
	o-Iodophenol	59	63	4[362]	130/18, (43)
	m-Fluorophenol	56	35	4[325]	103/46
		97	95	5[535]	84/20
	m-Bromophenol	93	95	5[485]	138/12, (33)
	p-Fluorophenol	97	74	5[534]	87/23
	p-Bromophenol	64	84	4[282]	150/30, (63)
	p-Iodophenol	56	72	4[324]	140/5, (94)
		64	80	4[298]	(94)
	2,6-Dichlorophenol	13	91	5[780]	(66)
C_7	o-Chlorobenzyl alcohol	79	96	5[89]	(65)
	o-Iodobenzyl alcohol	81	90	5[511]	(71)
	m-Chlorobenzyl alcohol	81	97	5[511]	119/10
	m-Bromobenzyl alcohol	81	89	5[511]	128/10
	p-Chlorobenzyl alcohol	79	92	5[89]	(72)
	p-Bromobenzyl alcohol	79	96	5[89]	(76)
		95	61†	5[465]	(78)
	p-Iodobenzyl alcohol	81	81	5[511]	(91)
		95	86	5[524]	(72)
C_8	β-Hydroxy-β-phenylethyl chloride	77	76	4[470]	111/6, 1.5400, 81NBz
	β-Hydroxy-β-phenylethyl bromide	77	50	4[469]	110/2, 1.5800[17]
		80	85	5[177]	134/12
		79	71	5[2]	1.5751[25]
	o-Chlorophenylmethyl-carbinol	88	69	5[271]	94/4
	o-Bromophenylmethyl-carbinol	88	73	5[271]	105/3
		88	87	5[330]	109/7, 1.5702
	m-Chlorophenylmethyl-carbinol	79	94	5[151]	103/3, 1.5438
		88	88	5[271]	99-104/4, 1.5405[25]
	m-Bromophenylmethyl-carbinol	88	74	5[271]	110/3
	p-Bromophenylmethyl-carbinol	88	64	5[271]	90/1
	p-Fluorophenylmethyl-carbinol	79	98	5[152]	91/10, 1.4980[25]
		88	66	5[329]	104-110/20, 1.5035[25]
	p-Chlorophenylmethyl-carbinol	80	81	5[193]	81-86/1, 1.5420
		88	59	5[271]	99/5

For explanations and symbols see pp. xi–xii.

TABLE 15 *(continued)*

C_n	Compound	Method	Yield (%)	Chapter[ref.]	B.p./mm., n_D^t, (M.p.), Deriv.
		Aromatic Halo Alcohols and Halo Phenols *(continued)*			
C_8	p-Iodophenylmethylcarbinol	80	93	5[190]	(42)
	Phenyltrichloromethyl-carbinol	102	41	5[736]	159/26, 1.5673
	p-Trifluoromethylbenzyl alcohol	84	94	5[74]	80/4, 1.4600
C_9	m-Trifluoromethylphenyl-methylcarbinol	88	83	5[271]	102/17, 1.4585
	Phenyltrichloromethyl-methylcarbinol	102	41	5[736]	
	3-Chloro-1-phenyl-1-propanol	79	70	5[150]	131/8, 63NBz
	1-Chloro-3-phenyl-2-propanol	90	18	5[468]	143/23, 121Db
	α-Methyl-α-phenyl-β-chloro-ethanol	89	55	5[395]	131/21
	2-Bromo-1-indanol	77	94	4[472]	(128)
C_{10}	1-Chloro-4-phenyl-2-butanol	90	45	5[469]	113/4, (47)
	6-Bromo-2-naphthol	64	100	4[281]	(129)
C_{11}	1-Chloro-5-phenyl-2-pentanol	90	13	5[468]	153/8, 107Db

For explanations and symbols see pp. xi–xii.

REFERENCES FOR CHAPTER 5

[1] Adams and Marvel, *J. Am. Chem. Soc.*, **42**, 315 (1920).

[2] Chaikin and Brown, *J. Am. Chem. Soc.*, **71**, 122 (1949); cf. refs. 3 and 4.

[3] Nystrom et al., *J. Am. Chem. Soc.*, **71**, 3245 (1949); cf. refs. 2 and 4.

[4] Nystrom and Brown, *J. Am. Chem. Soc.*, **69**, 1197 (1947); cf. refs. 2 and 3.

[5] Ford and Marvel, *Org. Syntheses*, Coll. Vol. II, 372 (1943).

[6] Kenyon and Platt, *J. Chem. Soc.*, 637 (1939); Dolique, *Ann. chim.*, (10) **15**, 483 (1931).

[7] Marvel and Tanenbaum, *J. Am. Chem. Soc.*, **44**, 2648 (1922).

[8] Koller and Kandler, *Monatsh.*, **58**, 234 (1931).

[9] Cason, *J. Am. Chem. Soc.*, **64**, 1108 (1942).

[10] Olivier, *Rec. trav. chim.*, **55**, 1031 (1936).

[11] Prins, *Rec. trav. chim.*, **42**, 1050 (1923).

[12] Hansley, *Ind. Eng. Chem.*, **39**, 55 (1947).

[13] Harmon and Marvel, *J. Am. Chem. Soc.*, **54**, 2515 (1932).

[14] McClellan and Connor, *J. Am. Chem. Soc.*, **63**, 484 (1941).

[15] Adkins and Billica, *J. Am. Chem. Soc.*, **70**, 3118, 3121 (1948); cf. ref. 46.

[16] Cason et al., *J. Am. Chem. Soc.*, **66**, 1766 (1944).

[17] Dirscherl and Nahm, *Ber.*, **76B**, 639 (1943).

[18] Dirscherl and Nahm, *Ber.*, **76B**, 709 (1943).

[19] Colonge, *Bull. soc. chim. France*, (5) **9**, 731 (1942).

[20] Adkins, Wojcik, and Covert, *J. Am. Chem. Soc.*, **55**, 1669 (1933).

[21] Leonard, *J. Am. Chem. Soc.*, **47**, 1774 (1925); cf. ref. 33.

[22] Hauser et al., *J. Am. Chem. Soc.*, **69**, 591 (1947); cf. ref. 33.

[23] Mozingo and Folkers, *J. Am. Chem. Soc.*, **70**, 229 (1948).

[24] Hamlin et al., *J. Am. Chem. Soc.*, **71**, 2735 (1949).

[25] Ford and Adams, *J. Am. Chem. Soc.*, **52**, 1260 (1930).

[26] Hickinbottom, *Reactions of Organic Compounds*, Longmans, Green & Co., New York, 2nd ed., 1948, p. 265.

[27] Rupe and van Walraven, *Helv. Chim. Acta*, **13**, 369 (1930).

[28] Adkins and Burgoyne, *J. Am. Chem. Soc.*, **71**, 3528 (1949).

[29] West, *J. Am. Chem. Soc.*, **42**, 1662 (1920).

[30] Adkins, *Reactions of Hydrogen*, University of Wisconsin Press, Madison, 1937.

[31] Bowden and Adkins, *J. Am. Chem. Soc.*, **56**, 689 (1934).

[32] Palfray, *Bull. soc. chim. France*, (5) **7**, 440 (1940).

[33] Folkers and Adkins, *J. Am. Chem. Soc.*, **54**, 1145 (1932).

[34] Adkins and Folkers, *J. Am. Chem. Soc.*, **53**, 1095 (1931).

[35] Guyer, Bieler, and Jaberg, *Helv. Chim. Acta*, **30**, 42 (1947).

[36] Niemann and Wagner, *J. Org. Chem.*, **7**, 227 (1942); cf. ref. 34.

[37] Bleyberg and Ulrich, *Ber.*, **64B**, 2510 (1931).

[38] Wasserman and Dawson, *J. Org. Chem.*, **8**, 76 (1943); Lazier, Hill, and Amend, *Org. Syntheses*, Coll. Vol. II, 325 (1943); cf. ref. 15.

[39] Manske, *Org. Syntheses*, Coll. Vol. II, 154 (1943).

[40] Ahmad, Bumpus, and Strong, *J. Am. Chem. Soc.*, **70**, 3392 (1948); cf. ref. 39.

[41] Bennett and Mosses, *J. Chem. Soc.*, 1697 (1931); cf. ref. 15.

[42] Adams and Kornblum, *J. Am. Chem. Soc.*, **63**, 199 (1941).

[43] Christian, Brown, and Hixon, *J. Am. Chem. Soc.*, **69**, 1961 (1947); cf. refs. 33 and 44.

[44] Nystrom and Brown, *J. Am. Chem. Soc.*, **70**, 3739 (1948).

[45] Cason, Brewer, and Pippen, *J. Org. Chem.*, **13**, 239 (1948).
[46] Wojcik and Adkins, *J. Am. Chem. Soc.*, **55**, 4939 (1933); cf. ref. 15.
[47] Karrer and Lee, *Helv. Chim. Acta*, **17**, 545 (1934); cf. ref. 46.
[48] Nenitzescu, Cioranescu, and Cantuniari, *Ber.*, **70B**, 282 (1937).
[49] Manske, *J. Am. Chem. Soc.*, **53**, 1107 (1931).
[50] Mozingo and Folkers, *J. Am. Chem. Soc.*, **70**, 228 (1948).
[51] Adkins and Burks, *J. Am. Chem. Soc.*, **70**, 4174 (1948).
[52] Owen and Robins, *J. Chem. Soc.*, 330 (1949).
[53] Rambaud, *Bull. soc. chim. France*, (5) **7**, 479 (1940).
[54] Amstutz and Plucker, *J. Am. Chem. Soc.*, **63**, 206 (1941).
[55] Barger, Robinson, and Smith, *J. Chem. Soc.*, 720 (1937).
[56] Hofmann, *J. Am. Chem. Soc.*, **67**, 421 (1945).
[57] Brehm, *J. Am. Chem. Soc.*, **71**, 3541 (1949).
[58] Renshaw et al., *J. Am. Chem. Soc.*, **61**, 639 (1939).
[59] Sandborn and Marvel, *J. Am. Chem. Soc.*, **50**, 565 (1928).
[60] Merchant and Marvel, *J. Am. Chem. Soc.*, **50**, 1200 (1928).
[61] Adkins et al., *J. Am. Chem. Soc.*, **56**, 2425 (1934).
[62] Sauer and Adkins, *J. Am. Chem. Soc.*, **60**, 402 (1938); cf. ref. 15.
[63] Blicke and Sheetz, *J. Am. Chem. Soc.*, **71**, 2856 (1949).
[64] Reid et al., *Org. Syntheses*, Coll. Vol. II, 468 (1943); Adkins and Gillespie, *ibid.*, **29**, 80 (1949).
[65] Kass and Burr, *J. Am. Chem. Soc.*, **62**, 1796 (1940).
[66] Gaubert, Linstead, and Rydon, *J. Chem. Soc.*, 1971 (1937).
[67] Paul, *Ann. chim.*, (10) **18**, 333 (1932).
[68] Cook and Dansi, *J. Chem. Soc.*, 500 (1935); Cook and Lawrence, *ibid.*, 822 (1937).
[69] Sauer and Adkins, *J. Am. Chem. Soc.*, **59**, 1 (1937).
[70] Folkers and Adkins, *J. Am. Chem. Soc.*, **53**, 1418 (1931).
[71] Goering, Cristol, and Dittmer, *J. Am. Chem. Soc.*, **70**, 3315 (1948).
[72] Martin, Schepartz, and Daubert, *J. Am. Chem. Soc.*, **70**, 2601 (1948).
[73] Gilman and Jones, *J. Am. Chem. Soc.*, **70**, 1281 (1948); Campbell, Knobloch, and Campbell, *ibid.*, **72**, 4380 (1950).
[74] Hass and Bender, *J. Am. Chem. Soc.*, **71**, 1768 (1949).
[75] Sroog et al., *J. Am. Chem. Soc.*, **71**, 1710 (1949).
[76] Adams, Harfenist, and Loewe, *J. Am. Chem. Soc.*, **71**, 1627 (1949).
[77] Hunter and Hogg, *J. Am. Chem. Soc.*, **71**, 1924 (1949).
[78] Guss, *J. Am. Chem. Soc.*, **71**, 3462 (1949).
[79] Bennett and Hock, *J. Chem. Soc.*, 475 (1927).
[80] Prelog and Seiwerth, *Ber.*, **72B**, 1640 (1939).
[81] Coleman and Johnson, *Org. Syntheses*, **21**, 10 (1941); cf. ref. 661.
[82] Barrow and Ferguson, *J. Chem. Soc.*, 410 (1935).
[83] Kerwin et al., *J. Am. Chem. Soc.*, **69**, 2963 (1947).
[84] Adkins and Pavlic, *J. Am. Chem. Soc.*, **69**, 3040 (1947); cf. ref. 15.
[85] Decombe, *Ann. chim.*, (10) **18**, 160 (1932).
[86] Magidson et al., *Arch. Pharm.*, **271**, 574 (1933); **272**, 78 (1934); cf. ref. 85.
[87] Adams and Voorhees, *Org. Syntheses*, Coll. Vol. I, 61 (1941).
[88] Clarke and Dreger, *Org. Syntheses*, Coll. Vol. I, 304 (1941).
[89] Carothers and Adams, *J. Am. Chem. Soc.*, **46**, 1675 (1924); **45**, 1071 (1923).
[90] Franke and Kroupa, *Monatsh.*, **69**, 190 (1936).
[91] Palfray, *Bull. soc. chim. France*, (5) **7**, 407 (1940).

[92] Adams and Garvey, *J. Am. Chem. Soc.*, **48**, 477 (1926).
[93] Cooke, Gillespie, and MacBeth, *J. Chem. Soc.*, 1825 (1938).
[94] Fieser, Joshel, and Seligman, *J. Am. Chem. Soc.*, **61**, 2137 (1939).
[95] Burdick and Adkins, *J. Am. Chem. Soc.*, **56**, 440 (1934).
[96] Scott and Johnson, *J. Am. Chem. Soc.*, **54**, 2554 (1932).
[97] Kaufmann and Adams, *J. Am. Chem. Soc.*, **45**, 3041 (1923); Brown and Hixon, *Ind. Eng. Chem.*, **41**, 1382 (1949); Bremner and Keeys, *J. Chem. Soc.*, 1068 (1947); cf. ref. 99.
[98] Panizzon, *Helv. Chim. Acta*, **24**, 26E (1941).
[99] Adkins and Connor, *J. Am. Chem. Soc.*, **53**, 1093 (1931).
[100] Hofmann et al., *J. Am. Chem. Soc.*, **69**, 193 (1947); cf. ref. 95.
[101] Campbell, Anderson, and Gilmore, *J. Chem. Soc.*, 820 (1940).
[102] Woods and Sanders, *J. Am. Chem. Soc.*, **68**, 2111 (1946).
[103] Montmollin and Martenet, *Helv. Chim. Acta*, **12**, 606 (1929).
[104] Wilson and Read, *J. Chem. Soc.*, 1123 (1935).
[105] Hochstein and Brown, *J. Am. Chem. Soc.*, **70**, 3484 (1948); cf. ref. 106.
[106] Hill and Nason, *J. Am. Chem. Soc.*, **46**, 2236 (1924); Tuley and Adams, *ibid.*, **47**, 3061 (1925).
[107] Kindler and Gehlhaar, *Arch. Pharm.*, **274**, 385 (1936).
[108] Woodward, *J. Am. Chem. Soc.*, **62**, 1480 (1940).
[109] Rapson and Robinson, *J. Chem. Soc.*, 1536 (1935).
[110] Sexton and Britton, *J. Am. Chem. Soc.*, **70**, 3606 (1948).
[111] Adkins and Billica, *J. Am. Chem. Soc.*, **70**, 696, 3118 (1948).
[112] Kayser, *Ann. chim.*, (11) **6**, 155, 188, 238 (1936).
[113] Whitmore and Homeyer, *J. Am. Chem. Soc.*, **55**, 4195 (1933); Whitmore and Krueger, *ibid.*, **55**, 1531 (1933).
[114] Ipatieff and Haensel, *J. Am. Chem. Soc.*, **64**, 520 (1942).
[115] Whitmore and Otterbacher, *Org. Syntheses*, Coll. Vol. II, 317 (1943).
[116] Lucas, *J. Am. Chem. Soc.*, **51**, 251 (1929).
[117] Slabey and Wise, *J. Am. Chem. Soc.*, **71**, 3252 (1949).
[118] Wiselogle and Sonneborn, *Org. Syntheses*, Coll. Vol. I, 90 (1941); Hughes, Ingold, and Taher, *J. Chem. Soc.*, 954 (1940); cf. refs. 119 and 120.
[119] Bachmann, *J. Am. Chem. Soc.*, **55**, 770 (1933).
[120] Zechmeister and Rom, *Ann.*, **468**, 123 (1929).
[121] Cramer and Glasebrook, *J. Am. Chem. Soc.*, **61**, 231 (1939); cf. ref. 99.
[122] Pines, Edeleanu, and Ipatieff, *J. Am. Chem. Soc.*, **67**, 2193 (1945); Ruzicka, Plattner, and Wild, *Helv. Chim. Acta*, **28**, 397 (1945); Kohler et al., *J. Am. Chem. Soc.*, **61**, 1059, 1061 (1939).
[123] Henshall, *J. Soc. Chem. Ind.*, **62**, 127 (1943).
[124] Cooke, Gillespie, and MacBeth, *J. Chem. Soc.*, 518 (1939).
[125] Lutz et al., *J. Am. Chem. Soc.*, **70**, 4137 (1948).
[126] Ungnade and Ludutsky, *J. Org. Chem.*, **10**, 520 (1945); Ungnade, *ibid.*, **14**, 333 (1949).
[127] Godchot, Cauquil, and Calas, *Bull. soc. chim. France*, (5) **6**, 1358, 1366 (1939); cf. ref. 125.
[128] Noller and Adams, *J. Am. Chem. Soc.*, **48**, 1080 (1926); cf. refs. 129 and 130.
[129] Edwards and Reid, *J. Am. Chem. Soc.*, **52**, 3235 (1930).
[130] Goheen, *J. Am. Chem. Soc.*, **63**, 745 (1941).
[131] Skita and Faust, *Ber.*, **64B**, 2878 (1931); Hückel and Hagenguth, *ibid.*, **64B**, 2892 (1931); cf. ref. 656.

[132] Hückel and Gelmroth, *Ann.*, **514**, 250 (1934).
[133] McElvain and Rorig, *J. Am. Chem. Soc.*, **70**, 1827 (1948).
[134] Mowry, Renoll, and Huber, *J. Am. Chem. Soc.*, **68**, 1108 (1946).
[135] Nenitzescu, Gavat, and Cocora, *Ber.*, **73B**, 237 (1940).
[136] Strong and McElvain, *J. Am. Chem. Soc.*, **55**, 818 (1933).
[137] Covert, Connor, and Adkins, *J. Am. Chem. Soc.*, **54**, 1651 (1932).
[138] Adkins and Cramer, *J. Am. Chem. Soc.*, **52**, 4354 (1930).
[139] Lazier and Arnold, *Org. Syntheses*, Coll. Vol. II, 142 (1943).
[140] Billica and Adkins, *Org. Syntheses*, **29**, 24 (1949).
[141] Levene and Walti, *Org. Syntheses*, Coll. Vol. II, 545 (1943).
[142] Fisher and Chittenden, *Ind. Eng. Chem.*, **22**, 870 (1930).
[143] Rupe and Klemm, *Helv. Chim. Acta*, **21**, 1539 (1938).
[144] Sprague and Adkins, *J. Am. Chem. Soc.*, **56**, 2669 (1934).
[145] Bartleson, Burk, and Lankelma, *J. Am. Chem. Soc.*, **68**, 2513 (1946).
[146] Foster and Hammelt, *J. Am. Chem. Soc.*, **68**, 1737 (1946).
[147] Jenkins, Buck, and Bigelow, *J. Am. Chem. Soc.*, **52**, 4495 (1930); Jenkins, *ibid.*, **54**, 1159 (1932); Weissberger and Bach, *J. prakt. Chem.*, **127**, 260 (1930).
[148] Hückel et al., *Ann.*, **477**, 122, 123 (1929).
[149] Fox, *J. Org. Chem.*, **12**, 537 (1947).
[150] Case, *J. Am. Chem. Soc.*, **55**, 2929 (1933).
[151] Emerson and Lucas, *J. Am. Chem. Soc.*, **70**, 1180 (1948).
[152] Renoll, *J. Am. Chem. Soc.*, **68**, 1159 (1946).
[153] Powell and Adams, *J. Am. Chem. Soc.*, **42**, 651 (1920).
[154] Bernstein and Wallis, *J. Am. Chem. Soc.*, **62**, 2873 (1940).
[155] Hurd and Perletz, *J. Am. Chem. Soc.*, **68**, 38 (1946).
[156] Buck and Jenkins, *J. Am. Chem. Soc.*, **51**, 2163 (1929).
[157] Gomberg and Van Natta, *J. Am. Chem. Soc.*, **51**, 2238 (1929); Gomberg and Bachmann, *ibid.*, **49**, 2584 (1927).
[158] Stutsman and Adkins, *J. Am. Chem. Soc.*, **61**, 3303 (1939).
[159] Blicke and Grier, *J. Am. Chem. Soc.*, **65**, 1726 (1943).
[160] Emerson et al., *J. Am. Chem. Soc.*, **68**, 674 (1946).
[161] Lochte and Pickard, *J. Am. Chem. Soc.*, **68**, 721 (1946).
[162] Kindler et al., *Ber.*, **76B**, 308 (1943).
[163] Scherp, *J. Am. Chem. Soc.*, **68**, 913 (1946); cf. ref. 46.
[164] Elderfield et al., *J. Am. Chem. Soc.*, **68**, 1579 (1946).
[165] Adkins, Connor, and Cramer, *J. Am. Chem. Soc.*, **52**, 5195 (1930); cf. ref. 30, p. 51.
[166] Davies and Powell, *J. Am. Chem. Soc.*, **67**, 1466 (1945).
[167] Hyde, Browning, and Adams, *J. Am. Chem. Soc.*, **50**, 2292 (1928).
[168] Elderfield et al., *J. Am. Chem. Soc.*, **68**, 1520 (1946).
[169] Fourneau and Barrelet, *Bull. soc. chim. France*, (4) **47**, 78 (1930).
[170] Smith and Adkins, *J. Am. Chem. Soc.*, **60**, 409 (1938).
[171] Cromwell, Wiles, and Schroeder, *J. Am. Chem. Soc.*, **64**, 2432 (1942).
[172] Ghigi, *Ann. chim. applicata*, **32**, 3 (1942).
[173] Wilds, *Organic Reactions*, Vol. 2, John Wiley & Sons, New York, 1944, p. 178.
[174] Kleiderer and Kornfeld, *J. Org. Chem.*, **13**, 457 (1948).
[175] Young, Hartung, and Crossley, *J. Am. Chem. Soc.*, **58**, 100 (1936); cf. ref. 173, p. 200.
[176] Peak and Robinson, *J. Chem. Soc.*, 1589 (1937).

[177] Lund, *Ber.*, **70B**, 1520 (1937).
[178] Crawford and Nelson, *J. Am. Chem. Soc.*, **68**, 134 (1946).
[179] Marvel and Overberger, *J. Am. Chem. Soc.*, **67**, 2250 (1945); cf. ref. 134.
[180] Campaigne and Diedrich, *J. Am. Chem. Soc.*, **70**, 391 (1948).
[181] Brown and Bluestein, *J. Am. Chem. Soc.*, **62**, 3256 (1940).
[182] Mannich and Salzmann, *Ber.*, **72B**, 506 (1939).
[183] Mannich and Lammering, *Ber.*, **55**, 3510 (1922).
[184] Mannich and Hof, *Arch. Pharm.*, **265**, 589 (1927).
[185] Mannich and Horkheimer, *Arch. Pharm.*, **264**, 167 (1926).
[186] Mannich, Borkowsky, and Wan Ho Lin, *Arch. Pharm.*, **275**, 54 (1937).
[187] Bartlett and Woods, *J. Am. Chem. Soc.*, **62**, 2933 (1940); Whitmore and Pedow, *ibid.*, **63**, 758 (1941).
[188] Macbeth et al., *J. Chem. Soc.*, **265**, 1532 (1939).
[189] Natelson and Gottfried, *J. Am. Chem. Soc.*, **64**, 2962 (1942).
[190] Strassburg, Gregg, and Walling, *J. Am. Chem. Soc.*, **69**, 2141 (1947).
[191] Kornblum and Iffland, *J. Am. Chem. Soc.*, **71**, 2140 (1949).
[192] Elderfield et al., *J. Am. Chem. Soc.*, **69**, 1259 (1947).
[193] Marvel and Schertz, *J. Am. Chem. Soc.*, **65**, 2055 (1943).
[194] Winstein, *J. Am. Chem. Soc.*, **61**, 1610 (1939).
[195] Schenck, *Ber.*, **67**, 1571 (1934).
[196] Goebel and Marvel, *J. Am. Chem. Soc.*, **55**, 1693 (1933).
[197] Whitmore and Homeyer, *J. Am. Chem. Soc.*, **55**, 4558 (1933).
[198] Whitmore, Marker, and Plambeck, *J. Am. Chem. Soc.*, **63**, 1628 (1941).
[199] Tsatsas, *Ann. Chim.*, (11) **19**, 237 (1944).
[200] Stiller et al., *J. Am. Chem. Soc.*, **62**, 1787 (1940); Ford, *ibid.*, **66**, 21 (1944).
[201] Marvel, Myers, and Saunders, *J. Am. Chem. Soc.*, **70**, 1694 (1948).
[202] Alexander and Marvell, *J. Am. Chem. Soc.*, **72**, 3945 (1950); Saunders, Murray, and Cleveland, *ibid.*, **65**, 1714 (1943).
[203] Backes, *Bull. soc. chim. France,* (5e) **9**, 79 (1942).
[204] Conant and Tuttle, *Org. Syntheses,* Coll. Vol. I, 199 (1941); Bourdiol et al., *Bull. soc. chim. France,* (5) **8**, 375 (1941).
[205] Colonge, *Bull. soc. chim. France,* (5) **1**, 1101 (1934).
[206] Spåth, Lorenz, and Freund, *Ber.*, **76B**, 1203 (1943).
[207] White and Haward, *J. Chem. Soc.*, 25 (1943).
[208] Landau and Irany, *J. Org. Chem.* **12**, 422 (1947); White, *J. Chem. Soc.*, 238 (1943).
[209] Kyrides, *J. Am. Chem. Soc.*, **55**, 3431 (1933).
[210] Smith, Chase, and Rhodes, *J. Am. Chem. Soc.*, **66**, 1548 (1944); Eccott and Linstead, *J. Chem. Soc.*, 911 (1930).
[211] Powell, Murray, and Baldwin, *J. Am. Chem. Soc.*, **55**, 1153 (1933).
[212] Powell, *J. Am. Chem. Soc.*, **46**, 2514 (1924).
[213] Haeussler and Dijkema, *Ber.*, **77B**, 601 (1944).
[214] Powell and Nielsen, *J. Am. Chem. Soc.*, **70**, 3627 (1948).
[215] Vavon and Flurer, *Bull. soc. chim. France*, **45**, 754 (1929).
[216] Kenner, Ritchie, and Statham, *J. Chem. Soc.*, 1170 (1937); Mannich and Brose, *Ber.*, **56**, 841 (1923).
[217] Haeussler and Brugger, *Ber.*, **77**, 152 (1944).
[218] Powell and Hagemann, *J. Am. Chem. Soc.*, **66**, 372 (1944).
[219] Shriner in Organic *Reactions,* Vol. I, John Wiley & Sons, New York, 1942, p. 1.

[220] Newman, *J. Am. Chem. Soc.,* 64, 2131 (1942).

[221] Hussey and Newman, *J. Am. Chem. Soc.,* 70, 3024 (1948).

[222] Fieser, Leffler, et al., *J. Am. Chem. Soc.,* 70, 3209 (1948); cf. ref. 239.

[223] Huston, Goerner, and György, *J. Am. Chem. Soc.,* 70, 390 (1948).

[224] Schwenk and Papa, *J. Am. Chem. Soc.,* 67, 1433 (1945); cf. ref. 219, p. 17.

[225] Natelson and Gottfried, *J. Am. Chem. Soc.,* 61, 970 (1939).

[226] Hauser and Breslow, *Org. Syntheses,* 21, 51 (1941).

[227] Baker and Holdsworth, *J. Chem. Soc.,* 728 (1945); Bohnsack, *Ber.,* 74B, 1582 (1941).

[228] Colonge and Joly, *Ann. chim.,* (11) 18, 310 (1943); Colonge, *Bull. soc. chim., France,* (5) 9, 732 (1942).

[229] Tsatsas, *Ann. chim.,* (12) 1, 352 (1946).

[230] Harvey, Heilbron, and Wilkinson, *J. Chem. Soc.,* 426 (1930).

[231] Abbott, Kon, and Satchell, *J. Chem. Soc.,* 2518 (1928).

[232] Bardhan, *J. Chem. Soc.,* 2603, 2615 (1928).

[233] Philippi, Hendgen, and Hernler, *Monatsh.,* 69, 277 (1936).

[234] Ziegler, Schumann, and Winkelmann, *Ann.,* 551, 120 (1942); Fuson, Arnold, and Cooke, *J. Am. Chem. Soc.,* 60, 2272 (1938); Jones, O'Sullivan, and Whiting, *J. Chem. Soc.,* 1415 (1949).

[235] Blaise and Luttringer, *Bull. soc. chim. France,* (3) 33, 635 (1905).

[236] Courtot, *Bull. soc. chim. France,* (3) 35, 114 (1906).

[237] Lipkin and Stewart, *J. Am. Chem. Soc.,* 61, 3295 (1939).

[238] Fuson and Cooke, *J. Am. Chem. Soc.,* 62, 1180 (1940).

[239] Cymerman, Heilbron, and Jones, *J. Chem. Soc.,* 147 (1944).

[240] Kuhn and Grundmann, *Ber.,* 70B, 1899 (1937).

[241] McBee and Truchan, *J. Am. Chem. Soc.,* 70, 2911 (1948).

[242] Müller and Töpel, *Ber.,* 72B, 273 (1939).

[243] Gilman and Van Ess, *J. Am. Chem. Soc.,* 61, 1365 (1939).

[244] Gilman, Bywater, and Parker, *J. Am. Chem. Soc.,* 57, 885 (1935).

[245] Gilman and Young, *J. Am. Chem. Soc.,* 57, 1122 (1935).

[246] Gilman and Jacoby, *J. Org. Chem.,* 3, 113 (1938).

[247] Komppa and Weckman, *J. prakt. Chem.,* 138, 115 (1933).

[248] Edwards and Teague, *J. Am. Chem. Soc.,* 71, 3548 (1949).

[249] Porter and Steel, *J. Am. Chem. Soc.,* 42, 2650 (1920).

[250] Ivanoff, *Bull. soc. chim. France,* 39, 47 (1926); Kharasch and Reynolds, *J. Am. Chem. Soc.,* 65, 501 (1943).

[251] Meerwein and Schmidt, *Ann.,* 444, 221 (1925).

[252] Reichstein, Ammann, and Trivelli, *Helv. Chim. Acta,* 15, 261 (1932).

[253] Chalmers, *Org. Syntheses,* Coll. Vol. II, 598 (1943).

[254] Arcus and Kenyon, *J. Chem. Soc.,* 698 (1938).

[255] Whitmore, Karnatz, and Popkin, *J. Am. Chem. Soc.,* 60, 2540 (1938).

[256] Whitmore and Johnston, *J. Am. Chem. Soc.,* 60, 2265 (1938).

[257] Hiers and Adams, *J. Am. Chem. Soc.,* 48, 2388 (1926).

[258] Whitmore and Badertscher, *J. Am. Chem. Soc.,* 55, 1559 (1933).

[259] Dauben, *J. Am. Chem. Soc.,* 70, 1377 (1948).

[260] Chu and Marvel, *J. Am. Chem. Soc.,* 53, 4449 (1931).

[261] Whitmore and Rothrock, *J. Am. Chem. Soc.,* 55, 1107 (1933); cf. ref. 262.

[262] Conant and Blatt, *J. Am. Chem. Soc.,* 51, 1227 (1929).

[263] Cavalieri, Pattison, and Carmack, *J. Am. Chem. Soc.,* 67, 1785 (1945); cf. ref. 264, p. 344.

[264] Wibaut et al., *Rec. trav. chim.*, **58**, 329 (1939).
[265] Conant and Blatt, *J. Am. Chem. Soc.*, **50**, 554 (1928); cf. ref. 13.
[266] Barrow and Atkinson, *J. Chem. Soc.*, 638 (1939).
[267] Drake and Cooke, *Org. Syntheses*, Coll. Vol. II, 406 (1943).
[268] Gilman and Catlin, *Org. Syntheses*, Coll. Vol. I, 188 (1949); cf. ref. 257.
[269] Bergs, *Ber.*, **67B**, 1619 (1934).
[270] Turkiewicz, *Ber.*, **72B**, 1061 (1939); cf. ref. 128.
[271] Overberger et al., *Org. Syntheses*, **28**, 28 (1948); cf. ref. 276.
[272] Davies, Dixon, and Jones, *J. Chem. Soc.*, 468 (1930).
[273] Duveen and Kenyon, *Bull. soc. chim. France*, (5) **5**, 1122 (1938).
[274] Barber, Slack, and Woolman, *J. Chem. Soc.*, 100 (1943).
[275] Gerrard and Kenyon, *J. Chem. Soc.*, 2564 (1928).
[276] Marvel et al., *J. Am. Chem. Soc.*, **68**, 736, 1088 (1946).
[277] Gattermann and Wieland, *Laboratory Methods of Organic Chemistry*, The Macmillan Co., New York, 1938, p. 337.
[278] Marvel et al., *J. Am. Chem. Soc.*, **63**, 1894 (1941); **66**, 914 (1944).
[279] Tsatsas, *Ann. chim.*, (12) **1**, 350 (1946).
[280] Bachmann and Boatner, *J. Am. Chem. Soc.*, **58**, 2098 (1936).
[281] Newman, *J. Am. Chem. Soc.*, **62**, 2298 (1940); cf. refs. 282 and 283.
[282] Smith and Spillane, *J. Am. Chem. Soc.*, **62**, 2640 (1940).
[283] Reichstein et al., *Helv. Chim. Acta*, **19**, 412 (1936).
[284] Dillon and Lucas, *J. Am. Chem. Soc.*, **50**, 1712 (1928).
[285] Freundler and Damond, *Bull. soc. chim. France*, (3), **35**, 110 (1906).
[286] Finkelstein and Elderfield, *J. Org. Chem.*, **4**, 374 (1939).
[287] Duveen and Kenyon, *J. Chem. Soc.*, 622 (1936); cf. ref. 288.
[288] Peters and Fischer, *J. Am. Chem. Soc.*, **52**, 2081 (1930).
[289] Clarke et al., *J. Org. Chem.*, **14**, 221 (1949).
[290] Walter, *Org. Syntheses*, **23**, 83 (1943).
[291] Coburn, *Org. Syntheses*, **27**, 65 (1947); Mulliken, Wakeman, and Gerry, *J. Am. Chem. Soc.*, **57**, 1606 (1935).
[292] Niemann, Benson, and Mead, *J. Org. Chem.*, **8**, 397 (1943); cf. ref. 294.
[293] Young, Winstein, and Prater, *J. Am. Chem. Soc.*, **58**, 290 (1936); cf. ref. 294.
[294] Delaby, *Ann. chim.*, (9) **19**, 275 (1923); Prevost, *ibid.*, (10) **10**, 147 (1928); Delaby and Lecomte, *Bull. soc. chim. France*, (5) **4**, 741 (1937).
[295] Arcus and Kenyon, *J. Chem. Soc.*, 317 (1938); cf. ref. 291.
[296] Airs, Balfe, and Kenyon, *J. Chem. Soc.*, 24 (1942); cf. ref. 299.
[297] Noller and Girvin, *J. Am. Chem. Soc.*, **59**, 607 (1937); cf. ref. 303.
[298] Hurd and Puterbaugh, *J. Org. Chem.* 2, 383 (1937); cf. ref. 291.
[299] Smith et al., *J. Am. Chem. Soc.*, **61**, 3080 (1939).
[300] Ginnings, Herring, and Coltrane, *J. Am. Chem. Soc.*, **61**, 807 (1939).
[301] Hunsdiecker, *Ber.*, **75B**, 467 (1942); cf. ref. 294.
[302] Henze, Allen, and Leslie, *J. Org. Chem.*, **7**, 326 (1942).
[303] Gredy, *Bull. soc. chim. France*, (5) 3, 1093 (1936).
[304] Platt, *J. Chem. Soc.*, 318 (1941).
[305] Amstutz, *J. Org. Chem.*, **9**, 310 (1944); Linstead and Rydon, *J. Chem. Soc.*, 1998 (1934).
[306] Roberts and Young, *J. Am. Chem. Soc.*, **67**, 148 (1945).
[307] Tamele, Ott, Marple, and Hearne, *Ind. Eng. Chem.*, **33**, 115 (1941).
[308] Yanko, Mosher, and Whitmore, *J. Am. Chem. Soc.*, **67**, 666 (1945).
[309] Ziegler, *Ber.*, **54**, 739 (1921).

[310] Kuhn and Grundmann, *Ber.*, **71B**, 444 (1938).
[311] Woods and Schwartzman, *J. Am. Chem. Soc.*, **70**, 3394 (1948).
[312] Duveen and Kenyon, *J. Chem. Soc.*, 1699 (1939); Burton and Ingold, *J. Chem. Soc.*, 915 (1928).
[313] Braude, Jones, and Stern, *J. Chem. Soc.*, 401 (1946).
[314] Urion, *Ann. chim.*, (11) **1**, 48 (1934).
[315] Ou Kiun-Houo, *Ann. chim.*, (11) **13**, 195 (1940).
[316] Duveen and Kenyon, *Bull. soc. chim. France*, (5) **5**, 706 (1938).
[317] Meerwein et al., *J. prakt. Chem.*, **147**, 226 (1936).
[318] Hennion and Lieb, *J. Am. Chem. Soc.*, **66**, 1289 (1944).
[319] Hennion and Sheehan, *J. Am. Chem. Soc.*, **71**, 1964 (1949).
[320] Newman and Wotiz, *J. Am. Chem. Soc.*, **71**, 1294 (1949).
[321] Jones and McCombie, *J. Chem. Soc.*, 733 (1942); Jones, Shen, and Whiting, *ibid.*, 239 (1950); cf. ref. 322.
[322] Rutan and May, *J. Am. Chem. Soc.*, **69**, 2017 (1947).
[323] Bartlett and Rosen, *J. Am. Chem. Soc.*, **64**, 544 (1942).
[324] McGrew and Adams, *J. Am. Chem. Soc.*, **55**, 1499 (1937).
[325] Gredy, *Ann. chim.*, (11) **4**, 31, 53 (1935).
[326] Gredy, *Bull. soc. chim. France*, (5) **2**, 1953 (1935).
[327] Tchao Yin Lai, *Bull. soc. chim. France*, (4) **53**, 683 (1933).
[328] Stevens, *J. Am. Chem. Soc.*, **56**, 1425 (1934), **57**, 1112 (1935).
[329] Bachman and Lewis, *J. Am. Chem. Soc.*, **69**, 2022 (1947).
[330] Marvel and Moon, *J. Am. Chem. Soc.*, **62**, 46 (1940).
[331] Bradsher, *J. Am. Chem. Soc.*, **62**, 487 (1940).
[332] Palomaa and Jansson, *Ber.*, **64B**, 1606 (1931).
[333] Prelog et al., *Ann.*, **545**, 255 (1940).
[334] Noller et al., *J. Am. Chem. Soc.*, **48**, 1079, 1091 (1926).
[335] McKenzie and Dennler, *J. Chem. Soc.*, 1600 (1926).
[336] Jacobs et al., *J. Org. Chem.*, **11**, 223 (1946).
[337] Pierotti and Stewart, *J. Am. Chem. Soc.*, **59**, 1773 (1937); cf. ref. 348.
[338] Huston and Hedrick, *J. Am. Chem. Soc.*, **59**, 2001 (1937).
[339] Whitmore and Laughlin, *J. Am. Chem. Soc.*, **54**, 4012, 4392 (1932); cf. ref. 264.
[340] Whitmore and George, *J. Am. Chem. Soc.*, **64**, 1240 (1942); cf. ref. 339.
[341] Huston and Guile, *J. Am. Chem. Soc.*, **61**, 70 (1939).
[342] Whitmore et al., *J. Am. Chem. Soc.*, **60**, 2571, 2573 (1938); cf. ref. 343.
[343] Whitmore et al., *J. Am. Chem. Soc.*, **55**, 361, 408, 813, 1120 (1933).
[344] Whitmore et al., *J. Am. Chem. Soc.*, **63**, 2040 (1941).
[345] Huston and Barrett, *J. Org. Chem.*, **11**, 657 (1946); cf. ref. 338.
[346] Greenburg and Aston, *J. Am. Chem. Soc.*, **62**, 3135 (1940).
[347] Young and Roberts, *J. Am. Chem. Soc.*, **66**, 1444 (1944).
[348] Church, Whitmore, and McGrew, *J. Am. Chem. Soc.*, **56**, 176 (1934).
[349] Edgar, Calingaert, and Marker, *J. Am. Chem. Soc.*, **51**, 1483 (1929); cf. ref. 264.
[350] Blicke and Powers, *J. Am. Chem. Soc.*, **51**, 3378 (1929).
[351] Deschamps, *J. Am. Chem. Soc.*, **42**, 2670 (1920); cf. ref. 264, p. 339.
[352] Moersch and Whitmore, *J. Am. Chem. Soc.*, **71**, 819 (1949).
[353] Nasarow, *Ber.*, **69B**, 23 (1936), **70B**, 599 (1937).
[354] Clarke, *J. Am. Chem. Soc.*, **33**, 529 (1911); cf. ref. 264, p. 351.
[355] Volkenburgh, Greenlee, Derfer, and Boord, *J. Am. Chem. Soc.*, **71**, 172 (1949).

[356] Dice, Loveless, and Cates, *J. Am. Chem. Soc.*, **71**, 3547 (1949); Bartlett and Bavley, *ibid.*, **60**, 2417 (1938).

[357] Signaigo and Cramer, *J. Am. Chem. Soc.*, **55**, 3329 (1933); Mosher, *ibid.*, **62**, 552 (1940).

[358] McLellan and Edwards, *J. Am. Chem. Soc.*, **66**, 409 (1944).

[359] Smith and Lo, *J. Am. Chem. Soc.*, **70**, 2210 (1948).

[360] Wallis and Bowman, *J. Org. Chem.*, 1, 383 (1936); Inglis, *J. Chem. Soc.*, 540 (1911).

[361] Coffman, *Org. Syntheses*, **20**, 40 (1940); Sung Wouseng, *Ann. chim.*, (10) 1, 343 (1924).

[362] Roblin, Davidson, and Bogert, *J. Am. Chem. Soc.*, **57**, 155, 156 (1935).

[363] Ramart-Lucas and Salmon-Legagneur, *Bull. soc. chim. France*, **51**, 1078 (1932).

[364] Fieser and Wieghard, *J. Am. Chem. Soc.*, **62**, 154 (1940); cf. ref. 372.

[365] Crane, Boord, and Henne, *J. Am. Chem. Soc.*, **67**, 1239 (1945).

[366] Young and Roberts, *J. Am. Chem. Soc.*, **67**, 319 (1945).

[367] Milas and McAlevy, *J. Am. Chem. Soc.*, **57**, 581 (1935).

[368] Fischer, *Ber.*, **76B**, 735 (1943); cf. ref. 371.

[369] Linstead et al., *J. Chem. Soc.*, 1136 (1937).

[370] Elliott and Linstead, *J. Chem. Soc.*, 662 (1938).

[371] Bacon and Farmer, *J. Chem. Soc.*, 1065 (1937); cf. ref. 372.

[372] Kohler, *Am. Chem. J.*, **38**, 511 (1907); Kyriakides, *J. Am. Chem. Soc.*, **36**, 661 (1914).

[373] Whitmore and Pedlow, *J. Am. Chem. Soc.*, **63**, 758 (1941).

[374] Gilman, *Organic Chemistry*, John Wiley & Sons, New York, 2nd ed., 1943, p. 672.

[375] Backer and van der Bij, *Rec. trav. chim.*, **62**, 561 (1943); Heilbron et al., *J. Chem. Soc.*, 1827 (1949).

[376] Cymerman, Heilbron, and Jones, *J. Chem. Soc.*, 144 (1944), 90 (1945).

[377] Newman, Fones, and Booth, *J. Am. Chem. Soc.*, **67**, 1053 (1945).

[378] Price and Meisel, *J. Am. Chem. Soc.*, **69**, 1497 (1947).

[379] Milas, Brown, and Phillips, *J. Am. Chem. Soc.*, **70**, 2862 (1948).

[380] Bartlett and Rosenwald, *J. Am. Chem. Soc.*, **56**, 1992 (1934).

[381] Turner and Connor, *J. Am. Chem. Soc.*, **69**, 1011 (1947).

[382] Froning and Hennion, *J. Am. Chem. Soc.*, **62**, 654 (1940).

[383] Campbell, Campbell, and Eby, *J. Am. Chem. Soc.*, **60**, 2882 (1938).

[384] Hennion and Banigan, *J. Am. Chem. Soc.*, **68**, 1202 (1946).

[385] Hurd and McPhee, *J. Am. Chem. Soc.*, **69**, 239 (1947); cf. refs. 361 and 362.

[386] McMahon et al., *J. Am. Chem. Soc.*, **70**, 2974 (1948).

[387] Thompson and Margnetti, *J. Am. Chem. Soc.*, **64**, 573 (1942).

[388] Thompson, Burr, and Shaw, *J. Am. Chem. Soc.*, **63**, 187 (1941).

[389] Henne and Greenlee, *J. Am. Chem. Soc.*, **67**, 484 (1945).

[390] Wittig and Waldi, *J. prakt. Chem.*, **160**, 243 (1942); cf. ref. 371.

[391] Willemart, *Ann. chim.*, (10) **12**, 362, 373 (1929); cf. ref. 325, p. 56.

[392] Bruson and Kroeger, *J. Am. Chem. Soc.*, **62**, 36, 41 (1940); cf. ref. 382.

[393] Milas, MacDonald, and Black, *J. Am. Chem. Soc.*, **70**, 1831 (1948); cf. ref. 394.

[394] Marvel, Mozingo, and Kirkpatrick, *J. Am. Chem. Soc.*, **61**, 2006 (1939); Pinkney et al., *ibid.*, **58**, 974 (1936).

[395] King, *J. Am. Chem. Soc.*, **61**, 2386 (1939).

[396] Barnes and Budde, *J. Am. Chem. Soc.*, 68, 2339 (1946).
[397] Hurd and Perletz, *J. Am. Chem. Soc.*, 68, 40 (1946).
[398] Freon, *Ann. chim.*, (11) 11, 453 (1939).
[399] Whitmore and Randall, *J. Am. Chem. Soc.*, 64, 1246 (1942); Whitmore and Lester, *ibid.*, 64, 1252 (1942).
[400] McKenzie and Ritchie, *Ber.*, 70B, 33 (1937).
[401] Kloetzel, *J. Am. Chem. Soc.*, 62, 1710 (1940).
[402] Marxer, *Helv. Chim. Acta*, 24, 216E, 223E (1941).
[403] Suter and Weston, *J. Am. Chem. Soc.*, 64, 2451 (1942).
[404] Spaeth, Geissman, and Jocobs, *J. Org. Chem.*, 11, 399 (1946).
[405] Huston and Bailey, *J. Am. Chem. Soc.*, 68, 1382 (1946).
[406] Calingaert et al., *J. Am. Chem. Soc.*, 66, 1391 (1944).
[407] Lewis, *J. Chem. Education*, 7, 856 (1930); Sherrill, Otto, and Pickett, *J. Am. Chem. Soc.*, 51, 3026 (1929).
[408] Coleman and Craig, *Org. Syntheses*, Coll. Vol. II, 179 (1943).
[409] Neunhoeffer and Schlüter, *Ann.*, 526, 71 (1936).
[410] Huston and Krantz, *J. Org. Chem.*, 13, 66 (1948).
[411] Farmer and Warren, *J. Chem. Soc.*, 3231 (1931).
[412] Dounce, Wardlow, and Connor, *J. Am. Chem. Soc.*, 57, 2556 (1935).
[413] Whitmore et al., *J. Am. Chem. Soc.*, 63, 643 (1941).
[414] Arnold and Liggett, *J. Am. Chem. Soc.*, 64, 2875 (1942).
[415] Whitmore and Forster, *J. Am. Chem. Soc.*, 64, 2966 (1942).
[416] Whitmore et al., *J. Am. Chem. Soc.*, 60, 2458, 2462 (1938).
[417] Whitmore et al., *J. Am. Chem. Soc.*, 60, 2788 (1938).
[418] Blicke, *J. Am. Chem. Soc.*, 49, 2848 (1927).
[419] Bateman and Marvel, *J. Am. Chem. Soc.*, 49, 2917 (1927).
[420] Bachmann and Hetzner, *Org. Syntheses*, 23, 98 (1943); cf. ref. 421.
[421] Gilman et al., *Rec. trav. chim.*, 48, 749 (1929); 49, 1177 (1930).
[422] Morton, Myles, and Emerson, *Org. Syntheses*, 23, 95 (1943).
[423] Schoepfle, *J. Am. Chem. Soc.*, 44, 188 (1922).
[424] Moyer and Marvel, *Org. Syntheses*, Coll. Vol. II, 602 (1943).
[425] Boyle, McKenzie, and Mitchell, *Ber.*, 70B, 2159 (1937).
[426] Smith and Hoehn, *J. Am. Chem. Soc.*, 63, 1177 (1941).
[427] Bachmann and Sternberger, *J. Am. Chem. Soc.*, 56, 171 (1934).
[428] Hibbit and Linstead, *J. Chem. Soc.*, 473 (1936).
[429] Johnson and Johnson, *J. Am. Chem. Soc.*, 62, 2617 (1940).
[430] Salzberg and Marvel, *J. Am. Chem. Soc.*, 50, 1740 (1928).
[431] Chauvelier, *Ann. chim.*, (12) 3, 410 (1948).
[432] Bradsher and Smith, *J. Am. Chem. Soc.*, 65, 1644 (1943).
[433] Gryszkiewicz-Trochimowski, *Rec. trav. chim.*, 66, 427 (1947).
[434] Weizmann and Bergmann, *J. Chem. Soc.*, 401 (1936); Moureu and Barrett, *Bull. soc. chim. France*, (4) 29, 993 (1921).
[435] Campbell and Campbell, *J. Am. Chem. Soc.*, 60, 1372 (1938).
[436] Bardan, *Bull. soc. chim. France*, (4) 49, 1429 (1931); (5) 1, 143 (1934).
[437] Avy, *Bull. soc. chim. France*, (4) 49, 12 (1931).
[438] Barrow and Ferguson, *J. Chem. Soc.*, 416 (1935).
[439] Campbell and McKenna, *J. Org. Chem.*, 4, 202 (1939).
[440] Spielman and Schmidt, *J. Am. Chem. Soc.*, 59, 2009 (1937).
[441] McKenzie and Mills, *Ber.*, 62B, 284 (1929).
[442] Dreger, *Org. Syntheses*, Coll. Vol. I, 306 (1941).

[443] Prout and Cason, *J. Org. Chem.*, 14, 134 (1949).

[444] Strating and Backer, *Rec. trav. chim.*, 55, 910 (1936); cf. ref. 446.

[445] Veibel et al., *Bull. soc. chim. France*, (5) 6, 990 (1939).

[446] Huston and Agett, *J. Org. Chem.*, 6, 123 (1942); Huston and Langham, *ibid.*, 12, 90 (1947).

[447] Schorigin et al., *Ber.*, 64B, 2589 (1931); cf. ref. 446.

[448] Blicke and Zienty, *J. Am. Chem. Soc.*, 61, 95 (1939); cf. refs. 334 and 446.

[449] Bradsher and Wert, *J. Am. Chem. Soc.*, 62, 2807 (1940).

[450] Bartlett and Berry, *J. Am. Chem. Soc.*, 56, 2684 (1934).

[451] Pilat and Turkiewicz, *Ber.*, 72B, 1528 (1939); Yohe and Adams, *J. Am. Chem. Soc.*, 50, 1505 (1928).

[452] Golumbic and Cottle, *J. Am. Chem. Soc.*, 61, 999 (1939).

[453] Bergmann and Blum-Bergmann, *J. Am. Chem. Soc.*, 58, 1679 (1936).

[454] Newman, *J. Org. Chem.*, 9, 525 (1944); Cook and Hewett, *J. Chem. Soc.*, 1107 (1933).

[455] Speer and Hill, *J. Org. Chem.*, 2, 143 (1937); Papa, Perlman, and Bogert, *J. Am. Chem. Soc.*, 60, 319 (1938); Kipping and Wild, *J. Chem. Soc.*, 1241 (1940).

[456] Karrer et al., *Helv. Chim. Acta*, 23, 586 (1940).

[457] Kayser, *Ann. chim.*, (11) 6, 223 (1936).

[458] Wooster, Segool, and Allan, *J. Am. Chem. Soc.*, 60, 1666 (1938).

[459] Schick and Hartough, *J. Am. Chem. Soc.*, 70, 1646 (1948); Cagniant and Deluzarche, *Bull. soc. chim. France*, (5) 15, 1084 (1948).

[460] Stone, *J. Am. Chem. Soc.*, 62, 571 (1940).

[461] Kharasch and Fuchs, *J. Org. Chem.*, 9, 370 (1944).

[462] Arvin and Adams, *J. Am. Chem. Soc.*, 50, 1792 (1928).

[463] Haynes and Jones, *J. Chem. Soc.*, 956 (1946).

[464] Suter and Weston, *J. Am. Chem. Soc.*, 63, 606 (1941).

[465] Gilman and Melstrom, *J. Am. Chem. Soc.*, 70, 4177 (1948).

[466] Huston and Bostwick, *J. Org. Chem.*, 13, 334 (1948).

[467] Koelsch and McElvain, *J. Am. Chem. Soc.*, 51, 3392 (1929); cf. ref. 168.

[468] Koelsch and McElvain, *J. Am. Chem. Soc.*, 52, 1164 (1930).

[469] Henze and Holder, *J. Am. Chem. Soc.*, 63, 1943 (1941); cf. ref. 468.

[470] Hardegger, Redlich, and Gal, *Helv. Chim. Acta*, 28, 631 (1945).

[471] Plimmer, Short, and Hill, *J. Chem. Soc.*, 695 (1938).

[472] Palomaa, *Ber.*, 74B, 297 (1941).

[473] Whitmore and Thorpe, *J. Am. Chem. Soc.*, 63, 1118 (1941); Taylor and Price, *J. Chem. Soc.*, 2052 (1929).

[474] Clemo, Haworth, and Walton, *J. Chem. Soc.*, 2375 (1929).

[475] Stevens and Beutel, *J. Am. Chem. Soc.*, 63, 311 (1941).

[476] Grillot and Gormley, *J. Am. Chem. Soc.*, 67, 1968 (1945).

[477] Morgan and Harrison, *J. Soc. Chem. Ind.*, 49, 417T (1930).

[478] Baker, *J. Chem. Soc.*, 478 (1937).

[479] Bachmann and Boatner, *J. Am. Chem. Soc.*, 58, 2195 (1936).

[480] Lothrop, *J. Am. Chem. Soc.*, 61, 2117 (1939).

[481] Mosettig and Stuart, *J. Am. Chem. Soc.*, 61, 1 (1939).

[482] Geissman and Tess, *J. Am. Chem. Soc.*, 62, 515 (1940).

[483] Fieser and Kennelly, *J. Am. Chem. Soc.*, 57, 1614 (1935).

[484] Caldwell, Tyson, and Lauer, *J. Am. Chem. Soc.*, 66, 1481 (1944).

[485] Hodgson, *J. Am. Chem. Soc.*, 62, 230 (1940); Koelsch, *ibid.*, 61, 969 (1939); Natelson and Gottfried, *ibid.*, 61, 1001 (1939).

[486] Willink and Wibaut, Rec. trav. chim., 53, 418 (1934).

[487] Erickson and Spoerri, J. Am. Chem. Soc., 68, 400 (1946).

[488] Higginbottom, Hill, and Short, J. Chem. Soc., 264 (1937).

[489] Woodward, Org. Syntheses, 25, 55 (1945); Woodward and Doering, J. Am. Chem. Soc., 67, 868 (1945); Icke et al., Org. Syntheses, 29, 63 (1949).

[490] Manske, Org. Syntheses, Coll. Vol. I, 404 (1941).

[491] Harvey and Robson, J. Chem. Soc., 99 (1938); Astle and Cropper, J. Am. Chem. Soc., 65, 2398 (1943).

[492] Silverman and Bogert, J. Org. Chem., 11, 43 (1946).

[493] King, McWhirter, and Barton, J. Am. Chem. Soc., 67, 2090 (1945).

[494] Ungnade and Henick, J. Am. Chem. Soc., 64, 1737 (1942).

[495] Blicke, Smith, and Powers, J. Am. Chem. Soc., 54, 1468 (1932).

[496] Carter and Hey, J. Chem. Soc., 152 (1948).

[497] Smith and Haller, J. Am. Chem. Soc., 61, 143 (1939); Haller and Schaffer, ibid., 55, 4954 (1933).

[498] Witt, Nölting, and Grandmougin, Ber., 23, 3635 (1890).

[499] Drake in Organic Reactions, Vol. 1, John Wiley & Sons, New York, 1942, p. 318.

[500] Clarke and Hartman, Org. Syntheses, Coll. Vol. I, 455 (1941).

[501] Neunhoeffer and Kölbel, Ber., 68B, 260 (1935).

[502] Hartshorn and Baird, J. Am. Chem. Soc., 68, 1562 (1946).

[503] Hartman, Byers, and Dickey, Org. Syntheses, Coll. Vol. II, 451 (1943).

[504] Geissman in Organic Reactions, Vol. 2, John Wiley & Sons, New York, 1944, p. 94.

[505] Horning, Horning, and Platt, J. Am. Chem. Soc., 69, 2930 (1947).

[506] Shortridge et al., J. Am. Chem. Soc., 70, 984 (1948); cf. ref. 512.

[507] Derfer, Greenlee, and Boord, J. Am. Chem. Soc., 71, 178 (1949).

[508] Wilson, Org. Syntheses, Coll. Vol. I, 276 (1941).

[509] Schurink, Org. Syntheses, Coll. Vol. I, 425 (1941); cf. ref. 504, p. 111.

[510] Davidson and Bogert, J. Am. Chem. Soc., 57, 905 (1935).

[511] Lock, Ber., 63, 855 (1930); cf. ref. 504, p. 112.

[512] Fourneau, Benoit, and Firmenich, Bull. soc. chim. France, (4) 47, 868 (1930).

[513] Davidson and Weiss, Org. Syntheses, Coll. Vol. II, 590 (1943).

[514] Blicke and Blake, J. Am. Chem. Soc., 53, 1019 (1931).

[515] Gattermann and Wieland, Laboratory Methods of Organic Chemistry, The Macmillan Co., New York, 1938, p. 115.

[516] Glacet, Ann. chim., (12) 2, 321, 323 (1947).

[517] Bennett and Heathcoat, J. Chem. Soc., 271, 273 (1929); cf. ref. 525.

[518] Hershberg, Helv. Chim. Acta, 17, 354 (1934).

[519] Healey and Robinson, J. Chem. Soc., 1626 (1934).

[520] Cason, Org. Syntheses, 21, 1 (1941).

[521] Carroll, J. Chem. Soc., 1267 (1940).

[522] Levene and Walti, Org. Syntheses, Coll. Vol. II, 5 (1943).

[523] Auwers, Ludewig, and Müller, Ann., 526, 143 (1936).

[524] Hartman and Rahrs, Org. Syntheses, 24, 81 (1944).

[525] Hill and Hibbert, J. Am. Chem. Soc., 45, 3130 (1923).

[526] Guest, J. Am. Chem. Soc., 69, 301 (1947); Mendel and Coops, Rec. trav. chim., 58, 1136 (1939).

[527] Benton and Dillon, J. Am. Chem. Soc., 64, 1128 (1942).

[528] Close, Tiffany, and Spielman, *J. Am. Chem. Soc.*, **71**, 1265 (1949).
[529] Prey, *Ber.*, **74B**, 1221 (1941); **75B**, 350 (1942).
[530] Weber and Sowa, *J. Am. Chem. Soc.*, **60**, 94 (1938).
[531] Marvel and White, *J. Am. Chem. Soc.*, **62**, 2739 (1940); Fieser, Jacobsen, and Price, *ibid.*, **58**, 2163 (1936).
[532] King and Sherred, *J. Chem. Soc.*, 416 (1942).
[533] Mottier, *Helv. Chim. Acta*, **18**, 840 (1935).
[534] Suter, Lawson, and Smith, *J. Am. Chem. Soc.*, **61**, 163 (1939); cf. ref. 535.
[535] Schiemann, *J. prakt. Chem.*, 143, 23 (1935).
[536] Pfeiffer and Loewe, *J. prakt. Chem.*, 147, 293 (1936).
[537] LaForge, *J. Am. Chem. Soc.*, **55**, 3045 (1933).
[538] Kirner and Richter, *J. Am. Chem. Soc.*, **51**, 2505 (1929).
[539] Levine, Eble, and Fischbach, *J. Am. Chem. Soc.*, **70**, 1930 (1948).
[540] Kornfeld, *J. Am. Chem. Soc.*, **70**, 1375 (1948).
[541] Gilman and Broadbent, *J. Am. Chem. Soc.*, **70**, 2620 (1948).
[542] Carter and West, *Org. Syntheses*, **20**, 81 (1940).
[543] Carter and West, *Org. Syntheses*, **20**, 101 (1940).
[544] Prey, *Ber.*, **76B**, 156 (1943).
[545] Le Sueur, *J. Chem. Soc.*, 1895 (1905).
[546] Hurtley, *J. Chem. Soc.*, 1870 (1929); Rosenmund and Harms, *Ber.*, **53**, 2226 (1920).
[547] Loevenich, Becker, and Schröder, *J. prakt. Chem.*, 127, 248 (1930).
[548] Smith et al., *J. Org. Chem.*, **4**, 320 (1939).
[549] Ashley et al., *J. Chem. Soc.*, 114 (1942).
[550] Schierholtz and Staples, *J. Am. Chem. Soc.*, **57**, 2710 (1935).
[551] Hatch and Moore, *J. Am. Chem. Soc.*, **66**, 285 (1944).
[552] Maier-Bode, *Ber.*, **69**, 1537 (1936).
[553] Sparks and Nelson, *J. Am. Chem. Soc.*, **58**, 1010 (1936).
[554] Marvel et al., *J. Am. Chem. Soc.*, **46**, 2840 (1924).
[555] Danilow and Venus-Danilowa, *Ber.*, **63B**, 2769 (1930).
[556] Witzemann, *J. Am. Chem. Soc.*, **39**, 109 (1917).
[557] Dworzak and Prodinger, *Monatsh.*, **50**, 467 (1928).
[558] Söderbaum and Widman, *Ber.*, **25**, 3291 (1892).
[559] Tarbell in *Organic Reactions*, Vol. 2, John Wiley & Sons, New York, 1944, p. 1.; *Chem. Revs.*, **27**, 495 (1940).
[560] Paul and Normant, *Bull. soc. chim. France*, (5) **5**, 1151 (1938).
[561] Frank, Berry, and Shotwell, *J. Am. Chem. Soc.*, **71**, 3891 (1949).
[562] Gattermann and Wieland, *Laboratory Methods of Organic Chemistry*, The Macmillan Co., New York, 1938, p. 239.
[563] Hartman, *Org. Syntheses*, Coll. Vol. I, 175 (1941).
[564] Fierz-David and Stamm, *Helv. Chim. Acta*, **25**, 368 (1942).
[565] Emerson et al., *J. Am. Chem. Soc.*, **68**, 1665 (1946).
[566] Robinson, *J. Am. Chem. Soc.*, **69**, 1942, 1945 (1947).
[567] Willson and Meyer, *Ber.*, **47**, 3162 (1914).
[568] Ungnade and McLaren, *J. Am. Chem. Soc.*, **66**, 118 (1944); cf. ref. 569.
[569] Ungnade and Nightingale, *J. Am. Chem. Soc.*, **66**, 1218 (1944); cf. ref. 568.
[570] Carlin, *J. Am. Chem. Soc.*, **67**, 931 (1945).
[571] Skita and Faust, *Ber.*, **72**, 1127 (1939); cf. ref. 722.
[572] Adkins and Krsek, *J. Am. Chem. Soc.*, **70**, 412 (1948); Papa, Schwenk, and Breiger, *J. Org. Chem.*, **14**, 366 (1949); Stork, *J. Am. Chem. Soc.*, **69**, 576 (1947); Dauben, McKusick, and Mueller, *J. Am. Chem. Soc.*, **70**, 4179 (1948).

[573] Price and Karabinos, *J. Am. Chem. Soc.*, **62**, 1160 (1940).
[574] Ungnade, *J. Org. Chem.*, **13**, 361 (1948).
[575] Adkins et al., *J. Am. Chem. Soc.*, **71**, 3629 (1949).
[576] Olberg, Pines, and Ipatieff, *J. Am. Chem. Soc.*, **66**, 1097 (1944).
[577] Wilson and Read, *J. Chem. Soc.*, 1270 (1935); cf. ref. 580.
[578] Ruggli, Leupin, and Businger, *Helv. Chim. Acta*, **24**, 341 (1941).
[579] Vavon and Mitchovitch, *Bull. soc. chim. France*, **45**, 963 (1929).
[580] Adkins, *Reactions of Hydrogen*, Wisconsin University Press, Madison, 1937, p. 58.
[581] Read and Prisley, *J. Am. Chem. Soc.*, **46**, 1512 (1924).
[582] King, *J. Chem. Soc.*, 1409 (1919).
[583] Adams, Kamm, and Marvel, *J. Am. Chem. Soc.*, **40**, 1955 (1918).
[584] Hearne, Tamele, and Converse, *Ind. Eng. Chem.*, **33**, 806 (1941).
[585] Burgin, Hearne, and Rust, *Ind. Eng. Chem.*, **33**, 385 (1941).
[586] Pressman and Lucas, *J. Am. Chem. Soc.*, **61**, 2276 (1939).
[587] Adams and Adams, *Org. Syntheses*, Coll. Vol. I, 459 (1941); Hill and Kropa, *J. Am. Chem. Soc.*, **55**, 2509 (1933).
[588] Bachmann, *J. Am. Chem. Soc.*, **55**, 1183 (1933).
[589] Bachmann, *J. Am. Chem. Soc.*, **55**, 2829 (1933).
[590] Gomberg and Bachmann, *J. Am. Chem. Soc.*, **49**, 236 (1927); Bachmann and Shankland, *ibid.*, **51**, 306 (1929).
[591] Bachmann, *Org. Syntheses*, Coll. Vol. II, 71 (1943); cf. ref. 590.
[592] Davis and Marvel, *J. Am. Chem. Soc.*, **53**, 3843 (1931).
[593] Barnett and Lawrence, *J. Chem. Soc.*, 1106 (1935); Backer, Strating, and Huisman, *Rec. trav. chim.*, **60**, 383 (1941).
[594] Oppenauer, *Rec. trav. chim.*, **58**, 321 (1939).
[595] Ramart-Lucas and Salmon-Legagneur, *Bull. soc. chim. France*, **45**, 726 (1929).
[596] Ayers, *J. Am. Chem. Soc.*, **60**, 2958 (1938).
[597] Roebuck and Adkins, *Org. Syntheses*, **28**, 35 (1948); cf. ref. 601.
[598] Swern, Billen, Findley, and Scanlan, *J. Am. Chem. Soc.*, **67**, 1786 (1945).
[599] English and Gregory, *J. Am. Chem. Soc.*, **69**, 2120 (1947).
[600] Swern, Billen, and Scanlan, *J. Am. Chem. Soc.*, **68**, 1504 (1946).
[601] Adkins and Roebuck, *J. Am. Chem. Soc.*, **70**, 4041 (1948).
[602] Glattfeld and Straitiff, *J. Am. Chem. Soc.*, **60**, 1385 (1938); Glattfeld and Chittum, *ibid.*, **55**, 3663 (1933); Braun, *ibid.*, **51**, 228 (1929).
[603] Milas and Sussman, *J. Am. Chem. Soc.*, **58**, 1302 (1936), **59**, 2343, 2345 (1937).
[604] Milas, Sussman, and Mason, *J. Am. Chem. Soc.*, **61**, 1844 (1939).
[605] Roberts and Sauer, *J. Am. Chem. Soc.*, **71**, 3925 (1949).
[606] Schindler and Reichstein, *Helv. Chim. Acta*, **25**, 552 (1942).
[607] Clarke and Owen, *J. Chem. Soc.*, 318 (1949).
[608] Braun, *J. Am. Chem. Soc.*, **52**, 3176, 3185, 3188 (1930).
[609] Glattfeld and Reitz, *J. Am. Chem. Soc.*, **62**, 974 (1940); Braun, *ibid.*, **54**, 1133 (1932); cf. ref. 608.
[610] Milas and Terry, *J. Am. Chem. Soc.*, **47**, 1412 (1925).
[611] Meerwein, *Ann.*, **542**, 127 (1939).
[612] Milas and Maloney, *J. Am. Chem. Soc.*, **62**, 1841 (1940).
[613] Scanlan and Swern, *J. Am. Chem. Soc.*, **62**, 2305, 2309 (1940).
[614] Wilson and Lucas, *J. Am. Chem. Soc.*, **58**, 2400 (1936); cf. ref. 616.

[615] Lucas, Schlatter, and Jones, *J. Am. Chem. Soc.*, **63**, 25 (1941).

[616] Moureu and Dode, *Bull. soc. chim. France*, (5) **4**, 289 (1937).

[617] Winstein, *J. Am. Chem. Soc.*, **64**, 2794 (1942).

[618] Hearne and deJong, *Ind. Eng. Chem.*, **33**, 941 (1941).

[619] Cahnmann, *Bull. soc. chim. France*, (5) **4**, 230 (1937).

[620] Witzemann et al., *Org. Syntheses*, Coll. Vol. II, 307 (1943).

[621] Kaufman and Reeve, *Org. Syntheses*, **26**, 83 (1946).

[622] Grummitt, Stearns, and Arters, *Org. Syntheses*, **29**, 89 (1949); cf. ref. 626.

[623] Schniepp, Geller, and Korff, *J. Am. Chem. Soc.*, **69**, 672 (1947).

[624] Baker, Cornell, and Cron, *J. Am. Chem. Soc.*, **70**, 1491 (1948).

[625] Woods, *Org. Syntheses*, **27**, 43 (1947); Schniepp and Geller, *J. Am. Chem. Soc.*, **68**, 1646 (1946); cf. ref. 102.

[626] Wilson, *J. Chem. Soc.*, **49**, (1945).

[627] Gilman, Swiss, and Cheney, *J. Am. Chem. Soc.*, **62**, 1964 (1940).

[628] Sawyer and Andrus, *Org. Syntheses*, **23**, 25 (1943).

[629] Brooks and Snyder, *Org. Syntheses*, **25**, 84 (1945); Gaubert, Linstead, and Rydon, *J. Chem. Soc.*, 1971 (1937); Paul and Normant, *Bull. soc. chim. France*, (5) **10**, 484 (1943).

[630] Smith and Nichols, *J. Am. Chem. Soc.*, **65**, 1742 (1943).

[631] Emerson and Smith, *J. Am. Chem. Soc.*, **62**, 142 (1940).

[632] Fieser et al., *J. Am. Chem. Soc.*, **61**, 3219 (1939).

[633] Fieser and Fieser, *J. Am. Chem. Soc.*, **61**, 602 (1939).

[634] Caldwell and Thompson, *J. Am. Chem. Soc.*, **61**, 765 (1939).

[635] Dodgson, *J. Chem. Soc.*, 2435 (1914).

[636] Snell and McElvain, *Org. Syntheses*, Coll. Vol. II, 114 (1943); Speck and Bost, *J. Org. Chem.*, **11**, 791 (1946); cf. ref. 637.

[637] Corson, Benson, and Goodwin, *J. Am. Chem. Soc.*, **52**, 3988 (1930).

[638] Kharasch, Sternfeld, and Mayo, *J. Org. Chem.*, **5**, 362 (1940).

[639] Hansley, *J. Am. Chem. Soc.*, **57**, 2303 (1935).

[640] Adams and Marvel, *Org. Syntheses*, Coll. Vol. I, 94 (1941).

[641] Buck and Ide, *J. Am. Chem. Soc.*, **53**, 2350, 2784 (1931).

[642] Fulton and Robinson, *J. Chem. Soc.*, 200 (1939).

[643] Dewar and Read, *J. Soc. Chem. Ind.*, **55**, 347T (1936); cf. ref. 541.

[644] Kinney, *J. Am. Chem. Soc.*, **51**, 1595 (1929); Jenkins, *ibid.*, **54**, 1159 (1932).

[645] Schorigin, *Ber.*, **66B**, 1431 (1933); Gomberg, *Rec. trav. chim.*, **48**, 850 (1929).

[646] Weissberger, *J. Chem. Soc.*, 225 (1935); Hodgson and Rosenberg, *ibid.*, 16 (1930); Lutz and Murphey, *J. Am. Chem. Soc.*, **71**, 480 (1949).

[647] Hartman and Dickey, *J. Am. Chem. Soc.*, **55**, 1228 (1933).

[648] Fuson, Weinstock, and Ullyot, *J. Am. Chem. Soc.*, **57**, 1803 (1935); Arnold and Fuson, *ibid.*, **58**, 1295 (1936).

[649] Fuson, Gray, and Gouza, *J. Am. Chem. Soc.*, **61**, 1937 (1939).

[650] Wegmann and Dahn, *Helv. Chim. Acta*, **29**, 101 (1946).

[651] Clemmensen, *Ber.*, **47**, 51 (1914); cf. ref. 797.

[652] Bruce and Ralls, *Org. Syntheses*, Coll. Vol. II, 191 (1943).

[653] Bruson and Kroeger, *J. Am. Chem. Soc.*, **62**, 41 (1940).

[654] Bernard and Colonge, *Bull. soc. chim. France*, (5) **12**, 357 (1945).

[655] Overberger and Roberts, *J. Am. Chem. Soc.*, **71**, 3620 (1949).

[656] Noyce and Denney, *J. Am. Chem. Soc.*, **72**, 5743 (1950).

[657] Hatch and Nesbitt, *J. Am. Chem. Soc.*, **72**, 730 (1950).

[658] Reeve and Sadle, *J. Am. Chem. Soc.*, **72**, 1253 (1950).

[659] Sherman and Amstutz, *J. Am. Chem. Soc.*, 72, 2198 (1950).
[660] Arnold, Amidon, and Dodson, *J. Am. Chem. Soc.*, 72, 2873 (1950).
[661] Conover and Tarbell, *J. Am. Chem. Soc.*, 72, 3586 (1950).
[662] Yale et al., *J. Am. Chem. Soc.*, 72, 3716 (1950).
[663] Siegel and Bergstrom, *J. Am. Chem. Soc.*, 72, 3816 (1950).
[664] Smith and McKenzie, *J. Org. Chem.*, 15, 79 (1950).
[665] Moffett, *J. Org. Chem.*, 14, 862 (1949).
[666] Ligthelm, Rudloff, and Sutton, *J. Chem. Soc.*, 3187 (1950).
[667] Clarke and Owen, *J. Chem. Soc.*, 2111 (1950).
[668] Goldschmidt and Veer, *Rec. trav. chim.*, 67, 503 (1948).
[669] Willimann and Schinz, *Helv. Chim. Acta*, 32, 2151 (1949).
[670] Colonge and Lagier, *Bull. soc. chim. France*, (5) 16, 15 (1949).
[671] Pascual, Sistare, and Regas, *J. Chem. Soc.*, 1944 (1949).
[672] Gruber and Renner, *Monatsh.*, 81, 759 (1950).
[673] Arnold, Smith, and Dodson, *J. Org. Chem.*, 15, 1258 (1950).
[674] Nightingale and Radford, *J. Org. Chem.*, 14, 1090 (1949).
[675] Hayes and Drake, *J. Org. Chem.*, 15, 873 (1950); Wenner, *ibid.*, 15, 301 (1950).
[676] Hass, Susie, and Heider, *J. Org. Chem.*, 15, 13 (1950).
[677] Swann in Weissberger, *Technique of Organic Chemistry*, Vol. II, Interscience Publishers, New York, 1948, pp. 180–182.
[678] Volkenburgh et al., *J. Am. Chem. Soc.*, 71, 3595 (1949).
[679] Eliel, *J. Am. Chem. Soc.*, 71, 3971 (1949); also refs. 91, 111, 114, and 138.
[680] Lutz, Wayland, and France, *J. Am. Chem. Soc.*, 72, 5511 (1950).
[681] Elderfield, Pitt, and Wempen, *J. Am. Chem. Soc.*, 72, 1342–1344 (1950).
[682] Alexander and Mudrak, *J. Am. Chem. Soc.*, 72, 1810 (1950).
[683] Hurd and Kreuz, *J. Am. Chem. Soc.*, 72, 5543 (1950).
[684] Mentzer and Pillon, *Bull. soc. chim. France*, (5) 17, 810 (1950).
[685] Linstead and Walpole, *J. Chem. Soc.*, 854 (1939).
[686] Macbeth and Mills, *J. Chem. Soc.*, 2646 (1949); Jackman, Macbeth, and Mills, *ibid.*, 2641 (1949).
[687] Meltzer and Doczi, *J. Am. Chem. Soc.*, 72, 4986 (1950).
[688] Alder and Haydn, *Ann.*, 570, 208 (1950).
[689] Mousseron and Nguyen Phuoc Du, *Bull. soc. chim. France*, (5) 15, 91 (1948).
[690] Golse, *Ann. chim.*, (12) 3, 548, 554 (1948).
[691] Valette, *Ann. chim.*, (12) 3, 661 (1948); Hanford and Fuller, *Ind. Eng. Chem.*, 40, 1175–1176 (1948).
[692] Gaylord and Becker, *J. Org. Chem.*, 15, 305 (1950).
[693] Whitmore, Whitmore, and Cook, *J. Am. Chem. Soc.*, 72, 51 (1950).
[694] Bradsher and Kittila, *J. Am. Chem. Soc.*, 72, 278 (1950).
[695] Taylor and Strong, *J. Am. Chem. Soc.*, 72, 4264 (1950).
[696] Hargreaves and Owen, *J. Chem. Soc.*, 757 (1947); cf. refs. 291 and 298.
[697] Heilbron, Jones, and Weedon, *J. Chem. Soc.*, 83 (1945).
[698] Braude and Timmons, *J. Chem. Soc.*, 2005, 2007 (1950).
[699] Doering and Zeiss, J. *Am. Chem. Soc.*, 72, 148 (1950).
[700] Saunders, *Org. Syntheses*, 29, 47 (1949).
[701] Bachmann and Raunio, *J. Am. Chem. Soc.*, 72, 2530 (1950).
[702] Elphimoff-Felkin, *Bull. soc. chim. France*, (5) 17, 499 (1950).
[703] Nenitzescu and Necsoiu, *J. Am. Chem. Soc.*, 72, 3483 (1950).
[704] Cottle and Hollyday, *J. Org. Chem.*, 12, 510 (1947).

[705] Lambooy, J. Am. Chem. Soc., 72, 5327 (1950).

[706] Prijs, Lutz, and Erlenmeyer, Helv. Chim. Acta, 31, 575 (1948).

[707] Lock, Monatsh., 55, 180, 183 (1930).

[708] Emerson and Patrick, J. Org. Chem., 14, 790 (1949).

[709] Synerholm, J. Am. Chem. Soc., 69, 2581 (1947).

[710] Wittcoff and Miller, J. Am. Chem. Soc., 69, 3139 (1947).

[711] Reid, Fortenbaugh, and Patterson, J. Org. Chem., 15, 579 (1950).

[712] Villani and Lang, J. Am. Chem. Soc., 72, 2301 (1950).

[713] Emerson et al., J. Am. Chem. Soc., 72, 5314 (1950).

[714] Buck and Zimmerman, Org. Syntheses, Coll. Vol. II, 549 (1943).

[715] Morris and Riemenschneider, J. Am. Chem. Soc., 68, 500 (1946); Baltzly and Buck, ibid., 65, 1984 (1943).

[716] Ungnade and Zilch, J. Org. Chem., 15, 1109 (1950).

[717] Rhoad and Flory, J. Am. Chem. Soc., 72, 2218 (1950).

[718] Lowenthal and Pepper, J. Am. Chem. Soc., 72, 3292 (1950).

[719] David, Dupont, and Paquot, Bull. soc. chim. France, (5) 11, 562 (1944).

[720] Clarke and Owen, J. Chem. Soc., 2111 (1950).

[721] Shreve and Lloyd, Ind. Eng. Chem., 42, 811 (1950).

[722] Nickels and Heintzelman, J. Org. Chem., 15, 1143 (1950).

[723] Jackman, Macbeth, and Mills, J. Chem. Soc., 1717 (1949).

[724] Baker and Schuetz, J. Am. Chem. Soc., 69, 1250 (1947).

[725] Clarke and Owen, J. Chem. Soc., 2105 (1950); Rigby, ibid., 1586, 1588 (1949).

[726] Allen, J. Am. Chem. Soc., 72, 3797 (1950); J. Org. Chem., 15, 435 (1950).

[727] Laude and Wiemann, Bull. soc. chim. France, (5) 13, 256 (1946).

[728] Young, Levanas, and Jasaitis, J. Am. Chem. Soc., 58, 2274 (1936); Urion, Ann. chim., (11) 1, 39, 67 (1934); Wiemann, ibid., (11) 5, 287 (1936).

[729] Booth, Boyland, and Turner, J. Chem. Soc., 1188 (1950).

[730] Elderfield and Dodd in Elderfield's Heterocyclic Compounds, Vol. I, John Wiley & Sons, New York, 1950, pp. 170–177; Paul, Bull. soc. chim. France, (5) 14, 158 (1947).

[731] Brandon, Derfer, and Boord, J. Am. Chem. Soc., 72, 2120 (1950); Jacobson, ibid., 72, 1490 (1950); cf. ref. 733.

[732] Adams and Vanderwerf, J. Am. Chem. Soc., 72, 4371 (1950).

[733] Combie and Harper, J. Chem. Soc., 1707, 1714 (1950).

[734] Mugdan and Young, J. Chem. Soc., 2988 (1949).

[735] Swern, Chem. Revs., 45, 25–30 (1949).

[736] Weizmann, Bergmann, and Sulzbacher, J. Am. Chem. Soc., 70, 1189 (1948); Bergmann, Ginsburg, and Lavie. ibid., 72, 5012 (1950).

[737] Howard, J. Am. Chem. Soc., 52, 5059 (1930); Ekeley and Klemme, ibid., 46, 1252 (1924).

[738] Wagner, J. Am. Chem. Soc., 71, 3215 (1949); cf. ref. 209.

[739] Dubois, Bull. soc. chim. France, (5) 16, 66 (1949).

[740] Colonge and Cumet, Bull. soc. chim. France, (5) 14, 838 (1947).

[741] Morgan, Megson, and Pepper, Chemistry & Industry, 16, 885 (1938).

[742] Long and Troutman, J. Am. Chem. Soc., 71, 2470 (1949).

[743] Reasenberg and Smith, J. Am. Chem. Soc., 66, 993 (1944); cf. ref. 746.

[744] Sprang and Degering, J. Am. Chem. Soc., 64, 1063 (1942); Cerf De Mauny, Bull. soc. chim. France, (5) 7, 135 (1940).

[745] Vanderbilt and Hass, Ind. Eng. Chem., 32, 34 (1940); Gakenheimer and Hartung, J. Org. Chem., 9, 86 (1944).

[746] Parham and Bleasdale, *J. Am. Chem. Soc.*, 72, 3844 (1950); Nightingale and Janes, *ibid.*, 66, 352 (1944).

[747] Marans and Zelinski, *J. Am. Chem. Soc.*, 72, 5329 (1950).

[748] Attenburrow, Elks, Hems, and Speyer, *J. Chem. Soc.*, 514 (1949); Blicke et al., *J. Am. Chem. Soc.*, 67, 206 (1945).

[749] Hoover and Hass, *J. Org. Chem.*, 12, 507 (1947).

[750] Schmidt, Ascherl, and Mayer, *Ber.*, 58, 2430 (1925); cf. ref. 746.

[751] Lambert and Lowe, *J. Chem. Soc.*, 1517 (1946).

[752] Grob and Tscharner, *Helv. Chim. Acta*, 33, 1075 (1950); Nightingale, Erickson, and Knight, *J. Org. Chem.*, 15, 782 (1950); Fraser and Kon, *J. Chem. Soc.*, 606 (1934).

[753] Sprang and Degering, *J. Am. Chem. Soc.*, 64, 1735 (1942).

[754] Gault and Roesch, *Bull. soc. chim. France*, (5) 4, 1411 (1937); Roesch, *ibid.*, (5) 4, 1643 (1937).

[755] Gault et al., *Bull. soc. chim. France*, (5) 5, 386 (1938); 3, 54 (1936).

[756] Burkhard, *Bull. soc. chim. France*, (5) 5, 1664 (1938); Wendling, *ibid.*, (5) 3, 790 (1936).

[757] Newman and Rosher, *J. Org. Chem.*, 9, 223 (1944).

[758] Henbest, Jones, and Walls, *J. Chem. Soc.*, 2696 (1949).

[759] Colonge and Dumont, *Bull. soc. chim. France*, (5) 14, 44 (1947).

[760] Ide and Buck in *Organic Reactions*, Vol. 4, John Wiley & Sons, New York, 1948, p. 269.

[761] Sheehan, O'Neill, and White, *J. Am. Chem. Soc.*, 72, 3376 (1950).

[762] Dupont, Dulou, and Duplessis-Kergomard, *Bull. soc. chim. France*, (5) 16, 314 (1949).

[763] Deschamps, King, and Nord, *J. Org. Chem.*, 14, 185 (1949).

[764] Kipnis, Soloway, and Ornfelt, *J. Am. Chem. Soc.*, 70, 142 (1948).

[765] Eistert in *Newer Methods of Preparative Organic Chemistry*, Interscience Publishers, New York, 1948, p. 540.

[766] Clarke and Taylor, *Org. Syntheses*, Coll. Vol. I, 150 (1941).

[767] Weizmann, Bergmann, and Sulzbacher, *J. Org. Chem.*, 15, 54 (1950).

[768] Horning, Horning, and Walker, *J. Am. Chem. Soc.*, 71, 169 (1949).

[769] Adkins, Richards, and Davis, *J. Am. Chem. Soc.*, 63, 1320 (1941).

[770] Linstead and Michaelis, *J. Chem. Soc.*, 1134 (1940).

[771] Ruzicka, *Helv. Chim. Acta*, 19, 419 (1936).

[772] Sowa, Hinton, and Nieuwland, *J. Am. Chem. Soc.*, 54, 3696 (1932).

[773] Huston and Hsieh, *J. Am. Chem. Soc.*, 58, 439 (1936).

[774] Kolloff and Page, *J. Am. Chem. Soc.*, 60, 948 (1938).

[775] Huston and Hedrick, *J. Am. Chem. Soc.*, 59, 2002 (1937).

[776] Shriner and Hull, *J. Org. Chem.*, 10, 228 (1945); Robinson and Weygand, *J. Chem. Soc.*, 387 (1941); Barclay, Burawoy, and Thomson, *ibid.*, 400 (1944); Burawoy and Chamberlain, *ibid.*, 624 (1949).

[777] Cornforth, Cornforth, and Robinson, *J. Chem. Soc.*, 682 (1942).

[778] Ipatieff, Pines, and Friedman, *J. Am. Chem. Soc.*, 60, 2495 (1938).

[779] McElvain in *Organic Reactions*, Vol. 4, John Wiley & Sons, New York, 1948, p. 256.

[780] Tarbell, Wilson, and Fanta, *Org. Syntheses*, 29, 35 (1949).

[781] Smith and Welch, *J. Chem. Soc.*, 730 (1934).

[782] Ritter, *J. Am. Chem. Soc.*, 70, 4253 (1948).

[783] Baker and Brown, *J. Chem. Soc.*, 2303 (1948).

[784] Hauser and Breslow, *J. Am. Chem. Soc.*, **61**, 793 (1939).

[785] Paul and Tchelitcheff, *Bull. soc. chim. France*, (5) **13**, 388 (1946).

[786] Emmert and Asendorf, *Ber.*, **72**, 1188 (1939); Emmert and Pirot, *ibid.*, **74**, 718 (1941).

[787] Tullock and McElvain, *J. Am. Chem. Soc.*, **61**, 962 (1939).

[788] Colonge and Rochas, *Bull. soc. chim. France*, (5) **15**, 818, 822, 825, 827 (1948).

[789] Arnold and Dowdall, *J. Am. Chem. Soc.*, **70**, 2590 (1948).

[790] Smith and Niederl, *J. Am. Chem. Soc.*, **53**, 807 (1931).

[791] Astle and Stephenson, *J. Am. Chem. Soc.*, **65**, 2402 (1943).

[792] Adams and Marvel, *Org. Syntheses*, Coll. Vol. I, 366 (1941); Kornblum et al., *J. Am. Chem. Soc.*, **69**, 309 (1947).

[793] Rabjohn in *Organic Reactions*, Vol. 5, John Wiley & Sons, New York, 1949, p. 338.

[794] Fourneau, Benoit, and Firmenich, *Bull. soc. chim. France*, (4) **47**, 896 (1930).

[795] Read and Wood, *Org. Syntheses*, **20**, 57 (1940).

[796] Hart, *J. Am. Chem. Soc.*, **71**, 1966 (1949).

[797] Nightingale and Radford, *J. Org. Chem.*, **14**, 1089 (1949).

[798] Wittcoff, *Org. Syntheses*, **31**, 101 (1951).

[799] Sethna, *Chem. Revs.*, **49**, 91 (1951).

[800] Brown in *Organic Reactions*, Vol. 6, John Wiley & Sons, New York, 1951, p. 469.

[801] Hansley, *Ind. Eng. Chem.*, **43**, 1759 (1951).

6

Ethers

115. Alkylation of Hydroxy Compounds by Halogen Compounds

$$RONa + R'X \rightarrow ROR' + NaX$$

Preparation of symmetrical and unsymmetrical aliphatic ethers can be accomplished by coupling alkyl halides and sodium alkoxides (Williamson). The formation of the alkoxide may be slow and incomplete because the slow-dissolving alkoxide coats the sodium. This difficulty can be overcome by using a large excess of alcohol. After the sodium has dissolved, the alkyl halide is added to form the ether which is finally removed by fractional distillation.[1] Sodium t-butoxide is not only formed slowly but also reacts very slowly with alkyl halides. The reaction of the t-alkyl halide with the sodium alcoholate is not any better, for the chief products are olefins. Consequently, another method must be considered for preparing t-alkyl ethers (method 118). Even in the conversion of s-alkyl halides, olefin formation occurs.

Syntheses of alkyl phenyl ethers, C_6H_5 OR, are carried out by refluxing aqueous or alcoholic solutions of alkali phenolates with alkyl halides; the yields vary with the nature of the alkyl halides (40-80%).[1, 6] The reactive halogen in benzyl halides is easily replaced by an alkoxyl group (95%).[9, 10] The choice of a solvent is sometimes important. Thus, in the preparation of the alkyl ethers of o- and p-hydroxybiphenyl from a mixture of the phenol, alkyl halide, and powdered potassium hydroxide, high yields are obtained using acetone as a solvent, whereas, with alcohol as solvent, only small yields are obtained.[11] Triarylmethyl chlorides react with alcohols directly (97%).[12]

$$Ar_3CCl + ROH \rightarrow Ar_3COR + HCl$$

In the preparation of substituted diaryl ethers (ArOAr′), the reaction of alkali phenoxides and aryl halides is catalyzed by copper (Ullmann).[14, 23] Further studies have shown that the yield varies considerably with different copper-catalyst preparations.[15, 24]

The chlorine atom in furfuryl chloride, like that in benzyl chloride, is very reactive and is readily replaced by the alkoxyl group (80%).[17] On the other hand, the chlorine atom in tetrahydrofurfuryl chloride is unreactive, so that the corresponding ethers are prepared from the alkali alcoholate and alkyl halides (80%).[18]

2-Pyridyl aryl or alkyl ethers are made by condensing 2-bromopyridine with the appropriate sodium phenoxide or sodium alkoxide, copper powder being an effective catalyst in certain instances.[158]

Certain diethers of the type $ROCH_2CH_2OR′$ have been prepared by adding alkyl halides to a solution of sodium in excess ethylene glycol monoalkyl ether, as in the preparation of ethylene glycol dimethyl ether (78%).[22] Chloromethyl methyl ether and alcohols react to give an acetal derivative of formaldehyde, CH_3OCH_2OR; the reaction is carried out in the presence of pyridine.[26] Aromatic diethers such as 2-methoxydiphenyl ether have been prepared by the Ullmann procedure.[23]

Allylic chlorides, e.g., allyl, methallyl, and crotyl chlorides, are very reactive and are employed in the synthesis of unsaturated ethers.[6, 27, 30] Besides the usual coupling of the sodium alcoholate and halide in alcohol solutions other conditions have been described, including reaction of the alcohol and unsaturated halide in the presence of potassium carbonate or sodium hydroxide in acetone or water. The combination of anhydrous potassium carbonate and acetone is widely used in the preparation of allyl aryl ethers;[30] the reaction is aided by the addition of finely powdered potassium iodide.[31]

Hydroxy ethers of the type $ROCH_2CH_2CH_2OH$ are obtained by adding alkyl halides to a hot solution of sodium in excess trimethylene glycol diluted with xylene (60–70%).[37, 43] A series of 2-alkoxyethanols is made in a similar way from ethylene glycol and various alkyl halides.[153] The interaction of sym-glycerol dichlorohydrin and sodium alcoholates leads to sym-dialkoxypropanols in an average yield of 40%.[39] In the preparation of the phenyl ethers, the sodium phenoxide is treated with the chlorohydrin.[41, 42]

Halo ethers are prepared by adding an alcoholic solution of the sodium alkoxide to the polymethylene halide, $X(CH_2)_nX$, in anhydrous ether[45] or benzene,[46] as illustrated by the preparation of 1-bromo-6-methoxyhexane (47%). In a somewhat different manner, an aromatic halo ether such as γ-phenoxypropyl bromide is synthesized by the action of phenol and the dihalide in the presence of hot aqueous sodium hydroxide (85%).[47] The syntheses of o- and p-chlorophenyl phenyl ethers have been successfully accomplished by the Ullmann procedure (40–55%), whereas chlorination of diphenyl ether yields an inseparable mixture of isomers.[14]

Dialkoxyaldehydes of the type $RCH(OCH_3)CR(OCH_3)CHO$ are prepared from the corresponding α,β-dichloroaldehydes by the action of very dilute solutions of sodium alkoxide below 15° (70–85%).[50] In these preparations, the presence of potassium iodide or an alkyl iodide has been helpful. The yield of phenoxyacetone from chloroacetone and sodium phenoxide is increased from 16–23% to more than 90% chiefly by the presence of potassium iodide in the reaction mixture.[51] The reaction of alkyl iodides with phenolic aldehydes in methanolic potassium hydroxide gives p-alkoxybenzaldehydes (60–75%).[63]

Alkoxy acids[53] and esters[58] have been prepared from the corresponding chloro derivatives. Reaction of the hydroxyl group of methyl lactate with methyl iodide is brought about by silver oxide (65%).[101] Alkylation of the isomeric hydroxy benzoic acids is readily accomplished.[97, 98]

Aromatic[14] and aliphatic[61] amino ethers have been synthesized by this method. An example of the formation of a cyano ether is the preparation of p-cyano benzyl methyl ether from the substituted benzyl bromide and sodium methoxide (84%).[62] Also, certain aryloxyacetonitriles, $ArOCH_2CN$, are made by the condensation of chloroacetonitrile with sodium phenoxides in a solution of methyl ethyl ketone containing a small amount of sodium iodide (70–80%).[155] Aromatic nitro ethers, like o- and p-nitrodiphenyl ether, have been prepared by the Ullmann procedure (84%).[24] The synthesis of alkyl p-nitrophenyl ethers has also been accomplished with good yields (55–92%).[63]

116. Alkylation of Hydroxy Compounds by Alkyl Sulfates, Sulfites, or Sulfonates

$$2RONa + (CH_3)_2SO_4 \rightarrow 2ROCH_3 + Na_2SO_4$$

Mixed aliphatic ethers containing methyl or ethyl radicals can be synthesized from the corresponding alkyl sulfate and magnesium alcoholates, e.g., methyl n-butyl, methyl cyclohexyl, and methyl isoamyl ethers (70-78%).[72] A higher yield of ethyl isobutyl ether is obtained by substituting sodium for magnesium (70% vs. 30%).[73]

The method finds more general use in the alkylation of phenols.[76, 77] One or both alkyl groups in the alkyl sulfate may be utilized. Thus, in the preparation of anisole, an aqueous solution of sodium phenoxide is treated at 10° with dimethyl sulfate (75%).[74] The first methyl group is readily furnished but the second only under reflux. The phenolic groups in certain phenanthrene compounds have been quantitatively methylated by adding dimethyl sulfate to a suspension of the compounds in acetone and aqueous potassium hydroxide.[79] In another instance, 1- and 4-methoxy-phenanthrenes are made in quantitative yields by treating the corresponding acetoxy compounds under these same conditions.[160] Methyl β-naphtha-lenesulfonate is a satisfactory methylating agent.[75]

Unsaturated ethers, $RCH=CHCH_2OCH_3$, have been prepared from the corresponding allylic alcohols and dimethyl sulfate in the presence of sodium amide (60-80%).[84] *Acetylenic ethers* are made in a similar manner from acetylenic alcohols.[85] The hydroxyethylation of phenols with ethylene sulfite or ethylene carbonate appears to be a promising reaction for the formation of *hydroxy ethers* of the type $ROCH_2CH_2OH$.[86]

$$ArOH + \begin{array}{c} CH_2-O \\ | \qquad \diagdown \\ | \qquad \qquad C=O \\ | \qquad \diagup \\ CH_2-O \end{array} \rightarrow ArOCH_2CH_2OH + CO_2$$

The semi-methylation of resorcinol with dimethyl sulfate leads to m-methoxyphenol (45%).[87]

Many *other groups* may be present in the alcohol or phenol during alkylation. Dimethyl sulfate and chlorohydrins give chloro ethers.[82, 88] Halo ethers are also prepared by the action of this reagent on halogenated phenols, e.g., m-bromoanisole (91%).[89] Phenolic aldehydes are converted in excellent yields to alkoxy aldehydes with dimethyl sulfate[90, 94] or alkyl p-toluenesulfonates.[92] The conversion of a phenolic ketone to an alkoxy ketone is illustrated by the preparation of p-methoxypropiophenone (88%).[96] Phenolic acids,[99] esters,[100] and cyanides,[103] and nitrophenols[104] respond favorably to this method for methylation. The sodium salt of mandelic acid, $C_6H_5CHOHCOOH$, is methylated with dimethyl sulfate to furnish, after acidification, α-methoxyphenylacetic acid (42%).[162]

117. Haloalkylation of Alcohols

$$RCHO + R'OH + HX \longrightarrow RCHXOR' + H_2O$$

α-Halo ethers are prepared in good yields by treating mixtures of aldehydes and alcohols at ice temperature with dry hydrogen halides, the aldehyde furnishing the haloalkyl radical. In the preparation of halomethyl
alkyl ethers, aqueous formaldehyde or paraformaldehyde is used. The
procedure is illustrated by the formation of chloromethyl methyl ether
(89%)[126] and chloromethyl n-propyl ether (64%).[127] These chloromethyl
ethers and others are relatively unstable, especially upon exposure to
moisture. Best results are obtained if the excess halogen acid is swept
from the product before distillation.[128] The original procedure for preparing the corresponding bromo derivatives has been successfully modified
so that branched alkyl bromomethyl ethers can be prepared (85–98%).[131]
Paraformaldehyde is preferred rather than the aqueous solution of formaldehyde; furthermore, the reaction is run in the presence of calcium chloride,
which removes the water liberated.

This reaction is applicable to higher aldehydes and primary or secondary alcohols. Thus, paraldehyde and alcohols combine to give α-chloro-
ethyl alkyl ethers (93–99%).[132] Similarly, propionaldehyde and n-butyr-
aldehyde yield α-chloro-n-propyl and α-chloro-n-butyl alkyl ethers,
respectively.[125]

By this same procedure, ethylene chlorohydrin and aldehydes yield *dihalo ethers*.[134]

$$ClCH_2CH_2OH + CH_3CHO + HCl \longrightarrow ClCH_2CH_2OCHClCH_3 \quad (60\%)$$

118. Dehydration of Alcohols

$$2ROH \xrightarrow{(H^+)} ROR + H_2O$$

Symmetrical aliphatic ethers (C_4–C_{16}) are prepared by the removal of
water from alcohols under acidic conditions. Thus, in the preparation of
diisoamyl ether, the alcohol is heated with concentrated sulfuric acid or
p-toluenesulfonyl chloride in a flask equipped with a condenser and a water
separator. The top layer of alcohol and ether is returned to the reaction
flask until water no longer separates. Any alcohol remaining in the ether
is converted to the higher-boiling triisoamyl borate, and the ether is purified by fractional distillation.[64] Several suitable water separators have
been described.[65] High reaction temperatures must be avoided to prevent
the formation of unsaturated hydrocarbons[1] (cf. method 19).

This method has special advantages in the preparation of mixed ethers containing the t-butyl and primary alkyl radicals.[3] For example, t-butyl alcohol added slowly to a boiling mixture of ethanol and 15% aqueous sulfuric acid gives a 95% yield of t-butyl ethyl ether.[66] Under these conditions, isopropyl alcohol reacts more slowly and the yield of t-butyl isopropyl ether is reduced by the large amount of isobutylene formed by the prolonged contact of the tertiary alcohol with the acid. However, the substitution of an aqueous solution of sodium hydrogen sulfate for the sulfuric acid gives an excellent yield of t-butyl isopropyl ether (82%).[3] The formation of an ether from a primary and a secondary alcohol requires a concentration of 50% sulfuric acid or greater; the three possible ethers result.

The dehydration of alcohols in the gaseous phase by solid catalysts such as alumina and "solid phosphoric acid" is used to a small extent in the laboratory.[67] In the conversion of phenol over thorium dioxide at 450°, the yield of diphenyl ether is 64%.[68]

An interesting synthesis of diglycerol, a *polyhydroxy ether,* has been reported involving the treatment of glycerol with calcium oxide and carbon dioxide.[70]

119. Interaction of Grignard Reagents and Halo Ethers

$$RCHClOCH_2CH_3 + R'MgX \longrightarrow RCHR'OCH_2CH_3$$

The ready availability of α-halo ethers (methods 65 and 117) and the ease of reaction of the reactive halogen atom with Grignard reagents provide a good method for obtaining branched ethers of the type $ROCHR'CH_2R''$ (60–85%).[118] If ethers without branching on the α-carbon atom are desired, then chloromethyl ether and normal Grignard reagents are used, as in the formation of methyl amyl ether from n-butylmagnesium bromide and chloromethyl methyl ether (67%).[119]

The reaction of Grignard reagents with α,β-dibromo ethers to form β-bromo ethers has been developed as the third step in the Boord synthesis of olefins (method 21).[120, 125] The coupling is carried out by adding the dibromo ether to the Grignard reagent at 0°, the bromine atom in the *beta* position being unreactive. The products may be put through a second process of dehydrobromination, bromination, and coupling to give more highly branched β-bromo ethers.[121, 122, 124]

$$RCHBrCH(R')OCH_2CH_3 \xrightarrow{KOH} RCH=C(R')OCH_2CH_3 \xrightarrow{Br_2}$$

$$RCHBrCBr(R')OCH_2CH_3 \xrightarrow{R''MgX} RCHBrCR''(R')OCH_2CH_3$$

In general, primary alkylmagnesium halides give better yields than the secondary derivatives, and the tertiary Grignard reagents do not react; allyl-[125] and phenyl-magnesium[123] halides respond favorably. If each alkyl group of the ether carries a halogen atom in the *beta* position, then a dihalo ether results,[135] viz., $RMgX + ClCH_2CH_2OCHBrCH_2Br \rightarrow ClCH_2CH_2OCHRCH_2Br$.

In a similar manner, Grignard reagents react with cyclic α,β-dihalo ethers derived from 3,4-dihydro-1,2-pyran[166, 167] and tetrahydrofuran[168] to form the corresponding 2-alkyl-3-halo derivatives. Thus, addition of 2,3-dibromotetrahydropyran to methylmagnesium halide at 0° followed by hydrolysis gives a 65% yield of 2-methyl-3-bromotetrahydropyran. These materials are valuable intermediates in the synthesis of olefinic alcohols (cf. method 99).

120. Addition of Halo Ethers to Olefins

$$(CH_3)_2C\!=\!CH_2 + ClCH_2OCH_3 \xrightarrow{HgCl_2} (CH_3)_2CClCH_2CH_2OCH_3 \quad (60\%)$$

The addition of a chloromethyl ether to olefinic linkages takes place under conditions similar to the Friedel-Crafts reaction and leads to γ-chloro ethers.[139] Substitution of zinc chloride for mercuric chloride as catalyst has improved the yields.[140] Allyl chloride and chloromethyl ether react to give a high yield of 1-methoxy-3,4-dichlorobutane (98%).[40]

$$CH_2\!=\!CHCH_2Cl + ClCH_2OCH_3 \xrightarrow[CS_2]{ZnCl_2} CH_3OCH_2CH_2CHClCH_2Cl$$

121. Addition of Hydroxy Compounds to Olefinic Compounds

$$ROH + CH_2\!=\!C(CH_3)_2 \xrightarrow{H+} ROC(CH_3)_3$$

The addition of alcohols to olefinic compounds provides an easy method for making ethers which may otherwise be difficult to obtain, particularly those which contain a second functional group.

In the preparation of mixed aliphatic ethers, the reaction between alcohol and olefin is catalyzed by dilute sulfuric acid. Those olefins that can be derived from tertiary alcohols are the most suitable, e.g., isobutylene and trimethylethylene, leading to tertiary alkyl ethers. Also, primary alcohols are more suitable as additants than secondary alcohols; tertiary alcohols are practically non-reactive. The procedure, typified by the preparation of ethyl t-amyl ether (90%),[105] is not as rapid and convenient as the dehydration reaction discussed above (method 118). Phenols have been condensed in the cold with unsaturated compounds under the influence of a mineral acid[106] or boron trifluoride.[107] Reaction at high temperatures causes the formation of alkyl-substituted phenols.

Olefinic linkages activated by *other groups* add alcohols. Thus vinylacetylene, $CH_2 = CH - C \equiv CH$, adds three molecules of methanol in the presence of boron trifluoride and mercuric oxide to yield 2,2,4-trimethoxybutane (65%).[108] On the other hand, in the presence of sodium methoxide, this unsaturated system adds only one molecule of methanol to form 4-methoxy-1-butyne (61%).[109] Also, unsaturated ketones react with alcohols in the presence of boron trifluoride etherate to yield β-alkoxy ketones, e.g., 4-methoxy-2-butanone from methanol and methyl vinyl ketone (61%).[110, 111] Sodium methoxide has also been used as the condensing agent.[112, 149] Primary and secondary, but not tertiary, alcohols and phenols in the presence of the corresponding sodium derivatives add to the unsaturated system of acrylic esters to produce β-alkoxy- and β-aryloxypropionates.[113, 164] The reaction has been extended for the preparation of β,β-dialkoxy esters by the catalytic addition of alcohols to β-alkoxyacrylic esters.[114] Similarly, primary and secondary alcohols add to acrylonitrile to give β-alkoxypropionitriles; potassium hydroxide, sodium methoxide, or aqueous 40% trimethylbenzylammonium hydroxide (Triton B) are employed as catalysts.[115–117] Alcohols and α-nitro olefins combine to form 2-nitroalkyl ethers, viz.,[165]

$$H_2C = CHNO_2 + ROH \rightarrow ROCH_2CH_2NO_2$$

122. Addition of Alcohols to Oxides

$$CH_3CH - CH_2 + ROH \xrightarrow{NaOCH_3} CH_3CHOHCH_2OR$$

The alcoholysis of α-epoxides gives hydroxy ethers in a *trans* opening of the ring. An example is the treatment of cyclohexene oxide with methanol under reflux in the presence of a small quantity of sulfuric acid, *trans*-2-methoxycyclohexanol being formed in 82% yield.[171] The mechanism and stereochemistry of the opening of oxide rings have been reviewed.[172]

When an unsymmetrical α-epoxide reacts, either a primary or a secondary alcohol is formed, depending on which carbon-oxygen bond is cleaved. With propylene oxide, for example, a base-catalyzed reaction favors the formation of the secondary alcohol almost exclusively, whereas, a noncatalytic or acid-catalyzed alcoholysis yields a mixture of the isomeric ethers.[141, 169] However, the reactions of other α-epoxides, such as 3,4-epoxy-1-butene, 3,4-epoxy-1-chloropropane (epichlorohydrin), 3,4-epoxy-1-propanol (glycidol), and styrene oxide, are more complicated with respect to which isomer is favored.[142, 162]

The 1-alkoxy-2-hydroxy-3-chloropropanols are obtained from the acid-catalyzed condensation of aliphatic alcohols and 1,2-epoxy-3-chloropropane. These compounds are treated with alkali for the synthesis of epoxy ethers, which, in turn, are valuable intermediates.[143]

$$\underset{H_2C-CHCH_2Cl}{\overset{O}{\triangle}} + ROH \xrightarrow{H_2SO_4} ROCH_2CHOHCH_2Cl \xrightarrow{KOH} \underset{H_2C-CHCH_2OR}{\overset{O}{\triangle}}$$

123. Halo Ethers by Action of Acyl Chlorides on Acetals

$$RCH(OR')_2 + CH_3COCl \rightarrow RCHClOR' + CH_3CO_2R'$$

The interaction of an acetal and an acyl chloride causes an exchange of chloro and alkoxyl groups, the corresponding α-chloro ether and an ester being formed.[146] The acetals of both aliphatic and aromatic aldehydes undergo the reaction. For example, the dimethyl acetal of n-butyraldehyde and acetyl chloride react vigorously to yield α-methoxy-n-butyl chloride, $CH_3(CH_2)_2CHClOCH_3$ (70–80%). The reaction may be catalyzed by a trace of copper-bronze filings.[148] Similarly, the dimethyl acetals of benzaldehyde and its derivatives react to give α-methoxybenzyl chlorides (80–98%).[147, 148]

Dihalo ethers, $RCHXOCH_2CH_2X$, can be synthesized by utilizing dichloroalkyl acetals, $RCH(OCH_2CH_2X)_2$. In this manner, chloromethyl β-chloroisopropyl ether is prepared from di-(β-chloroisopropyl)-formal and benzoyl chloride (66%).[137]

$$H_2C[OCH(CH_3)CH_2Cl]_2 \xrightarrow{C_6H_5COCl} ClCH_2OCH(CH_3)CH_2Cl$$

124. α-Alkoxy Ketones by Interaction of Alcohols and Diazoketones[173]

$$C_6H_5COCHN_2 + ROH \xrightarrow{BF_3} C_6H_5COCH_2OR + N_2$$

TABLE 16. ETHERS 235

TABLE 16. ETHERS

C_n	Compound	Method	Yield (%)	Chapter[ref.]	B.p./mm., n_D^t, (M.p.), Deriv.
		Alicyclic and Aliphatic Ethers			
C_4	Methyl cyclopropyl ether	....	50	6^6	43
C_5	Methyl n-butyl ether	115	70	6^{72}	70
		115	71	6^1	70.5/766, 1.3736
	Methyl t-butyl ether	118	95	6^3	55/760, 1.3690 *
	Ethyl n-propyl ether	115	60	6^{72}	64
C_6	Methyl cyclopentyl ether	115	29	6^6	105.4/760, 1.4206
		115	26	6^5	105/763
	Methyl n-amyl ether	115	84	6^1	99/763, 1.3873
		119	67	6^{119}	100, 1.3862^{22}
	Methyl isoamyl ether	115	70	6^{72}	91
	Ethyl n-butyl ether	115	71	6^1	91.5/757, 1.3818
		115	60	6^{72}	91
	Ethyl isobutyl ether	115	70	6^{73}	80 *
	Ethyl s-butyl ether	119	76	6^{118}	81/776, 1.3802
	Ethyl t-butyl ether	118	95	6^3	73/760, 1.3755 *
C_7	Methyl n-hexyl ether	115	72	6^1	126/770, 1.3972
	Ethyl n-amyl ether	115	47	6^1	117.5/768, 1.3927
	Ethyl t-amyl ether	121	90	6^{105}	102
	Ethyl neopentyl ether	115	38	6^4	90.5/729, 1.3830
	n-Propyl isobutyl ether	115	67	6^2	106/720
	Isopropyl n-butyl ether	115	72	6^2	108/738
	t-Butyl n-propyl ether	118	68	6^3	97/760, 1.3830^{25}
	t-Butyl isopropyl ether	118	82	6^3	88/760, 1.3798 *
	Methyl cyclohexyl ether	5	76	6^6	
		115	78	6^{72}	135
		115	27	6^5	133.5/762
	Ethyl cyclopentyl ether	115	35	6^5	122.5/763
C_8	Ethyl n-hexyl ether	115	57	6^1	143/773, 1.4008
	n-Butyl ether	118	60	6^{66}	144, 1.3989 *
	t-Butyl n-butyl ether	118	52	6^3	124/760, 1.3928^{25}
C_9	Ethyl n-heptyl ether	119	77	6^{118}	51/15, 1.4066
C_{10}	Isoamyl ether	118	75	6^{64}	61/10, 1.4085 *
		Aromatic Ethers			
C_7	Anisole	116	75	6^{74}	154/748
C_8	Ethyl phenyl ether (phenetole)	115	60	6^1	169/766, 1.5074
	Methyl benzyl ether	115	90	6^6	170/760, 1.5022
	Methyl 4-tolyl ether	116	92	6^{76}	57/9, 1.5060^{25}
C_9	n-Propyl phenyl ether	115	73	6^1	187/751, 1.5103
		115	63	6^6	189/760, 1.5014

For explanations and symbols see pp. xi–xii.

TABLE 16 (continued)

C_n	Compound	Method	Yield (%)	Chapter[ref.]	B.p./mm., n_D^t, (M.p.), Deriv.
		Aromatic Ethers (continued)			
C_9	Isopropyl phenyl ether	115	40	6^1	174/758, 1.4975
		115	54	6^6	177/760, 1.4975
		121	54	6^{107}	178, 1.4992
	m-Ethylanisole	116	87	6^{78}	76/12
C_{10}	n-Butyl phenyl ether	115	80	6^1	207/755, 1.4971
	s-Butyl phenyl ether	115	59	6^6	72/5, 194/760, 1.4926^{25}
	Isobutyl phenyl ether	115	90	6^7	196, 1.4932^{24}
	n-Propyl benzyl ether	115	93	6^9	68/8, 1.4905
	Isopropyl benzyl ether	115	84	6^6	83/16, 1.4859
C_{11}	n-Amyl phenyl ether	115	72	6^1	226/751, 1.4947
	n-Butyl benzyl ether	115	74	6^{20}	112/23
	s-Butyl benzyl ether	115	55	6^{20}	109/29, 1.4787^{25}
	Ethyl p-ethylbenzyl ether	115	95	6^{10}	107/14, 1.4918^{25}
	p-t-Butylanisole	116	60	6^6	223/760, 1.5030
	Methyl α-naphthyl ether	116	70	6^{76}	102/2, 1.6940^{25}
	Methyl β-naphthyl ether	116	73	6^{71}	(71)
	6-Methoxytetralin	116	65 †	6^{159}	138/18
	1,2,3,4-Tetrahydro-2-methoxynaphthalene	4	58	6^{174}	115/9, 1.5293
C_{12}	Isoamyl benzyl ether	119	85	6^{118}	119/19, 1.4810
	Diphenyl ether	115	82	6^{14}	259/754
	Ethyl α-naphthyl ether	116	77	6^{76}	138/14, 1.5953^{25}
	Ethyl β-naphthyl ether	116	84	6^{76}	132/5, (38)
C_{13}	Phenyl benzyl ether	115	73	6^{13}	(39)
	Phenyl o-tolyl ether	115	77	6^{14}	267/738, 124/9, 1.5710^{25}
	Phenyl m-tolyl ether	115	81	6^{14}	275/738, 155/25, 1.5711^{25}
	Phenyl p-tolyl ether	115	69	6^{14}	278/745, 126/9, 1.5701^{25}
	Methyl 2-biphenyl ether	116	89	6^{76}	122/2, (29)
	4-Methyldiphenyl ether	14	60	6^{176}	278/744, 150/7
	Methyl 4-cyclohexylphenyl ether	116	64	6^{76}	116/4, (59)
C_{14}	Di-p-tolyl ether	115	87	6^{145}	(50)
	Ethyl 2-biphenyl ether	115	75	6^{11}	(34)
		116	87	6^{76}	132/6, (34)
	Ethyl 3-biphenyl ether	116	90	6^{76}	158/8, (35)
	Ethyl 4-biphenyl ether	115	80	6^{11}	(76)
		116	71	6^{76}	188/13, (74)
	Ethyl 2-cyclohexylphenyl ether	116	59	6^{76}	99/1
	Ethyl 4-cyclohexylphenyl ether	116	57	6^{76}	131/3, (42)
C_{15}	1-Methoxyphenanthrene	116	100	6^{160}	(103)
	4-Methoxyphenanthrene	116	100	6^{160}	(67)

TABLE 16. ETHERS   237

TABLE 16 (continued)

C_n	Compound	Method	Yield (%)	Chapter[ref.]	B.p./mm., n_D^t, (M.p.), Deriv.
		Aromatic Ethers (continued)			
C_{15}	9-Ethoxyfluorene	115	73	6^{16}	(54)
	2-Methoxy-9,10-dihydro-phenanthrene	116	100	6^{79}	(55)
C_{19}	9-Phenoxyfluorene	115	87	6^{16}	(156)
C_{21}	Ethyl triphenylmethyl ether	115	97	6^{12}	(83)
		Heterocyclic Ethers			
C_5	2,3-Dihydropyran	19	70	39^{209}	86
	Tetrahydropyran	554	100	39^{167}	86
C_6	Methyl α-furfuryl ether	115	66	6^{17}	135/762, 1.4570
	Methyl tetrahydrofurfuryl ether	115	73	6^{18}	141/716, 1.4292
C_7	Ethyl α-furfuryl ether	115	81	6^{17}	150/770, 1.4523
	Ethyl tetrahydrofurfuryl ether	115	85	6^{18}	154/726, 1.4298
C_8	n-Propyl α-furfuryl ether	115	79	6^{17}	170/767, 1.4523
	n-Propyl tetrahydrofurfuryl ether	115	86	6^{18}	176/728, 1.4313
C_9	n-Butyl α-furfuryl ether	115	78	6^{17}	191/777, 1.4522
	n-Butyl tetrahydrofurfuryl ether	115	79	6^{18}	196/721, 1.4357
	6-Methoxyindole	559	80	39^{202}	(92)
	3-(4-Piperidyl)-1-methoxy-propane	554	88	39^{125}	112/17
C_{10}	Di-α-furfuryl ether	115	84	6^{17}	89/1, 1.5088
	6-Methoxyquinoline	575	63	39^{128}	102/0.5, (20)
	7-Methoxyquinoline	575	27	39^{146}	287/758, (210), 229Pi
	8-Methoxyquinoline	575	27	39^{147}	175/29, (45), 162Pi
	bz-Tetrahydro-6-methoxy-quinoline	554	93	39^{149}	130/1, (43), 1.5718^{50}
C_{13}	4-Methoxydibenzofuran	116	97	6^{80}	165/5, (52)
	4-Methoxydibenzothio-phene	116	94	6^{81}	(123)
C_{14}	3-Ethoxycarbazole	557	90	39^{158}	(106)
C_{19}	5-Phenoxyacridine	115	98	6^{19}	(128)

For explanations and symbols see pp. xi–xii.

TABLE 17. DIETHERS

C_n	Compound	Method	Yield (%)	Chapter[ref.]	B.p./mm., n_D^t, (M.p.)
C_4	Dimethyl ether of ethylene glycol	115	78	6^{22}	84, 1.3813
C_7	Methyl n-butyl ether of ethylene glycol	115	46	6^{20}	146, 1.3988[25]
C_8	Ethyl n-butyl ether of ethylene glycol	115	90	6^{21}	165
	1,2-Dimethoxybenzene (veratrole)	116	95	6^{77}	205, (15)
C_9	Ethyl n-pentyl ether of ethylene glycol	115	48	6^{21}	183
	Methoxymethyl benzyl ether	115	50	6^{26}	211/756
C_{12}	1,4-Dimethoxynaphthalene	116	70	6^{83}	(85)
C_{13}	2-Methoxydiphenyl ether	115	67	6^{23}	(78)
	3-Methoxydiphenyl ether	115	96	6^{25}	175/20
	4-Methoxydiphenyl ether	115	96	6^{25}	186/32
C_{16}	4,4′-Dimethoxydibenzyl	9	60	6^{175}	(125)
C_{18}	o-Diphenoxybenzene	115	81	6^{14}	(93)
	p-Diphenoxybenzene	115	83	6^{14}	(77)

For explanations and symbols see pp. xi–xii.

TABLE 18. OLEFINIC ETHERS

C_n	Compound	Method	Yield (%)	Chapter [ref.]	B.p./mm., n_D^t, (M.p.)
	Aliphatic and Alicyclic Olefinic Ethers				
C_4	Ethyl vinyl ether	20	43	2^{144}	36, 1.3737[21]
		23	42	2^{140}	36/760, 1.3768
	Divinyl ether	20	61	2^{141}	28/760
	Dioxene	22	49	2^{267}	94
	Dioxadiene	22	48	2^{267}	75/746, 1.4350
C_5	2-Methoxy-2-butene	20	52	2^{140}	65/770, 1.4000[15]
	2-Methoxy-1,3-butadiene	23	60	2^{505}	75/745, 1.4442
	Methyl methallyl ether	115	72	6^6	66/760, 1.3943
	2-Ethoxypropene	20	64	2^{139}	62/760, 1.3913
		20	83	2^{138}	62/748, 1.3915
		27	91	2^{140}	62/765, 1.3927
	Vinyl allyl ether	20	67	2^{450}	67
C_6	Ethyl crotyl ether	115	82	6^{28}	101/765, 1.4030[23]
	2-Ethoxy-1-butene	20	65	2^{253}	86, 1.4011[25]
		20	70	2^{138}	86/745, 1.4018
	3-Ethoxy-1-butene	115	53	6^{28}	77/760, 1.3882[23]

TABLE 18. OLEFINIC ETHERS 239

TABLE 18 (*continued*)

C_n	Compound	Method	Yield (%)	Chapter[ref.]	B.p./mm., n_D^t, (M.p.)

Aliphatic and Alicyclic Olefinic Ethers (*continued*)

C_n	Compound	Method	Yield (%)	Chapter[ref.]	B.p./mm., n_D^t, (M.p.)
C_6	2-Ethoxy-1,3-butadiene	23	59	2[505]	97/760, 1.4401
		121	53	6[163]	95, 1.4400[19]
	1,3-Dimethoxy-2-butene	23	66	2[505]	130/748, 1.4145[25]
	3,3-Dimethoxy-1-butene	23	29	2[505]	99/745, 1.4038
	trans-1,2-Diethoxyethylene	23	80	2[507]	79
C_7	1-Methoxy-5-hexene	29	60	2[192]	123/745, 1.4109
		29	50	2[191]	124/742, 1.4117
	2-Methoxy-1-hexene	23	92	2[506]	120/740, 1.4179[19]
	3-Methoxy-3-hexene	20	79	2[253]	115, 1.4130[25]
	Allyl methallyl ether	115	90	6[27]	115, 1.4236
	Isopropyl methallyl ether	115	57	6[6]	104/760, 1.4014
	Ethyl allyl ether of ethylene glycol	115	60	6[21]	142
C_8	1-Methoxy-6-heptene	29	56	2[192]	148/751, 1.4182
	Dimethallyl ether	115	65	6[6]	134/760, 1.4285
	t-Butyl methallyl ether	115	33	6[6]	120/760, 1.4082
	1-Ethoxy-2-cyclohexene	115	46	6[29]	153/728
C_9	*trans*-1-Methoxy-2-octene	116	78	6[84]	70/18, 1.4249[22]

Aromatic Olefinic Ethers

C_n	Compound	Method	Yield (%)	Chapter[ref.]	B.p./mm., n_D^t, (M.p.)
C_8	Phenyl vinyl ether	20	69	2[143]	155
C_9	Phenyl allyl ether	115	74	6[31]	89/26
	α-Methoxystyrene	23	86	2[504]	74/10
	β-Methoxystyrene	23	36	2[504]	212
	2-Methoxystyrene	27	40	2[255]	62/3, 1.5608
	3-Methoxystyrene	19	69	2[145]	89/14, 1.5540
	4-Methoxystyrene	19	65	2[166]	46/0.5, 1.5553[25]
		20	33	2[145]	93/13, 1.5608
		27	71	2[255]	54/2, 1.5612
C_{10}	Crotyl phenyl ether	115	73	6[33]	98/14
	Methallyl phenyl ether	115	70	6[6]	80/8, 1.5157
	Allyl *p*-tolyl ether	115	93	6[32]	98/16
	α-Methoxy-β-methylstyrene	20	42	2[253]	97/19, 1.5271[26]
	α Ethoxystyrene	20	62	2[253]	110/30, 1.5287[25]
	trans-3-Methoxy-1-phenyl-1-propene	116	64	6[84]	112/15, 1.5452[21]
	p-Ethoxystyrene	19	69	2[166]	58/1.0, 1.5454[25]
C_{11}	1-Phenoxy-2-pentene	115	57	6[34]	119/20
	5-Phenoxy-2-pentene	20	70	2[142]	132/32, 1.5005[30]
C_{12}	1-Phenoxy-2-hexene	115	57	6[36]	107/5, 1.5109
	3-Ethoxy-4-propyl-3-heptene	19	90	2[112]	109/17

For explanations and symbols see pp. xi-xii.

TABLE 18 (*continued*)

C_n	Compound	Method	Yield (%)	Chapter[ref.]	B.p./mm., n_D^t, (M.p.)
		Aromatic Olefinic Ethers (*continued*)			
C_{14}	4-Phenoxystyrene	19	77	2[145]	116/3, 1.6037
C_{15}	Cinnamyl phenyl ether	115	92	6[35]	(67)
	cis-4-Methoxystilbene	27	60	2[438]	142/3
	trans-4-Methoxystilbene	28	49	2[273]	(136)

For explanations and symbols see pp. xi-xii.

TABLE 19. ACETYLENIC ETHERS

C_n	Compound	Method	Yield (%)	Chapter[ref.]	B.p./mm., n_D^t
C_4	Ethoxyacetylene	43	55	3[57]	28/300
	Methyl propargyl ether	43	60	3[59]	64, 1.3975[19]
C_5	4-Methoxy-1-butyne	44	60	3[23]	88/748, 1.4117[22]
	4-Methoxy-2-butyne	121	61	6[109]	100
C_6	4-Ethoxy-1-butyne	44	60	3[23]	104/747, 1.4148[22]
C_8	Phenoxyacetylene	43	70	3[48]	62/25, 1.5171
C_9	1-Methoxy-2-octyne	116	80	6[85]	77/19, 1.4380
		119	63	6[85]	77/20, 1.4383[18]

For explanations and symbols see pp. xi-xii.

TABLE 20. HALO ETHERS

C_n	Compound	Method	Yield (%)	Chapter[ref.]	B.p./mm., n_D^t, (M.p.)
		Aliphatic and Alicyclic Halo Ethers			
C_2	Chloromethyl methyl ether	117	89	6[126]	55-60
C_3	Chloromethyl ethyl ether	117	90	6[128]	82, 1.0282[12]
	Chloromethyl β-chloro-ethyl ether	117	55	6[134]	46/10, 1.4578
	Methyl α-chloroethyl ether	117	97	6[132]	73, 1.4004
	Methyl β-chloroethyl ether	116	27	6[82]	90
C_4	Chloromethyl *n*-propyl ether	117	64	6[127]	28/32, 110/755, 1.4106
	Bromomethyl *n*-propyl ether	117	80	6[130]	48/20, 1.4515
	γ-Methoxypropyl chloride	116	65	6[88]	112

TABLE 20. HALO ETHERS 241

TABLE 20 (*continued*)

C_n	Compound	Method	Yield (%)	Chapter[ref.]	B.p./mm., n_D^t, (M.p.)
		Aliphatic and Alicyclic Halo Ethers (*continued*)			
C_4	γ-Methoxypropyl bromide	52	32	4[126]	30/15, 131/736, 1.4467
		52	27	4[124]	133
	Chloromethyl isopropyl ether	117	49	6[127]	36/45, 101/750, 1.4095
		117	90	6[128]	98, 1.4592[16]
	Bromomethyl isopropyl ether	117	87	6[131]	76/196, 1.4251[25]
	Chloromethyl β-chloro-isopropyl ether	117	57	6[137]	107/146, 1.4521
		123	66	6[137]	59/16, 1.4528
	1-Chloro-2-methoxy-propane	77	56	4[629]	101/743, 1.4147
	2-Chloro-2-methoxy-propane	123	90	6[148]	15/12
	α-Chloroethyl ethyl ether	65	42	4[633]	100
		117	94	6[132]	98/750, 1.3950
	Ethyl β-chloroethyl ether	53	80	4[617]	109
		118	66	6[82]	109
	Ethyl β-bromoethyl ether	52	66	4[123]	127/760
	Ethyl β-iodoethyl ether	55	89	4[384]	155
	α,α'-Dichlorodiethyl ether	65	57	4[633]	114, 1.4183[24]
	β-Chloroethyl α-chloro-ethyl ether	117	60	6[134]	51/10, 1.4473
	β-Bromoethyl α-chloro-ethyl ether	117	69	6[136]	84/37, 1.4770
	α,β-Dibromoethyl ethyl ether	65	91	4[384]	91/20
	β,β'-Dichlorodiethyl ether	118	75	6[71]	178, 1.457
		77	61	4[629]	178/752, 1.4568
	β,β'-Dibromodiethyl ether	52	81	4[576]	93/12
	β,β'-Diiododiethyl ether	55	74	4[385]	124/10
C_5	Chloromethyl n-butyl ether	117	37	6[129]	134/760
	Bromomethyl n-butyl ether	117	78	6[130]	57/20, 1.4514
	α-Methoxy-n-butyl chloride	123	80	6[148]	29/12
	1-Chloro-4-methoxybutane	115	36	6[149]	143, 1.4244
	1-Bromo-4-methoxybutane	115	53	6[46]	70–82/34–35
	1-Methoxy-3,4-dichloro-butane	120	98	6[40]	170/760, 73/20
	Bromomethyl isobutyl ether	117	98	6[131]	53/30, 1.4400[25]
	Chloromethyl isobutyl ether	117	35	6[129]	121/760

For explanations and symbols see pp. xi–xii.

TABLE 20 *(continued)*

C_n	Compound	Method	Yield (%)	Chapter[ref.]	B.p./mm., n_D^t, (M.p.)
	Aliphatic and Alicyclic Halo Ethers (continued)				
C_5	3-Methoxy-2-methyl-1-chloropropane	53	92	4[583]	124, 1.4143[27]
	2-Methoxy-3-iodobutane	77	95	4[628]	1.5012[17]
	2-Methoxy-3-bromobutane	77	50	4[630]	56/40, 1.4478[25]
	Chloromethyl s-butyl ether	117	90	6[128]	123, 1.4205[16]
	Bromomethyl s-butyl ether	117	97	6[131]	108/357, 1.4453[25]
	α-Chloroethyl n-propyl ether	117	93	6[132]	48/40, 1.4013
	α-Chloro-n-propyl ethyl ether	117	74	6[125]	36/25, 1.4120
	γ-Ethoxypropyl chloride	52	67	4[124]	128
	γ-Ethoxypropyl bromide	52	65	4[124]	150, 87/100
		52	75	4[125]	152/760, 65/33, 48/13
	α,β-Dibromoethyl n-propyl ether	65	93	4[482]	97/27
	α,β-Dibromopropyl ethyl ether	65	97	4[480]	82/20, 1.5000
	1,3-Dichloropropyl ethyl ether	117	66	6[138]	65/18, 1.4478
	β-Chloroethyl α-chloro-n-propyl ether	117	51	6[134]	60/10, 1.4496
	β-Ethoxy-n-propyl bromide	119	77	6[120]	138
		119	42	6[122]	29/10, 1.4422
	2-Methyl-3-chlorotetrahydrofuran *(trans)*	119	82	6[168]	130, 1.4420
	(cis)				145, 1.4520
	2,3-Dibromotetrahydropyran	74	100	4[621]	….
	2,3-Dichlorotetrahydropyran	74	91	4[620]	83/13, 1.4930[25]
C_6	Bromoethyl n-amyl ether	117	99	6[130]	72/7, 83/15, 1.4512
	1-Bromomethoxy-2-methylbutane	117	98	6[131]	68/16, 1.4671[25]
	Bromomethyl isoamyl ether	117	98	6[131]	129/247, 1.4489[25]
	2-Chloro-3-methyl-3-methoxybutane	77	45	4[629]	135/749, 1.4279
	1-Methoxy-3-methyl-3-chlorobutane	120	60	6[139]	81/120, 136/751
	2-Chloro-3-methoxypentane	77	78	4[629]	77/100, 1.4246
	α-Chloroethyl n-butyl ether	117	95	6[132]	50/11, 1.4155

TABLE 20. HALO ETHERS 243

TABLE 20 (*continued*)

C_n	Compound	Method	Yield (%)	Chapter[ref.]	B.p./mm., n_D^t, (M.p.)
	Aliphatic and Alicyclic Halo Ethers (*continued*)				
C_6	α-Chloro-*n*-butyl ethyl	117	81	6[125]	51/25, 1.4168
	ether	123	80	6[148]	47/12
	β-Chloroethyl α-chloro-*n*-butyl ether	117	70	6[134]	71/10, 1.4471
	α,β-Dibromoethyl *n*-butyl ether	65	95	4[482]	115/36
	α,β-Dibromo-*n*-butyl ethyl ether	65	90	4[480]	101/27, 1.4968
	α-Chloroisobutyl ethyl ether	117	90	6[121]	43/24, 1.4130
	α,β-Dibromoisobutyl ethyl ether	65	92	4[424]	89/22, 1.4450
	α-Chloroethyl *s*-butyl ether	117	83	6[133]	39/20, 1.4149
	β-Ethoxy-*n*-butyl bromide	119	61	6[120]	166, 67/34
	β-Chloroethyl β-bromo-α-ethylethyl ether	118	81	6[135]	93/12, 1.4770
	β-Propoxy-*n*-propyl bromide	119	61	6[120]	65/32
	2-Methyl-3-chlorotetrahydropyran (*trans*)	119	61	6[167]	51/18, 1.4551
	(*cis*)				66/18, 1.4626
	2-Methyl-3-bromotetrahydropyran	119	65	6[166]	61/17, 1.4834
	1-Bromo-6-methoxyhexane	115	47	6[45]	113/30, 1.4469[25]
	1-Methoxy-4-chlorohexane	53	65	4[128]	70/15
	3-Chloro-4-methoxyhexane	77	63	4[629]	95/98, 1.4288
	4-Bromo-3-methoxyhexane	119	68	6[121]	66/12, 1.4495
	α-Chloroethyl *n*-amyl ether	117	99	6[132]	66/8, 1.4218
	1-Bromo-5-ethoxypentane	52	78	4[127]	85/14
	β-Ethoxy-*n*-amyl bromide	119	57	6[120]	82/34
	1-Bromo-2-ethoxy-2-methylbutane	119	27	6[122]	57/13, 1.4508
	2-Chloro-3-ethoxypentane	77	57	4[629]	70/50, 1.4236
	β-Propoxy-*n*-butyl bromide	119	73	6[120]	66/15
	Chloromethyl cyclohexyl ether	117	90	6[128]	185, 1.4713[9]
	1-Chloro-2-methoxycyclohexane	77	66	4[629]	74/20, 1.4648
	trans-1-Bromo-2-methoxycyclohexane	77	70	4[630]	75/10, 1.4900[25]

For explanations and symbols see pp. xi–xii.

TABLE 20 (*continued*)

C_n	Compound	Method	Yield (%)	Chapter[ref.]	B.p./mm., n_D^t, (M.p.)
	Aliphatic and Alicyclic Halo Ethers (*continued*)				
C_8	1-Chloro-7-methoxyheptane	53	67	4[162]	78/6.5, 1.4375
	1-Bromo-7-methoxyheptane	52	50	4[128]	97/8, 1.4592[25]
	1-Bromomethoxy-1-methylhexane	117	96	6[131]	69/4, 1.4537[25]
	1-Bromo-2-ethoxyhexane	119	78	6[121]	86/19, 1.4485
	1-Bromo-2-ethoxy-3-methylpentane	119	30	6[121]	75/13, 1.4503
	1-Bromo-2-ethoxy-4-methylpentane	119	48	6[121]	85/25, 1.4455
	2-Bromo-3-ethoxyhexane	119	60	6[121]	73/12, 1.4474
	1-Bromo-2-ethoxy-2-methylpentane	119	71	6[121]	82/19, 1.4532
	2-Bromo-3-ethoxy-2-methylpentane	119	49	6[121]	67/20, 1.4376
	2-Bromo-3-ethoxy-3-methylpentane	119	55	6[121]	79/25, 1.4458
	1-Bromo-2-ethoxy-2-ethylbutane	119	75	6[121]	81/17, 1.4548
	1-Bromo-2-ethoxy-2,3-dimethylbutane	119	71	6[121]	79/15, 1.4560
	4,4'-Dichlorodibutyl ether	54	54	4[415]	118/10, 1.4562[25]
	β-Propoxy-n-amyl bromide	119	70	6[120]	82/13
	1-(Methoxymethyl)-2-chlorocyclohexane	120	27	6[140]	91/17
C_9	1-Bromomethoxy-1-methylheptane	117	93	6[131]	72/3, 1.4562[25]
	β-Ethoxyisoheptyl bromide	119	65	6[120]	109/33
	β-Propoxy-n-hexyl bromide	119	81	6[120]	93/14
C_{10}	4,4'-Dichlorodiamyl ether	54	24	4[415]	69–75/0.3, 1.4533[25]
	Aromatic Halo Ethers				
C_7	o-Bromoanisole	56	93	4[318]	116/29
	m-Bromoanisole	116	91	6[89]	105/16
	p-Chloroanisole	64	58	4[592]	85–90, 1.5354[25]
	p-Bromoanisole	65	90	4[479]	216
	p-Iodoanisole	65	73	4[283]	139, (52)
	p-Fluoroanisole	56	52	4[303]	157

TABLE 20. HALO ETHERS 245

TABLE 20 (*continued*)

C_n	Compound	Method	Yield (%)	Chapter[ref.]	B.p./mm., n_D^t, (M.p.)
	Aromatic Halo Ethers (*continued*)				
C_7	2-Bromo-4-chloroanisole	64	66	4[592]	125–130/11, (29.1)
	2,4-Dibromoanisole	64	72	4[592]	106/1, (62.3)
C_8	β-Phenoxyethyl chloride	53	53 ‡	4[161]	221
	Phenoxyethyl bromide	115	56	6[47]	125–130/18
	Chloromethyl benzyl ether	117	77	6[129]	125/40
	α-Methoxybenzyl chloride	123	80	6[147]	72/0.1
	p-Chloro-α-methoxybenzyl chloride	123	98	6[148]	82/0.15
	Ethyl o-iodophenyl ether	56	68	4[323]	131/18
	Ethyl p-bromophenyl ether	65	85	4[479]	236
	m-Methoxybenzyl chloride	53	91	4[164]	115/10
	m-Methoxybenzyl bromide	51	90 ‡	4[65]	129/18
	p-Methoxybenzyl chloride (anisyl chloride)	51	80	4[66]	113/10, 1.5491
C_9	γ-Phenoxypropyl bromide	115	85	6[47]	136–142/20
	Benzyl β-iodoethyl ether	55	60	4[386]	149/14
	1-Chloro-2-phenoxypropane	77	35	4[629]	113/22, 1.5218
	α-Ethoxybenzyl chloride	123	95	6[148]	37/0.06
	β-o-Anisylethyl chloride	53	85	4[163]	112/12
	β-m-Anisylethyl bromide	52	61	4[65]	139/13
	p-Methyl-α-methoxybenzyl chloride	123	98	6[148]	70/0.15
	3,4-Dimethoxybenzyl chloride	53	90	4[165]	(51)
C_{10}	1-Bromo-4-phenoxybutane	52	70	4[129]	156/18
	1-Chloro-4-phenoxybutane	115	60	6[48]	138/12
	γ-Chloropropyl benzyl ether	53	83	4[386]	129/16
	γ-Bromopropyl benzyl ether	52	34	4[124]	132/8
C_{11}	2-Bromo-1-phenyl-1-ethoxypropane	119	56	6[123]	114/9
C_{12}	6-Phenoxyhexyl bromide	115	79	6[152]	174–180/13
	o-Chlorophenyl phenyl ether	115	40	6[14]	153/15, (40)
	o-Iodophenyl phenyl ether	56	68	4[322]	185/15, (55)
	p-Chlorophenyl phenyl ether	115	55	6[14]	162/19, 1.5865[25]
		65	90	4[284]	150/7

For explanations and symbols see pp. xi–xii.

TABLE 21. HYDROXY ETHERS

C_n	Compound	Method	Yield (%)	Chapter[ref.]	B.p./mm., n_D^t, (M.p.), Deriv.
		Aliphatic and Alicyclic Hydroxy Ethers			
C_4	2-Methoxy-1-propanol	84	40	5[658]	130/758, 97Db, 60Nu
	1-Methoxy-2-propanol	122	63	6[151]	119/765, 80Db
	3-Methoxy-1-propanol	115	64	6[37]	149
C_5	4-Methoxy-1-butanol	88	37	5[332]	64/7, 1.4213
	3-Ethoxy-1-propanol	84	78	5[50]	161
		115	62	6[37]	157-163
	1-Ethoxy-2-propanol	122	81	6[141]	138, 1.4100
	3-Methoxy-2-methyl-1-propanol	79	94	5[681]	155, 1.4140[27], 64Db
	1,3-Dimethoxy-2-propanol	115	60	6[39]	66/9, 1.4192
C_6	5-Methoxy-1-pentanol	88	47	5[332]	84/9, 1.4281
	4-Ethoxy-1-butanol	88	29	5[332]	72/8, 1.4229
	4-Methoxy-3-methyl-1-butanol	88	67	5[681]	89/25, 1.4213[27], 57Db
C_7	1-Methoxy-4-hexanol	88	47	5[164]	91/15
	5-Ethoxy-1-pentanol	84	71	5[80]	90/9
		88	28	5[332]	91/9, 1.4291
	5-Methoxy-4-methyl-1-pentanol	90	74	5[681]	97/15, 1.4272[27]
	5-Methoxy-2-methyl-1-pentanol	84	85	5[681]	94/10
	1-Methoxy-2-ethyl-2-butanol	85	80	5[654]	155/750, 1.4258[15]
	3-Ethoxy-2-methyl-2-butanol	91	79	5[436]	141, 226Pu
	1-Methoxy-2,3-dimethyl-2-butanol	89	52	5[396]	36/10, 1.4202[23]
	γ-n-Butoxypropyl alcohol	115	83	6[38]	78-85/10
	1,3-Diethoxy-2-propanol	115	46	6[39]	62/2, 1.4200
		122	75	6[144]	111/60, 1.420
	2-Amyloxyethanol	115	42	6[153]	188/753, 1.4239
	trans-2-Methoxycyclohexanol	122	82	6[171]	73/10, 1.4586[25]
	3-Methoxycyclohexanol	86	60	5[575]	89/8
	4-Methoxycyclohexanol	86	74	5[578]	99/12
C_8	7-Methoxy-1-heptanol	88	35	5[164]	109/8, 1.4334[25]
		90	53	5[472]	97/3, 1.4357
	3-Methyl-5-ethoxy-1-pentanol	115	45	6[52]	111/20
	2-Ethyl-4-ethoxy-1-butanol	84	60	5[681]	92/10
	1-Methoxy-3-methyl-2-ethyl-2-butanol	89	58	5[396]	55/11, 1.4288[22]
	trans-2-Ethoxycyclohexanol	122	80	6[170]	86/15, 1.4537[25]

TABLE 21. HYDROXY ETHERS   247

TABLE 21 (*continued*)

C_n	Compound	Method	Yield (%)	Chapter[ref.]	B.p./mm., n_D^t, (M.p.), Deriv.
	Aliphatic and Alicyclic Hydroxy Ethers (*continued*)				
C_9	3-Ethyl-4-ethoxy-3-pentanol	91	75	5[436]	68/14, 231Pu
	2-Ethoxycyclohexyl-1-methanol	115	60	6[40]	75/10
	Aromatic Hydroxy Ethers				
C_7	m-Methoxyphenol	116	45	6[87]	242
C_8	o-Methoxybenzyl alcohol	84	56	5[23]	135/20, 82NBz
	m-Methoxybenzyl alcohol	79	100	5[108]	150/25
	p-Methoxybenzyl alcohol	79	97	5[91]	138/14, (24)
	(anisyl alcohol)	79	96	5[2]	(24), 93Pu *
		84	89	5[23]	151/27, 94NBz
C_9	1-Phenoxy-2-propanol	79	75	5[155]	130/21, 1.5232
		122	90	6[169]	117/10, 1.5200[25]
	2-Phenoxy-1-propanol	79	100	5[110]	120/10, 1.4760[25]
	γ-Phenoxypropyl alcohol	115	80	6[41]	160/25
	α-Glyceryl phenyl ether	115	64	6[42]	187/15, (70)
	2-Phenyl-2-methoxyethanol	122	42	6[162]	93/4, 1.5182[25]
	β-Methoxy-α-phenylethyl alcohol	115	61	6[150]	131/18, 1.5165[26]
	Benzyl β-hydroxyethyl ether	115	69	6[44]	138/15
	m-Methoxyphenylethyl alcohol	84	90	5[77]	145/13
	2,3-Dimethoxybenzyl alcohol	81	71	5[505]	173/33, (48)
	3,4-Dimethoxybenzyl alcohol	79	91	5[107]	170/14, 118Pu *
	3,5-Dimethoxybenzyl alcohol	84	93	5[76]	(46)
C_{10}	1-Phenoxy-2-butanol	88	86	5[333]	134/20, (29)
	4-Phenoxy-1-butanol	84	68	5[7]	163/19, 1.520[27], 91NBz
	γ-Benzyloxypropyl alcohol	115	72	6[69]	142/10
		115	73	6[37]	150/13
	1-Phenoxy-2-methyl-2-propanol	89	88	5[397]	125/21, 1.5100
	β-Ethoxy-α-phenylethyl alcohol	115	65	6[150]	131–135/18, 1.5109[25]
C_{11}	Benzyl 4-hydroxybutyl ether	84	37	5[79]	157/12
	Methyl-γ-phenoxypropylcarbinol	79	75	5[153]	163/20, 1.5123[25]

For explanations and symbols see pp. xi–xii.

TABLE 21 *(continued)*

C_n	Compound	Method	Yield (%)	Chapter ref.	B.p./mm., n_D^t, (M.p.), Deriv.
		Aromatic Hydroxy Ethers *(continued)*			
C_{12}	o-Hydroxyphenyl phenyl ether	97	91	5 716	(105)
	m-Hydroxyphenyl phenyl ether	93	40	5 707	320/743
	p-Hydroxyphenyl phenyl ether	97	70	5 707	176/10, (85)
	β-Hydroxyethyl β-naphthyl ether	116	98	6 86	(77.5)
C_{13}	1-(β-Naphthoxy)-2-propanol	79	88	5 155	(83)
C_{14}	1-Phenyl-2-phenoxy-ethanol	80	87	5 78	(64), 84NBz
	2-Phenyl-2-phenoxy-ethanol	84	84	5 78	(81), 87NBz
C_{15}	α,γ-Glycerol diphenyl ether	122	80	6 144	(81)

For explanations and symbols see pp. xi–xii.

REFERENCES FOR CHAPTER 6

[1] Vogel, J. *Chem. Soc.*, 616 (1948).
[2] Henstock, J. *Chem. Soc.*, 371 (1931).
[3] Norris and Rigby, J. *Am. Chem. Soc.*, 54, 2088 (1932).
[4] Whitmore, Wittle, and Popkin, J. *Am. Chem. Soc.*, 61, 1589 (1939).
[5] Vogel, J. *Chem. Soc.*, 1809 (1948).
[6] Olson et al., J. *Am. Chem. Soc.*, 69, 2451 (1947).
[7] Smith, J. *Am. Chem. Soc.*, 56, 717 (1934).
[8] Sprung and Wallis, J. *Am. Chem. Soc.*, 56, 1717 (1934).
[9] Monacelli and Hennion, J. *Am. Chem. Soc.*, 63, 1722 (1941).
[10] Emerson et al., J. *Am. Chem. Soc.*, 69, 1905 (1947).
[11] Brewster and Putman, Jr., J. *Am. Chem. Soc.*, 61, 3083 (1939).
[12] Nixon and Branch, J. *Am. Chem. Soc.*, 58, 492 (1936).
[13] Short and Stewart, J. *Chem. Soc.*, 553 (1929).
[14] Ullmann and Sponagel, *Ann.*, 350, 83 (1906); Suter and Green, J. *Am. Chem. Soc.*, 59, 2578 (1937); also, ref. 20.
[15] Weston and Adkins, J. *Am. Chem. Soc.*, 50, 859 (1928).
[16] Loevenich, Becker, and Schröder, J. *prakt. Chem.*, 127, 248 (1930).
[17] Kirner, J. *Am. Chem. Soc.*, 50, 1955 (1928).
[18] Kirner, J. *Am. Chem. Soc.*, 52, 3251 (1930).
[19] Dupré and Robinson, J. *Chem. Soc.*, 549 (1945).
[20] Van Duzee and Adkins, J. *Am. Chem. Soc.*, 57, 147 (1935).
[21] Liston and Dehn, J. *Am. Chem. Soc.*, 60, 1264 (1938).
[22] Capinjola, J. *Am. Chem. Soc.*, 67, 1615 (1945).
[23] Ungnade and Orwoll, *Org. Syntheses*, 26, 50 (1946).
[24] Brewster and Groening, *Org. Syntheses*, Coll. Vol. II, 445 (1943).
[25] Lea and Robinson, J. *Chem. Soc.*, 411 (1926); cf. ref. 23.
[26] Cocker, Lapworth, and Walton, J. *Chem. Soc.*, 451 (1930).
[27] Tamele et al., *Ind. Eng. Chem.*, 33, 115 (1941).
[28] Roberts, Young, and Winstein, J. *Am. Chem. Soc.*, 64, 2157 (1942).
[29] Kohlrausch, *Monatsh.*, 70, 223 (1937).
[30] Tarbell in *Organic Reactions*, Vol. 2, John Wiley & Sons, New York, 1944, pp. 22, 26.
[31] Smith, Hoehn, and Whitney, J. *Am. Chem. Soc.*, 62, 1863 (1940); cf. ref. 30.
[32] Hurd and Yarnall, J. *Am. Chem. Soc.*, 59, 1686 (1937).
[33] Claisen and Tietze, *Ber.*, 59, 2344 (1926).
[34] Lauer and Filbert, J. *Am. Chem. Soc.*, 58, 1388 (1936).
[35] Hurd and Schmerling, J. *Am. Chem. Soc.*, 59, 107 (1937).
[36] Hurd and McNamee, J. *Am. Chem. Soc.*, 54, 1648 (1932).
[37] Smith and Sprung, J. *Am. Chem. Soc.*, 65, 1276 (1943).
[38] Hurd and Fowler, J. *Am. Chem. Soc.*, 61, 249 (1939).
[39] Henze and Rogers, J. *Am. Chem. Soc.*, 61, 433 (1939); 62, 1758 (1940).
[40] Nenitzescu and Przemetzky, *Ber.*, 74, 676 (1941).
[41] Powell, J. *Am. Chem. Soc.*, 45, 2708 (1923).
[42] Wheeler and Willson, *Org. Syntheses*, Coll. Vol. I, 296 (1941).
[43] Bennett and Hock, J. *Chem. Soc.*, 472 (1927).
[44] Bennett, J. *Chem. Soc.*, 1277 (1925); cf. ref. 69.
[45] Drake et al., J. *Am. Chem. Soc.*, 68, 1536 (1946); Baudart, *Bull. soc. chim. France*, (5) 11, 336 (1944).
[46] Schmid, *Helv. Chim. Acta*, 27, 134 (1944).

[47] Marvel and Tanenbaum, *Org. Syntheses, Coll.* Vol. I, 435 (1941).

[48] Sayles and Degering, *J. Am. Chem. Soc.,* **71**, 3161 (1949).

[49] Rapson and Robinson, *J. Chem. Soc.,* 1540 (1935).

[50] Lechtenberger and Naftali, *Bull. soc. chim. France,* (5) **4**, 325 (1937).

[51] Hurd and Perletz, *J. Am. Chem. Soc.,* **68**, 38 (1946).

[52] Karrer and Lee, *Helv. Chim. Acta,* **17**, 543 (1934).

[53] Fuson and Wojcik, *Org. Syntheses, Coll.* Vol. II, 260 (1943).

[54] Rothstein, *Bull. soc. chim. France,* **51**, 691 (1932).

[55] Mason and Manning, *J. Am. Chem. Soc.,* **62**, 1635 (1940).

[56] Scheibler and Baumann, *Ber.,* **62**, 2057 (1929).

[57] Munch-Petersen and Hauser, *J. Am. Chem. Soc.,* **71**, 770 (1949).

[58] Bardan, *Bull. soc. chim. France,* **49**, 1426 (1931); cf. ref. 57.

[59] Niemann, Benson, and Mead, *J. Org. Chem.,* **8**, 401 (1943); cf. ref. 101.

[60] Guss, *J. Am. Chem. Soc.,* **71**, 3460 (1949).

[61] Richmond and Wright, *J. Am. Chem. Soc.,* **67**, 2272 (1945).

[62] Hass and Bender, *J. Am. Chem. Soc.,* **71**, 1767 (1949).

[63] Weygand and Gabler, *J. prakt. Chem.,* **155**, 332 (1940).

[64] Schorigin and Makaroff-Semljanski, *Ber.,* **65**, 1293 (1932); also, Weygand, *Organic Preparations,* Interscience Publishers, New York, 1945, p. 163.

[65] Natelson and Gottfried, *Org. Syntheses,* **23**, 37 (1943).

[66] Hultman, Davis, and Clarke, *J. Am. Chem. Soc.,* **43**, 366 (1921).

[67] Clarke, Graham, and Winter, *J. Am. Chem. Soc.,* **47**, 2748 (1925); Ipatieff and Burwell, Jr., *ibid.,* **63**, 969 (1941); Cullinane and Chard, *J. Chem. Soc.,* 821 (1945).

[68] Briner, Bron-Stalet, and Paillard, *Helv. Chim. Acta,* **15**, 619 (1932).

[69] Butler, Renfrew, and Clapp, *J. Am. Chem. Soc.,* **60**, 1472 (1938).

[70] Wright and Du Puis, *J. Am. Chem. Soc.,* **68**, 446 (1946).

[71] Kamm and Waldo, *J. Am. Chem. Soc.,* **43**, 2223 (1921).

[72] Cerchez, *Bull. soc. chim. France,* **43**, 762 (1928).

[73] Marks, Lipkin, and Bettman, *J. Am. Chem. Soc.,* **59**, 946 (1937).

[74] Hiers and Hager, *Org. Syntheses, Coll.* Vol. I, 58 (1941).

[75] Rodionow, *Bull. soc. chim. France,* (4) **45**, 118 (1929).

[76] Musser and Adkins, *J. Am. Chem. Soc.,* **60**, 667 (1938).

[77] Perkin and Weizmann, *J. Chem. Soc.,* **89**, 1649 (1906).

[78] Baker, *J. Am. Chem. Soc.,* **65**, 1576 (1943); footnote 12.

[79] Mosettig and Stuart, *J. Am. Chem. Soc.,* **61**, 1 (1939).

[80] Gilman and Young, *J. Am. Chem. Soc.,* **57**, 1121 (1935).

[81] Gilman and Jacoby, *J. Org. Chem.,* **3**, 108 (1938).

[82] Swallen and Boord, *J. Am. Chem. Soc.,* **52**, 651 (1930).

[83] Sah, *Rec. trav. chim.,* **59**, 1032 (1940).

[84] Gredy, *Bull. soc. chim. France,* (5) **3**, 1093 (1936).

[85] Gredy, *Ann. chim.,* (11) **4**, 42 (1935).

[86] Carlson and Cretcher, *J. Am. Chem. Soc.,* **69**, 1952 (1947).

[87] Perkin, Ray, and Robinson, *J. Chem. Soc.,* 945 (1926).

[88] Paul, *Bull. soc. chim. France,* (10) **18**, 315 (1932).

[89] Natelson and Gottfried, *J. Am. Chem. Soc.,* **61**, 1001 (1939).

[90] Icke et al., *Org. Syntheses,* **29**, 63 (1949).

[91] Levine, Eble, and Fishbach, *J. Am. Chem. Soc.,* **60**, 1930 (1948); cf. ref. 92.

[92] Kanewskaja, *Arch. Pharm.,* **271**, 462 (1933).

[93] Weissberger and Dym, *Ann.,* **502**, 78 (1933); cf. ref. 92.

[94] Buck, *Org. Syntheses, Coll.* Vol. II, 619 (1943); cf. ref. 92.

[95] Weijlard, Swanezy, and Tashjian, *J. Am. Chem. Soc.*, **71**, 1889 (1949); cf. Kindler and Gehlhaar, *Arch. Pharm.*, **274**, 387 (1936).

[96] Bernstein and Wallis, *J. Am. Chem. Soc.*, **62**, 2872 (1940).

[97] McElvain and Carney, *J. Am. Chem. Soc.*, **68**, 2598 (1946).

[98] Pierce, Salsbury, and Fredericksen, *J. Am. Chem. Soc.*, **64**, 1691 (1942).

[99] Bell and Robinson, *J. Chem. Soc.*, 814 (1934); cf. ref. 77.

[100] Marshall, Kuck, and Elderfield, *J. Org. Chem.*, **7**, 444 (1942); cf. Amstutz, Fehnel, and Neumoyer, *J. Am. Chem. Soc.*, **68**, 351 (1946).

[101] Cowdrey, Hughes, and Ingold, *J. Chem. Soc.*, 1228 (1937).

[102] Scarrow and Allen, *Org. Syntheses*, Coll. Vol. II, 387 (1943).

[103] Silverman and Bogert, *J. Org. Chem.*, **11**, 43 (1946); Meisenheimer and Weibezahn, *Ber.*, **54**, 3195 (1921).

[104] Li and Adams, *J. Am. Chem. Soc.*, **57**, 1565 (1935); Haworth and Lapworth, *J. Chem. Soc.*, **123**, 2986 (1923).

[105] Evans and Edlund, *Ind. Eng. Chem.*, **28**, 1186 (1936).

[106] Niederl and Natelson, *J. Am. Chem. Soc.*, **53**, 272, 1928 (1931).

[107] Sowa, Hinton, and Nieuwland, *J. Am. Chem. Soc.*, **54**, 2019, 3695 (1932).

[108] Killian, Hennion, and Nieuwland, *J. Am. Chem. Soc.*, **56**, 1786 (1934).

[109] Jacobson, Dykstra, and Carothers, *J. Am. Chem. Soc.*, **56**, 1169 (1934).

[110] Killian, Hennion, and Nieuwland, *J. Am. Chem. Soc.*, **58**, 892 (1936); also, refs. 111, 112, and 149.

[111] Milas et al., *J. Am. Chem. Soc.*, **70**, 1602 (1948).

[112] Puetzer, Nield, and Barry, *J. Am. Chem. Soc.*, **67**, 835 (1945).

[113] Rehberg, Dixon, and Fisher, *J. Am. Chem. Soc.*, **68**, 544 (1946); **69**, 2970 (1947).

[114] Croxall, Van Hook, and Luckenbaugh, *J. Am. Chem. Soc.*, **71**, 2736 (1949).

[115] Koelsch, *J. Am. Chem. Soc.*, **65**, 437 (1943); cf. ref. 116.

[116] Utermohlen, *J. Am. Chem. Soc.*, **67**, 1505 (1945).

[117] Christian and Hixon, *J. Am. Chem. Soc.*, **70**, 1333 (1948).

[118] Waterman et al., *Rec. trav. chim.*, **56**, 437 (1937).

[119] Gredy, *Bull. soc. chim. France*, (5) 3, 1094 (1936).

[120] Boord et al., *J. Am. Chem. Soc.*, **52**, 651, 3396 (1930).

[121] Schmitt and Boord, *J. Am. Chem. Soc.*, **54**, 751 (1932).

[122] Sherrill and Walter, *J. Am. Chem. Soc.*, **58**, 742 (1936).

[123] Bossert and Brode, *J. Am. Chem. Soc.*, **56**, 165 (1934).

[124] Soday and Boord, *J. Am. Chem. Soc.*, **55**, 3293 (1933).

[125] Shoemaker and Boord, *J. Am. Chem. Soc.*, **53**, 1505 (1931).

[126] Marvel and Porter, *Org. Syntheses*, Coll. Vol. I, 377 (1941).

[127] Henze et al., *J. Am. Chem. Soc.*, **64**, 1222 (1942).

[128] Farren et al., *J. Am. Chem. Soc.*, **47**, 2419 (1925).

[129] Hill and Keach, *J. Am. Chem. Soc.*, **48**, 259 (1926).

[130] Blair and Henze, *J. Am. Chem. Soc.*, **54**, 399 (1932).

[131] Lucien and Mason, *J. Am. Chem. Soc.*, **71**, 258 (1949).

[132] Henze and Murchison, *J. Am. Chem. Soc.*, **53**, 4077 (1931); cf. ref. 118.

[133] Speer and Henze, *J. Am. Chem. Soc.*, **61**, 1226 (1939).

[134] Lingo and Henze, *J. Am. Chem. Soc.*, **61**, 1574 (1939); cf. ref. 135.

[135] Cottle et al., *J. Org. Chem.*, **11**, 289 (1946); Summerbell and Umhoefer, *J. Am. Chem. Soc.*, **61**, 3019 (1939).

[136] Clark and Henze, *J. Org. Chem.*, **2**, 508 (1938).

[137] Spurlock and Henze, *J. Org. Chem.*, **4**, 234 (1939).

[138] Wilson and Henze, *J. Am. Chem. Soc.*, **63**, 2112 (1941).
[139] Straus and Thiel, *Ann.*, **525**, 151 (1936).
[140] Nenitzescu and Przemetzki, *Ber.*, **69**, 2706 (1936).
[141] Chitwood and Freure, *J. Am. Chem. Soc.*, **68**, 680 (1946).
[142] Bartlett and Ross, *J. Am. Chem. Soc.*, **70**, 926 (1948); Swern, Billen, and Knight, *ibid.*, **71**, 1152 (1949).
[143] Flores-Gallardo and Pollard, *J. Org. Chem.*, **12**, 831 (1947); cf. Koelsch, *J. Am. Chem. Soc.*, **65**, 2460 (1943).
[144] Fairbourne, Gibson, and Stephens, *J. Chem. Soc.*, 1965 (1932).
[145] Reilly, Drumm, and Barrett, *J. Chem. Soc.*, 67 (1927).
[146] Post, *J. Org. Chem.*, **1**, 231 (1936).
[147] Straus and Heinze, *Ann.*, **493**, 203 (1932).
[148] Straus and Weber, *Ann.*, **498**, 120 (1932).
[149] Elderfield, Pitt, and Wempen, *J. Am. Chem. Soc.*, **72**, 1340 (1950).
[150] Emerson, *J. Am. Chem. Soc.*, **67**, 516 (1945).
[151] Reeve and Sadle, *J. Am. Chem. Soc.*, **72**, 1251 (1950).
[152] Buckle, Pattison, and Saunders, *J. Chem. Soc.*, 1476 (1949).
[153] Cooper and Partridge, *J. Chem. Soc.*, 462 (1950).
[154] Manske and Ledingham, *J. Am. Chem. Soc.*, **72**, 4797 (1950).
[155] Djerassi and Scholz, *J. Am. Chem. Soc.*, **69**, 1688 (1947).
[156] Partridge, *J. Chem. Soc.*, 3043 (1949).
[157] Tarbell and Noble, *J. Am. Chem. Soc.*, **72**, 2657 (1950).
[158] Hill and McGraw, *J. Org. Chem.*, **14**, 783 (1949); Adams and Jones, *J. Am. Chem. Soc.*, **69**, 1803 (1947).
[159] Burnop, Elliott, and Linstead, *J. Chem. Soc.*, 730 (1940).
[160] Duvall and Mosettig, *J. Am. Chem. Soc.*, **60**, 2409 (1938).
[161] Shepard and Noth, *J. Am. Chem. Soc.*, **72**, 4364 (1950).
[162] Reeve and Christoffel, *J. Am. Chem. Soc.*, **72**, 1480 (1950).
[163] Braude et al., *J. Chem. Soc.*, 613 (1949).
[164] Rehberg and Dixon, *J. Am. Chem. Soc.*, **72**, 2205 (1950); Hall and Stern, *J. Chem. Soc.*, 2035 (1949).
[165] Lambert, Scaife, and Wilder-Smith, *J. Chem. Soc.*, 1474 (1947).
[166] Brandon, Derfer, and Boord, *J. Am. Chem. Soc.*, **72**, 2120 (1950).
[167] Crombie and Harper, *J. Chem. Soc.*, 1707 (1950).
[168] Crombie and Harper, *J. Chem. Soc.*, 1714 (1950).
[169] Sexton and Britton, *J. Am. Chem. Soc.*, **70**, 3606 (1948).
[170] Winstein and Buckles, *J. Am. Chem. Soc.*, **65**, 613 (1943).
[171] Winstein and Henderson, *J. Am. Chem. Soc.*, **65**, 2196 (1943).
[172] Winstein and Henderson in Elderfield's *Heterocyclic Compounds*, Vol. I, John Wiley & Sons, New York, 1950, pp. 22–42.
[173] Newman and Beal, *J. Am. Chem. Soc.*, **72**, 5161 (1950).
[174] Arbit, *J. Am. Chem. Soc.*, **68**, 1662 (1946).
[175] Dewar and Read, *J. Soc. Chem. Ind. (London)*, **55**, 347T (1936).
[176] Kornblum in *Organic Reactions*, Vol. 2, John Wiley & Sons, New York, 1944, p. 297.

7

Oxides

CONTENTS

125. Action of Alkali on Halohydrins

$$\text{RCHClCHOHR} \xrightarrow{\text{KOH}} \overset{\displaystyle O}{\overset{\displaystyle /\ \backslash}{\text{RCH}-\text{CHR}}}$$

Epoxy compounds are prepared by heating halohydrins with strong caustic solutions and, where possible, distilling the product as it is formed. By this procedure, 3-chloro-2-butanol yields a mixture of *cis*- and *trans*-2,3-epoxybutane (90%), which can be readily separated by fractional distillation. Another example is the conversion of 2-chlorocyclohexanol to cyclohexene oxide (73%).[6] The reaction is included in an excellent discussion of the chemistry of ethylene and trimethylene oxides.[48]

The reaction has been applied to the preparation of many substituted ethylene oxides in which one to all four hydrogen atoms are replaced by alkyl groups.[3-5] It is noted that alkyl substituents enhance oxide ring closure which occurs by a *trans* mechanism.

Aryl-substituted ethylene oxides have also been prepared. The simplest of these is styrene oxide, which is prepared by the alkali treatment of the iodohydrin made by the action of iodine, water, and mercuric oxide on styrene (51%).[7] Aryl chlorohydrins resulting from the action of chloroacetone and aromatic Grignard reagents, $C_6H_5(CH_2)_nMgX$, have been converted by alkali or sodium ethoxide to oxides of the type

$$C_6H_5(CH_2)_n(CH_3)\overset{\displaystyle O}{\overset{\displaystyle /\ \backslash}{C-CH_2}}$$

253

(n = 0 to 4) in 20-40% over-all yields.[8,9] Halohydrins from the aluminum isopropoxide reduction of 1-naphthyl halomethyl ketones are converted in excellent yields to α-naphthylethylene oxides.[10]

Trimethylene oxide and its homologs are prepared from the corresponding trimethylene chlorohydrins and alkali. The yield is higher when γ-chloropropyl acetate is substituted for the chlorohydrin (44% vs. 25%).[11] Pentamethylene oxide is obtained in almost quantitative yield by the action of zinc and water on α,ϵ-dibromopentane.[13]

Epoxy compounds containing another functional group are important materials in synthetic work. Among these are 3,4-epoxy-1-butene,[14] 2,3-epoxy-1-propanol (glycidol),[15] 2,3-epoxy-1-chloropropane (epichlorohydrin,[16,17] 2,3-epoxy-1-methoxypropane and homologs,[18] 2,3-epoxybutanoic acid,[20] and 1-diethylamino-2,3-epoxypropane,[45] all of which are prepared by treating the appropriate chlorohydrin with base under various conditions.

The condensation of ethyl dichloroacetate with aldehydes or ketones aided by magnesium amalgam gives good yields of α-chloro-β-hydroxy esters, which by treatment with sodium ethoxide are converted quantitatively to glycidic esters (cf. method 127).[32]

$$RCHO + CHCl_2CO_2C_2H_5 \xrightarrow[\text{then } H_2O]{\text{Hg-Mg;}} RCHOHCHClCO_2C_2H_5 \xrightarrow{C_2H_5ONa}$$

$$RCH\!\!-\!\!CHCO_2C_2H_5$$
$$\diagdown\!\!O\!\!\diagup$$

The initial step closely resembles the well-known Reformatsky reaction for the formation of β-hydroxy esters (cf. method 103).

126. Action of Peracids on Olefinic Compounds

$$RCH\!\!=\!\!CH_2 + C_6H_5CO_3H \rightarrow RCH\!\!-\!\!CH_2 + C_6H_5CO_2H$$
$$\diagdown\!\!O\!\!\diagup$$

Olefinic compounds are conveniently converted to epoxy compounds by treatment with an organic peracid, commonly perbenzoic acid or peracetic acid in chloroform solution at 0-5°. The preparation of perbenzoic acid has been described.[24] Performic and monoperphthalic acids have also been successfully employed.[50,51] The reaction has been reviewed.[48,52]

The rate of reaction of peracetic acid in acetic acid or perbenzoic acid in chloroform solution is quite sensitive to the number and kind of substituents on the ethylenic carbon atoms. In general, alkyl and aryl groups enhance the reactivity whereas carboxyl, carboalkoxy, and carbonyl groups slow or prevent the reaction.[51] However, α,β-unsaturated carbonyl compounds respond to treatment with hydrogen peroxide in basic medium. The conversion of alkyl- and aryl-substituted ethylenes is illustrated by the preparation of 1,1-dineopentylethylene oxide (88%)[22] and styrene oxide (75%).[23]

The epoxidation of high-molecular-weight olefins (C_8–C_{18}) with peracetic acid in acetic acid solution is accompanied by appreciable quantities of hydroxy acetoxy compounds, which arise by reaction of the oxides with the solvent.[26] Similar treatment of the high-molecular-weight unsaturated *fatty esters* has been more successful.[27]

Perbenzoic acid in chloroform solution reacts with propylvinylcarbinol to give a *hydroxy epoxide,* 1,2-epoxy-3-hydroxyhexane (50%).[28]

Epoxy ketones are prepared by the action of hydrogen peroxide on unsaturated ketones in alkaline medium.[29,30] In this manner, dibenzoylethylene oxide (86%) is prepared from both *cis-* and *trans-*dibenzoylethylene.[46]

$$C_6H_5COCH\!=\!CHCOC_6H_5 \xrightarrow{H_2O_2} C_6H_5COCH\!-\!CHCOC_6H_5$$
$$\underset{O}{\diagdown\diagup}$$

Certain α,β-olefinic nitriles with *alpha* branching $\left(\diagup\!\!\diagdown C\!=\!C(R)CN\right)$ give epoxyamides with hydrogen peroxide instead of the corresponding unsaturated amides (cf. method 354). For example, α-phenylcrotononitrile, $CH_3CH\!=\!C(C_6H_5)CN$, reacts with hydrogen peroxide in the presence of sodium carbonate and aqueous acetone to give an excellent yield of α-phenyl-β-methylglycidamide. On the other hand, the double bond in allyl cyanide is not attacked, and the unsaturated amide is obtained.[47]

127. Condensation of Carbonyl Compounds with Halogenated Compounds

$$R'COR'' + XCHR'''CO_2C_2H_5 \xrightarrow{NaOC_2H_5} R'R''C\!-\!CR'''CO_2C_2H_5 +$$
$$\underset{O}{\diagdown\diagup}$$

$$NaX + C_2H_5OH$$

The condensation of aldehydes and ketones with ethyl chloroacetate in the presence of sodium ethoxide or sodium amide produces α,β-epoxy esters (Darzens). The scope, limitations, typical experimental procedures, and examples have been given.[33,36,48] Briefly, aliphatic and aromatic ketones, and aromatic aldehydes react satisfactorily, whereas aliphatic aldehydes give poor yields. α-Halopropionic and α-halobutyric esters have also been employed. The α-chloro esters are preferable to the bromo or iodo esters.

Other halogenated compounds have been substituted for the halo esters. Aromatic α-halo ketones have been condensed with aromatic aldehydes to give α,β-epoxy ketones.[39, 41]

$$RCHO + ClCH_2COR' \xrightarrow{C_2H_5ONa} RCH\overset{O}{\overset{\diagup\diagdown}{-}}CHCOR'$$

For example, the reaction of benzaldehyde and ω-chloroacetophenone yields α-phenyl-β-benzoylethylene oxide (80%)[39]

Substituted benzyl halides and aromatic aldehydes have also been condensed to yield epoxy compounds.[42]

$$RCHO + R'CH_2Cl \xrightarrow[CH_3OH]{KOH} RCH\overset{O}{\overset{\diagup\diagdown}{-}}CHR'$$

128. Dehydration of Glycols

$$HOCH_2(CH_2)_nCH_2OH \xrightarrow{H_2SO_4} CH_2(CH_2)_nCH_2 \overset{\overbrace{O---}}{}$$

Treatment of polymethylene glycols with 50% sulfuric acid gives mixtures of cyclic oxides. Thus, 1,6-hexanediol yields a mixture containing 16% 1,6-, 25% 1,5-, and 65% 1,4-oxidohexane. In other instances, formation of the 1,4-oxido derivatives is also favored.[43]

By passing trans-1,4-cyclohexanediol over activated alumina at 275°, a 73% yield of 1,4-epoxycyclohexane is obtained.[54]

TABLE 22. OXIDES   257

TABLE 22. OXIDES

C_n	Compound	Method	Yield (%)	Chapter[ref.]	B.p./mm., n_D^t, (M.p.)
C_2	Ethylene oxide	125	61	7[4]	12/760
C_3	Propylene oxide	125	65	7[4]	35/760, 1.3681[17]
	Trimethylene oxide	125	44	7[11]	48, 1.3905[23]
	Epichlorohydrin	125	81	7[16]	115–117
		125	72	7[17]	115–117
	Epibromohydrin	125	89	7[17]	136, 62/50
	2,3-Epoxy-1-propanol (glycidol)	125	90	7[15]	66/2.5, 1.4302[25]
C_4	1,2-Epoxybutane	125	53	7[4]	62/760, 1.3855[17]
	trans-2,3-Epoxybutane	125	90	7[1]	54/747, 1.3736
	cis-2,3-Epoxybutane				60/747, 1.3826
	2-Methyl-1,2-epoxypropane	125	47	7[4]	56/760
	3,4-Epoxy-1-butene	125	84	7[14]	65–72, 1.4162
	1,2-Epoxy-3-methoxypropane	125	68	7[18]	54/85, 1.4012[25]
	2,3-Epoxybutanoic acid	125	54[†]	7[20]	(88.5)
C_5	Pentamethylene oxide	125	100	7[13]	88/760, 1.4195[25]
	trans-2,3-Epoxypentane	125	96	7[2]	80/748, 1.3867
	cis-2,3-Epoxypentane				85/748, 1.3941
	2-Methyl-2,3-epoxybutane	125	62	7[12]	74–78, 1.3896[18]
	1,2-Epoxycyclopentane	125	40	7[49]	102, 1.4330[23]
	1,2-Epoxy-3-ethoxypropane	125	75	7[18]	61/65, 1.4046[25]
C_6	2,3-Dimethyl-2,3-epoxybutane	125	15[†]	7[5]	91/753
	Cyclohexene oxide	125	73	7[6]	129–134
		126	60	7[21]	131
	1,4-Epoxycyclohexane	128	73	7[54]	120/760, 1.4477
	1,2-Epoxy-3-hydroxy-n-hexane	126	50	7[28]	90/25
C_7	1,2-Dimethyl-1,2-epoxycyclopentane	126	85	7[25]	122/20
	Ethyl β,β-dimethylglycidate	127	53	7[34]	183, 74/12, 1.4202[18]
	1-Diethylamino-2,3-epoxypropane	125	63	7[45]	62–65/20

For explanations and symbols see pp. xi–xii.

TABLE 22 (*continued*)

C_n	Compound	Method	Yield (%)	Chapter[ref.]	B.p./mm., n_D^t, (M.p.)
C_8	Styrene oxide	125	51	7[7]	88/23, 1.5331[25]
		126	75	7[23]	188–192
	Ethyl β-isopropyl-glycidate	125	68 †	7[32]	
	Ethyl β-methyl-β-ethylglycidate	127	56	7[35]	91–95/17
C_9	2-Phenyl-1,2-epoxy-propane	125	79	7[8]	75/11
	1,2-Epoxy-3-phenyl-propane	125	63	7[19]	116/4
	1-Phenyl-2,3-epoxy-1-propanol	126	72	7[31]	115/5, 1.5441[26]
	3-Phenyl-2,3-epoxy-1-propanol	126	65	7[31]	127/2, (25)
	Epoxypropiophenone	126	40	7[29]	(53)
C_{10}	1,2-Epoxydecane	126	56	7[26]	89/10, 1.4288
	2-Methyl-3-phenyl-1,2-epoxypropane	125	20 †	7[9]	90/10
	Ethyl α,β-epoxycyclo-hexylideneacetate	125	97 †	7[32]	
C_{11}	2-Methyl-4-phenyl-1,2-epoxybutane	125	13 †	7[9]	105/10
C_{12}	1,1-Dineopentylethylene oxide	126	88	7[22]	88/15, 1.4330[22]
	2-Methyl-5-phenyl-1,2-epoxypentane	125	41 †	7[9]	116/4
	Ethyl β-methyl-β-phenylglycidate	125	95 †	7[32]	
		127	64	7[37]	111–114/3
C_{13}	Ethyl α-methyl-β-tolylglycidate	127	56	7[38]	148–152/12
C_{15}	α-Phenyl-β-benzoyl-ethylene oxide	127	80	7[39]	(90)
C_{16}	Dibenzoylethylene oxide	126	86	7[46]	(129)
C_{17}	Ethyl β,β-diphenyl-glycidate	127	30	7[53]	145/0.45, (47)
C_{19}	Methyl 9,10-epoxy-stearate	126	45	7[27]	(16.5)

For explanations and symbols see pp. xi–xii.

REFERENCES FOR CHAPTER 7

[1] Wilson and Lucas, *J. Am. Chem. Soc.*, **58**, 2396 (1936).
[2] Lucas, Schlatter, and Jones, *J. Am. Chem. Soc.*, **63**, 22 (1941).
[3] Rothstein, *Bull. soc. chim. France*, (5) 2, 1936 (1935).
[4] Moureu and Dodé, *Bull. soc. chim. France*, (5) **4**, 288 (1937).
[5] Norton and Hass, *J. Am. Chem. Soc.*, **58**, 2147 (1936).
[6] Osterberg, *Org. Syntheses*, Coll. Vol. I, 185 (1944).
[7] Golumbic and Cottle, *J. Am. Chem. Soc.*, **61**, 996 (1939).
[8] King, *J. Am. Chem. Soc.*, **61**, 2383 (1939).
[9] Ramart-Lucas and Labaune, *Ann. chim.*, (10) **16**, 282 (1931).
[10] Winstein et al., *J. Org. Chem.*, **11**, 157 (1946).
[11] Noller, *Org. Syntheses*, **29**, 92 (1949).
[12] Read and Reid, *J. Chem. Soc.*, 1487 (1928); cf. ref. 5.
[13] Clarke, *J. Chem. Soc.*, 1802 (1912); Allen and Hibbert, *J. Am. Chem. Soc.*, **56**, 1400 (1934).
[14] Kadesch, *J. Am. Chem. Soc.*, **68**, 44 (1946).
[15] Rider and Hill, *J. Am. Chem. Soc.*, **52**, 1521 (1930).
[16] Clarke and Hartman, *Org. Syntheses*, Coll. Vol. I, 233 (1941).
[17] Braun, *Org. Syntheses*, Coll. Vol. II, 256 (1943).
[18] Flores-Gallardo and Pollard, *J. Org. Chem.*, **12**, 831 (1947); cf. ref. 19.
[19] Fairbourne, Gibson, and Stephens, *J. Chem. Soc.*, 1965 (1932).
[20] Braun, *J. Am. Chem. Soc.*, **52**, 3185 (1930).
[21] Böeseken and Schneider, *J. prakt. Chem.*, **131**, 287 (1931).
[22] Bartlett, Fraser, and Woodward, *J. Am. Chem. Soc.*, **63**, 495 (1941).
[23] Hibbert and Burt, *Org. Syntheses*, Coll. Vol. I, 494 (1941).
[24] Braun, *Org. Syntheses*, Coll. Vol. I, 431 (1941).
[25] Bartlett and Bavley, *J. Am. Chem. Soc.*, **60**, 2416 (1938).
[26] Swern, Billen, and Scanlan, *J. Am. Chem. Soc.*, **68**, 1504 (1946); cf. ref. 3.
[27] Finley, Swern, and Scanlan, *J. Am. Chem. Soc.*, **67**, 412 (1945).
[28] Niemann, Benson, and Mead, *J. Org. Chem.*, **8**, 397 (1943).
[29] Cahnmann, *Bull. soc. chim. France*, (5) **4**, 229 (1937).
[30] Rohrmann, Jones, and Shonle, *J. Am. Chem. Soc.*, **66**, 1856 (1944).
[31] Darmon and Weill, *Bull. soc. chim. France*, (5) **8**, 407, 413 (1941).
[32] Darzens, *Compt. rend.*, **151**, 883 (1910); **203**, 1374 (1936); **204**, 272 (1937).
[33] Newman and Magerlein in *Organic Reactions*, Vol. 5, John Wiley & Sons, New York, 1949, p. 413.
[34] Rutowski and Dajew, *Ber.*, **64**, 693 (1931); Darzens, *Compt. rend.*, **139**, 1214 (1904); Culvenor et al., *J. Chem. Soc.*, 2573 (1949).
[35] Linstead and Mann, *J. Chem. Soc.*, 2070 (1930).
[36] Yarnall and Wallis, *J. Org. Chem.*, **4**, 270 (1939).
[37] Allen and Van Allen, *Org. Syntheses*, **24**, 82 (1944).
[38] Ruzicka and Ehmann, *Helv. Chim. Acta*, **15**, 160 (1932); ref. 33.
[39] Widman, *Ber.*, **49**, 477 (1916).
[40] Bodforss, *Ber.*, **49**, 2795 (1916); **51**, 192 (1918); **52**, 142 (1919).
[41] Jörlander, *Ber.*, **49**, 2782 (1916); **50**, 406, 1457 (1917).
[42] Kleucker, *Ber.*, **55**, 1634 (1922); Bergmann and Hervey, *ibid.*, **62**, 902 (1929).
[43] Franke and Kroupa, *Monatsh.*, **69**, 172 (1936); *C. A.*, **31**, 1360 (1937).
[44] Weizmann and Malkowa, *Bull. soc. chim. France*, **47**, 356 (1930).
[45] Gilman et al., *J. Am. Chem. Soc.*, **68**, 1291 (1946).
[46] Lutz and Wilder, *J. Am. Chem. Soc.*, **56**, 1987 (1934).

[47] Murray and Cloke, *J. Am. Chem. Soc.*, **56**, 2749 (1934).

[48] Winstein and Henderson in Elderfield's *Heterocyclic Compounds*, Vol. I, John Wiley & Sons, New York, 1950, pp. 1–60.

[49] McCasland and Smith, *J. Am. Chem. Soc.*, **72**, 2190 (1950).

[50] Chakravorty and Levin, *J. Am. Chem. Soc.*, **64**, 2317 (1942); Böhme, *Org. Syntheses*, **20**, 70 (1940).

[51] Swern, *J. Am. Chem. Soc.*, **69**, 1692 (1947).

[52] Swern, *Chem. Revs.*, **45**, 1 (1949).

[53] Ecary, *Ann. chim.*, (12) **3**, 450 (1948).

[54] Olberg, Pines, and Ipatieff, *J. Am. Chem. Soc.*, **65**, 2260 (1943).

8

Acetals and Ketals

CONTENTS

In addition to the procedures given here, which are concerned with making the acetal or ketal group, acetals or ketals having a second functional group are made by adaptations of methods employed for the second group. Thus, olefinic and acetylenic acetals are made by the dehydrohalogenation of halo acetals (methods 20 and 43); ketene acetals by the elimination of halo and alkoxyl groups from bromoörthoesters (method 21); halo acetals by direct halogenation of acetals (method 66) and by the action of phosphorus tribromide on hydroxy acetals (method 52); hydroxy acetals by the action of Grignard reagents on keto and carbethoxy acetals (methods 89 and 91), by the hydrolysis of halo acetals (method 96), and by the oxidation of olefinic acetals (method 107); alkoxy acetals by interaction of sodium alkoxides and halo acetals (method 115); amino acetals by amination of halo acetals (methods 435 and 436); and cyano acetals by the action of alkali cyanides on halo acetals (method 378) and by the dehydration of amido acetals (method 384).

129. Interaction of Alcohols and Carbonyl Compounds

$$RCHO + 2R'OH \rightleftharpoons RCH(OR')_2 + H_2O$$

In the formation of acetals from carbonyl compounds and low-molecular-weight alcohols, an equilibrium is attained and the percentage conversion varies widely, depending on the structures of the reactants. With normal aliphatic aldehydes and primary alcohols, the average conversion is 80% and with secondary alcohols 46%; the yields become progressively lower as branching on the α-carbon of the aldehyde increases.[3] Hydrogen chloride and ferric chloride are the most efficient catalysts in the production of methylal, $HC(OCH_3)_2$, from paraformaldehyde and methanol, and ferric chloride has been used for the combination of higher alcohols with this aldehyde.[4] On the other hand, calcium chloride is preferred for the preparation of diethyl acetal since it has the advantage of removing water from the system.[1] This advantage is less marked with high-molecular-weight alcohols.[2]

In the reaction of higher aldehydes employing hydrogen chloride or still another catalyst, p-toluenesulfonic acid,[4,5] the water is conveniently removed by an azeotropic distillation with benzene. The vapors containing the ternary mixture of alcohol, benzene, and water are condensed in a water separator,[14] and the benzene-alcohol mixture is automatically returned to the reaction flask either directly[8] or after drying with *calcium carbide*.[50]

The acid catalyst must be quickly and completely neutralized before diluting the reaction mixture with water; otherwise the reverse reaction occurs.[2] A soluble base such as alcoholic sodium ethoxide has been recommended since its action is quick and thorough.[50]

The preparation of ketals of monohydric alcohols is not as readily accomplished.

Dialkyl sulfites, which are prepared in good yields from thionyl chloride and alcohols, react with aldehydes in the presence of dry methanolic hydrochloric acid to form acetals (80%);[6] moreover, high-molecular-weight alcohols not only act as solvent but also enter into the reaction to give higher acetals.[7]

$$(CH_3O)_2SO + 2ROH \rightleftharpoons (RO)_2SO + 2CH_3OH$$

$$(RO)_2SO + R'CHO \rightleftharpoons R'CH(OR)_2 + SO_2$$

Aromatic and aliphatic carbonyl compounds condense with glycols, such as ethylene, propylene, and trimethylene glycols, to form *cyclic acetals;* p-toluenesulfonic acid has proved to be an excellent catalyst.[8,10] As before, the water formed in these reactions is conveniently removed by an azeotropic distillation with benzene. Representative aldehydes and ketones that undergo this acetalization include acetone, cyclohexanone, pinacolone, acetophenone, benzophenone, n-heptaldehyde, furfural, benzaldehyde, and substituted benzaldehydes (70–90%). Sulfuric acid,[11] phosphoric acid,[12,30] and hydrogen chloride[13] have also been used as catalysts in this cyclization reaction.

Unsaturated acetals can be prepared by the acetalization of an unsaturated aldehyde. Acrolein diethyl acetal, $CH_2 = CH — CH(OCH_2CH_3)_2$, is prepared in this manner and also by the dehydrohalogenation of β-chloropropionaldehyde diethyl acetal (cf. method 20); however, the former method has definite advantages in that it involves a single-step process and gives a more stable product.[17,34] The double bond may also be in the alcohol fragment, as in acetaldehyde diallyl acetal,

$$CH_3CH(OCH_2CH = CH_2)_2.[18]$$

Halo acetals have been prepared by the action of alcohol on halo ketones[26,27] and halo aldehydes.[19,25] An indirect application of this reaction consists in the halogenation of enol acetates with subsequent reaction of the brominated products with alcohols to give the halo acetals.[20,22]

$$RCH = CHOCOCH_3 \xrightarrow{Br_2} RCHBrCHBrOCOCH_3 \xrightarrow{C_2H_5OH}$$

$$RCHBrCH(OC_2H_5)_2 + CH_3CO_2C_2H_5$$

The reaction of carbonyl compounds with glycerin-α-monochlorohydrin, $CH_2OHCHOHCH_2Cl$, leads to cyclic halo acetals.[26,29,30] Treatment of α,β-olefinic aldehydes with alcohols *saturated* with dry hydrogen chloride causes the addition of the halogen acid to the double bond as well as acetalization to give β-halo acetals.[23,24]

Isopropylideneglycerol, a five-membered cyclic *hydroxy ketal* from acetone and glycerol, is prepared in 90% yield by removing the liberated water by an azeotropic distillation.[32] In another procedure, *calcium carbide* is added directly to the reaction mixture as a desiccant.[31] Acetaldehyde and benzaldehyde, unlike acetone, react with glycerol to form a mixture of the five- and six-membered cyclic hydroxy acetals.[33]

Alkoxy acetals are made by the acetalization of α,β-olefinic aldehydes in weakly acidic solutions; however, the addition of alcohol to the double bond may not go to completion.[34,35]

Other functional groups may be present in acetals or ketals prepared by these procedures. Some of these groups are keto,[36,37] e.g., phenylglyoxal diethyl acetal; carbethoxyl,[26,28] e.g., ethyl acetoacetate ethylene ketal; amino,[26,29] e.g., β-diethylaminopropyl methyl ketone ethylene ketal; and nitro,[40,41] e.g., *m*-nitrobenzaldehyde dimethyl acetal. In addition, amino ketals can be prepared by the hydrogenation of nitro ketals over Raney nickel catalysts.[40,119]

130. Interaction of Orthoesters and Carbonyl Compounds

$$RCHO + HC(OR')_3 \rightarrow RCH(OR')_2 + HCO_2R'$$

Acetals and ketals are readily prepared from carbonyl compounds and orthoformic esters in alcohol solution in the presence of a catalyst such as concentrated sulfuric acid, anhydrous hydrogen chloride, or ammonium chloride (60–95%).[42] The reaction mixture must be neutralized before processing since the acetals are very sensitive to an acid hydrolysis. The methyl and ethyl esters of orthosilicic acid have been substituted for the orthoformic esters with good results (70–90%); however, steps must be taken to remove compounds of silicon.[47,112]

Acetals and ketals having a *second functional group* are made by these procedures. For example, acrolein reacts with ethyl orthoformate in alcohol solution with ammonium nitrate as catalyst to give acrolein diethyl acetal (73%).[48] On the other hand, it reacts with ethyl orthosilicate with anhydrous hydrogen chloride as catalyst to furnish β-ethoxypropionaldehyde diethyl acetal (76%).[112] p-Bromoacetophenone and ethyl orthoformate give the corresponding ketal in 65% yield.[113] p-Methoxy- and m-amino-benzaldehyde diethyl acetals are made in a similar way in 96% and 85% yields, respectively.[42,49]

α-Keto esters like ethyl α-keto-n-butyrate and ethyl α-keto-n-valerate are converted to their diethyl ketals in excellent yields by the action of orthoformic ester in ethanol-hydrochloric acid solution. If the reaction is carried out in the presence of ethylene glycol instead of ethanol and, in addition, the volatile products are removed by distillation, then the ethylene ketal is formed in almost quantitative yield[114] (cf. method 133).

131. Interaction of Grignard Reagents and Orthoformic Esters

$$RMgBr + HC(OC_2H_5)_3 \rightarrow RCH(OC_2H_5)_2 + C_2H_5OMgBr$$

The preparation of acetals is effected by refluxing an ethereal solution of ethyl orthoformate and a Grignard reagent. Prolonged heating is necessary for maximum yields. The reaction mixtures are then carefully processed by the addition of ice and dilute acetic acid followed by extraction with ether and distillation to give the acetal (80–90%).[52] Further studies have been made in conjunction with the preparation of aldehydes (method 165).[57]

The procedure has been extended to the formation of *difunctional compounds* like 3-methyl-3-butenal diethyl acetal (24%),[54] 1,1-diethoxy-2-butyne (80%),[118] and β-ethoxyethyl methyl ketone diethyl ketal (92%).[63]

A somewhat related reaction is the formation of diethyl acetals of α-formyl esters by treatment of α-bromo esters with zinc and ethyl orthoformate (45–60%).[121]

$$RCHBrCO_2C_2H_5 + HC(OC_2H_5)_3 \xrightarrow{Zn} \begin{matrix} RCHCO_2C_2H_5 \\ | \\ HC(OC_2H_5)_2 \end{matrix}$$

132. Interaction of Alcohols and Vinyl Esters

$$CH_2 = CHOCOCH_3 + 2ROH \xrightarrow{Catalyst} CH_3CH(OR)_2 + CH_3COOH$$

Acetaldehyde acetals are produced in 80–90% yields by the addition of primary aliphatic alcohols to vinyl acetate in the presence of an acidic mercury-boron catalyst. In a similar manner, acetone ketals are produced from isopropenyl acetate.[69]

133. Interchange of Alkoxyl Groups

$$ClCH_2CH(OC_2H_5)_2 + CH_2OHCH_2OH \xrightarrow{H^+} ClCH_2\overline{CHOCH_2CH_2O} + 2C_2H_5OH$$

Cyclic acetals have been prepared in 75–90% yields by an alcohol exchange between dimethyl or diethyl acetals and a glycol. Thus, anhydrous glycerol and chloroacetal, on heating under a fractionating column to remove the liberated alcohol, give chloroethylidene glycerol (88%).[70] The reaction, catalyzed by a small amount of concentrated sulfuric acid, has been extended to the formation of numerous halo cyclic acetals[71] and mixed acetals.[72]

134. Addition of Alcohols to Acetylenic Compounds

$$RC \equiv CH + 2R'OH \xrightarrow{Catalyst} RC(OR')_2CH_3$$

Acetals are formed by the action of acetylene with alcohols in the presence of a catalyst consisting of boron trifluoride and mercuric oxide.[58] The method has been extended to the condensation of substituted acetylenes, $RC \equiv CH$, with alcohols to give ketals,[59,60] as illustrated by the preparation of 2-hexanone dimethyl ketal (70%).[59] The acidic catalyst must be carefully neutralized with powdered anhydrous potassium carbonate before contacting the acetal or ketal with water.

For the reaction of higher straight-chain monohydric alcohols a small amount of trichloroacetic acid is added to the above catalyst.[61]   The addition of alcohols to vinylacetylene, H_2C=CHC≡CH, gives *β-alkoxy ketals*, $ROCH_2CH_2C(OR)_2CH_3$.[64,66]   On the other hand, allylacetylenes, CH_2=CHCH$_2$C≡CR, add only two molecules of methanol under the same conditions to yield 5,5-dimethoxy-1-alkenes, CH_2=CHCH$_2$CH$_2$C(OCH$_3$)$_2$R.[65]

Reaction of 1-chloro- or 1-bromo-heptyne, C_5H_{11}C≡CX, in the same way gives the corresponding 1-halo-2,2-dimethoxyheptanes, C_5H_{11}C(OCH$_3$)$_2$CH$_2$X, in 30 and 60% yield, respectively.[115]

135. Addition of Alcohols to Dihydropyran

The formation of cyclic acetals by the acid-catalyzed addition of hydroxy compounds (both aromatic and aliphatic) to dihydropyran takes place in excellent yields.[73,74]   The simple procedure consists in allowing the two compounds to stand in the presence of a trace of concentrated hydrochloric acid for several hours, followed by neutralization and distillation.   The method is valuable for protecting the hydroxyl group in reactions that are conducted in basic media.[74]

136. Interaction of Carbonyl Compounds and Epoxides

Epoxides react with aldehydes and ketones in the presence of stannic chloride to form cyclic acetals of dihydric alcohols.[75,76]   Undesirable side reactions are repressed by adding the reactants, dissolved in *dry* carbon tetrachloride, to a dilute solution of the catalyst in the same solvent at 20° to 30°.   In most instances, the reaction is practically instantaneous and the mixture may be processed immediately by washing with aqueous alkali and distilling.   The yields for the interaction of γ-halopropylene oxides and typical carbonyl compounds, such as propionaldehyde, diethyl ketone, or benzophenone, are 69–70%.

137. β-Keto Acetals by Interaction of β-Chlorovinyl Ketones and Methanolic Alkali

$$RCOCH = CHCl \xrightarrow[\text{NaOH, }-10°]{CH_3OH} RCOCH_2CH(OCH_3)_2$$

β-Keto dimethyl acetals are made in 80–90% yields by treating β-chlorovinyl alkyl ketones with a solution of sodium hydroxide in absolute methanol at $-10°$. The starting materials are readily obtained by adding acyl chlorides to acetylene in cold carbon tetrachloride solution in the presence of aluminum chloride, viz.,

$$HC \equiv CH + RCOCl \rightarrow RCOCH = CHCl$$

(R = methyl, isobutyl, isoamyl, and isohexyl, 60–80% yield).[117]
    The β-keto acetals may be converted by the Grignard reaction to β-hydroxy acetals, $RR'COHCH_2CH(OCH_3)_2$, in 55–70% yields (cf. method 89).[117]

138. Ketene Acetals by Pyrolysis of Orthoesters[94,116]

$$C_6H_5 CH_2C(OR)_3 \xrightarrow{\text{Heat}} C_6H_5 CH = C(OR)_2 + ROH \quad \text{(cf. method 23)}$$

139. α-Hydroxy Ketals from α-Halo Ketones[92,93]

$$RCOCH_2X \xrightarrow{C_2H_5 ONa} C_2H_5 OC(R) - CH_2 \xrightarrow{C_2H_5 OH} RC(OC_2H_5)_2CH_2OH$$

TABLE 23. ACETALS

C_n	Compound	Method	Yield (%)	Chapter[ref.]	B.p./mm., n_D^t, (M.p.)
			Acetals		
C_3	Methylal	129	97	8[2]	41.5/754, 1.35298
	Glycolformal	129	25	8[12]	75
C_4	Methyl ethyl formal	115	13	8[97]	65/745, 1.3543
	Acetaldehyde dimethyl acetal	132	84	8[69]	64, 1.3665
	Acetaldehyde ethylene acetal	129	87	8[11]	85
C_5	Methyl n-propyl formal	115	17	8[97]	93/760, 1.3779
C_6	Acetaldehyde diethyl	129	64	8[1]	101-103.5, 1.3805
	acetal (acetal)	130	58	8[44]	
		132	88	8[69]	104, 1.3809
C_7	Propionaldehyde diethyl acetal	131	75	8[51]	123
C_8	n-Butyraldehyde diethyl acetal	131	80	8[52]	144
	Isobutyraldehyde diethyl	130	61	8[43]	134-138
	acetal	131	83	8[52]	136
C_9	n-Heptaldehyde ethylene acetal	129	81	8[10]	94/20, 1.4306
	Isovaleraldehyde diethyl	129	32	8[50]	153
	acetal	131	90	8[52]	158
	Benzaldehyde ethylene acetal	129	83	8[10]	101/10, 1.5269
	Furfural diethyl acetal	129	24	8[15]	79/16, 185/740
		130	97	8[42]	189-191
	Thiophene 2-aldehyde diethyl acetal	131	51	8[56]	97-102/15
C_{11}	Malonaldehyde tetraethyl acetal	164	35[†]	8[105]	78/3, 1.4101[25]
	Cyclohexylacetaldehyde diethyl acetal	131	60	8[53]	96-101/11, 1.4390[25]
	Benzaldehyde diethyl	129	66	8[50]	
	acetal	130	99	8[42]	217-223
		131	55	8[51]	93/10
C_{13}	Glutaraldehyde tetraethyl diacetal	129	....	8[16]	100/3, 1.4232[25]
C_{15}	Benzaldehyde di-n-butyl acetal	129	80	8[7]	145-150/14
		Olefinic and Acetylenic Acetals			
C_6	Crotonaldehyde dimethyl acetal	130	50	8[47]	124-128/760

TABLE 23. ACETALS 269

TABLE 23 (*continued*)

C_n	Compound	Method	Yield (%)	Chapter[ref.]	B.p./mm., n_D^t, (M.p.)
				Olefinic and Acetylenic Acetals (*continued*)	
C_7	Propiolaldehyde diethyl acetal	43	63	8[82]	139
	Acrolein diethyl acetal	20	75	8[77]	122–126
		129	30	8[17]	45/24, 40/18, 92/32
		130	73	8[48]	120–125
C_8	α-Butenal diethyl acetal	20	41	8[83]	49/21
	1,1-Diethoxy-2-butyne	43	78	8[118]	62/11, 1.4310[18]
		131	80	8[118]	63/14, 1.4300[18]
	Isobutenal diethyl acetal	20	64	8[83]	137
	Acetaldehyde diallyl acetal	129	68	8[18]	149
C_9	α-Pentenal diethyl acetal	20	90	8[80]	165/750
	α-Isopentenal diethyl acetal	20	62	8[83]	60/16
	3-Methyl-3-buten-1-al diethyl acetal	131	24	8[54]	155, 1.4098
	β-Ethoxyacrolein diethyl acetal	20	80	8[81]	96/20
C_{11}	1,1-Diethoxy-2-heptyne	131	69	8[51]	98/10, 1.4320[27]
				Ketene Acetals	
C_4	Ketene dimethyl acetal	21	65	8[85]	91/740, 1.3962[25]
C_6	Ketene diethyl acetal	20	75	8[78]	83–86/200
		21	66	8[84]	68/100, 1.4110[25]
C_7	n-Propylketene dimethyl acetal	21	68	8[86]	68/47, 1.4235[24]
	Methylketene diethyl acetal	21	80	8[84]	78/100, 1.4083[25]
C_9	n-Propylketene diethyl acetal	21	71	8[83]	108/100, 1.4204[25]
	Isopropylketene diethyl acetal	21	65	8[83]	97/100, 1.4158[25]
C_{10}	Phenylketene dimethyl acetal	138	59	8[94]	87/0.5, 1.5390[24]
C_{11}	n-Heptylketene dimethyl acetal	21	87	8[86]	100–105/10, 1.4370
C_{12}	Phenylketene diethyl acetal	138	70	8[94]	88/0.2, 1.5385
				Halo Acetals	
C_4	Chloroacetaldehyde dimethyl acetal	129	53	8[21]	126, 1.4150

For explanations and symbols see pp. xi–xii.

TABLE 23 (*continued*)

C_n	Compound	Method	Yield (%)	Chapter[ref.]	B.p./mm., n_D^t, (M.p.)
		Halo Acetals (*continued*)			
C_4	Bromoacetaldehyde dimethyl acetal	129	83	8[20]	49/14, 1.4450
	Chloroacetaldehyde ethylene acetal	133	90	8[71]	155-159/740, 1.4465[25]
	Bromoacetaldehyde ethylene acetal	129	80	8[25]	71/15
		133	90	8[71]	175/745, 1.4805[25]
	Dibromoacetaldehyde ethylene acetal	133	90	8[71]	104/9, 1.5351[25]
	Methyl β-chloroethyl formal	....	63	8[110]	134-139
C_5	β-Bromopropionaldehyde ethylene acetal	129	65	8[24]	73/10
	Acetaldehyde γ-chloropropylene acetal	136	45	8[76]	158-162/760
	Ethyl β-chloroethyl formal	....	72	8[110]	65/50
C_6	2,3-Dichlorobutanal dimethyl acetal	129	40	8[28]	86-90/13, 1.4498
	β-Bromo-*n*-butyraldehyde ethylene acetal	129	56	8[24]	78/10
	α-Bromoisobutyraldehyde dimethyl acetal	129	50	8[28]	69/28, 1.4468[23]
		129	76	8[22]	54/10, 1.4480[25]
	Propionaldehyde γ-chloropropylene acetal	136	64	8[76]	65-70/18
	Chloroacetaldehyde diethyl acetal	129	83	8[21]	54/16, 1.4171
	Bromoacetaldehyde diethyl acetal	66		8[90]	49/3, 167-170
		129	58	8[19]	65/18
		129	77	8[20]	65/16, 1.4418
	Iodoacetaldehyde diethyl acetal	55	77	8[88]	70/8
	Dichloroacetaldehyde diethyl acetal	66	37	8[111]	66-71/12
	Dibromoacetaldehyde diethyl acetal	21	50	8[87]	97/12, 1.4790[25]
C_7	*n*-Butyraldehyde γ-chloropropylene acetal	136	61	8[76]	78-85/14
	β-Chloropropionaldehyde diethyl acetal	129	34	8[23]	58-62/8
	α-Bromopropionaldehyde diethyl acetal	66	70	8[103]	79/20, 1.441
C_8	α-Bromo-*n*-butyraldehyde diethyl acetal	66	20	8[83]	84/12
	α-Bromoisobutyraldehyde diethyl acetal	66	48	8[89]	100/40

TABLE 23. ACETALS   271

TABLE 23 (*continued*)

C_n	Compound	Method	Yield (%)	Chapter[ref.]	B.p./mm., n_D^t, (M.p.)
		Halo Acetals (*continued*)			
C_9	α-Bromo-n-heptaldehyde dimethyl acetal	129	78	8 [22]	119/17, 1.4520 [25]
	α-Bromo-n-valeraldehyde diethyl acetal	66	80	8 [80]	92-96/12
	α-Bromoisovaleraldehyde diethyl acetal	66	40	8 [83]	93/14, 1.4438 [25]
		66	75	8 [91]	89/13, 1.4489
C_{10}	α-Bromophenylacetaldehyde dimethyl acetal	129	82	8 [22]	135/10, 1.5395 [25]
	α-Bromophenylacetaldehyde ethylene acetal	133	90	8 [71]	165/9, 1.5628 [25], (39)
C_{13}	Diphenoxymethyl chloride	....	64	8 [109]	132/0.7
		Ether Acetals			
C_7	β-Methoxy-n-butyraldehyde dimethyl acetal	129	74	8 [35]	62/20, 54/16, 1.405 [15]
C_8	Ethoxyacetaldehyde diethyl acetal	115	20	8 [122]	64/21, 74/28, 1.3982 [28]
C_9	γ-Methoxybutyraldehyde diethyl acetal	131	18	8 [55]	74/6, 1.4105
	β-Ethoxypropionaldehyde diethyl acetal	129	52	8 [34]	97/39
		130	76	8 [112]	73/13, 1.4035 [25]
C_{10}	β-Ethoxy-n-butyraldehyde diethyl acetal	129	60	8 [35]	86/18, 1.4080
	n-Butoxyacetaldehyde diethyl acetal	115	38	8 [122]	86/14, 1.4115 [14]
C_{12}	Phenoxyacetaldehyde diethyl acetal	115	77	8 [98]	134/10
	p-Methoxybenzaldehyde diethyl acetal	130	96	8 [42]	263
C_{14}	n-Octoxyacetaldehyde diethyl acetal	115	39	8 [99]	122/5
		Amino Acetals			
C_6	Aminoacetaldehyde diethyl acetal	435	73	8 [102]	162, 99-103/100, 1.4182 [25]
	Formaldehyde γ-dimethylaminopropylene acetal	436	60	8 [29]	68/21
C_7	β-Aminopropionaldehyde diethyl acetal	435	80	8 [104]	71/10
	Acetaldehyde γ-dimethylaminopropylene acetal	436	47	8 [29]	65/17

For explanations and symbols see pp. xi-xii.

TABLE 23 (continued)

C_n	Compound	Method	Yield (%)	Chapter[ref.]	B.p./mm., n_D^t, (M.p.)
		Amino Acetals (continued)			
C_7	Methylaminoacetaldehyde diethyl acetal	436	40	8[103]	165/735, 1.4140[22]
C_8	α-Methylaminopropion-aldehyde diethyl acetal	436	40	8[103]	74/26, 1.415
C_9	m-Aminobenzaldehyde dimethylacetal	425	78	8[119]	124/4, 112/1.5
C_{11}	m-Aminobenzaldehyde diethyl acetal	130	85	8[49]	139/5
C_{12}	Phenylaminoacetaldehyde diethyl acetal	436	46	8[120]	142/6
		Other Substituted Acetals			
C_6	Glycolic aldehyde diethyl acetal	96	95	8[88]	167
	Glyoxal semidiethyl acetal	160	54	8[48]	43/13
	β-Keto-n-butyraldehyde dimethyl acetal	137	81	8[117]	38/2, 1.4139[25]
	Diethoxyacetamide	352	84	8[106]	(78)
	Diethoxyacetonitrile	384	79	8[106]	70/20, 1.3937[25]
C_7	DL-Glyceraldehyde diethyl acetal	107	67	8[100]	121/8
	β,β-Diethoxypropion-amide	352	80	8[105]	(53)
	Cyanoacetaldehyde diethyl acetal	378	14	8[107]	99/14, 1.4155
		384	81	8[105]	93/11, 1.4153[25]
C_8	α-Hydroxyisobutyralde-hyde diethyl acetal	91	70	8[95]	75/19, 1.4111[21]
	Piperonylic acid	253	84	8[101]	(228)
	Methyl 2-nitrophenyl formal	115	80	8[96]	154/16, (30.5)
C_9	Ethyl β,β-diethoxy-propionate	129	35	8[39]	65/2, 1.4101[25]
	bis-(2-Nitroisobutoxy)-methane	129	95	8[40]	(62)
	m-Nitrobenzaldehyde dimethyl acetal	129	85	8[41]	143/8
C_{10}	Ethyl α-formylpropionate diethyl acetal	131	44	8[121]	102/20
C_{11}	m-Nitrobenzaldehyde diethyl acetal	129	78	8[50]	178/21

TABLE 24. KETALS   273

TABLE 23 (*continued*)

C_n	Compound	Method	Yield (%)	Chapter[ref.]	B.p./mm., n_D^t, (M.p.)
		Other Substituted Acetals (*continued*)			
C_{12}	Cyclohexylglyoxal diethyl acetal	129	80	8[36]	128/18
	Phenylglyoxal diethyl acetal	129	65	8[37]	132/7, 1.5012[25]

For explanations and symbols see pp. xi–xii.

TABLE 24. KETALS

C_n	Compound	Method	Yield (%)	Chapter[ref.]	B.p./mm., n_D^t, (M.p.)
			Ketals		
C_5	Acetone ethylene ketal	132	49	8[69]	92, 1.3980
C_6	Methyl ethyl ketone ethylene ketal	129	80	8[8]	116/763, 1.4096
	Acetone trimethylene ketal	129	80	8[8]	124/758, 1.4201
C_7	Methyl ethyl ketone trimethylene ketal	129	80	8[8]	147/747, 1.4288
	Acetone diethyl ketal	130	75	8[18]	113–115
		132	55	8[69]	113, 1.3891
C_8	2-Hexanone dimethyl ketal	134	70	8[59]	60/30, 1.4053[25]
	Methyl isobutyl ketone ethylene ketal	129	84	8[10]	48/10, 1.4180
	Pinacolone ethylene ketal	129	81	8[10]	139/760, 1.4236
	Cyclohexanone dimethyl ketal	129	79	8[6]	65/22.5
		130	89	8[47]	56/13
	Cyclohexanone ethylene ketal	129	85	8[10]	65/10, 1.4580[21]
C_9	2-Heptanone ethylene ketal	134	75	8[59]	181/745, 1.4224[27]
	Cyclopentanone diethyl ketal	130	75	8[45]	65/20
C_{10}	3-Octanone dimethyl ketal	134	55	8[62]	92/26, 1.4171[25]
	Cyclohexanone diethyl ketal	130	83	8[45]	78–85/18
	Acetophenone ethylene ketal	129	85	8[10]	110/30

For explanations and symbols see pp. xi–xii.

TABLE 24 (*continued*)

C_n	Compound	Method	Yield (%)	Chapter[ref.]	B.p./mm., n_D^t, (M.p.)
		Ketals (*continued*)			
C_{12}	Acetophenone diethyl ketal	130	75	8 [46]	101/15, 1.4773
C_{15}	Benzophenone ethylene ketal	129	81	8 [10]	168/10, 1.5901
		Halo Ketals			
C_5	Chloroacetone ethylene ketal	129	93	8 [26]	64/18
	Bromoacetone ethylene ketal	129	60	8 [26]	78/16
	sym-Dichloroacetone dimethyl ketal	129	85	8 [27]	(81.5)
	sym-Dichloroacetone ethylene ketal	129	85	8 [26]	105/12
C_6	1-Chloro-3-butanone ethylene ketal	129	61	8 [123]	55/11, 1.4456 [16]
	1-Bromo-3-butanone ethylene ketal	52	41	8 [123]	76/11, 1.4685
	Acetone γ-chloropropylene ketal	129	71	8 [30]	162/757, 1.4487 [15]
C_8	Diethyl ketone γ-bromopropylene ketal	136	69	8 [76]	85/2
C_9	1-Bromo-2,2-dimethoxyheptane	134	60	8 [115]	88/5, 1.4531 [26]
C_{10}	ω-Chloroacetophenone ethylene ketal	129	95	8 [26]	146/15
	ω-Bromoacetophenone ethylene ketal	129	92	8 [26]	142/11, (61)
C_{11}	Acetophenone γ-chloropropylene ketal	129	71	8 [26]	140/15
C_{12}	p-Bromoacetophenone diethyl ketal	130	65	8 [113]	155/24
C_{16}	Benzophenone γ-chloropropylene ketal	136	71	8 [76]	(44.5)
		Hydroxy Ketals			
C_5	2,2-Dimethoxy-1-propanol	139	34	8 [93]	65/12, 1.4216
C_6	DL-Isopropylideneglycerol	129	90	8 [32]	81/11, 1.4339 [25]
C_7	3,3-Dimethoxy-2-methyl-2-butanol	134	80	8 [68]	81/50, 1.4248
		139	77	8 [92]	161/730, 1.4238
C_8	3,3-Dimethoxy-2-methyl-2-pentanol	139	66	8 [92]	82/100, 1.4088
C_9	Cyclohexylideneglycerol	129	64	8 [26]	135/15

TABLE 24. KETALS 275

TABLE 24 (*continued*)

C_n	Compound	Method	Yield (%)	Chapter[ref.]	B.p./mm., n_D^t, (M.p.)
		Alkoxy Ketals			
C_7	β-Methoxyethyl methyl ketone dimethyl ketal	134	56	8[67]	65/25, 1.4080[26]
	β-Methoxyethyl methyl ketone dimethyl ketal	134	65	8[64]	65/25, 1.4082[26]
C_9	Methyl β-methoxyethyl ketone diethyl ketal	134	57	8[62]	69/30
C_{10}	β-Ethoxyethyl methyl ketone diethyl ketal	131	92	8[63]	75/9, 1.4148
		134	55	8[66]	107–111/54, 1.4142
		Other Substituted Ketals			
C_8	Ethyl acetoacetate ethylene ketal	129	87	8[38]	101/18
C_{10}	Ethyl α-keto-n-butyrate diethyl ketal	130	89	8[114]	87/11, 1.4200[18]
	β-Diethylaminoethyl methyl ketone ethylene ketal	129	70	8[26]	94/13
C_{11}	Ethyl α-keto-n-valerate diethyl ketal	130	95	8[114]	98/11
C_{13}	5,5-Dimethoxy-5-phenyl-1-pentene	134	80	8[65]	118/16, 1.5011[23]

For explanations and symbols see pp. xi–xii.

REFERENCES FOR CHAPTER 8

[1] Adkins and Nissen, *Org. Syntheses*, Coll. Vol. I, 1 (1941).
[2] Adams and Adkins, *J. Am. Chem. Soc.*, **47**, 1358 (1925); cf. ref. 4.
[3] Dunbar and Adkins, *J. Am. Chem. Soc.*, **56**, 442 (1934).
[4] Vogel, *J. Chem. Soc.*, 616 (1948).
[5] Zaganiaris, *Ber.*, **71**, 2002 (1938).
[6] Voss, *Ann.*, **485**, 283 (1931); *C. A.*, **25**, 1798 (1931); ref. 7.
[7] Weygand, *Organic Preparations*, Interscience Publishers, New York, 1945, p. 188.
[8] Salmi and Rannikko, *Ber.*, **72**, 600 (1939); cf. *Ber.*, **71**, 1803 (1938).
[9] Salmi et al., *C. A.*, **34**, 423 (1940); **41**; 5480 (1947); **42**, 537 (1948).
[10] Salzbacher, Bergmann, and Pariser, *J. Am. Chem. Soc.*, **70**, 2827 (1948).
[11] Hibbert and Timm, *J. Am. Chem. Soc.*, **46**, 1283 (1924).
[12] Leutner, *Monatsh.*, **60**, 317 (1932); cf. **66**, 230 (1935).
[13] Backer, *Rec. trav. chim.*, **55**, 1036 (1936).
[14] Natelson and Gottfried, *Org. Syntheses*, **23**, 38 (1943).
[15] Adkins, Semb, and Bolander, *J. Am. Chem. Soc.*, **53**, 1855 (1931).
[16] Baudart, *Bull. soc. chim. France*, (5) **11**, 336 (1944).
[17] Pingert, *Org. Syntheses*, **25**, 1 (1945).
[18] Hurd and Pollack, *J. Am. Chem. Soc.*, **60**, 1905 (1938).
[19] Wizinger and Al-Attar, *Helv. Chim. Acta*, **30**, 197 (1947); Dey, *J. Chem. Soc.*, 1059 (1937).
[20] Bedoukian, *J. Am. Chem. Soc.*, **66**, 651 (1944); McElvain and Kundiger, *Org. Syntheses*, **23**, 8 (1943).
[21] Filachione, *J. Am. Chem. Soc.*, **61**, 1705 (1939).
[22] Bedoukian, *J. Am. Chem. Soc.*, **66**, 1325 (1944); *Org. Syntheses*, **29**, 15 (1949).
[23] Witzemann et al., *Org. Syntheses*, Coll. Vol. II, 137 (1943).
[24] Hill and Potter, *J. Am. Chem. Soc.*, **51**, 1512 (1929).
[25] Hill and Pidgeon, *J. Am. Chem. Soc.*, **50**, 2723 (1928).
[26] Kühn, *J. prakt. Chem.*, **156**, 103 (1940).
[27] Prjanischnikow and Leontowitsch, *Ber.*, **68**, 1866 (1935).
[28] Naftali, *Bull. soc. chim. France*, (5) **4**, 338 (1937).
[29] Fourneau and Chantalou, *Bull. soc. chim. France*, (5) **12**, 845 (1945).
[30] Smith and Lindberg, *Ber.*, **64**, 505 (1931).
[31] Maglio and Burger, *J. Am. Chem. Soc.*, **68**, 529 (1946).
[32] Renoll and Newman, *Org. Syntheses*, **28**, 73 (1948); ref. 31.
[33] Hill and Hibbert, *J. Am. Chem. Soc.*, **50**, 2242 (1928).
[34] Simpson, *J. Am. Chem. Soc.*, **71**, 754 (1949).
[35] Meier, *Ber.*, **76**, 1016 (1943); Krausz, *Ann. chim.*, (12) **4**, 819 (1949).
[36] Rubin, Paist, and Elderfield, *J. Org. Chem.*, **6**, 268 (1941).
[37] Torrey, Kuck, and Elderfield, *J. Org. Chem.*, **6**, 292 (1941).
[38] Salmi, *Ber.*, **71**, 1803 (1938).
[39] Dyer and Johnson, *J. Am. Chem. Soc.*, **56**, 222 (1934); cf. ref. 105.
[40] Senkus, *J. Am. Chem. Soc.*, **69**, 1380 (1947).
[41] Icke et al., *Org. Syntheses*, **29**, 72 (1949).
[42] Claisen, *Ber.*, **40**, 3903 (1907).
[43] Hamer and Rathbone, *J. Chem. Soc.*, 595 (1945).
[44] Post, *J. Org. Chem.*, **5**, 244 (1940).
[45] Böeseken and Tellegen, *Rec. trav. chim.*, **57**, 133 (1938); cf. ref. 47.

[46] Fuson and Burness, *J. Am. Chem. Soc.*, **68**, 1270 (1946); cf. ref. 42.
[47] Helferich and Hausen, *Ber.*, **57**, 795 (1924); Weygand, *Organic Preparations*, Interscience Publishers, New York, 1945, p. 187.
[48] Fisher and Baer, *Helv. Chim. Acta*, **18**, 514 (1935).
[49] Bottomley, Cocker, and Nanney, *J. Chem. Soc.*, 1891 (1937).
[50] Haworth and Lapworth, *J. Chem. Soc.*, **121**, 76 (1922).
[51] Kranzfelder and Vogt, *J. Am. Chem. Soc.*, **60**, 1714 (1938).
[52] McElvain, Clarke, and Jones, *J. Am. Chem. Soc.*, **64**, 1966 (1942); Bachman, *Org. Syntheses*, Coll. Vol. II, 323 (1943).
[53] Fried and Elderfield, *J. Org. Chem.*, **6**, 574 (1941).
[54] Kritchevsky, *J. Am. Chem. Soc.*, **65**, 487 (1943).
[55] Palomaa and Kaski, *Ber.*, **72**, 317 (1939).
[56] Weygand, *Organic Preparations*, Interscience Publishers, New York, 1945, p. 378.
[57] Smith and Nichols, *J. Org. Chem.*, **6**, 489 (1941).
[58] Nieuwland et al., *J. Am. Chem. Soc.*, **52**, 1018, 2892 (1930).
[59] Hennion et al., *J. Am. Chem. Soc.*, **56**, 1130 (1934).
[60] Killian, Hennion, and Nieuwland, *J. Am. Chem. Soc.*, **56**, 1384 (1934).
[61] Killian, Hennion, and Nieuwland, *J. Am. Chem. Soc.*, **58**, 80 (1936).
[62] Hennion and Nieuwland, *J. Am. Chem. Soc.*, **57**, 2006 (1935).
[63] Dykstra, *J. Am. Chem. Soc.*, **57**, 2255 (1935).
[64] Killian, Hennion, and Nieuwland, *J. Am. Chem. Soc.*, **56**, 1786 (1934).
[65] Killian, Hennion, and Nieuwland, *J. Am. Chem. Soc.*, **58**, 892 (1936).
[66] Norris, Verbanc, and Hennion, *J. Am. Chem. Soc.*, **61**, 887 (1939).
[67] Norris, Verbanc, and Hennion, *J. Am. Chem. Soc.*, **60**, 1159 (1938).
[68] Froning and Hennion, *J. Am. Chem. Soc.*, **62**, 653 (1940)
[69] Croxall, Glavis, and Neher, *J. Am. Chem. Soc.*, **70**, 2805 (1948).
[70] Hallonquist and Hibbert, *Can. J. Research*, **8**, 129 (1933).
[71] McElvain and Curry, *J. Am. Chem. Soc.*, **70**, 3781 (1948).
[72] Alquier, *Bull. soc. chim. France*, (5) **10**, 197 (1943).
[73] Woods and Kramer, *J. Am. Chem. Soc.*, **69**, 2246 (1947).
[74] Parham and Anderson, *J. Am. Chem. Soc.*, **70**, 4187 (1948).
[75] Bogert and Roblin, *J. Am. Chem. Soc.*, **55**, 3741 (1933).
[76] Willfang, *Ber.*, **74**, 145 (1941); **70**, 2167 (1937).
[77] Witzemann et al., *Org. Syntheses*, Coll. Vol. II, 17 (1943).
[78] McElvain and Kundiger, *Org. Syntheses*, **23**, 45 (1943).
[79] McElvain and Walters, *J. Am. Chem. Soc.*, **64**, 1059 (1942).
[80] Kuhn and Grundmann, *Ber.*, **70**, 1894 (1937).
[81] Price and Moos, *J. Am. Chem. Soc.*, **67**, 207 (1945).
[82] Sheehan and Robinson, *J. Am. Chem. Soc.*, **71**, 1436 (1949).
[83] McElvain, Clarke, and Jones, *J. Am. Chem. Soc.*, **64**, 1966 (1942).
[84] Walters and McElvain, *J. Am. Chem. Soc.*, **62**, 1482 (1940).
[85] McElvain, Anthes, and Shapiro, *J. Am. Chem. Soc.*, **64**, 2525 (1942).
[86] McElvain, Kent, and Stevens, *J. Am. Chem. Soc.*, **68**, 1922 (1946).
[87] Beyerstedt and McElvain, *J. Am. Chem. Soc.*, **59**, 2266 (1937).
[88] Beyerstedt and McElvain, *J. Am. Chem. Soc.*, **58**, 529 (1936).
[89] Alexander, *J. Am. Chem. Soc.*, **70**, 2592 (1948).
[90] Hartung and Adkins, *J. Am. Chem. Soc.*, **49**, 2517 (1927).
[91] Fisher, Ertel, and Löwenberg, *Ber.*, **64**, 30 (1931).
[92] Aston and Greenburg, *J. Am. Chem. Soc.*, **62**, 2590 (1940).
[93] Bergmann and Miekeley, *Ber.*, **64**, 802 (1931).

[94] McElvain and Stevens, *J. Am. Chem. Soc.*, **68**, 1917 (1946); McElvain and Venerable, *ibid.*, **72**, 1661 (1950).
[95] Avy, *Bull. soc. chim. France*, (4) **49**, 12 (1931).
[96] Brand and Schreber, *Ber.*, **75**, 156 (1942).
[97] Palomaa and Kantola, *Ber.*, **65**, 1593 (1932).
[98] Dey, *J. Chem. Soc.*, 1057 (1937).
[99] Rotbart, *Ann. chim.*, (11) **1**, 458 (1934).
[100] Witzemann et al., *Org. Syntheses*, Coll. Vol. II, 307 (1943).
[101] Shriner and Kleiderer, *Org. Syntheses*, Coll. Vol. II, 538 (1943).
[102] Allen and Clark, *Org. Syntheses*, **24**, 3 (1944); Woodward and Doering, *J. Am. Chem. Soc.*, **67**, 868 (1945).
[103] Johnson et al., *J. Am. Chem. Soc.*, **69**, 2364 (1947).
[104] Albers, Kallischnigg, and Schmidt, *Ber.*, **77**, 623 (1944).
[105] McElvain and Clarke, *J. Am. Chem. Soc.*, **69**, 2657 (1947).
[106] McElvain and Clarke, *J. Am. Chem. Soc.*, **69**, 2661 (1947).
[107] Uhle and Jacobs, *J. Org. Chem.*, **10**, 81 (1945); Hartung and Adkins, *J. Am. Chem. Soc.*, **69**, 1535 (1947).
[108] Wibaut and Beets, *Rec. trav. chim.*, **59**, 653 (1940).
[109] Scheibler and Depner, *Ber.*, **68**, 2151 (1935).
[110] Bergel, Morrison, and Rinderknecht, *J. Chem. Soc.*, 265 (1944).
[111] Magnani and McElvain, *J. Am. Chem. Soc.*, **60**, 2210 (1938).
[112] Feazel and Berl, *J. Am. Chem. Soc.*, **72**, 2278 (1950).
[113] Kaslow and Lawton, *J. Am. Chem. Soc.*, **72**, 1723 (1950).
[114] Vogel and Schinz, *Helv. Chim. Acta*, **33**, 127 (1950).
[115] McCusker and Vogt, *J. Am. Chem. Soc.*, **59**, 1307 (1937).
[116] McElvain, *Chem. Revs.*, **45**, 453 (1949).
[117] Price and Pappalardo, *J. Am. Chem. Soc.*, **72**, 2613 (1950).
[118] Lunt and Sondheimer, *J. Chem. Soc.*, 3361 (1950).
[119] Icke et al., *Org. Syntheses*, **29**, 6 (1949).
[120] Janetzky, Verkade, and Meerburg, *Rec. trav. chim.*, **66**, 321 (1947).
[121] Deno, *J. Am. Chem. Soc.*, **69**, 2233 (1947).
[122] Kraus, *Ann. chim.*, (12) **4**, 817 (1949).
[123] Willimann and Schinz, *Helv. Chim. Acta*, **32**, 2151 (1949).

9

Aldehydes

CONTENTS

CONTENTS *(continued)*

A large number of methods exist for the preparation of aldehydes, many of which are very limited in their scope. The more general methods are given here. An excellent review on the synthesis of aromatic aldehydes has been published.[120]

140. Formylation with Carbon Monoxide (Gattermann-Koch)

$$ArH + CO + HCl \xrightarrow{AlCl_3\text{-}CuCl_2} ArCHO$$

Aromatic aldehydes are prepared by passing carbon monoxide and dry hydrogen chloride through an ether or nitrobenzene solution of an aromatic hydrocarbon in the presence of a catalyst, commonly aluminum chloride with cuprous chloride as a carrier. The process is illustrated by the synthesis of p-tolualdehyde (51%).[70] A convenient procedure for obtaining an equimolar mixture of anhydrous hydrogen chloride and carbon monoxide consists in dropping chlorosulfonic acid on formic acid,[266] viz.,

$$HSO_3Cl + HCO_2H \rightarrow HCl + CO + H_2SO_4$$

In most reactions at atmospheric pressure the yields are about 30–50%, whereas at a high pressure of carbon monoxide the yields are 80–90%.[73] This method is particularly suitable for the reaction of mono- and poly-alkylbenzenes. It is not applicable to phenols and aromatic ethers. The reaction has been considered in detail.[243]

141. Formylation with Cyano Compounds (Gattermann)

$$ArH + HCN + HCl \xrightarrow{ZnCl_2} ArCH=NH \cdot HCl \xrightarrow{H_2O} ArCHO$$

A mixture of hydrogen cyanide and hydrogen chloride in the presence of zinc chloride reacts with an aromatic compound to form an aldimine hydrochloride which on hydrolysis produces the corresponding aldehyde.

The reaction can be carried out more conveniently and in equally good yields by substituting zinc cyanide for the hydrogen cyanide (70–90%).[71, 72] Potassium chloride impurity in this catalyst is necessary.[75] Sodium cyanide has also been used.[79] With these modifications, phenols[71] and ethers[72] as well as hydrocarbons[74, 78, 79] react (cf. method 140).

142. Formylation with N-Methylformanilide

$$ArH + C_6H_5 N(CH_3)CHO \xrightarrow{POCl_3} ArCHO + C_6H_5 NHCH_3$$

This synthesis is applicable to many aromatic compounds, including alkoxyl or N,N-dimethylamino derivatives of benzene[103] and naphthalene,[101] naphthols,[106] indole,[105] and certain reactive hydrocarbons, namely, anthracene,[101] 1,2-benzanthracene,[102] 3,4-benzpyrene,[102] and pyrene.[104] The high-melting polynuclear hydrocarbons react best in the presence of a solvent, such as o-dichlorobenzene. For example, a solution of anthracene, methyl formanilide, and phosphorus oxychloride in o-dichlorobenzene is heated 1 hour at 90–95°; then an aqueous solution of sodium acetate is added, and the solvent and N-methylaniline are removed by steam distillation. The solid residue is readily purified to yield 9-anthraldehyde (84%).[101] With liquid or low-melting compounds a solvent is not required.

The conversion of thiophene and its derivatives to the corresponding aldehydes by this procedure has been extensively studied, the yield of 2-thiophenealdehyde being 76%.[260]

unsym-Diarylethylenes react in a similar manner to yield unsaturated aldehydes, $Ar_2C=CHCHO$.[202]

Other catalysts and reagents have been used. In the presence of aluminum chloride, 2-naphthol reacts with formamide to give 2-naphthol-1-aldehyde (45%).[106]

143. Formylation of Phenols with Chloroform (Reimer-Tiemann)

$$C_6H_5 OH + CHCl_3 \xrightarrow[HCl]{NaOH;} o\text{- and } p\text{-HOC}_6H_4CHO$$

Substituted phenols react with chloroform and alkali in alcohol solution to yield o- and p-hydroxybenzaldehydes. The yields are often less than 50%, the para- isomer predominating.[81] The procedure involves heating an alkaline ethanolic solution of the reactants for several hours, followed by acidification and isolation of the product by steam distillation or crystallization. An example is the synthesis of 2-hydroxy-1-naphthaldehyde (48%).[80]

144. Formylation of Phenols (or Amines) with Hexamine (Duff)

$$C_6H_5OH + (CH_2)_6N_4 \rightarrow o\text{-}HOC_6H_4CH=NCH_3 \rightarrow o\text{-}HOC_6H_4CHO$$

This reaction is readily accomplished by heating the phenolic compound at 150–160° for 10 to 30 minutes with a mixture of glycerol, boric acid, and hexamine. The phenolic aldehyde is liberated by acidification and steam distillation. By this general procedure, sixteen phenolic aldehydes have been prepared. Although the yields are only 15–20%, the method requires little time and furnishes a reasonably pure product which is the *ortho* isomer[96] (cf. method 143).

The method has been extended to the formation of *p*-dialkylaminobenzaldehydes in 35–45% yields.[99]

145. Hydroformylation of Unsaturated Compounds

$$RCH=CH_2 + CO + H_2 \xrightarrow[\text{Catalyst}]{\text{Pressure}} RCH_2CH_2CHO$$

Addition of carbon monoxide and hydrogen to an alkene linkage in the presence of cobalt catalysts gives aldehydes in an average yield of 50%.[190] The reactions may be carried out in the usual hydrogenation apparatus. The poisonous properties of carbon monoxide and cobalt carbonyls call for considerable care. Compounds made by hydroformylation include cyclopentanealdehyde from cyclopentene (65%), β-carbethoxypropionaldehyde from ethyl acrylate (74%), and ethyl β-formylbutyrate from ethyl crotonate (71%).

146. Formylation of Ketones with Formic Esters

$$CH_3COCH_2CH_3 \xrightarrow[\text{Na}]{HCO_2C_2H_5} CH_3COCH(CHO)CH_3$$

Acylation of ketones having reactive methylene groups by higher esters has been shown to be an excellent method for preparing β-diketones (method 203). If the acylating ester is an alkyl formate, then a keto aldehyde is formed (50–80%).[171–174] The formylation is simply brought about by adding sodium metal to a mixture of the ketone and ester in anhydrous ether. Oftentimes, the product is isolated as the sodium salt of the hydroxymethylene form. The point of attack is unpredictable in unsymmetrical ketones, CH_3COCH_2R.[173, 174]

147. Interaction of Halomethyl Compounds and Hexamine (Sommelet)

$$ArCH_2X \xrightarrow{(CH_2)_6N_4} [ArCH_2(CH_2)_6N_4]^+Cl^- \xrightarrow{H_2O} ArCHO$$

Substituted benzyl halides react with hexamine in boiling alcohol to form addition compounds which decompose on heating with water to give aldehydes.[85-90] An excellent discussion of the reaction has been presented, and improvements in the conditions have been made.[244] Aqueous acetic acid (1 : 1) is recommended as solvent for the entire process, and there is no need to isolate the intermediate salt. The procedure is illustrated by the synthesis of 1-naphthaldehyde (82%).[245] In other instances, the addition compound is first prepared in chloroform solution, isolated, and then decomposed with water or dilute acetic acid, as in the synthesis of 2-thiophenaldehyde (53%).[84]

The reaction is applicable to the formation of *m*- and *p*-dialdehydes, but not the *ortho* isomer, from the *bis*-(chloromethyl)-benzenes,[246] as well as aldehyde esters, e.g., *p*-carbomethoxybenzaldehyde,[85] and halo aldehydes, e.g., 1-bromo-2-naphthaldehyde.[87]

A somewhat similar reaction is the conversion of substituted benzylamines to the corresponding benzaldehydes by treating their formaldehyde condensation product with hexamine.[97]

148. Interaction of Benzyl Halides and Sodium 2-Propanenitronate

$$ArCH_2Br + [(CH_3)_2CNO_2]^- Na^+ \longrightarrow ArCHO + (CH_3)_2C{=}NOH + NaBr$$

A general procedure for the conversion of *p*-substituted benzyl halides to the corresponding benzaldehydes consists in treating the halide with sodium 2-propanenitronate suspended in absolute ethanol. The resulting instable nitronic ester breaks down into acetoxime and the carbonyl compound. The yields are in the range 68–77% for benzaldehydes having a methyl, bromo, carbomethoxyl, cyano, or trifluoromethyl group in the *para* position. However, *p*-nitrobenzyl chloride undergoes C-alkylation to furnish the stable substituted nitropropane, $p\text{-}NO_2C_6H_4CH_2C(CH_3)_2NO_2$.[261] The reaction has been extended to the synthesis of *o*-tolualdehyde (73%).[262]

149. Decomposition of Arylsulfonohydrazides

$$ArCONHNH_2 \xrightarrow{C_6H_5SO_2Cl} ArCONHNHSO_2C_6H_5 \xrightarrow{Na_2CO_3} ArCHO$$

Aromatic and heterocyclic aldehydes have been prepared from hydrazides, *via* the arylsulfonyl derivative, in 50–65%[123] and 20–40% yields,[124] respectively; the method fails in the aliphatic series. The hydrazide is treated with benzenesulfonyl chloride in pyridine, and the subsequent product is isolated by precipitation with water and decomposed by heating with sodium carbonate in ethylene glycol or glycerol at 160°.

Benzhydrazides in small quantities have been oxidized to the aldehydes with potassium ferricyanide in excess ammonium hydroxide (30-60%).[127]

150. Cleavage of Schiff Bases

$$ArCH = NR + H_2O \rightarrow ArCHO + RNH_2$$

Several preparations of aldehydes have been developed that involve the formation and cleavage of Schiff bases. The condensation of anilines or phenols with formaldehyde and p-nitrosodimethylaniline leads to such intermediates. These substances can be isolated and converted by an exchange reaction with formaldehyde in acetic acid to the corresponding aldehydes. p-Dimethylaminobenzaldehyde is made in this manner in 59% yield.[187]

$$(CH_3)_2NC_6H_5 \xrightarrow[CH_2O]{p\text{-}(CH_3)_2NC_6H_4NO} p\text{-}(CH_3)_2NC_6H_4CH = NC_6H_4N(CH_3)_2 \xrightarrow{CH_2O}$$

$$p\text{-}(CH_3)_2NC_6H_4CHO$$

When a methyl group on an aromatic nucleus is activated by a nitro group in the *ortho* or *para* position, condensation with nitrosobenzenes can occur to give a Schiff base; subsequent hydrolysis furnishes the aldehyde. An example is the synthesis of 2,4-dinitrobenzaldehyde (32%).[186]

$$(NO_2)_2C_6H_3CH_3 \xrightarrow{p\text{-}(CH_3)_2NC_6H_4NO} (NO_2)_2C_6H_3CH = NC_6H_4N(CH_3)_2 \xrightarrow{H_2O}$$

$$(NO_2)_2C_6H_3CHO$$

Condensation of diethylaniline and formaldehyde in the presence of sulfanilic acid gives the structure

$$p\text{-}(CH_3CH_2)_2NC_6H_4CH_2NCH_6H_4SO_3H,$$

which can be isolated and oxidized with potassium dichromate to the benzylidene compound; the latter on alkaline hydrolysis gives p-diethylaminobenzaldehyde in 50% yield.[188]

Imino chlorides, which are readily prepared by the action of phosphorus pentachloride on anilides, are reduced by anhydrous stannous chloride to imino intermediates which on hydrolysis yield aromatic aldehydes (50-90%); applications in the aliphatic series are poorly described.[128-132]

$$RCONHC_6H_5 \xrightarrow{PCl_5} \underset{\overset{|}{Cl}}{RC} = NC_6H_5 \xrightarrow[HCl]{SnCl_2} \underset{\overset{|}{H}}{RC} = NC_6H_5 \xrightarrow{H_2O} RCHO$$

In most cases, the crude imino chloride is treated directly by adding it to a solution of stannous chloride saturated with dry hydrogen chloride; the aldehyde is then liberated by steam distillation. The procedure is illustrated by the synthesis of o-tolualdehyde (70%).[128] Imino chlorides have also been prepared by treatment of ketoximes with phosphorus pentachloride, viz., $RR'C = NOH \rightarrow RCCl = NR'$, in preparations of benzaldehyde and p-chlorobenzaldehyde (70-85%).[133] As in the Stephen reaction (method 164), groups ortho to the imino chloride group hinder the reaction.

Schiff bases from other sources furnish aldehydes (methods 166 and 170).

151. Hydrolysis of gem-Dihalides

$$ArCH_3 \xrightarrow{X_2} ArCHX_2 \xrightarrow{H_2O} ArCHO$$

Toluenes substituted with chloro, bromo, fluoro, or cyano groups can be dichlorinated or dibrominated and the resulting benzal halides hydrolyzed directly to the corresponding aldehydes in the presence of calcium carbonate or sulfuric acid (50-70%).[135, 136] o- and p-Xylene have been converted to the corresponding dialdehydes.[139, 140] In the halogenation of certain cresols, the carbonate or acetate esters are used in order to prevent nuclear halogenation.[141, 216]

Aliphatic gem-dihalides require more vigorous conditions for hydrolysis than do the benzal halides. Examples are found in the treatment of certain 1,1-dichloroalkanes, like 1,1-dichloro-3-methylbutane and 1,1-dichloro-3,3-dimethylbutane, with water and, in some cases, magnesium oxide for 4 hours at 200-300°. The aldehydes are formed in 60-96% yields (cf. method 222).

152. Interaction of Pyridinium Salts and p-Nitrosodimethylaniline

$$ArCH_2COCH_2Cl \xrightarrow{Pyridine} [ArCH_2COCH_2\overset{+}{N}C_5H_5]Br^-$$

$$\downarrow (CH_3)_2NC_6H_4NO$$

$$ArCH_2COCHO \xleftarrow[H_2O]{H^+} ArCH_2COCH = NOC_6H_4N(CH_3)_2$$

Compounds containing reactive halogens ($ArCH = CHCH_2X$ or $ArCOCH_2X$) readily form pyridinium salts. Rearrangement of these products with p-nitrosodimethylaniline to a nitrone followed by hydrolysis with acid gives α,β-unsaturated aldehydes or substituted glyoxals.[189] Substituted benzyl halides, $ArCH_2X$, undergo the series of reactions to give the corresponding aldehydes, $ArCHO$. Terephthaldehyde is made in this way in a 70% over-all yield.[189]

153. Hydrolysis of 2-Alkoxy-3,4-dihydro-1,2-pyrans

Hydrolysis of 2-alkoxy-3,4-dihydro-1,2-pyrans with dilute hydrochloric acid furnishes a convenient synthesis of glutaraldehyde ($R = H$) and other 1,5-dicarbonyl compounds. The starting materials are obtained by the 1,4-addition of vinyl ethers to α,β-unsaturated carbonyl compounds. The wide selection of diene systems includes acrolein, crotonaldehyde, methacrolein, cinnamaldehyde, β-furylacrolein, methyl vinyl ketone, benzalacetone, and benzalacetophenone. Ethyl vinyl ether is preferred as the dienophile. The yields in the cyclization step are in the range of 25-87% and in the subsequent hydrolysis step, 59-85%.[265]

154. Hydrolysis of Aldehyde Derivatives

$$RCH = NOH + C_6H_5CHO \longrightarrow RCHO + C_6H_5CH = NOH$$

Oftentimes, aldehydes are isolated and purified as their derivatives, and their regeneration is then of importance (cf. method 195). The fission of the oxime, semicarbazone, hydrazone, etc., may be accomplished by acid hydrolysis or by an exchange of the nitrogenous moiety with another carbonyl compound, such as benzaldehyde, for which it has a greater affinity.

Semicarbazones of volatile aldehydes may be hydrolyzed by steam distillation in the presence of phthalic anhydride.[107] A synthetic route for aromatic aldehydes involves the hydrolysis of semicarbazones which have been prepared by the interaction of dithio acids and semicarbazide hydrochloride in pyridine solution.[17, 28]

$$ArCSSH \xrightarrow{H_2NNHCONH_2} ArCH = NNHCONH_2 \xrightarrow{H_2O} ArCHO$$

The hydrolysis of succinaldehyde dioxime must be carried out with care because of the instability of the dialdehyde. This step has been accomplished in 60% yield by treating the dioxime with ethyl nitrite in dioxane or with sodium nitrite in dilute sulfuric acid.[108]

The adducts formed from amine bisulfites and aldehydes are readily purified by crystallization from organic solvents and, like the sodium bisulfite addition products, are readily decomposed by the action of dilute acids.[122]

Acetals are readily hydrolyzed by dilute mineral acids; however, the yields are not always satisfactory. These substances are not affected by alkaline reagents. The sensitive dl-glyceraldehyde acetal is converted to its aldehyde in 80% yield by the action of dilute sulfuric acid under mild conditions.[238] Other procedures are illustrated by the treatment of acetals which are formed by the interaction of Grignard reagents and orthoformic esters (method 165).

Olefinic aldehydes have been prepared by bromination of the diethyl-acetal derivatives followed by dehydrobromination (cf. Acetals and Ketals); the unsaturated aldehydes are readily liberated by mild acid treatment of their acetals.[6] *Alkoxy aldehydes* have also been synthesized through acetal intermediates, which in turn are prepared from sodium alkoxides and bromoacetals.[111]

α-Hydroxy aldehydes have been prepared by hydrolysis of the oximes resulting from the action of Grignard reagents on certain isonitroso ketones.[175]

$$RCH_2COCH=NOH \xrightarrow{R'MgX} R'RCHC(OH)CH=NOH \xrightarrow{H_2O} R'RCHC(OH)CHO$$

155. Oxidation of Aromatic Side Chains

$$ArCH_3 \xrightarrow[(CH_3CO)_2O]{CrO_3} ArCH(OCOCH_3)_2 \xrightarrow[H_2O]{HCl} ArCHO$$

Oxidation of the methyl group in substituted toluenes with chromium trioxide in acetic anhydride forms crystalline diacetates, which are stable to further oxidation. These compounds are readily hydrolyzed in acid solution to the corresponding aldehydes (40–50% over-all).[149, 150] The procedure is generally applicable to the preparation of benzaldehydes carrying nitro, halo, and cyano substituents.

Other oxidative procedures have been described. The heterogeneous liquid-phase oxidation of toluene with manganese dioxide in 65% sulfuric acid is important in the production of benzaldehyde and salicylaldehyde. An example of its application in the laboratory is found in the preparation of 3,5-dimethylbenzaldehyde (48%) from mesitylene.[153] In a comparison of other oxidants, chromyl chloride is outstanding; however, it must be employed with care. The hydrocarbon is added slowly to a chloroform solution of this reagent, and the addition complex is carefully decomposed with dilute sulfurous acid to give the aldehyde. Yields range up to 80% (Etard reaction).[215] The internal oxidation-reduction of nitrotoluenes can be brought about by refluxing with alkaline sodium polysulfide, e.g., p-aminobenzaldehyde from p-nitrotoluene (75%).[156]

Benzyl halides have been oxidized directly with selenium dioxide[91] or copper nitrate.[92]

156. Oxidation of Olefinic Compounds

$$RCH=CH_2 \xrightarrow[H_2O]{O_3;} RCHO + CH_2O$$

Aldehydes result from the decomposition of certain ozonides. The technique is similar to that used for the preparation of ketones (method 182). High yields are obtained by catalytic hydrogenation of the ozonides.[114] This step coupled with Grignard and dehydration reactions has been used as a procedure for the degradation of an aldehyde to its next lower homolog, viz.,

$$RCH_2CHO \xrightarrow[H_2O]{C_6H_5MgX;} RCH_2CHOHC_6H_5 \xrightarrow{-H_2O} RCH=CHC_6H_5 \xrightarrow[H_2]{O_3;} RCHO$$

Dialdehydes result when cyclic olefins are ozonized.[115] Improved directions for the ozonolysis of unsaturated esters in glacial acetic acid to yield aldehyde esters have been given.[116] The same procedure is applied to the preparation of aliphatic aldehydes containing halo,[117] hydroxyl,[118] and ether groups.[121]

Oxidation of olefinic side chains with ozone to form aromatic aldehydes gives erratic results and therefore other oxidants are employed.[120] For this purpose, the most widely used oxidant is nitrobenzene in dilute alkali; the mixture is allowed to react at moderate temperatures for several hours. Thus, hydroxy benzaldehydes may be obtained from propenyl-phenols, which in turn are readily prepared by the Claisen rearrangement of O-alkyl ethers (method 100). Sodium dichromate in the presence of sulfanilic acid, which removes the aldehyde as it is formed, gives yields as high as 86% in the oxidation of isoeugenol and isosafrole.[267]

157. Oxidation of Methyl Ketones by Selenium Dioxide

$$ArCOCH_3 \xrightarrow{SeO_2} ArCOCHO$$

The preparation of certain substituted benzils by treatment of aryl benzyl ketones with selenium dioxide is discussed later (method 183). If a methyl ketone is treated under these conditions, the methyl group is oxidized to an aldehyde group.[176] The reaction is carried out by refluxing a mixture of selenium dioxide and ketone in dioxane or alcohol for several hours. Preparative details are found in the procedures for phenylglyoxal (72%)[177] and glyoxal (74%);[178] the latter is isolated as its bisulfite derivative.

4-Methylquinoline and 1-methylisoquinoline, which have reactive methyl groups, are converted to quinoline-4-aldehyde (61%) and isoquinaldehyde (42%), respectively, by means of this reagent.[183, 184]

158. Oxidation of Primary Alcohols

$$RCH_2OH \xrightarrow{(O)} RCHO$$

Controlled oxidation of a primary alcohol with a mixture of sulfuric and chromic acids gives the corresponding aldehyde. In the preparation of low-molecular-weight aldehydes, an aqueous medium is used and the product is removed by steam distillation, thus preventing further oxidation. This procedure is well illustrated by the preparation of propionaldehyde (49%)[1] and isovaleraldehyde (60%).[2] Certain benzyl alcohols are dissolved in aqueous acetic acid for chromic acid oxidation.[4] *Olefinic aldehydes* are produced by a rapid low-temperature (5–20°) oxidative procedure, as illustrated by the preparation of 2-heptenal (75%) from 2-heptenol.[10] *Aldehyde ethers* such as methoxyacetaldehyde and ethoxyacetaldehyde have been prepared by the chromic acid oxidation of the corresponding alcohols in 17% and 10% yields, respectively.[11]

Aldehydes have been formed from alcohols by the use of other oxidizing agents. Dihydroxyacetone has been oxidized with excess cupric acetate to *hydroxypyruvic aldehyde* in 87% yield.[12] *p*-Cyanobenzyl alcohol treated at 0° with a chloroform solution of nitrogen tetroxide gives practically pure *p*-cyanobenzaldehyde (90%).[13] Aromatic alcohols containing nitro groups have been oxidized to the corresponding *nitro aldehydes* with concentrated nitric acid, e.g., *o*- and *p*-nitrobenzaldehydes (80–85%).[14] *m*-Nitrobenzenesulfonic acid in basic media has been used for the oxidation of substituted benzyl alcohols, most satisfactorily for the water-soluble phenolic benzyl alcohols.[217] Selenium dioxide, or less effectively tellurium dioxide, oxidizes benzyl alcohol slowly to benzaldehyde.[218]

The Oppenauer reaction has been applied in the conversion of aliphatic and aromatic alcohols.[269] The alcohol, a high-boiling aldehyde (such as cinnamaldehyde), and aluminum alkoxide catalyst are heated, and the volatile aldehyde is removed as it is formed.

$$RCH_2OH + R'CHO \xrightarrow[\text{alkoxide}]{\text{Aluminum}} RCHO{\uparrow} + R'CH_2OH$$

In this manner, benzaldehyde and n-butyraldehyde have been obtained in 95% and 72% yields, respectively.[15] This procedure is employed more extensively in the preparation of ketones (method 180).

159. Dehydrogenation of Primary Alcohols

$$RCH_2OH \xrightarrow{\text{Catalyst}} RCHO + H_2$$

Catalytic dehydrogenation of primary alcohols in the vapor phase has been studied in detail.[226] Formerly, a copper catalyst[32] was used; however, it has been found that this catalyst is easily poisoned.[39] A copper chromite catalyst at 300–345° and atmospheric pressure gives improved and consistent yields (50–70%) and retains its activity over long periods.[33, 34, 38] Side reactions, such as dehydration, condensation, and ester formation, do not occur appreciably under these conditions.[38] Preparation of the catalyst and the apparatus have been described.[34–36, 38]

Catalytic dehydrogenation of alcohols has been conducted with yields as high as 90% by passing the vapor mixed with air over silver or copper-silver catalysts.[41, 195, 225] A three-step synthesis of DL-glyceraldehyde from glycerol consists in protecting two of the hydroxyl groups by ketal formation with acetone, followed by air oxidation over a silver catalyst and then hydrolysis of the ketal (59% over-all yield).[221] Methacrolein, $H_2C = C(CH_3)CHO$, is made by the air oxidation of methallyl alcohol (95%).[227] A laboratory-scale model for the air oxidation of tetrahydrofurfuryl alcohol over a silver gauze catalyst has been described.[228]

Liquid-phase dehydrogenation is carried out under a pressure of ethylene, which serves as a hydrogen acceptor.[40]

Ethoxyacetaldehyde, an *aldehyde ether*, is readily prepared in 35% yield from Cellosolve by the vapor-phase dehydrogenation technique.[36]

Similar techniques are employed for the catalytic dehydrogenation of secondary alcohols (method 181).

160. Oxidative Cleavage of Glycols

$$RCHOHCHOHR' \xrightarrow[\text{Pb(OOCCH}_3)_4]{\text{HIO}_4 \text{ or}} RCHO + R'CHO$$

Certain β-amino alcohols and glycols and their dehydroderivatives, i.e., α-ketols, α-ketals, and diketones, are readily oxidized with periodic acid or lead tetraacetate to aldehydes. A review of the method has been made.[144]

The reactions are usually carried out at a moderate temperature, using water as the solvent for periodic acid and organic solvents for lead tetraacetate; however, both reagents can be used in aqueous solvents. Addition of the oxidizing reagent to the glycol instead of the reverse gives an improved yield.[169] The yields are high, and the method has found extensive application in both analytical and preparative procedures. It has been applied in the preparation of aldehydes containing a double bond or hydroxyl, carboxyl, ester, or ether groups.[147, 148, 169] Oxidation of 1,2-cyclohexanediols with lead tetraacetate leads to substituted adipic aldehydes in 68% yields.[249]

Several small-scale synthetic routes for obtaining intermediates for cleavage to aldehydes by lead tetraacetate have been proposed.[145, 146]

(a) $RMgX \xrightarrow[80\%]{CH_2=CHCH_2Br} RCH_2CH=CH_2 \xrightarrow[KOAc]{Br_2;} RCH_2CHOHCH_2OH \xrightarrow{(O)}$
$$60\%$$

$$RCH_2CHO$$

(b) $RCOCl \xrightarrow[90\%]{CH_2N_2} RCOCHN_2 \xrightarrow[90\%]{HOAc} RCOCH_2OAc \xrightarrow[80\%]{H^+}$

$$RCOCH_2OH \xrightarrow{(O)} RCHO$$

161. Selective Reduction of Olefinic Aldehydes

$$RCH=CHCHO \xrightarrow[Catalyst]{H_2} RCH_2CH_2CHO$$

Aldehydes may be prepared by selective hydrogenation of substituted acroleins in much the same manner as the selective reduction of unsaturated ketones (method 196); however, there are few examples adequately described.[93-95, 100, 236]

162. Reduction of Acyl Chlorides (Rosenmund)

$$RCOCl \xrightarrow[Catalyst]{H_2} RCHO + HCl$$

Selective catalytic hydrogenation of an acyl chloride to an aldehyde can be accomplished with varying yields; the method has been reviewed.[58] The preferred catalyst is palladium suspended on barium sulfate. The reaction may be carried out in the liquid phase by bubbling hydrogen through a hot solution of the acyl chloride in xylene or tetralin in which the catalyst is suspended, or in the vapor phase by passing the acyl chloride over palladinized asbestos at about 200°.[64] In the former procedure, the reduction has been arrested at the aldehyde stage by careful control of the temperature [62] (lowest point at which hydrogen chloride is evolved) or by use of a catalyst "regulator" which inactivates the catalyst for reduction of the aldehyde. Typical reductions with and without catalyst poisons are found in the preparation of β-naphthaldehyde (81%)[56] and 2,4,6-trimethylbenzaldehyde (80%),[57] respectively. The reaction is applicable to acyl chlorides carrying halogen, nitro, or ester groups,[65, 67, 233] and even a double bond although this may migrate during the reaction.[66] Hydroxyl groups should be protected by acetylation.

Phosphorus- or sulfur-containing compounds formed in the preparation of the acyl chlorides hinder the reaction and therefore must be removed.[223]

163. Reduction of Thiol Esters

$$RCOSR' \xrightarrow[Ni]{(H)} RCHO + H_2S + R'H$$

The reduction of a carboxyl group to an aldehyde group can be effected by a reductive desulfurization of the thiol ester with Raney nickel. The thiol esters are prepared by the reaction of the acyl chloride with an excess of ethyl mercaptan in pyridine or by reaction with lead mercaptide in dry ether. The hydrogenolysis is then carried out by refluxing an ethanolic solution of the thiol ester with Raney nickel for 6 hours. By this new synthesis, propionaldehyde and benzaldehyde have been prepared in 73% and 62% yields, respectively.[160]

164. Reduction of Nitriles (Stephen)

$$RCN \xrightarrow{HCl} RC(Cl)=NH \cdot HCl \xrightarrow[HCl]{SnCl_2} (RCH=NH)_2SnCl_4 \xrightarrow{H_2O} RCHO$$

Nitriles may be converted to their imino chloride salts by the action of dry hydrogen chloride in ether. These intermediates are reduced by anhydrous stannous chloride to stannic aldimonium chlorides, which on hydrolysis yield aldehydes. Chloroform may be added to facilitate the solution of the nitrile. The quality of the stannous chloride catalyst is important; the preparation of an active and dependable form has been described.[49] The yields are usually high for many aromatic nitriles, as in the preparation of β-naphthaldehyde (95%).[49] The reaction has also been employed in the heterocyclic series, as in the synthesis of 4-methylthiazole-5-aldehyde (40%).[51] The reduction of the cyano group in the presence of an ester group leads to an aldehyde ester, e.g., methyl cyanobenzoate to methyl p-formylbenzoate (90%).[53] However, it has been shown that the method may not be as general as originally supposed, especially in the preparation of the aliphatic aldehydes.[50, 52, 55] Also, groups *ortho* to the nitrile group hinder the reaction. Instead of reducing the imino chloride with stannous chloride, as indicated above, sodium amalgam may be used in the presence of phenylhydrazine. The resulting phenylhydrazone is then hydrolyzed.[54]

165. Interaction of Grignard Reagents and Orthoformic Esters

$$RMgX + HC(OC_2H_5)_3 \rightarrow RCH(OC_2H_5)_2 \xrightarrow{H^+} RCHO$$

The reaction of ethyl orthoformate and Grignard reagents gives acetals which are hydrolyzed readily by dilute acid to aldehydes. This method has been employed extensively for the preparation of aliphatic and aromatic aldehydes. A study of the optimum conditions has been made, using the conversion of bromobenzene to benzaldehyde as a model synthesis (90%).[17, 21] Comparative studies of various aldehyde syntheses that employ Grignard reagents (methods 154, 166, and 167) show that this one is the most practical;[16, 17] however, the possibility of a sudden exothermic reaction limits the size of the run. Longer reaction times at room or reflux temperature help overcome this difficulty.[16, 18] Examples of the better preparative procedures are found in those for n-hexaldehyde (50%),[18] p-tolualdehyde (79%),[17] and phenanthrene-9-aldehyde (42%).[224] N,N-Dialkylformamide[16, 19] or ethyl formate[20] and Grignard reagents have been used with some success; however, the former reaction is complicated and frequently produces tertiary amines as the chief product, and the latter forms secondary alcohols by further reaction of the aldehyde. Substituted benzaldehydes have been prepared from aryllithium compounds and N-methylformanilide in good yields.[122]

166. Interaction of Grignard Reagents and Ethoxymethyleneaniline

$$ArMgX + C_6H_5N = CHOC_2H_5 \rightarrow ArCH = NC_6H_5 \xrightarrow{H^+} ArCHO$$

Aromatic Grignard reagents react smoothly with ethoxymethyleneaniline to give imines which are easily hydrolyzed to aldehydes. The reaction is easy to cary out, is adaptable to large-scale preparations, and gives high yields (65–82%).[17] Its use is limited by the availability of the ethoxymethyleneaniline, which may be prepared in a pure condition from the dry silver salt of formanilide and ethyl iodide.

167. Decomposition of Glycol Monoalkyl Ethers

$$2RMgX + C_2H_5OCH_2CO_2C_2H_5 \rightarrow C_2H_5OCH_2C(OH)R_2$$

$$\downarrow H_2SO_4$$

$$R_2CHCHO \leftarrow [R_2C = CHOH] \leftarrow [C_2H_5OCH = CR_2]$$

A large number of symmetrical diaryl- or dialkyl-acetaldehydes, difficult to obtain by other means, have been prepared by the reaction of ethyl ethoxyacetate, or ethyl phenoxyacetate, with Grignard reagents followed by treatment of the resulting glycol monoalkyl ether with anhydrous oxalic acid or dilute sulfuric acid.[29] The yield in the first step is 40–80%, and the yield in the subsequent transformation is 50–80%.

Unsymmetrical dialkylacetaldehydes may be obtained by starting with an α-keto ether.[30]

$$RMgX + R'COCH_2OC_2H_5 \rightarrow RR'C(OH)CH_2OC_2H_5 \rightarrow RR'CHCHO$$

By this procedure, 2-(α-naphthyl)-propionaldehyde has been obtained in a 74% yield.[31]

The method has been further studied in its application for the synthesis of ketones (method 202).

168. Thermal Decomposition of Acids

$$RCOOH + HCOOH \xrightarrow{ThO_2} RCHO + CO_2 + H_2O$$

The old method of heating the calcium salts of formic and a second carboxylic acid for aldehyde formation has been modified by the use of a catalytic decomposition technique. By this scheme, the acid vapors are passed over thorium oxide, titanium oxide, or magnesium oxide at 300°;[213] or the acids are heated under pressure at 260° in the presence of titanium dioxide.[214] In the latter procedure, non-volatile acids can be used. With aliphatic acids over titanium oxide, reaction occurs only when more than seven carbon atoms are present, the yields increasing with increase in the molecular weight (78–90%). Aromatic acids having halo and phenolic groups are converted in high yields to aldehydes, e.g., salicylaldehyde (92%) and p-chlorobenzaldehyde (89%). Preparation of a thorium oxide catalyst has been described[268] (cf. method 186).

169. Decomposition of α-Hydroxy Acids

$$RCHOHCO_2H \xrightarrow{Heat} RCHO + CO + H_2O$$

High-molecular-weight aliphatic aldehydes have been made by the distillation of α-hydroxy acids, which are prepared by the hydrolysis of the corresponding α-bromo acids. The reaction is carried out under diminished pressure or in an atmosphere of carbon dioxide. Details for the procedure are found in the preparation of octanal (57%)[43] and undecanal (96%).[44] Preparation of the α-bromo acid and its subsequent hydrolysis are also described. A later modification has been the distillation of the α-methoxy acid in the presence of copper. This procedure gives an almost quantitative yield in the preparation of heptadecanal.[45]

Aldehydes have also been prepared from α-hydroxy acids by oxidation with lead tetraacetate in glacial acetic acid, e.g., tridecanal (55%) and pentadecanal (58%)[46] (cf. method 160).

170. Decarboxylation of α-Keto Acids

$$RCOCOOH \xrightarrow[\text{Heat}]{C_6H_5NH_2} RCH = NC_6H_5 \xrightarrow{H_2O} RCHO$$

α-Keto acids are readily decomposed to aldehydes and carbon dioxide. The decarboxylation may be brought about by heating the α-keto acid or its arylimino derivative. By the latter procedure, a solution of the keto acid in aniline is boiled, which causes the formation of water, carbon dioxide, and a Schiff base, $RCH = NC_6H_5$; hydrolysis of this product gives the aldehyde.[164] Oftentimes, decarboxylation is accomplished in higher yields by heating the glyoxylic acid in N,N-dimethyl-p-toluidine at 170°[170] or in diphenylamine at 150–200°.[256]

Another modification is the decomposition of the bisulfite-addition compound of the keto acid as illustrated by the synthesis of phthalaldehydic acid (41%).[166]

171. Decarboxylation of Glycidic Acids

$$RR'C\!-\!CCO_2H \xrightarrow{HCl} RR'CHCHO$$
$$\diagdown\!\diagup$$
$$O$$

Aromatic and aliphatic aldehydes have been prepared in good yields by the decarboxylation and isomerization of the corresponding glycidic acids. Esters of the latter are obtained by treating a ketone with ethyl chloroacetate in the presence of sodium amide (method 127). The glycidic esters are first converted to the sodium salts with sodium ethoxide and then treated with aqueous hydrochloric acid under gentle reflux. By this procedure, α-phenylpropionaldehyde has been prepared from acetophenone in an over-all yield of 38%.[157] Other details have been discussed.[161]

A similar route is the formation and isomerization of substituted ethylene oxides.[159] This synthesis has been carried out without isolating the intermediates.[30]

$$RCOCH_2Cl \xrightarrow{R'MgX} RR'COHCH_2Cl \xrightarrow{KOH} RR'C\overset{O}{\overset{/\backslash}{-}}CH_2 \xrightarrow{HCl} RR'CHCHO$$

172. Hydrolysis of Olefin Dibromides [113]

$$(CH_3)_3COH \xrightarrow{Br_2} (CH_3)_2CBrCH_2Br \xrightarrow{H_2O} (CH_3)_2CHCHO$$

Over-all yield 75%

173. Degradation of Acid Amides and Azides

(a) α-Bromo Azides [112] (cf. method 220).

$$RCHBrCON_3 \xrightarrow{Heat} RCHBrNCO \xrightarrow{H_2O} (RCHBrNH_2) \xrightarrow{H_2O} RCHO$$

(b) Monosubstituted Malonyl Azides. [240]

$$RCH_2CH(CON_3)_2 \xrightarrow{C_2H_5OH} RCH_2CH(NHCO_2C_2H_5)_2 \xrightarrow{H_2O} RCH_2CHO$$

(c) α,β-Olefinic Amides. [168]

$$RCH=CHCONH_2 \xrightarrow[CH_3OH]{NaOCl} RCH=CHNHCO_2CH_3 \xrightarrow{H_2O} RCH_2CHO$$

174. Acid Treatment of Primary Acinitroparaffins [194]

$$RCH_2NO_2 \xrightarrow{NaOH} RCH=NONa \xrightarrow[80-85\%]{H^+} RCHO$$
$$\downarrow$$
$$O$$

R = methyl, ethyl, isopropyl, and n-butyl.

175. Isomerization of Unsaturated Alcohols [195]

$$H_2C=\underset{\underset{CH_3}{|}}{C}-CH_2OH \xrightarrow[96\%]{H_2SO_4} (CH_3)_2CHCHO$$

176. Condensation of Aromatic Hydrocarbons with Chloral[120,197]

$$ArCH_3 + Cl_3CCHO \xrightarrow{OH^-} ArCH_2CHOHCCl_3 \xrightarrow{(O)} ArCH_2CHO$$

177. Formylation of Acetylenes[211, 225]

(a) $C_6H_5C \equiv CNa + HCO_2R \xrightarrow[18\%]{} C_6H_5C \equiv C-CHO$

(b) $CH_3(CH_2)_3C \equiv CNa + HCO_2R \xrightarrow[24\%]{-20^\circ} CH_3(CH_2)_3C \equiv C-CHO$

TABLE 25. ALDEHYDES

C_n	Compound	Method	Yield (%)	Chapter ref.	B.p./mm., n_D^t, (M.p.), Deriv.
			Aliphatic and Alicyclic Aldehydes		
C_1	Formaldehyde	159	35	9^{142}	-21/760, 169Se, 166Dn *
C_2	Acetaldehyde	158	72	9^3	162Se *
		158	50	9^{142}	147Dn *
		....	74	9^{207}	20/760, $1.3353^{12 \cdot 5}$, 168Dn *
C_3	Propionaldehyde	158	49	9^1	55, 1.364, 99Se*
		159	67	9^{33}	154Se *
		163	73	9^{160}	154Dn
		165	82	9^{21}	49
		174	80	9^{194}	
C_4	n-Butyraldehyde	158	72	9^{15}	82/760, 1.3843 *, 104Se *
		159	62	9^{33}	77, 122Dn *
		165	76	9^{21}	75
		174	85	9^{194}	
	Isobutyraldehyde	158	64	9^8	63/741, 125Se *
		172	75 †	9^{113}	65/740, 182Dn *
		175	96	9^{195}	64, 1.3730
C_5	n-Valeraldehyde	158	50	9^6	102, 1.3947 *, 106Dn *
		159	72	9^{37}	
		159	58	9^{33}	
		165	50	9^{25}	
	Isovaleraldehyde	158	60	9^2	95, 1.3902*, 107Se *
		159	61	9^{33}	123Dn *
		162	100	9^{64}	92
	Methylethylacetaldehyde	158	52	9^9	92, 1.3942 *, 120Dn *
		159	63	9^{33}	
		165	25 †	9^{26}	93, 103Se
		171	35	9^9	91/751
	Trimethylacetaldehyde	159	66	9^{39}	76, 191Se *
		165	35	9^{20}	74/730, 1.3791, 210Dn *
		170	40	9^{256}	78
C_6	n-Hexaldehyde (caproic aldehyde)	159	53	9^{33}	128 *, 106Se *
		165	50	9^{18}	128/747, 1.4068 *, 104Dn *
	Methyl-n-propylacetaldehyde	161	68	9^{100}	116/737, 102Se *, 103Dn *
	Isobutylacetaldehyde	165	86	9^{23}	127Se, 99Dn
		168	86	9^{213}	121/743
	Diethylacetaldehyde	159	55	9^{33}	
		167	60 †	9^{29}	118, 94Se
	Dimethylethylacetaldehyde	159	66	9^{39}	104
	t-Butylacetaldehyde	151	60	9^{248}	103, 1.4150, 147Dn
	Methylisopropylacetaldehyde	167	61	9^{30}	114, 1.3998^{25}, 124Dn
		....	14 †	9^{30}	114

TABLE 25. ALDEHYDES   299

TABLE 25 (continued)

C_n	Compound	Method	Yield (%)	Chapter[ref.]	B.p./mm., n_D^t, (M.p.), Deriv.

Aliphatic and Alicyclic Aldehydes (continued)

C_n	Compound	Method	Yield (%)	Chapter[ref.]	B.p./mm., n_D^t, (M.p.), Deriv.
C_6	Cyclopentylaldehyde	161	60	9[94]	136/758, 34/10, 124Se
C_7	n-Heptaldehyde (oe-nanthol) (from castor oil)	....	....	9[208]	155/760, 1.4125 *, 109Se * 108Dn *
	5-Methylhexanal	156	62	9[114]	144/750, 1.4114, 117Dn, 117Se
	3,3-Dimethylpentanal	151	80	9[248]	134, 1.4292, 102Dn
	Ethylpropylacetaldehyde	167	60 †	9[29]	141
	Ethylisopropylacetaldehyde	167	60	9[30]	133.5, 1.4086[25], 121Dn
	Cyclohexanealdehyde	161	86	9[236]	63/24, 1.4503[18], 172Dn
C_8	n-Octaldehyde	164	100	9[50]	65/11, 60-Ox, 98Se, 80pN
		168	90	9[213]	1.4217 *
		169	57	9[43]	81/32, 59-Ox, 101Se
	Ethyl-n-butylacetaldehyde	159	58	9[33]	163 *, 254dSe *, 121Dn *
	Di-n-propylacetaldehyde	167	60 †	9[29]	161, 1.4142[15], 101Se
	Ethylisobutylacetaldehyde	167	60 †	9[29]	155, 98Se
	Cyclohexylacetaldehyde	165	47	9[22]	58/10, 1.4509[25], 159Se, 125Dn
C_9	Nonanal (pelargonic aldehyde)	159	90	9[42]	78/3, 1.4273 *
		160	33 †	9[147]	100/15, 64-Ox, 106Dn
		168	78	9[214]	
		168	85	9[213]	80/13, 64-Ox, 100Se
	Methyl-n-hexylacetaldehyde	167	60 †	9[29]	83/20, 80Se
	7-Methyloctanal	156	67	9[114]	103/140, 94/120, 100Dn, 80Se
	3,5-Dimethylhexahydrobenzaldehyde	171	65	9[253]	71/14, 171Se
C_{10}	Decanal	169	40	9[48]	98/13, 102Se *
C_{11}	Undecanal	169	96	9[44]	120/20, 1.4324[23], 103Se *, 104Dn *
C_{12}	Dodecanal (lauric aldehyde)	168	90	9[214]	238, (39.5), 78-Ox *, 106Dn *
C_{13}	Tridecanal	169	55	9[46]	136/8, (15), 106Se, 108Dn
C_{14}	Tetradecanal (myristaldehyde)	164	100	9[50]	155/10, (23), 83-Ox, 107Se, 95pN
		169	35	9[47]	166/24, (24), 106Se, 83-Ox
C_{15}	Pentadecanal	169	58	9[46]	160/14, (25), 109Se, 108Dn

For explanations and symbols see pp. xi-xii.

TABLE 25 (*continued*)

C_n	Compound	Method	Yield (%)	Chapter[ref.]	B.p./mm., n_D^t, (M.p.), Deriv.
		Aliphatic and Alicyclic Aldehydes (*continued*)			
C_{16}	Hexadecanal (palmitalde-	164	100	9[50]	(34), 88-Ox, 107Se, 97pN
	hyde	169	47	9[47]	202/29, (34), 107Se, 88-Ox
C_{17}	Heptadecanal (margaric	160	80	9[146]	(63)
	aldehyde)	169	52	9[47]	204/26, (36), 108Se, 90-Ox
C_{18}	Octadecanal (stearalde-	164	100	9[50]	(38), 89-Ox, 109Se, 101pN
	hyde				
		Aromatic Aldehydes			
C_7	Benzaldehyde	147	70	9[98]	
		148	73	9[261]	64/13, 1.5446, 235Dn
		149	73	9[123]	222Se *
		150	85	9[133]	88/40, 158Ph *
		151	70	9[142]	179
		155	44	9[215]	
		158	95	9[15]	
		162	96	9[64]	
		163	62	9[160]	235Dn
		165	89	9[16]	
		168	93	9[214]	
		....	97	9[52]	
C_8	Phenylacetaldehyde	160	72	9[145]	84/14, 97-Ox
		162	80	9[65]	156Se *
		164	33	9[52]	
		165	58	9[21]	195, 99-Ox
		171	50	9[158]	95/22, 121Dn *
		173	75	9[240]	82/12, 58Ph *
	o-Tolualdehyde	147	70	9[89]	88/19, 111Ph
		148	73	9[262]	72/6, 1.5430[25], 193Dn *
		150	70	9[128]	93/19, 101Ph *
		155	65	9[215]	
		165	73	9[17]	
		166	81	9[27]	
	m-Tolualdehyde	155	60	9[215]	84Ph *
		164	50	9[230]	198/756, 212Dn
	p-Tolualdehyde	140	51	9[70]	205
		140	65	9[74]	114Ph *
		148	70	9[261]	72/6, 1.5420, 234Se
		149	60	9[127]	198pN
		155	80	9[215]	
		164	77	9[52]	106/10, 200pN *
		165	74	9[17]	
		166	82	9[27]	
C_9	α-Phenylpropionalde-	171	38 †	9[157]	93/10, 76/4, 135Dn
	hyde				

TABLE 25. ALDEHYDES 301

TABLE 25 (*continued*)

C_n	Compound	Method	Yield (%)	Chapter[ref.]	B.p./mm., n_D^t, (M.p.), Deriv.
		Aromatic Aldehydes (*continued*)			
C_9	β-Phenylpropionaldehyde	162	62	9[232]	119/11
		165	67	9[24]	100/13, 127Se
	2,6-Dimethylbenzaldehyde	162	67	9[63]	228/742, 158Se
	3,5-Dimethylbenzaldehyde	155	48	9[153]	78/3.5, 1.5385, 201Se
C_{10}	3-Phenyl-2-methylpropanal	171	55	9[159]	90/6, 123Se
	p-n-Propylbenzaldehyde	170	65	9[167]	114/13
	p-Isopropylbenzaldehyde	140	60	9[243]	133/35, 1.5301*, 211Se*
	2,3,6-Trimethylbenzaldehyde	165	61	9[17]	114/10, 126-Ox, 169Se
	2,4,5-Trimethylbenzaldehyde	165	72	9[17]	121/10, (44)*, 243Se*, 127Ph*
	2,4,6-Trimethylbenzaldehyde	140	83	9[78]	128/15, 1.5524
		162	80	9[57]	98/6
		162	80	9[164]	98/6
		165	57	9[17]	188Se
		170	50	9[164]	98/6
	1,2,3,4-Tetrahydro-2-naphthaldehyde	162	67	9[231]	92/0.5, 197Se
C_{11}	p-s-Butylbenzaldehyde	165	66	9[122]	118/15, 1.5240[25]
	2,3,5,6-Tetramethylbenzaldehyde	165	61	9[17]	135/11, (20), 270dSe, 125-Ox
	α-Naphthaldehyde	147	68	9[88]	152/13, 98-Ox, 219Se
		147	82	9[245]	107/0.2, 162/18, (2.5)
		158	42	9[5]	
	β-Naphthaldehyde	147	50	9[90]	150/15
		162	81	9[56]	(60)
		164	95	9[49]	(58), 154-Ox*
		165	70	9[27]	(61), 245dSe
C_{13}	2,4,6-Triethylbenzaldehyde	140	69	9[78]	149/21
	p-Phenylbenzaldehyde	140	73	9[243]	(60), 189dPh*
	o-Phenylbenzaldehyde	149	55 †	9[241]	162/12
	2-(α-Naphthyl)-propionaldehyde	167	74	9[31]	132/2, 204Se
	1-Acenaphthaldehyde	162	72	9[59]	(100.5)
C_{14}	Diphenylacetaldehyde	171	90	9[255]	146/5, 114-Ox
	9-Formylfluorene	....	71	9[199]	172/2
C_{15}	α,β-Diphenylpropionaldehyde	150	50	9[129]	170/11, (54), 125Se,
	9-Anthraldehyde	142	84	9[101]	(105), 187-Ox*, 207Ph*
	1-Phenanthraldehyde	150	75	9[134]	(111.5), 189-Ox

For explanations and symbols see pp. xi–xii.

TABLE 25 *(continued)*

C_n	Compound	Method	Yield (%)	Chapter[ref.]	B.p./mm., n_D^t, (M.p.), Deriv.
			Aromatic Aldehydes *(continued)*		
C_{15}	2-Phenanthraldehyde	150	85	9^{130}	(59)*, 195-Ox *
		162	70	9^{60}	(59.5), 282Se *
	3-Phenanthraldehyde	150	85	9^{130}	275Se *
		162	90	9^{60}	(80), 145-Ox *
	9-Phenanthraldehyde	150	90	9^{131}	(101), 223Se
		162	90	9^{60}	(101)
		165	42 †	9^{224}	(101)
	1,2,3,4-Tetrahydrophe-nanthrene-9-aldehyde	150	68	9^{133}	(129)
C_{16}	2,4,6-Triisopropylbenz-aldehyde	140	65	9^{78}	126/4
C_{17}	Pyrene-3-aldehyde	142	53	9^{104}	(126)
C_{19}	1,2-Benzanthracene-10-aldehyde	142	64	9^{102}	(148)
C_{21}	3,4-Benzpyrene-5-aldehyde	142	90	9^{102}	(203)
			Heterocyclic Aldehydes		
C_5	Furfural	560	....	39^{6}	90/65, 159/745
	3-Furaldehyde	162	62	9^{61}	68/39, 1.4945*, 211Se
	Tetrahydrofurfuraldehyde	159	60	9^{228}	43/15, 1.4473, 134Dn
	2-Thiophenealdehyde	142	76	9^{260}	92/25, 1.5888^{25}, 139Ph
		147	53 †	9^{84}	91/21, 1.5880^{25}, 242Dn
		158	65	9^{223}	79/12, 1.5880^{25}
		165	70	9^{257}	78/20, 1.5950^{16}
		170	45 †	9^{162}	198, 119Ph
	3-Thenaldehyde	147	32 †	9^{86}	199/744, 1.5860, 137Ph
	α-Pyrrole aldehyde	143	33	9^{83}	109/14, (50)
	4-Methylthiazole-5-aldehyde	149	40	9^{124}	118/21, (75), 159Ph
		164	65	9^{51}	(72.5), 161Ph
C_6	5-Methylfurfural	7	22 †	39^{210}	85/15
		560	22	39^{5}	85/15
	3-Methyl-2-thiophenealde-hyde	142	83	9^{260}	114/25, 1.5833^{25}, 149Ph
	5-Methyl-2-thiophenealde-hyde	142	81	9^{260}	114/25, 1.5782^{29}, 126Ph
	Nicotinaldehyde	149	23	9^{125}	99/26, 158Ph
C_7	β-Furylpropionaldehyde	161	46	9^{95}	70/14, 1.4470, 80Se
C_9	Thianaphthene-3-aldehyde	147	31	9^{247}	(58)
		162	43	9^{235}	(54)
	Indole-3-aldehyde	142	54	9^{105}	(195)
		143		9^{82}	198Ph *
		170	74	9^{163}	(198)
	Coumarin-3-aldehyde	162	75	9^{62}	(132)

TABLE 27. OLEFINIC ALDEHYDES   303

TABLE 25 (continued)

C_n	Compound	Method	Yield (%)	Chapter[ref.]	B.p./mm., n_D^t, (M.p.), Deriv.
		Heterocyclic Aldehydes (continued)			
C_{10}	Quinoline-2-aldehyde	176	50	9[198]	(69)
	Quinoline-4-aldehyde	157	61	9[184]	(84.5), 182-Ox
		176	36 †	9[197]	123/4, (51), 179Pi
	Isoquinaldaldehyde	157	42	9[183]	(55.5), 197Se
C_{13}	Dibenzofuran-2-aldehyde	140	81	9[77]	(68), 162Ph

For explanations and symbols see pp. xi–xii.

TABLE 26. DIALDEHYDES

C_n	Compound	Method	Yield (%)	Chapter[ref.]	B.p./mm., n_D^t, (M.p.), Deriv.
C_2	Glyoxal	157	74	9[178]	51*, 178-Ox*
C_3	Malonaldehyde	154	45 †	9[206]	(74)
C_4	Succinaldehyde	154	60	9[108]	67/13, 172-Ox, 280Dn
C_5	Glutaraldehyde	153	59	9[265]	75–81/15, 1.4330[25], 169pN
C_6	Adipic dialdehyde	156	60	9[115]	94/12, 186-Ox*
		160	68	9[249]	70/3, 1.4350, 206Se*
C_8	Phthaldehyde	151	58	9[139]	(55.5), 191Ph*
	Isophthaldehyde	155	31 †	9[151]	(89), 242Ph*, 180-Ox*
	Terephthalaldehyde	147	34	9[244]	(114), 278dPh*
		151	84	9[140]	(116), 200-Ox*
		152	70 †	9[189]	(118)
		158	80	9[14]	(116)

For explanations and symbols see pp. xi–xii.

TABLE 27. OLEFINIC ALDEHYDES

C_n	Compound	Method	Yield (%)	Chapter[ref.]	B.p./mm., n_D^t, (M.p.), Deriv.
		Aliphatic and Alicyclic Olefinic Aldehydes			
C_3	Acrolein	....	48	9[191]	55.5, 171Se*
		....	85	9[192]	54, 1.4025, 165Dn*
C_4	Methacrolein (2-Methyl-2-propenal)	159	95	9[227]	73.5/760, 1.4191*, 198Se*
		159	90	9[195]	206Dn*
C_5	2-Pentenal	158	50	9[10]	125, 1.4350[21], 180Se
		154	70	9[6]	125, 123pN*
	2-Methyl-2-butenal	36	30	2[315]	116–119, 216Se
	β-Methylcrotonaldehyde	19	40	2[439]	130–135, 1.4526*, 223Se

For explanations and symbols see pp. xi–xii.

TABLE 27 (continued)

C_n	Compound	Method	Yield (%)	Chapter[ref.]	B.p./mm., n_D^t, (M.p.), Deriv.
	Aliphatic and Alicyclic Olefinic Aldehydes (continued)				
C_6	2-Hexenal	158	50	9[10]	150, 1.4470[13], 176Se, 139pN
	3-Hexenal	160	40	9[146]	150, 147Dn
	Hexadienal	36	50	2[317]	65/11, 160-Ox, 102Ph
	α-Isopropylacrolein	24	50	2[167]	109, 1.4223
		26	53	2[167]	107, 1.4223, 165Dn
	1-Cyclopentenylformaldehyde	....	28 †	9[94]	146/760, 48/11, 1.4828[21]
C_7	2-Heptenal	158	75	9[10]	85/14, 1.4314, 169Se, 116pN
	1-Cyclohexenealdehyde	20	77	2[451]	70/13, 1.4921[17], 213Se, 99-Ox *
	2-Cyclopentenylacetaldehyde	159	85	9[229]	50/15
C_8	4-Octenal	158	35	9[219]	84/13, 1.4463[25], 108Dn
	Octatrienal	36	40	2[317]	(55)
	2-Ethyl-2-hexenal	36	58	2[73]	73/30, 152Se, 125Dn
	2-Ethyl-3-hexenal	....	78	9[196]	84/52, 156Se
	3,6-Dihydro-o-tolualdehyde	34	31	2[520]	66/2, 1.5248[28], 219Dn, 230Se
C_9	2-Nonenal	158	50	9[10]	126/21, 1.4426, 165Se, 113pN
		160	67	9[147]	58/0.1, 1.4502[25], 165Se, 126Dn
C_{11}	11-Undecenal	160	64	9[146]	103/10, 91Dn
	Aromatic and Heterocyclic Olefinic Aldehydes				
C_7	β-Furylacrolein	36	54	2[313]	95/9, (52)
C_9	p-Formylstyrene (p-Vinylbenzaldehyde	27	52	2[493]	93/14, 1.5960[25], 131Ph
C_{10}	α-Methylcinnamaldehyde	36	67	2[314]	124/14, 208Se *
C_{11}	5-Phenylpentadienal	36	20	2[318]	161/12
	α-Ethylcinnamaldehyde	36	58	2[312]	112/7, 1.5822[25]
C_{15}	Stilbene-2-aldehyde	149	80	9[126]	(83)
	α-Phenylcinnamaldehyde	36	25	2[316]	200/16, (95), 141Ph, 195Se
	β-Phenylcinnamaldehyde	142	60	9[202]	210/14, 196Dn, 173Ph *

For explanations and symbols see pp. xi–xii.

TABLE 29. HALO ALDEHYDES   305

TABLE 28. ACETYLENIC ALDEHYDES

C_n	Compound	Method	Yield (%)	Chapter[ref.]	B.p./mm., n_D^t, Deriv.
C_3	Propargyl aldehyde	158	46	9^{220}	55
C_4	2-Butynal	177	28 †	9^{225}	105–110/755, 1.446[19]
					136Dn
C_7	2-Heptynal	177	24	9^{225}	54/13, 1.4521[17], 74Dn
C_9	Phenylpropargyl aldehyde	43	70 †	3^{33}	116/17, 1.6032[25], 108-Ox *
		154	81	9^{238}	117/17, 1.6032[25]

For explanations and symbols see pp. xi–xii.

TABLE 29. HALO ALDEHYDES

C_n	Compound	Method	Yield (%)	Chapter[ref.]	B.p./mm., n_D^t, (M.p.), Deriv.
	Aliphatic and Alicyclic Halo Aldehydes				
C_2	Trifluoroacetaldehyde	....	46	9^{222}	–20, 151Dn
	Tribromoacetaldehyde (bromal)	66	57	4^{513}	74/18
C_3	β-Chloropropionaldehyde	73	43	4^{197}	130, 50/10 *
	β,β,β-Trifluoropropion-aldehyde	158	57	9^{222}	56/745, 1.3168[22], 151Dn
C_4	α-Bromoisobutyraldehyde	66	18 †	4^{642}	115, 1.4518[25]
		154	47	9^{239}	108–113
C_5	α-Bromo-n-valeraldehyde	66	70	4^{514}	54/13
	2,3-Dibromo-2-methyl-butanal	74	70	4^{430}	73/3.5, 1.5228
C_6	Bromoparacetaldehyde	66	32	4^{516}	(104)
	2-Methyl-2,3-dichloro-pentanal	74	81	4^{438}	67/13, 1.4586[19,5]
C_7	α-Bromoheptaldehyde	66	40 †	4^{642}	92/17, 1.4580–1.4600[25]
	1-Bromocyclohexanealde-hyde	66	80	4^{639}	91/20, 1.500[18]
C_9	9-Chlorononaldehyde	156	66	9^{117}	100/3, 1.4501[25]
	Aromatic Halo Aldehydes				
C_7	o-Fluorobenzaldehyde	151	71	9^{137}	91/45, 90Ph *, 63-Ox *
	o-Chlorobenzaldehyde	149	61	9^{242}	98/20, 209Dn *
		162	70	9^{65}	
	o-Iodobenzaldehyde	150	80	9^{132}	129/14, 108-Ox *, 79Ph *
	m-Fluorobenzaldehyde	151	44	9^{137}	93/45, 114Ph *
		162	60	9^{67}	173/760, 63-Ox
	m-Chlorobenzaldehyde	56	79	4^{329}	86/8, 107/26, 135Ph *
	m-Bromobenzaldehyde	56	67	4^{329}	92/4, 205Se *
	p-Fluorobenzaldehyde	151	49	9^{137}	94/45, 147Ph *
	p-Chlorobenzaldehyde	149	77	9^{123}	75/3, (47) *, 232Se *
		150	81	9^{133}	(47), 220pN *

For explanations and symbols see pp. xi–xii.

TABLE 29 (continued)

C_n	Compound	Method	Yield (%)	Chapter[ref.]	B.p./mm., n_D^t, (M.p.), Deriv.
		Aromatic Halo Aldehydes (continued)			
C_7	p-Chlorobenzaldehyde	151	60	9^{136}	111/25, (47)
		168	89	9^{214}	
	p-Bromobenzaldehyde	148	75	9^{261}	(57), 229Se
		151	69	9^{135}	(57)
		155	51 †	9^{149}	(57)
		164	62	9^{230}	(57), 257Dn
	p-Iodobenzaldehyde	56	100	4^{330}	(77), 121Ph *
		164	56	9^{230}	(77), 257Dn
C_8	p-Trifluoromethylbenz-aldehyde	148	77	9^{261}	67/13, 1.4630
C_9	α-Bromobenzylacetalde-hyde hydrate	66	90	4^{515}	(82)
C_{11}	1-Bromo-2-naphthalde-hyde	147	40	9^{87}	(118)

For explanations and symbols see pp. xi–xii.

TABLE 30. HYDROXY ALDEHYDES

C_n	Compound	Method	Yield (%)	Chapter[ref.]	B.p./mm., n_D^t, (M.p.), Deriv.
		Aliphatic Hydroxy Aldehydes			
C_2	Glycolaldehyde	156	25	9^{118}	(76), 162Ph *
		....	25	9^{205}	(87)
		....	96	9^{212}	
C_3	α-Hydroxypropionalde-hyde	96	35	5^{557}	114/9, 127pN
	dl-Glyceraldehyde	154	80	9^{237}	139
		159	59 †	9^{221}	(133)
	Hydroxypyruvic aldehyde	158	87	9^{12}	(160), 135-Ox
C_4	4-Hydroxybutanal	160	42	9^{250}	60/8, 1.4403, 118Dn
C_5	5-Hydroxypentanal	99	79	5^{625}	55/3, 1.4514^{25}
	Methylethylglycolic aldehyde	154	50	9^{175}	
	3-Methyl-3-hydroxy-butanal	156	75	9^{119}	67/13, 142pN
	α,α-Dimethyl-β-hydroxy-propionaldehyde	102	80	5^{200}	85/15, (97)
C_6	2-Methyl-3-hydroxy-pentanal	102	86	5^{206}	86/12, 1.4373
	2-Isopropyl-3-hydroxy-propionaldehyde	102	52	5^{201}	84/10, 1.4603, 126Dn

TABLE 31. ALDO ETHERS 307

TABLE 30 (continued)

C_n	Compound	Method	Yield (%)	Chapter[ref.]	B.p./mm., n_D^t, (M.p.), Deriv.
	Aliphatic Hydroxy Aldehydes (continued)				
C_7	Methyl-n-butylglycolic	89	15 †	5[398]	87/35, 143Se
	aldehyde	154	50	9[175]	88/35, 143Se
C_8	2,2,4-Trimethyl-3-	102	....	5[202]	110/13, 1.4443
	hydroxypentanal				
C_9	9-Hydroxynonanal	160	23 †	9[147]	120/0.1, (54)
	Aromatic Hydroxy Aldehydes				
C_7	Salicylaldehyde	143	50	9[109]	196, 59-Ox *
		144	20	9[96]	197, 142Ph
		149	55	9[123]	230Se *
		151	50	9[141]	248Dn *
		168	92	9[214]	
	m-Hydroxybenzaldehyde	93	56	5[489]	(104), 88-Ox, 130Ph *
	Resorcyl aldehyde	141	95	9[71]	(136)
	3,4-Dihydroxybenzalde-	154	61 †	9[264]	(154d), 230dSe *
	hyde	97	61	5[714]	(154), 157d-Ox *
C_9	Benzylglycolic aldehyde	96	50	5[555]	121/4, (52), 70Bz, 137Se
	Methylphenylglycolic	89	19 †	5[398]	101/4, 182Se
	aldehyde	154	36	9[175]	101/4, 183Se
	2-Ethyl-4-hydroxybenz-	141	21	9[76]	145/1, (53)
	aldehyde				
C_{10}	Ethylphenylglycolic	89	11 †	5[398]	110/5, 188Se
	aldehyde	154	28	9[175]	111/5, 188Se
C_{11}	1-Naphthol-2-aldehyde	141	72	9[71]	(178)
	2-Naphthol-1-aldehyde	141	85	9[71]	(81)
		142	45	9[106]	161/11, (84)
		143	48	9[80]	(80)
		144	20	9[96]	(82), 157-Ox
C_{14}	Diphenylglycolic alde-	89	25 †	5[398]	(163), 124-Ox
	hyde	154	65	9[175]	(163), 242Se

For explanations and symbols see pp. xi–xii.

TABLE 31. ALDO ETHERS

C_n	Compound	Method	Yield (%)	Chapter[ref.]	B.p./mm., n_D^t, (M.p.), Deriv.
	Aliphatic Aldo Ethers				
C_3	Methoxyacetaldehyde	158	17	9[11]	92, 125Dn
		160	51	9[148]	89, 124Dn

For explanations and symbols see pp. xi–xii.

TABLE 31 (*continued*)

C_n	Compound	Method	Yield (%)	Chapter[ref.]	B.p./mm., n_D^t, (M.p.), Deriv.
		Aliphatic Aldo Ethers (*continued*)			
C_4	γ-Methoxypropionaldehyde	121	63	6[149]	
	Ethoxyacetaldehyde	158	10	9[11]	106, 117Dn
		159	35	9[36]	106/760*, 1.3956*
		160	40	9[148]	91, 116Dn
C_5	β-Methoxyisobutyraldehyde	121	51	6[149]	129, 1.4030[27], 102Dn
	n-Propoxyacetaldehyde	160	28	9[148]	68/100, 119/748, 86Dn
C_6	5-Methoxyvaleraldehyde	156	78	9[121]	59/14.5
	α-Methyl-γ-methoxybutyraldehyde	171	59	9[254]	66/55, 1.4280[25], 88Dn
C_8	2-Methyl-2,3-dimethoxypentanal	115	85	6[50]	67/12, 1.4196[19]
		Aromatic Aldo Ethers			
C_8	Phenoxyacetaldehyde	154	60	9[111]	105/10, 95-Ox*
		160	45	9[148]	94/6, 146Se, 138Dn
		160	60	9[169]	83/5, 1.5360
	o-Methoxybenzaldehyde	116	92	6[91]	(37), 205pN*
	m-Methoxybenzaldehyde	116	72 †	6[90]	90/3, 171pN*
	p-Methoxybenzaldehyde	141	100	9[72]	248, 203Se*
		149	77	9[123]	161pN*
C_9	o-Ethoxybenzaldehyde	116	90	6[93]	125/15, 59-Ox, 219Se*
	3,4-Dimethoxybenzaldehyde (veratraldehyde)	116	87	6[94]	153/8, (46), 90-Ox
C_{10}	2-Ethyl-4-methoxybenzaldehyde	141	53	9[76]	134/12, 1.5543[28]
	3-Ethoxy-4-methoxybenzaldehyde	116	93	6[161]	155/10
	3-Methoxy-4-ethoxybenzaldehyde	116	79	6[161]	(64)
	3,4,5-Trimethoxybenzaldehyde	162	64	9[143]	(75)
C_{11}	3,4-Diethoxybenzaldehyde	116	95	6[95]	130/2
C_{13}	o-Phenoxybenzaldehyde	115	22	6[154]	153/1, 215Se
	2-Ethoxy-1-naphthaldehyde	142	84	9[101]	(112), 258Dn*
C_{14}	m-Benzyloxybenzaldehyde	115	97	6[49]	218/20, (54)

For explanations and symbols see pp. xi–xii.

REFERENCES FOR CHAPTER 9

[1] Hurd and Meinert, *Org. Syntheses,* Coll. Vol. II, 541 (1943).
[2] Bouveault and Rousest, *Bull. soc. chim. France,* (3) 11, 300 (1894); Weygand, *Organic Preparations,* Interscience Publishers, New York, 1945, p. 143.
[3] Wertheim, *J. Am. Chem. Soc.,* 44, 2658 (1922).
[4] Smith et al., *J. Org. Chem.,* 4, 323 (1939).
[5] West, *J. Am. Chem. Soc.,* 42, 1663 (1920).
[6] Kühn and Grundmann, *Ber.,* 70, 1897 (1937).
[7] v. Braun, *Ber.,* 56, 2272 (1923).
[8] Fossek, *Montash.,* 2, 614 (1881); 4, 660 (1883).
[9] Neustädter, *Monatsh.,* 27, 882 (1906).
[10] Delaby and Guillot-Allègre, *Bull. soc. chim. France,* 53, 308 (1933); Martin, Schepartz, and Daubert, *J. Am. Chem. Soc.,* 70, 2601 (1948).
[11] Hurd and Abernethy, *J. Am. Chem. Soc.,* 63, 1966 (1941).
[12] Evans, Carr, and Krantz, *J. Am. Chem. Soc.,* 60, 1628 (1938).
[13] Ashley et al., *J. Chem. Soc.,* 115 (1942).
[14] Helferich, Streech, and Günther, *J. prakt. Chem.,* 151, 251 (1938).
[15] Davies and Hodgson, *J. Soc. Chem. Ind. (London),* 62, 109 (1943); Lauchenauer and Schinz, *Helv. Chim. Acta,* 32, 1265 (1949).
[16] Smith and Bayliss, *J. Org. Chem.,* 6, 437 (1941).
[17] Smith and Nichols, *J. Org. Chem.,* 6, 489 (1941).
[18] Bachman, *Org. Syntheses,* Coll. Vol. II, 323 (1943).
[19] Maxim and Mavrodineanu, *Bull. soc. chim. France,* (5) 2, 591 (1935).
[20] Campbell, *J. Am. Chem. Soc.,* 59, 1980 (1937).
[21] Wood and Comley, *J. Soc. Chem. Ind. (London),* 42, 429T (1923).
[22] Fried and Elderfield, *J. Org. Chem.,* 6, 574 (1941); cf. ref. 21.
[23] Brunner and Farmer, *J. Chem. Soc.,* 1044 (1937).
[24] Cohen, *J. Chem. Soc.,* 432 (1935).
[25] Letch and Linstead, *J. Chem. Soc.,* 450 (1932); cf. ref. 21.
[26] Linstead and Mann, *J. Chem. Soc.,* 2069 (1930).
[27] Sah, *Rec. trav. chim.,* 59, 1024 (1940).
[28] Wuyts, Berman, and Lacourt, *Bull. soc. chim. Belg.,* 40, 665 (1931).
[29] Behal and Sommelet, *Bull. soc. chim. France,* (3) 31, 300 (1904); (4) 1, 401 (1907); Stoermer, *Ber.,* 39, 2288 (1906).
[30] Barnes and Budde, *J. Am. Chem. Soc.,* 68, 2339 (1946).
[31] Fieser, Joshel, and Seligman, *J. Am. Chem. Soc.,* 61, 2136 (1939).
[32] Bouveault, *Bull. soc. chim. France,* (3) 11, 300 (1894); (4) 3, 119 (1908).
[33] Dunbar and Arnold, *J. Org. Chem.,* 10, 501 (1945); *Ind. Eng. Chem., Anal. Ed.,* 16, 441 (1944).
[34] Dunbar, *J. Org. Chem.,* 3, 242 (1938).
[35] Lazier and Arnold, *Org. Syntheses,* Coll. Vol. II, 142 (1943).
[36] Redemann and Icke, *J. Org. Chem.,* 8, 160 (1943).
[37] Kraft and Herbst, *J. Org. Chem.,* 10, 492 (1945); cf. ref. 36.
[38] Adkins et al., *J. Am. Chem. Soc.,* 55, 2992 (1933).
[39] Conant, Webb, and Mendum, *J. Am. Chem. Soc.,* 51, 1246 (1929).
[40] Reeve and Adkins, *J. Am. Chem. Soc.,* 62, 2874 (1940).
[41] Davies and Hodgson, *J. Chem. Soc.,* 282 (1943).
[42] Weygand, *Organic Preparations,* Interscience Publishers, New York, 1945, p. 145.
[43] Blaise, *Bull. soc. chim. France,* (3) 31, 483 (1904).

[44] Davies and Hodgson, J. Soc. Chem. Ind. (London), 62, 128 (1943).
[45] Darzens and Levy, Compt. rend., 196, 348 (1933).
[46] Laurer, Gensler, and Miller, J. Am. Chem. Soc., 63, 1153 (1941); cf. ref. 47.
[47] Le Sueur, J. Chem. Soc., 87, 1888 (1905); 85, 827 (1904).
[48] Pickard and Kenyon, J. Chem. Soc., 103, 1947 (1913).
[49] Williams, Org. Syntheses, 23, 63 (1943).
[50] Stephen, J. Chem. Soc., 1874 (1925).
[51] Harington and Moggridge, J. Chem. Soc., 445 (1939).
[52] Williams, J. Am. Chem. Soc., 61, 2248 (1939).
[53] Slotta and Kethur, Ber., 71, 335 (1938).
[54] Henle, Ber., 35, 3039 (1902); 38, 1362 (1905).
[55] Lieber, J. Am. Chem. Soc., 71, 2862 (1949).
[56] Hershberg and Cason, Org. Syntheses, 21, 84 (1941).
[57] Barnes, Org. Syntheses, 21, 110 (1941).
[58] Mosettig and Mozingo in Organic Reactions, Vol. 4, John Wiley & Sons, New York, 1948, p. 362.
[59] Fieser and Hershberg, J. Am. Chem. Soc., 62, 52 (1940); cf. ref. 58.
[60] Mosettig and van de Kamp, J. Am. Chem. Soc., 55, 2995 (1933); cf. ref. 58.
[61] Hayes, J. Am. Chem. Soc., 71, 2581 (1949).
[62] Boehm, Schumann, and Hansen, Arch. Pharm., 271, 490 (1933).
[63] Lock and Schmidt, J. prakt. Chem., 140, 231 (1934).
[64] Weygand and Meusel, Ber., 76, 503 (1943); Fröschl and Danoff, J. prakt. Chem., (2) 144, 217 (1936); Rosenmund, Ber., 51, 585 (1918).
[65] Rosenmund and Zetzsche, Ber., 54, 425 (1921).
[66] English, Jr., and Velick, J. Am. Chem. Soc., 67, 1413 (1945).
[67] Shoesmith et al., J. Chem. Soc., 2760 (1926).
[68] Harris et al., J. Am. Chem. Soc., 67, 2098 (1945).
[69] Glattfeld and Straitiff, J. Am. Chem. Soc., 60, 1386 (1938).
[70] Coleman and Craig, Org. Syntheses, Coll. Vol. II, 583 (1943).
[71] Adams and Levine, J. Am. Chem. Soc., 45, 2373 (1923).
[72] Adams and Montgomery, J. Am. Chem. Soc., 46, 1518 (1924).
[73] Holloway and Krase, Ind. Eng. Chem., 25, 497 (1933).
[74] Hinkel, Ayling, and Morgan, J. Chem. Soc., 2793 (1932).
[75] Arnold and Sprung, J. Am. Chem. Soc., 60, 1699 (1938).
[76] Baker, J. Am. Chem. Soc., 65, 1576 (1943).
[77] Hinkel, Ayling, and Beynon, J. Chem. Soc., 778 (1937).
[78] Fuson et al., J. Am. Chem. Soc., 64, 30 (1942); Org. Syntheses, 23, 57 (1943).
[79] Niedzielski and Nord, J. Org. Chem., 8, 147 (1943).
[80] Russell and Lockhart, Org. Syntheses, 22, 63 (1942).
[81] Hodgson and Jenkinson, J. Chem. Soc., 469 (1929).
[82] Boyd and Robson, Biochem. J., 29, 555 (1935).
[83] Weygand, Organic Preparations, Interscience Publishers, New York, 1945, p. 403.
[84] Dunn, Waugh, and Dittmer, J. Am. Chem. Soc., 68, 2118 (1946); Wiberg, Org. Syntheses, 29, 87 (1949).
[85] Fuson and Cooke, Jr., J. Am. Chem. Soc., 62, 1180 (1940).
[86] Campaigne and LeSuer, J. Am. Chem. Soc., 70, 1557 (1948).
[87] Hewett, J. Chem. Soc., 297 (1940).
[88] Coles and Dodds, J. Am. Chem. Soc., 60, 853 (1938); Mayer and Stieglitz, Ber., 55, 1846 (1922); Rupe and Brentano, Helv. Chim. Acta, 19, 586 (1936); Ruggli and Bruckhardt, ibid., 23, 443 (1940).

[89] Weygand, *Organic Preparations*, Interscience Publishers, New York, 1945, p. 156; Grammaticakis, *Bull. soc. chim. France*, (5) 7, 537 (1940).

[90] Badger, *J. Chem. Soc.*, 536 (1941).

[91] Fisher, *J. Am. Chem. Soc.*, 56, 2056 (1934).

[92] Baker, Nathan, and Shoppee, *j. Chem. Soc.*, 1848 (1935).

[93] Palfray, *Bull. soc. chim. France*, (5) 7, 414 (1940).

[94] Urion, *Ann. chim.*, (11) 1, 43 (1934).

[95] Burdick and Adkins, *J. Am. Chem. Soc.*, 56, 438 (1934).

[96] Duff, *J. Chem. Soc.*, 547 (1941).

[97] Graymore and Davies, *J. Chem. Soc.*, 293 (1945).

[98] Sommelet, *Compt. rend.*, 157, 852 (1913).

[99] Duff, *J. Chem. Soc.*, 276 (1945).

[100] Skita, *Ber.*, 48, 1491 (1915).

[101] Fieser, Hartwell, and Jones, *Org. Syntheses*, 20, 11 (1940).

[102] Fieser and Hershberg, *J. Am. Chem. Soc.*, 60, 2547, 2558 (1938).

[103] Vilsmeier and Haack, *Ber.*, 60, 119 (1927).

[104] Vollmann et al., *Ann.*, 531, 108 (1937).

[105] Shabica et al., *J. Am. Chem. Soc.*, 68, 1156 (1946).

[106] Ruggli and Burckhardt, *Helv. Chim. Acta*, 23, 447 (1940).

[107] Tiemann, *Ber.*, 33, 3721 (1900).

[108] Keagle and Hartung, *J. Am. Chem. Soc.*, 68, 1609 (1946); Mannich and Budde, *Arch. Pharm.*, 270, 283 (1932); and Weygand, *Organic Preparations*, Interscience Publishers, New York, 1945, p. 161.

[109] Gattermann and Wieland, *Laboratory Methods of Organic Chemistry*, The Macmillan Co., New York, 1938, p. 235.

[110] Moses, *Ber.*, 33, 2624 (1900).

[111] Dey, *J. Chem. Soc.*, 1059 (1937); Rotbart, *Ann. chim.*, (11) 1, 439 (1934).

[112] Newman, *J. Am. Chem. Soc.*, 57, 732 (1935).

[113] Whitmore et al., *J. Am. Chem. Soc.*, 55, 1136 (1933).

[114] Henne and Hill, *J. Am. Chem. Soc.*, 65, 752 (1943); Henne and Perilstein, *ibid.*, 65, 2183 (1943).

[115] Fisher and Loewenberg, *Ber.*, 66, 666 (1933); Gattermann and Wieland, *Laboratory Methods of Organic Chemistry*, The Macmillan Co., New York, 1938, p. 384.

[116] Noller and Adams, *J. Am. Chem. Soc.*, 48, 1074 (1926).

[117] Noller and Bannerot, *J. Am. Chem. Soc.*, 56, 1563 (1934).

[118] Fisher and Feldmann, *Ber.*, 62, 856 (1929).

[119] Fisher, *Ber.*, 76, 734 (1943).

[120] Ferguson, *Chem. Revs.*, 38, 227 (1946).

[121] Pummerer and Schönamsgruber, *Ber.*, 72, 1840 (1939).

[122] Adams and Lipscomb, *J. Am. Chem. Soc.*, 71, 519 (1949).

[123] McFadyen and Stevens, *J. Chem. Soc.*, 584 (1936).

[124] Buchman and Richardson, *J. Am. Chem. Soc.*, 61, 892 (1939).

[125] Niemann, Lewis, and Hays, *J. Am. Chem. Soc.*, 64, 1678 (1942); Panizzon, *Helv. Chim. Acta*, 24, 24E (1941).

[126] Natelson and Gottfried, *J. Am. Chem. Soc.*, 63, 487 (1941); 64, 2962 (1942).

[127] Kalb and Gross, *Ber.*, 59, 727 (1926).

[128] Williams, Witten, and Krynitsky, *Org. Syntheses*, 26, 97 (1946).

[129] Burton and Shoppee, *J. Chem. Soc.*, 548 (1937).

[130] Bachmann and Kloetzel, *J. Am. Chem. Soc.*, 59, 2209 (1937).

[131] Shoppee, *J. Chem. Soc.*, 40 (1933).

[132] Rapson and Shuttleworth, *J. Chem. Soc.*, 488 (1941).

[133] Coleman and Pyle, *J. Am. Chem. Soc.*, 68, 2007 (1946).

[134] Bachmann and Boatner, *J. Am. Chem. Soc.*, 58, 2100 (1936).

[135] Coleman and Honeywell, *Org. Syntheses*, Coll. Vol. II, 89 (1943).

[136] McEwen, *Org. Syntheses*, Coll. Vol. II, 133 (1943).

[137] Brooks, *J. Am. Chem. Soc.*, 66, 1296 (1944); Marvel and Hein, *ibid.*, 70, 1896 1948.

[138] Wiley and Smith, *J. Am. Chem. Soc.*, 70, 1560 (1948).

[139] Wawzonek and Karll, *J. Am. Chem. Soc.*, 70, 1666 (1948).

[140] Snell and Weissberger, *Org. Syntheses*, 20, 92 (1940).

[141] Copisarow, *J. Chem. Soc.*, 588 (1929).

[142] Gattermann and Wieland, *Laboratory Methods of Organic Chemistry*, The Macmillan Co., New York, 1938, Chapter V.

[143] Huang, Tarbell, and Arnstein, *J. Am. Chem. Soc.*, 70, 4182 (1948).

[144] Jackson in *Organic Reactions*, Vol. 2, John Wiley & Sons, New York, 1944, p. 341.

[145] Hershberg, *Helv. Chim. Acta*, 17, 351 (1934).

[146] Grundmann, *Ann. chim.*, 524, 31 (1936).

[147] Scanlan and Swern, *J. Am. Chem. Soc.*, 62, 2305, 2309 (1940).

[148] Hatch and Nesbitt, *J. Am. Chem. Soc.*, 67, 39 (1945).

[149] Lieberman and Connor, *Org. Syntheses*, Coll. Vol. II, 441 (1943); Walton, Tipson, and Cretcher, *J. Am. Chem. Soc.*, 67, 1501 (1945).

[150] Tsang, Wood, and Johnson, *Org. Syntheses*, 24, 75 (1944).

[151] Johnston and Williams, *J. Am. Chem. Soc.*, 69, 2065 (1947).

[152] Marvel and Hein, *J. Am. Chem. Soc.*, 70, 1897 (1948).

[153] Marvel, Saunders, and Overberger, *J. Am. Chem. Soc.*, 68, 1085 (1946).

[154] Charlot, *Ann. chim.*, (11) 2, 415 (1934).

[155] Marek and Hahn, *Catalytic Oxidation of Organic Compounds in Vapor Phase*, A.C.S. Monograph 61, Chemical Catalog Co., New York, 1932.

[156] Beard and Hodgson, *J. Chem. Soc.*, 4 (1944).

[157] Allen and Van Allen, *Org. Syntheses*, 24, 82, 87 (1944); Newman and Closson, *J. Am. Chem. Soc.*, 66, 1554 (1944).

[158] Scheibler and Tutundzitsch, *Ber.*, 64, 2916 (1931); Ruggli and Hegedüs, *Helv. Chim. Acta*, 25, 1291 (1942).

[159] Ramart-Lucas and Labaune, *Ann. chim.*, (10) 16, 282 (1931).

[160] Wolfrom and Karabinos, *J. Am. Chem. Soc.*, 68, 1455 (1946).

[161] Newman and Magerlein in *Organic Reactions*, Vol. 5, John Wiley & Sons, New York, 1949, pp. 413–440.

[162] Barger and Easson, *J. Chem. Soc.*, 2100 (1938); Biedermann, *Ber.*, 19, 636 (1886).

[163] Elks, Elliott, and Hems, *J. Chem. Soc.*, 629 (1944).

[164] Barnes, Pierce, and Cochrane, *J. Am. Chem. Soc.*, 62, 1084 (1940).

[165] Fuson, *J. Am. Chem. Soc.*, 48, 1093 (1926).

[166] Gardner and Naylor, Jr., *Org. Syntheses*, Coll. Vol. II, 523 (1943).

[167] Weygand, *Organic Preparations*, Interscience Publishers, New York, 1945, p. 447.

[168] Weerman, *Ann.*, 401, 1 (1913); *Rec. trav. chim.*, 29, 18 (1910); 37, 1 (1917); Rinkes, *Rec. trav. chim.*, 39, 200, 704 (1920); 45, 819 (1926); 46, 268 (1927); 48, 960 (1929).

[169] Speer and Mahler, *J. Am. Chem. Soc.*, 71, 1133 (1949).

[170] Guyot and Gry, *Bull. soc. chim. France*, (4) 7, 911 (1910).

[171] Levine et al., *J. Am. Chem. Soc.*, **67**, 1510 (1945).
[172] Long, *J. Am. Chem. Soc.*, **69**, 992 (1947).
[173] Mariella, *J. Am. Chem. Soc.*, **69**, 2670 (1947); Tracy and Elderfield, *J. Org. Chem.*, **6**, 63 (1941).
[174] Petrow, *J. Chem. Soc.*, 694 (1942); Plattner, *Helv. Chim. Acta*, **28**, 773 (1945).
[175] Freon, *Ann. chim.*, (11) **11**, 478 (1939).
[176] Rabjohn in *Organic Reactions*, Vol. 5, John Wiley & Sons, New York, 1949, pp. 331–386.
[177] Riley and Gray, *Org. Syntheses*, Coll. Vol. II, 509 (1943).
[178] Ronzio and Waugh, *Org. Syntheses*, **24**, 61 (1944).
[179] Gray and Fuson, *J. Am. Chem. Soc.*, **56**, 739 (1934).
[180] Fuson, Gray, and Gouza, *J. Am. Chem. Soc.*, **61**, 1938 (1939).
[181] Hahn and Schales, *Ber.*, **67**, 1821 (1934).
[182] Rubin, Paist, and Elderfield, *J. Org. Chem.*, **6**, 268 (1941).
[183] Barrows and Lindwall, *J. Am. Chem. Soc.*, **64**, 2430 (1942).
[184] Kwartler and Lindwall, *J. Am. Chem. Soc.*, **59**, 524 (1937).
[185] Rappen, *J. prakt. Chem.*, **157**, 197 (1941).
[186] Bennett and Bell, *Org. Syntheses*, Coll. Vol. II, 223 (1943).
[187] Adams and Coleman, *Org. Syntheses*, Coll. Vol. I, 214 (1941).
[188] Dippy et al., *J. Soc. Chem. Ind. (London)*, **56**, 346T (1937).
[189] Kröhnke and Börner, *Ber.*, **69**, 2006 (1936); Kröhnke, *ibid.*, **71**, 2583 (1938); Reich, *Helv. Chim., Acta*, **23**, 219 (1940); Karrer and Epprecht, *ibid.*, **24**, 1039 (1941).
[190] Adkins and Krsek, *J. Am. Chem. Soc.*, **70**, 383 (1948); **71**, 3051 (1949).
[191] Adkins and Hartung, *Org. Syntheses*, Coll. Vol. I, 15 (1941).
[192] Bremner, Jones, and Beaumont, *J. Chem. Soc.*, 1019 (1946).
[193] Shriner and Wolf, *Org. Syntheses*, **23**, 74 (1943); Ullyot et. al., *J. Org. Chem.*, 10, 433 (1945).
[194] Johnson and Degering, *J. Org. Chem.*, **8**, 10 (1943).
[195] Hearne, Tamele, and Converse, *Ind. Eng. Chem.*, **33**, 805 (1941).
[196] Mannich and Kniss, *Ber.*, **74**, 1640 (1941).
[197] Clemo and Hoggarth, *J. Chem. Soc.*, 1241 (1939); Pauly and Schanz, *Ber.*, **56**, 979 (1923).
[198] Cooper and Cohen, *J. Chem. Soc.*, 723 (1932).
[199] Von and Wagner, *J. Org. Chem.*, **9**, 162 (1944); Brown and Bluestein, *J. Am. Chem. Soc.*, **65**, 1082 (1943).
[200] Oroshnik and Spoerri, *J. Am. Chem. Soc.*, **63**, 3338 (1941).
[201] Peak, Robinson, and Walker, *J. Chem. Soc.*, 752 (1936).
[202] Lorenz and Wizinger, *Helv. Chim. Acta*, **28**, 600 (1945).
[203] Blumenfeld, *Ber.*, **74B**, 527 (1941).
[204] Jitkow and Bogert, *J. Am. Chem. Soc.*, **63**, 1981 (1941).
[205] Bell and Hirst, *J. Chem. Soc.*, 1777 (1939); cf. Fischer and Taube, *Ber.*, 1707 (1927).
[206] Hüttel, *Ber.*, **74**, 1827 (1941); Reitzenstein and Bönitsch, *J. prakt. Chem.*, (2) 86, 36 (1912).
[207] Dolliver et al., *J. Am. Chem. Soc.*, **60**, 440 (1938).
[208] Johnson, *J. Am. Chem. Soc.*, **61**, 2486 (1939).
[209] Schönberg, Moubasher, and Mostafa, *J. Chem. Soc.*, 176 (1948); Baddar, *ibid.*, S163 (1949).

[210] Spense and Wild, *J. Chem. Soc.*, 338 (1935); Walker, *J. Am. Chem. Soc.*, **55**, 2821 (1933).

[211] Moureu and Delange, *Compt. rend.* **133**, 105 (1901); *Chem. Zentr.*, ii, 461 (1901).

[212] Milas, Sussman, and Mason, *J. Am. Chem. Soc.*, **61**, 1844 (1939).

[213] Sabatier and Mailhe, *Compt. rend.*, **154**, 561 (1912); **158**, 986 (1914).

[214] Davies and Hodgson, *J. Chem. Soc.*, 84 (1943).

[215] Law and Perkin, *J. Chem. Soc.*, 259 (1907).

[216] Segesser and Calvin, *J. Am. Chem. Soc.*, **64**, 825 (1942).

[217] Hanus, *J. prakt. Chem.*, **158**, 254 (1941).

[218] Astin, Newman, and Riley, *J. Chem. Soc.*, 391 (1933); Fisher and Eisner, *ibid.*, **6**, 169 (1941); Weygand, Kinkel, and Tietjen, *Chem. Ber.*, **83**, 394 (1950).

[219] Jacobson, *J. Am. Chem. Soc.*, **72**, 1491 (1950).

[220] Wille and Saffer, *Ann.*, **568**, 34 (1950).

[221] Gresham and Grigsby, *J. Org. Chem.*, **14**, 1103 (1949).

[222] Henne, Pelley, and Alm, *J. Am. Chem. Soc.*, **72**, 3370 (1950).

[223] Emerson and Patrick, *J. Org. Chem.*, **14**, 790 (1949).

[224] Dornfeld and Coleman, *Org. Syntheses*, **28**, 83 (1948).

[225] Lunt and Sondheimer, *J. Chem. Soc.*, 3361 (1950).

[226] Marek and Hahn, *Catalytic Oxidation of Organic Compounds in the Vapor Phase*, Chemical Catalog Co., New York, 1932, pp. 37–99.

[227] Church and Lynn, *Ind. Eng. Chem.*, **42**, 768 (1950).

[228] Bremner et al., *J. Chem. Soc.*, S25 (1950).

[229] Moureu, Chovin, and Brunet, *Bull. soc. chim. France*, (5) **15**, 96 (1948).

[230] Bowen and Wilkinson, *J. Chem. Soc.*, 750 (1950).

[231] Newman and Mangham, *J. Am. Chem. Soc.*, **71**, 3342 (1949).

[232] Kumler, Strait, and Alpen, *J. Am. Chem. Soc.*, **72**, 1463 (1950).

[233] Eliel and Burgstahler, *J. Am. Chem. Soc.*, **71**, 2251 (1949).

[234] Detweiler and Amstutz, *J. Am. Chem. Soc.*, **72**, 2882 (1950).

[235] Elliot and Harington, *J. Chem. Soc.*, 1377 (1949).

[236] Heilbron et al., *J. Chem. Soc.*, 737 (1949).

[237] Witzemann et al., *Org. Syntheses*, Coll. Vol. II, 304 (1943).

[238] Allen and Edens, *Org. Syntheses*, **25**, 92 (1945).

[239] Alexander, *J. Am. Chem. Soc.*, **70**, 2592 (1948).

[240] Curtius, *J. prakt. Chem.*, **94**, 273 (1917); Smith in *Organic Reactions*, Vol. 3, John Wiley & Sons, New York, 1946, p. 384.

[241] Cook et al., *J. Chem. Soc.*, 142 (1950).

[242] McCoubrey and Mathieson, *J. Chem. Soc.*, 701 (1949).

[243] Crounse in *Organic Reactions*, Vol. 5, John Wiley & Sons, New York, 1949, pp. 290–300.

[244] Angyal et al., *J. Chem. Soc.*, 2700, 2704 (1949); 2141 (1950).

[245] Angyal, Tetaz, and Wilson, *Org. Syntheses*, **30**, 67 (1950); cf. Gaylord and Becker, *J. Org. Chem.*, **15**, 312 (1950).

[246] Wood et al., *J. Am. Chem. Soc.*, **72**, 2992 (1950).

[247] King and Nord, *J. Org. Chem.*, **13**, 635 (1948).

[248] Schmerling, *J. Am. Chem. Soc.*, **68**, 1653 (1946).

[249] English and Barber, *J. Am. Chem. Soc.*, **71**, 3310 (1949).

[250] Paul and Tchelitcheff, *Bull. soc. chim. France*, (5) **15**, 200 (1948).

[251] Bergmann and Pinchas, *J. Org. Chem.*, **15**, 1184 (1950).

[252] Horrom and Zaugg, *J. Am. Chem. Soc.*, **72**, 723 (1950).

[253] Horning, Horning, and Platt, *J. Am. Chem. Soc.*, **71**, 1771 (1949).

[254] Elderfield, Pitt, and Wempen, *J. Am. Chem. Soc.*, **72**, 1334 (1950).

[255] Ecary, *Ann. chim.*, (12) **3**, 450 (1948).

[256] Trister and Hibbert, *Can. J. Research*, **14B**, 421 (1936).

[257] Cagniant, *Bull. soc. chim. France*, (5) **16**, 849 (1949).

[258] Kipnis and Ornfelt, *J. Am. Chem. Soc.*, **70**, 3948 (1948).

[259] Johnson and Shelberg, *J. Am. Chem. Soc.*, **67**, 1745 (1945).

[260] Weston and Michaels, *J. Am. Chem. Soc.*, **72**, 1422 (1950) *Org. Syntheses,* 31, 108 (1951); cf. refs. 223 and 247.

[261] Hass and Bender, *J. Am. Chem. Soc.*, **71**, 1767 (1949).

[262] Hass and Bender, *Org. Syntheses*, **30**, 99 (1950).

[263] Ruzicka et al., *Helv. Chim. Acta*, **31**, 433 (1948).

[264] Buck and Zimmermann, *Org. Syntheses*, Coll. Vol. II, 549 (1943).

[265] Longley and Emerson, *J. Am. Chem. Soc.*, **72**, 3079 (1950).

[266] Bert, *Compt. rend.*, **221**, 77 (1945).

[267] Davies and Hodgson, *J. Soc. Chem. Ind. (London)*, **62**, 90 (1943).

[268] Herbst and Manske, *Org. Syntheses*, Coll. Vol. II, 389 (1943).

[269] Djerassi in *Organic Reactions*, Vol. 6, John Wiley & Sons, New York, 1951, p. 207.

10

Ketones

CONTENTS

CONTENTS *(continued)*

178. Acylation of Hydrocarbons (Friedel-Crafts)

$$\text{ArH} + \text{RCOCl} \xrightarrow{\text{Catalyst}} \text{ArCOR} + \text{HCl}$$

Many organic compounds react with carboxylic acids, acyl halides, or anhydrides in the presence of certain metallic halides, metallic oxides, iodine, or inorganic acids to form carbonyl compounds. The reaction is generally applicable to aromatic hydrocarbons. Benzene, alkylbenzenes, biphenyl, fluorene, naphthalene, anthracene, acenaphthene, phenanthrene, higher aromatic ring systems, and many derivatives undergo the reaction. In addition, olefinic and heterocyclic compounds have been converted to ketonic compounds. Therefore, a large number of ketones have been prepared by this reaction. Excellent reviews are available.[10]

Benzene is usually acylated by the addition of anhydrous aluminum chloride to a benzene or carbon disulfide-benzene solution of the aliphatic or aromatic acyl halide, as in the preparation of phenyl benzyl ketone (83%),[1] benzophenone (90%),[2] and stearoylbenzene (65%).[3]

The mono- and poly-alkylated benzenes are treated using modifications of the above procedure. Monoalkylbenzenes are added to a preformed complex of acyl halides and aluminum chloride in carbon tetrachloride[4] (Perrier modification). In this manner, the manipulation is easier, no tars are encountered, and the yields are improved (85-90%). The procedure shows no advantage, however, in the acylation of alkoxy- or chloro-aromatic compounds. The addition of benzoyl chloride to p-alkylbenzenes in the presence of aluminum chloride in cold carbon disulfide is a good procedure for making p-alkylbenzophenones (67-87%).[5] The condensation of homologs of benzene with oxalyl chloride under similar conditions yields p,p'-dialkylbenzophenones (30-55%).[27] Polyalkylbenzenes have been acylated with acetic anhydride and aluminum chloride (2.1:1 molar ratio) in carbon disulfide in 54-80% yields.[6,7] Ferric chloride catalyst has been used under similar conditions.[8] Acetylation of p-cymene with acetyl chloride and aluminum chloride in carbon disulfide yields 2-methyl-5-isopropylacetophenone (55%).[9]

Studies on the conditions of the reaction have been made using simple compounds as model substances. A comparison of thirty-nine metallic chlorides shows aluminum chloride to be the most effective in the preparation of p-methylacetophenone.[11] Optimum yields result when the molar ratios of aluminum chloride to anhydride, acyl chloride, and acid are 3.3, 1.0, and 2.5, respectively. Halogen and oxyhalogen carriers are not helpful.[12] Inconsistent yields in the Friedel-Crafts reaction have been attributed to the presence of ferric chloride or moisture in the aluminum chloride catalyst.[13] Prolonged heating causes condensation of the ketone product. It has been shown that cessation of hydrogen chloride evolution may not be a satisfactory criterion for judging completeness or optimum period of reaction.[14] For the most part, the success of the reaction depends on the use of mild conditions and pure reagents.[15-17]

Other aromatic compounds have been acylated by varying procedures. A general procedure for the preparation of alkyl biphenyl ketones has been described whereby the acyl halide is added to a mixture of biphenyl, aluminum chloride, and carbon disulfide (62-90%).[18] Nitrobenzene or carbon disulfide is used as the solvent in the preparation of 2-acetylfluorene (83%)[19,31] and the isomeric 2- and 3-acylphenanthrenes.[20,21] A convenient method for obtaining pure 2-acylphenanthrene is the acylation of 9,10-dihydrophenanthrene followed by sulfur dehydrogenation. In this case, only the 2-position is attacked; the over-all yield is about 48%.[22] Anthracene is acylated in the 9-position (60%).[32] The isomeric acetylacenaphthenes have been prepared from the hydrocarbon and acetic acid, using hydrogen fluoride as catalyst.[23,24] Substituted tetralins have been prepared by the Friedel-Crafts reaction under mild conditions. Thus, tetralin or its 7-alkylated derivative reacts with acid anhydrides in the presence of aluminum chloride and nitrobenzene solvent at $0°$ (60–80%).[25] Naphthalene is acetylated or benzoylated almost exclusively in the alpha position by the action of an acyl chloride and aluminum chloride in methylene or ethylene chloride solution.[30] Also, on treatment with benzoyl chloride in the presence of iodine, it is converted predominantly to the α-benzoyl isomer (52%).[26] Aroyl halides respond better than anhydrides to this treatment.

Heterocyclic ketones derived from furan or thiophene have been prepared similarly using an iodine catalyst. Short reaction time and low temperature are used. Thus, thiophene and acetic anhydride heated for 1 hour with a small quantity of iodine at about $100°$ yields 2-acetylthiophene (86%); similarly, furan yields 2-acetylfuran (75%).[59] Other catalysts for the acylation of furan and thiophene have been used, namely, zinc chloride,[60] silica-metal oxides,[61] stannic chloride,[62] aluminum chloride,[63] boron trifluoride,[64,65,68] and orthophosphoric acid.[66] The last-named catalyst has been employed for the preparation of eleven compounds including 2-acetylthiophene (94%), 2-benzoylthiophene (99%), and 2-acetyl-5-methyl-thiophene (91%). Other oxygenated acids have been studied, but orthophosphoric acid is the most effective and produces the fewest side reactions. In general, the acid anhydride as acylating agent is preferred over the acyl halide. In introducing large acyl groups, it is convenient to use merely the organic acid and phosphorus pentoxide. Yields of acylated thiophene range from 45% with acetic acid to 97% with oleic acid.[66]

γ-Aryl-substituted acids, $Ar(CH_2)_3COOH$, or their halides undergo an internal Friedel-Crafts reaction to give 1-tetralones.[15] The acids may be cyclized directly with 85–95% sulfuric acid as in the preparation of 4-methyl-1-tetralone (74%).[80] However, sulfonation by-products may occur. Thus, 1-tetralone from γ-phenylbutyric and sulfuric acid mixture is obtained in 49% yield, whereas it is prepared from the acyl chloride and aluminum chloride in 92% yield.[79] A better catalyst for direct cyclization is hydrofluoric acid. The organic acid is simply treated at room temperature with 10 parts hydrofluoric acid for several hours. In this manner, 1-tetralone (92%), 1-hydrindone (73%), 1,2-benz-10-anthrone (75%), and other difficultly obtained anthrones have been prepared.[24] In preparing acyl chlorides with thionyl chloride for the Friedel-Crafts reaction, care must be taken to remove this reagent completely since it may lead to side reactions. Better results have been obtained by employing phosphorus pentachloride for formation of the acyl halide, but again the harmful phosphorus oxychloride must be removed. This is readily accomplished by codistillation with benzene. The acyl chloride may be cyclized without further purification. A solution in benzene, nitrobenzene, or chlorobenzene *is added to* aluminum chloride below 25°.[17] Polyphosphoric acid has also been applied in the synthesis of cyclic ketones.[75]

Ring closure of this type has been brought about by the reaction of a lactone, namely, γ,γ-dimethylbutyrolactone, with benzene and aluminum chloride to give 4,4-dimethyl-1-tetralone (70%).[86] Tetralones containing halogen atoms[87] or alkoxyl groups[17,88] have been prepared. Also, β-haloalkyl ketones of the type $ArCOCH_2CH_2Cl$ undergo intramolecular condensation to furnish 1-indanones.[74]

Diketones have been prepared by the Friedel-Crafts method. Both acyl chloride groups in adipyl chloride react with benzene in the presence of aluminum chloride to form the diketo compound, 1,4-dibenzoylbutane (81%).[89] When diketene is treated with benzene under the conditions of the Friedel-Crafts reaction, benzoylacetone, $C_6H_5 COCH_2COCH_3$, is formed (73%).[90]

$$CH_2 = C - CH_2 + C_6H_6 \xrightarrow{AlCl_3} C_6H_5 COCH_2COCH_3$$
$$\overset{|}{O} - \overset{|}{C} = O$$

This synthesis of 1,3-diketones may be extended by the use of other available diketenes.

Olefinic ketones have been obtained from the reaction of acyl chlorides or anhydrides with olefins using the conditions of the Friedel-Crafts reaction. The intermediate chloro ketones are oftentimes stable and must be treated with sodium bicarbonate or dimethylaniline to complete the dehydrohalogenation. In this manner, 1-acetyl-1-cyclohexene (62%)[92,103] and 1-butyryl-1-cyclohexene (60%)[93] are prepared.

$$RCOCl + \bigcirc \xrightarrow{ZnCl_2} \overset{COR}{\underset{Cl}{\bigcirc}} \xrightarrow{Base} \overset{COR}{\bigcirc}$$

More recently, it has been shown that acetylation of cyclohexene with acetic anhydride in the presence of stannic chloride is less troublesome and does not necessitate dehydrohalogenation.[97]

The reaction has been investigated in detail using diisobutylene and acetic anhydride whereby methyl octenyl ketones are formed in yields as high as 60%. Studies of catalysts show zinc chloride to be the most effective. It is used in relatively small concentrations compared with the catalyst requirements for aromatic hydrocarbons. A low temperature (40°) is maintained to prevent polymerization of the olefin. On a small scale, a preformed complex of the anhydride and zinc chloride is prepared and treated with the olefin.[94,95]

Under these conditions, the addition of acyl chlorides to acetylene leads to β-chlorovinyl ketones (62–80%).[99]

$$RCOCl + HC \equiv CH \xrightarrow{AlCl_3} RCOCH = CHCl$$

Ketones containing a double bond have also been prepared by the reaction of unsaturated acyl halides with aromatic hydrocarbons[96] in the usual Friedel-Crafts manner. Acylation of benzene and its homologs with β,β-dimethylacroyl chloride leads to dimethylvinyl aryl ketones, $(CH_3)_2C = CHCOAr$ (75–90%).[100] The latter compounds are stable and do not undergo intramolecular condensation.

Three types of *halo ketones,* differing in the position of the halogen atom, have been prepared by the Friedel-Crafts reaction: (1) a halogenated acyl chloride and an aromatic hydrocarbon give a haloalkyl aryl ketone, e.g., β-bromopropiophenone, $C_6H_5COCH_2CH_2Br$, (93%)[112] from benzene and β-bromoacetyl chloride; (2) an aryl halide upon acylation gives a haloaryl alkyl ketone, e.g., *p*-fluoroacetophenone (74%) from fluorobenzene and a preformed acetic anhydride-aluminum chloride complex[110] or *p*-bromoacetophenone (79%)[113] from bromobenzene and acetic anhydride; and (3) an aryl-substituted alkyl halide on acylation gives an aryl alkyl ketone containing a halogenated side chain, e.g., β-(*p*-acetylphenyl)-ethyl bromide, *p*-$CH_3COC_6H_4CH_2CH_2Br$ (83%),[112] from β-phenylethyl bromide and acetyl chloride. In general, the reactions are carried out in carbon disulfide with aluminum chloride catalyst.

Phenolic ketones have been prepared by modifications of the Friedel-Crafts reaction. In preparing acyl derivatives of phenol, a preformed complex of phenol and aluminum chloride is treated with an acyl chloride. *Ortho* and *para* isomers are formed with the latter predominating.[123] On the other hand, in preparing acyl derivatives of the polyhydric phenols and naphthols, a preheated solution of zinc chloride and acylating acid is treated with the hydroxy compound (Nencki reaction).[124-126] This procedure gives poor yields when applied to the monohydroxy phenols.[127] Phloroglucinol, *sym*-$C_6H_3(OH)_3$, condenses with acetonitrile in the presence of zinc chloride and hydrochloric acid to give phloroacetophenone (87%) (Hoesch-Houben reaction).[128,129] An imino chloride is probably formed, viz., $CH_3CN + HCl \rightarrow CH_3C(Cl) = NH$, which reacts with the phenol to give an intermediate ketimine hydrochloride.

$$sym\text{-}(HO)_3C_6H_3 + CH_3C(Cl)=NH \xrightarrow[\text{HCl}]{\text{ZnCl}_2} sym\text{-}(HO)_3C_6H_2C(=NH \cdot HCl)CH_3$$

$$\xrightarrow{H_2O} sym\text{-}(HO)_3C_6H_2COCH_3$$

Acylation of aromatic ethers yields the corresponding *keto ethers*.[131] Typical examples are found in the conversion of anisole with aluminum chloride and appropriate acyl halide to *p*-methoxybutyrophenone (85%)[132] and *p*-methoxyphenyl benzyl ketone (84%).[133] Mild catalysts like iodine[26] and phosphorus pentoxide[29] are also effective.

Aryl-substituted *γ-keto acids* are readily obtained by acylation of aromatic compounds with succinic anhydride, e.g., *β*-benzoylpropionic acid (85%).[135]

$$C_6H_6 + \begin{array}{c} CH_2CO \\ | \quad\quad O \\ CH_2CO \end{array} \rightarrow C_6H_5\,CO(CH_2)_2CO_2H$$

Phenol,[136] bromobenzene,[87] *t*-butylbenzene,[137] and acenaphthene[138] give keto acids in good yields. The reaction is applicable to other aliphatic dibasic acid anhydrides like glutaric anhydride,[139] adipic polyanhydride,[140] and maleic anhydride,[141] furnishing *ω*-aroyl acids. An excellent discussion including experimental conditions and procedures has been given.[142]

Optimum conditions for the reaction of naphthalene,[670] biphenyl,[144] and chlorobenzene[145] with phthalic anhydride have been determined. The corresponding keto acids are obtained in 90–98% yields. In this type of condensation, nitrobenzene is stated to be far superior to other solvents with respect to solvent power and ability to slow side reactions.[146]

Another variation consists in the reaction between an aromatic nucleus and the ester-acyl chloride of a dibasic acid followed by hydrolysis of the resulting keto ester. This synthesis affords *ω*-aroyl aliphatic acids in 85–95% yields and is applicable to benzene, its alkyl, halo, alkoxy, and alkylalkoxy derivatives as well as to thiophene and naphthalene.[139,147]

When the interaction of an ester-acyl chloride and an aromatic nucleus is employed for the synthesis of a *keto ester,* then a reesterification step is recommended.[147] Certain *α-keto esters* have been prepared by using ethyl oxalyl chloride, $CO_2ClCO_2C_2H_5$, as the acylating agent, e.g., ethyl *α*-thienyl glyoxylate (50%),[150] ethyl *α*-naphthylglyoxylate (46%),[151] and ethyl *p*-biphenylylglyoxylate (70%).[152] An example of acylation of an aromatic ester is found in the preparation of the *para* and *meta* isomers of ethyl acetylphenylacetate (80%).[153]

Nitro- and *amino*-aromatic compounds do not respond favorably. However, acylations of acetanilide with acetic anhydride using iodine

catalyst[26] or with acetyl chloride and aluminum chloride catalyst[154] have
been reported. o-Nitrophenyl 2-thienyl ketone has been prepared.[155]

Use of α-cyanopropionyl chloride results in a *cyano ketone*, e.g., α-
cyanopropiomesitylene, $C_6H_2(CH_3)_3COCHCNCH_3$ (20%).[156]

179. Oxidation of Secondary Alcohols

$$R_2CHOH \xrightarrow{(O)} R_2CO$$

Oxidation of secondary alcohols to ketones with sulfuric-chromic acid
mixture proceeds readily. In general, the reaction is carried out in an
aqueous medium keeping the temperature at 20-40°. Occasionally, the
reaction temperature is elevated to 50-80° for additional periods.[157,158]
Vigorous stirring is required for slightly soluble alcohols. The yields
vary from 60% to 80% for the C_5-C_{10} aliphatic ketones. Isopropyl s-butyl
ketone is prepared by carrying out the oxidation of the alcohol at 40°
for 36 hours (68%).[159] Substituted cyclohexanones have been prepared in
good yields (70-93%) with widely varying reaction times and temperatures.[169-172,675] Oxidation of insoluble aromatic carbinols is carried out
with acetic acid as the solvent. Thus, m-biphenylmethylcarbinol and 2-
phenylcyclohexanol are oxidized at 45-50° to the corresponding ketones
in 80% yield.[173,47] Concentrated nitric acid at reflux temperature for 20
minutes has been used for the preparation of hexamethylacetone (81%).[174]
The mechanism of chromic acid oxidation of alcohols has been discussed.[168,175,186]

Among the *diketones* prepared by oxidation of an alcohol group are the
the benzils from the corresponding benzoins and aliphatic α-diketones
from the acyloins. The oxidation of the former is accomplished with
copper sulfate in pyridine, e.g., benzoin to benzil (86%),[190] and the latter
with cupric acetate in 70% acetic acid, e.g., 4-hydroxy-3-hexanone to
dipropionyl (70%).[191] Ferric chloride in a boiling ether-water mixture is
also used as an oxidant.[191] Certain alicyclic 1,2-diketones are prepared
by oxidation of the acyloins with chromic anhydride in glacial acetic
acid, e.g., 3,3,6,6-tetramethyl-1,2-cyclohexanedione (64%).[201] Improvements in carrying out oxidations of benzoins and in processing the reaction mixtures have been described.[192-194] In one oxidation procedure, a
catalytic quantity of cupric acetate is employed, which is continuously
regenerated by the action of ammonium nitrate. The reduction product of
the latter is ammonium nitrite, which is decomposed simultaneously to
nitrogen and water.[194] Benzoins carrying halo,[195] methoxyl,[198,212] and dialkylamino[199] groups have been oxidized.

Secondary acetylenic alcohols, prepared in good yields from acetylenic
Grignard reagents and aldehydes, are oxidized to *acetylenic ketones*

(40-80%).[203,204] The oxidation is carried out at 0-20° by means of chromic acid with acetone as solvent. An acetone layer of the unsaturated ketone separates, preventing further oxidation.

Preparations of *halo ketones,* such as α,α'-dichloroacetone (75%)[205] and 1-chloro-4-phenyl-2-butanone (82%),[143] and *keto ethers,* such as 4-methoxycyclohexanone (65%)[207] and *sym*-dialkoxyacetones (40-70%),[208] have been carried out by the oxidation of the corresponding alcohols with chromic-sulfuric acid mixture. Methyl esters of certain α-hydroxy acids can be oxidized to the *α-keto esters* with lead tetraacetate in boiling benzene as in the preparation of methyl phenylglyoxylate (84%).[213] Also, esters of lactic acid, $CH_3CHOHCO_2R$, have been converted to pyruvic esters by the action of potassium permanganate.[218,692] This same reagent has been employed for changing mandelic acid to the *α-keto acid,* benzoylformic acid (72%).[214]

A general synthesis for γ-keto acids involves the oxidation of γ-lactones with bromine in the presence of magnesium hydroxide.[216,217] The lactones are readily obtained by interaction of oxides and sodiomalonic esters with subsequent hydrolysis and decarboxylation (method 323). The over-all yields are excellent.

Nitro alcohols from the condensation of aromatic aldehydes with sodium salts of nitroparaffins are oxidized to *α-nitro ketones* with chromic-acetic acids, as illustrated by the preparation of α-nitroacetophenone, $C_6H_5COCH_2NO_2$ (80%).[219]

180. Oxidation of Alcohols by Ketones (Oppenauer)

$$R_2CHOH + R'_2CO \underset{\text{alkoxide}}{\overset{\text{Metal}}{\rightleftharpoons}} R_2CO + R'_2CHOH$$

Oxidation of alcohols by ketones in the presence of a metallic alkoxide has proved especially valuable in the steroid field.[221,222] The literature to 1951 has been reviewed.[693] An extensive investigation of experimental conditions using aluminum *t*-butoxide has been carried out.[223] The merits of various ketones as hydrogen acceptors have been considered. In general, methyl ethyl ketone and cyclohexanone are best for high-molecular-weight alcohols. The condensation products from these ketones may be removed by steam distillation. Benzil is recommended for preparing aldehydes and ketones capable of being distilled from the reaction mixture below 100°. Benzil or quinone may be used for ketone products boiling from 100° to 200°, especially if they are likely to condense. The optimum temperature, duration of reaction, and concentration of reactants may vary for the alcohol oxidized. In general, 0.5 mole of alkoxide per mole of alcohol gives good results; however, an additional 0.5

mole of alkoxide is recommended to remove any water present in the reaction mixture. A high ratio of 40 to 80 moles of ketone for 1 mole of a
steroid is desirable. For simpler alcohols, 20 moles of acetone or methyl
ethyl ketone, 3-10 moles of cyclohexanone, or 1-3 moles of quinone or
benzil are satisfactory. The equilibrium is displaced by the large excess
of the ketone reactant to give the desired product. It is preferable to
carry out the oxidation at 55-60°. The use of an inert diluent, such as
benzene, toluene, or dioxane, minimizes ketone condensation products.

The reaction has been extended to nitrogen-containing compounds by
the use of an alkali alkoxide, such as potassium t-butoxide.[224]

181. Catalytic Dehydrogenation of Secondary Alcohols

$$R_2CHOH \xrightarrow[\text{Catalyst}]{-H_2} R_2CO$$

Ketones are formed in good yields by vapor-phase dehydrogenation of
secondary alcohols over copper chromite catalyst. An example is the
conversion of cyclohexanol to cyclohexanone (60%).[225] A liquid-phase
dehydrogenation using Raney nickel catalyst at 170° has proved successful for preparing C_4-C_9 aliphatic ketones (79-95%).[226] The catalyst can
be reused. The procedure has been modified by employing a hydrogen
acceptor, such as cyclohexanone. The mixture of catalyst, hydrogen
acceptor, alcohol, and toluene is merely refluxed for short periods.[227]

The reaction may also be performed over a mixed-oxide catalyst at
280° and 100 atm. of ethylene, which serves as the hydrogen acceptor,[363]
as illustrated by the preparation of β-tetralone from 1,2,3,4-tetrahydro-
2-naphthol.[485] By the same procedure, diisobutyryl, a diketone, has been
prepared from the acyloin (27%).[228]

Dehydrogenation of 1,4-pentanediol over a copper chromite catalyst in
the liquid phase yields the corresponding hydroxy ketone, 5-hydroxy-2-
pentanone (30%).[229]

182. Oxidation of Olefinic Compounds (Ozonolysis)

$$R_2C=CHR \xrightarrow[\text{H}_2\text{O}]{\text{O}_3;} R_2CO + RCHO$$

Ozonolysis of olefins has found little application in the preparation of
ketones for synthetic purposes. Since the ozonides may be explosive,
the method has been limited to the reaction of small quantities of olefins,
mostly for degradation studies and location of double bonds.

Improved conditions for the oxidation of olefins with ozone to ketones
(60-70%) have been described.[231-233] The use of Dry Ice temperature and
methylene chloride as solvent lessens the loss of volatile olefins in the

oxygen stream. The ozonides are decomposed by zinc and water in the presence of acetic acid or by catalytic hydrogenation with 1% palladium-calcium carbonate catalyst. Ozonides also react with Raney nickel to give aldehydes and ketones.[234] A new ozonizer has been described.[231] Several olefinic compounds have been oxidized with potassium permanganate or chromic acid to furnish ketones. An example is the oxidation of diisobutylene to methyl neopentyl ketone (56%).[235]

Methylenecyclobutane has been converted to cyclobutanone by oxidation to the corresponding glycol with performic acid and subsequent cleavage of the glycol with lead tetraacetate (75% over-all).[237]

183. Oxidation of Methylene Groups

$$ \text{ArCOCH}_2\text{Ar} \xrightarrow[\text{or Nitrogen oxides}]{\text{SeO}_2} \text{ArCOCOAr} $$

Compounds containing reactive methylene groups are readily converted by suitable oxidizing agents to carbonyl derivatives. Reviews of the reaction employing selenium dioxide[564] or nitrogen oxides[565] are given.

Selenium dioxide is commonly applied to a methylene group activated by a carbonyl group, although an adjacent double bond, aromatic ring, or heterocyclic ring may also subject it to attack. The conversion of aldehydes and methyl ketones leads to glyoxals (method 157). Best results are obtained when only one methylene group is present. For example, aryl benzyl ketones have been oxidized almost quantitatively to substituted benzils by treatment with selenium dioxide and acetic anhydride at 140-150° for 3 to 4 hours.[566] Dioxane has been used as solvent with this oxidizing agent. The products are purified by activated-charcoal treatment. Other experimental details are illustrated in the preparation of methyl phenyl diketone (60%)[567] and 2,4,6-trimethylbenzil (83%).[568]

Cyclic ketones like cyclohexanone[569] and cycloheptanone[570] yield the corresponding α-diketones in 35% and 90% yields, respectively.

Compounds having methylene groups situated between two activating groups—ketone, acid, or ester—are readily oxidized with selenium dioxide to furnish *triketones,*[571] *keto diesters,*[572] *α,β-diketo esters,*[573] or *α-keto acids.*[574]

Another procedure utilizes oxides of nitrogen. An example is the oxidation of diethyl malonate to diethyl oxomalonate, $CO(CO_2C_2H_5)_2$, with nitrous anhydride (76%).[575] Synthesis of alkyl aryl α-diketones has been accomplished under similar conditions (30-40%).[576]

A benzyl side chain is changed to a benzoyl group by vigorous oxidation. For example, 4,4'-diacetylaminodiphenylmethane[248] is converted with chromic acid to the benzophenone in 70% yield. Also, 2-benzoylpyridine is made from 2-benzylpyridine in 86% yield by the action of potassium permanganate.[244]

Oxidation of cyclohexene with chromic anhydride in acetic acid gives a 37% yield of 2-cyclohexenone; likewise, 1-methylcyclohexene goes to 3-methyl-2-cyclohexen-1-one (20%).[441]

Certain aromatic compounds containing alkyl groups have been converted to carbonyl derivatives by liquid-phase oxidation of these groups with air in the presence of chromium oxide catalysts.

$$ArCH_2CH_3 \xrightarrow[\text{Catalyst}]{O_2} ArCOCH_3$$

By the simple procedure of passing dispersed air through a suspension of m-diethylbenzene, 1% chromia, and 4% calcium carbonate at 130° for 40 hours, a 50% yield of m-ethylacetophenone is obtained.[238] Likewise, aromatic esters,[239,246,247] acetophenones,[4] and halogenated benzenes[245] containing alkyl groups yield the corresponding *keto esters, diketones,* and *halo ketones,* respectively. Manganese dioxide catalyst has also been used.[240] Tetralin can be oxidized to α-tetralone with dispersed air in the absence of a catalyst (56%).[241]

184. Cleavage of β-Keto Esters

The formation of β-keto esters and their cleavage represents an important synthesis for many types of ketones. The methods of synthesis of various β-keto esters are considered under methods 211 to 215 and have been reviewed.[614] Quite often the intermediate β-keto esters are not isolated but are cleaved directly to ketones. With few exceptions (methods 266 and 308), the cleavage always results in the formation of a ketone. Syntheses involving these cleavages are considered here.

Monoalkylation of ethyl acetoacetate and subsequent ketonic hydrolysis gives methyl ketones of the type CH_3COCH_2R (acetoacetic ester synthesis).

$$CH_3COCH_2CO_2C_2H_5 \xrightarrow[RX]{NaOC_2H_5 \; ;} CH_3COCHRCO_2C_2H_5 \xrightarrow{H^+} CH_3COCH_2R$$
$$\downarrow NaOC_2H_5 \; ;R'X$$
$$CH_3COCHRR' + CO_2 + C_2H_5OH \xleftarrow{H^+} CH_3COCRR'CO_2C_2H_5$$

The over-all yields resulting from the use of primary alkyl bromides are 50-70%. The method is illustrated by the preparation of methyl n-amyl ketone. (61%).[256] Monoalkylation with secondary alkyl bromides is less complete, and the over-all yields are lower (20-30%).

Dialkylation followed by hydrolysis gives methyl ketones of the type $CH_3COCHRR'$ The over-all yields are 30-40%, often depending on which alkyl group is introduced first when R and R′ are different.[250,251] For example, in the preparation of methyl methylisopropylacetoacetate, better results are obtained if the methyl group is substituted first (60% ester yield)[252] (cf. method 213). Hydrolysis of disubstituted acetoacetic esters, $CH_3COCRR'CO_2C_2H_3$, in which R and R′ are methyl or ethyl groups usually gives ketones in 60 to 80% yields.[253,254] When R is a n-butyl group and R′ is either a n- or s-butyl group, the ketones are formed in low yields, ester formation being favored (cf. method 308); however, these particular ketones are available in good yields by cleaving the corresponding t-butyl acetoacetates.[255]

Sulfuric[256] or phosphoric[257] acids are used for the ketonic hydrolysis, as in the preparation of methyl n-amyl ketone. Also, the hydrolysis is brought about by boiling with acetic-sulfuric acid mixture,[258] hot 5% potassium hydroxide solution,[259] or hydriodic acid if the hydrolysis is especially difficult.[260] Benzylacetone, $C_6H_5CH_2CH_2COCH_3$, is formed by hydrolysis of the corresponding β-keto ester with water at 150–250° and 200 atm. Dialkylated β-keto esters are stable to this treatment; therefore, a single ketone can be obtained from a mixture of mono- and di-alkylated β-keto esters.[253]

Difunctional compounds have been prepared by this series of reactions. Alkylation with unsaturated halides[284-287] or alkylation of unsaturated β-keto esters[262] leads to *olefinic ketones*. Halogenation of a substituted acetoacetate followed by acetic-sulfuric acid hydrolysis gives α-halo ketones. An example of this transformation is the chlorination of ethyl benzylacetoacetate with sulfuryl chloride (69%) followed by hydrolysis and decarboxylation to give α-benzyl-α-chloroacetone (84%).[288] If alkoxy halides are used, *keto ethers* result. In this manner, δ-ethoxybutyl methyl ketone (35% over-all)[291] and δ-phenoxybutyl methyl ketone (61%)[292] have been prepared. Similarly, alkylation using dialkylamino halides yields *dialkylamino ketones* in about 60% over-all yield,[306] as illustrated by the conversion of γ-diethylaminopropyl chloride and ethyl sodioacetoacetate to 1-diethylamino-5-hexanone (60%).[307] An example of the reaction of a halogenated ester leading to a *keto acid* is found in the preparation of 8-ketononoic acid (68%).[297] γ-Keto-α-alkyl acids have been prepared by a one-step hydrolysis and decarboxylation of certain cyanoacetoacetic esters.[296]

$$RCHCNCH(COCH_3)CO_2C_2H_5 \xrightarrow{H^+} RCH(COOH)CH_2COCH_3 + CO_2 + C_2H_5OH$$

α-Keto acids have also been obtained by treating α-oxalyl esters with boiling dilute sulfuric acid for 6 hours (8–94%).[295] These starting materials are prepared by condensation of ethyl oxalate and a second ester (method 211).

$$(CO_2C_2H_5)_2 + RCH_2CO_2C_2H_5 \xrightarrow{NaOC_2H_5} C_2H_5O_2CCOCHRCO_2C_2H_5$$

$$\downarrow H^+$$

$$RCH_2COCO_2H + CO_2 + C_2H_5OH$$

β-Keto esters prepared by additional methods (methods 211–215) are cleaved to give other types of ketones. (1) Acylation of the sodium enolates of disubstituted acetic esters followed by hydrolysis and decarboxylation gives ketones of the type $R'COCHR_2$.

$$HCR_2CO_2C_2H_5 \xrightarrow{(C_6H_5)_3CNa} Na^+(CR_2CO_2C_2H_5)^-$$

$$\downarrow R'COCl$$

$$R'COCHR_2 + CO_2 + C_2H_5OH \xleftarrow{H^+} R'COCR_2CO_2C_2H_5$$

The over-all yield from ester and acid chloride is 38–58%.[262] (2) Self-condensation of high-molecular-weight esters and hydrolysis of the resulting β-keto esters gives symmetrical ketones of the type RCH_2COCH_2R.

$$RCH_2CO_2C_2H_5 \xrightarrow{NaOC_2H_5} RCH_2COCHRCO_2C_2H_5 \xrightarrow{H^+} RCH_2COCH_2R$$

The over-all yields (R equals n-C_3–C_8, n-C_{11}, and n-C_{12}) from the esters vary from 55% to 78%.[259] Certain heterocyclic ketones, namely, 8-acetylquinoline and β-acetylpyridine, have been prepared through a mixed ester condensation.[279,280] (3) If acetoacetic ester is acylated in the form of its sodium enolate and carefully hydrolyzed, a new β-keto ester is formed. Alkylation of this keto ester followed by hydrolysis gives ketones of the type $RCOCH_2R'$.

$$CH_3COCH_2CO_2C_2H_5 \xrightarrow[RCOCl]{NaOC_2H_5;} CH_3COCH(COR)CO_2C_2H_5$$

$$\downarrow NH_3$$

$$RCOCHR'CO_2C_2H_5 \xleftarrow[R'X]{NaOC_2H_5;} RCOCH_2CO_2C_2H_5$$

$$\downarrow H^+$$

$$RCOCH_2R'$$

The over-all yields are stated to be 13–20% from the acid chloride;[303] however, the directions are not clear.[304,305] If the chloride of a dibasic acid is used, a *diketone* results. Thus, terephthalic acid chloride gives p-diacetylbenzene (15% over-all).[283] o-Chloroacetophenone, a *halo ketone*, has been prepared from ethyl acetoacetate and o-chlorobenzoyl chloride (54%).[290]

Aminomethyl ketones have been prepared by the α-oximination of β-keto esters followed by reduction and cleavage.[310]

$$RCOCH_2CO_2C_2H_5 \xrightarrow{HNO_2} RCOC(NOH)CO_2C_2H_5 \xrightarrow[(CH_3CO)_2O]{Zn}$$

$$RCOCH(NHAc)CO_2C_2H_5 \xrightarrow{HCl} RCOCH_2NH_2 \cdot HCl$$

Symmetrical ketones are sometimes prepared from acyl chlorides by way of diketenes and β-keto acids.[691]

$$2RCH_2COCl \xrightarrow{(C_2H_5)_3N} RCH_2COC(R)=C=O \xrightarrow{H_2O} (RCH_2)_2CO + CO_2$$

The addition of ethyl sodiomalonate to olefinic ketones followed by ring closure and β-keto ester cleavage leads to 1,3-cyclohexanediones. The reaction has been applied to the formation of 2-alkyl-5-phenyl-1,3-cyclohexanediones[583] and is typified by the preparation of 5,5-dimethyl-1,3-cyclohexanedione (85%).[584] Other cyclizations for formation of four- and five-membered rings have been described.[585,586]

185. Decarboxylation of Acylmalonic Acids

$$RCOCl + C_2H_5OMgCH(CO_2C_2H_5)_2 \rightarrow RCOCH(CO_2C_2H_5)_2 \xrightarrow{H^+} RCOCH_3$$

A convenient method for preparing alicyclic or aromatic methyl ketones consists in the acylation of the ethoxymagnesium derivative of diethyl malonate with the appropriate acyl chloride, followed by acid hydrolysis and decarboxylation of the resulting β-keto diester.[312-314] The last step is carried out like the ketonic cleavage of β-keto esters.[262] The over-all yields are 60–85%.

The method is especially valuable for the preparation of certain substituted acetophenones, namely, *o*- and *p*-nitroacetophenone and *o*-chloroacetophenone.[314] Methods involving Grignard, Friedel-Crafts, or nitration reactions are apparently not applicable for the preparation of these nitro compounds, and the Friedel-Crafts reaction is not applicable to the preparation of *o*-chloroacetophenone. Although the acetoacetic ester synthesis has been used for the preparation of these and other substituted acetophenones, it may be complicated by O-acylation and also by cleavage at either acyl group (cf. method 212).

High-molecular-weight aliphatic ketones of the type RCOCH$_2$R' are made by acylation of substituted dibenzyl esters of malonic acid followed by hydrogenolysis and decarboxylation.[316]

$$R'CH(CO_2CH_2C_6H_5)_2 \xrightarrow[\text{RCOCl}]{\text{NaOC}_2\text{H}_5;} RCOCR'(CO_2CH_2C_6H_5)_2$$

$$\xrightarrow[\text{Pd}]{\text{H}_2} RCOCR'(CO_2H)_2 \xrightarrow{-CO_2} RCOCH_2R'$$

Decomposition of acylated malonic esters over aromatic sulfonic acids leads to β-keto esters (method 214).

186. Thermal Decarboxylation of Acids

$$RCO_2H \xrightarrow[\text{Heat}]{\text{Catalyst}} R_2CO + CO_2$$

Symmetrical ketones (R equals ethyl, propyl, isopropyl, n-butyl, isobutyl, and n-heptyl) have been prepared in nearly "quantitative" yields by passing the acid vapors over thoria at high temperatures. Studies have been made of metallic oxide catalysts and temperature of reaction. In general, a thoria catalyst has been favored at temperatures of 400–500°.[318] The apparatus and catalyst preparation have been described.[319] More recently, it has been shown that a thoria "aerogel" catalyst is superior to the thoria-hydrogel and thoria-on-pumice catalysts. High yields at a lower temperature (310°) and high flow rates are obtained.[320] The distillation of lauric acid (or other high-boiling acids) over the catalyst bed is difficult and gives poor yields; however, when the lower-boiling methyl ester is used, laurone is obtained in a 93% yield.[321] Similarly, the ethyl ester of 9-undecenoic acid gives undecylenone (86%). A large number of unsymmetrical ketones have been prepared by the thermal decarboxylation method;[322, 323] however, the yields are not recorded. In general, by using a large excess of the short-chain acid (which minimizes formation of the long-chain symmetrical ketone) over thoria at 400°, yields of about 50% are obtained.[35, 303] Methyl benzyl ketone and other alkyl aryl ketones have been synthesized in this manner (65%).[319] The use of manganese oxide catalyst at 400° gives about the same results.[324]

The thermal decarboxylation of a mixture of barium salts has been used to prepare unsymmetrical ketones; the yields are not stated.[325] The earlier procedure has been modified by carrying out the reaction *in vacuo*[326] in an iron flask. Glass reaction vessels are inferior. In this manner, a large number of the high-molecular-weight methyl ketones, C_9, C_{10}, C_{12}–C_{17}, and C_{19}, are prepared in 54–67% yields. Cyclopentanone has been synthesized in 80% yield by distillation of adipic acid from barium hydroxide at 295°.[327] In a study of metallic oxides and carbonates, magnesium oxide is preferred for the liquid-phase ketonization of stearic acid at 330–360° (95%).[328] A convenient method for the preparation of dibenzyl ketone is the reaction of phenylacetic acid, acetic anhydride, and fused potassium acetate at 150° (41%).[330] Several pyridyl ketones have been made in a similar way.[339, 340]

Acids which have no α-hydrogen atoms may yield unsymmetrical ketones on decarboxylation instead of the anticipated symmetrical compounds.[331]

187. Interaction of Grignard Reagents and Nitriles

$$R'MgX + RCN \longrightarrow RR'C{=}NMgX \xrightarrow{H_2O} RCOR'$$

Grignard reagents react with nitriles to form ketimine salts which on hydrolysis give ketones. For the most part, the procedure is successful only for high-molecular-weight aliphatic and aromatic nitriles, although the lower-membered aliphatic nitriles respond favorably with aromatic Grignard reagents.[353,354,388] Poor results have been associated with a competing reaction of the Grignard reagent at the α-hydrogen of the nitrile to form a hydrocarbon and a magnesium derivative which may react further at the nitrile group, viz., $RCH_2CN + R'MgX \longrightarrow R'H + (RCHCN)MgX$.[677]

Alkyl α-naphthyl ketones from α-cyanonaphthalene and RMgX are prepared when R is methyl through n-hexyl, cyclohexyl, or phenyl (35–60%).[346] The Grignard reagents are treated with the cyanide for 5 hours in boiling toluene or benzene-ether mixture. The intermediate ketimine salt is then hydrolyzed with aqueous ammonium chloride. Acylated aromatic compounds can be prepared readily in this way, avoiding isomeric mixtures encountered by the Friedel-Crafts method. Thus, the pure acetyl-, propionyl-, and benzoyl-phenanthrenes have been synthesized (50–87%).[21,347,348]

Ketones from fatty acid nitriles and high-molecular-weight Grignard reagents are often contaminated with hydrocarbons.[349,350] This difficulty can be avoided by discarding the ethereal solution containing the hydrocarbon products before the hydrolysis of the ketimine salt.[351] The ketone-hydrocarbon mixture has been separated by dissolving the ketone in warm concentrated sulfuric acid, removing the insoluble hydrocarbons, and then reclaiming the ketone by diluting the acid solution with water.[303]

The reaction of olefinic Grignard reagents with nitriles to give *olefinic ketones* is not common. An example is the preparation of 4-hexen-3-one from allylmagnesium bromide and propionitrile (25%).[371]

Nitriles carrying relatively unreactive halogen atoms have been used to prepare *halo ketones*. Thus, 4-chloro-2-ethoxybutyronitrile, $CH_2ClCH_2CH(OC_2H_5)CN$, has been converted to 3-chloro-1-ethoxypropyl alkyl ketones in 40–75% yields.[369] Reaction of methyl Grignard reagent and o-bromophenyl cyanide gives o-bromoacetophenone (80%).[470]

Diphenylacetoin, a *hydroxy ketone,* has been prepared in 45–60% yield by the action of benzyl Grignard reagent on phenylacetaldehyde cyanohydrin.[372]

An important method for the preparation of *keto ethers* is the reaction of cyano ethers with Grignard reagents. In this manner, a large number of α-alkoxy aliphatic ketones have been made (30-70%).[208,373-377] Likewise, phenoxymethyl alkyl ketones have been prepared (20-64%).[380] When the Grignard reagent contains an ω-alkoxy group, ω-alkoxy ketones are formed.[379]

Ethyl β-oxovalerate, a *β-keto ester,* is prepared from ethyl Grignard reagent and ethyl cyanoacetate (58%).[386,387] *Amino ketones* are conveniently made by the action of aromatic Grignard reagents on γ-diethylaminobutyronitrile, $(C_2H_5)_2NCH_2CH_2CH_2CN$, in 80-90% yields.[388]

188. Interaction of Organometallic Reagents and Anhydrides

$$(RCO)_2O \xrightarrow{R'MgX} RC \overset{\displaystyle OMgX}{\underset{\displaystyle R'}{\diagup \diagdown}} OCOR \xrightarrow{H_2O} RCOR'$$

A large number of ketones have been prepared by treating anhydrides with Grignard reagents. It has been shown that the yields are best at low temperatures ($-75°$). Primary, secondary, and tertiary aliphatic or aromatic Grignard reagents give high yields when treated with acetic, propionic, or butyric anhydrides.[389-391]

A variety of ketones may be made using cadmium alkyls (50-70%). In the preparation of alkyl aryl ketones, reaction of the aliphatic rather than the aromatic anhydride is preferred.[392] *Keto acids* result when phthalic anhydride[392-394] or dimethylsuccinic anhydride (60-70%)[395] is used.

Acetylenic ketones of the type $RC \equiv CCOCH_3$ are prepared by the reaction of acetic anhydride and acetylenic Grignard reagents. The latter compounds are readily made from acetylenic hydrocarbons and ethylmagnesium chloride, and are added slowly to the anhydride at a low temperature. This procedure prevents a secondary reaction of the desired product with a second molecule of Grignard reagent. In this manner, 3-octyn-2-one (58%) and 3-nonyn-2-one (55%) are prepared.[396] Sodium phenylacetylide has been treated with various anhydrides, including acetic, benzoic, cinnamic, and crotonic, to give the corresponding phenylacetylenic ketones.[397]

189. Interaction of Organometallic Reagents and Acyl Chlorides

$$2RCOCl + R'_2Cd \rightarrow 2RCOR' + CdCl_2$$

Addition of cadmium alkyls to acyl chlorides yields the corresponding ketones. The method has been reviewed,[400] and the experimental condi-

tions have been studied.[401] The cadmium reagents are readily prepared by
adding anhydrous cadmium chloride to Grignard reagents. It is advisable
to check the completeness of the cadmium alkyl formation by the standard
Gilman test for Grignard reagent. The use of an alkyl bromide for formation of the cadmium reagent and of benzene as solvent during the coupling
reaction has improved the yield. A variety of ketones have been prepared,
and yields of 50–80% may be expected if highly reactive ketones are not
formed and if the cadmium alkyl is not secondary or tertiary.[401, 402] In the
preparation of methyl n-butyl ketone (74%), n-propyl-n-heptadecyl ketone
(65%), acetophenone (85%), and ethyl α-furyl ketone (61%), the smaller
alkyl fragment comes from the cadmium alkyl. Either the aryl or alkyl
cadmium compound is satisfactory for formation of alkyl aryl ketones.

The reaction has been extended to the formation of difunctional compounds. High-molecular-weight *keto esters* and *halo ketones* are formed
by using carbalkoxy acyl chlorides and halogenated acyl chlorides, respectively. Methyl 4-keto-7-methyloctanoate (75%) and 1-chloro-2-
hexanone (51%) have been prepared in this way.[401, 403] Also, β-aroyl-
propionic esters are made by the reaction of diarylcadmium reagents with
β-carbomethoxypropionyl chloride.[678] In the preparation of a carbalkoxy
acyl chloride having a branched carbon skeleton, an ester interchange may
occur to give a mixture of the two possible carbalkoxy acyl chlorides.[581]
Alkoxy acyl chlorides react with cadmium alkyls to give *keto ethers*, as
in the preparation of γ-phenoxypropyl methyl ketone (78%) from γ-phenoxy-
butyryl chloride and methylcadmium[292] and of certain 2-alkoxyethyl phenyl
ketones from β-alkoxypropionyl chloride and diphenylcadmium.[404]

A large number of methyl and ethyl ketones have been prepared in about
70% yields by employing zinc alkyls; however, full directions are not
given.[405] Reaction of zinc alkyls and unsaturated acyl chlorides in the
presence of a zinc-copper couple gives *olefinic ketones* in 75–90% yields.
By this procedure, 5-ethyl-4-hepten-3-one (74%) and 3,4-diethyl-4-hexen-2-
one (83%) are made.[406] High-molecular-weight *keto acids* (C_{28}–C_{35}) have
been prepared in good yields (77–92%) by adding ethereal Grignard reagents
to anhydrous zinc chloride, replacing the ether with benzene as solvent,
and then treating with carbethoxy acyl chlorides under reflux.[407, 408]

In general, the cadmium reagent is preferred to the zinc reagent because it is more readily prepared and is less reactive toward the carbonyl group.

Grignard reagents have been used directly in mono-[409, 410, 539] and diketone[415] formation. More recently, it has been found that a catalytic
quantity of cuprous chloride greatly increases the yields.[416, 419] An example is the formation of hexamethylacetone in 70–80% yield from t-
butylmagnesium chloride and trimethylacetyl chloride. Diketones have

also been prepared by coupling magnesium enolates of certain ketones with high-molecular-weight acyl chlorides.[539]

190. Interaction of Grignard Reagents and Amides

$$RCONH_2 \xrightarrow{2R'MgX} RC \begin{matrix} NHMgX \\ \diagup \\ \diagdown \\ R' \end{matrix} OMgX \xrightarrow{H_2O} RCOR'$$

This reaction has been used extensively for the preparation of neo-pentyl and t-butyl ketones from n-alkyl Grignard reagents and t-butyl-acetamide and trimethylacetamide, respectively, (52-78%).[427,428] In addition, a large number of *halo ketones* have been prepared by the reaction of aromatic Grignard reagents with chloro-substituted aromatic amides (60-80%).[429-432] For example, benzyl Grignard reagent and m-chloro-phenylacetamide react to give benzyl m-chlorophenyl ketone (80%). In a similar manner, the use of mandelamide or p-methoxyphenylacetamide leads to *hydroxy ketones* or *keto ethers,* respectively.[429]

191. Interaction of Grignard Reagents and α,β-Olefinic Ketones

$$RCH{=}CHCOR + R'MgX \rightarrow RR'CHCH{=}C(OMgX)R \xrightarrow{H_2O} RR'CHCH_2COR$$

Aliphatic and aromatic ketones have been prepared by this method. The Grignard reagent adds 1:4 to the conjugated ketone system. This is illustrated by the addition of ethyl Grignard reagent to ethylideneacetone, $CH_3CH{=}CHCOCH_3$, to give a 75% yield of 4-methyl-2-hexanone.[437] Highly branched ketones have been prepared in small yields.[438,439] The amount of 1:4 addition varies considerably with the Grignard reagent[440,441] (cf. method 89). Certain methoxy-substituted chalcones, $ArCH{=}CHCOAr$, have been treated successfully.[132]

192. Interaction of Grignard Reagents and Halo Ketones

The most successful application of this method has been the synthesis of 2-substituted cyclohexanones by the action of either aliphatic[444] or aromatic[445] Grignard reagents on 2-chlorocyclohexanone. An example is the formation of 2-phenylcyclohexanone (R = C_6H_5) in 60% yield.[443] The

aromatic moiety may also be substituted with alkyl or alkoxyl groups.
The method has been extended to the preparation of 2-phenylcyclopentanone
(50%).[446]

193. Interaction of Organometallic Reagents and Esters [447-450]
(cf. method 91)

$$RCO_2C_2H_5 + R'MgX \rightarrow RC\overset{OC_2H_5}{\underset{R'}{\diagdown}}\!\!-OMgX \overset{H_2O}{\longrightarrow} RCOR'$$

194. Interaction of Organometallic Reagents and Salts of Carboxylic Acids[449, 451]

$$RCO_2Na + R'MgX \rightarrow RC\overset{ONa}{\underset{R'}{\diagdown}}\!\!-OMgX \overset{H_2O}{\longrightarrow} RCOR'$$

195. Hydrolysis of Ketone Derivatives

$$R_2C=NOH + H_2CO \overset{H_2O}{\underset{H^+}{\longrightarrow}} R_2CO + H_2C=NOH$$

Oximes, which are produced by several synthetic routes (cf. Chapter 27),
are readily hydrolyzed to carbonyl compounds. Thus, the acetylbenzoyl
monoxime, prepared by the nitrosation of propiophenone, has been converted to the diketone by hydrolysis with dilute sulfuric acid.[452]

In another instance, the action of aliphatic Grignard reagents on methyl
α-nitrosoethyl ketone with subsequent acid hydrolysis furnishes α-hydroxy
ketones of the type $CH_3(R)COHCOCH_3$.[456] The oxime of 1-methylcyclo-
penten-5-one is hydrolyzed by dilute sulfuric acid (54%). It is prepared
by the action of nitrosyl chloride on 1-methylcyclopentene with subsequent
dehydrohalogenation with pyridine.[598]

A method for hydrolyzing p-quinone oximes with the aid of cuprous chloride has been described; the yields are excellent.[459]
Aliphatic ketones have been prepared by a five-step synthesis from nitroparaffins.

$$R'CH_2NO_2 \xrightarrow{RCHO} RCHOHCHR'NO_2$$

$$RCH_2COR' \leftarrow RCH_2CR' = NOH \leftarrow RCH = CR'NO_2$$

The nitroparaffins are condensed with aldehydes to yield nitro alcohols (70-80%), which on acetylation and treatment with an aqueous methanolic solution of sodium bicarbonate are converted to nitroölefins (80-84%). These compounds are reduced to the corresponding ketoximes by zinc and acetic acid (50-60%).[453] Reduction with iron and dilute hydrochloric acid gives good yields of either ketones or ketoximes, depending upon the amount of hydrochloric acid used.[679] The ketoximes can be hydrolyzed to ketones by refluxing with dilute sulfuric acid in the presence of formalin, which acts as a hydroxylamine acceptor (80%). The over-all yields from the nitroölefins are 40-60%. In this manner, certain otherwise difficultly obtainable ketones are prepared. Semicarbazones have been converted to ketones by treatment with sodium nitrite in glacial acetic acid,[454] with aqueous oxalic acid,[455] or with phthalic anhydride.[490]

α-Keto acids or esters may be prepared by the hydrolysis of the corresponding oximino esters with 85% formic acid and nitrosylsulfuric acid at 0°.[457] Although α-oximino acids can be obtained in excellent yield from α-halo acids or substituted acetoacetic or malonic esters,[458] their hydrolysis may proceed poorly.[295]

Elimination of carbon dioxide from a carboxylic acid in the presence of a diazonium salt leads to an aryl hydrazone (Japp-Klingemann). Subsequent hydrolysis in the presence of pyruvic acid furnishes the carbonyl compound, as illustrated by the preparation of 2-n-butyrylpyridine (81%).[535]

196. Selective Reduction of α,β-Olefinic Ketones

$$RCH = CHCOR \xrightarrow[\text{Catalyst}]{H_2} RCH_2CH_2COR$$

Selective hydrogenation of α,β-olefinic ketones to saturated ketones can be accomplished through careful control of the temperature, duration of reaction, and use of a catalyst active enough to permit low-temperature hydrogenation.[464] Thus, mesityl oxide, benzalacetone, and benzalacetophenone have been reduced in 90-100% yields to the corresponding saturated ketones.[465] Preparations of nickel catalysts used in these reductions are described.[465,466]

Other olefinic ketones have been reduced selectively at room temperature and atmospheric pressure over a platinum or palladium catalyst to give good yields of the ketones, namely, 5-methyl-3-heptanone (94%),[467, 468] diisobutyl ketone (100%),[469] and α-benzylacetophenone (81-95%).[688] Selective hydrogenations of some 3-alkyl-2-cyclohexenones have been carried out over palladinized charcoal in essentially quantitative yields.[475] Preparation of platinum catalyst has been described.[470] Many olefinic ketones prepared by the aldol condensation or by acylation of olefins have been hydrogenated; however, the yields are not always stated.[471] Benzalacetone, $C_6H_5CH\!=\!CHCOCH_3$, is selectively reduced to benzylacetone in a 63% yield by the action of sodium amalgam in acetic acid-alcohol solution.[476]

Unsaturated keto esters obtained by the Knoevenagel condensation have been selectively hydrogenated in good yields with Raney nickel catalyst at room temperature and 45 atm. to saturated *keto esters, e.g.*, ethyl α-heptylacetoacetate (97%) from ethyl α-heptylideneacetoacetate.[689]

197. Partial Reduction of Phenols

Phenols can be partially hydrogenated in the presence of alkali to cyclohexanones. An example is the synthesis of dihydroresorcinol, or 1,3-cyclohexanedione, by hydrogenation of resorcinol in the presence of Raney nickel and an equimolar quantity of sodium hydroxide (95%).[481] Under these same conditions, pyrogallol furnishes a stable enediolone.[482]

Hydrogenation of 2-naphthol in the presence of palladium and an organic base like N-ethylmorpholine gives 2-tetralone (40%);[483] other conditions for its reduction lead to other products.[484, 485] By means of Raney nickel and alkali, 1,6-dihydroxynaphthalene has been partially reduced to 6-hydroxy-1-tetralone.[484]

Reductions of this type may also be carried out by the action of sodium and ammonia, sodium and alcohol,[486] or Raney nickel-aluminum alloy and alkali.[484]

198. Alkylation of Ketones

$$RCH_2COCH_2R \xrightarrow[R'X]{NaNH_2;} RCH_2COCHRR'$$

Many highly branched ketones have been prepared by the alkylation of simpler ketones, sodium amide or sodium alkoxides generally being used to form the enolate ion. For example, ketones of the type RCOR', where R and R' represent many combinations of methyl (Me), ethyl (Et), n-propyl (Pr), isopropyl, n-butyl, s-butyl, t-butyl, isoamyl, Et_2CH-, Et_3C-, $n-Pr_2CH-$, $n-PrMeCH-$, $isoPrCH_2-$, and $n-PrMe_2C-$, have been prepared; however, the yields are not always reported.[488] Alkylation of alicyclic ketones like cyclopentanone and cyclohexanone has also been studied. In these reactions all available α-hydrogens may be replaced, disubstitution on one side of the carbonyl group occurring first.[489-493] Alkyl aryl ketones of the types $ArCOCH_2R$, ArCOCHR'R'', and ArCOCR'R''R''' are made by alkylating acetophenone and its derivatives with allyl or benzyl halides.[495] In general, the reactivity of the alkyl halide decreases with increasing carbon content and complexity. Oftentimes, an alkyl sulfate is employed as the alkylating agent. A review of the earlier work has been presented.[494] The method is illustrated by the conversion of diisopropyl ketone to hexamethylacetone in the presence of sodium amide (52%).[165]

Methyl γ-chloropropyl ketone, $CH_3CO(CH_2)_3Cl$, undergoes intramolecular cyclization to methyl cyclopropyl ketone under the influence of 50% aqueous sodium hydroxide.[694]

The effect of the basic reagent has been studied in the methylation of phenylacetone. Monomethylation proceeds better with sodium isopropoxide than with sodium ethoxide. Introduction of a second alkyl group is accomplished best with potassium t-butoxide. Sodium t-amylate allows many alkylations that fail or give poor results when carried out with sodium amide.[493] 1,1-Disubstituted 2-tetralones are conveniently prepared by alkylation in the presence of sodium hydride, no monosubstituted products being formed with this reagent.[496]

The temperature of the reaction has been shown to be important. For example, in the alkylation of 2-methylcyclopentyl phenyl ketone, the reaction carried out at the temperature of the refluxing benzene solution gives the desired product; however, the use of boiling xylene leads to O-alkylated products, and boiling toluene gives mixtures.[668]

Diketones have been alkylated by a modified procedure.[500,501] The monosodio derivative is prepared in ether by treating the diketone with powdered sodium. It is then allowed to react with the alkyl iodide in acetone or dioxane solution. This scheme has been applied in the prep-

aration of n-butylbenzoylacetone, $PhCOCH(n\text{-}Bu)COCH_3$, ethylacetylace-
tone, $CH_3COCH(C_2H_5)COCH_3$, and other high-molecular-weight compounds.
In a similar manner, acyloin enolates are alkylated with primary halides
in ethyl ether or toluene to furnish α,α-dialkyl-α'-*hydroxy ketones*.[502]
Alkylation with allyl bromide leads to *olefinic ketones*, e.g., 2-allyl-
cyclohexanone (62%) and α-allylethyl ethyl ketone (56%) from the corresponding ketones.[286,503] Desoxybenzoin, $C_6H_5CH_2COC_6H_5$, and β-diethyl-
aminoethyl chloride, $(C_2H_5)_2NCH_2CH_2Cl$, combine to form the corresponding *amino ketone*.[504]

199. Interaction of Diazomethane and Carbonyl Compounds

$$RCHO + CH_2N_2 \rightarrow RCOCH_3 + N_2$$

Diazomethane reacts with carbonyl compounds to introduce methylene
groups.[505] In the case of aldehydes, nitrogen is lost and the corresponding epoxide, methyl ketone, or higher homolog of the starting aldehyde is formed, depending on the nature of the R group and catalytic
influences. Similarly, ketones yield epoxides and homologous ketones.
The latter may react further with additional diazomethane. For these
reasons, the reaction may be complicated.

Cyclic ketones react to form the higher homologs; for example, cyclohexanone is converted to cycloheptanone (63%).[506]

An extension of this reaction has been the use of other aliphatic diazoalkanes. Benzaldehyde and the appropriate diazo compound give
propiophenone, butyrophenone, and valerophenone in almost quantitative
yield.[507] Furylaldehyde also reacts to form furyl alkyl ketones[526]

200. Catalytic Hydration of Acetylenic Compounds

$$RC\equiv CH + H_2O \xrightarrow{\text{Catalyst}} RCOCH_3$$

This method finds commercial application in the production of acetaldehyde from acetylene. Mercuric salts in the presence of dilute sulfuric
acid act as the catalyst. The reaction has been extended to higher
alkylacetylenes, which are obtained in about 60% yield from sodium
acetylide and alkyl halides. These compounds are readily hydrated in
aqueous solutions of acetone, methanol, or acetic acid to give 80–90%
yields of the corresponding methyl ketones, for example, methyl butyl,
methyl amyl, and methyl hexyl ketones.[508] Hydration has been accomplished by passing the acetylenic hydrocarbon and steam over a phosphoric acid catalyst at 150–204° and atmospheric pressure.[509]

Acetylenic carbinols (from sodium acetylide and a ketone) are readily
hydrated in the presence of mercuric sulfate to give the corresponding

hydroxy ketones in high yields.[510, 511] β-*Keto acids* have been prepared
by hydration of acetylenic acids.[512] α-Acyloxy ketones,
$R_2C(OCOCH_3)COCH_3$, are made by the action of carboxylic acids on
acetylenic carbinols.[657]

201. Dehydration and Rearrangement of α-Diols

$$R_2COHCOHR_2 \xrightarrow{H^+} R_3CCOR + H_2O$$

The classical example of this method is the rearrangement of pinacol
to pinacolone (72%).[513] The reaction is usually brought about by dilute
sulfuric acid. A second procedure is the passage of a mixture of the
pinacol and steam over silica-phosphoric acid at 275–300°; the yield of
pinacolone is 94%.[514] Benzopinacol, $(C_6H_5)_2COHCOH(C_6H_5)_2$, is dehydrated and rearranged by iodine in acetic acid (96%).[515] Under the same
conditions, diphenyl-(1-hydroxy-1-cyclopentyl)-carbinol undergoes rearrangement accompanied by ring expansion to form 2,2-diphenylcyclo-
hexanone (98%).[516]

The reaction has been extended to other pinacols; however, their
preparation may involve lengthy procedures.[517] Certain benzoins on reduction with metals and acids yield diols which are then converted to
desoxybenzoins.[518-520] These conversions involve the migration of a
hydrogen atom rather than an alkyl group. Similarly, aromatic *keto ethers*
and *amino ketones* have been prepared.[520, 521]

A modification of this reaction is the hydrolysis and rearrangement of
olefin dibromides.[522] The most successful of these conversions is the
preparation of methylisopropyl ketone (59%) from trimethylethylene
dibromide.[523]

202. Decomposition of Glycol Monoalkyl Ethers

$$RCHBrCO_2C_2H_5 \xrightarrow[65\%]{NaOC_2H_5} RCH(OC_2H_5)CO_2C_2H_5 \xrightarrow[75\%]{R'MgX} RCH(OC_2H_5)COHR'_2$$

$$RCOCHR'_2 \xleftarrow[68-96\%]{H^+} RC(OC_2H_5)=CR'_2 \quad H^+\downarrow 90\%$$

Ketones of the type $RCOCHR'_2$, where R represents methyl, ethyl, isopropyl, *n*-butyl, *n*-hexyl, or phenyl, and R′ represents ethyl, *n*-propyl,
n-butyl, or phenyl, have been prepared by a series of reactions similar
to that used in the preparation of aldehydes (method 167).[525]

In an analogous manner, the monoethyl ether of dihydroresorcinol reacts
with alkylmagnesium halides to form 3-alkyl-2-cyclohexenones.[475]

203. β-Diketones by Acylation of Ketones

$$CH_3COCH_2R \begin{cases} \xrightarrow[BF_3]{(R'CO)_2O} R'COCH_2COCH_2R \quad \text{(Type I)} \\ \xrightarrow[Base]{R'CO_2C_2H_5} R'COCHRCOCH_3 \quad \text{(Type II)} \end{cases}$$

The acylation of ketones having reactive methylene groups by esters [501,541] or anhydrides [542,543] is a common and convenient method for preparing β-diketones. An ester is used in the presence of a base, and an anhydride with boron trifluoride. From an unsymmetrical ketone two types of ketones result, depending on which α-hydrogen atom reacts. In general, the boron trifluoride method leads to the formation of type I ketones, $R'COCH_2COCH_2R$, whereas the basic reagent method favors type II ketones, $R'COCHRCOCH_3$. Either sodium amide [544,549] or sodium hydride [545,549] is preferred as the basic reagent. Unsymmetrical ketones having only one reactive side (such as acetophenone) respond the same by either method. [542] Also, symmetrical ketones take the same course by both methods, e.g., acetone to acetylacetone. [546,547] Many representative ketones—methyl ethyl, methyl isopropyl, methyl isobutyl, methyl *t*-butyl, diisobutyl, methyl *n*-amyl, cyclohexanone, and acetophenone—have been converted to diketones. The acylating agents are varied and include ethyl esters or anhydrides of acetic, propionic, *n*-butyric, isobutyric, *n*-valeric, *n*-caproic, benzoic, anisic, phenylacetic, lauric, and nicotinic acids. Thus, a large number of β-diketones have been prepared in varying yields, mostly in the range of 30–60%.

β-Diketones are also formed by acylation of the enol esters of ketones with anhydrides in the presence of boron trifluoride. [673]

$$(RCO)_2O + R'\overset{\displaystyle OCOR}{\underset{}{C}}=CHR'' \xrightarrow[CH_3CO_2Na]{BF_3 \text{ then}} RCOCHR''COR'$$

If the acylating ester is diethyl oxalate, then an α,γ-*diketo ester*, or a substituted glyoxalate, is formed. [555-557] These substances are important intermediates in the synthesis of certain β-keto esters (method 307).

$$RCOCH_3 + (CO_2C_2H_5)_2 \xrightarrow{NaOC_2H_5} RCOCH_2COCO_2C_2H_5$$

204. α, β-Olefinic Ketones from Acetylenic Carbinols

$$RCH_2COH(R')C \equiv CH \xrightarrow{HCO_2H} RCH = C(R')COCH_3$$

Ethynyl carbinols on heating with formic acid are isomerized to α,β-olefinic ketones; for example, isohexylmethylethynylcarbinol is taken to 3,7-dimethyl-3-octen-2-one (48%)[264] and 1-ethynyl-1-cyclohexanol to 1-acetyl-1-cyclohexene (70%).[594] Small amounts of unsaturated aldehydes may contaminate the product.

205. γ, δ-Olefinic Ketones from Alkenyl Esters of β-Keto Acids

$$CH_3COCH_2CO_2CH_2CH = CH_2 \xrightarrow{170-250°} CH_3COCH_2CH_2CH = CH_2 + CO_2$$

Acetoacetates or benzoylacetates of β,γ-unsaturated alcohols—methallyl alcohol, crotyl alcohol, methylvinylcarbinol, cinnamyl alcohol, etc.—on heating at 170-250° evolve carbon dioxide and produce γ,δ-olefinic ketones (23-88%).[595] The unsaturated acetoacetates are readily prepared by the action of diketene on the corresponding unsaturated alcohols.

206. Cyclopentenones from Lactones

γ-Methyl-γ-lactones having a methylene group adjacent to the γ-carbon are converted conveniently to 2-alkyl-3-methyl-2-cyclopentenones (30-50%). The method is not applicable, however, to the preparation of 2-cyclopentenone and 3-methyl-2-cyclopentenone. The lactone is simply warmed over phosphorus pentoxide, and the product is distilled from the reaction mixture.[596]

207. β-Halo Ketones from Acyl Chlorides and Olefins

$$R'COCl + RCH = CHR \xrightarrow{Catalyst} RCHClCHRCOR'$$

Addition of acyl halides to olefins in the presence of catalytic amounts of aluminum chloride, stannic chloride, or zinc chloride gives β-halo ketones.[599] An example is the addition of propionyl chloride to ethylene to form ethyl β-chloroethyl ketone (45%).[98] Sometimes the addition products are very unstable and undergo spontaneous dehydrohalogenation to olefinic ketones[101] (cf. methods 20 and 178).

208. α-Halo Ketones from Alkenyl Esters

$$RCO_2CR' = CH_2 \xrightarrow{Br_2} RCO_2CR'BrCH_2Br \rightarrow RCOBr + R'COCH_2Br$$

The dibromide derivatives of alkenyl esters spontaneously cleave in the cold to form α-bromo ketones and acyl halides. In this manner, 1-bromo-2-hexanone (67%) and 1-bromo-2-heptanone (80%) are prepared. The alkenyl esters are prepared by the catalytic addition of organic acids to alkylacetylenes (30–35%).[601]

209. Hydroxy Ketones from Phenolic Esters (Fries)

An ester of a phenol may be converted to the isomeric o or p-hydroxy ketone, or a mixture of both, by treatment with aluminum chloride. Critical discussions of the reaction have been presented[602] with respect to the influence of temperature, solvents, ester-reagent ratio, and the structure of the acyl[603] and phenoxy groups.[604] By varying the first three factors, it is often possible to prepare predominantly either of the isomeric ketones. The reaction is exemplified in the preparation of o- and p-propiophenol (35% and 40%, respectively)[605] and 2-hydroxy-4,6-dimethylacetophenone (80%).[606]

210. α-Keto Acids from Azlactones

Hydrolysis of certain unsaturated azlactones with aqueous sodium hydroxide followed by treatment with dilute hydrochloric acid yields

α-keto acids. The azlactones are readily prepared from substituted benzaldehydes and hippuric acid.[608,609] In this manner, phenylpyruvic acid (72% over-all)[610] and m-chlorophenylpyruvic acid (52% over-all)[611] have been prepared. Other applications have been described.[608,612,613]

211. β-Keto Esters by Condensation of Esters

$$2RCH_2CO_2C_2H_5 \xrightleftharpoons{\text{NaOC}_2\text{H}_5} RCH_2COCHRCO_2C_2H_5 + C_2H_5OH$$

The acetoacetic ester condensation consists of a base-catalyzed reaction of two esters (at least one having an α-hydrogen atom) to form a β-keto ester. The scope, limitations, experimental procedures, and applications have been reviewed.[614,615,626]

Variations of the reaction include condensation of the same ester, a mixed ester condensation, and ester cyclizations. Improvement in yield of the self-condensation reaction is obtained by removing the alcohol produced, the reaction being forced to completion. In this manner, methyl esters[616] catalyzed by sodium methoxide and ethyl esters[148] catalyzed by sodium ethoxide are self-condensed (50-85%). Ethyl isobutyrate and ethyl isovalerate do not respond to sodium alkoxide catalysis; however, these compounds are readily self-condensed with the aid of diisopropyl-aminomagnesium bromide.[626] Another promising reagent is sodium hydride.[545] Mixed ester condensations in which only one ester has an α-hydrogen atom are satisfactory. These are less complicated than a condensation of two different esters each having reactive α-hydrogens. Thus methyl benzoate condensed under "forcing" conditions with methyl acetate, propionate, or butyrate forms the α-alkylbenzoylacetates, $C_6H_5COCHRCO_2CH_3$, in 45%, 61%, and 41% yields, respectively.[616] Similarly, condensation between ethyl oxalate and these esters produces α-ethoxalyl esters.[295,617]

$$RCH_2CO_2C_2H_5 + (CO_2C_2H_5)_2 \xrightarrow{\text{NaOC}_2\text{H}_5} RCH(COCO_2C_2H_5)CO_2C_2H_5 + C_2H_5OH$$

An example is the synthesis of ethyl α-ethoxalylpropionate (R = CH$_3$) in 70% yield.[618] Ethyl oxalate and ethyl succinate form ethyl α-ethoxalyl-succinate (83%).[624] In a mixed ester condensation, the use of a more reactive ester, such as the phenyl or biphenyl ester, helps to prevent side reactions.[619,620] Simple heterocyclic esters, namely, ethyl nicotinate and ethyl 8-quinolinecarboxylate, undergo the mixed ester condensation in good yields.[280,281,630] The internal condensation of ethyl adipate to give 2-carbethoxycyclopentanone (Dieckmann reaction) is an example of cyclization (81%).[627]

212. β-Keto Esters by Selective Cleavage of α,α-Diacyl Esters

$$CH_3COCH_2CO_2C_2H_5 \xrightarrow[\text{RCOCl}]{\text{NaOC}_2\text{H}_5;} RCOCH(COCH_3)CO_2C_2H_5 \xrightarrow{\text{NH}_3}$$

$$RCOCH_2CO_2C_2H_5 + CH_3CONH_2$$

The acylation of simple β-keto esters with acyl chlorides to form diacylacetic esters proceeds readily; however, the subsequent cleavage for removing the smaller acyl group is complicated in that the original keto ester may be regenerated. The optimum conditions for the conversion of benzoylacetoacetic ester to benzoylacetic ester with ammonium chloride and ammonium hydroxide have been studied.[631] The over-all synthesis of this ester has been described (57%).[632] An improved procedure for the ammonolysis of ethyl α-acetyl-β-oxocaproate using gaseous ammonia has been described.[386] By a similar process, a series of alicyclic β-keto esters has been prepared in over-all yields of 20-40%.[633]

Variations of the above procedures are sometimes employed. β-Keto esters may be obtained by alcoholysis of the intermediate diacyl esters by sodium methoxide in methanol,[634] as in the preparation of methyl β-oxocaprylate (88%).[635] The starting β-keto ester can be converted to the new β-keto ester in a single step. Thus, in the synthesis of ethyl benzoylacetate (55%), ethyl acetoacetate and ethyl benzoate are converted directly to this keto ester by distilling the lower-boiling product, ethyl acetate, thereby forcing the reaction to completion.[636]

$$CH_3COCH_2CO_2C_2H_5 + C_6H_5CO_2C_2H_5 \xrightarrow{\text{NaOCH}_3} C_6H_5COCH_2CO_2C_2H_5 +$$

$$CH_3CO_2C_2H_5\uparrow$$

Finally, the sodium enolate of the new β-keto ester may be alkylated directly to give β-keto esters of the type $RCOCHRCO_2C_2H_5$.[637]

213. β-Keto Esters by Alkylation of β-Keto Esters

$$RCOCH_2CO_2C_2H_5 \xrightarrow[\text{R'X}]{\text{NaOC}_2\text{H}_5;} RCOCHR'CO_2C_2H_5$$

This reaction has been considered above (method 184) with respect to ease of mono- and di-alkylation. A large number of condensing agents have been compared, including sodium and potassium ethoxide, sodium in dioxane or toluene, sodium hydride, sodium amide, and sodium or potassium t-butoxide.[642] In general, sodium ethoxide is recommended in the alkylation of acetoacetic ester with primary halides (73%); potassium ethoxide with branched halides, such as isobutyl and s-butyl halides

(61% and 55%); and potassium *t*-butoxide for introducing a second alkyl group in α-substituted acetoacetic esters (60-80%). The other reagents are successful in certain cases. Alkylation of 2-carbethoxycyclopentanone with methyl, ethyl, or isopropyl iodides gives the corresponding β-keto esters in 82%, 74%, and 59% yields, respectively.[268,643] Other examples are found in the preparation of ethyl monomethyl- (71%) and dimethyl-acetoacetic esters (54%)[644] and ethyl *n*-butylacetoacetate (72%).[645] Alkylations by ethyl benzenesulfonate,[623] isopropyl acetate or isopropyl alcohol in the presence of boron trifluoride,[646,647] and dimethyl sulfate[648] have proved more successful than those by the corresponding alkyl halides.

β-Keto esters containing a double bond,[284-287] an alkoxyl group,[291,292] or an amino group[306,307] are formed by alkylating acetoacetic ester with a substituted alkyl halide.

214. β-Keto Esters from Ethyl *t*-Butyl Acylmalonic Esters

$$C_2H_5OMgCH(CO_2C_2H_5)CO_2C(CH_3)_3 \xrightarrow{RCOCl} RCOCH(CO_2C_2H_5)CO_2C(CH_3)_3$$

$$\rightarrow RCOCH_2CO_2C_2H_5 + CH_2 {=\!=} C(CH_3)_2 + CO_2$$

Olefin elimination and decarboxylation of ethyl *t*-butyl acylmalonates proceeds easily on treatment with toluenesulfonic acid to form β-keto esters of the type $RCOCH_2CO_2C_2H_5$.[650,651] By this procedure, acyl acetates where R is ethyl (63%), cyclohexyl (65%), 2-furyl (70%), benzyl (46%), or propenyl (35%) have been prepared. The limiting factor in this excellent method is the availability of ethyl *t*-butyl malonate; its synthesis has been described.[651]

A reaction similar to the above involves the acylation of malonic ester through its magnesium enolate. Thus, the reaction of propionyl chloride with the ester enolate leads to diethyl propionylmalonate. Thermal decomposition of this compound with β-naphthalenesulfonic acid yields ethyl propionylacetate (57%). This modification appears to be general in that it has been extended to the use of aliphatic, aromatic, and carbalkoxy acyl chlorides.[652]

215. β-Keto Esters by Acylation of Ester Enolates

$$RCOCl + Na^+[CR'_2CO_2C_2H_5]^- \rightarrow RCOCR'_2CO_2C_2H_5 + NaCl$$

The acylation of the sodium enolates of esters (prepared by sodium triphenylmethide) with acyl chlorides gives the corresponding α,α-disubstituted β-keto esters, $RCOCR'_2CO_2C_2H_5$. The synthesis is direct, and the product is free from monoalkylation products usually encountered by the dialkylation of β-keto esters. By this procedure, ethyl dimethyl-acetoacetate (51%), ethyl *n*-butyryldimethylacetate (58%), and ethyl benzoyldimethylacetate (65%) have been prepared.[523,653] In a similar manner, the acylation of malonic ester is performed through its magnesium enolate.[652,653,655]

216. β-Keto Nitriles by Acylation of Nitriles

$$RCH_2CN + R'CO_2C_2H_5 \xrightarrow{Base} R'COCHRCN + C_2H_5OH$$

In the presence of sodium ethoxide, nitriles having reactive α-methylene groups may be acylated with esters to form β-keto nitriles. The method is general and is illustrated by the reaction of alkyl cyanides, where R is C_1 to *n*-C_4, with ethyl benzoate to form the corresponding alkylbenzoyl-acetonitriles in 53–60% yield.[659] Aliphatic esters also react; for example, phenylacetonitrile with ethyl acetate gives α-phenylacetoacetonitrile, $C_6H_5CH(CN)COCH_3$ (64%).[660] In the case of the higher-boiling nitriles, the alcohol product is removed by distillation, thereby increasing the yield and decreasing the reaction time.[661]

The method has been extended to the preparation of numerous acyl-acetonitriles in the benzene, naphthalene, furan, and the thiophene series. Modifications of the procedure including the substitution of commercial sodium methoxide for sodium ethoxide and the use of an inert solvent to facilitate stirring have been employed.[662]

If the acylating ester is capable of undergoing self-condensation in the presence of sodium ethoxide, sodium triphenylmethide is substituted for the latter. An example is the reaction of acetonitrile with ethyl *n*-butyrate to give *n*-butyrylacetonitrile (52%).[663]

217. Hydrogenolysis of 1,3-Diketones [487]

$$CH_3COCH_2COCH_2CH(CH_3)_2 \xrightarrow[42\%]{H_2, \text{ Catalyst}} CH_3CH_2CH_2COCH_2CH(CH_3)_2$$

218. Acid Treatment of *Aci*nitroparaffins [540]

$$R_2CHNO_2 \xrightarrow{NaOH} R_2C{=}N{-}ONa \xrightarrow[80-85\%]{H^+} R_2CO$$
$$\downarrow$$
$$O$$

219. Pyrolysis of Glycidic Acids [341,342,367]

$$R_2\overset{O}{\overset{/\backslash}{C}} {-} CR'CO_2H \xrightarrow[-CO_2]{Heat} R_2CHCOR'$$

220. Rearrangement of α-Bromo Azides [83, 343, 344]

$$R_2CBrCON_3 \xrightarrow{Heat} R_2CBrNCO \xrightarrow{H_2O} (R_2CBrNH_2) \xrightarrow{H_2O} R_2CO$$

Where R equals ethyl, n-butyl, or cyclopentyl, over-all yields of 35%, 77%, and 60%, respectively, have been obtained.

221. Degradation of Disubstituted Glycolic Acids [345]

$$R_2COHCO_2H \xrightarrow{Pb(OAc)_4} R_2CO + H_2O + CO$$

222. Hydrolysis of gem-Dihalides [460-463] (cf. method 151)

$$R_2CX_2 \xrightarrow{H_2O} R_2CO$$

223. Isomerization of Vinyl Carbinols [528]

$$CH_2=CHCHO \xrightarrow[30-50\%]{RMgX} CH_2=CHCHOHR \xrightarrow[50-70\%]{Cu} CH_3CH_2COR$$

224. Condensation of Furans with Unsaturated Ketones

Furans and unsaturated ketones undergo a condensation similar to the Diels-Alder type (cf. method 34) to give furyl-substituted ketones; for example, α-methylfuran and methyl vinyl ketone react under mild acidic conditions to yield 5-methylfurfurylacetone (65%). [529]

225. Condensation of Anhydrides [533]

$$2(RCH_2CO)_2O \xrightarrow{BF_3} (RCH_2COCHRCO)_2O \xrightarrow[-CO_2]{H_2O} RCH_2COCH_2R$$

226. Acylation of Certain Heterocyclic Compounds [534]

227. Addition of Aldehydes to Olefins [536]

$$RCHO + R'CH = CH_2 \xrightarrow[\text{peroxide}]{\text{Diacetyl}} RCOCH_2CH_2R'$$

Typical compounds prepared include 4-decanone (41%), 4-dodecanone (57%), and 7-pentadecanone (75%).

228. Interaction of Hydriodic Acid and Diazo Ketones [537,538]

$$RCOCHN_2 + HI \rightarrow RCOCH_3 + N_2 + I_2$$

229. γ-Diketones from Substituted Furans [589-591]

$$\xrightarrow[86\%]{\text{H}_2\text{O, H}_2\text{SO}_4} CH_3COCH_2CH_2CO(CH_2)_5CH_3$$

230. α-Diketones by Oxidation of Aryl Acetylenes [592]

$$ArC \equiv CAr \xrightarrow[60\%]{CrO_3 - CH_3CO_2H} ArCOCOAr$$

231. γ-Diketones from Ketones [593]

$$2RR'CHCOCHRR' \xrightarrow{\text{Diacetyl peroxide}} \begin{array}{c} RR'CCOCHRR' \\ | \\ RR'CCOCHRR' \end{array}$$

232. Olefinic Ketones from Hydrocarbons and Carbon Monoxide [597]

$$3CH_3CH_2CH_3 + CO \xrightarrow[23\%]{AlCl_3, \ 125 \ atm., \ 12 \ hr.} (CH_3)_2CH = CHCH_2COCH(CH_3)_2$$

233. α,β-Olefinic Ketones from Diketene and Aldehydes [90]

234. β-Keto Esters by the Reformatsky Reaction[658,666]

$$C_6H_5CO_2C_6H_5 + (CH_3)_2CBrCO_2C_2H_5 \xrightarrow[\text{(52\%)}]{\text{Zn}} C_6H_5COC(CH_3)_2CO_2C_2H_5$$

235. Hydrolysis of β-Iminonitriles[682]

$$ArCN + CH_3CN \xrightarrow[\text{40–60\%}]{\text{NaNH}_2} ArC(=NH)CH_2CN \xrightarrow[\text{60–70\%}]{\text{H}_2\text{O}} ArCOCH_2CN$$

TABLE 32. MONOKETONES

C_n	Compound	Method	Yield (%)	Chapter[ref.]	B.p./mm., n_D^t, (M.p.), Deriv.
		Aliphatic Ketones			
C_3	Acetone	186	61	10^{317}	56, 1.3592*, 187Se*
	(purification only)	....		10^{667}	56*, 1.3592*, 187Se*
C_4	Methyl ethyl ketone	181	79	10^{226}	82, 1.3791*, 135Se*
C_5	Methyl n-propyl ketone	179	74	10^{157}	102
		184	70	10^{254}	102/747, 110Se
		186	44	10^{324}	102/756, 1.3902, 110Se
	Methyl isopropyl ketone	201	59	10^{523}	94, 1.3879*, 113Se*
	Diethyl ketone	179	57	10^{157}	103, 156Dn*
		186	59	10^{324}	102/751, 1.3922, 139Se
C_6	Methyl n-butyl ketone	179	64	10^{160}	127
		179	80	10^{161}	127
		182	60	10^{233}	124/738, 1.4002, 107Dn
		184	50 †	10^{256}	128
		188	56 †	10^{392}	126/760, 121Se
		188	83	10^{389}	
		189	74	10^{402}	127, 125Se
		200	80	10^{508}	127
	Methyl isobutyl ketone	184	20 †	10^{256}	119, 1.3956*, 135Se*, 95Dn*
		188	80	10^{389}	119
		196	100	10^{465}	116/740
	Methyl s-butyl ketone	179	81	10^{163}	116/734, 1.4002
		188	78 †	10^{390}	118
	Methyl t-butyl ketone	188	78	10^{389}	106
		189	40	10^{409}	106, 158Se*
		190	52	10^{427}	105/746, 1.3960, 127Dn, 80-Ox
		201	72	10^{513}	107
		201	94	10^{514}	106, 1.4019²⁵, 124Dn
	Ethyl n-propyl ketone	179	85	10^{162}	123, 130Dn*
		181	86	10^{226}	126, 113Se
		186	62	10^{324}	125/760, 1.4007, 113Se
		190	45	10^{433}	124
		223	57	10^{528}	124
C_7	Methyl n-amyl ketone	179	70	10^{158}	150/750, 123Se
		179	83	10^{168}	1.4073²⁵*, 74Dn
		184	61 ‡	10^{256}	151/750, 127Se*
		184	95	10^{257}	150
		200	87	10^{508}	149
	Methyl isoamyl ketone	184	60	10^{254}	142/746, 143Se
		194	50	10^{451}	144
	4-Methyl-2-hexanone	184	30 †	10^{256}	142
		184	52	10^{261}	139, 1.4057²⁵, 120Se
		191	75	10^{437}	139/762, 128Se*
	3-Methyl-2-hexanone	184	30 †	10^{251}	137, 70Se*
	3-Ethyl-2-pentanone	184	45	10^{254}	139/746, 1.4073*, 99Se

TABLE 32. MONOKETONES   353

TABLE 32 (continued)

C_n	Compound	Method	Yield (%)	Chapter[ref.]	B.p./mm., n_D^t, (M.p.), Deriv.
				Aliphatic Ketones (continued)	
C_7	Methyl neopentyl ketone	182	56	10^{235}	125/760, 1.4018[25]
		222	96	10^{463}	122, 100Dn
	Methyl t-amyl ketone	179	36	10^{164}	130/733, 1.4100, 112Dn
	3,4-Dimethyl-2-pentanone	184	36†	10^{252}	138, 1.4094*, 113Se*
	Ethyl n-butyl ketone	179	70	10^{158}	148/756, 103Se
		181	89	10^{226}	148, 101Se
		186	46	10^{35}	146/767, 1.4092*
		195	48†	10^{453}	
	Ethyl isobutyl ketone	189	70	10^{405}	135/735, 1.407*, 152Se*
		195	48†	10^{453}	
	Ethyl s-butyl ketone	179	63	10^{168}	78Dn
		184	78	10^{262}	136/760, 1.402*, 137Se*
	Ethyl t-butyl ketone	190	78	10^{427}	125/729, 1.4052, 144Dn
	Di-n-propyl ketone	179	70	10^{158}	144/756, 132Se
		186	50	10^{324}	145/767, 1.4069, 134Se
		225	60	10^{533}	145
	n-Propyl isopropyl ketone	184	79	10^{262}	136/760, 1.4075, 119Se
		189	60	10^{402}	132, 119Se
	Diisopropyl ketone	179	74	10^{165}	125/742, 1.4001, 98Dn*
		184	78	10^{262}	125/760, 160Se
		187	58	10^{356}	125, 160Se
C_8	Methyl n-hexyl ketone	179	96	10^{166}	173, 1.4154
		181	95	10^{226}	172, 121Se
		184	70	10^{263}	172, 122Se*
		200	91	10^{508}	170
	Methyl isohexyl ketone	184	47†	10^{264}	171, 1.4146
		184	77	10^{254}	164/746, 154Se
		....	....	10^{455}	164/757, 1.4144[19], 77Dn
	3-Methyl-2-heptanone	179	68	10^{167}	162/760, 1.415, 82Se
	3,4-Dimethyl-2-hexanone	191	20	10^{439}	158, 120Se
		196	80	10^{472}	155, 118Se
		196	90	10^{468}	158, 126Se
	4-Ethyl-2-hexanone	195	48†	10^{453}	
	3-Methyl-3-ethyl-2-pentanone	189	48	10^{164}	79/20, 1.4206*, 74Dn
	Ethyl isoamyl ketone	189	40	10^{410}	163, 132Se
		196	92	10^{472}	160, 132Se
	5-Methyl-3-heptanone	196	94	10^{467}	161
	Ethyl neopentyl ketone	189	51	10^{411}	92/150, 1.4160*, 136Dn
	n-Propyl n-butyl ketone	201	25	10^{527}	170, 96Se
	n-Propyl isobutyl ketone	217	42	10^{487}	150/750, 124Se
	n-Propyl t-butyl ketone	179	41	10^{168}	124Dn
		190	67	10^{427}	145/738, 1.4107, 116Dn
	Isopropyl s-butyl ketone	179	68	10^{159}	65/50, 1.4080, 71Dn
		189	70	10^{414}	145, 1.4059

For explanations and symbols see pp. xi–xii.

TABLE 32 *(continued)*

C_n	Compound	Method	Yield (%)	Chapter[ref.]	B.p./mm., n_D^t, (M.p.), Deriv.
		Aliphatic Ketones *(continued)*			
C_8	Isopropyl *t*-butyl ketone	190	20	10^{427}	135/744, 1.4065, 144-Ox
		198	54	10^{497}	135, 132Se*
C_9	Methyl *n*-heptyl ketone	181	83	10^{226}	118Se
		185	93	10^{313}	80/10, 118Se
		186	54	10^{326}	192/743, 120Se*
	4-Methyl-2-octanone	182	69	10^{233}	94/40, 70Se
	3-Methyl-3-ethyl-2-hexanone	189	47	10^{420}	110/86, 1.4222^{30}, 81Dn
	Ethyl *n*-hexyl ketone	186	41	10^{35}	187/751, 112Se*
		195	48 †	10^{453}	
	5-Ethyl-3-heptanone	187	40	10^{357}	173, 134Se
		195	48 †	10^{453}	
	Di-*n*-butyl ketone	184	72	10^{259}	88/22
		186	99	10^{320}	93/24, 90Se*
	n-Butyl isobutyl ketone	188	20	10^{398}	168, 132Se
	n-Butyl *t*-butyl ketone	190	68	10^{427}	166/745, 1.4167, 145Se
		198	38	10^{498}	166/745
	Diisobutyl ketone	196	100	10^{469}	56/11, 122Se
	Isobutyl *s*-butyl ketone	184	75	10^{262}	167/760, 133Se
		188	21	10^{399}	169, 132Se
	Isobutyl *t*-butyl ketone	198	35	10^{498}	158, 145Se*
	Isopropyl neopentyl ketone	193	55	10^{447}	107/180, 129Dn
	Isopropyl *t*-amyl ketone	189	87	10^{419}	87/35, 1.4214
	Di-*t*-butyl ketone	179	81	10^{249}	154, 1.4188^{22}
		185	81	10^{174}	154
		189	80	10^{416}	153, 1.4392
		198	52	10^{165}	150/740, 1.4194
C_{10}	Methyl *n*-octyl ketone	196	92	10^{473}	142/100, (14), 126Se
C_{11}	*sym*-Tetraethylacetone	225	57	10^{533}	104/30
	Di-*n*-amyl ketone	225	64	10^{533}	125/35
		184	81	10^{259}	106/13, (15)
		184	72 †	10^{691}	100/15
		186	69	10^{35}	223/760
C_{12}	Methyl *n*-decyl ketone	185	94	10^{313}	107/5, 123Se
C_{13}	Di-*n*-hexyl ketone	184	82	10^{259}	264, (30)
	Methyl *n*-undecyl ketone	185	97	10^{313}	(28), 117Se
C_{15}	Di-*n*-heptyl ketone	184	93	10^{259}	178, (42), 120-Ox*
C_{17}	Di-*n*-octyl ketone	184	93	10^{259}	(53), 112-Ox*
C_{19}	Methyl *n*-heptadecyl ketone	185	96	10^{313}	(56), 77-Ox
	Di-*n*-nonyl ketone	184	95	10^{259}	(59)
C_{21}	Di-*n*-decyl ketone	184	90	10^{265}	(64)

TABLE 32. MONOKETONES   355

TABLE 32 *(continued)*

C_n	Compound	Method	Yield (%)	Chapter[ref.]	B.p./mm., n_D^t, (M.p.), Deriv.
		Aliphatic Ketones *(continued)*			
C_{23}	Di-*n*-undecyl ketone	184	98	10^{259}	(69), 40-Ox*
	(laurone)	184	55†	10^{691}	(69)
		186	93	10^{321}	(69)
C_{27}	Di-*n*-tridecyl ketone	184	97	10^{259}	(79), 51-Ox*
	(myristone)				
C_{35}	Di-*n*-heptadecyl ketone	186	95	10^{328}	(89), 63-Ox*
	(stearone)				
		Alicyclic Ketones			
C_4	Cyclobutanone	182	91	10^{237}	100, 1.4189^{25}, 146Dn
C_5	Methyl cyclopropyl	198	83	10^{694}	111, 1.4226^{25}
	ketone				
	Cyclopentanone	186	80	10^{327}	131, 1.4370, 203Se*
C_6	Methyl cyclobutyl ketone	186	60	10^{332}	137/767, 149Se
		189	66	10^{423}	136, 1.4283^{28}, 149Se
	2-Methylcyclopentanone	184	80	10^{267}	140, 182Se
		184	56†	10^{266}	140/758
	3-Methylcyclopentanone	186	76	10^{333}	145/755, 1.4329, 185Se
	Cyclohexanone	179	85	10^{176}	155, 160Dn*
		181	60	10^{225}	156, 165Se
C_7	Methyl cyclopentyl	179	54†	10^{177}	155, 143Se
	ketone				
	3,3-Dimethyl-1-cyclo-	186	30	10^{334}	153/748, 178Se
	pentanone				
	1-Ethylcyclopentanone	184	64	10^{268}	161/755, 189Se
	2-Methylcyclohexanone	179	85	10^{169}	165, 1.4487, 191Se
	3-Methylcyclohexanone	179	90	10^{170}	65/30
		179	78	10^{169}	169, 1.4463, 182Se
		179	88	10^{675}	64/20, 1.4460
		196	100	10^{475}	93/15, 1.4446, 185Se
	4-Methylcyclohexanone	179	74	10^{171}	168, 1.4448, 193Se
		179	70	10^{169}	172, 1.4462, 196Se
		179	70	10^{172}	170
	Cycloheptanone	186	40	10^{335}	66/15, 163Se
		199	63	10^{506}	182
C_8	2-Isopropylcyclo-	196	88	10^{178}	174, 1.4395^{29}, 202Se
	pentanone				
	2-Methyl-5-ethylcyclo-	184	88	10^{269}	165/750
	pentanone				
	Methyl cyclohexyl ketone	179	85	10^{163}	67/12, 1.4514
		185	66†	10^{312}	65/12
	2-Ethylcyclohexanone	179	86	10^{675}	76/20, 1.4522
		184	74	10^{271}	74/35, 162Dn
		192	41	10^{444}	42/2, 1.4530^{16}, 162Se
		198	43	10^{493}	67/12, 1.4543^{15}, 163Se

For explanations and symbols see pp. xi–xii.

356 KETONES Ch. 10

TABLE 32 (continued)

C_n	Compound	Method	Yield (%)	Chapter[ref.]	B.p./mm., n_D^t, (M.p.), Deriv.
				Alicyclic Ketones (continued)	
C_8	3-Ethylcyclohexanone	179	84	10^{171}	192, 1.4511, 182Se
		196	100	10^{475}	41/0.8, 1.4537, 175Se
	2,2-Dimethylcyclohexanone	198	30	10^{490}	170/761, 1.4482, 201Se
		198	26†	10^{493}	171/760, 1.4499^{18}, 193Se
	2,4-Dimethylcyclohexanone	179	79	10^{178}	176, 1.4430^{25}, 200Se
	2,6-Dimethylcyclohexanone	179	93	10^{675}	69/20, 1.4470
		179	49	10^{179}	174, 1.4500
		184	91	10^{270}	58/10
	3,4-Dimethylcyclohexanone	179	93	10^{675}	81/20, 1.4520
	3,5-Dimethylcyclohexanone	179	92	10^{675}	75/20, 1.4434
		196	78	10^{474}	182/750, 1.4427, 201Se
C_9	α-Methyl-α-cyclopentylacetone	184	69	10^{272}	79/17, 1.4470, 98Se
	2,2,5,5-Tetramethylcyclopentanone	198	35	10^{493}	155/760, 1.4280
	2-n-Propylcyclohexanone	192	30	10^{444}	88/17, 120Se
	3-n-Propylcyclohexanone	196	100	10^{475}	42/0.7, 1.4530, 169Se
	3-Isopropylcyclohexanone	196	100	10^{475}	51/1, 1.4540, 195Se
	4-n-Propylcyclohexanone	179	82	10^{180}	212/740, 1.4514^{25}, 180Se
	4-Isopropylcyclohexanone	179	82	10^{181}	91/13, 1.4560, 188Se
	3-Methyl-5-ethylcyclohexanone	196	94	10^{474}	205/747, 1.4452
	2,2,6-Trimethylcyclohexanone	198	27	10^{491}	179/767, 1.4480, 209Se, 141Dn
C_{10}	2,2,6,6-Tetramethylcyclohexanone	198	26	10^{492}	184/772, 1.4473, (15)
	cis-α-Decalone	180	80	10^{693}	116/18, 1.4939, 220dSe
	2-Decalone	179	94	10^{182}	114/15
C_{11}	Dicyclopentyl ketone	220	60	10^{344}	112/12, 162Se
	1-Methyl-2-decalone	179	80	10^{183}	107/7
C_{12}	4-Cyclohexylcyclohexanone	179	87	10^{184}	100/0.1, (31), 216Se
				Aromatic Ketones	
C_8	Acetophenone	178	83	10^6	88/16, (20)
		178	86	10^{12}	(19), 60-Ox*
		183	63	10^{240}	
		187	70	10^{353}	205/760, 1.541, 199Se

TABLE 32. MONOKETONES 357

TABLE 32 (continued)

C_n	Compound	Method	Yield (%)	Chapter[ref.]	B.p./mm., n_D^t, (M.p.), Deriv.
				Aromatic Ketones (continued)	
C_8	Acetophenone (continued)	188	75	10^{389}	202
		188	75†	10^{392}	104/31, 199Se
		189	85	10^{402}	∪ 91/16, 203Se
C_9	Methyl benzyl ketone	178	32	10^{33}	114/22, 188Se
		184	86	10^{273}	112/24
		185	71†	10^{312}	98/13, 190Se
		186	65	10^{319}	120/22
		188	52†	10^{390}	
		190	65	10^{434}	125/50, 153Dn
		195	77	10^{679}	216
	Phenyl ethyl ketone	178	58	10^{35}	215/763
		178	84	10^{34}	220, 189Dn*
		187	83	10^{354}	106/17, 1.5270, 173Se
		189	81†	10^{401}	103/16, 179Se
	o-Methylacetophenone	179	60†	10^{185}	105/20, 203Se
		184	35	10^{274}	95/15, 210Se
		189	60	10^{413}	108/25
		189	85	10^{412}	94/13, 206Se
	m-Methylacetophenone	189	83	10^{402}	108/19, 203Se
	p-Methylacetophenone	178	88	10^{28}	108/18, 1.5348, 88-Ox
		178	89	10^{6}	93/7, 87-Ox*
		178	93	10^{12}	227/764
		179	50†	10^{185}	109/12, 197Se
		189	84	10^{402}	138/13, 198Se
	1-Indanone (α-hydrindone)	178	55	10^{74}	(41)
		178	84	10^{76}	120/13, 146-Ox*
		178	93	10^{77}	(38)
		....	60	10^{78}	126/17, (41), 233Se*
	2-Indanone	201	75	10^{76}	(57), 153-Ox
C_{10}	Phenyl n-propyl ketone	178	65	10^{36}	115/17
		187	82	10^{354}	123/20, 1.5203
	Phenyl isopropyl ketone	179	75	10^{186}	....
		184	81	10^{262}	102/15, 181Se*
		188	72†	10^{392}	217/760, 57-Ox
	Ethyl benzyl ketone	195	68	10^{679}	102/10
	Benzylacetone	184	35†	10^{276}	110/7, 142Se
		184	88	10^{275}	124/16
		184	97	10^{253}	
		196	63	10^{476}	235, 87-Ox*
		196	67	10^{477}	236/748, 142Se
		196	96	10^{465}	133/15
	3-Phenyl-2-butanone	198	74	10^{499}	107/22, 1.5092
		187	28	10^{358}	78/1.5, 1.5088^{25}, 158Se

For explanations and symbols see pp. xi–xii.

TABLE 32 (continued)

C_n	Compound	Method	Yield (%)	Chapter[ref.]	B.p./mm., n_D^t, (M.p.), Deriv.

Aromatic Ketones (continued)

C_n	Compound	Method	Yield (%)	Chapter[ref.]	B.p./mm., n_D^t, (M.p.), Deriv.
C_{10}	p-Methylpropiophenone	178	86	10^6	106/8
	o-Ethylacetophenone	186	74	10^{337}	108/18, 180Se
		187	62	10^{336}	118/29, 1.5249
	m-Ethylacetophenone	183	50	10^{238}	116/14, 1.5232[25]
	p-Ethylacetophenone	178	98	10^4	117/13, 1.5275[25]
		186	38†	10^{336}	125/20, 1.5298
	2,4-Dimethylaceto-	178	48	10^8	97/4, 1.5381, 234Se*
	phenone	178	54	10^7	113/18, 64-Ox*
		178	74	10^8	94/5, 1.5340, 187Se*
	2,5-Dimethylaceto-	178	68	10^8	94/8, 1.5291, 169Se*
	phenone	186	69	10^{336}	127/31, 1.5306
	3,4-Dimethylaceto-	186	58	10^{336}	132/19, 1.5400
	phenone				
	3,5-Dimethylaceto-	187	63	10^{336}	129/22, 1.5276[25]
	phenone				
	α-Tetralone	178	91	10^{17}	170/49
		178	91†	10^{79}	107/2, 102-Ox
		178	92	10^{24}	123/8, 217Se
		183	56	10^{241}	124/9
	β-Tetralone	181	42	10^{485}	121-132/8, 1.5555[25], (18)
		197	40	10^{483}	194Se
		197	56	10^{486}	131/11, 88-Ox*
C_{11}	Phenyl n-butyl ketone	179	93	10^{186}	
		187	83	10^{354}	141/24, 1.5146, 166Se*
		195	50	10^{679}	107/10
	3-Phenyl-2-pentanone	198	55	10^{499}	110/18, 1.5051, 191Se
	4-Phenyl-2-pentanone	178	39	10^{530}	115/13, 1.5124, 137Se
	5-Phenyl-2-pentanone	184	25†	10^{276}	122/6, 130Se
	Phenyl isobutyl ketone	178	62	10^{36}	235, 210Se*
	Phenyl s-butyl ketone	184	69	10^{262}	109/10
	Phenyl t-butyl ketone	179	64	10^{187}	108/16, 150Se*
		189	67	10^{417}	84/3, 1.5102, 195Dn
		198	77	10^{187}	104/14, 166-Ox
	5-Phenyl-3-pentanone	196	82	10^{479}	244/760, 1.5125, 80Se
	Pivalophenone	187	82	10^{355}	224/750, 1.5082
	3-Methyl-3-phenyl-2-	187	61	10^{358}	77/15, 1.5078[25], 186Se
	butanone	198	50	10^{499}	99/12, 1.5083, 186Se
	3-Methyl-4-phenyl-2-	....	65	10^{681}	106/9, 1.5065[18], 114Se
	butanone	196	83	10^{479}	130/17, 1.5090[19], 112Se
	2,4,5-Trimethylaceto-	178	75	10^{37}	124/5, 204Se*
	phenone	178	80	10^7	123/10, 86-Ox*
	2,4,6-Trimethylaceto-	178	72	10^7	123/18
	phenone	178	83	10^{29}	102/1
	2-Phenylcyclopentanone	192	50	10^{446}	135-140/9, (37), 214Se

TABLE 32. MONOKETONES 359

TABLE 32 *(continued)*

C_n	Compound	Method	Yield (%)	Chapter[ref.]	B.p./mm., n_D^t, (M.p.), Deriv.
		Aromatic Ketones (continued)			
C_{11}	2-Methyl-1-tetralone	178	71	10^{82}	138/16, 1.5538^{25}
		178	92	10^{81}	80/1, 1.5447, 195Se
		184	95	10^{80}	116/2.5, 205Se
	3-Methyl-1-tetralone	178	73†	10^{84}	96/0.3, 123-Ox
		178	86	10^{83}	136/14, 242Dn
	4-Methyl-1-tetralone	178	74	10^{80}	111/1, 211Se
	7-Methyl-1-tetralone	178	89†	10^{85}	109/1.5-2, (33)
C_{12}	Phenyl neopentyl ketone	178	87	10^{478}	116/11, 1.5078, 218Se, 114-Ox
	m-Propyl propiophenone	187	82	10^{360}	145/20, 128Se
	Mesitylacetone	185	83†	10^{312}	(60), 205Se
		187	50	10^{359}	130/10, (60), 197Se
	p-n-Butylacetophenone	178	78	10^{38}	141/14, 185Se
	p-Isobutylacetophenone	178	38	10^{38}	135/16
	p-s-Butylacetophenone	178	74	10^{39}	135/11, 1.5195
	p-t-Butylacetophenone	178	83	10^4	138/16, 1.5195^{25}
	2-Methyl-5-isopropylacetophenone	178	55	10^9	125/12
	Acetodurene	178	80	10^7	131/10
		178	86	10^{40}	(73)
	Acetoisodurene	178	81	10^7	137/16
	Acetoprehnitene	178	70	10^7	124/8
	2-Phenylcyclohexanone	179	80	10^{173}	160/15, (63), 190Se
		192	60	10^{443}	155/13, (60), 139Dn
		201	80	10^{532}	150/9, (59)
	4-Phenylcyclohexanone	179	40	10^{188}	(78), 212Se
	Methyl α-naphthyl ketone	178	35	10^{42}	151/7, 237Se*
		178	93	10^{30}	163/15, (9.0)
		187	52	10^{346}	150/8, 1.6257, 116Pi*
	Methyl β-naphthyl ketone	178	40	10^{43}	(53), 82Pi
	6-Acetyltetralin	178	74	10^{41}	115/2
		178	93	10^4	121/2.0, 1.5591^{25}
		178	60	10^{25}	156/10, 1.5593^{29}, 234Se
	1,1-Dimethyl-2-tetralone	198	80	10^{496}	96/0.5, 1.538, 204Se
	7-Acenaphthenone	179	65	10^{189}	(121)
		....	45	10^{531}	(121)
C_{13}	Benzylpinacolone	196	75	10^{478}	261/746, 1.4972, 158Se
	p-n-Amylacetophenone	178	73	10^{38}	159/17
	p-Isoamylacetophenone	178	73	10^{38}	153/16
	p-s-Amylacetophenone	178	58	10^{39}	145/11, 1.5150
	p-t-Amylacetophenone	178	59	10^{38}	146/13
	Acetopentamethylbenzene	178	80	10^7	145/8, (84)
	Benzophenone	178	76	10^{44}	(49), 167Se*
		178	90	10^2	(48), 144-Ox*
		183	87	10^{577}	140-Ox

For explanations and symbols see pp. xi–xii.

TABLE 32 *(continued)*

C_n	Compound	Method	Yield (%)	Chapter ref.	B.p./mm., n_D^t, (M.p.), Deriv.
			Aromatic Ketones *(continued)*		
C_{13}	Benzophenone *(con-*	186	87	10^{329}	(48)
	tinued)	189	57	10^{402}	172/19
		222	89	10^{460}	190/15, (48)
	Ethyl α-naphthyl ketone	187	37	10^{346}	170/11, 1.6109, 58-Ox*
		187	89	10^{685}	146/1, 79Pi
	6-Propionyltetralin	178	68	10^{25}	163/11, 1.5508^{29}, 209Se
	Fluorenone	183	70	10^{242}	(83.5)
		186	82	10^{242}	(84), 195-Ox*
		222	90	10^{462}	(83.5)
C_{14}	Phenyl benzyl ketone	178	83	10^{1}	160/5, (56), 148Se*
	(desoxybenzoin)	190	77	10^{429}	(57), 98-Ox
		201	88	10^{519}	(58)
	p-Methylbenzophenone	178	55	10^{46}	185/17, 122Se*
	4-Phenylhexahydroace-tophenone	178	60	10^{45}	121/1-2, 191Se
	p-Cyclohexylaceto-phenone	178	91	10^{4}	129/1.5, (69)
	2-Acetylbiphenyl	188	48†	10^{391}	105/1, 197Se
	3-Acetylbiphenyl	179	81	10^{47}	138/1, 1.6140^{25}
		188	46†	10^{391}	151/1, 223Se
	4-Acetylbiphenyl	178	70	10^{47}	150/2, (121)
		178	80	10^{48}	(121)
		178	90	10^{18}	(121)
	1-Acetoacenaphthene	178	45	10^{49}	(105)
	Anthrone	178	28	10^{50}	(154)
		....	83	10^{51}	(153)
C_{15}	Benzylacetophenone	196	95	10^{688}	(73), 144Se*
	Dibenzyl ketone	186	41	10^{330}	320, (30), 146Se*
		186	85	10^{338}	187/15
		187	11	10^{210}	(35)
	α,α-Diphenylacetone	....	57†	10^{680}	(61)
	Di-o-tolyl ketone	189	40	10^{687}	(67), 105-Ox
	o-Ethylbenzophenone	178	83†	10^{52}	165/18
	p-Ethylbenzophenone	178	80	10^{5}	144/0.2, 315/730
	p,p'-Dimethylbenzo-phenone	178	55	10^{27}	(95), 140Se
	Ethyl 4-biphenylyl ketone	178	79	10^{18}	(89)
	2-Acetylfluorene	178	63	10^{31}	192/4, (130)
		178	83	10^{19}	(129)
	9-Acetylfluorene	....	60	10^{199}	(75.5), 139Ph
		....	60	10^{53}	(75)
C_{16}	p-n-Propylbenzo-phenone	178	67	10^{5}	114/0.05

TABLE 32. MONOKETONES 361

TABLE 32 (continued)

C_n	Compound	Method	Yield (%)	Chapter$^{ref.}$	B.p./mm., n_D^t, (M.p.), Deriv.
		Aromatic Ketones (continued)			
C_{16}	p-Isopropylbenzophenone	178	55	10^{46}	197/16
		187	40	10^{361}	118/0.04
	Mesityl phenyl ketone	183	83	10^{568}	(137), 232Dn
	1-Acetylphenanthrene	187	85	10^{347}	(113)
	2-Acetylphenanthrene	178	15	10^{20}	(143), 260Se
		178	53†	10^{22}	(143)
	3-Acetylphenanthrene	178	64	10^{20}	(72), 230Se
	9-Acetylphenanthrene	184	83†	10^{277}	(74), 201Se
		187	59	10^{347}	170/1, (74)
	9-Acetylanthracene	178	60	10^{32}	(76)
C_{17}	p-n-Butylbenzophenone	178	69	10^{5}	164/0.65
	p-s-Butylbenzophenone	178	88	10^{39}	188/9, 1.5760
		187	50	10^{361}	139/0.04
	p-t-Butylbenzophenone	178	74	10^{5}	205/15, (37.5)
	Benzoylisodurene	178	78	10^{54}	164/4, (61)
	Phenyl α-naphthyl ketone	178	52	10^{26}	169/1, (75), 161-Ox
		178	86	10^{30}	225/15, (73)
	2-Propionylphenanthrene	178	23	10^{21}	(105), 107Pi
		178	45†	10^{22}	(104)
		187	77	10^{21}	(105), 107Pi
	3-Propionylphenanthrene	178	23	10^{21}	(57), 113Pi
		187	22	10^{21}	(57), 113Pi
	9-Propionylphenanthrene	187	86	10^{21}	(57), 107Pi
	9-Propionylanthracene	178	11	10^{55}	(75)
C_{18}	Laurophenone	187	90	10^{362}	(44), 63-Ox
	p-s-Amylbenzophenone	178	60	10^{39}	190/5, 1.5672
	2,2-Diphenylcyclohexanone	201	98	10^{516}	(99)
C_{19}	Dimesityl ketone	189	56	10^{418}	(137)
	Phenyl 3-biphenylyl ketone	187	46	10^{686}	(79)
	Phenyl 4-biphenylyl ketone	178	75	10^{18}	(106)
	1-Benzoylacenaphthene	190	95	10^{23}	(92)
	3-Benzoylacenaphthene	178	70	10^{24}	(99)
C_{21}	β,β-Diphenylpropiophenone	178	85	10^{56}	(92), 133-Ox
		191	90	10^{442}	(96)
	Di-α-naphthyl ketone	187	75	10^{351}	(100), 200-Ox*
	1-Benzoylphenanthrene	178	8	10^{58}	(149)
	2-Benzoylphenanthrene	187	85	10^{58}	(118)
	3-Benzoylphenanthrene	178	20	10^{58}	(112)
		187	60	10^{58}	(112)

For explanations and symbols see pp. xi–xii.

TABLE 32 *(continued)*

C_n	Compound	Method	Yield (%)	Chapter ref.	B.p./mm., n_D^t, (M.p.), Deriv.
		Aromatic Ketones *(continued)*			
C_{21}	9-Benzoylphenanthrene	187	65	10^{348}	(90)
	9-Anthraphenone	178	65	10^{57}	(148)
	2,3-Diphenyl-1-indenone	19	71	2^{78}	238/6, (151)
C_{24}	Stearoylbenzene	178	65	10^3	(65)
C_{26}	Phenyl triphenylmethyl ketone	201	96	10^{515}	(180)
C_{27}	sym-Tetraphenylacetone	189	52	10^{422}	(134)
		189	36	10^{278}	
		...	39	10^{278}	(134)
C_{33}	Pentaphenylacetone	189	70	10^{422}	(181)
		Heterocyclic Ketones			
C_4	3-Thiophanone	560	22	39^7	85/24, 192Se
C_6	2-Acetylfuran	178	66	10^{60}	48/5, (32), 150Se*
		178	48	10^{65}	90/43, 1.5015^{30}, (32)
		178	77	10^{64}	48/5
		178	76	10^{59}	48/5, 220Dn
		189	28	10^{421}	58/3
		199	75	10^{526}	169-173, 148Se
	2-Acetylthiophene	178	70	10^{65}	88/8, 1.5666
		178	83	10^{62}	91/9, 1.566
		178	79	10^{66}	90/10, (10.5), 1.5662
		178	73	10^{64}	81/7
		178	86	10^{59}	78/4, 1.5666
C_7	α-Furylacetone	195	40	10^{679}	180
	Ethyl 2-furyl ketone	178	52	10^{67}	77/17, (28), 189Se
		178	81	10^{64}	63/6
		189	61	10^{402}	82/15, 189Se
		199	100	10^{526}	183, (30), 189Se
	2-Acetyl-5-methylfuran	178	42	10^{68}	73/8, 191Se
	α-Thienylacetone	219	87	10^{367}	106/12, 1.5366^{14}, 195Se
	Ethyl 2-thienyl ketone	178	79	10^{64}	89/6
	2-Acetyl-5-methyl-thiophene	178	91	10^{66}	83/2, 1.5622, 217Se
	Methyl 2-pyridyl ketone	184	50	10^{279}	190, 121-Ox*
	Methyl 3-pyridyl ketone	184	81	10^{279}	218, 137Ph*
		184	96	10^{280}	92/5, (14), 177HCl
		186	36	10^{399}	108/23
		187	50	10^{364}	220, 113-Ox
	Methyl 4-pyridyl ketone	184	80	10^{279}	212, 142-Ox*
C_8	n-Propyl 2-furyl ketone	178	93	10^{64}	78/7
	1-(α-Furyl)-2-butanone	195	70	10^{679}	76/12, 1.4680^{25}
	1-(α-Tetrahydrofuryl)-3-butanone	196	73	10^{683}	81/2, 1.4459^{19}

TABLE 33. DIKETONES 363

TABLE 32 *(continued)*

C_n	Compound	Method	Yield (%)	Chapter[ref.]	B.p./mm., n_D^t, (M.p.), Deriv.
	Heterocyclic Ketones *(continued)*				
C_8	5-Methyl-2-propiofuran	199	100	10^{526}	96/14, 164Se
	n-Propyl 2-thienyl ketone	178	89	10^{64}	96/4
	n-Propyl 3-pyridyl ketone	189	30	10^{365}	98/3, 1.5128, 104Pi
	3-Pyridylacetone	186	40	10^{340}	123/1, 185Se
C_9	2-Furyl 2-thienyl ketone	178	66	10^{69}	136/3, 1.6694^{24}
	2-Furyl 2-pyrryl ketone	189	42	10^{69}	144/1.5, (70)
	n-Propyl 3-pyridyl ketone	187	40	10^{365}	98/3, 1.5136, 130Ph
	2-n-Butyrylpyridine	195	81	10^{535}	217, 1.5078, 75Pi
C_{10}	Methyl 2-benzofuryl ketone	178	37	10^{71}	119/5, (72), 207Se
		570	80	39^{60}	136/11, (76), 154Ph
	3-Acetylthianaphthene	178	70	10^{70}	137/3, 250Se
C_{11}	2-Benzoylfuran	178	70	10^{66}	150/3, (44), 122-Ox
	Phenyl 2-thienyl ketone	178	90	10^{63}	209/40, (56), 93-Ox
	2-Acetylquinoline	201	62	10^{518}	(46), 54Ph
	3-acetylquinoline	184	95	10^{311}	(98.5)
	8-Acetylquinoline	184	52	10^{281}	116/0.7, (43.5), 253Dn
C_{12}	2-Benzoylpyridine	183	86	10^{244}	133/2, 1.6056, 199Dn
C_{13}	2-Phenacylpyridine	226	57	10^{534}	150-160/4, (54)
C_{14}	2-Acetyldibenzofuran	178	57	10^{73}	220/18
	2-Acetyldibenzothiophene	178	25	10^{72}	(112), 235Se

For explanations and symbols see pp. xi–xii.

TABLE 33. DIKETONES

C_n	Compound	Method	Yield (%)	Chapter[ref.]	B.p./mm., n_D^t, (M.p.), Deriv.
	Aliphatic Diketones				
C_5	Acetylacetone	203	45	10^{547}	136
		203	54	10^{544}	141/758
		203	85	10^{546}	136, 150-Ox*
C_6	Dipropionyl	179	70	10^{191}	35/10, 185-Ox*
	Propionylacetone	203	35	10^{500}	157
		203	46	10^{542}	157/754, 199Cu
		203	60	10^{541}	158, 198Cu
	Acetonylacetone	229	90	10^{591}	79/15, 89/25
	Methyldiacetylmethane	203	32	10^{542}	79/30
C_7	Dipropionylmethane	203	51	10^{545}	80/30
		203	57	10^{544}	80/30, 210Cu

For explanations and symbols see pp. xi–xii.

TABLE 33 (continued)

C_n	Compound	Method	Yield (%)	Chapter ref.	B.p./mm., n_D^t, (M.p.), Deriv.
			Aliphatic Diketones (continued)		
C_7	n-Butyrylacetone	203	45	10^{500}	90/38
		203	48	10^{542}	73/20, 165Cu
	Isobutyrylacetone	203	30	10^{541}	67/20, 172Cu
		203	41	10^{545}	64/19
		203	54	10^{500}	164
	3-Methyl-2,4-hexane-dione	203	31	10^{542}	91/30, 177Cu
		203	45	10^{541}	183, 177Cu
		203	60	10^{545}	184
	3-Methyl-2,5-hexane-dione	184	83	10^{282}	71/10, 1.4260, 220Se
	Diacetylethylmethane	198	30	10^{500}	178/740
C_8	n-Valerylacetone	203	62	10^{500}	81/17
	Propionyl-n-butyryl-methane	203	70	10^{544}	86/20, 158Cu
	3-Methyl-2,4-heptanedione	203	44	10^{542}	96/20, 163Cu
		203	47	10^{500}	100/45
	Isovalerylacetone	203	64	10^{500}	77/17
	Pivaloylacetone	203	43	10^{544}	71/20, 192Cu
	Diisobutyryl	181	27	10^{228}	148, 172-Ox*
	Isopropyldiacetyl-methane	198	35	10^{501}	183/740
C_9	Caproylacetone	203	54	10^{549}	98/11, 1.4222[25]
		203	61	10^{541}	105/20, 138Cu
	Di-n-butyrylmethane	203	76	10^{544}	102/20, 157Cu
	Methylpropionylbutyryl-methane	203	46	10^{542}	108/20, 152Cu
	Propionyl-isovaleryl-methane	203	75	10^{545}	93/19
	Diisobutyrylmethane	203	28	10^{548}	63/3
	n-Butyldiacetylmethane	198	38	10^{501}	94/10
		203	53	10^{542}	106/20
		203	67	10^{673}	106/20
	Diacetyldiethylmethane	198	32	10^{501}	100/10
C_{10}	Dipivaloyl	179	36	10^{196}	73/24
		179	50	10^{201}	62/14, 1.4144
C_{11}	2,5-Undecandione	229	86	10^{590}	(33)
	Diisovalerylmethane	203	76	10^{549}	116/20, 1.4565[25]
			Alicyclic Diketones		
C_5	Cyclopentan-1,2-dione	184	67	10^{561}	97/20
C_6	4-Methyl-cyclopentan-1,2-dione	184	65	10^{562}	98/17
	1,2-Cyclohexanedione	183	30	10^{569}	97/25, 188-Ox

TABLE 33. DIKETONES 365

TABLE 33 *(continued)*

C_n	Compound	Method	Yield (%)	Chapter[ref.]	B.p./mm., n_D^t, (M.p.), Deriv.

Alicyclic Diketones *(continued)*

C_6	1,3-Cyclohexanedione	197	95	10^{481}	(104), 156-Ox*
	1,4-Cyclohexanedione	184	85	10^{587}	132/20, (79), 188-Ox*
C_7	1,2-Cycloheptanedione	183	90	10^{570}	109/17, 182-Ox
C_8	Tetramethyl-1,3-cyclo-butanedione	....	38	10^{585}	161, (116)
	2-Acetylcyclohexanone	203	35	10^{541}	115/20
		203	35	10^{542}	97/10
		203	56	10^{543}	101/11
	5,5-Dimethyl-1,3-cyclo-hexanedione	184	85	10^{584}	(148), 176-Ox*
C_9	5-Isopropyl-1,3-cyclo-hexanedione	184	80	10^{588}	(62)
	2-Propionylcyclohexanone	203	29	10^{545}	125/20
		203	35	10^{542}	125/20, 185Cu
C_{10}	2-Ethyl-4-*n*-propyl-1,3-cy-clopentanedione	....	32	10^{586}	176/1, (120)

Aromatic Diketones

C_9	Acetylbenzoyl	183	20	10^{576}	128/20, 232Se*
		183	60	10^{567}	115/15
		195	70	10^{452}	116/20, 240-Ox*
	Ninhydrin (triketohy-drindene)	183	35	10^{571}	(243), 201-Ox
C_{10}	1-Phenyl-1,2-butanedione	183	35	10^{576}	132/20
	Benzoylacetone	178	73	10^{90}	141/15, (59)
		203	50	10^{542}	141/18
		203	66	10^{545}	(61)
		203	68	10^{673}	146/20
		203	70	10^{500}	136/16, (60)
		203	83	10^{543}	(60)
	o-Diacetylbenzene	183	71	10^{243}	147/16, (38.5)
	p-Diacetylbenzene	183	76	10^{4}	130/3, (114)
		184	15	10^{283}	(114), 240-Ox*
C_{11}	*w*-Propionylace-tophenone	203	30	10^{542}	152/10, 153Cu
		203	55	10^{541}	127/5, 149Cu
		203	61	10^{550}	122/5, 1.5837, 151Cu
	3-Phenyl-2,4-pentane-dione	203	41	10^{542}	134/20, (60), 224Cu
C_{12}	1,3,5-Triacetylbenzene	....	51	10^{563}	(161)
C_{14}	Benzil	179	86	10^{190}	(95), 244Se*
		179	95	10^{193}	(95), 225Ph*
		179	100	10^{194}	(95)
		183	93	10^{566}	

For explanations and symbols see pp. xi–xii.

TABLE 33 (continued)

C_n	Compound	Method	Yield (%)	Chapter[ref.]	B.p./mm., n_D^t, (M.p.), Deriv.
		Aromatic Diketones (continued)			
C_{15}	Dibenzoylmethane	203	71	10^{552}	(78)
		202	80	10^{551}	(78)
	Diphenyl triketone	222	59†	10^{461}	(70)
	4-Methylbenzil	183	75	10^{566}	221/15
	Mesityl t-butyl ketone	179	83	10^{197}	118/2, 1.5068, 139-Ox*
C_{16}	1,2-Dibenzoylethane	196	76	10^{480}	(147), 204-Ox*
	p-Tolil	179	47	10^{194}	(102), 225-Ox*
	p,p'-Diacetylbiphenyl	178	45	10^{18}	(191)
C_{18}	1,4-Dibenzoylbutane	178	81	10^{89}	(107)
		Heterocyclic Diketones			
C_8	Acetyl-2-furoylmethane	203	43	10^{553}	110/10, 222Cu
		203	45	10^{500}	110/10
	Tetrahydrofuroylacetone	203	60	10^{500}	97/8
	Acetyl-2-thenoylmethane	203	81	10^{554}	131/8, 230Cu
C_9	Propionyl-2-thenoylmethane	203	62	10^{554}	126/4, 194Cu
	Nicotinylacetylmethane	203	63	10^{690}	135/6, (83.5)
C_{10}	Furil	179	63	10^{200}	(166)
		179	91	10^{194}	(165)
C_{11}	Di-2-thenoylmethane	203	64	10^{554}	(100), 263Cu
	2-Furoyl-2-thenoyl-methane	203	75	10^{553}	195/6, (55.5), 274Cu
C_{13}	Benzoyl-2-furoylmethane	203	55	10^{500}	165/3, (68)
		203	87	10^{553}	169/3, 248Cu
	Benzoyl-2-thenoylmethane	203	58	10^{554}	201/4, (78), 278Cu

For explanations and symbols see pp. xi–xii.

TABLE 34. OLEFINIC KETONES

C_n	Compound	Method	Yield (%)	Chapter[ref.]	B.p./mm., n_D^t, (M.p.), Deriv.
		Aliphatic Olefinic Ketones			
C_4	Methyl vinyl ketone	26	81†	2^{478}	81/734
		36	15†	2^{70}	81, 1.4095[22]
			15	10^{665}	81, 1.4095[22], 140Se*
		181	63	10^{230}	
C_5	Methyl propenyl ketone	36	42	2^{76}	119-125
	Ethyl vinyl ketone	178	22	10^{98}	102/740, 1.4192, 129Dn
	Methyl isopropenyl ketone	24	98	2^{488}	38/85, 1.4235, 173Se, 181Dn
		26	92	2^{478}	97/734

TABLE 34. OLEFINIC KETONES · · · · · · · · · · 367

TABLE 34 *(continued)*

C_n	Compound	Method	Yield (%)	Chapter ref.	B.p./mm., n_D^t, (M.p.), Deriv.
					Aliphatic Olefinic Ketones *(continued)*
C_5	Methyl isopropenyl ketone *(continued)*	36	80	2^{291}	58/200, 1.4232
		200	91	10^{98}	
C_6	5-Hexen-2-one-(allylacetone)	184	48†	10^{284}	132/760, 1.4170^{27}
		205	31	10^{595}	128/ 1.4174^{25}, 108Dn, 102Se*
		188	42	10^{390}	
	4-Hexen-3-one	187	25	10^{371}	139, 1.4388, 157Se
	1,2-Diacetylethylene	....	15	2^{521}	90/15, (77)
	2-Methyl-1-penten-3-one	20	65	2^{149}	119/751, 1.4270^{24}, 161Se
	3-Methyl-3-penten-2-one	36	87	2^{487}	97/200, 1.4489
		36	90	2^{71}	140
	4-Methyl-3-penten-2-one	36	80	2^{67}	128
	(mesityl oxide)	36	100	2^{69}	129
C_7	*trans*-3-Hepten-2-one	36	33	2^{72}	60/16, 1.4421, 125Se
	5-Hepten-2-one (crotylacetone)	184	81†	10^{284}	154/770, 1.4280^{25}
		205	80	10^{595}	153, 1.4272^{25}, 105Se
	3-Methyl-1-hexen-5-one	205	37	10^{595}	138, 1.4197^{25}, 112Se
	5-Methyl-4-hexen-3-one	20	30	2^{150}	148/760, 1.4496^{15}, 163Se
		178	30†	10^{101}	148/760, 163Se
	5-Methyl-5-hexen-2-one (methallylacetone)	184	69	10^{284}	145-150/760, 1.4278^{27}, 137Se
		205	26	10^{595}	149, 1.4285^{25}, 137Se
	3,4-Dimethyl-3-penten-2-one	178	54†	10^{101}	147, 200Se
	3,4-Dimethyl-3-penten-2-one	20	54	2^{150}	147, 1.4506^{14}, 200Se
	3,4-Dimethyl-4-penten-2-one				144, 114Se
	3,4-Dimethyl-4-penten-2-one	178	54†	10^{101}	144, 114Se
	4,4-Dimethyl-1-penten-3-one	20	60	2^{149}	66/105, 1.4219^{14}
C_8	3-Methyl-3-hepten-2-one	36	93	2^{71}	175, 164Se
	3-Methyl-3-hepten-5-one	36	72	2^{319}	82-86/42, 1.4488^{25}, 114Se
	4-Methyl-6-hepten-3-one	198	56	10^{286}	156, 80Dn
	2-Methyl-2,5-heptadien-4-one	194	30	10^{449}	72/16, 1.4922^{21}, 141Dn
	3-Ethyl-5-hexen-2-one	184	48	10^{286}	152, 1.4260^{25}, 53Dn
	2-Ethyl-1-hexen-3-one	20	55	2^{149}	158/742, 1.4408^{18}, 119Se
	3,4-Dimethyl-3-hexen-2-one	36	....	2^{322}	158, 1.4476^{15}, 142Se
	5,5-Dimethyl-3-hexen-2-one	36	40	2^{292}	79/40, 1.4430, 178Se
	4,5-Dimethyl-4-hexen-3-one	178	57†	10^{101}	166/750, 209Se
	4,5-Dimethyl-5-hexen-3-one	178	57†	10^{101}	162/750, 110Se

For explanations and symbols see pp. xi–xii.

TABLE 34 *(continued)*

C_n	Compound	Method	Yield (%)	Chapter[ref.]	B.p./mm., n_D^t, (M.p.), Deriv.
		Aliphatic Olefinic Ketones *(continued)*			
C_9	7-Methyl-5-octen-4-one	36	45	2^{74}	86/25, 1.4413
	5-Ethyl-4-hepten-3-one	189	74	10^{406}	179/740, 105Se
	2,3-Dimethyl-2-hepten-6-one	184	86	10^{285}	76/13, 163Se
	3-Propyl-3-hexen-2-one	19	68	2^{75}	72/9, 142Se
	2,4,5-Trimethyl-4-hexen-3-one	178	40 †	10^{101}	174/755
		Alicyclic Olefinic Ketones			
C_6	2-Methyl-2-cyclopen-tenone	179	67	10^{202}	53/12, 220Se
		195	54	10^{598}	161/760, 1.4771, 127-Ox
	2-Cyclohexenone	19	35	2^{79}	68/22, 172Se, 163Dn
		183	38	10^{441}	67/25, 1.4879, 168Se, 117Dn
C_7	1-Acetyl-1-cyclopen-tene	178	50†	10^{102}	74/12, 211Se
	2,3-Dimethyl-2-cyclopen-tenone	206	30	10^{596}	92/25, 1.4830, 250Se
	3-Methyl-2-cyclohexen-1-one	183	20	10^{441}	78/14, 1.4938, 201Se, 176Dn
		202	34	10^{475}	40/0.8, 1.4945, 178Dn, 199Se
C_8	1-Cyclopentenylacetone	184	90	10^{287}	67/12, 150Se
	α-Propylidenecyclopen-tanone	36	65	2^{77}	80/10, 225Se
	2,2,3-Trimethyl-4-cyclo-pentenone	206	6	10^{596}	66/19, 1.4601, 190Se
	3-Ethyl-2-cyclohexenone	202	75	10^{475}	57/0.9, 1.4913, 160Dn, 136Se
	3,5-Dimethyl-2-cyclo-hexen-1-one	36	55	2^{409}	85/9
	1-Acetyl-1-cyclohexene	178	50 †	10^{103}	93/14
		178	54	10^{97}	69/5, 1.4883^{25}, 220Se, 59-Ox
		178	62 †	10^{92}	200, 221Se
		204	70	10^{594}	88/22, 1.4892
C_9	3-Methyl-2-n-propyl-1-cyclopentenone	206	32	10^{596}	58/2, 1.4778, 210Se
	1-Propionyl-1-cyclo-hexene	178	36†	10^{104}	102/14, 189Se, 78-Ox
		178	40†	10^{93}	90/10, 195Se
	2-Allylcyclohexanone	184	66	10^{286}	79/11, 1.4662^{25}, 70-Ox
		198	62	10^{503}	92/17
	3-n-Propyl-2-cyclohex-enone	202	75	10^{475}	60/0.4, 1.4876^{25}, 156Dn, 175Se
	3-Isopropyl-2-cyclohex-enone	202	12	10^{475}	60/0.3, 1.4842, 155Dn, 179Se
	3-Methyl-5-ethyl-2-cyclo-hexen-1-one	36	66	2^{409}	100/9, 1.4880*

TABLE 34. OLEFINIC KETONES 369

TABLE 34 (continued)

C_n	Compound	Method	Yield (%)	Chapter[ref.]	B.p./mm., n_D^t, (M.p.), Deriv.
				Alicyclic Olefinic Ketones (continued)	
C_{10}	2,2-Dimethyl-1-acetyl-1-cyclohexene	204	56	10^{490}	118/49, 1.4810^{25}, 201Se
C_{12}	2-Cyclohexylidenecyclohexanone	36	70	2^{320}	150/22, 1.5084^{25}, 188Se
				Aromatic Olefinic Ketones	
C_9	Phenyl vinyl ketone	20	78	2^{148}	
C_{10}	Phenyl propenyl ketone	178	61	10^{96}	95/2
	Benzalacetone	36	78	2^{294}	128/8, (42)
	α-Methylacrylophenone	26	70	2^{285}	60/3, 1.5354
C_{11}	Isopropylideneacetophenone	178	35	10^{550}	106/5, 1.5579^{23}
		178	40	10^{100}	
		194	40	10^{449}	121/4, 1.5598^{19}, 168pN
C_{12}	1-Phenyl-1-hexen-5-one	205	88	10^{595}	99/0.30, 1.5458^{25}, 132Se
	1-Phenyl-4-hexen-1-one	205	83	10^{595}	97/1, 1.5270^{25}, 130Se
	3-Phenyl-1-hexen-5-one	205	74	10^{595}	86/1, 1.5193^{25}, 103Dn
	Phenyl 2-methyl-3-butenyl ketone	205	76	10^{595}	100/2.1, 1.5223^{25}, 177Se
	o-Methylstyryl ethyl ketone	36	26	2^{302}	152/14, 178Se
C_{13}	Benzalpinacolone	36	93	2^{296}	146/10, (43)
	1-Benzoyl-1-cyclohexene	178	40†	10^{92}	147/8
C_{14}	1-Naphthalacetone	36	75	2^{297}	170/1, 1.6665
	2-Naphthalacetone	36	69	2^{297}	(104)
C_{15}	Benzalacetophenone (chalcone)	36	82	2^{295}	(55–57)
C_{16}	trans-Dibenzoylethylene	178	83	10^{91}	(110), 211-Ox*
	2,4-Diphenyl-2-buten-4-one	36	82	2^{321}	139/1, 1.6273^{25}, 135-Ox
C_{17}	Dibenzalacetone	36	94	2^{293}	(111)
				Heterocyclic Olefinic Ketones	
C_8	Furfuralacetone	36	66	2^{307}	116/10, (38)
C_{11}	Furfuralacetofuran	36	89	2^{309}	(90)
C_{13}	Furfuralacetophenone	36	90	2^{308}	179/7, (26)
	2-Thenalacetophenone	36	96	2^{482}	(59)

For explanations and symbols see pp. xi–xii.

TABLE 35. ACETYLENIC KETONES

C_n	Compound	Method	Yield (%)	Chapter[ref.]	B.p./mm., n_D^t, (M.p.), Deriv.
C_4	Methyl ethynyl ketone	179	40	10^{208}	86, 181Dn, 143pN
C_5	3-Pentyn-2-one	179	67	10^{204}	74/95, 1.4380[23], 149Dn
C_6	n-Propyl ethynyl ketone	179	70	10^{203}	66/100, 137Dn
C_8	3-Octyn-2-one	179	80	10^{203}	76/15, 88Dn, 109Se
		188	58†	10^{396}	76/15, 1.4446[25]
C_9	3-Nonyn-2-one	188	55†	10^{396}	87/13, 1.4463[25]
	Phenyl ethynyl ketone	179	80	10^{203}	(51), 214Dn
C_{10}	4-Phenyl-3-butyn-2-one	188	45†	10^{396}	102/3, 1.5735[25]
		188	55	10^{397}	125/14
C_{15}	Phenyl phenylethynyl	189	74	10^{424}	(55)
	ketone	193	85	10^{424}	(66)

For explanations and symbols see pp. xi–xii.

TABLE 36. HALO KETONES

C_n	Compound	Method	Yield (%)	Chapter[ref.]	B.p./mm., n_D^t, (M.p.), Deriv.
	Aliphatic and Alicyclic Halo Ketones				
C_3	Chloroacetone	66	72	4^{495}	120
		184		10^{90}	
	Bromacetone	66	44	4^{483}	42/13
	α,α'-Dibromoacetone	66	60	4^{634}	98/22, (26.5)
	α,γ-Dichloroacetone	179	75	10^{205}	175, (45)*
	α,α,α'-Tribromoacetone	66	60	4^{634}	116/14, (29)
	Hexafluoroacetone hydrate	182	60	10^{236}	57/93, 1.3288
C_4	Methyl α-chloroethyl ketone	66	62	4^{496}	113, 1.4171
	Methyl α-bromoethyl ketone	66	50	4^{484}	34/12, 1.4571
	Methyl β-chloroethyl ketone	73	67	4^{124}	50/15
		207	40	10^{599}	48/15
	Chloromethyl ethyl ketone	66	21	4^{496}	138, 1.4372
	Bromomethyl ethyl ketone	57	55	4^{519}	155, 1.4670
		66	17	4^{484}	50/12, 1.4670
	Chloromethyl β-chloroethyl ketone	207	45	10^{599}	81/2.5
	Chloromethyl β-iodoethyl ketone	57	84	4^{523}	(55)
	α,α'-Dibromodiacetyl	66	71	4^{493}	(117)

TABLE 36. HALO KETONES 371

TABLE 36 (continued)

C_n	Compound	Method	Yield (%)	Chapter[ref.]	B.p./mm., n_D^t, (M.p.), Deriv.
				Aliphatic and Alicyclic Halo Ketones (continued)	
C_5	Methyl α-chloro-n-propyl	66	44	4[494]	66/56
	ketone	66	37	4[488]	38/12
	Methyl γ-chloro-n-	184	91	10[694]	71/20, 1.4375[25]
	propyl ketone				
	Methyl α-bromo-n-	66	50	4[485]	78/50, 1.4563[22]
	propyl ketone	66	53	4[488]	53/14, 1.4629
	Chloromethyl n-propyl	179	83	10[206]	66/26
	ketone				
	Bromomethyl n-propyl	57	27	4[519]	92/50, 1.4575
	ketone	66	33	4[485]	92/50, 1.4620[23]
	Methyl α-chloroisopropyl	66	58	4[496]	146, 1.4390, 116Dn
	ketone				
	Methyl α-bromoisopropyl	66	35	4[485]	84/150, 1.4590[16]
	ketone				
	Bromomethyl isopropyl	57	46	4[519]	86/50, 1.4467[14·5]
	ketone				
	1-Bromo-5-chloro-2-	57	80	4[519]	114/13, 1.5009[19·5]
	pentanone				
	Ethyl β-chloroethyl	207	45	10[98]	33/2.5, 1.4361
	ketone				
	α-Chloroethyl β-chloro-	207	60	10[599]	65/1.5, 1.4631
	ethyl ketone				
	Di-β-chloroethyl ketone	207	48	10[600]	77/2, 1.4710[16]
	Bromoethyl β-bromoethyl	207	60	10[599]	77/0.1
	ketone				
	2,3-Dibromo-3-methyl-	74	97	4[442]	53/1
	2-butanone				
	1,5-Dibromoacetyl-	184	67	10[289]	(7), 152Cu
	acetone				
	Acetyltrifluoroacetone	203	80	10[560]	107/760, 1.3893[21], 189Cu
C_6	6-Bromo-2-hexanone	54	58	4[125]	105/15, 1.4713, 81Dn
	1-Chloro-2-hexanone	189	51†	10[401]	72.5/15, 1.4370[24*]
	1-Bromo-2-hexanone	57	50	4[519]	108/50, 1.4486[15·5]
		208	67†	10[601]	88/30
	Bromomethyl isobutyl	57	70	4[519]	102/50, 1.4595[17]
	ketone				
	2-Methyl-1-chloro-3-	70	50	4[348]	64/9, 70Se
	pentanone				
	2-Chloro-2-methyl-4-	53	74	4[167]	52/14
	pentanone				
	2,3-Dibromo-3-methyl-2-	74	90	4[442]	82/5
	pentanone				
	1-Chloro-3,3-dimethyl-	66	85	4[496]	76/15, 1.4422, 144Dn
	2-butanone				
	1-Bromo-3,3-dimethyl-2-	66	68	4[489]	49/1, 72/10
	butanone				

For explanations and symbols see pp. xi–xii.

TABLE 36 *(continued)*

C_n	Compound	Method	Yield (%)	Chapter[ref.]	B.p./mm., n_D^t, (M.p.), Deriv.
		Aliphatic and Alicyclic Halo Ketones *(continued)*			
C_6	2-Chlorocyclohexanone	66	57	4[498]	79/7, (23), 1.4825
		66	66	4[497]	91/15
	2-Bromocyclohexanone	66	31†	4[643]	113/20, 1.5085[25]
C_7	1-Chloro-2-heptanone	57	90	4[522]	84/16
	1-Bromo-2-heptanone	208	85†	10[601]	110/30, 1.4644[25]
		57	70	4[519]	96/14, 1.4645[18]
	3-Bromo-2-heptanone	66	21†	4[643]	88/20, 1.4620[25]
		66	43	4[487]	80/9, 1.4613
	2-Chloro-3-heptanone	189	43†	10[401]	68/15
	1-Bromo-6-heptanone	51	47	4[67]	108/8
	3-Methyl-6-bromo-2-hexanone	54	44	4[370]	74/1.5
	3,4-Dimethyl-4-chloro 2-pentanone	207	42	10[101]	64/14
C_8	Chloromethyl n-hexyl ketone	57	92	4[522]	103/16
	3-Bromo-3-methyl-4-heptanone	66	45	4[486]	88/22, 1.4630
	2-Ethyl-1-chloro-3-hexanone	70	50	4[348]	92/12, 115Se
	4,5-Dimethyl-5-chloro-3-hexanone	207	57	10[101]	78/17
	Methyl α-bromocyclohexyl ketone	66	54	4[635]	58-65/3, 1.5027, (-8)
	Bromomethyl cyclohexyl ketone	57	95	4[635]	1.5033, (-2), 131Dn
	1-Acetyl-1,2-dibromocyclohexane	74	60	4[442]	(48)
	1-(Dibromoacetyl)-1-bromocyclohexane	66	80	4[645]	(74)
C_{13}	1-Bromo-2-tridecanone	57	92	4[524]	(53)
		Aromatic Halo Ketones			
C_8	ω-Fluoroacetophenone	178	46	10[105]	95/12, (28)
	ω-Bromoacetophenone	66	96	4[499]	(51)
	ω-Dichloroacetophenone	66	97	4[637]	134/13, 144/25
	ω-Dibromoacetophenone	66	50	4[502]	160/13, (37)
	ω-Trifluoroacetophenone	178	64	10[108]	67/37, 1.4576
	ω-Trichloroacetophenone	66	95	4[636]	102/3.5, 1.5685
		178	70	10[115]	121/15
	m-Bromophenacyl bromide	64	40	4[332]	174/14, (51), 164Se
	p-Bromophenacyl bromide	66	72	4[500]	(109)
	o-Chloroacetophenone	184	54†	10[290]	229/758
		185	81†	10[312]	87/5, 160Se*

TABLE 36. HALO KETONES 373

TABLE 36 (continued)

C_n	Compound	Method	Yield (%)	Chapter[ref.]	B.p./mm., n_D^t, (M.p.), Deriv.
		Aromatic Halo Ketones (continued)			
C_8	o-Bromoacetophenone	56	80	4[332]	112/10, 177Se
		187	80	10[370]	189Dn
		212	65	10[684]	117/12, 177Se*
	m-Chloroacetophenone	56	83	4[334]	113/11, 1.5494*
		183	76	10[245]	92/3, 232Se*
	m-Bromoacetophenone	56	56	4[331]	132/17, 1.5755, 233Se
	m-Iodoacetophenone	56	53	4[334]	117/4, 1.6220
	p-Fluoroacetophenone	178	74	10[110]	79/10, 1.5081[25]
		178	76	10[111]	196, 219Se
	p-Chloroacetophenone	178	78	10[113]	126/24
		178	83	10[12]	(12), 204Se*
	p-Bromoacetophenone	178	79	10[113]	117/7, (50.5), 129-Ox*
	p-Iodoacetophenone	56	52	4[335]	140/9, (84)
		178	95	10[114]	(85)
C_9	α-Chloro-α-phenyl-acetone	66	84	4[510]	118/16, 1.5373
	α-Bromo-α-phenyl-acetone	66	69	4[504]	127/7
	Chloromethyl benzyl ketone	57	85	4[520]	135/19, 98/1
	Bromomethyl benzyl ketone	57	62	4[519]	106/0.2, 1.5593[19.5]
	α-Chloropropiophenone	178	66	10[109]	133/26
	α-Bromopropiophenone	66	42†	4[643]	139/20, 1.5686[25]
	β-Chloropropiophenone	178	65	10[107]	(50)
		178	85	10[106]	(48)
	β-Bromopropiophenone	178	93	10[112]	(59)
	α,α-Dibromopropio-phenone	66	83	4[651]	180/64, (30.5)
	α,β-Dibromopropio-phenone	178	98	10[116]	(56)
	o-Chlorobenzyl methyl ketone	189	60	10[669]	130/15, 120-Ox
	p-Chlorobenzyl methyl ketone	178	16	10[117]	86/1
	o-Chloropropiophenone	56	85	4[333]	106/12, 173Se
	o-Bromopropiophenone	56	77	4[333]	118/11, 179Se
	m-Chloropropiophenone	56	73	4[333]	(46), 180Se
	m-Bromopropiophenone	56	44	4[333]	(40), 183Se
	p-Chloropropiophenone	56	76	4[333]	118/2, (35), 177Se
	p-Bromopropiophenone	56	58	4[333]	140/2, (46), 171Se
	p-Methylphenacyl bromide	66	94	4[501]	(50)
	p-Acetobenzyl bromide	54	46	4[369]	136/5
	m-Trifluoromethylace-tophenone	187	50	10[368]	202
		189	91	10[368]	202

For explanations and symbols see pp. xi-xii.

TABLE 36 *(continued)*

C_n	Compound	Method	Yield (%)	Chapter[ref.]	B.p./mm., n_D^t, (M.p.), Deriv.
		Aromatic Halo Ketones *(continued)*			
C_{10}	α-Bromo-*n*-propyl phenyl ketone	66	98	4[503]	154/23
	Chloromethyl β-phenyl-	57	85	4[510]	(40), 146Dn
	ethyl ketone	179	82	10[143]	111/5, (41), 147Dn
	4-Phenyl-3-chloro-2-	184	60 †	10[288]	99/4, 1.5268, 139Dn
	butanone				
	4-Phenyl-3-bromo-2-	66	81	4[503]	155-160/30
	butanone				
	Benzalacetone dichloride	74	34	4[440]	(93)
	Benzalacetone dibromide	74	57	4[439]	(125)
	1,3-*bis*-Chloroacetyl-	57	83	4[526]	(98)
	benzene				
C_{11}	α-Bromoisobutyl phenyl	66	80	4[503]	145-155/20, (52)
	ketone				
C_{12}	α-Bromoacetylnaph-	66	80	4[638]	215/15
	thalene				
C_{13}	α-Bromoisobutyryl-	178	70	10[122]	170/24
	mesitylene				
	o-Chlorobenzophenone	178	86†	10[118]	180/15, (44)
	o-Bromobenzophenone	178	52	10[120]	153/0.05, 133-Ox*
		178	80	10[121]	190/14
	p-Chlorobenzophenone	178	82	10[119]	(78), 106Ph*, 185Dn*
C_{14}	Phenyl α-chlorobenzyl	53	79	4[183]	(67)
	ketone	62	65	4[407]	(68)
	o-Chlorobenzyl phenyl	190	73	10[430]	(71), 86-Ox
	ketone				
	m-Chlorobenzyl phenyl	190	42	10[432]	(43), 102-Ox
	ketone				
	p-Chlorobenzyl phenyl	190	70	10[431]	(138), 96-Ox
	ketone				
	o-Chlorophenyl benzyl	190	71	10[430]	178/5, 132-Ox
	ketone				
	m-Chlorophenyl benzyl	190	72	10[429]	(62), 120-Ox*
	ketone				
	p-Chlorophenyl benzyl	190	77	10[431]	(108), 123-Ox
	ketone				
	4-Chlorobenzil	183	93	10[566]	(73)
	4-Bromobenzil	183	94	10[566]	(87)
	2,2′-Dichlorobenzil	179	39†	10[195]	(129)
C_{15}	α-Chlorodibenzyl	66	80	4[511]	195/12, (68.5)
	ketone				
	α-Bromodibenzyl ketone	66	99	4[506]	(49)
	Benzalacetophenone di-	74	96	4[441]	(113)
	chloride				

TABLE 37. HYDROXY KETONES 375

TABLE 36 *(continued)*

C_n	Compound	Method	Yield (%)	Chapter[ref.]	B.p./mm., n_D^t, (M.p.), Deriv.
		Aromatic Halo Ketones *(continued)*			
C_{15}	α-Bromo-4-propionylbiphenyl	66	75	4 [505]	(79)
C_{16}	9-ω-Bromoacetylanthracene	66	50	4 [508]	(107)
		Heterocyclic Halo Ketones			
C_6	2-Chloroacetylfuran	57	88 †	4 [527]	93–108/4
	2-Chloroacetylthiophene	66	77	4 [512]	113/5, (48)
	2-Bromoacetylthiophene	66	80	4 [509]	98/1.5, 1.6258
C_{10}	2-Chloroacetylbenzofuran	57	95	4 [644]	(105)
C_{11}	4-Quinolyl chloromethyl ketone	57	50	4 [525]	(101)

For explanations and symbols see pp. xi–xii.

TABLE 37. HYDROXY KETONES

C_n	Compound	Method	Yield (%)	Chapter[ref.]	B.p./mm., n_D^t, (M.p.), Deriv.
		Aliphatic and Alicyclic Hydroxy Ketones			
C_3	Acetol (1-hydroxy-2-propanone)	95	58	5 [522]	42/12
C_4	1-Hydroxy-3-butanone	84	44 †	5 [669]	74/13, 1.4302 [15]
		102	28	5 [207]	71/12, 1.435 [15]
C_5	1-Hydroxy-2-pentanone	95	15	5 [711]	152/760
	4-Hydroxy-2-pentanone	79	35	5 [158]	94/43, 1.4238 [25], 104Ph
	5-Hydroxy-2-pentanone	99	31	5 [623]	75/3, 1.4350 [25]
		181	30	10 [229]	86/10, 155Se
	3-Methyl-4-hydroxy-2-butanone	102	93	5 [208]	84/19
	Dimethylacetylcarbinol	89	26 †	5 [398]	140, 87-Ox, 165Se
	2-Hydroxycyclopentanone	104	16	5 [761]	74/10, 1.4701 [25]
C_6	5-Hydroxy-2-hexanone	184	69	5 [732]	61/2, 1.4312 [25], 151Se
	4-Hydroxy-3-hexanone (propionoin)	104	55	5 [636]	60–65/12
	5-Hydroxy-3-hexanone	79	51	5 [158]	76/12, 1.4280 [25]
	3-Methyl-3-hydroxy-2-pentanone	200	60	10 [511]	73/50, 1.4200, 150Se

For explanations and symbols see pp. xi–xii.

TABLE 37 *(continued)*

C_n	Compound	Method	Yield (%)	Chapter[ref.]	B.p./mm., n_D^t, (M.p.), Deriv.
	Aliphatic and Alicyclic Hydroxy Ketones *(continued)*				
C_6	3-Methyl-4-hydroxy-2-pentanone	102	67	5[738]	76/10, 1.4350
	4-Methyl-4-hydroxy-2-pentanone (diacetone alcohol)	102	71	5[204]	73/23
	2-Methyl-1-hydroxy-3-pentanone	102	57	5[740]	94/15, 1.4346
	3-Ethyl-4-hydroxy-2-butanone	102	55	5[740]	96/17, 1.4362[18]
	2-Hydroxycyclohexanone	96	76	5[187]	
		104	55	5[761]	(117)
C_7	4-Hydroxy-2-heptanone	102	80	5[210]	95/12, 1.4357
	2-Hydroxy-4-heptanone	79	58	5[158]	101/24, 1.4300[25]
	3-Methyl-4-hydroxy-2-hexanone	102	61	5[211]	95/20, 1.435[24]
	2-Methyl-5-hydroxy-3-hexanone	79	50	5[158]	73/9, 1.4278[25]
	2-Hydroxymethyl-1-cyclohexanone	102	20	5[216]	115/16, 129Ph, 145pN
C_8	2-Hydroxy-4-octanone	79	66	5[158]	91/8, 1.4333[25]
	5-Hydroxy-4-octanone (butyroin)	104	70	5[636]	80–86/12
	3-Methyl-3-hydroxy-2-heptanone	89	46[†]	5[398]	84/19, 152Se
	3-Methyl-4-hydroxy-2-heptanone	102	45	5[212]	110/16, 1.442
		102	82	5[209]	115/30
	5-Methyl-5-hydroxy-3-heptanone	102	67	5[205]	86/14, 1.4386[14], 125Se
	5-Methyl-2-hydroxy-4-heptanone	79	64	5[158]	114/36, 1.4318[25]
	6-Methyl-2-hydroxy-4-heptanone	79	49	5[158]	86/9, 1.4294[25], 112Ph
	4-Ethyl-4-hydroxy-3-hexanone	193	54	10[502]	178/742
		198	59	10[502]	89/35, 177Se
	2,2-Dimethyl-5-hydroxy-3-hexanone	79	68	5[158]	73/10, 1.4243[25]
	2,5-Dimethyl-4-hydroxy-3-hexanone (isobutyroin)	104	75	5[636]	70–75/14
	2-(α-Hydroxy-n-propyl)-cyclopentanone	102	45	5[215]	105/9
C_9	3-Methyl-4-hydroxy-2-octanone	102	35	5[211]	98/16, 1.4404[29]

TABLE 37. HYDROXY KETONES 377

TABLE 37 *(continued)*

C_n	Compound	Method	Yield (%)	Chapter[ref.]	B.p./mm., n_D^t, (M.p.), Deriv.
		Aliphatic and Alicyclic Hydroxy Ketones *(continued)*			
C_{10}	2,2,5,5-Tetramethyl-4-hydroxy-3-hexanone (pivaloin)	104	60	5 [636]	85–95/12
	2-(1'-Hydroxycyclopentyl)-cyclopentanone	102	40	5 [205]	99/3, (31), 78-Ox
		Aromatic Hydroxy Ketones			
C_8	m-Hydroxyacetophenone	93	48	5 [493]	(95)
	2,4-Dihydroxyacetophenone	178	65	10 [124]	(144)
	2,5-Dihydroxyacetophenone	209	77	10 [607]	(203)
	2,3,4-Trihydroxyacetophenone	178	57	10 [125]	(172)
	2,4,6-Trihydroxyacetophenone	178	87	10 [129]	(219)
C_9	Acetylphenylcarbinol	95	72	5 [523]	123/13, 113-Ox, 126Dn
		190	50	10 [435]	137/24, 194Se, 170Dn
	Methylbenzoylcarbinol	95	87	5 [523]	123/14, 134-Ox
	α,β-Dihydroxypropiophenone	98	90	5 [619]	(82)
	o-Propiophenol	209	35	10 [605]	115/6
	p-Propiophenol	178	82	10 [130]	(149), 170Se
		209	50	10 [605]	(148)
C_{10}	Acetylphenylmethylcarbinol	105	48	5 [650]	132/10
C_{12}	Phenyltrimethylacetylcarbinol	105	49	5 [649]	(47)
C_{13}	2-Hydroxybenzophenone	97	96	5 [536]	(153)
	3-Hydroxybenzophenone	97	88	5 [536]	(116)
	4-Hydroxybenzophenone	97	95	5 [536]	(134)
C_{14}	Benzoin	79	93	5 [156]	(134)
		79	97	5 [157]	
		104	92	5 [640]	(129)
		105	90	5 [648]	(133)
	o,o'-Dichlorobenzoin	104	40	5 [646]	(57)
	m,m'-Dichlorobenzoin	104	22	5 [646]	(76)
	p,p'-Dichlorobenzoin	104	88	5 [646]	(88)
	4,4'-Dihydroxybenzil	97	89	5 [541]	(235)
C_{15}	p-Methoxybenzoin (benzanisoin)	104	31	5 [644]	(106)

For explanations and symbols see pp. xi–xii.

TABLE 37 (continued)

C_n	Compound	Method	Yield (%)	Chapter[ref.]	B.p./mm., n_D^t, (M.p.), Deriv.
				Aromatic Hydroxy Ketones (continued)	
C_{16}	Diphenylacetoin	187	45	10^{372}	(52), 169 Se, 84NBz
	p,p'-Dimethoxybenzoin (anisoin)	104	73	5^{643}	(113)
C_{17}	$2',4',6'$-Trimethylbenzoin	105	63	5^{648}	(103)
C_{22}	β-Naphthoin	104	78	5^{642}	(126), 172-Ox
				Heterocyclic Hydroxy Ketones	
C_6	2-Hydroxyacetylfuran	114	74	5^{764}	(82)
C_{10}	α-Furoin	104	38	5^{647}	(135)
	$2,2'$-Thenoin	104	30	5^{763}	(109)

For explanations and symbols see pp. xi–xii.

TABLE 38. KETO ETHERS

C_n	Compound	Method	Yield (%)	Chapter[ref.]	B.p./mm., n_D^t, (M.p.), Deriv.
				Aliphatic and Alicyclic Keto Ethers	
C_4	Mexthoxymethyl methyl ketone	179	29	10^{209}	115/756, 1.3982, 111pN, 163Dn
		187	48	10^{373}	114/746, 1.3980, 159Dn*, 109pN*
C_5	1-Methoxyethyl methyl ketone	187	37	10^{375}	116/739, 1.3936, 141Se
	4-Methoxy-2-butanone	121	73	6^{110}	66/50, 138/745, 1.4050
		195	75	10^{578}	140/745
	Methoxymethyl ethyl ketone	187	49	10^{373}	133/757, 1.4063
		187	59	10^{379}	132, 198Dn*
	sym-Dimethoxyacetone	187	45	10^{208}	78/18, 1.4174, 120Se
	Ethoxyacetone	187	65	10^{381}	36/28, 1.4000, 96Se*
C_6	1-Methoxypropyl methyl ketone	187	29	10^{378}	71/95, 1.4015^{25}, 147Se
	Methoxymethyl n-propyl ketone	187	51	10^{373}	153/745, 1.4119
	Methoxymethyl isopropyl ketone	187	30	10^{374}	144, 163Dn
		187	44	10^{373}	145/748, 1.4078
	1-Methoxyethyl ethyl ketone	187	22	10^{375}	136/750, 1.4019, 120Se
	4-Ethoxy-2-butanone	121	77	6^{111}	150/764, 74/50
	Ethoxymethyl ethyl ketone	187	84	10^{377}	147/752, 1.4068
	n-Propoxymethyl methyl ketone	187	52	10^{376}	49/6, 1.4052

TABLE 38. KETO ETHERS 379

TABLE 38 *(continued)*

C_n	Compound	Method	Yield (%)	Chapter[ref.]	B.p./mm., n_D^t, (M.p.), Deriv.
	\multicolumn{5}{c}{Aliphatic and Alicyclic Keto Ethers *(continued)*}				
C_6	Isopropoxymethyl methyl ketone	187 187	48 53	10^{376} 10^{374}	35/10, 1.4004, 144Dn 142, 142Dn
C_7	1-Methoxy-5-hexanone	187	23	10^{379}	67/8, 1.4180[25], 70Dn
	Methoxymethyl n-butyl ketone	187	34	10^{373}	169/744, 1.4173
	Methoxymethyl isobutyl ketone	187	30	10^{373}	164/751, 1.4140
	Methoxymethyl s-butyl ketone	187	32	10^{373}	164/757, 1.4162
	Methoxymethyl t-butyl ketone	187	19	10^{373}	159/743, 1.4193
	1-Methoxyethyl n-propyl ketone	187 187	33 73	10^{375} 10^{382}	155/746, 1.4091, 169Se 93/100, 170Se
	1-Methoxyethyl isopropyl ketone	187	13	10^{375}	58/31, 1.4092, 146Se
	1-Methoxypropyl ethyl ketone	187	79	10^{378}	63/40, 1.4080[25], 145Se
	α-Methoxypinacolone	124	59	6^{173}	83/4, 189Dn
	n-Propoxymethyl ethyl ketone	187	46	10^{376}	56/4, 1.4122
	Isopropoxymethyl ethyl ketone	187	41	10^{376}	47/11, 1.4082, 103Dn
	sym-Diethoxyacetone	187	67	10^{208}	105/35, 1.4202, 91Se
	2-Methoxycyclohexanone	179	46	10^{210}	59/8, 1.4519[25]
	4-Methoxycyclohexanone	179	65	10^{207}	85/14, 1.4560, 178Se, 150Dn
C_8	Methoxymethyl n-amyl ketone	187	46	10^{373}	191/753, 1.4220
	Methoxymethyl isoamyl ketone	187	71	10^{373}	186/752, 1.4210
	1-Methoxyethyl n-butyl ketone	187	63	10^{375}	82/36, 1.4160, 154Se
	1-Methoxyethyl isobutyl ketone	187	21	10^{375}	52/9, 1.4128, 145Se
	1-Methoxyethyl s-butyl ketone	187	43	10^{375}	77/36, 1.4158, 127Se
	1-Methoxyethyl t-butyl ketone	187	14	10^{375}	64/34, 1.4130, 121Se
	1-Methoxypropyl n-propyl ketone	187	69	10^{378}	86/42, 1.4131[25], 157Se
	1-Methoxypropyl isopropyl ketone	187	44	10^{378}	66/23, 1.4159, 136Se
	6-Ethoxy-2-hexanone	184	60†	10^{291}	92/13, 64Dn
	Ethoxymethyl s-butyl ketone	187	29	10^{377}	173/743, 1.4158

For explanations and symbols see pp. xi–xii.

TABLE 38 (continued)

C_n	Compound	Method	Yield (%)	Chapter[ref.]	B.p./mm., n_D^t, (M.p.), Deriv.
	Aliphatic and Alicyclic Keto Ethers (continued)				
C_8	1-Isopropoxy-3-methyl-2-butanone	187	17	10^{374}	160, 88Dn
	Methyl α-(s-butoxy)-ethyl ketone	187	69	10^{383}	163/750, 1.4080, 118Se
	Methoxymethyl cyclopentyl ketone	187	22	10^{384}	87/14, 1.4486^{25}, 129Dn
C_9	3-Methyl-6-ethoxy-2-hexanone	184	69†	10^{293}	99/17
	Methoxymethyl cyclohexyl ketone	187	33	10^{384}	111/21, 1.4552^{25}, 102Se
	Aromatic Keto Ethers				
C_9	Phenoxyacetone	115	93	6^{51}	120/19
		187	16	10^{380}	112/12, 1.5228, 176Se
	α-Methoxyacetophenone	124	79	6^{173}	126/19, 129Se
	p-Methoxyacetophenone	178	66	10^{26}	125/5, 198Se
		178	96	10^6	139/15, (37), 87-Ox*
C_{10}	Phenoxymethyl ethyl ketone	187	62	10^{380}	100/5, 1.5201, 102Se
	α-Methoxypropiophenone	124	60	6^{173}	89–95/4, 160Dn
	β-Methoxyethyl phenyl ketone	189	90	10^{404}	1.5250, 176Dn
	α-Ethoxyacetophenone	124	81	6^{173}	127/11, 128Se
		187	68	10^{377}	122/15, 1.5250
	p-Methoxypropiophenone	116	88	6^{96}	152/19
		178	87	10^6	125/4
	p-Ethoxyacetophenone	178	77	10^{29}	147/16, 1.5429^{25}
	2,5-Dimethoxyacetophenone	178	71	10^{134}	160/15
	3,5-Dimethoxyacetophenone	190	57	10^{436}	(43)
C_{11}	γ-Phenoxypropyl methyl ketone	189	78	10^{292}	121/2, (50), 110Dn
	Phenoxymethyl n-propyl ketone	187	64	10^{380}	112/4, 1.5148, 108Se
	β-Ethoxyethyl phenyl ketone	189	82	10^{404}	1.5190, 161Dn
	n-Propoxymethyl phenyl ketone	187	37	10^{376}	118/6, 1.5150
C_{12}	δ-Phenoxybutyl methyl ketone	184	61†	10^{292}	130/2, 1.5071^{25}, 101Dn
	β-n-Propoxyethyl phenyl ketone	189	82	10^{404}	1.5193, 158Dn

TABLE 30. KETO ALDEHYDES 381

TABLE 38 *(continued)*

C_n	Compound	Method	Yield (%)	Chapter[ref.]	B.p./mm., n_D^t, (M.p.), Deriv.
		Aromatic Keto Ethers *(continued)*			
C_{12}	β-Isopropoxyethyl phenyl ketone	189	89	10^{404}	1.5083, 175Dn
C_{13}	β-Naphthoxyacetone	115	85	6^{51}	(77)
C_{14}	Phenoxymethyl phenyl ketone	187	45	10^{380}	187/8, (74), 187Se
	m-Methoxybenzophenone	179	25 †	10^{211}	(38)
		187	77	10^{385}	185/4, (40)
	p-Methoxybenzophenone	178	89	10^{26}	(62.5), 180Dn
	p-Phenoxyacetophenone	178	68	10^{107}	154/2, (49)
C_{15}	*p*-Methoxyphenyl benzyl ketone	190	74	10^{429}	(77), 118-Ox
	2-Methoxybenzil	179	60 †	10^{212}	(72)
	4-Methoxybenzil	179	90	10^{198}	(63), 124-Ox
C_{16}	2-Ethoxybenzil	179	60 †	10^{212}	(102)
	4-Ethoxybenzil	179	60 †	10^{212}	(71)
	Desoxyanisoin	221	98	10^{345}	(112)
	2,2'-Dimethoxybenzil	179	40 †	10^{212}	(129)
	3,3'-Dimethoxybenzil	179	60 †	10^{212}	(83)
	4,4'-Dimethoxybenzil	179	52 †	10^{212}	(133)
	(anisil)	179	97	10^{194}	(132), 255Se*

For explanations and symbols see pp. xi–xii.

TABLE 39. KETO ALDEHYDES

C_n	Compound	Method	Yield (%)	Chapter[ref.]	B.p./mm., n_D^t, (M.p.), Deriv.
C_3	Methylglyoxal	157	50	9^{181}	52/12, 148Ph, 254Se
C_5	3-Formyl-2-butanone	146	75	9^{173}	
C_6	*t*-Butylglyoxal	157	52	9^{180}	115, 172Dn, 101-Ox
C_7	Pivaloylacetaldehyde	146	50	9^{171}	45/13, 126Cu
	Hydroxymethylene-methyl isobutyl ketone	146	80	9^{173}	
	α-Formylcyclohexanone	146	60	9^{174}	88/14, 1.5130
C_8	Cyclohexylglyoxal	157	59	9^{182}	72/17
	1-Methyl-3-hydroxy-methylene-2-cyclohexanone	146	45	9^{263}	87/12
	Phenylglyoxal	152	87 †	9^{189}	(73)
		157	72	9^{177}	97/25
C_9	*p*-Acetylbenzaldehyde	162	43	9^{234}	190Ph, 181-Ox

For explanations and symbols see pp. xi–xii.

TABLE 39 *(continued)*

C_n	Compound	Method	Yield (%)	Chapter[ref.]	B.p./mm., n_D^t, (M.p.), Deriv.
C_{11}	Mesitylglyoxal	157	83	9[179]	106/4, 1.5520[19]
	2-Hydroxymethylene-1-tetralone	146	94	9[259]	180/28
C_{12}	β-Naphthylglyoxal	152	30	9[189]	(109)
C_{14}	p-Xenylglyoxal	152	90	9[189]	(121)

For explanations and symbols see pp. xi–xii.

REFERENCES FOR CHAPTER 10

[1] Bergmann, Schapiro, and Eschinazi, *J. Am. Chem. Soc.*, **64**, 559 (1942); Allen and Barker, *Org. Syntheses,* Coll. Vol. II, 156 (1943).
[2] Grummitt and Case, *J. Am. Chem. Soc.*, **64**, 880 (1942).
[3] Seidel and Engelfried, *Ber.*, **69B**, 2578 (1936).
[4] Mowry, Renoll, and Huber, *J. Am. Chem. Soc.*, **68**, 1105 (1946).
[5] Bachmann, Carlson, and Moran, *J. Org. Chem.*,**13**, 916 (1948).
[6] Noller and Adams, *J. Am. Chem. Soc.*, **46**, 1889 (1924).
[7] Smith and Guss, *J. Am. Chem. Soc.*, **59**, 805 (1937).
[8] Marvel, Saunders, and Overberger, *J. Am. Chem. Soc.*, **68**, 1086 (1946).
[9] Allen, *Org. Syntheses,* Coll. Vol. II, 3 (1943).
[10] Groggins, *Unit Processes in Organic Synthesis,* McGraw-Hill Book Co., New York, 1947, pp. 759–770; Thomas, *Anhydrous Aluminum Chloride in Organic Chemistry,* Reinhold Publishing Corp., New York, 1941, pp. 205–393.
[11] Dermer et al., *J. Am. Chem. Soc.*, **63**, 2881 (1941).
[12] Groggins and Nagel, *Ind. Eng. Chem.*, **26**, 1313 (1934).
[13] Riddell and Noller, *J. Am. Chem. Soc.*, **52**, 4365 (1930).
[14] Calloway and Green, *J. Am. Chem. Soc.*, **59**, 809 (1937).
[15] Johnson in *Organic Reactions,* Vol. 2, John Wiley & Sons, New York, 1944, p. 114.
[16] Calloway, *Chem. Revs.*, **17**, 327 (1935).
[17] Johnson and Glenn, *J. Am. Chem. Soc.*, **71**, 1092 (1949).
[18] Long and Henze, *J. Am. Chem. Soc.*, **63**, 1939 (1941).
[19] Bachmann and Sheehan, *J. Am. Chem. Soc.*, **62**, 2688 (1940).
[20] Mosettig and van de Kamp, *J. Am. Chem. Soc.*, **52**, 3707 (1930).
[21] Bachmann and Struve, *J. Am. Chem. Soc.*, **58**, 1660 (1936).
[22] Riegel, Gold, and Kubico, *J. Am. Chem. Soc.*, **64**, 2221 (1942).
[23] Fieser and Cason, *J. Am. Chem. Soc.*, **61**, 1742 (1939).
[24] Fieser and Hershberg, *J. Am. Chem. Soc.*, **61**, 1272 (1939).
[25] Smith and Lo, *J. Am. Chem. Soc.*, **70**, 2209 (1948).
[26] Chodroff and Klein, *J. Am. Chem. Soc.*, **70**, 1647 (1948).
[27] Fahim, *J. Chem. Soc.*, 520 (1949).
[28] Pines, Strehlau, and Ipatieff, *J. Am. Chem. Soc.*, **71**, 3536 (1949).
[29] Kosolapoff, *J. Am. Chem. Soc.*, **69**, 1651 (1947).
[30] Baddeley, *J. Chem. Soc.*, S99 (1949).
[31] Ray and Rieveschl, *Org. Syntheses,* **28**, 3 (1948); cf. ref. 4.
[32] Merritt and Braun, *Org. Syntheses,* **30**, 1 (1950).
[33] Mason and Terry, *J. Am. Chem. Soc.*, **62**, 1622 (1940).
[34] Read, *J. Am. Chem. Soc.*, **44**, 1751 (1922).
[35] Vogel, *J. Chem. Soc.*, 612 (1948).
[36] Fourneau and Barrelet, *Bull. soc. chim. France*, **47**, 77 (1930).
[37] Maxwell and Adams, *J. Am. Chem. Soc.*, **52**, 2959 (1930).
[38] Weygand and Mensdorf, *Ber.*, **68B**, 1831 (1935).
[39] Hennion and McLease, *J. Am. Chem. Soc.*, **64**, 2421 (1942).
[40] Kadesch and Weller, *J. Am. Chem. Soc.*, **63**, 1311 (1941).
[41] Kloetzel and Herzog, *J. Am. Chem. Soc.*, **72**, 1991 (1950).
[42] Williams and Osborn, *J. Am. Chem. Soc.*, **61**, 3438 (1939).
[43] Immediata and Day, *J. Org. Chem.*, **5**, 516 (1940).
[44] Sachanen and Caesar, *Ind. Eng. Chem.*, **38**, 45 (1946).
[45] Johnson and Offenhauer, *J. Am. Chem. Soc.*, **67**, 1046 (1945).

[46] Hughes, Ingold, and Taher, *J. Chem. Soc.*, 953 (1940).
[47] Huber et al., *J. Am. Chem. Soc.*, **68**, 1109 (1946).
[48] Drake and Bronitsky, *J. Am. Chem. Soc.*, **52**, 3718 (1930).
[49] Fieser and Kilmer, *J. Am. Chem. Soc.*, **62**, 1357 (1940).
[50] Steyermark and Gardner, *J. Am. Chem. Soc.*, **52**, 4886 (1930).
[51] Meyer, *Org. Syntheses*, Coll. Vol. I, 60 (1941).
[52] Bergmann, *J. Org. Chem.*, **4**, 4, (1939).
[53] Von and Wagner, *J. Org. Chem.*, **9**, 163 (1944).
[54] Fuson et al., *J. Am. Chem. Soc.*, **66**, 682 (1944).
[55] May and Mosettig, *J. Am. Chem. Soc.*, **70**, 686, 688 (1948).
[56] Shildneck, *Org. Syntheses*, Coll. Vol. II, 236 (1943).
[57] Cook, *J. Chem. Soc.*, 1284 (1926).
[58] Bachmann, *J. Am. Chem. Soc.*, **57**, 555 (1935).
[59] Hartough and Kosak, *J. Am. Chem. Soc.*, **68**, 2639 (1946).
[60] Hartough and Kosak, *J. Am. Chem. Soc.*, **69**, 1012 (1947).
[61] Hartough, Kosak, and Sardella, *J. Am. Chem. Soc.*, **69**, 1014 (1947).
[62] Johnson and May, *Org. Syntheses*, Coll. Vol. II, 8 (1943); cf. ref. 4.
[63] Minnis, *Org. Syntheses*, Coll. Vol. II, 520 (1943); refs. 59 and 60.
[64] Levine et al., *J. Org. Chem.*, **13**, 409 (1948); *J. Am. Chem. Soc.*, **71**, 1207 (1949).
[65] Hartough and Kosak, *J. Am. Chem. Soc.*, **70**, 867 (1948).
[66] Hartough et al., *J. Am. Chem. Soc.*, **69**, 3093, 3096, 3098 (1947); Kosak and Hartough, *Org. Syntheses*, **28**, 1 (1948).
[67] Emling, Beatty, and Stevens, *J. Am. Chem. Soc.*, **71**, 703 (1949).
[68] Farrar and Levine, *J. Am. Chem. Soc.*, **72**, 3695 (1950).
[69] Gilman, Rowe, and Dickey, *Rec. trav. chim.*, **52**, 396 (1933).
[70] Hansch and Lindwall, *J. Org. Chem.*, **10**, 383 (1945); cf. ref. 71.
[71] Farrar and Levine, *J. Am. Chem. Soc.*, **72**, 4433 (1950).
[72] Burger and Bryant, *J. Org. Chem.*, **4**, 119 (1939).
[73] Buu-Hoi and Royer, *Rec. trav. chim.*, **69**, 866 (1950).
[74] Hart and Tebbe, *J. Am. Chem. Soc.*, **72**, 3286 (1950).
[75] Snyder and Werber, *J. Am. Chem. Soc.*, **72**, 2965 (1950).
[76] Levin, Graham, and Kolloff, *J. Org. Chem.*, **9**, 384 (1944).
[77] Cope and Field, *J. Am. Chem. Soc.*, **71**, 1591 (1949).
[78] Pacaud and Allen, *Org. Syntheses*, Coll. Vol. II, 336 (1943).
[79] Martin and Fieser, *Org. Syntheses*, Coll. Vol. II, 569 (1943).
[80] Kloetzel, *J. Am. Chem. Soc.*, **62**, 1708 (1940).
[81] Alexander and Mudrak, *J. Am. Chem. Soc.*, **72**, 3194 (1950).
[82] Adkins and Davis, *J. Am. Chem. Soc.*, **71**, 2955 (1949).
[83] Weygand and Schröder, *Ber.*, **74B**, 1847 (1941).
[84] Bachmann and Struve, *J. Am. Chem. Soc.*, **62**, 1618 (1940).
[85] Newman, *J. Am. Chem. Soc.*, **62**, 1685 (1940).
[86] Arnold, Buckley, and Richter, *J. Am. Chem. Soc.*, **69**, 2323 (1947).
[87] Fieser and Seligman, *J. Am. Chem. Soc.*, **60**, 170 (1938).
[88] Thomas and Nathan, *J. Am. Chem. Soc.*, **70**, 331 (1948).
[89] Fuson and Walker, *Org. Syntheses*, Coll. Vol. II, 169 (1943).
[90] Boese, *Ind. Eng. Chem.*, **32**, 16 (1940).
[91] Lutz, *Org. Syntheses*, **20**, 29 (1940).
[92] Christ and Fuson, *J. Am. Chem. Soc.*, **59**, 893 (1937).
[93] Colonge and Duroux, *Bull. soc. chim. France*, (5e) 7, 459 (1940).
[94] Colonge and Mostafavi, *Bull. soc. chim. France*, (5) 5, 1478 (1938).

[95] Byrans and Doumani, *Ind. Eng. Chem.*, **35**, 349 (1943).
[96] Fuson, Christ, and Whitman, *J. Am. Chem. Soc.*, **58**, 2451 (1936).
[97] Royals and Hendry, *J. Org. Chem.*, **15**, 1147 (1950).
[98] McMahon et al., *J. Am. Chem. Soc.*, **70**, 2971 (1948).
[99] Price and Pappalardo, *J. Am. Chem. Soc.*, **72**, 2613 (1950).
[100] Darzens, *Compt. rend.*, **211**, 435 (1940).
[101] Colonge and Mostafavi, *Bull. soc. chim. France*, (5) **6**, 341–354 (1939).
[102] Hawthorne and Robinson, *J. Chem. Soc.*, 763 (1936).
[103] Ruzicka, Koolhaas, and Wind, *Helv. Chim. Acta*, **14**, 1157 (1931).
[104] Jones and Ramage, *J. Chem. Soc.*, 1856 (1938).
[105] Truce and Sack, *J. Am. Chem. Soc.*, **70**, 3959 (1948).
[106] Campbell, LaForge, and Campbell, *J. Org. Chem.*, **14**, 348 (1949).
[107] Conant and Kirner, *J. Am. Chem. Soc.*, **46**, 239 (1924).
[108] Cohen, Wolosinski, and Scheuer, *J. Am. Chem. Soc.*, **71**, 3440 (1949).
[109] Baker and Barkenbus, *J. Am. Chem. Soc.*, **58**, 263 (1936).
[110] Renoll, *J. Am. Chem. Soc.*, **68**, 1160 (1946).
[111] Fosdick and Campaigne, *J. Am. Chem. Soc.*, **63**, 974 (1941); Buu-Hoi, Hoan, and Jacquignon, *Rec. trav. chim.*, **68**, 784 (1949).
[112] Foreman and McElvain, *J. Am. Chem. Soc.*, **62**, 1436 (1940).
[113] Adams and Noller, *Org. Syntheses*, Coll. Vol. I, 109 (1941).
[114] Kimura, *Ber.*, **67**, 395 (1934).
[115] Houben and Fischer, *J. prakt. Chem.*, **123**, 313 (1929).
[116] Davis, *J. Am. Chem. Soc.*, **63**, 1677 (1941).
[117] Patrick, McBee, and Hass, *J. Am. Chem. Soc.*, **68**, 1135 (1946).
[118] Berliner, *J. Am. Chem. Soc.*, **66**, 534 (1944).
[119] Newton and Groggins, *Ind. Eng. Chem.*, **27**, 1397 (1935).
[120] Bergmann, *J. Org. Chem.*, **4**, 9 (1939).
[121] Borsche and Scriba, *Ann.*, **540**, 90 (1939).
[122] Fisher, Oakwood, and Fuson, *J. Am. Chem. Soc.*, **52**, 5038 (1930).
[123] Sandulesco and Girard, *Bull. soc. chim. France*, (4) **47**, 1300 (1930); cf. Close, Tiffany, and Spielman, *J. Am. Chem. Soc.*, **71**, 1265 (1949).
[124] Cooper, *Org. Syntheses*, **21**, 103 (1941).
[125] Badhwar and Venkataraman, *Org. Syntheses*, Coll. Vol. II, 304 (1943).
[126] Brewster and Watters, *J. Am. Chem. Soc.*, **64**, 2578 (1942).
[127] Coulthard, Marshall, and Pyman, *J. Chem. Soc.*, 280 (1930).
[128] Spoerri and Dubois in *Organic Reactions*, Vol. 5, John Wiley & Sons, New York, 1949, p. 387.
[129] Gulati, Seth, and Venkataraman, *Org. Syntheses*, Coll. Vol. II, 522 (1943).
[130] v. Auwers, Potz, and Noll, *Ann.*, **535**, 228 (1938).
[131] Ungnade, *Chem. Revs.*, **38**, 419 (1946).
[132] Stuart and Tallman, *J. Am. Chem. Soc.*, **65**, 1579 (1943); Skraup and Nieten, *Ber.*, **57**, 1294 (1924).
[133] Buck and Ide, *J. Am. Chem. Soc.*, **54**, 3012 (1932).
[134] Villani and Lang, *J. Am. Chem. Soc.*, **72**, 2301 (1950).
[135] Somerville and Allen, *Org. Syntheses*, Coll. Vol. II, 81 (1943).
[136] Fieser, Gates, and Kilmer, *J. Am. Chem. Soc.*, **62**, 2968 (1940).
[137] Fieser and Price, *J. Am. Chem. Soc.*, **58**, 1841 (1936).
[138] Fieser and Peters, *J. Am. Chem. Soc.*, **54**, 4347 (1932).
[139] Fieser et al., *J. Am. Chem. Soc.*, **70**, 3197 (1948).
[140] Hill, *J. Am. Chem. Soc.*, **54**, 4105 (1932).
[141] Papa et al., *J. Am. Chem. Soc.*, **70**, 3356 (1948).

[142] Berliner in *Organic Reactions*, Vol. 5, John Wiley & Sons, New York, 1949, p. 229.

[143] Henze and Holder, *J. Am. Chem. Soc.*, **63**, 1943 (1941).

[144] Groggins, *Ind. Eng. Chem.*, **22**, 620 (1930).

[145] Groggins and Newton, *Ind. Eng. Chem.*, **21**, 369 (1929).

[146] Fieser, *Org. Syntheses*, **20**, 1 (1940).

[147] Papa, Schwenk, and Hankin, *J. Am. Chem. Soc.*, **69**, 3018 (1947).

[148] McElvain, *J. Am. Chem. Soc.*, **51**, 3124 (1929); Roberts and McElvain, *ibid.*, **59**, 2007 (1937).

[149] Sengupta, *J. prakt. Chem.*, **151**, 87 (1938).

[150] Blicke and Tsao, *J. Am. Chem. Soc.*, **66**, 1645 (1944).

[151] Blicke and Feldkamp, *J. Am. Chem. Soc.*, **66**, 1089 (1944).

[152] Blicke and Grier, *J. Am. Chem. Soc.*, **65**, 1726 (1943).

[153] Papa et al., *J. Am. Chem. Soc.*, **68**, 2133 (1946).

[154] Ferber and Brückner, *Ber.*, **72B**, 999 (1939).

[155] Steinkopf and Günther, *Ann.*, **522**, 31 (1936).

[156] Fuson, Ullyot, and Gehrt, *J. Am. Chem. Soc.*, **60**, 1200 (1938).

[157] Yoke, Louder, and Smith, *J. Chem. Education*, **10**, 374 (1933).

[158] Sherrill, *J. Am. Chem. Soc.*, **52**, 1990 (1930).

[159] Young and Roberts, *J. Am. Chem. Soc.*, **67**, 321 (1945).

[160] Bennett and Elder, *J. Chem. Education*, **13**, 273 (1936).

[161] Grignard and Fluchaire, *Ann. chim.*, (10) **9**, 14 (1928).

[162] Smith et al., *J. Am. Chem. Soc.*, **61**, 3082 (1939).

[163] Wagner and Moore, *J. Am. Chem. Soc.*, **72**, 974 (1950).

[164] Whitmore and Lewis, *J. Am. Chem. Soc.*, **64**, 2965 (1942).

[165] Whitmore and Stahly, *J. Am. Chem. Soc.*, **55**, 4155 (1933).

[166] Mann and Porter, *J. Chem. Soc.*, 456 (1944).

[167] Powell, *J. Am. Chem. Soc.*, **46**, 2516 (1924).

[168] Mosher and Langerak, *J. Am. Chem. Soc.*, **71**, 286 (1949).

[169] Signaigo and Cramer, *J. Am. Chem. Soc.*, **55**, 3329 (1933).

[170] Macbeth and Mills, *J. Chem. Soc.*, 711 (1945).

[171] Ungnade and McLaren, *J. Org. Chem.*, **10**, 30 (1945).

[172] Pezold and Shriner, *J. Am. Chem. Soc.*, **54**, 4709 (1932).

[173] Price and Karabinos, *J. Am. Chem. Soc.*, **62**, 1160 (1940).

[174] Bartlett and Schneider, *J. Am. Chem. Soc.*, **67**, 143 (1945).

[175] Westheimer, *Chem. Revs.*, **45**, 419 (1949).

[176] Osterburg and Kendall, *J. Am. Chem. Soc.*, **42**, 2618 (1920).

[177] Gredy, *Ann. chim.*, (11) **4**, 22 (1935).

[178] Kornfeld, Jones, and Parke, *J. Am. Chem. Soc.*, **71**, 150 (1949).

[179] Carlin, *J. Am. Chem. Soc.*, **67**, 932 (1945).

[180] Ungnade and Ludutsky, *J. Org. Chem.*, **10**, 521 (1945).

[181] Frank, Berry, and Shotwell, *J. Am. Chem. Soc.*, **71**, 3889 (1949).

[182] Adkins and Hager, *J. Am. Chem. Soc.*, **71**, 2965 (1949).

[183] Adkins and Hager, *J. Am. Chem. Soc.*, **71**, 2967 (1949).

[184] Shunk and Wilds, *J. Am. Chem. Soc.*, **71**, 3946 (1949).

[185] Lock and Schreckeneder, *Ber.*, **72B**, 516 (1939).

[186] Neidig et al., *J. Am. Chem. Soc.*, **72**, 4617 (1950).

[187] Tsatsas, *Ann. chim.*, (12) **1**, 348 (1946).

[188] Ungnade, *J. Org. Chem.*, **13**, 364 (1948).

[189] Fieser and Cason, *J. Am. Chem. Soc.*, **62**, 434 (1940).

[190] Clarke and Dreger, *Org. Syntheses*, Coll. Vol. I, 87 (1941).

[191] Ruggli and Herzog, *Helv. Chim. Acta*, **29**, 111 (1946).

[192] Kinney, *J. Am. Chem. Soc.*, **51**, 1596 (1929).

[193] Pearl and Dehn, *J. Am. Chem. Soc.*, **60**, 57 (1938).

[194] Weiss and Appel, *J. Am. Chem. Soc.*, **70**, 3666 (1948); Klein, *ibid.*, **63**, 1474 (1941).

[195] Gilman and Broadbent, *J. Am. Chem. Soc.*, **70**, 2619 (1948).

[196] Backer, *Rec. trav. chim.*, **57**, 978 (1938).

[197] Fuson and Robertson, *J. Org. Chem.*, **7**, 469 (1942).

[198] Kinney, *J. Am. Chem. Soc.*, **51**, 1596 (1929); cf. ref. 190.

[199] Jenkins, Buck, and Bigelow, *J. Am. Chem. Soc.*, **52**, 4496 (1930).

[200] Hartman and Dickey, *J. Am. Chem. Soc.*, **55**, 1229 (1933).

[201] Leonard and Mader, *J. Am. Chem. Soc.*, **72**, 5390 (1950).

[202] Dane, Schmitt, and Rautenstrauch, *Ann.*, **532**, 37 (1937).

[203] Bowden, Heilbron, Jones, and Weedon, *J. Chem. Soc.*, 39 (1946).

[204] Braude et al., *J. Chem. Soc.*, 612 (1949).

[205] Conant and Quayle, *Org. Syntheses*, Coll. Vol. I, 211 (1941).

[206] Elderfield and Ressler, *J. Am. Chem. Soc.*, **72**, 4067 (1950).

[207] Marvel and Walton, *J. Org. Chem.*, **7**, 88 (1942).

[208] Henze and Rodgers, *J. Am. Chem. Soc.*, **61**, 433 (1939); **62**, 1759 (1940).

[209] Mariella and Leech, *J. Am. Chem. Soc.*, **71**, 3558 (1949).

[210] Adkins et al., *J. Am. Chem. Soc.*, **71**, 3629 (1949).

[211] Lea and Robinson, *J. Chem. Soc.*, 2354 (1926).

[212] Leonard et al., *J. Am. Chem. Soc.*, **71**, 2997 (1949).

[213] Baer and Kates, *J. Am. Chem. Soc.*, **67**, 1482 (1945).

[214] Hurd and McNamee, *Org. Syntheses*, Coll. Vol. I, 244 (1941), note 11.

[215] Dimroth and Resin, *Ber.*, **75B**, 322 (1942).

[216] Russell and Vanderwerf, *J. Am. Chem. Soc.*, **69**, 11 (1947).

[217] McRae, Charlesworth, and Alexander, *Can. J. Research*, **21B**, 1 (1943).

[218] Colonge, Watteau, and Cumet, *Bull. soc. chim. France*, (5) **14**, 246 (1947).

[219] Long and Troutman, *J. Am. Chem. Soc.*, **71**, 2469 (1949); Parkes and Williams, *J. Chem. Soc.*, 67 (1934).

[220] Ford-Moore and Rydon, *J. Chem. Soc.*, 679 (1946).

[221] Bersin in *Newer Methods of Preparative Organic Chemistry*, Interscience Publishers, New York, 1948, p. 143.

[222] Oppenauer, *Org. Syntheses*, **21**, 18 (1941).

[223] Adkins and Franklin, *J. Am. Chem. Soc.*, **63**, 2381 (1941).

[224] Woodward, Wendler, and Brutschy, *J. Am. Chem. Soc.*, **67**, 1425 (1945); Lutz, Jordan, and Truett, *ibid.*, **72**, 4085 (1950).

[225] Hurd, Greengard, and Roe, *J. Am. Chem. Soc.*, **61**, 3359 (1939).

[226] Paul, *Bull. soc. chim. France*, (5e) **8**, 514–518 (1941).

[227] Kleiderer and Kornfeld, *J. Org. Chem.*, **13**, 455 (1948).

[228] Speck and Bost, *J. Org. Chem.*, **11**, 788 (1946).

[229] Kyrides and Zienty, *J. Am. Chem. Soc.*, **68**, 1385 (1946).

[230] Kolfenbach et al., *Ind. Eng. Chem.*, **37**, 1178 (1945).

[231] Henne and Perilstein, *J. Am. Chem. Soc.*, **65**, 2183 (1943).

[232] Church, Whitmore, and McGrew, *J. Am. Chem. Soc.*, **56**, 181 (1934).

[233] Henne and Hill, *J. Am. Chem. Soc.*, **65**, 752 (1943).

[234] Cook and Whitmore, *J. Am. Chem. Soc.*, **63**, 3540 (1941).

[235] Moersch and Whitmore, *J. Am. Chem. Soc.*, **71**, 819 (1949); Mosher and Cox, *ibid.*, **72**, 3701 (1950).

[236] Henne, Shepard, and Young, *J. Am. Chem. Soc.*, **72**, 3577 (1950).

[237] Roberts and Sauer, *J. Am. Chem. Soc.*, **71**, 3928 (1949).
[238] Mowry, *J. Am. Chem. Soc.*, **67**, 1050 (1945).
[239] Emerson et al., *J. Am. Chem. Soc.*, **68**, 1666 (1946).
[240] Senseman and Stubbs, *Ind. Eng. Chem.*, **25**, 1286 (1933).
[241] Thompson, *Org. Syntheses*, **20**, 94 (1940).
[242] Huntress, Hershberg, and Cliff, *J. Am. Chem. Soc.*, **53**, 2720 (1931).
[243] Winkler, *Chem. Ber.*, **81**, 256 (1948).
[244] Huntress and Walter, *J. Am. Chem. Soc.*, **70**, 3704 (1948).
[245] Emerson and Lucas, *J. Am. Chem. Soc.*, **70**, 1180 (1948).
[246] Emerson et al., *J. Am. Chem. Soc.*, **68**, 674 (1946).
[247] Emerson et al., *J. Am. Chem. Soc.*, **69**, 1905 (1947).
[248] Rivier and Farine, *Helv. Chim. Acta*, **12**, 865 (1929).
[249] Bartlett and Schneider, *J. Am. Chem. Soc.*, **67**, 141 (1945).
[250] Clarke, *J. Am. Chem. Soc.*, **34**, 679 (1911).
[251] Clarke, *J. Am. Chem. Soc.*, **33**, 529 (1911).
[252] Willstätter and Hatt, *Ann.*, **418**, 152 (1919).
[253] Connor and Adkins, *J. Am. Chem. Soc.*, **54**, 3420 (1932).
[254] Renfrow, *J. Am. Chem. Soc.*, **66**, 144 (1944).
[255] Renfrow and Walker, *J. Am. Chem. Soc.*, **70**, 3957 (1948).
[256] Johnson and Hager, *Org. Syntheses*, Coll. Vol. I, 351 (1941).
[257] Dehn and Jackson, *J. Am. Chem. Soc.*, **55**, 4284 (1933).
[258] Adams, Abramovitch, and Hauser, *J. Am. Chem. Soc.*, **65**, 552 (1943)
[259] Briese and McElvain, *J. Am. Chem. Soc.*, **55**, 1697 (1933).
[260] Leuchs, Heller, and Hoffman, *Ber.*, **62**, 875 (1929).
[261] Cope, Hofmann, and Hardy, *J. Am. Chem. Soc.*, **63**, 1855 (1941).
[262] Hudson and Hauser, *J. Am. Chem. Soc.*, **63**, 3163 (1941).
[263] Bouveault and Locquin, *Bull. soc. chim. France*, (3) **31**, 1153 (1940).
[264] Price and Meisel, *J. Am. Chem. Soc.*, **69**, 1497 (1947).
[265] Strating and Backer, *Rec. trav. chim.*, **55**, 904 (1936).
[266] Hückel and Kindler, *Chem. Ber.*, **80**, 203 (1947).
[267] Shive, Crouch, and Lochte, *J. Am. Chem. Soc.*, **63**, 2983 (1941).
[268] Case and Reid, *J. Am. Chem. Soc.*, **50**, 3064 (1928).
[269] Cornubert and Borrel, *Bull. soc. chim. France*, (4) **47**, 307 (1930).
[270] Cornubert et al., *Bull. soc. chim. France*, (5e) **12**, 371 (1945).
[271] King, Barltrop, and Walley, *J. Chem. Soc.*, 279 (1945).
[272] Rydon, *J. Chem. Soc.*, 1549 (1939).
[273] Julian and Oliver, *Org. Syntheses*, Coll. Vol. II, 391 (1943).
[274] Mercer, Robertson, and Cahn, *J. Chem. Soc.*, 999 (1935).
[275] Heilbron et al., *J. Chem. Soc.*, 1338 (1931).
[276] Ramart-Lucas and Labaune, *Ann. chim.*, (10) **16**, 295 (1931).
[277] Mosettig and van de Kamp, *J. Am. Chem. Soc.*, **55**, 3445 (1933).
[278] Dean, Dickinson, Quayle, and Lester, *J. Am. Chem. Soc.*, **72**, 1740 (1950).
[279] Kolloff and Hunter, *J. Am. Chem. Soc.*, **63**, 492 (1941).
[280] Strong and McElvain, *J. Am. Chem. Soc.*, **55**, 816 (1933).
[281] Campball et al., *J. Am. Chem. Soc.*, **68**, 1845 (1946).
[282] Youtz and Perkins, *J. Am. Chem. Soc.*, **51**, 3514 (1929).
[283] Ruggli and Gassenmeier, *Helv. Chim. Acta*, **22**, 501 (1939).
[284] Schechter, Green, and LaForge, *J. Am. Chem. Soc.*, **71**, 3165 (1949).
[285] Ruzicka and Schinz, *Helv. Chim. Acta*, **23**, 964 (1940).
[286] Cope, Hoyle, and Heyl, *J. Am. Chem. Soc.*, **63**, 1843 (1941).
[287] v. Braun and Rudolph, *Ber.*, **67**, 278 (1934).

[288] McPhee and Klingsberg, *J. Am. Chem. Soc.*, **66**, 1132 (1944).
[289] Becker, *Helv. Chim. Acta*, **32**, 1584 (1949).
[290] Sharp, Sutherland, and Wilson, *J. Chem. Soc.*, 346 (1943).
[291] Anderson, Crawford, and Sherrill, *J. Am. Chem. Soc..* **68**, 1294 (1946).
[292] Brown and Partridge, *J. Am. Chem. Soc.* **67**, 1423 (1945).
[293] Finkelstein and Elderfield, *J. Org. Chem.*, **4**, 371 (1939).
[294] Howard and Fraser, *Org. Syntheses*, Coll. Vol. I, 475 (1941).
[295] Adickes and Andresen, *Ann.*, **555**, 41 (1943).
[296] Huan, *Bull. soc. chim. France*, (5e) **5**, 1341 (1938).
[297] Gaubert, Linstead, and Rydon, *J. Chem. Soc.*, 1977 (1937).
[298] Ames and Bowman, *J. Chem. Soc.*, 329 (1950).
[299] Kögl, Halberstadt, and Barendregt, *Rec. trav. chim.*, **68**, 387 (1949).
[300] Openshaw and Robinson, *J. Chem. Soc.*, 944 (1937).
[301] Fieser et al., *J. Am. Chem. Soc.*, **57**, 1852 (1935); **58**, 2320 (1936).
[302] Friedmann, *J. prakt. Chem.*, **146**, 159 (1936).
[303] Oldham and Ubbelohde, *J. Chem. Soc.*, 201 (1939).
[304] Bouveault and Bongert, *Bull. soc. chim. France*, (3) **27**, 1038, 1046, 1088 (1902).
[305] Bouveault and Locquin, *Bull. soc. chim. France*, (3) **31**, 588, 1153 (1940).
[306] Breslow et al., *J. Am. Chem. Soc.*, **66**, 1921 (1944).
[307] Elderfield et al., *J. Am. Chem. Soc..* **69**, 1258 (1947).
[308] Mannick and Margotte, *Ber.*, **68B**, 278 (1935).
[309] Elderfield et al., *J. Am. Chem. Soc.*, **68**, 1584 (1946).
[310] Jackman et al., *J. Am. Chem. Soc.*, **70**, 2884 (1948).
[311] Jones et al., *J. Am. Chem. Soc.*, **70**, 2846 (1948).
[312] Walker and Hauser, *J. Am. Chem. Soc.*, **68**, 1386 (1946); cf. ref. 313.
[313] Bowman, *J. Chem. Soc.*, 322 (1950).
[314] Reynolds and Hauser, *Org. Syntheses*, **30**, 70 (1950).
[315] Long and Troutman, *J. Am. Chem. Soc.*, **71**, 2473 (1949).
[316] Bowman, *J. Chem. Soc.*, 325 (1950).
[317] Noyce, *J. Chem. Education*, **26**, 275 (1949).
[318] Sabatier and Mailhe, *Compt. rend.*, **158**, 831 (1914); Senderens, *Ann. chim.*, (8) **28**, 243–343 (1913).
[319] Herbst and Manske, *Org. Syntheses*, Coll. Vol. II, 389 (1943).
[320] Kistler, Swann, and Appel, *Ind. Eng. Chem.*, **26**, 388 (1934).
[321] Swann, Appel, and Kistler, *Ind. Eng. Chem.*, **26**, 1014 (1934).
[322] Senderens, *Bull. soc. chim. France*, (4) **3**, 824 (1908).
[323] Perkins and Kenyon, *J. Chem. Soc.*, **99**, 57 (1911); **101**, 629 (1912); **103**, 1936 (1913).
[324] Cowan, Jeffery, and Vogel, *J. Chem. Soc.*, 171 (1940).
[325] Krafft, *Ber.*, **15**, 1712 (1879).
[326] Morgan and Holmes, *J. Soc. Chem. Ind. (London)*, **44**, 109T (1925).
[327] Thorpe and Kon, *Org. Syntheses*, Coll. Vol. I, 192 (1941).
[328] Curtis, Dobson, and Hatt, *J. Soc. Chem. Ind. (London)*, **66**, 402 (1947).
[329] Dougherty, *J. Am. Chem. Soc.*, **50**, 571 (1928).
[330] Hurd and Thomas, *J. Am. Chem. Soc.*, **58**, 1240 (1936).
[331] Miller, Cook, and Whitmore, *J. Am. Chem. Soc.*, **72**, 2732 (1950).
[332] Wibaut et al., *Rec. trav. chim.*, **58**, 362 (1939).
[333] Vogel, *J. Chem. Soc.*, 912 (1931).
[334] Henshall, *J. Soc. Chem. Ind. (London)*, **62**, 127 (1943).
[335] Vogel, *J. Chem. Soc.*, 2033 (1928).

[336] Birch et al., *J. Am. Chem. Soc.*, **71**, 1362 (1949).
[337] Winkler, *Chem. Ber.*, **81**, 258 (1948).
[338] Maeder, *Helv. Chim. Acta*, **29**, 124 (1946).
[339] Webb and Webb, *J. Am. Chem. Soc.*, **71**, 2285 (1949).
[340] Burger and Walter, *J. Am. Chem. Soc.*, **72**, 1988 (1950).
[341] Yarnall and Wallis, *J. Org. Chem.*, **4**, 270 (1939).
[342] Newman and Magerlein in *Organic Reactions*, Vol. 5, John Wiley & Sons, New York, 1949, p. 421.
[343] v. Braun and Kroper, *Ber.*, **62**, 2880 (1929); v. Braun and Teuffert, *ibid.*, **62**, 235 (1929).
[344] v. Braun, *Ber.*, **67**, 218 (1934); Newman, *J. Am. Chem. Soc.*, **57**, 732 (1935).
[345] Rohrmann, Jones, and Shonle, *J. Am. Chem. Soc.*, **66**, 1856 (1944).
[346] Nunn and Henze, *J. Org. Chem.*, **12**, 541 (1947).
[347] Bachmann and Boatner, *J. Am. Chem. Soc.*, **58**, 2098 (1936); Callen, Dornfeld, and Coleman, *Org. Syntheses*, **28**, 6 (1948).
[348] Bachmann, *J. Am. Chem. Soc.*, **56**, 1365 (1934).
[349] Whitmore et al., *J. Am. Chem. Soc.*, **67**, 2059 (1945).
[350] Sherk, Augur, and Soffer, *J. Am. Chem. Soc.*, **67**, 2239 (1945).
[351] Blicke, *J. Am. Chem. Soc.*, **49**, 2847 (1927).
[352] Gilman and Jacoby, *J. Org. Chem.*, **3**, 108 (1938).
[353] Shriner and Turner, *J. Am. Chem. Soc.*, **52**, 1268 (1930).
[354] Hauser, Humphlett, and Weiss, *J. Am. Chem. Soc.*, **70**, 426 (1948).
[355] Pearson, *J. Am. Chem. Soc.*, **72**, 4169 (1950).
[356] Hauser and Renfrow, *J. Am. Chem. Soc.*, **59**, 1823 (1937).
[357] Rhinesmith, *J. Am. Chem. Soc.*, **58**, 596 (1936).
[358] Kumler, Strait, and Alpen, *J. Am. Chem. Soc.*, **72**, 1463 (1950).
[359] Alpen, Kumler, and Strait, *J. Am. Chem. Soc.*, **72**, 4560 (1950).
[360] Baddeley and Kenner, *J. Chem. Soc.*, 303 (1935).
[361] Bachmann, Carlson, and Moran, *J. Org. Chem.*, **13**, 920 (1948).
[362] Whitmore et al., *J. Am. Chem. Soc.*, **69**, 236 (1947).
[363] Reeve and Adkins, *J. Am. Chem. Soc.*, **62**, 2874 (1940).
[364] LaForge, *J. Am. Chem. Soc.*, **50**, 2477 (1928).
[365] Frank and Weatherbee, *J. Am. Chem. Soc.*, **70**, 3482 (1948).
[366] Vogel and Schinz, *Helv. Chim. Acta*, **33**, 123 (1950).
[367] Cagniant, *Bull. soc. chim. France*, (5) **16**, 847 (1949).
[368] Behrens et al., *J. Am. Chem. Soc.*, **70**, 2837 (1948).
[369] Wilson and Henze, *J. Am. Chem. Soc.*, **63**, 2112 (1941).
[370] Borsche and Herbert, *Ann.*, **546**, 297 (1941).
[371] Young, McKinnis, Webb, and Roberts, *J. Am. Chem. Soc.*, **68**, 295 (1946).
[372] Ruggli and Hegedus, *Helv. Chim. Acta*, **25**, 1292 (1942); Ruggli and Zeller, *ibid.*, **28**, 744 (1945).
[373] Henze and Rigler, *J. Am. Chem. Soc.*, **56**, 1350 (1934).
[374] Barnes and Budde, *J. Am. Chem. Soc.*, **68**, 2339 (1946).
[375] Wallace and Henze, *J. Am. Chem. Soc.*, **64**, 2882 (1942).
[376] Henze et al., *J. Am. Chem. Soc.*, **64**, 1222 (1942).
[377] Rigler and Henze, *J. Am. Chem. Soc.*, **58**, 474 (1936).
[378] Henze, Benz, and Sutherland, *J. Am. Chem. Soc.*, **71**, 2122 (1949).
[379] Elderfield, Pitt, and Wempen, *J. Am. Chem. Soc.*, **72**, 1334 (1950).
[380] Whitney and Henze, *J. Am. Chem. Soc.*, **60**, 1148 (1938).
[381] Cross and Henze, *J. Am. Chem. Soc.*, **61**, 2730 (1939).
[382] Niemann, Benson, and Mead, *J. Org. Chem.*, **8**, 397 (1943).

[383] Speer and Henze, *J. Am. Chem. Soc.*, **61**, 1226 (1939).
[384] Rubin, Paist, and Elderfield, *J. Org. Chem.*, **6**, 260 (1941).
[385] Bachmann and Ferguson, *J. Am. Chem. Soc.*, **56**, 2082 (1934).
[386] Anderson et al., *J. Am. Chem. Soc.*, **67**, 2197 (1945).
[387] Decombe, *Ann. chim.*, (10) **18**, 92 (1932).
[388] Humphlett, Weiss, and Hauser, *J. Am. Chem. Soc.*, **70**, 4020 (1948).
[389] Newman and Smith, *J. Org. Chem.*, **13**, 592 (1948).
[390] Newman and Booth, *J. Am. Chem. Soc.*, **67**, 154 (1945).
[391] Campaigne and Reid, *J. Am. Chem. Soc.*, **68**, 1663 (1946).
[392] de Benneville, *J. Org. Chem.*, **6**, 462 (1941).
[393] Ullyot et al., *J. Org. Chem.*, **10**, 440 (1945).
[394] Weizmann et al., *J. Chem. Soc.*, 1367, 1371 (1935).
[395] Fieser and Daudt, *J. Am. Chem. Soc.*, **63**, 785 (1941).
[396] Kroeger and Nieuwland, *J. Am. Chem. Soc.*, **58**, 1861 (1936).
[397] Nightingale and Wadsworth, *J. Am. Chem. Soc.*, **67**, 416 (1945).
[398] Hopff, Nenitzescu, Isacesu, and Cantuniau, *Ber.*, **69**, 2249 (1936).
[399] Hopff et al., *Ber.*, **69B**, 2249 (1936).
[400] Cason, *Chem. Revs.*, **40**, 15 (1947).
[401] Cason, *J. Am. Chem. Soc.*, **68**, 2078 (1946); cf. ref. 426.
[402] Gilman and Nelson, *Rec. trav. chim.*, **55**, 520 (1936).
[403] Bunnett and Tarbell, *J. Am. Chem. Soc.*, **67**, 1944 (1945).
[404] Leslie and Henze, *J. Am. Chem. Soc.*, **71**, 3480 (1949).
[405] Michael, *J. Am. Chem. Soc.*, **41**, 411 (1919).
[406] Colonge and Joly, *Ann. chim.*, (11) **18**, 314 (1943).
[407] Jones, *J. Am. Chem. Soc.*, **69**, 2350 (1947).
[408] Schmidt and Shirley, *J. Am. Chem. Soc.*, **71**, 3804 (1949).
[409] Badertscher and Whitmore, *J. Am. Chem. Soc.*, **55**, 1564 (1933).
[410] Thoms, *Arch. Pharm.*, **263**, 246 (1925).
[411] Whitmore et al., *J. Am. Chem. Soc.*, **60**, 2790 (1938).
[412] Baker, *J. Chem. Soc.*, 447 (1938).
[413] Kadesch, *J. Am. Chem. Soc.*, **66**, 1211 (1944).
[414] Whitmore, Whitmore, and Cook, *J. Am. Chem. Soc.*, **72**, 51 (1950).
[415] Hurd and Kelso, *J. Am. Chem. Soc.*, **62**, 2184 (1940).
[416] Cook and Percival, *J. Am. Chem. Soc.*, **71**, 4141 (1949).
[417] Ford, Thompson, and Marvel, *J. Am. Chem. Soc.*, **57**, 2621 (1935).
[418] Kohler and Baltzly, *J. Am. Chem. Soc.*, **54**, 4023 (1932).
[419] Stehman, Cook, and Whitmore, *J. Am. Chem. Soc.*, **71**, 1509 (1949).
[420] Lester and Proffitt, *J. Am. Chem. Soc.*, **71**, 1877 (1949).
[421] Kipnis and Ornfelt, *J. Am. Chem. Soc.*, **70**, 3948 (1948).
[422] Kantor and Hauser, *J. Am. Chem. Soc.*, **72**, 3290 (1950).
[423] Pinson and Friess, *J. Am. Chem. Soc.*, **72**, 5333 (1950).
[424] Hurd and Cohen, *J. Am. Chem. Soc.*, **53**, 1071 (1931).
[425] McKennis and du Vigneaud, *J. Am. Chem. Soc.*, **68**, 832 (1946); cf. ref. 426.
[426] Cason and Prout, *Org. Syntheses*, **28**, 75 (1948).
[427] Whitmore, Noll, and Meunier, *J. Am. Chem. Soc.*, **61**, 683 (1939).
[428] Whitmore et al., *J. Am. Chem. Soc.*, **60**, 2462 (1938).
[429] Jenkins, *J. Am. Chem. Soc.*, **55**, 703 (1933).
[430] Jenkins, *J. Am. Chem. Soc.*, **55**, 1618 (1933).
[431] Jenkins, *J. Am. Chem. Soc.*, **56**, 682 (1934).
[432] Jenkins, *J. Am. Chem. Soc.*, **55**, 2896 (1933).
[433] Montagne, *Ann. chim.*, (10) **13**, 53 (1930).

[434] Whitmore and Sloat, *J. Am. Chem. Soc.*, 64, 2969 (1942).

[435] Hey, *J. Chem. Soc.*, 1232 (1930).

[436] Adams, Harfenist, and Loewe, *J. Am. Chem. Soc.*, 71, 1628 (1949).

[437] Kohler, *Am. Chem. J.*, 38, 511 (1907).

[438] Colonge, *Bull. soc. chim. France*, (5) 3, 413 (1936).

[439] Colonge, *Bull. soc. chim. France*, (5) 2, 754 (1935).

[440] Smith, Chase, and Rhodes, *J. Am. Chem. Soc.*, 66, 1547 (1944).

[441] Whitmore and Pedlow, *J. Am. Chem. Soc.*, 63, 758 (1941).

[442] Kohler, *Am. Chem. J.*, 29, 352 (1902).

[443] Newman and Farbman, *J. Am. Chem. Soc.*, 69, 1550 (1944); Bachmann et al., 72, 1997 (1950).

[444] Dice, Loveless, and Gates, *J. Am. Chem. Soc.*, 71, 3546 (1949).

[445] Newman and Booth, *J. Org. Chem.*, 12, 737 (1947); Mueller and May, *J. Am. Chem. Soc.*, 71, 3313 (1949).

[446] Arnold, Buckley, and Dodson, *J. Am. Chem. Soc.*, 72, 3154 (1950).

[447] Whitmore and Forster, *J. Am. Chem. Soc.*, 64, 2967 (1942).

[448] Sah, *Rec. trav. chim.*, 59, 1025 (1940).

[449] Braude and Coles, *J. Chem. Soc.*, 2012 (1950).

[450] Wieland, *Chem. Ber.*, 81, 314 (1948).

[451] Salkind and Beburuschwili, *Ber.*, 42, 4500 (1909).

[452] Hartman and Roll, *Org. Syntheses*, 23, 1 (1943).

[453] Nightingale and Janes, *J. Am. Chem. Soc.*, 66, 352 (1944).

[454] St. Goldschmidt and Veer, *Rec. trav. chim.*, 65, 796 (1946); Hey and Morris, *J. Chem. Soc.*, 2319 (1948); Keagle and Hartung, *J. Am. Chem. Soc.*, 68, 1608 (1946).

[455] Hey and Morris, *J. Chem. Soc.*, 48 (1948).

[456] Freon, *Ann. chim.*, (11) 11, 465 (1939).

[457] Locquin, *Bull. soc. chim. France*, (3) 31, 1147 (1904).

[458] Barry and Hartung, *J. Org. Chem.*, 12, 460 (1947).

[459] Sumerford and Dalton, *J. Am. Chem. Soc.*, 66, 1330 (1944).

[460] Marvel and Sperry, *Org. Syntheses*, Coll. Vol. I, 95 (1941).

[461] Bigelow and Hanslick, *Org. Syntheses*, Coll. Vol. II, 244 (1943).

[462] Wittig and Vidal, *Chem. Ber.*, 81, 368 (1948).

[463] Schmerling, *J. Am. Chem. Soc.*, 68, 1650 (1946).

[464] Adkins, *Reactions of Hydrogen*, U. of Wisconsin Press, 1937, p. 129.

[465] Covert, Connor, and Adkins, *J. Am. Chem. Soc.*, 54, 1658 (1932).

[466] Covert and Adkins, *J. Am. Chem. Soc.*, 54, 4116 (1932).

[467] Powell and Secoy, *J. Am. Chem. Soc.*, 53, 765 (1931).

[468] Colonge, *Bull. soc. chim. France*, (4) 49, 444 (1931).

[469] Vavon, *Ann. chim.*, (9) 1, 144, 196 (1914); Skita, *Ber.*, 43, 3393 (1910).

[470] Adams, Voorhees, and Shriner, *Org. Syntheses*, Coll. Vol. I, 463 (1941).

[471] Colonge, *Bull. soc. chim. France*, (4) 49, 441 (1931); (4) 41, 327 (1927); (5) 3, 416 (1936); (5) 6, 335, 342 (1939); Morgan and Hardy, *J. Soc. Chem. Ind. (London)*, 11, 518 (1933); Thoms, *Arch. Pharm.*, 263, 241 (1925); Powell, Murray, and Baldwin, *J. Am. Chem. Soc.*, 55, 1153 (1933).

[472] Haeussler and Dijkema, *Ber.*, 77, 601 (1944).

[473] Rupe and Willi, *Helv. Chim. Acta*, 15, 845 (1932).

[474] Henze, Wilson, and Townley, *J. Am. Chem. Soc.*, 65, 964 (1943).

[475] Woods et al., *J. Am. Chem. Soc.*, 71, 2028 (1949).

[476] Dippy and Lewis, *Rec. trav. chim.*, 56, 1000 (1937).

[477] Raiford and Peterson, *J. Org. Chem.*, 1, 549 (1937).

[478] Berliner and Berliner, *J. Am. Chem. Soc.*, **72**, 222 (1950).

[479] Metayer, *Ann. chim.*, (12) **4**, 201 (1949).

[480] Bailey and Lutz, *J. Am. Chem. Soc.*, **70**, 2412 (1948).

[481] Thompson, *Org. Syntheses*, **27**, 21 (1947).

[482] Pecherer, Jampolsky, and Wuest, *J. Am. Chem. Soc.*, **70**, 2587 (1948).

[483] Stork and Foreman, *J. Am. Chem. Soc.*, **68**, 2173 (1946).

[484] Papa, Schwenk, and Breiger, *J. Org. Chem.*, **14**, 366 (1949); Papa, *J. Am. Chem. Soc.*, **71**, 3246 (1949).

[485] Adkins, Rossow, and Carnahan, *J. Am. Chem. Soc.*, **70**, 4247 (1948).

[486] Cornforth, Cornforth, and Robinson, *J. Chem. Soc.*, 690 (1942).

[487] Sprague and Adkins, *J. Am. Chem. Soc.*, **56**, 2670 (1934).

[488] Haller and Bauer, *Ann. chim.*, (8) **29**, 313 (1913); Nasarow, *Ber.*, **70**, 594 (1937).

[489] Cornubert et al., *Bull. soc. chim. France*, (4) **49**, 1260, 1498–1528 (1931); (5) **2**, 195 (1935).

[490] Chanley, *J. Am. Chem. Soc.*, **70**, 244 (1948); Fischer and Wunderlich, *Ber.*, **74**, 1546 (1941).

[491] Sobotka and Chanley, *J. Am. Chem. Soc.*, **71**, 4136 (1949).

[492] Colonge, *Bull. soc. chim. France*, (5e) **5**, 99 (1938); cf. ref. 491.

[493] Conia, *Bull. soc. chim. France*, (5) **17**, 537 (1950).

[494] Haller and Bauer, *Ann. chim.*, (8) **28**, 373 (1913).

[495] Haller, *Bull. soc. chim. France*, (4) **31**, 1073–1144 (1922).

[496] Soffer et al., *J. Am. Chem. Soc.*, **72**, 3704 (1950).

[497] Whitmore and Laughlin, *J. Am. Chem. Soc.*, **55**, 3732 (1933).

[498] Haller, *Ann. chim.*, (8) **29**, 313 (1913).

[499] Suter and Weston, *J. Am. Chem. Soc.*, **64**, 534 (1942).

[500] Sprague, Beckman, and Adkins, *J. Am. Chem. Soc.*, **56**, 2665 (1934).

[501] Adkins, Kutz, and Coffman, *J. Am. Chem. Soc.*, **52**, 3218 (1930).

[502] Speck and Bost, *J. Org. Chem.*, **11**, 788 (1946).

[503] Vanderwerf and Lemmerman, *Org. Syntheses*, **28**, 8 (1948).

[504] Eisleb, *Ber.*, **74**, 1437 (1941).

[505] Eistert in *Newer Methods of Preparative Organic Chemistry*, Interscience Publishers, New York, 1948, p. 513.

[506] Kohler et al., *J. Am. Chem. Soc.*, **61**, 1059 (1939).

[507] Adamson and Kenner, *J. Chem. Soc.*, 184 (1939).

[508] Thomas, Campbell, and Hennion, *J. Am. Chem. Soc.*, **60**, 719 (1938).

[509] Schaad and Ipatieff, *J. Am. Chem. Soc.*, **62**, 178 (1940).

[510] Leers, *Bull. soc. chim. France*, **39**, 423 (1926).

[511] Hennion, Davis, and Maloney, *J. Am. Chem. Soc.*, **71**, 2813 (1949).

[512] Moureu and Delange, *Bull. soc. chim. France*, (3) **29**, 666 (1903).

[513] Hill and Flosdorf, *Org. Syntheses*, Coll. Vol. I, 462 (1941).

[514] Emerson, *J. Am. Chem. Soc.*, **69**, 1212 (1947).

[515] Bachmann, *Org. Syntheses*, Coll. Vol. II, 73 (1943).

[516] Burger and Bennet, *J. Am. Chem. Soc.*, **72**, 5414 (1950).

[517] Bouveault and Locquin, *Bull. soc. chim. France*, (3) **35**, 629–649 (1906); Leers, *ibid.*, (4) **35**, 597 (1924); (4) **39**, 421, 423, 433, 655 (1926); Parry, *J. Chem. Soc.*, 107, 108 (1915); Meerwein, *Ann.*, **396**, 201, 250 (1913).

[518] Kohler and Nygaard, *J. Am. Chem. Soc.*, **52**, 4133 (1930).

[519] Ballard and Dehn, *J. Am. Chem. Soc.*, **54**, 3969 (1932).

[520] Jenkins, Buck, and Bigelow, *J. Am. Chem. Soc.*, **52**, 4495, 5198 (1930).

[521] v. Wacek, *Ber.*, **77B**, 85 (1944).

[522] Evers et al., *J. Am. Chem. Soc.*, 55, 1136 (1933).

[523] Whitmore, Evers, and Rothrock, *Org. Syntheses*, Coll. Vol. II, 408 (1943).

[524] Brown, *J. Chem. Soc.*, 2577 (1949).

[525] Bardan, *Bull. soc. chim. France*, (4) 49, 1426, 1551, 1875 (1931); (5) 1, 141 368, 370 (1934); Elphimoff-Felkin, *ibid.*, (5) 17, 497 (1950).

[526] Ramonczai and Vargha, *J. Am. Chem. Soc.*, 72, 2737 (1950).

[527] Bouveault, *Bull. soc. chim. France*, (3) 35, 629–649 (1906).

[528] Delaby and Dumoulin, *Bull. soc. chim. France*, (4) 33, 602 (1923); (4) 39, 1583 (1923).

[529] Alder and Schmidt, *Ber.*, 76, 192 (1943).

[530] Nenitzescu and Gavat, *Ann.*, 519, 260 (1935).

[531] Rule and Thompson, *J. Chem. Soc.*, 1762 (1937).

[532] Goldschmidt and Veer, *Rec. trav. chim.*, 67, 504 (1948).

[533] Man and Hauser, *J. Am. Chem. Soc.*, 72, 3294 (1950).

[534] Weiss and Hauser, *J. Am. Chem. Soc.*, 71, 2023 (1949).

[535] Frank and Phillips, *J. Am. Chem. Soc.*, 71, 2804 (1949).

[536] Kharasch, Urry, and Kuderna, *J. Org. Chem.*, 14, 248 (1949).

[537] Wolfrom et al., *J. Am. Chem. Soc.*, 65, 1516 (1943); 67, 1793 (1945); 71, 3509 (1949).

[538] Truitt et al., *J. Am. Chem. Soc.*, 71, 3511 (1949).

[539] Whitmore and Randall, *J. Am. Chem. Soc.*, 64, 1244 (1942).

[540] Johnson and Degering, *J. Org. Chem.*, 8, 10 (1943).

[541] Levine, Conroy, Adams, and Hauser, *J. Am. Chem. Soc.*, 67, 1510 (1945).

[542] Adams and Hauser, *J. Am. Chem. Soc.*, 67, 284 (1945); 66, 345 (1944).

[543] Meerwein and Vossen, *J. prakt. Chem.*, 141, 157 (1934).

[544] Adams and Hauser, *J. Am. Chem. Soc.*, 66, 1220 (1944).

[545] Swamer and Hauser, *J. Am. Chem. Soc.*, 72, 1352 (1950).

[546] Denoon, *Org. Syntheses*, 20, 6 (1940).

[547] Adkins and Rainey, *Org. Syntheses*, 20, 7 (1940).

[548] Smith and King, *J. Am. Chem. Soc.*, 65, 442 (1943).

[549] Green and LaForge, *J. Am. Chem. Soc.*, 70, 2287 (1948); cf. ref. 545.

[550] Smith and Engelhardt, *J. Am. Chem. Soc.*, 71, 2671 (1949).

[551] Allen, Abell, and Normington, *Org. Syntheses*, Coll. Vol. I, 205 (1941).

[552] Magnani and McElvain, *Org. Syntheses*, 20, 32 (1940).

[553] Harris and Levine, *J. Am. Chem. Soc.*, 71, 1120 (1949).

[554] Harris and Levine, *J. Am. Chem. Soc.*, 70, 3360 (1948).

[555] Royals, *J. Am. Chem. Soc.*, 67, 1508 (1945).

[556] Dessert and Halverstadt, *J. Am. Chem. Soc.*, 70, 2595 (1948).

[557] Snyder, Brooks, and Shapiro, *Org. Syntheses*, Coll. Vol. II, 531 (1943).

[558] Jackman, Bergman, and Archer, *J. Am. Chem. Soc.*, 70, 499 (1948).

[559] Elks, Elliott, and Hems, *J. Chem. Soc.*, 629 (1944).

[560] Reid and Calvin, *J. Am. Chem. Soc.*, 72, 2948 (1950).

[561] Hesse and Bücking, *Ann.*, 563, 31 (1949).

[562] Hesse and Böckmann, *Ann.*, 563, 37 (1949).

[563] Frank and Varland, *Org. Syntheses*, 27, 91 (1947); Mowry and Ringwald, *J. Am. Chem. Soc.*, 72, 2037 (1950).

[564] Waitkins and Clark, *Chem. Revs.*, 36, 235 (1945); Rabjohn in *Organic Reactions*, Vol. 5, John Wiley & Sons, New York, 1949, p. 331.

[565] Riebsomer, *Chem. Revs.*, 36, 157 (1945).

[566] Hatt, Pilgrim, and Hurran, *J. Chem. Soc.*, 93 (1936).

[567] Wegmann and Dahn, *Helv. Chim. Acta*, 29, 1248 (1946).

[568] Weinstock and Fuson, *J. Am. Chem. Soc.*, **58**, 1233 (1936); Fuson and Hoch, *ibid.*, **71**, 1585 (1949).
[569] Rauh, Smith, Banks, and Diehle, *J. Org. Chem.*, **10**, 199 (1945).
[570] Harr, Voter, and Banks, *J. Org. Chem.*, **14**, 836 (1949).
[571] Teeters and Shriner, *J. Am. Chem. Soc.*, **55**, 3026 (1933).
[572] Astin, Newman, and Riley, *J. Chem. Soc.*, 391 (1933); ref. 573.
[573] Müller, *Ber.*, **66**, 1668 (1933).
[574] Chakravarti and Swaminathan, *J. Indian Chem. Soc.*, **11**, 715 (1934); *C. A.*, **29**, 1080 (1935).
[575] Dox, *Org. Syntheses*, Coll. Vol. I, 266 (1941).
[576] Coles, Manske, and Johnson, *J. Am. Chem. Soc.*, **51**, 2269 (1929).
[577] Postowsky and Lugowkin, *Ber.*, **68**, 852 (1935).
[578] Killian, Hennion, and Nieuwland, *J. Am. Chem. Soc.*, **56**, 1786 (1934).
[579] Muller and Krauss, *Monatsh.*, **61**, 206 (1932).
[580] Franke, Kroupa, and Schmid, *Monatsh.*, **66**, 412 (1935).
[581] Cason, *J. Org. Chem.*, **13**, 227 (1948).
[582] Yale, *J. Am. Chem. Soc.*, **69**, 1547 (1947).
[583] Mattar, Hastings, and Walker, *J. Chem. Soc.*, 2455 (1930).
[584] Shriner and Todd, *Org. Syntheses*, Coll. Vol. II, 200 (1943).
[585] Erickson and Kitchens, *J. Am. Chem. Soc.*, **68**, 492 (1946).
[586] Woodward and Blout, *J. Am. Chem. Soc.*, **65**, 562 (1943).
[587] Vincent, Thompson, and Smith, *J. Org. Chem.*, **3**, 606 (1939).
[588] Frank and Hall, *J. Am. Chem. Soc.*, **72**, 1645 (1950).
[589] Lutz and Wilder, *J. Am. Chem. Soc.*, **56**, 978 (1934).
[590] Hunsdiecker, *Ber.*, **75B**, 452 (1942).
[591] Young and Allen, *Org. Syntheses*, Coll. Vol. II, 219 (1943); note 2.
[592] Ruggli and Zaeslin, *Helv. Chim. Acta*, **18**, 848 (1935).
[593] Kharasch, McBay, and Urry, *J. Am. Chem. Soc.*, **70**, 1269 (1948).
[594] Saunders, *Org. Syntheses*, **29**, 1 (1949).
[595] Kimel and Cope, *J. Am. Chem. Soc.*, **65**, 1992 (1943).
[596] Frank, Armstrong, Kwiatek, and Price, *J. Am. Chem. Soc.*, **70**, 1379 (1948).
[597] Pines and Ipatieff, *J. Am. Chem. Soc.*, **69**, 1337 (1947).
[598] Gaddis and Butz, *J. Am. Chem. Soc.*, **69**, 1203 (1947).
[599] Catch et al., *J. Chem. Soc.*, 278 (1948).
[600] Cardwell and McQuillin, *J. Chem. Soc.*, 714 (1949); cf. ref. 599.
[601] Slanina, Hennion, and Nieuwland, *J. Am. Chem. Soc.*, **58**, 891 (1936).
[602] Blatt in *Organic Reactions*, Vol. 1, John Wiley & Sons, New York, Chapter 11; Blatt, *Chem. Revs.*, **27**, 413 (1940).
[603] Tarbell and Fanta, *J. Am. Chem. Soc.*, **65**, 2169 (1943).
[604] Ralston, McCorkle, and Baurer, *J. Org. Chem.*, **5**, 645 (1940).
[605] Miller and Hartung, *Org. Syntheses*, Coll. Vol. II, 543 (1943).
[606] Smith and Opie, *J. Org. Chem.*, **6**, 427 (1941).
[607] Amin and Shah, *Org. Syntheses*, **28**, 42 (1948).
[608] Carter in *Organic Reactions*, Vol. 3, John Wiley & Sons, New York, 1946, p. 198.
[609] Buck and Ide, *Org. Syntheses*, Coll. Vol. II, 55 (1943).
[610] Herbst and Shemin, *Org. Syntheses*, Coll. Vol. II, 1, 519 (1943).
[611] Buck and Ide, *J. Am. Chem. Soc.*, **54**, 3307 (1932).
[612] Buck, Baltzly, and Ide, *J. Am. Chem. Soc.*, **60**, 1789 (1938).
[613] Johnson in *Organic Reactions*, Vol. 1, John Wiley & Sons, New York, 1942, p. 253.

[614] Hauser and Hudson in *Organic Reactions,* Vol. 1, John Wiley & Sons, New York, 1942, p. 266.

[615] Shivers, Dillon, and Hauser, *J. Am. Chem. Soc.,* 69, 119 (1947); Hamell and Levine, *J. Org. Chem.,* 15, 162 (1950).

[616] Royals, *J. Am. Chem. Soc.,* 70, 489 (1948).

[617] Floyd and Miller, *J. Am. Chem. Soc.,* 69, 2354 (1947).

[618] Cox and McElvain, *Org. Syntheses,* Coll. Vol. II, 272 (1943); Steck, Hallock, and Holland, *J. Am. Chem. Soc.,* 68, 131 (1946).

[619] Shivers, Hudson, and Hauser, *J. Am. Chem. Soc.,* 65, 2051 (1943).

[620] Abramovitch and Hauser, *J. Am. Chem. Soc.,* 64, 2271 (1942).

[621] Inglis and Roberts, *Org. Syntheses,* Coll. Vol. I, 235 (1941).

[622] Hauser and Walker, *J. Am. Chem. Soc.,* 69, 295 (1947).

[623] Hudson and Hauser, *J. Am. Chem. Soc.,* 63, 3156 (1941).

[624] Friedman and Kosower, *Org. Syntheses,* 26, 42 (1946).

[625] Albertson, *J. Am. Chem. Soc.,* 70, 669 (1948).

[626] Frostick and Hauser, *J. Am. Chem. Soc.,* 71, 1350 (1949).

[627] Pinkney, *Org. Syntheses,* Coll. Vol. II, 116 (1943).

[628] Zanetti and Beckmann, *J. Am. Chem. Soc.,* 50, 1438 (1928).

[629] Barger, Robinson, and Smith, *J. Chem. Soc.,* 721 (1937).

[630] Gilman and Broadbent, *J. Am. Chem. Soc.,* 70, 2755 (1948); Bloom, Breslow, and Hauser, *ibid.,* 67, 2206 (1945).

[631] Shriner and Schmidt, *J. Am. Chem. Soc.,* 51, 3636 (1929).

[632] Shriner, Schmidt, and Roll, *Org. Syntheses,* Coll. Vol. II, 266 (1943).

[633] Jackman, Bergman, and Archer, *J. Am. Chem. Soc.,* 70, 499 (1948).

[634] Hunsdiecker, *Ber.,* 75B, 447, 455, 460 (1942).

[635] Soloway and LaForge, *J. Am. Chem. Soc.,* 69, 2677 (1947).

[636] McElvain and Weber, *Org. Syntheses,* 23, 35 (1943).

[637] Bouveault and Locquin, *Bull. soc. chim. France,* (5) 31, 388 (1940).

[638] Spassow, *Org. Syntheses,* 21, 46 (1941).

[639] Coulson, *J. Chem. Soc.,* 1409 (1934).

[640] Cardwell, *J. Chem. Soc.,* 719 (1949).

[641] Newman and Walborsky, *J. Am. Chem. Soc.,* 72, 4296 (1950).

[642] Renfrow and Renfrow, *J. Am. Chem. Soc.,* 68, 1801 (1946).

[643] Bartlett and Bavley, *J. Am. Chem. Soc.,* 60, 2416 (1938).

[644] Folkers and Adkins, *J. Am. Chem. Soc.,* 53, 1416 (1931).

[645] Marvel and Hager, *Org. Syntheses,* Coll. Vol. I, 248 (1941).

[646] Breslow and Hauser, *J. Am. Chem. Soc.,* 62, 2611 (1940).

[647] Adams, Levine, and Hauser, *Org. Syntheses,* 27, 35 (1947).

[648] Bowden, *J. Am. Chem. Soc.,* 60, 131 (1938).

[649] Wallingford, Thorpe, and Homeyer, *J. Am. Chem. Soc.,* 64, 580 (1942).

[650] Miller, Dessert, and Anderson, *J. Am. Chem. Soc.,* 70, 500 (1948).

[651] Breslow, Baumgarten, and Hauser, *J. Am. Chem. Soc.,* 66, 1286 (1944).

[652] Riegel and Lilienfeld, *J. Am. Chem. Soc.,* 67, 1273 (1945).

[653] Hauser and Renfrew, *Org. Syntheses,* Coll. Vol. II, 268 (1943).

[654] Lund, *Ber.,* 67, 935 (1934).

[655] Hunter and Hogg, *J. Am. Chem. Soc.,* 71, 1924 (1949).

[656] von Doering and Wiberg, *J. Am. Chem. Soc.,* 72, 2608 (1950).

[657] Froning and Hennion, *J. Am. Chem. Soc.,* 62, 653 (1940).

[658] Bloom and Hauser, *J. Am. Chem. Soc.,* 66, 152 (1944).

[659] Dorsch and McElvain, *J. Am. Chem. Soc.,* 54, 2960 (1932).

[660] Julian et al., *Org. Syntheses,* Coll. Vol. II, 487 (1943).

[661] Wiley and Adkins, *J. Am. Chem. Soc.*, **60**, 914 (1938).

[662] Long, *J. Am. Chem. Soc.*, **69**, 990 (1947).

[663] Abramovitch and Hauser, *J. Am. Chem. Soc.*, **64**, 2720 (1942).

[664] Kroeker and McElvain, *J. Am. Chem. Soc.*, **56**, 1172 (1934).

[665] Milas et al., *J. Am. Chem. Soc.*, **70**, 1602 (1948).

[666] Shriner in *Organic Reactions*, Vol. 1, John Wiley & Sons, New York, 1942, p. 9.

[667] Livingston, *J. Am. Chem. Soc.*, **69**, 1220 (1947).

[668] Wash, Shive, and Lochte, *J. Am. Chem. Soc.*, **63**, 2975 (1941).

[669] Johns and Burch, *J. Am. Chem. Soc.*, **60**, 919 (1938).

[670] Groggins and Newton, *Ind. Eng. Chem.*, **22**, 157 (1930).

[671] Adams, Chiles, and Rassweiler, *Org. Syntheses*, Coll. Vol. I, 10 (1941).

[672] Winterfeld and Rönsberg, *Arch. Pharm.*, **274**, 40 (1936).

[673] Young et al., *J. Am. Chem. Soc.*, **72**, 3635 (1950).

[674] Bergmann and Sulzbacher, *J. Org. Chem.*, **15**, 918 (1950).

[675] Nickels and Heintzelman, *J. Org. Chem.*, **15**, 1142 (1950).

[676] Shapiro, *J. Org. Chem.*, **15**, 1030 (1950).

[677] Hauser and Humphlett, *J. Org. Chem.*, **15**, 359 (1950).

[678] Dauben and Tilles, *J. Org. Chem.*, **15**, 785 (1950).

[679] Hass, Susie, and Heider, *J. Org. Chem.*, **15**, 10 (1950).

[680] Schultz and Mickey, *Org. Syntheses*, **29**, 38 (1949).

[681] Colonge and Pichat, *Bull. soc. chim. France*, (5) **16**, 177, 853 (1949).

[682] Dornow, Kuhlcke, and Baxmann, *Chem. Ber.*, **82**, 254 (1949).

[683] Kaufmann and Adams, *J. Am. Chem. Soc.*, **45**, 3043 (1923).

[684] Helberger, *Ann.*, **529**, 214 (1937).

[685] Kloetzel and Wildman, *J. Org. Chem.*, **11**, 391 (1946).

[686] Hatt, Pilgrim, and Stephenson, *J. Chem. Soc.*, 481 (1941).

[687] Cook, *J. Chem. Soc.*, 1091 (1930).

[688] Adams, Kern, and Shriner, *Org. Syntheses*, Coll. Vol. I, 101 (1941); cf. ref. 465.

[689] Leonard, Herbrandson, and Van Heyningen, *J. Am. Chem. Soc.*, **68**, 1281 (1946).

[690] Kuick and Adkins, *J. Am. Chem. Soc.*, **57**, 143 (1935).

[691] Sauer, *Org. Syntheses*, **31**, 68 (1951) including note 5.

[692] Cornforth, *Org. Syntheses*, **31**, 59 (1951).

[693] Djerassi in *Organic Reactions*, Vol. 6, John Wiley & Sons, New York, 1951, p. 207.

[694] Cannon, Ellis, and Leal, *Org. Syntheses*, **31**, 74 (1951).

11

Quinones

CONTENTS

236. Oxidation of Aromatic Hydrocarbons

Polycyclic quinones are prepared by careful oxidation of the corre-sponding hydrocarbons with chromic-sulfuric acid mixture in acetic acid solution or as an agitated aqueous suspension, e.g., 2,3-dimethyl-1,4-naphthoquinone (80%),[1] 9,10-phenanthroquinone (80%),[2] and acenaphthene-quinone (60%).[4] A laboratory reactor has been described in which an acetic acid solution of chromic acid and another solution of hydrocarbon are mixed as a film at 90°. The reaction mixture is then fed into water to prevent further oxidation. By this procedure, the yield of 2-methyl-1,4-naphthoquinone has been raised from 29% by the usual process to 45%.[5,6]

Other oxidizing agents have been used. Sodium chlorate with vanadium pentoxide catalyst attacks anthracene readily but is not powerful enough for the conversion of hydrocarbons of the naphthalene and phenanthrene series.[7,8] An acetic acid solution of 30% hydrogen peroxide has also been used.[9,10]

237. Oxidation of Phenols, Aminophenols, and Aryl Diamines

$$p\text{-HOC}_6\text{H}_4\text{OH} \xrightarrow{(O)} O = C_6H_4 = O$$

Derivatives of phenol or aniline can be oxidized to quinones, the yield and ease of oxidation depending on the substituents. If an amino or hydroxyl group is in the *para* position, the reaction proceeds readily, as illustrated by the synthesis of quinone from hydroquinone by oxidation with a sodium chlorate-vanadium pentoxide mixture (96%)[7] or with chromic-sulfuric acid mixture (92%).[13] A *para* halogen atom usually has a favorable effect. Any group in the *para* position is eliminated or oxidized. o-Quinones are usually prepared from the corresponding catechols. A survey of procedures for the synthesis of benzoquinones by oxidation has been made.[35]

Polymethylquinones and certain polycyclic quinones are prepared by the oxidation of aminophenols and their polycyclic analogs. The latter substances are readily obtained by coupling the corresponding phenolic compound with diazotized sulfanilic acid followed by a reductive cleavage of the azo compound.

Oxidation of the crude aminophenol is carried out with chromic acid[14, 15] or manganese dioxide.[17] The over-all yields are good (50–90%). For the preparation of 1,2-naphthoquinone, ferric chloride is a milder and a better oxidant than chromic acid (94%).[21] Similarly, diamines are oxidized with ferric chloride, as in the synthesis of duroquinone (90%).[20]

238. Oxidation of 2-Hydroxy-1,4-naphthoquinones

The conversion of 2-hydroxy-3-alkyl-1,4-naphthoquinones by the action of alkaline permanganate into the next lower homolog has been extensively studied.[33] A modified procedure involves the treatment of the naphthoquinone with hydrogen peroxide in dioxane-soda solution followed by the action of copper sulfate and alkali on an intermediate acid (93% over-all). It has been established that the hydroxyl and alkyl groups change places in the course of the oxidation. The method has been found valuable in the synthesis of certain homologs difficult to obtain by direct alkylation (method 239).[32]

239. Alkylation of Quinones

Diacyl peroxides are good agents for the alkylation of p-benzo- and 1,4-naphthoquinones having a free position in the quinoid ring, particularly when the normal- or iso-alkyl chains are desired (30–60%).[11,32] The method has been widely applied in the synthesis of 2-hydroxy-1,4-naphthoquinones substituted in the 3-position. The procedure consists in adding slowly a solution of the diacyl peroxide in ether to a solution of the quinone in acetic acid at 90–95°.

Alkyl groups in the low-molecular-weight range are also introduced by heating the quinone with the corresponding acid, excess red lead, and a promoter, which is a compound containing an active hydrogen, such as malonic ester or acetoacetic ester.[12]

240. Quinones by Ring Closure

The intramolecular condensation of o-aroylbenzoic acids in the presence of concentrated sulfuric acid gives substituted anthraquinones. The acid strength, reaction temperature, and period of heating are carefully controlled to insure optimum yields and to avoid sulfonation products.[22,23] Boric acid has been added as a sulfonation inhibitor.[22] Substitution in the *para* position of the aroyl group leads to 2-alkyl-,[23] 2-chloro-,[25] and 2-bromo-anthraquinones.[26]

A number of anthraquinones have been synthesized by adding dienes to aroylacrylic acids, dehydrogenating the adducts in the form of the esters, and cyclizing as before.[27]

$$R = H, CH_3, C_6H_5; \quad R' = H, CH_3; \quad R'' = H, CH_3, OCH_3$$

The diene synthesis[28, 30] with quinones is valuable in providing hydro-aromatic systems which are readily dehydrogenated, as illustrated by the synthesis of 2,3-dimethylanthraquinone (90% over-all).[29]

The synthesis has been adapted to the preparation of 1,2-naphthoquinone and its derivatives by an improved procedure.[30]

TABLE 40. QUINONES

C_n	Compound	Method	Yield (%)	Chapter ref.	(M.p.)
C_6	Benzoquinone	237	96	11^7	(112)
		237	92	11^{13}	
	Chlorobenzoquinone	237	92	11^8	(54–64)
	Bromobenzoquinone	237	94	11^8	(56)
C_7	Methylbenzoquinone	237	90	11^8	(69)
C_8	o-Xyloquinone	237	62	11^{17}	(57.5)
	m-Xyloquinone	237	75 †	11^{14}	(75)
	p-Xyloquinone	237	81 †	11^{19}	(124)
		237	40	11^{18}	(125)
C_9	Trimethylbenzoquinone	237	95 †	11^{14}	(26)
	4,7-Hydrindenequinone	237	93	11^{17}	(205)
C_{10}	Duroquinone	237	90	11^{20}	(110)
		237	60 †	11^{14}	(112)
	1,2-Naphthoquinone	237	94	11^{21}	(147)
	1,4-Naphthoquinone	237	81	11^{16}	(125)
		240	88	11^{30}	(124)
	1,2,3,4-Tetrahydro-5,8-naphthoquinone	237	60 †	11^{17}	(56)
	2-Chloro-1,4-naphthoquinone	66	75 †	11^{30}	(118)
	2-Hydroxy-1,4-naphthoquinone	97	46 †	11^{31}	(192)
		240	95	11^{30}	(196)
C_{11}	2-Methyl-1,4-naphthoquinone	236	29	11^5	(106)
		236	45	11^6	(105)
C_{12}	2-Ethyl-1,4-naphthoquinone	236	39	11^5	(87)
	2,3-Dimethyl-1,4-naphthoquinone	236	78	11^9	(127)
		236	80	11^1	(127)
	Acenaphthenequinone	236	60	11^4	(245)
C_{13}	2-Methyl-3-ethyl-1,4-naphthoquinone	239	41	11^{12}	(73)
C_{14}	1,2-Phenanthraquinone	237	96 †	11^{15}	(222)
	9,10-Phenanthraquinone	236	80	11^2	(207)
	9,10-Anthraquinone	236	91	11^8	(275)
	α-Chloroanthraquinone	....	98	11^{34}	(160)
	β-Chloroanthraquinone	240	99	11^{26}	(209)
	β-Bromoanthraquinone	240	95	11^{25}	(209)
	β-Aminoanthraquinone	240	96	11^{25}	(306) *
		435	97	11^{36}	
C_{15}	β-Methylanthraquinone	240	90	11^{23}	(174)
C_{16}	2,3-Dimethylanthraquinone	240	96	11^{29}	(210)
C_{18}	β-t-butylanthraquinone	240	75	11^{24}	(104)
C_{22}	2,3-Diphenyl-1,4-naphthoquinone	236	50	11^3	(139)

For explanations and symbols see pp. xi–xii.

REFERENCES FOR CHAPTER 11

[1] Smith and Webster, *J. Am. Chem. Soc.*, 59, 662 (1937).
[2] Linstead et al., *J. Am. Chem. Soc.*, 64, 1998, 2023 (1942); Moore and Huntress, *ibid.*, 49, 1328 (1927); Steck and Day, *ibid.*, 65, 454 (1943).
[3] Crawford and Nelson, *J. Am. Chem. Soc.*, 68, 134 (1946).
[4] Maxwell and Allen, *Org. Syntheses*, 24, 1 (1944).
[5] Fieser et al., *J. Am. Chem. Soc.*, 61, 3218 (1939); Sah, *Rec. trav. chim.*, 59, 1027 (1940).
[6] Veldstra and Wiardi, *Rec. trav. chim.*, 62, 82 (1943).
[7] Underwood and Walsh, *Org. Syntheses*, Coll. Vol. II, 553 (1943).
[8] Underwood and Walsh, *J. Am. Chem. Soc.*, 58, 646 (1936); cf. ref. 7.
[9] Arnold and Larson, *J. Org. Chem.*, 5, 250 (1940).
[10] Greenspan, *Ind. Eng. Chem.*, 39, 848 (1947).
[11] Fieser and Oxford, *J. Am. Chem. Soc.*, 64, 2060 (1942).
[12] Fieser and Chang, *J. Am. Chem. Soc.*, 64, 2043 (1942).
[13] Vliet, *Org. Syntheses*, Coll. Vol. I, 482 (1941).
[14] Smith et al., *J. Org. Chem.*, 4, 318 (1939).
[15] Fieser, *J. Am. Chem. Soc.*, 51, 1900 (1929).
[16] Fieser, *Org. Syntheses*, Coll. Vol. I, 383 (1941).
[17] Arnold and Zaugg, *J. Am. Chem. Soc.*, 63, 1317 (1941); Emerson and Smith, *ibid.*, 62, 141 (1940).
[18] James, Snell, and Weissberger, *J. Am. Chem. Soc.*, 60, 2084 (1938).
[19] Smith and Nichols, *J. Am. Chem. Soc.*, 65, 1742 (1943); cf. ref. 14.
[20] Smith, *Org. Syntheses*, Coll. Vol. II, 254 (1943); Smith and Denyes, *J. Am. Chem. Soc.*, 58, 304 (1936).
[21] Fieser, *Org. Syntheses*, Coll. Vol. II, 430 (1943).
[22] Groggins and Newton, *Ind. Eng. Chem.*, 22, 157 (1930).
[23] Fieser, *Org. Syntheses*, Coll. Vol. I, 353 (1941).
[24] Peters and Rowe, *J. Chem. Soc.*, 181 (1945).
[25] Groggins, Stirton, and Newton, *Ind. Eng. Chem.*, 23, 893 (1931).
[26] Groggins and Newton, *Ind. Eng. Chem.*, 21, 369 (1929).
[27] Fieser and Fieser, *J. Am. Chem. Soc.*, 57, 1679 (1935).
[28] Butz and Rytina in *Organic Reactions*, Vol. 5, John Wiley & Sons, New York, 1949, p. 136.
[29] Allen and Bell, *Org. Syntheses*, 22, 37 (1942).
[30] Fieser, *J. Am. Chem. Soc.*, 70, 3165 (1948).
[31] Fieser and Martin, *Org. Syntheses*, 21, 56 (1941).
[32] Fieser et al., *J. Am. Chem. Soc.*, 70, 3174 (1948).
[33] Fieser and Fieser, *J. Am. Chem. Soc.*, 70, 3215 (1948).
[34] Scott and Allen, *Org. Syntheses*, Coll. Vol. II, 128 (1943).
[35] Cason in *Organic Reactions*, Vol. 4, John Wiley & Sons, New York, 1948, pp. 305–361.
[36] Groggins, Stirton, and Newton, *Ind. Eng. Chem.*, 23, 893 (1931).

12

Ketenes and Ketene Dimers

CONTENTS

A critical discussion of methods for the preparation of ketenes and ketene dimers including many experimental procedures has been elegantly presented.[1] For the most part, the methods are modifications of those used for the synthesis of olefins. Ketenes are very reactive substances and are prepared for immediate consumption. The simplest member, ketene, reacts with various groups which contain hydrogen to form acetyl derivatives.[25,27,28] Even t-butyl alcohol reacts readily to form t-butyl acetate when a small amount of sulfuric acid is present as a catalyst.[28]

241. Pyrolysis of Acids, Anhydrides, Ketones, and Esters

$$CH_3COCH_3 \xrightarrow{550^\circ} H_2C = C = O + CH_4$$

Ketene, $H_2C = C = O$, has been obtained by the pyrolysis of many compounds containing the CH_3CO- group.[1] However, its preparation from acetone has been the most successful from the standpoint of the laboratory and is carried out by passing the vapors through a combustion furnace at 650° (30%)[2] or over a hot Chromel A wire filament at 700–750° (90%).[3,4] The product is contaminated with ethylene, carbon monoxide, and methane. It may be purified by dimerization[26] followed by depolymerization (cf. method 246).[25] More often than not, since ketene dimerizes readily, it is passed directly from the generator into a reaction vessel for immediate consumption.

This method has no value for the synthesis of higher homologs.

242. Decomposition of Malonic Acid Derivatives

$$\begin{array}{c} R \\ \diagdown \\ C \\ \diagup \\ R \end{array} \begin{array}{c} CO \\ \diagup \diagdown \\ O \\ \diagdown \diagup \\ CO \end{array} \xrightarrow{\text{Heat}} R_2C{=}C{=}O + CO_2$$

The thermal decomposition of disubstituted malonic anhydrides gives ketoketenes, $R_2C{=}C{=}O$. A similar synthesis of an aldoketene, $RHC{=}C{=}O$, from a monosubstituted malonic anhydride has never been accomplished.

The anhydrides can be prepared by the action of acetic anhydride on the corresponding malonic acid in the presence of a small amount of sulfuric acid, followed by neutralization of the mineral acid with powdered barium carbonate and evaporation to dryness in a high vacuum. The residual malonic anhydride is then heated to the decomposition point at a low pressure, and the ketene is collected in a cold receiver. This procedure has been applied to the synthesis of low-molecular-weight dialkylketenes (R is methyl, ethyl, n-propyl, or isopropyl) in 50–80% yields.[5]

A second procedure consists in heating mixed anhydrides prepared from disubstituted malonic acids and diphenylketene.

$$R_2C(CO_2H)_2 \xrightarrow{(C_6H_5)_2C-CO} R_2C \begin{array}{l} {}^{\displaystyle /CO \cdot O \cdot COCH(C_6H_5)_2} \\ {}_{\displaystyle \diagdown CO \cdot O \cdot COCH(C_6H_5)_2} \end{array} \xrightarrow{\text{Heat}}$$

$$R_2C{=}C{=}O + [(C_6H_5)_2CHCO]_2O$$

The high-boiling ketenes are separated from the diphenylacetic anhydride by extraction rather than by distillation in order to avoid a ketene interchange. In this manner, many types of ketoketenes have been formed, including dimethylketene (49%), diallylketene (80%), dibenzylketene (74%), ethylchloroketene $C_2H_5ClC{=}CO$ (50%), and methylphenylketene (75%).[6,7]

Malonic acid and its esters yield carbon suboxide, $O{=}C{=}C{=}C{=}O$, when treated with excess phosphorus pentoxide at 300° (10–12%).[8] Better yields are obtained by the pyrolysis of diacetyltartaric anhydride at 200° (41%).[9] A review of the chemistry of this interesting substance has been made.[10]

243. Dehalogenation of α-Haloacyl Halides

$$R_2CXCOX + Zn \rightarrow R_2C=C=O + ZnX_2$$

The dehalogenation of α-haloacyl halides with zinc occurs readily, particularly for the formation of aromatic ketoketenes like methylphenylketene (90%),[11] diphenylketene (95%),[12] and di-p-xenylketene (60%).[13] The dehalogenation is carried out in anhydrous ether solution under reflux with excess zinc. The ether-soluble zinc chloride is then precipitated by the addition of petroleum ether. The resulting solution may be used directly or distilled to obtain the pure ketene.

An interesting extension of the reaction is the preparation of a ketene carrying an ester group, such as ethylcarbethoxyketene, from a malonic ester derivative (34%).[17]

$$C_2H_5C \underset{\displaystyle CO_2C_2H_5}{\overset{\displaystyle CO_2C_2H_5}{\Big\langle}} Br \xrightarrow{Zn} C_2H_5C \underset{\displaystyle CO_2C_2H_5}{\overset{}{=}} C=O$$

It is becoming increasingly apparent that the action of zinc on monosubstituted α-haloacetyl halides is not a general reaction for the formation of aldoketenes. It has been shown that the treatment of the various dihalo compounds of acetic acid—bromoacetyl bromide, chloroacetyl bromide, bromoacetyl chloride, and chloroacetyl chloride—gives poor or negative results.[14] Likewise, monosubstituted ketenes, such as methylketene, ethylketene, and phenylketene, can be obtained only in low yields (4–13%).

244. Decomposition of Diazo Ketones

$$ArCCOAr \xrightarrow[CaSO_4]{HgO} ArCOCN_2Ar \xrightarrow{Heat} Ar_2C=C=O + N_2$$
$$\underset{NNH_2}{\|}$$

Although this method has had limited application, it represents the most convenient synthesis for the important diphenylketene. This consists in converting benzil monohydrazone to the diazo compound by the action of mercuric oxide suspended in benzene. The presence of anhydrous calcium sulfate is needed to remove the water formed in the oxidation. The benzene solution is then dropped slowly into a distilling flask maintained at 100–110°, whereby the benzene distils and the diazo compound is transformed to diphenylketene (64%).[15] In a similar manner, di-p-tolylketene has been prepared.[16]

β-Keto esters, such as methyl acetoacetate and methyl benzoylacetate, have been converted to carbethoxyketenes by nitrosation, reduction, diazotization, and finally decomposition of the intermediate diazoketo ester.[18,19]

$$RCOCH_2CO_2CH_3 \rightarrow \underset{\underset{NO}{|}}{RCOCHCO_2CH_3} \rightarrow \underset{\underset{NH_2}{|}}{RCOCHCO_2CH_3} \rightarrow$$

$$RCOCN_2CO_2CH_3 \rightarrow \underset{\underset{CO_2CH_3}{|}}{RC=C=O}$$

245. Dehydrohalogenation of Acyl Halides

$$R_2CHCOCl + R'_3N \rightarrow R_2C=C=O + R_3'N \cdot HCl$$

Certain disubstituted acetyl chlorides readily undergo dehydrohalogenation with tertiary amines to yield ketoketenes. For example, in the preparation of di-n-heptylketene, di-n-heptylacetyl chloride is added under anhydrous conditions to excess trimethylamine dissolved in benzene. After the mixture has stood at room temperature for 29 hours, the precipitated amine hydrochloride is filtered with exclusion of moisture, the solution is concentrated in vacuum, and diheptylketene is distilled (60%).[1] Trimethylamine is preferred in the preparation of aliphatic ketoketenes because of the low solubility of its hydrochloride in organic solvents. In a similar manner, diphenylacetyl chloride is treated with tripropylamine in ether to give diphenylketene (83%).[20]

The method is apparently limited to the preparation of certain aryl and high-molecular-weight ketoketenes, which are relatively resistant to dimerization. Thus, the dehydrohalogenation of a low-molecular-weight acyl chloride such as isobutyryl chloride gives dimethyl ketene dimer (60%).[22] It is quite possible that the tertiary amine salt catalyzes the dimerization.[23]

Monoalkylacetyl halides, RCH_2COX, are converted to aldoketene dimers. These materials are useful in the synthesis of β-keto acid derivatives.[24]

246. Depolymerization of Ketene Dimers

The depolymerization of diketene by pyrolysis is a rapid and convenient method for obtaining high-purity ketene (cf. method 241). The conversion can be carried out in high yields by decomposition over hot filaments or in tubes at 550–600°.[25]

Examples for the treatment of other ketenes are few. The ordinary ketene lamp has been modified for the depolymerization of dimethylketene dimer (86%).[1] Ethylcarbethoxyketene can be obtained from its dimer in 80–90% yields by heating at 180–200° under a pressure of 15 mm.[17]

TABLE 41. KETENES 409

TABLE 41. KETENES

C_n	Compound	Method	Yield (%)	Chapter[ref.]	B.p./mm., n_D^t, (M.p.)
C_2	Ketene	241	29	12^1	$-41/760$
		246	100	12^{25}	
C_4	Dimethylketene	242	80	12^5	34
		242	49	12^6	
		246	86	12^1	
	Ketene dimer	245	50	12^{24}	96/400
		....	55	12^{26}	69/92
	Ethylchloroketene	242	50	12^6	
C_5	Methylethylketene	242	65	12^5	
C_6	Diethylketene	242	64	12^6	
		242	55	12^5	92*
	Methylketene dimer	245	74	12^{24}	58/12, 1.4280^{25}
	Ethylethoxyketene	246	85	12^{17}	48/15
C_7	Ethylcarboethoxyketene	243	34	12^{17}	
C_8	Di-n-propylketene	242	32	12^7	30/11
		242	50	12^5	
	Diisopropylketene	242	50	12^5	
	Ethylketene dimer	245	70	12^{24}	96/32, 1.4387^{25}
	Dimethylketene dimer	245	60	12^{22}	
	Diallylketene	242	80	12^7	30/9
	Phenoxyketene	245	32	12^{28}	(93)
C_9	Methylphenylketene	242	75	12^7	78/15*
		243	90	12^{11}	74/12
C_{10}	n-Propylketene dimer	245	93	12^{24}	135/30, 1.4433^{25}
	Isopropylketene dimer	245	57	12^{24}	110/35, 1.4343^{25}
	Phenylcarbomethoxyketene	244	70	12^{19}	80–85/0.2
C_{12}	n-Butylketene dimer	245	65	12^1	116/4, 1.4513
C_{14}	Diphenylketene	243	95	12^{12}	146/12
		244	64	12^{15}	121/3.5
		245	83	12^{20}	
	Ethylcarboethoxyketene dimer	243	61	12^{17}	116/0
C_{16}	Di-n-heptylketene	245	60	12^1	135/5
	Dibenzylketene	242	74	12^7	122/0.08
C_{17}	Mesitylphenylketene	245	78†	12^{21}	150/12
C_{26}	Di-p-xenylketene	243	60	12^{13}	(197)

For explanations and symbols see pp. xi–xii.

REFERENCES FOR CHAPTER 12

[1] Hanford and Sauer in *Organic Reactions*, Vol. 3, John Wiley & Sons, New York, 1946, p. 108.

[2] Hurd, *Org. Syntheses*, Coll. Vol. I, 330 (1941).

[3] Williams and Hurd, *J. Org. Chem.*, 5, 122 (1940); Wang and Schueler, *J. Chem. Education*, 26, 323 (1949).

[4] Dunbar and Bolstad, *J. Org. Chem.*, 9, 219 (1944).

[5] Staudinger, *Helv. Chim. Acta*, 8, 306 (1925); cf. ref. 1, p. 135.

[6] Staudinger, Anthes, and Schneider, *Ber.*, 46, 3539 (1913).

[7] Staudinger et al., *Helv. Chim. Acta*, 6, 291 (1923); cf. ref. 1, p. 135.

[8] Diels and Wolf, *Ber.*, 39, 689 (1906); Diels and Meyerheim, *ibid.*, 40, 355 (1907).

[9] Ott and Schmidt, *Ber.*, 55, 2126 (1922).

[10] Reyerson and Kobe, *Chem. Revs.*, 7, 479 (1930).

[11] Staudinger and Ruzicka, *Ann.*, 380, 298 (1911).

[12] Staudinger, *Ann.*, 356, 71 (1907).

[13] Schilow and Burmistrow, *Ber.*, 68, 582 (1935).

[14] Hurd, Cashion, and Perletz, *J. Org. Chem.*, 8, 367 (1943).

[15] Smith and Hoehn, *Org. Syntheses*, 20, 47 (1940).

[16] Gilman and Adams, *Rec. trav. chim.*, 48, 464 (1929).

[17] Staudinger and St. Bereza, *Ber.*, 42, 4908 (1909); cf. ref. 1, p. 138.

[18] Schroeter, *Ber.*, 49, 2738 (1916).

[19] Staudinger and Hirzel, *Ber.*, 49, 2522 (1916).

[20] Staudinger, *Ber.*, 44, 1619 (1911).

[21] Fuson et al., *J. Am. Chem. Soc.*, 66, 1464 (1944); cf. ref. 1, p. 139.

[22] Miller and Johnson, *J. Org. Chem.*, 1, 135 (1936).

[23] Staudinger and Klever, *Ber.*, 41, 594 (1908).

[24] Sauer, *J. Am. Chem. Soc.*, 69, 2444 (1947).

[25] Boese, *Ind. Eng. Chem.*, 32, 16 (1940).

[26] Williams and Krynitsky, *Org. Syntheses*, 21, 64 (1941).

[27] Rice et al., *J. Am. Chem. Soc.*, 56, 1760 (1934).

[28] Morey, *Ind. Eng. Chem.*, 31, 1129 (1939).

[29] Hill, Senter, and Hill, *J. Am. Chem. Soc.*, 72, 2286 (1950).

13

Carboxylic Acids

CONTENTS

CONTENTS *(continued)*

Thirty-eight methods for the preparation of carboxylic acids are described in this chapter. No special emphasis has been given to higher-molecular-weight aliphatic acids, the chemistry of which has been elegantly reviewed.[577–579] Another field abounding in well-organized literature is that of amino acids.[33, 584–587] Also worthy of mention is a review of syntheses of α-keto acids.[18]

247. Hydrolysis of Nitriles

$$RCN + H_2O \xrightarrow[OH^-]{H^+ \text{ or}} RCO_2H + (NH_3)$$

Hydrolysis of nitriles to carboxylic acids is best effected by refluxing with concentrated solutions of sulfuric acid or sodium hydroxide. The progress of the reaction with the latter reagent is indicated by the evolution of ammonia gas.[228] Excellent directions are numerous. Hydrolysis by concentrated alkali is described for valeric acid (81%)[138] and isocaproic acid (82%).[81] A solution of potassium hydroxide in glycol monomethyl ether is used for 2-phenanthroic acid (98%),[228] and alcoholic bases are employed for the preparation of nicotinic acid (90%)[253] and tetrahydrofurylacetic acid (75%).[262] Acid hydrolysis has been used for phenylacetic acid (78%),[148] o- and m-toluic acids (96%),[137,150] mesitylacetic acid (87%),[178] and 3-quinolinecarboxylic acid (97%).[274] Acetic acid is sometimes added to increase the solubility of the nitrile as in the preparations of o-tolylacetic acid (73%)[159] and 1-naphthoic acid (98%).[185] Di-o-substituted benzonitriles are sometimes difficult to hydrolyze. Several of these compounds have been successfully converted to acids by heating with 100% phosphoric acid.[192] Occasionally, the intermediate amide is formed, but this compound then resists further hydrolysis. Complete conversion can usually be accomplished by the action of nitrous acid on the amide as in the preparation of 2,2-diphenylbutanoic acid (81% over-all).[596]

A convenient method for preparing acids from halides is through the cyanides. It is usually unnecessary to isolate or purify the cyanide.[65, 81] By this method the carbon content is increased by one carbon atom. Primary aliphatic nitriles are readily formed in high yields from the halides; however, secondary and tertiary cyanides are less easily made in this manner.[23, 74, 88]

Another promising procedure for lengthening the carbon chain by one carbon atom is a five-step conversion of an aldehyde to an acid (rhodanine synthesis, method 385). Yields of 90% or better are obtained for each step including an alkaline hydrolysis of a nitrile as the last reaction in the series.[248]

Several *dibasic acids* have been made from dicyanides by refluxing with concentrated hydrochloric acid. Among those prepared in this manner are glutaric acid (85%)[289] and suberic acid (92%).[312] α-β-Diphenylsuccinic acid (86%)[362] is prepared similarly using a mixture of water, acetic acid, and sulfuric acid, whereas alkaline hydrolysis is employed for 1,13-tridecanedicarboxylic acid (93%).[326] Preparations of malonic acid (80%)[284] and β,β-dimethyladipic acid (48%)[315] illustrate a process for making dibasic acids from halo acids through the intermediate cyano acids. Alkaline reagents are used in both cases to effect the hydrolysis. Methylsuccinic acid is made in 70% yield by hydrolysis of ethyl β-cyanobutyrate with barium hydroxide.[292] The most economical preparation of phenylsuccinic acid is the hydrolysis of the β-cyano ester obtained by the addition of aqueous potassium cyanide to benzalmalonic ester; the over-all yield is 70%.[166]

$$C_6H_5 CH = C(CO_2C_2H_5)_2 \xrightarrow[H_2O]{KCN} C_6H_5CH(CN)CH_2CO_2C_2H_5 \xrightarrow{HCl}$$

$$C_6H_5CH(CO_2H)CH_2CO_2H$$

Acid hydrolysis of the simpler olefinic nitriles to *olefinic acids* occurs without appreciable migration of the double bond. Acrylic acid is made by hydrolysis of acrylonitrile with sulfuric acid (78%).[363] Concentrated hydrochloric acid is used to convert allyl cyanide to vinylacetic acid (75-82%).[365] Similarly, 3-pentenonitrile furnishes a 70% yield of 3-pentenoic acid, but the isomeric 2-methyl-3-butenonitrile is not hydrolyzed under the same conditions.[370] The alkaline hydrolysis of higher-molecular-weight branched α,β-olefinic nitriles gives mixtures of isomeric α,β- and β,γ-olefinic acids.[2]

A series of *acetylenic acids* has been made from the corresponding acetylenic chlorides by way of the cyanides in over-all yields of 52-84%.[62]

Few *halo acids* have been made by this method because of the reactivity of the halogen atom; e.g., hydrogen chloride is removed from γ-chloro-

butyronitrile to give cyclopropanecarboxylic acid (79%),[128] and the bromine
atom of p-cyanobenzyl bromide is replaced by a hydroxyl group during
hydrochloric acid hydrolysis to give p-hydroxymethylbenzoic acid (90%).[460]
However, p-chloromethylbenzoic acid (78%) and p-bromomethylbenzoic acid
(73%) may be made from the halo cyanides by refluxing with the appropriate
halogen acid.[435] Halogens directly attached to an aromatic nucleus are
stable to hydrolysis.[430, 433] Both carboxyl and halogen groups are introduced in one operation in the preparation of β-bromopropionic acid (83%)
from ethylene cyanohydrin and 40% hydrobromic acid.[417]

The cyanohydrin synthesis of α-*hydroxy acids* is very often carried out
without isolation or purification of the cyanohydrins. The various techniques for the preparation of the cyanohydrins are discussed elsewhere
(method 390). Hydrolysis to the α-hydroxy acids is usually effected by
heating with concentrated hydrochloric acid. Excellent directions are
given for mandelic acid (52% over-all from benzaldehyde),[457] α-methyl-
α-hydroxybutyric acid (65% from methyl ethyl ketone),[444] and eighteen
dialkyl- and alkylphenyl-glycolic acids (60–80%).[447] Sodium hydroxide
solution is used in the preparation of β-hydroxypropionic acid from the
β-hydroxy nitrile (80%).[442]

The preparation of γ-phenoxybutyric acid (61%) by acid hydrolysis of
the phenoxycyanide is a typical example of the formation of an *ether acid*
by this method.[443] Nine alkoxypropionic acids, $ROCH_2CH_2CO_2H$, have been
made in 49–86% yields by acid hydrolysis of the alkoxy nitriles. Basic
hydrolysis gives readily polymerizable material propably because of partial
decomposition of the alkoxy nitrile into the alcohol and acrylonitrile.[473]

Two *aldehyde acids*, $R(C_2H_5)C(CHO)CH_2CH_2CO_2H$, where R is C_2H_5 or
n-C_4H_9, have been prepared by the alkaline hydrolysis of the cyano aldehydes obtained by direct cyanoethylation (method 388) of the corresponding
aldehydes by acrylonitrile.[511]

Several α-*keto acids* are easily obtained by hydrolysis of acyl cyanides.
An improved procedure using cuprous cyanide in the preparation of the
acyl cyanides is described.[496, 508] Hydrolysis of the acyl cyanides by cold
concentrated hydrochloric acid is described for pyruvic acid (73%),[496]
α-ketobutyric acid,[496] and benzoylformic acid (77%).[508] Isovaleryl cyanide
is not hydrolyzed under these conditions. Alkaline hydrolysis has been
found to be more successful than acid hydrolysis in the preparation of the
γ-keto acid, α-phenyl-β-benzoylpropionic acid (76%).[232]

Similar to the cyanohydrin synthesis for hydroxy acids is the Strecker
synthesis of α-*amino acids*. Aldehydes and ketones are converted to
α-amino cyanides by ammonia and hydrogen cyanide[519] or by aqueous ammonium chloride and sodium cyanide solutions.[543, 551, 553] Amino cyanides
may also be obtained by the action of gaseous ammonia on cyanohydrins[531]
(cf. method 391). The preparation of DL-alanine (60%) is typical.[520]

$$CH_3CHO \xrightarrow[NaCN]{NH_4Cl} CH_3CH(NH_2)CN \xrightarrow[HCl]{H_2O} CH_3CH(NH_3Cl)CO_2H \xrightarrow{Pb(OH)_2}$$

$$CH_3CH(NH_2)CO_2H$$

Hydrolysis of the amino cyanides has been critically discussed.[519] Acid hydrolysis is preferred. The free amino acids have been obtained from the hydrohalide salts by the use of yellow lead oxide,[520] lead hydroxide,[543] ammonia,[551] pyridine,[531, 553] and anion-exchange resins.[521] Substitution of methylamine hydrochloride for ammonium chloride gives N-methylamino acids.[537] Formaldehyde, sodium cyanide, and ammonium chloride give methyleneaminoacetonitrile, $CH_2\!=\!NCH_2CN$, from which aminoacetonitrile is readily obtained by alcoholysis. Glycine is formed by hydrolysis of the amino nitrile with barium hydroxide (87%)[55, 518] or 40% sulfuric acid (92%).[519] When ethoxyacetaldehyde is used, the ethoxyl group in the amino cyanide is converted to hydroxyl during hydrolysis by hydrobromic acid to give serine (51%).[528]

The addition of ammonia to acrylonitrile gives β-aminopropionitrile and bis-(β-cyanoethyl)-amine. The former is hydrolyzed directly to β-aminopropionic acid (90%) by barium hydroxide,[521-523] and the latter may also be converted through the intermediate phthalimide to the same amino acid (69%).[525] A variation of this procedure involves condensation of phthalimide and acrylonitrile to β-phthalimidopropionitrile. Both amino and carboxyl groups are formed during the subsequent hydrolysis by hydrochloric acid. The free β-alanine (75%) is liberated from the hydrochloride by lithium hydroxide.[524]

Nitro acids such as m- and p-nitrophenylacetic acids are prepared in 62% and 95% yields, respectively, by acid hydrolysis of the corresponding nitrobenzyl cyanides.[569, 570]

248. Hydrolysis of Amides

$$RCONH_2 + H_2O \xrightarrow[OH^-]{H^+ \text{ or}} RCO_2H + (NH_3)$$

Hydrolysis of amides may be carried out in acid or alkaline medium. For example, the former is used for α-phenylbutyric acid (90%)[164] and the latter for 2- and 4-dibenzofurylacetic acids (87%).[279, 280] A mixture of hydrochloric and acetic acids is employed for insoluble amides.[237] Amides obtained from the Willgerodt and Arndt-Eistert reactions (methods 361 and 360) are excellent sources of acids.

Certain amides are hydrolyzed with difficulty. Some success has been achieved by heating with 100% phosphoric acid.[192] It is usually advantageous to convert these compounds to acids by treatment with nitrous acid at room temperature; the yields are excellent.[38, 597]

$$RCONH_2 + [HONO] \rightarrow RCO_2H + N_2 + H_2O$$

A large number of trialkylacetic acids have been made by the following process, which involves treatment of the corresponding amides with nitrous acid.[100]

$$C_6H_5COCRR'R'' \xrightarrow{NaNH_2} RR'R''CCONH_2 \xrightarrow[H_2SO_4]{(HONO)} RR'R''CCO_2H$$

A phenyl alkyl ketone is subjected to two successive alkylations by sodium amide and an alkyl iodide. Higher-molecular-weight acids containing two large alkyl groups are best made by introducing a small and then a large alkyl group into a phenyl ketone already containing a large alkyl group. Cleavage of the trialkylacetophenones by sodium amide in boiling benzene gives trialkylacetamides. The method fails for the preparation of acids containing more than twelve carbon atoms unless two of the alkyl groups are methyl groups. Several of these compounds have been obtained, however, by hydrolysis of trisubstituted acetonitriles.[597]

p-Methoxyphenylacetic acid (85%) is obtained by hydrolysis of the corresponding amide by alcoholic potassium hydroxide.[483]

α-Keto acids, $RCOCO_2H$, have been prepared from N,N-diethyl amides obtained by the action of Grignard reagents on ethyl N,N-diethyloxamate, $C_2H_5O_2CCON(C_2H_5)_2$.[18]

Oximes of cyclopentanone and cyclohexanone undergo the Beckmann rearrangement to cyclic amides from which amino acids may be obtained, e.g., δ-aminovaleric acid (71-80%)[533, 534] and ε-aminocaproic acid (92%).[540, 541]

249. Hydrolysis of Esters

$$RCO_2R' + NaOH \rightarrow RCO_2Na + R'OH$$

The hydrolysis of esters is accomplished by refluxing with aqueous or alcoholic alkali hydroxides. Acid-catalyzed hydrolysis is an equilibrium reaction usually favoring ester formation. High-molecular-weight esters with branching in either acid or alcohol portions are sometimes hydrolyzed with difficulty.

Saponification of an ester is the last step in an elegant synthesis of highly branched trialkylacetic acids from acetoacetic ester. An α,α-dialkylacetoacetate is reduced to the β-hydroxy ester, which, in turn, is dehydrated to a β,γ-olefinic ester. Catalytic hydrogenation followed by saponification then gives the desired product.[273]

Partial saponification of malonic ester occurs with cold alcoholic potassium hydroxide to give potassium ethyl malonate in 82% yield.[234] Esters of dibasic acids having the carboxyl groups farther apart are cleaved in a similar manner under these conditions, e.g., the preparation of the half-ester of α-methylpimelic acid (59%).[235]

Mild conditions should be employed in alkaline hydrolysis of *olefinic* esters. Double bonds in many acids migrate readily during saponification. Aqueous alcoholic sodium hydroxide is used in the preparations of 3-ethyl-3-pentenoic acid (56%)[383] and β-methylcinnamic acid (41%).[403]

α-*Bromo-β-alkoxy acids* are obtained from the corresponding esters by stirring at room temperature with aqueous sodium hydroxide.[422, 424] However, the halogen atom of ethyl 3-bromocrotonate is hydrolyzed during saponification by aqueous potassium carbonate to give 3-hydroxycrotonic acid (28%).[368] α-Methoxypropionic acid (79%) is prepared by refluxing the methyl ester with 25% aqueous sodium hydroxide.[471] The opening of a lactone ring with aqueous base is sometimes an important step in the preparation of *hydroxy acids*.[264, 443, 450]

α-*Keto esters* are sensitive to alcoholic hydroxide solutions.[35] However, excellent results are obtained by shaking the esters with cold, dilute, aqueous sodium hydroxide[510] or by refluxing with alcoholic sodium carbonate.[203, 503] A mixture of glacial acetic and hydrochloric acids has been successfully employed in the conversion of high-molecular-weight β-keto esters to the corresponding acids.[236]

Low-molecular-weight α- and β-amino esters are easily hydrolyzed merely by boiling with water.[34] Also, aqueous barium hydroxide is employed in the preparation of several *amino acids*, e.g., β-aminopropionic acid (72%)[527] and α-methyl-γ-dimethylaminobutyric acid (90%).[549]

m-Nitrobenzoic acid (96%) is best prepared from the corresponding methyl ester by boiling for 10 minutes with 20% sodium hydroxide. Longer heating gives a colored product, and the use of a more dilute base is unsatisfactory.[564] γ-Nitrovaleric acid is obtained from its methyl ester by hydrolysis with concentrated hydrochloric acid.[301]

250. Hydrolysis of Acyl Halides and Anhydrides

$$RCOCl \text{ or } (RCO)_2O \xrightarrow{H_2O} RCO_2H$$

Although hydrolysis of acyl halides and anhydrides is infrequently used in the preparation of acids, several important examples are noted. The acyl chlorides, $Ar_2C=CHCOCl$, from the action of oxalyl chloride on diarylethylenes are hydrolyzed to β,β-diarylacrylic acids by stirring with ice-cold sodium carbonate solution.[1] α-Halo acids prepared by the Hell-Volhard-Zelinsky reaction are obtained from the α-halo acid halide by stirring with cold water (method 67).

Citraconic anhydride is hydrolyzed to the *cis unsaturated dibasic acid,* citraconic acid, by heating with the theoretical amount of water until the mixture is homogeneous.[294] Hydrolysis by dilute nitric acid gives the *trans* acid, mesaconic acid.[295]

251. Hydrolysis of Trihalides

$$C_6H_5CCl_3 \xrightarrow{H_2O} C_6H_5CO_2H$$

Few simple acids are prepared by this method because the corresponding trihalides are not readily available. Several modifications are important in the preparation of acids containing an additional functional group.

Di-(p-chlorophenyl)-acetic acid is prepared in 70% yield from 1,1-di-(p-chlorophenyl)-2,2,2-trichloroethane, $(p\text{-ClC}_6H_4)_2CHCCl_3$ (DDT). This reaction differs from a straightforward hydrolysis since hydrogen chloride is eliminated and an intermediate, 1,1-di-(p-chlorophenyl)-2,2-dichloroethylene, $(p\text{-ClC}_6H_4)_2C=CCl_2$, is readily isolated in 97% yield.[441]

Twelve α-alkoxyisobutyric acids have been made by alkaline alcoholysis of the trichlorohydrin formed by the condensation of acetone and chloroform.

$$(CH_3)_2C(OH)CCl_3 \xrightarrow{KOH} (CH_3)_2C-CCl_2 \xrightarrow[ROH]{KOH} (CH_3)_2C(OR)CO_2H$$
$$\diagdown \diagup$$
$$O$$

The oxide intermediate is postulated to account for the alkylation.[475]

Chloral, Cl_3CCHO, reacts with α-naphthylmagnesium bromide to give the corresponding trichloro alcohol, which may be hydrolyzed by sodium carbonate to α-naphthylglycolic acid in 50% over-all yield.[396]

252. Hydrolysis of Primary Nitro Compounds

$$RCH_2NO_2 \xrightarrow[H^+]{H_2O} RCONHOH \xrightarrow[H^+]{H_2O} RCO_2H$$

Propionic, butyric, and isobutyric acids have been prepared in better than 90% yields by heating the corresponding nitro compounds for 8 hours at 120–140° with 85% sulfuric acid.[60] The reaction may be stopped at the hydroxamic acid stage by using milder conditions. This peculiar rearrangement of the nitro compound to the hydroxamic acid has been reviewed.[37] α-Nitroölefins are hydrolyzed to α-hydroxy acids.[397]

253. Oxidation of Primary Alcohols and Aldehydes

$$RCH_2OH \xrightarrow{(O)} RCHO \xrightarrow{(O)} RCO_2H$$

Although aldehydes are more easily oxidized than alcohols, reagents and conditions are similar in the conversion of both substances to acids. Sulfuric-chromic acid mixture has been used to prepare propionic acid from the alcohol (65%),[61] heptanoic acid from the aldehyde (70%),[86] and furoic acid from furfural (75%).[240] Alkaline permanganate is employed in the preparation of methyldiphenylacetic acid from the aldehyde (45%)[219] and ethyl-n-butylacetic acid from the aldehyde or alcohol (74%).[102] Acid permanganate is used for the oxidation of heptaldehyde to heptanoic acid (78%)[87] and 6-methyl-1-octanol to 6-methyloctanoic acid (66%).[399]

Oxidation of alcohols by acidic reagents gives appreciable quantities of ester formed from the acid obtained and the original alcohol. For this reason, alkaline permanganate is sometimes preferred.

Oxidations are usually carried out at room temperature or with cooling by an ice bath. Vigorous stirring is important. The yields are seldom quantitative; carbon dioxide and lower acids are the principal by-products. The first step in this degradation is an oxidation of the α-carbon atom at the aldehyde stage.[10]

Silver oxide, easily prepared from silver nitrate and sodium hydroxide, is probably the best reagent for the preparation of pure acids from aldehydes. An additional advantage is that it does not attack other easily oxidizable groups in the molecule. Typical examples are 3-thiophenecarboxylic acid (97%),[245] palmitic acid (98%),[41] and anthracene-9-carboxylic acid (72%).[223] Its use in the preparation of *olefinic acids* from olefinic aldehydes is illustrated by the preparation of 2-methyl-2-pentenoic acid (60%).[369] Organic peracids have also been used in the oxidation of aldehydes to carboxylic acids.[477, 565]

Low yields of *acetylenic acids* are obtained by direct oxidation of the corresponding acetylenic alcohols by chromic-sulfuric acid mixture.[409]

Halo acids, such as β-chloropropionic acid (81%)[414, 415] or α,β-dihalopropionic acids (85%),[419–421] have been made by nitric acid oxidation of the halo aldehydes or alcohols.

β-Phenoxypropionic acid (45%) is made from the phenoxy alcohol by permanganate oxidation in magnesium sulfate solution at 15–20°.[479]

Alanine,[526] α-amino-*n*-butyric acid, and α-aminoisobutyric acid[529] are prepared by permanganate oxidation of the N-benzoyl derivatives of the corresponding amino alcohols. The free *amino acids* are obtained from the benzoyl derivatives by hydrolysis with hydrochloric acid followed by treatment with aniline. Over-all yields for the four step process are 45–60%.

254. Oxidation of Ketones and Quinones

$$\xrightarrow{(O)} HO_2C(CH_2)_4CO_2H$$

Cleavage of ketones by oxidation is infrequently used for preparation of monocarboxylic acids. Trimethylacetic acid is made in 75% yield from pinacolone, $(CH_3)_3CCOCH_3$, by oxidation with chromic anhydride in aqueous acetic acid.[71] Cleavage on only one side of the carbonyl group is possible in this case.

The *dibasic acids,* glutaric acid (85%),[290] adipic acid (60%),[296] and related substituted adipic acids,[308, 334, 336] are prepared from the cyclic ketones or corresponding alcohols by nitric acid oxidation using vanadium pentoxide catalyst. It is important to add the ketone dropwise to the hot acid since the reaction may become violent if the ketone is not instantaneously oxidized.

Diphenic acid (70–85%) is obtained by acid chromate oxidation of phenanthraquinone[355, 356] or phenanthrene.[357, 358] It is unnecessary to isolate or purify the quinone in the latter process.

255. Oxidation of the Double Bond

$$RCH = CH_2 \xrightarrow{(O)} RCO_2H$$

Several compounds are best prepared by this reaction, although it has been used chiefly for proof of organic structure. The Barbier-Wieland degradation is a classical method for the removal of one carbon atom from a chain.

$$RCH_2CO_2H \xrightarrow[H^+]{C_2H_5OH} RCH_2CO_2C_2H_5 \xrightarrow{C_6H_5MgBr} RCH_2C(OH)(C_6H_5)_2$$

$$\downarrow \triangle$$

$$RCO_2H \xleftarrow{CrO_3} RCH = C(C_6H_5)_2$$

In this way, pentadecanoic acid has been prepared in 58% over-all yield from palmitic acid.[120] A modification of the process, whereby three carbon atoms may be removed, has been reviewed.[31] In this procedure, the olefin is brominated in the "allylic position" by N-bromosuccinimide. Dehydrohalogenation then gives a diene, $R'CH = CH - CH = C(C_6H_5)_2$, which is oxidized with the loss of three carbon atoms.

Alkaline permanganate oxidation is frequently employed. Examples are 2,6-dimethylheptanoic acid (45%)[113] from 3,7-dimethyl-1-octene, m-ethylphenylacetic acid (24%)[160] from m-ethylallylbenzene, and azelaic acid (36%)[320] from ricinoleic acid.

Degradation of the carbon chain does not always occur. Dichromate oxidation of triisobutylenes gives acids with the same carbon content as the olefins.[15] The keto acid, benzoylformic acid (55%), is made by hot alkaline permanganate oxidation of styrene.[509]

256. Ozonization of the Double Bond

$$RCH = CH_2 \xrightarrow{O_3} R\underset{\underset{O_3}{\diagdown\diagup}}{CH - CH_2} \xrightarrow{Ag_2O} RCO_2H$$

The literature of this reaction to 1940 has been adequately reviewed.[16] The emphasis up to that time was placed on obtaining higher yields of carbonyl compounds by hydrolysis of the ozonides. Several methods have been described for the oxidative cleavage of ozonides to acids. These procedures may prove valuable in the synthesis of certain acids. By adding the ozonide of 1-tridecene to an alkaline silver oxide suspension at 95°, a 94% yield of lauric acid is obtained.[41] Decomposition of ozonides with 30% hydrogen peroxide is described for the preparation of 5-methylhexanoic acid (67%) from 6-methyl-1-heptene and of adipic acid (60%) from cyclohexene.[93] A study of solvents for ozonolysis has been made.[36]

257. Oxidation of Alkyl Groups to Carboxyl Groups

$$ArCH_3 \xrightarrow{(O)} ArCO_2H$$

As a preparative method, this reaction has found limited use. One methyl group of o- or p-xylene is oxidized by dilute nitric acid to give the corresponding toluic acid (55%).[149, 152] Similarly, oxidation of mesitylene by concentrated nitric acid gives a 20% yield of 3,5-dimethylbenzoic acid.[163] Catalytic oxidation by oxygen gas in the liquid phase appears very promising.[151] Butyric acid serves as a solvent, and acetates of cobalt, lead, and manganese are catalysts. Yields of 25-68% of aromatic acids are obtained from the corresponding alkylbenzenes and their chloro, nitro, or alkoxyl derivatives.[259] Permanganate oxidation of α- and γ-picolines is used to prepare picolinic and isonicotinic acids (45–60%).[249, 256, 257] The ethyl group of 4-ethylpyridine is converted to a carboxyl group with equal ease.[258] The acetyl and methyl groups of p-methylacetophenone are both oxidized to carboxyl groups by refluxing first with dilute nitric acid then with alkaline permanganate. The yield of the resulting *dibasic acid*, terephthalic acid, is 88%.[339] The t-butyl group is resistant to most oxidizing agents.[506]

An oxidizable alkyl group is not necessarily attached to an aromatic nucleus. Oxidation of a methyl group of trimethylacetic acid by heating for 7 hours with alkaline permanganate gives dimethylmalonic acid (35%).[123] Other examples include the α-*keto acids*, trimethylpyruvic acid (40%)[502] from pinacolone and β-naphthylglyoxylic acid (40%)[517] from β-acetylnaphthalene.

Halo and *nitro* groups on the benzene ring are unaffected by the oxidation of an alkyl group. o- and p-Nitro-,[562, 566] o-chloro-,[429] and p-iodobenzoic acids[432] have been made from the substituted toluenes.

258. Oxidation of 5-Alkyl-2-furoic Acids

$$\underset{O}{\overset{HC-CH}{\underset{HC}{\parallel}}} \overset{\parallel}{C} -CO_2C_2H_5 \xrightarrow[AlCl_3]{R_3CX} \underset{O}{\overset{HC-CH}{\underset{R_3CC}{\parallel}}} \overset{\parallel}{C} -CO_2C_2H_5 \xrightarrow[H^+]{NaOH;\ KMnO_4} R_3CCO_2H$$

Ethyl furoate undergoes a Friedel-Crafts condensation with tertiary chlorides in carbon disulfide solution. The free alkylfuroic acids are oxidized by alkaline potassium permanganate to trialkylacetic acids. Dimethylethylacetic acid (65%) and 1-methyl-1-cyclohexylcarboxylic acid (44%) have been prepared in this manner.[83]

259. Oxidation and Decarboxylation of α-Keto Acids

$$RCOCO_2H \xrightarrow{H_2O_2} RCO_2H$$

Oxidative degradation of substituted pyruvic acids is accomplished by treating an aqueous solution of the sodium salt with 30% hydrogen peroxide (Superoxol) at 0–15°. Good descriptions have been published for the preparations of o-hydroxyphenylacetic acid (34%),[646] 3,4-dimethoxyphenylacetic acid (60%),[486] m-chlorophenylacetic acid (57%),[434] and o-nitrophenylacetic acid.[568]

260. Haloform Reaction

$$RCOCH_3 + 4NaOH + 3X_2 \rightarrow RCO_2Na + CHX_3 + 3NaX + 3H_2O$$

By this method an acetyl group is converted to carboxyl by substitution of halogen for the three hydrogen atoms followed by cleavage of the resulting trihaloketone. For preparative purposes, it is desirable that no similarly replaceable hydrogen atom be present in the R radical. It has been observed, however, that methylene groups are not as easily substituted as might be expected. For example, β-phenylisovaleric acid is obtained in 84% yield[592] from 4-methyl-4-phenyl-2-pentanone, $(CH_3)_2C(C_6H_5)CH_2COCH_3$, and β-methoxyisovaleric acid is formed to the extent of 38% from 4-methyl-4-methoxy-2-pentanone.[588]

It has recently been shown that higher alkyl ketones are cleaved in a somewhat similar manner.[591]

$$ArCOCH_2R \xrightarrow{NaOBr} ArCOCBr_2R \xrightarrow{NaOH} ArCOCOR \xrightarrow[NaOH]{NaOBr} ArCO_2Na + RCO_2Na$$

Common reagents for the substitution are bromine in sodium hydroxide solution at $0°$,[72, 85, 516] chlorine in sodium hydroxide solution at 55-80°,[145,188, 376] aqueous sodium or potassium hypochlorite,[375, 515] and commercial bleaching agents.[176, 208, 366] Cleavage of the carbon chain by base usually occurs during the steam distillation of the haloform. This distillation is necessary for complete conversion of pinacolone to trimethylacetic acid (74%).[72]

Olefinic acids prepared by this method include β,β-dimethylacrylic acid (53%) from mesityl oxide,[375, 376] cinnamalacetic acid (70%) from cinnamalacetone,[176] and *trans*-α-alkylcinnamic acids from the corresponding methyl ketones (80%).[405]

A *halo acid*, p-(β-bromoethyl)-benzoic acid (87%),[439] a *hydroxy acid*, β-hydroxyisovaleric acid (9%),[376] and an acetylated *amino acid*, p-(β-acetyl-aminoethyl)-benzoic acid (78%),[558] have been made by this method. Attempts to prepare 3-nitro- and 4-hydroxy-benzoic acids from the corresponding acetophenones have failed.[145] Oxidation of the methylene group of 2-acetylfluorene occurs during the reaction to give fluorenone-2-carboxylic acid (60%).[589]

261. Intermolecular Oxidation-Reduction of Aldehydes (Cannizzaro)

$$2R_3CCHO + NaOH \rightarrow R_3CCH_2OH + R_3CCO_2Na$$

This dismutation occurs to a small extent with most aldehydes in the presence of a strong base. It is the primary reaction only with aldehydes that lack an α-hydrogen atom and, therefore, cannot undergo aldol condensation. The reaction has been reviewed[29, 582] (cf. method 81). It is used in the preparation of 2-furancarboxylic acid (63%),[241] nitrobenzoic acids (91%), and halobenzoic acids (84–96%).[563] Aldehydes with halogen atoms in both *ortho* positions lose the carbonyl group as potassium formate to give excellent yields of *m*-dihalobenzenes.[45] The three hydroxybenzaldehydes are completely converted into the potassium salts of the corresponding acids by fusion with potassium hydroxide. This complete conversion is due to the following reaction.

$$m\text{-HOC}_6\text{H}_4\text{CH}_2\text{OH} + 2\text{KOH} \xrightarrow{190°} m\text{-KOC}_6\text{H}_4\text{CO}_2\text{K} + 2\text{H}_2 + \text{H}_2\text{O}$$

The *m*-hydroxybenzoic acid is obtained in 94% yield.[583] *m*- and *p*-Dimethylaminobenzaldehydes are unaffected by concentrated potassium hydroxide solution.

262. Carbonation of Organometallic Compounds

$$\text{RLi} \xrightarrow{\text{CO}_2} \text{RCO}_2\text{Li} \xrightarrow[\text{H}^+]{\text{H}_2\text{O}} \text{RCO}_2\text{H}$$

$$\text{RMgX} \xrightarrow{\text{CO}_2} \text{RCO}_2\text{MgX} \xrightarrow[\text{H}^+]{\text{H}_2\text{O}} \text{RCO}_2\text{H}$$

This is an excellent reaction for the conversion of most halides to acids containing one additional carbon atom. Carbonation of Grignard reagents and organoalkali compounds gives acids in yields of 50–85%. Ether solutions of the organometallic compounds formerly were treated with carbon dioxide gas at 10° to –10°.[67, 72, 183] A more recent technique involves pouring the solution onto excess crushed Dry Ice.[184, 224, 277] Carbon dioxide under pressure is sometimes required for tertiary Grignard reagents.[615] Factors influencing the yield have been studied.[66] A low temperature and vigorous stirring are important. The yield of *n*-valeric acid from *n*-butylmagnesium bromide decreases from 79% at 0° to 47% at the reflux temperature of the ether solution.[66] Small amounts of magnesium alcoholates greatly inhibit the reaction.[21]

The chief by-products of the reaction are symmetrical ketones and tertiary alcohols formed by the action of the organometallic compound on the carboxylic acid salt. The amount of these products is greatly diminished by jetwise addition of the organometallic reagent to excess powdered Dry Ice (spray technique).[17, 54]

Allylic rearrangements occur in the carbonation of Grignard reagents from 3-furylmethyl chloride[612] and *m*-methylbenzyl bromide;[613] part of the product in each case contains a nuclear carboxyl group.

Appreciable quantities of *dibasic acids* are sometimes obtained as a result of α-metalation of the monobasic salt.[24,571] In fact, it is possible to prepare phenylmalonic acid (60%)[342] and *t*-butylmalonic acid (45%)[311] from the corresponding monobasic acids by this method.

The only *olefinic acid* isolated from the carbonation of the Grignard reagent prepared from the isomeric mixture of crotyl and methylvinylcarbinyl bromides is 2-methyl-3-butenoic acid (70%).[373, 374] Separation of the halides is unnecessary because of this fortunate allylic isomerization.

α-*Acetylenic acids*, $RC \equiv CCO_2H$, where R is ethyl to *n*-amyl, are prepared in 40-49% over-all yields from sodium acetylide by alkylation, conversion to the sodio derivative, and carbonation.[408] Carbonation of the magnesium compound formed from 1-hexyne and ethylmagnesium bromide gives 72% *n*-butylpropiolic acid. In a similar manner, *acetylenic hydroxy acids* are obtained in good yields from hydroxyacetylenic Grignard reagents in benzene solution. Carbonations are carried out at room temperature in an autoclave.[410]

$$CH_3C(OH)C \equiv CH \xrightarrow{C_2H_5MgBr} CH_3C(OMgX)C \equiv CMgX \xrightarrow[H^+]{CO_2;}$$

$$CH_3C(OH)C \equiv CCO_2H$$

Grignard reagents have been prepared from β-acetylenic bromides, $RC \equiv C-CH_2Br$. Carbonation of these compounds gives mixtures of acetylenic acids, $RC \equiv CCH_2CO_2H$, and allenic acids, $RC(CO_2H) = C = CH_2$.[618]

Highly branched ketones enolize in the presence of Grignard reagents to give bromomagnesium enolates. These compounds resemble true Grignard reagents, giving β-*keto acids* upon carbonation.[572] Several ketones have been converted to sodium enolates by sodium triphenylmethide in ether solution. The enolates are carbonated by pouring onto Dry Ice, and the β-keto acids are isolated as the methyl esters.[573]

$$RCOCH_3 \xrightarrow{(C_6H_5)_3CNa} [RCOCH_2]^- Na^+ \xrightarrow[H^+]{CO_2;} RCOCH_2CO_2H$$

263. Direct Carboxylation of the Aromatic Nucleus

$$C_6H_6 \xrightarrow{COCl_2 \cdot AlCl_3} C_6H_5COCl \cdot AlCl_3 \xrightarrow{H_2O} C_6H_5CO_2H$$

Direct introduction of the carboxyl group into an aromatic ring is accomplished with urea hydrochloride, phosgene, oxalyl chloride, or carbon dioxide.[11, 221] Carboxylation of benzene is effected in 15-58% yields by treating with liquid phosgene and aluminum chloride.[144] No catalyst is required in the conversion of dimethylaniline and phosgene to *p*-dimethylaminobenzoic acid (50%).[619] 9-Anthroic acid (67%) is prepared from anthracene by heating to 240° with oxalyl chloride and nitrobenzene.[221]

A similar carboxylation affords a general method for the preparation of β,β-diarylacrylic acids. Oxalyl chloride attacks the terminal carbon atom of 1,1-diarylethylenes, giving acyl chlorides of the type $Ar_2C{=}CHCOCl$. Hydrolysis to the corresponding acids is effected by stirring with cold sodium carbonate solution.[1]

o-Xylene is carboxylated to 3,4-dimethylbenzoic acid through 3,4-dimethylbenzodiphenylamide.[162]

$$o\text{-}(CH_3)_2C_6H_4 \xrightarrow[\text{AlCl}_3]{(C_6H_5)_2NCOCl} (CH_3)_2C_6H_3CON(C_6H_5)_2 \xrightarrow[\text{H}^+]{H_2O} (CH_3)_2C_6H_3CO_2H$$

More active aromatic compounds, such as resorcinol and α-naphthol, are carboxylated in excellent yields by heating their alkali salts with carbon dioxide (Kolbe reaction).[455, 466] The carboxyl group of salicylic acid migrates to the *para* position when this compound is heated to 240° with potassium carbonate; the *p*-hydroxybenzoic acid is obtained in 80% yield.[454]

264. Decarboxylation of Di- and Poly-basic Acids (Malonic Ester Synthesis)

$$CH_2(CO_2C_2H_5)_2 \xrightarrow[\text{RX}]{NaOC_2H_5;} CHR(CO_2C_2H_5)_2 \xrightarrow[\text{H}^+, \triangle]{NaOH;} RCH_2CO_2H$$

$$CHR(CO_2C_2H_5)_2 \xrightarrow[\text{R'X}]{NaOC_2H_5;} CRR'(CO_2C_2H_5)_2 \xrightarrow[\text{H}^+, \triangle]{NaOH;} RR'CHCO_2H$$

Many high-molecular-weight branched acids are best prepared from alkyl halides by this method. Monoalkylation of malonic ester proceeds readily (75–90%) with primary and some secondary halides.[20, 78, 110] The second hydrogen atom may be replaced by an alkyl group in 60–85% yield. Even α-naphthylmalonic ester may be further alkylated in 55–80% yields when R' equals CH_3 to n-C_4H_9.[203] Excess malonic ester favors the formation of the monalkyl ester.[19, 449] Thus, the use of twice the theoretical quantity of malonic ester increases the yield of β-phenylethylmalonic ester from 50% to 95%.[40] Dialkylated esters may be separated from the monoalkylated compounds by refluxing for 2 hours with 50% potassium hydroxide solution. Under these conditions the monoalkylmalonates are saponified whereas the dialkylated compounds are unaffected.[8]

It is usually recommended that substitution by the larger radical be made first.[27, 69] However, ethylisopropylacetic acid is best prepared by first introducing the ethyl group.[98] Also, n-butylisopropylacetic acid (77%)[116] and methylisohexylacetic acid (52%)[112] have been prepared by introducing the smaller of the two groups first. Direct substitution of both hydrogen atoms by isopropyl groups is difficult.[7, 97] Tertiary and higher secondary halides give inferior results. A further discussion of the alkylation of malonic ester appears elsewhere (method 299).

The substituted malonic esters are saponified and the free acids decarboxylated in excellent yields by refluxing with concentrated hydrochloric acid[65] or by heating to 170–190° until the evolution of carbon dioxide ceases.[78,110] Monoalkylmalonic acids begin to decompose at lower temperatures (98–123°) than malonic acid (129°), whereas the dialkylated acids require temperatures higher than those for the corresponding monoalkylated compounds.[8] α-Naphthylalkylmalonic acids decompose spontaneously at room temperature.[203]

The malonic ester synthesis has been applied successively to build up the even-carbon fatty acids from C_{22} to C_{30}.[127] Several series of branched acids have also been made.[9,122]

5-(α-Furyl)-pentanoic acid (50%)[267] and 3-tetrahydrofurfurylpropionic acid (75%)[262] may be prepared without destruction of the heterocyclic ring. β,β,β-Triphenylpropionic acid is made by merely heating triphenylcarbinol and malonic acid at 160° until the evolution of gas ceases (64%).[238]

Dicarboxylic acids may be synthesized in three ways by this method.

1. Hydrolysis of alkylmalonic esters leads to alkylmalonic acids and is invariably carried out with aqueous or alcoholic potassium hydroxide.

2. Dicarboxylic acids having the carboxyl groups farther apart are made by alkylation of malonic esters with a halo ester[324,352] or halo cyanide[354] followed by hydrolysis and decarboxylation; e.g., alkylation of ethylmalonic ester, $C_2H_5CH(CO_2C_2H_5)_2$, with ethyl δ-iodovalerate gives heptane-1,5,5-tricarboxylic ester, $C_2H_5O_2C(CH_2)_4C(C_2H_5)(CO_2C_2H_5)_2$, which is hydrolyzed and decarboxylated to heptane-1,5-dicarboxylic acid (85%).[322] A series of α-alkylglutaric acids have been prepared by this process from alkylmalonic esters and ethyl β-iodopropionate.[621] In a modification of this process acrylonitrile is condensed with an alkylmalonic ester by the Michael reaction (method 301) and the resulting cyanodicarboxylic ester is hydrolyzed and decarboxylated to α-alkylglutaric acids.[622] In another variation, equimolar quantities of an alkylmalonic ester and trimethylene bromide are used, whereby only one bromine atom in the latter is attacked. The other bromine atom is replaced by a cyanide group, and the resulting cyanodicarboxylic ester is hydrolyzed and decarboxylated to an α-alkyladipic acid.[316,325] Preparation of certain branched homologs is complicated. For example, alkylation of ethyl malonate by ethyl α-bromoisobutyrate gives 33% of the carbethoxyglutaric ester, $CH_3CH(CO_2C_2H_5)CH_2CH(CO_2C_2H_5)_2$, in addition to the expected isomeric carbethoxysuccinic ester, $(CH_3)_2C(CO_2C_2H_5)CH(CO_2C_2H_5)_2$.[14]

3. Alkylation of malonic ester by one-half equivalent of an α,ω-polymethylene bromide gives an α,α,ω,ω-tetracarboxylic ester which is hydrolyzed and decarboxylated to an α,ω-dicarboxylic acid having four more carbon atoms than the dibromide. Good descriptions include those for 1,12-

dodecanedicarboxylic acid (64%) from 1,10-dibromodecane,[326] pimelic acid (64%) from trimethylene bromide,[306] and α,α'-dimethylpimelic acid (45%) from trimethylene bromide and methylmalonic ester.[321] Equimolar portions of trimethylene bromide and ethyl sodiomalonate give intramolecular alkylation to form the cyclobutane ring. Hydrolysis then gives 1,1-cyclobutane-dicarboxylic acid (23%).[131] Glutaric acid (80%) is prepared by hydrolysis and decarboxylation of the tetracarboxylic ester obtained by condensing two moles of malonic ester with one mole of formaldehyde.[291]

Olefinic halides may be used as alkylating agents in the malonic ester synthesis. The olefinic malonic acids are decarboxylated to *olefinic acids* at lower temperatures (140–160°) than those employed for alkylmalonic acids. Examples include the conversion of 4-pentenylmalonic acid to 6-heptenoic acid (67%),[318] allylmalonic acid to allylacetic acid (70%),[371] and 2-cyclopentenylmalonic acid to 2-cyclopentenylacetic acid (99%).[394] γ,δ-Olefinic acids are usually contaminated with appreciable amounts of γ- or δ-lactones, into which they are readily converted in acid medium. Lactone formation is reduced by employing an immiscible solvent during the final acidification. In this way 5-methyl-4-hexenoic acid (52%) is obtained free from lactone.[371] Isobutylideneacetic acid is removed from isocaprolactone by fractional distillation.[381]

Olefinic dicarboxylic acids and esters from the Knoevenagel condensation are readily decarboxylated to olefinic acids. Decarboxylation frequently occurs during the condensation and is discussed elsewhere (method 37).

α-*Halo acids* are readily prepared by chlorinating[623] or brominating alkylmalonic acids before decarboxylation. Bromination is rapid at room temperature in ether solution. Crude malonic acids may be used. Decarboxylations are effected by heating the α-bromomalonic acids at 130°. Excellent directions are given for α-bromocaproic acid (71%),[425] α-bromo-β-methylvaleric acid (67%),[426] and α-bromoisovaleric acid (66%).[423]

The *hydroxy acid, trans*-cyclopentanol-2-acetic acid (57%), is made by refluxing *trans*-cyclopentanol-2-malonic acid for 10 minutes in pyridine solution.[449]

A number of substituted mandelic acids have been prepared in fair yields by the following series of reactions (Ando synthesis), where Z may be alkyl, aryl, acyl, or halogen.[462, 468]

Among the *ether acids* prepared by the malonic ester synthesis are 6-phenoxycaproic acid (65% over-all) from δ-phenoxybutyl bromide[493] and γ-(o-anisyl)-butyric acid (80%) from β-(o-anisyl)-ethyl bromide.[489]

Use of α-bromoethyl methyl ketone as alkylating agent for malonic ester gives a 74% yield of ethyl α-carbethoxy-β-methyllevulinate. The second α-hydrogen atom may be replaced by a methyl group in 76% yield. The *keto acids*, β-methyllevulinic acid (40%) and α,β-dimethyllevulinic acid (83%), are then obtained by decarboxylation of the dibasic acids at 140° and 120°, respectively.[501]

An *amino acid*, β-amino-β-phenylpropionic acid (70%), is made by adding ammonia to benzalmalonic ester (45%) followed by hydrolysis and decarboxylation by boiling hydrochloric acid.[46, 555] A single-step process to achieve the same result involves heating a mixture of malonic acid, benzaldehyde, and ammonium acetate on the steam bath until evolution of carbon dioxide ceases.[554]

265. Hydrolysis and Decarboxylation of α-Cyano Acids (Cyanoacetic Ester Synthesis)

$$NCCH_2CO_2C_2H_5 \xrightarrow[RX]{NaOC_2H_5;} NCCHRCO_2C_2H_5 \xrightarrow[R'X]{NaOC_2H_5;} NCCRR'CO_2C_2H_5 \xrightarrow[H^+]{NaOH;}$$

$$NCCRR'CO_2H \xrightarrow[165°]{HCl} RR'CHCO_2H$$

Few acids have been prepared by this method. It is important in the preparation of diisopropylacetic acid, which is made with difficulty by the malonic ester synthesis. Ethyl cyanoacetate is readily alkylated[28] (method 386). n-Propyl and isopropyl groups are substituted in 65-75% yields.[6, 7] Alkaline hydrolysis of diisopropylcyanoacetate gives diisopropylmalonamidic acid, $[(CH_3)_2CH]_2C(CONH_2)(CO_2H)$, which is stable to further hydrolysis or decarboxylation[7] but may be converted to diisopropylacetic acid by treatment with nitrous acid[108] (cf. method 248). On the other hand, the cyano ester may be hydrolyzed and decarboxylated directly to diisopropylacetic acid by refluxing with concentrated hydrochloric acid (90%).[109]

The cyanoacetic ester synthesis with ethylene bromide is preferred to the malonic ester synthesis for the preparation of cyclopropanecarboxylic acid.[129]

Indirect substitution by a cyclopentyl group in 80% yield may be accomplished by hydrogenation of the unsaturated ester formed by condensation of cyclopentanone and cyanoacetic ester (Knoevenagel reaction) (method 37). Alkaline hydrolysis followed by thermal decarboxylation gives cyclopentylacetic acid (82%).[132]

The *dibasic acid*, α-methylsuccinic acid (85%), is prepared by using ethyl α-bromopropionate as the alkylating agent followed by hydrolysis and decarboxylation by boiling with concentrated hydrochloric acid.[293] Phenylsuccinic acid (95%) is obtained from the α,β-dicyano ester, $C_6H_5CH(CN)CH(CN)CO_2C_2H_5$, made by adding hydrogen cyanide to the Knoevenagel condensation product, $C_6H_5CH = C(CN)CO_2C_2H_5$, of benzaldehyde and cyanoacetic ester.[56, 348] This synthesis has been extended to succinic acids of the type $HO_2CCR_2CH_2CO_2H$.[115]

Substituted malonic acids are obtained by alkaline hydrolysis of alkylcyano esters prepared either by direct alkylation or by reduction of unsaturated cyano esters from the Knoevenagel reaction.[300]

The Guareschi reaction (method 275) is a modification of this method.

266. Cleavage of β-Keto Acids (Acetoacetic Ester Synthesis)

$$CH_3COCH_2CO_2C_2H_5 \xrightarrow[RX]{NaOC_2H_5;} CH_3COCHRCO_2C_2H_5$$

$$\downarrow \begin{matrix} NaOC_2H_5; \\ R'X \end{matrix}$$

$$RR'CHCO_2H \xleftarrow[H^+]{NaOH;} CH_3COCRR'CO_2C_2H_5$$

Contrary to popular belief, the acetoacetic ester synthesis is not a good general method for the preparation of acids. Alkylation of acetoacetic ester is discussed elsewhere (method 213). Cleavage of the substituted esters by concentrated alkali gives salts of carboxylic acids. This reaction is always accompanied by varying amounts of ketonic cleavage (method 184). Factors influencing the ratio of ketone to acid formation have been studied.[12] Cleavage to acids is very sensitive to small changes in alkali concentration. Thus, the yield of caproic acid decreases from 60% to 28% when the alkali concentration is reduced from 60% to 50%.[75] Increased branching of butyl radicals in α-α-dialkylacetoacetates favors cleavage to dialkylacetic esters.[625] Methylethylacetic acid (60%)[70] is the only other simple acid for which an adequate preparation by this method is described.

A concentrated solution of sodium hydroxide in methanol is used to open the ring of 2-carbethoxycyclohexanone to give the dibasic acid, pimelic acid (88%).[302, 303] 1-Hydroxyhydrindene-2-acetic acid (60%) is prepared by alkylating acetoacetic ester with the bromohydrin followed by cleavage with 43% potassium hydroxide.[465] Preparation of γ-phenoxy-α-methylbutyric acid (87%) is accomplished using phenoxyethylbromide as alkylating agent and 20% alcoholic sodium hydroxide for the cleavage.[488] More concentrated alkali is used in the preparation of 6-phenoxyhexanoic acid (50%).[626]

An alternative method for the introduction of the carboxyl group by the acetoacetic ester synthesis involves alkylation by a bromo ester followed by a ketonic cleavage (method 308). In this manner, the keto acid, cyclopentanone-2-acetic acid (87%), is made from cyclopentanone-2-carboxylic acid and ethyl bromoacetate.[504]

267. Reduction of Unsaturated Acids

$$RCH=CHCO_2H + H_2 \xrightarrow{\text{Catalyst}} RCH_2CH_2CO_2H$$

Olefinic acids have been reduced to saturated acids in excellent yields by a variety of methods. Catalytic hydrogenation at room temperature over platinum oxide catalyst is described for 4-phenyl-3-pentenoic acid (98%).[175] Behenic and undecanoic acids are prepared from the naturally occurring erucic and undecylenic acids with this catalyst.[121, 126] New and "aged" platinum oxide catalysts have been compared.[48] Reduction by nickel-aluminum alloy has been preferred to catalytic hydrogenation over platinum catalyst in the preparation of γ-isopropylvaleric acid.[629]

β-Phenylpropionic acid is conveniently prepared from cinnamic acid by electrolytic reduction (90%),[157] by high-pressure hydrogenation over copper chromite catalyst (100%),[155] or by reduction with phosphorus and potassium iodide in phosphoric acid (80%).[156]

A palladium catalyst has been used for the quantitative hydrogenation of β,β-diphenylacrylic acid to β,β-diphenylpropionic acid.[1]

Sodium amalgam serves to reduce selectively the double bond in an olefinic acid containing the thiophene or furan ring.[263, 268, 628] This reagent is also employed to prepare *olefinic acids* by partial reduction of certain polyenoic acids, e.g., 3-pentenoic acid (60%) from vinylacrylic acid.[369]

Among the *dibasic acids* prepared by this method are succinic acid from maleic acid (98%) by catalytic hydrogenation over Raney nickel catalyst[285] and alkylsuccinic acids from alkenylsuccinic acids made by the Diels-Alder reaction of simple olefins and maleic anhydride.[310]

268. Reduction of Hydroxy Acids

$$ArRCOHCO_2H \rightarrow ArRCHCO_2H$$

Aryl-substituted glycolic acids have been successfully reduced in high yields by several procedures. Refluxing with phosphorus and iodine in glacial acetic acid is described for the preparations of diphenylacetic acid (97%),[213] 4-fluorenecarboxylic acid (92%),[220] and a series of α-naphthylalkylacetic acids[203] and biphenylalkylacetic acids.[212] In a slight variation of this procedure, a mixture of potassium iodide, phosphorus, and phosphoric acid is used.[156] Stannous chloride in a mixture of hydrochloric, hydriodic, and acetic acids has been employed in the preparation of

o-methoxyphenylacetic acid (90%) from o-methoxybenzaldehyde cyanohydrin.[480] Catalytic hydrogenation of mandelic acid, $C_6H_5CHOHCO_2H$, over
palladium catalyst in the presence of hydrobromic[482] or perchloric[146] acids
gives a 90% yield of phenylacetic acid. Similar hydrogenations of O-benzoyl
or O-acetyl derivatives give satisfactory results for preparations of various
aromatic acids.[22, 136, 161]

Catalytic hydrogenation of the γ-hydroxy acid over copper chromite
catalyst has been employed for the preparation of γ-(p-tolyl)-valeric acid.[193]

269. Reduction of Keto Acids

$$RCOCH_2CH_2CO_2H \xrightarrow{(H)} RCH_2CH_2CH_2CO_2H$$

Preparation of acids by the reduction of keto acids is possible when the
carbonyl group is in the *alpha* or *gamma* positions or further removed from
the carboxyl group. The α-keto acid, phthalonic acid, is reduced to o-car-
boxyphenylacetic acid (homophthalic acid) in excellent yield by phosphorus
and potassium iodide in phosphoric acid[345] or by constant-boiling hydriodic
acid.[346]

The Martin modification of the Clemmensen reduction (cf. method 3)
gives good results with a number of γ-keto acids.[168, 191] In this method
zinc amalgam and hydrochloric acid are used in the presence of an immiscible solvent such as toluene. The concentration of organic acid in
the aqueous reducing phase is small, and the formation of resinous products which coat the surface of the zinc is avoided. β-Benzoylpropionic
acid gives γ-phenylbutyric acid in 90% yield.[5, 169] The thiophene nucleus
is unaffected in the conversion of β-(α-thienoyl)-propionic acid to γ-(α-
thienyl)-butyric acid (83%).[266] Partial removal of halogen from the aromatic
ring occurs in the preparation of γ-p-bromophenylbutyric acid (75%).[440]
Hydroxyl groups on the benzene ring are unaffected.[464] In preparing
methoxy acids, the methoxyl group is partially cleaved during the reduction
but is easily replaced by treating the crude product with dimethyl sulfate.[5]

Catalytic hydrogenation over palladium-on-charcoal with perchloric acid
promoter is more satisfactory than the Clemmensen method for the reduction
of α-phenyl-β-benzoylpropionic acid to α,γ-diphenylbutyric acid (83%).[232]
Several other keto acids have been successfully hydrogenated over this
catalyst.[631]

A modified Wolff-Kishner reduction employing hydrazine in glycol has
been used to prepare 10-phenyldecanoic acid from the 10-keto acid (70%)[191]
and palmitic acid labeled with C_{14} at carbon atom 6 from the corresponding
5-keto acid.[125] As in the Clemmensen reduction, the thiophene nucleus is
unaffected.[266]

270. Reduction of Aromatic Acids

$$C_6H_5CO_2H \xrightarrow{(H)} C_6H_{11}CO_2H$$

Several catalytic hydrogenations of aromatic rings in compounds containing free carboxyl groups are described (cf. method 4). Low-pressure hydrogenation over platinum oxide catalyst has been used. p-Toluic acid in acetic acid at $60°$ gives 4-methylcyclohexanecarboxylic acid (95%). The reaction is rapid at first, but the catalyst is quickly exhausted.[135] p-Hydroxybenzoic acid gives 4-hydroxycyclohexanecarboxylic acid (49%) and cyclohexanecarboxylic acid (27%).[448] Less success is achieved in the preparation of aminocyclohexanecarboxylic acids.[52] Rates of hydrogenation of eleven phenyl-substituted aliphatic acids have been studied.[4] With increased molecular complexity, higher pressures and larger amounts of catalyst are required.[633]

Hexahydronicotinic acid (90%) is obtained by catalytic hydrogenation of nicotinic acid at 3 atm. pressure over colloidal platinum. Preparation of the catalyst is described.[254] The 9,10 double bond in the acridine nucleus is reduced at $10°$ by sodium amalgam in dilute sodium carbonate solution to give 9,10-dihydroacridine-9-carboxylic acid in 70% yield.[224] 2-Phenylcyclohexanecarboxylic acid (96%) is prepared by the selective reduction of 2-phenylbenzoic acid by a large excess of sodium in refluxing amyl alcohol.[204]

271. Hydrolysis and Rearrangement of Diazoketones (Arndt-Eistert)

$$RCOCl \xrightarrow{CH_2N_2} RCOCHN_2 \xrightarrow[Ag_2O]{H_2O} RCH_2CO_2H$$

This valuable method for the conversion of an acid to its next higher homolog has been used to prepare aliphatic, aromatic, and heterocyclic acids. Excellent reviews of the reaction have been published.[47, 49] Diazomethane preparations are described elsewhere (method 500). The acyl chloride is added to an excess of diazomethane in ether or benzene solution. Diazoketones are usually not purified.

Rearrangement to acids is accomplished by adding a dioxane solution of diazoketone to a suspension of silver oxide in warm aqueous sodium thiosulfate solution. Examples include biphenyl-2-acetic acid (86%),[210] 1-acenaphthylacetic acid (64%),[215] decane-1,10-dicarboxylic acid (72%),[314] and o-bromophenylacetic acid (63%).[215]

Rearrangement to amides (method 360) or esters (method 295) often gives higher yields.

272. Alkali Fusion of Unsaturated Acids (Varrentrapp)

$$CH_3(CH_2)_nCH = CHCO_2H \xrightarrow[300°]{KOH} CH_3(CH_2)_nCO_2K$$

Olefinic acids are cleaved by heating with alkali hydroxides and a small amount of water. The other products of the reaction are hydrogen gas and potassium acetate. The double bond may be in any position in the chain of the original olefinic acid, but it is isomerized to the α,β-position before cleavage. Examples are n-decanoic acid (74%) from dodecenoic acid[119] and palmitic acid from 9-octadecenoic acid (oleic acid).[458, 576] The reaction is of little value in preparative work.

273. Friedel-Crafts Reaction

$$2C_6H_6 + CH_3C(Cl) = CHCO_2H \xrightarrow{AlCl_3} CH_3C(C_6H_5)_2CH_2CO_2H$$

Benzene may be alkylated by certain unsaturated,[581] halo,[233, 594] hydroxy,[595] and keto[218, 596] acids. The yields of phenyl-substituted acids are usually low (18–65%). In the alkylation of benzene by cinnamic and crotonic acids the major products are 3-phenyl- and 3-methyl-hydrindones, respectively, formed by subsequent ring closures by Friedel-Crafts acylation.[233]

274. Alkaline Cleavage of β-Ketoalkylpyridinium Iodides

$$ArCOCH_3 \xrightarrow[C_5H_5N]{I_2} (ArCOCH_2\overset{+}{N}C_5H_5)I \xrightarrow{NaOH} ArCOONa$$

Methyl aryl ketones react with iodine in the presence of excess pyridine to give pyridinium salts. Cleavage of the salts is readily accomplished by heating with aqueous-alcoholic sodium hydroxide. Over-all yields of 60–83% are reported.[187, 635] This two-step procedure affords a method similar to the haloform reaction for degradation of certain methyl ketones to acids with one less carbon atom.

Nine hydroxyacetophenones have been converted to the corresponding hydroxybenzoic acids by this method.[452] Some nuclear iodination occurs with the m- and p-hydroxy compounds.

275. Substituted Glutaric Acids by the Guareschi Reaction

$$RCOR' \xrightarrow[NH_3]{NCCH_2CO_2C_2H_5} \begin{matrix} R & CH(CN)CO \\ & \diagup \qquad \diagdown \\ C & \qquad NH \xrightarrow{H^+} RR'C(CH_2CO_2H)_2 \\ & \diagdown \qquad \diagup \\ R' & CH(CN)CO \end{matrix}$$

Ethyl cyanoacetate condenses with ketones and ammonia in absolute
ethanol at 0–5° to give 44–73% yields of cyclic dicyanoimides. Endocyclic
ketones may be used, giving imides in which the two radicals are part of
an alicyclic ring. The imides are hydrolyzed and decarboxylated in almost
theoretical yields to β,β-disubstituted glutaric acids.[309] A similar reaction takes place between aldehydes or ketones and cyanoacetamide,
$NCCH_2CONH_2$, in the presence of piperidine [42, 297] or potassium hydroxide.[298]
When aldehydes are used, the condensation products are dicyanoamides,
$RCH[CH(CN)CONH_2]_2$, rather than cyclic imides.

276. α-Hydroxy Acids by the Benzilic Acid Rearrangement

$$RCOCOR + KOH \rightarrow R_2C(OH)CO_2K$$

This reaction is exhibited by a number of alkyl and alkoxy benzils,
phenanthraquinone,[469] and certain aliphatic [50] and alicyclic [26] α-diketones.
A similar rearrangement occurs when α-epoxyketones are refluxed with 30%
aqueous sodium hydroxide.[470] Best directions are those for benzilic acid
(90%) from benzoin, sodium bromate, and sodium hydroxide.[467] Oxidation
of the benzoin to benzil and rearrangement of benzil to benzilic acid are
accomplished in one step. α-Ketoaldehydes [446] and potential α-ketoaldehydes [456] undergo a similar internal oxidation-reduction reaction in excellent yields, viz.,

$$C_6H_5COCHCl_2 \xrightarrow{NaOH} C_6H_5CHOHCO_2Na$$

277. α-Isopropoxy Acids by Reductive Cleavage of Dioxolones

Six α-isopropoxy acids have been made in 20–80% yield by the hydrogenolysis of dioxolones by t-butylmagnesium chloride. The Grignard reagent is oxidized to isobutylene. An improved procedure for preparing the
dioxolones from α-hydroxy acids and acetone is described.[492]

278. α-Amino Acids by Hydrolysis and Decarboxylation of Acylaminomalonic Acids (Modified Sörensen Reaction)

$$RCONHCH(CO_2C_2H_5)_2 \xrightarrow[R'X]{Na;} RCONHCR'(CO_2C_2H_5)_2 \xrightarrow[H^+]{H_2O} R'CH(NH_2)CO_2H$$

A large number of α-amino acids have been prepared by various modifications of the Sörensen method[205, 539] in which acylaminomalonic esters are alkylated and degraded. Ethyl acetamidomalonate $(R = CH_3)$,[538, 542, 557] ethyl benzamidomalonate $(R = C_6H_5)$,[53, 561] and ethyl formamidomalonate $(R = H)$[532] have been used. The acetyl group is more easily introduced and removed than the benzoyl group.[542, 548, 557]

C-Alkylation of the sodio derivative is accomplished by a technique similar to the alkylation of malonic ester. Primary halogen compounds,[542, 548, 557] quaternary ammonium salts,[560, 561] and an alkene oxide[43] have been used as alkylating agents. Alkylation by secondary halides has been less successful.[557, 644] Hydrolysis of the substituted esters to acetylated amino acids is described for leucine (64%) and phenylalanine (83%).[557] Hydrolysis with deacylation has been used to prepare histidine (45%) and phenylalanine (67%).[542] Glutamic acid (75%) is obtained from substituted acylaminomalonates prepared by the Michael condensation of methyl acrylate and the acylated amino esters.[535, 557]

$$RCONHCH(CO_2C_2H_5)_2 \xrightarrow[CH_2=CHCO_2CH_3]{NaOC_2H_5;} CH_3O_2C(CH_2)_2C(NHCOR)(CO_2C_2H_5)_2$$

$$\downarrow H_2O, -CO_2$$

$$HO_2C(CH_2)_2CH(NH_2)(CO_2H)$$

A more recent modification of the Sörensen process employs acylaminocyanoacetic esters, $RCONHCH(CN)CO_2C_2H_5$, in place of the malonates.[44] An alkylated acetylaminocyanoacetate may be hydrolyzed to an amino acid in acidic or basic medium.[548]

Olefinic amino acids[548] and alkoxy amino acids[51, 559] are obtained by this method from olefinic halides and halo ethers, respectively.

279. Reduction of Azlactones

$$ArCH = C \underset{N = C - R}{\overset{CO - O}{\diagup}} \xrightarrow[H_2O]{(H)} ArCH_2CH(NH_2)CO_2H$$

β-Aryl-α-aminopropionic acids are obtained by reduction of azlactones with phosphorus and 50% aqueous hydriodic acid in glacial acetic acid.[556] Many other reducing agents have been used. Reviews of this synthesis and related reactions have been made.[32, 33, 586, 587] The azlactones are conveniently prepared in good yields from aromatic aldehydes and N-acyl derivatives of glycine.[39, 556] Potassium carbonate has been found to be a superior catalyst for this condensation.[645] Ketones cannot be substituted for the aromatic aldehydes.[647]

280. Hydrolysis of Hydantoins

$$\text{H}_2\text{C}-\text{CO} \quad \xrightarrow[\text{Base}]{\text{RCHO}} \quad \text{RCH}=\text{C}-\text{CO} \quad \xrightarrow[\text{H}_2\text{O}]{\text{(H)}} \quad \text{RCH}_2\text{CH(NH}_2)\text{CO}_2\text{H}$$

A variety of aldehydes—aliphatic, aromatic, and heterocyclic—have been condensed with hydantoin. Sodium acetate in a mixture of acetic acid and acetic anhydride[30] as well as pyridine containing traces of piperidine[3] serves as condensing agent. Reduction of the double bond is accomplished with phosphorus and hydriodic acid,[30] ammonium sulfide,[3] or stannous chloride.[552] In a more recent modification, the hydantoins are synthesized from aldehyde or ketone cyanohydrins and ammonium carbonate.[650]

$$\text{RCOR}' \quad \xrightarrow[\text{(NH}_4)_2\text{CO}_3]{\text{KCN}} \quad \text{RR}'\text{C}-\text{CO}$$

Hydrolysis to α-amino acids is effected by various reagents in acid or basic medium. Barium hydroxide is used for α-aminopelargonic acid (92%),[552] and 60% sulfuric acid for α-aminoisobutyric acid (76%).[530] Higher-molecular-weight dialkylhydantoins require treatment with concentrated hydrochloric acid in a sealed tube at 160–180°.[648] The over-all process has been reviewed for certain important α-amino acids.[32, 33, 650]

281. Carboxymethylation of Amines[600]

$$\text{RNH}_2 + 2\text{NaCN} + 2\text{CH}_2\text{O} + 2\text{H}_2\text{O} \rightarrow \text{RN(CH}_2\text{CO}_2\text{Na)}_2 + 2\text{NH}_3$$

282. Carboxylation of Olefins[601]

$$\text{RCH}=\text{CH}_2 + \text{CO} + \text{H}_2\text{O} \xrightarrow[\text{Pressure}]{\text{Catalyst}} \text{RCH(CH}_3)\text{CO}_2\text{H}$$

283. Keto Acids by Oxidation of Tertiary Alcohols[605]

$$\text{R}-\underset{\substack{| \\ \text{OH}}}{\overset{\substack{\text{CH}_2 \\ \diagup \diagdown}}{\text{C}}}(\text{CH}_2)_n \xrightarrow{\text{CrO}_3} \text{RCO(CH}_2)_{n+1}\text{CO}_2\text{H}$$

284. Cleavage of Acylcyclohexanones [606]

$$
\begin{array}{c}
\underset{\displaystyle \overset{\displaystyle O}{\parallel}}{\underset{\displaystyle C}{}} \\
\end{array}
$$

$$
\text{RCOCH} \quad \text{CH}_2 \\
\quad | \qquad\quad | \qquad \xrightarrow[\text{H}^+]{\text{NaOH;}} \text{RCO(CH}_2)_5\text{CO}_2\text{H} \\
\text{CH}_2 \quad \text{CH}_2 \\
\qquad \text{CH}_2
$$

TABLE 42. MONOCARBOXYLIC ACIDS   439

TABLE 42. MONOCARBOXYLIC ACIDS

C_n	Compound	Method	Yield (%)	Chapter[ref.]	B.p./mm., n_D^t, (M.p.), Deriv.
		Aliphatic Monocarboxylic Acids			
C_2	Acetic acid (anhydrous)	....	....	13[57]	118 *, (16.635), 114An *
		....	....	13[58]	1.3721 * (16.55), 147To *
C_3	Propionic acid	247	90	13[59]	141, 1.3862 *, 80Am
		252	96 †	13[60]	124To *
		253	65	13[61]	141, 106An
C_4	n-Butyric acid	252	94 †	13[60]	163, 1.3983 *, 116Am
		253	74	13[63]	96An
	Isobutyric acid	252	90 †	13[60]	155, 1.3920 *, 129Am
		253	84	13[64]	105An
C_5	n-Valeric acid	247	81	13[65]	187 *, 70To *
		262	80	13[66]	87/15, 106Am
	Methylethylacetic acid	262	86	13[67]	174, 1.4050 *, 112Am
		262	86	13[68]	175, 110An
		264	84	13[69]	
		266	60	13[70]	
	Trimethylacetic acid	254	75	13[71]	164/760, 129An
	(pivalic acid)	260	74	13[73]	78/20, (35)
		262	70	13[72]	112/124, 154Am *
C_6	n-Caproic acid	247	100	13[74]	101/16, 101Am
		264	74	13[65]	205, 1.4168 *, 96An *
		266	60	13[75]	110/16
	Methyl-n-propylacetic	264	63	13[69]	103/12, 1.4140 *, 78Am *
	acid	264	50	13[76]	105/12, 95An *
		264	63	13[77]	103/12
	3-Methylpentanoic acid	253	60	13[79]	92/10, 125Am
		264	65	13[78]	196/743, 1.4159 *, 112An *
	Isobutylacetic acid	247	82	13[81]	94/15, 1.4144 *, 120Am
		264	70	13[80]	111An *
	Dimethylethylacetic acid	258	79	13[83]	81/11, 1.4141 *, 104Am *
		262	60	13[82]	86 pP *
	Methylisopropylacetic	260	70	13[84]	90/16, 1.4146, 129Am
	acid	264	80	13[69]	
	t-Butylacetic acid	260	89	13[85]	96/26, 1.4096, (7), 132Am
C_7	Heptanoic acid (enanthic	253	70	13[86]	115/13, 1.4243 *, 96Am
	acid	253	98	13[41]	98/3, 71An *
		253	78	13[87]	161/100, 72p B *
	2-Methylhexanoic acid	247	25	13[88]	98An *
		264	80	13[69]	209 *, 1.4189[25] *, 73Am *
	3-Methylhexanoic acid	264	42 †	13[89]	112/16, 1.4222, 98Am
	4-Methylhexanoic acid	262	67	13[90]	115/16, 1.4211 *, 98Am
	5-Methylhexanoic acid	256	67	13[93]	207/752, 1.4220, 100Am
		264	100	13[91]	110/10, 103Am
		264	92	13[92]	212/762, 75An *

For explanations and symbols see pp. xi-xii.

TABLE 42 (*continued*)

C_n	Compound	Method	Yield (%)	Chapter[ref.]	B.p./mm., n_D^t, (M.p.), Deriv.
		Aliphatic Monocarboxylic Acids (*continued*)			
C_7	3-Ethylpentanoic acid	264	40 †	13[620]	105/13, 1.4250
	2,3-Dimethylpentanoic acid	264	46	13[94]	92/15, 102Am
	Methyldiethylacetic acid	262	42	13[96]	204 *, 1.4250 *, 78Am
	Ethylisopropylacetic acid	264	48 †	13[97]	105/15, 119Ar
		264	80	13[98]	101/14, 135Am
C_8	Methyl-*n*-amylacetic acid	264	82	13[99]	122/13
	4-Methylheptanoic acid	262	86	13[90]	132/22
	5-Methylheptanoic acid	262	50	13[90]	128/20
	2,2-Dimethylhexanoic acid	248	20	13[100]	218, 89Am
	4,5-Dimethylhexanoic acid	262	59	13[101]	92/1
		267	64	13[629]	81/1, 1.4315[25]
	Ethyl-*n*-butylacetic acid	253	74	13[102]	121/14
	3-Ethylhexanoic acid	262	50	13[103]	159/79
	Methylneopentylacetic acid	262	52	13[104]	108/14, 123Am
	3,4,4-Trimethylpentanoic acid	267	83	13[105]	98/4, 1.4320[21], 167Am
	Ethylisobutylacetic acid	264	72	13[106]	115/20, 89Am
	Di-*n*-propylacetic acid	264	61	13[107]	124Am
	n-Propylisopropylacetic acid	265	60	13[108]	116/12, 131Am
	Methylethyl-*n*-propyl-acetic acid	262	25 †	13[615]	82/1
	Diisopropylacetic acid	265	90	13[109]	109/12, 149Am
	Triethylacetic acid	247	82	13[82]	105/5, (35)
C_9	Nonanoic acid (pelargonic acid)	264	75 †	13[110]	142/12, 57An *
	3-Methyloctanoic acid	265	82	13[122]	141/20
	4-Methyloctanoic acid	262	80	13[90]	149/22
	5-Methyloctanoic acid	264	68 †	13[90]	127/5
	6-Methyloctanoic acid	253	66	13[399]	149/23, 1.4337, 91Am
		264	68 †	13[90]	139/20
	7-Methyloctanoic acid	269	79	13[111]	105/2, 106Am
	Dimethyl-*n*-amylacetic acid	262	22	13[96]	118/10, 103Am
	2,6-Dimethylheptanoic acid	255	45	13[113]	115/3, 143Sb
		264	90	13[112]	136/14, 100Am
	3-Ethylheptanoic acid	264	42 †	13[90]	130/12
	2-Ethyl-3-methylhexanoic acid	264	64	13[114]	232, 1.4302[25]
	2-Methyl-2-ethylhexanoic acid	248	24	13[100]	125/22
	2-Ethyl-5-methylhexanoic acid	264	66	13[114]	110Am

TABLE 42. MONOCARBOXYLIC ACIDS 441

TABLE 42 (continued)

C_n	Compound	Method	Yield (%)	Chapter[ref.]	B.p./mm., n_D^t, (M.p.), Deriv.
		Aliphatic Monocarboxylic Acids (continued)			
C_9	Isopropyl-n-butylacetic acid	264	77	13[116]	223, 93Am
	Dimethylneopentylacetic acid	262	34	13[117]	230/732, (45), 71Am
	3,3,4,4-Tetramethyl-pentanoic acid	262	59	13[118]	(67), 138Am
	n-Propylisobutylacetic acid	264	76	13[108]	127/12, 121Am
C_{10}	Decanoic (capric) acid	272	74	13[119]	164/12, (31), 108Am *
C_{11}	Undecanoic (hendecanoic) acid	247	80	13[120]	158/11, (29), 103Am *
		267	84	13[121]	122/1.5
C_{12}	Dineopentylacetic acid	253	80	13[123]	(88), 140Am
C_{13}	Tridecanoic acid	247	75	13[120]	177/10, (43), 75pB *
C_{14}	Tetradecanoic (myristic) acid	249	95	13[124]	(53), 102Am *
C_{15}	Pentadecanoic acid	255	71	13[120]	(51), 77pB *
C_{16}	Hexadecanoic acid	253	98	13[41]	106Am *
C_{17}	Heptadecanoic (margaric) acid	253	54 †	13[120]	(60), 106Am *
C_{19}	Nonadecanoic acid	247	35	13[120]	230/10, (66)
C_{20}	Eicosanoic (arachidic) acid	264	55	13[126]	(75), 109Am *
C_{22}	Docosanoic (behenic) acid	267	84	13[126]	(80), 111Am *
C_{24}	Tetracosanoic acid	264	98	13[127]	(85)
		Alicyclic Monocarboxylic Acids			
C_4	Cyclopropanecarboxylic acid	247	79	13[128]	95/26
		247	96	13[130]	81/13, 125Am
		260	64	13[590]	97/27, (17)
		265	49	13[129]	186
C_5	Cyclobutanecarboxylic acid	264	60 †	13[131]	105/21, 153Am *
	Cyclopropylacetic acid	264	90	13[281]	190/750, 1.4320[25], 83pP
C_6	Cyclopentanecarboxylic acid	262	50 †	13[574]	110/14, 179Am *
		313	53	13[132]	123/27
C_7	Cyclohexanecarboxylic acid	262	55 †	13[133]	(31), 186Am *
		262	83	13[617]	131/20, (30), 142An *
	2-Methylcyclopentane-carboxylic acid	260	81	13[134]	107/9, 1.4504[22], 148Am
	Cyclopentylacetic acid	265	82	13[132]	137/27

For explanations and symbols see pp. xi-xii.

TABLE 42 (*continued*)

C_n	Compound	Method	Yield (%)	Chapter[ref.]	B.p./mm., n_D^t, (M.p.), Deriv.
	Alicyclic Monocarboxylic Acids (*continued*)				
C_8	1-Methylcyclohexane-1-carboxylic acid	258	44	13[83]	(37)
	cis-4-Methylcyclohexane-carboxylic acid	270	95	13[135]	130/13, 175Am
	trans-4-Methylcyclohexanecarboxylic acid	270	60	13[135]	(111), 226Am
	Cyclohexylacetic acid	268	81	13[146]	100/15, 172Am *
		268	95	13[136]	237
	β-Cyclopentylpropionic acid	269	71	13[138]	135/15, 162Phz
C_{10}	γ-Cyclohexylbutyric acid	272	9	13[139]	139/4, (28)
	5-Cyclopentylpentanoic acid	264	85	13[140]	123/4.5, (14), 136Am
C_{11}	Decalin-2-carboxylic acid	262	50 †	13[141]	(101)
	Aromatic Monocarboxylic Acids				
C_7	Benzoic acid	257	49	13[259]	(122)
		260	85	13[145]	(121), 128Am *
		263	58	13[144]	160An *
C_8	Phenylacetic acid	247	78	13[148]	(76)
		248	84	13[147]	(77), 117An *
		268	90	13[156]	139/13, (76), 156Am
		268	88	13[146]	(76), 89pB *
	o-Toluic acid	247	89	13[137]	(103)
		257	55	13[149]	(101), 142Am *
		257	56	13[259]	(105)
	m-Toluic acid	247	96	13[150]	(111), 97Am *
		257	49	13[259]	(112) *
	p-Toluic acid	257	56	13[259]	(182)
		257	17	13[151]	(179), 158Am *
		257	51	13[152]	(177), 140An *
		260	68	13[153]	(181), 153pB *
		260	96	13[145]	(177)
C_9	β-Phenylpropionic (hydrocinnamic) acid	248	65 †	13[211]	129/6, (47), 92An *
		267	90	13[157]	147/18, (48), 95pP *
		267	80	13[156]	170/18, (40), 82Am *
		267	100	13[155]	
	o-Tolylacetic acid	247	65 †	13[158]	(88), 161Am
		247	73	13[159]	(90)
	p-Tolylacetic acid	247	45	13[160]	159/15, (94), 185Am *
		268	60	13[161]	(91)

TABLE 42. MONOCARBOXYLIC ACIDS 443

TABLE 42 (*continued*)

C_n	Compound	Method	Yield (%)	Chapter[ref.]	B.p./mm., n_D^t, (M.p.), Deriv.
		Aromatic Monocarboxylic Acids (*continued*)			
C_9	3,4-Dimethylbenzoic acid	248	100	13[162]	(166), 108An
		257	21	13[163]	(166), 130Am *
C_{10}	α-Phenylbutyric acid	247	85 †	13[165]	86Am *
		248	90	13[164]	138/3, (42)
	β-Phenylbutyric acid	267	80	13[167]	157/12, 107Am *
	γ-Phenylbutyric acid	248	36 †	13[211]	(51), 84Am *
		264	52 †	13[171]	130/3, (52)
		269	89	13[169]	181/19, (48)
		271	60	13[170]	(50)
	m-Ethylphenylacetic acid	255	24	13[160]	(63)
	p-Ethylphenylacetic acid	255	27	13[160]	(89)
		247	50	13[172]	170/11, (90)
		268	50	13[146]	(93)
	2,4,6-Trimethylbenzoic acid	262	61	13[614]	(152)
	1-Indenecarboxylic acid	262	20 ‡	13[174]	(161)
		262	53 †	13[224]	(157)
	5-Indanecarboxylic acid	274	75	13[635]	(183)
C_{11}	2-Phenylpentanoic acid	247	70 †	13[165]	(52) *, 85Am *
	4-Phenylpentanoic acid	267	98	13[175]	166/12
	5-Phenylpentanoic acid	264	86	13[176]	189/19, (60)
		248	14 †	13[211]	(59), 90An *
		267	70	13[176]	150/3, 109Am *
		269	63	13[630]	166/5, (53)
	2-Methyl-2-phenylbutanoic acid	262	43 †	13[177]	137/3, (58)
	2-Methyl-3-phenylbutanoic acid	267	95	13[175]	125/0.2, (132)
	2-Methyl-4-phenylbutanoic acid	269	85	13[631]	130/0.2, 1.5115, 64pP
	β-Phenylisovaleric acid	260	84	13[592]	162/13, (59)
	Mesitylacetic acid	247	87	13[178]	(168), 210Am *
	p-n-Butylbenzoic acid	260	100	13[179]	(101)
	p-s-Butylbenzoic acid	262	56 †	13[180]	(92)
	p-t-Butylbenzoic acid	262	78 †	13[181]	(164)
	α-Naphthoic acid	247	98	13[185]	(161)
		260	87	13[515]	(160)
		262	70 †	13[183]	(161), 205Am *
		262	90 †	13[184]	135pB *
		273	10	13[186]	(161), 164An
		274	90	13[187]	(161)
	β-Naphthoic acid	247	20 †	13[190]	(186)
		260	88	13[188]	(185), 195Am *
		262	63	13[189]	173An *

For explanations and symbols see pp. xi-xii.

TABLE 42 (*continued*)

C_n	Compound	Method	Yield (%)	Chapter[ref.]	B.p./mm., n_D^t, (M.p.), Deriv.
			Aromatic Monocarboxylic Acids (*continued*)		
C_{11}	1,2,3,4-Tetrahydro-2-naphthoic acid	270	53	13[634]	(97), 139Am
C_{12}	α-Naphthylacetic acid	247	92	13[197]	(135), 160An
		271	45	13[195]	(131), 181Am
		273	34	13[594]	(132)
	β-Naphthylacetic acid	248	81 †	13[198]	(143), 205Am
	p-n-Amylbenzoic acid	260	100	13[179]	(88)
	Pentamethylbenzoic acid	262	40 †	13[199]	(210), 206Am *
C_{13}	2,4,6-Triethylbenzoic acid	262	66	13[207]	(113), 156Am
	o-Phenylbenzoic acid	....	96	13[204]	(113), 177Am *
	p-Phenylbenzoic acid	262	50 †	13[206]	(221), 223Am *
	2-Phenylcyclohexanecarboxylic acid	270	73	13[204]	(107)
	α-(1-Naphthyl)-propionic acid	264	91	13[203]	(149)
	β-(1-Naphthyl)-propionic acid	264	92	13[202]	(156), 104Am
	1-Acenaphthoic acid	260	96	13[208]	(256), 228Am
C_{14}	γ-1-Naphthylbutyric acid	269	80	13[168]	(113)
	γ-2-Naphthylbutyric acid	269	87	13[168]	(102)
	β-(1-Naphthyl)-isobutyric acid	264	73	13[209]	(93)
	o-Biphenylylacetic (o-xenylacetic) acid	271	86	13[210]	(116)
	m-Biphenylylacetic (m-xenylacetic) acid	248	45	13[640]	(137)
	p-Biphenylacetic (p-xenylacetic) acid	248	89 †	13[211]	(165)
		268	70	13[212]	(162)
	Diphenylacetic acid	262	90 †	13[214]	(148), 167Am *
		268	94	13[156]	(147), 180An *
		268	97	13[213]	(145)
	1-Acenaphthylacetic acid	271	64	13[215]	(164)
	7-Acenaphthylacetic acid	264	96	13[216]	(117)
	2-Fluorenecarboxylic acid	269	43	13[589]	(275)
	4-Fluorenecarboxylic acid	268	92	13[220]	(190)
	9-Fluorenecarboxylic acid	259	95	13[514]	(225)
		262	89 †	13[214]	(227), 251Am
		262	75 †	13[223]	(230)
		273	83	13[595]	(229)

TABLE 42. MONOCARBOXYLIC ACIDS   445

TABLE 42 (continued)

C_n	Compound	Method	Yield (%)	Chapter[ref.]	B.p./mm., n_D^t, (M.p.), Deriv.
		Aromatic Monocarboxylic Acids (continued)			
C_{15}	α,α-Diphenylpropionic	247	66	13[154]	(175)
	acid	273	55	13[218]	(171), 149Am *
	Methyldiphenylacetic	253	45	13[219]	(174)
	acid				
	2-Fluoreneacetic acid	248	98	13[220]	(187), 266Am
	4-Fluoreneacetic acid	271	89	13[220]	(179)
	9-Fluoreneacetic acid	264	89	13[220]	(132)
	1-Phenanthroic acid	248	77	13[225]	(232) *, 284Am *
	2-Phenanthroic acid	260	70	13[226]	(260), 243Am
	3-Phenanthroic acid	260	75	13[226]	(270), 234Am
	9-Phenanthroic acid	12	93	13[602]	(250)
		247	98	13[228]	(253)
		247	90	13[229]	(252)
		262	30	13[227]	(251), 233Am *
	1-Anthroic acid	274	80	13[187]	(252), 260Am *
	9-Anthroic acid	253	72	13[223]	(216)
		262	72	13[222]	(216)
		263	67	13[221]	(212)
	9,10-Dihydroanthracene-	262	75 †	13[224]	(209)
	9-carboxylic acid				
C_{16}	α,α-Diphenylbutyric	247	71	13[154]	(175)
	acid	248	88	13[596]	(174)
	α,γ-Diphenylbutyric	247	95	13[231]	(72)
	acid	265	100	13[230]	(76)
		269	83	13[232]	(75)
	β,β-Diphenylbutyric acid	273	37	13[233]	225/20, (103)
	2-Phenanthrylacetic acid	248	81	13[638]	(188)
	3-Phenanthrylacetic acid	248	76	13[637]	(178), 176Am
C_{21}	β,β,β-Triphenylpropionic	264	64 †	13[238]	192Am
	acid				
		Heterocyclic Monocarboxylic Acids			
C_5	2-Furancarboxylic (2-	253	75	13[240]	141Am *
	furoic) acid	260	59	13[591]	(132)
		261	63	13[241]	77/15, 123An *
	3-Furoic acid	264	80	13[242]	169Am
		264	75	13[612]	(121)
	Tetrahydro-2-furoic acid	554	40	39[97]	132/14, (21), 1.4585[19]
	2-Thiophenecarboxylic	260	85	13[516]	(129)
	(2-thenoic) acid	262	60	13[243]	(129), 180Am *
	3-Thiophenecarboxylic	247	62 †	13[247]	(138)
	acid	253	97	13[245]	(138), 180Am
		262	42 †	13[246]	(138), 130pB *
	α-Tetrahydropyrrylcar-	560	20 †	39[15]	(204), 151HC
	boxylic acid (proline)				

For explanations and symbols see pp. xi–xii.

TABLE 42 (continued)

C_n	Compound	Method	Yield (%)	Chapter[ref.]	B.p./mm., n_D^t, (M.p.), Deriv.
	Heterocyclic Monocarboxylic Acids (continued)				
C_6	α-Furylacetic acid	247	96	13[248]	(67), 85An *
	2-Tetrahydrofurylacetic acid	247	75	13[262]	140/11
	2-Thienylacetic acid	248	77	13[641]	(64), 148Am
	3-Thienylacetic acid	247	25 †	13[245]	(80)
	2-Pyridinecarboxylic (picolinic) acid	257	63	13[249]	(138), 107Am *
	3-Pyridinecarboxylic	247	90	13[253]	(232), 85An *
	(nicotinic) acid	257	77	13[251]	(235), 122Am *
	4-Pyridinecarboxylic (isonicotinic) acid	257	64	13[257]	(324), 156Am
	Piperidine-4-carboxylic acid	554	100	39[117]	242HCl
	Hexahydronicotinic acid	270	90	13[254]	(240)
C_7	3-α-Furylpropionic acid	262	25 †	13[260]	(58)
	2,5-Dimethyl-3-furoic acid	561	68	39[23]	163/20
	3-Pyridylacetic acid	248	74	13[639]	(146), 155HCl
	4-Pyridylacetic acid	248	86	13[639]	131HCl
	Piperidinoacetic acid	554	100	39[116]	216HCl
C_8	γ-(α-Thienyl)-butyric acid	269	72	13[266]	134/1.5, (15)
	2-Thenylmalonic acid	267	85	13[628]	(137)
	β-(4-Piperidyl)-propionic acid	554	100	39[122]	(242)
C_9	5-α-Furylvaleric acid	264	50	13[267]	(43), 76An
	γ-(2-Pyridyl)-butyric acid	264	58 †	39[123]	(85), 112HCl
	γ-(2-Piperidyl)-butyric acid	554	97	39[123]	(171d), 195HCl
	Indole-2-carboxylic acid	571	58	39[66]	(204)
		572	65	39[63]	(204)
	2-Thianaphthenecarboxylic acid	262	56 †	13[270]	(236), 177Am *
	3-Thianaphthenecarboxylic acid	262	60 †	13[272]	(175), 198Am
		262	70	13[271]	(175), 173An *
C_{10}	2-Benzofurylacetic acid	249	75	13[337]	(99), 164Am
	Thianaphthene-2-acetic acid	247	93	13[143]	(142)
	Thianaphthene-3-acetic acid	247	52	13[271]	(109)
	3-Indoleacetic acid	248	88 †	13[217]	168
	3-Quinolinecarboxylic acid	247	98	13[274]	(272), 198Am *
		262	52 †	13[250]	(272)

TABLE 43. DICARBOXYLIC ACIDS 447

TABLE 42 (*continued*)

C_n	Compound	Method	Yield (%)	Chapter[ref.]	B.p./mm., n_D^t, (M.p.), Deriv.
	Heterocyclic Monocarboxylic Acids (*continued*)				
C_{10}	8-Quinolinecarboxylic acid	575	53	39[131]	(189)
	4-Isoquinolinecarboxylic acid	247	90	13[276]	(266)
		247	90	13[275]	
	6-Isoquinolinecarboxylic acid	247	90	13[276]	(360)
	7-Isoquinolinecarboxylic acid	247	90	13[276]	(297)
	8-Isoquinolinecarboxylic acid	247	90	13[276]	(294)
C_{11}	6-Quinolineacetic acid	575	39	39[138]	(220)
C_{13}	4-Dibenzofurancarboxylic acid	262	58 †	13[277]	(208)
	3-Carbazolecarboxylic acid	260	92 †	13[278]	
C_{14}	2-Dibenzofurylacetic acid	248	87	13[279]	(163), 210Am
	4-Dibenzofurylacetic acid	248	82	13[280]	(214), 212Am
	4-Dibenzothienylacetic acid	248	89	13[279]	(162), 206Am
C_{15}	β-Dibenzofuran-3-acrylic acid	38	95	2[392]	(240)

For explanations and symbols see pp. xi-xii.

TABLE 43. DICARBOXYLIC ACIDS

C_n	Compound	Method	Yield (%)	Chapter[ref.]	B.p./mm., n_D^t, (M.p.), Deriv.
	Aliphatic Dicarboxylic Acids				
C_2	Oxalic acid (anhydrous)	....	90	13[282]	257An *
		....	100	13[283]	242pB *
C_3	Malonic acid	247	80 †	13[284]	(130), 170Am *
C_4	Succinic acid	267	98	13[285]	(185), 242Am *
C_5	Glutaric acid	247	85	13[288]	(98), 174Am *
		247	85	13[289]	(98), 137pB *
		253	75	13[398]	(91)
		254	85	13[290]	(94), 152pP *
		264	80	13[291]	(97)
	Methylsuccinic acid	247	70 †	13[292]	(111), 225Am *
		265	85	13[293]	(109)

For explanations and symbols see pp. xi-xii.

TABLE 43 (*continued*)

C_n	Compound	Method	Yield (%)	Chapter[ref.]	B.p./mm., n_D^t, (M.p.), Deriv.
		Aliphatic Dicarboxylic Acids (*continued*)			
C_5	Dimethylmalonic acid	257	32	13[123]	269Am *
C_6	Adipic acid	254	55	13[296]	(152), 220Am *
	β-Methylglutaric acid	275	56 †	13[297]	(86)
		275	95	13[298]	(87)
	Ethylsuccinic acid	265	60	13[115]	(100)
	α,α-Dimethylsuccinic acid	265	76	13[115]	(139)
	Isopropylmalonic acid	265	75	13[300]	(89)
C_7	Pimelic acid	247	94	13[305]	(106) *
		264	64	13[306]	148pP *
		266	85	13[302]	(105), 155An *
		266	88	13[303]	(104), 137pB *
		....	50	13[304]	(105)
	β-Methyladipic acid	254	45	13[307]	(85), 200An *
		254	35	13[308]	223/18, (91)
	α-Ethylglutaric acid	264	66	13[621]	(61)
	β-Ethylglutaric acid	275	90	13[289]	(73)
	β,β-Dimethylglutaric acid	254	98	13[484]	(99)
		260	96	13[651]	(101)
		275	68 †	13[309]	(101)
	Isopropylsuccinic acid	265	78	13[115]	(116)
	α-Methyl-α-ethylsuccinic acid	265	73	13[115]	(102)
	t-Butylmalonic acid	262	45	13[311]	(157)
C_8	Suberic acid	247	92	13[312]	(143), 216Am *
		255	....	13[313]	(140), 187An *
		264	95	13[305]	(141)
		271	75	13[314]	(141)
	α-Methylpimelic acid	249	44	13[338]	(57)
	α-Ethyladipic acid	264	....	13[316]	167/1, (53)
	β,β-Dimethyladipic acid	247	48 †	13[315]	(87)
	α-n-Propylglutaric acid	264	72	13[621]	(70)
	β-n-Propylglutaric acid	275	85	13[575]	(52)
		275	90	13[298]	(52)
	α-Isopropylglutaric acid	264	89 †	13[317]	(95)
	β-Methyl-β-ethylglutaric acid	275	63 †	13[309]	(85)
C_9	Azelaic acid	255	36	13[320]	(106), 131pB *
		264	65 †	13[319]	(105), 175Am *
	α-Ethylpimelic acid	249	45	13[338]	168/1, (42)
		264	85	13[322]	223/17, (43), 145An *
	α,α-Dimethylpimelic acid	264	95	13[321]	
	α-n-Butylglutaric acid	264	46	13[621]	(41)

TABLE 43. DICARBOXYLIC ACIDS 449

TABLE 43 (continued)

C_n	Compound	Method	Yield (%)	Chapter[ref.]	B.p./mm., n_D^t, (M.p.), Deriv.
			Aliphatic Dicarboxylic Acids (continued)		
C_9	β-Methyl-β-n-propyl-glutaric acid	275	64 †	13[309]	(93)
	β,β-Diethylglutaric acid	275	44 †	13[309]	(106)
	n-Hexylmalonic acid	264	58 †	13[323]	(106), 208Am
C_{10}	n-Hexylsuccinic acid	264	75	13[324]	(89)
C_{12}	1,10-Decanedicarboxylic acid	271	72	13[314]	(128), 185Am
	α-n-Hexyladipic acid	264	80 †	13[325]	175/0.2, (65)
C_{14}	1,12-Dodecanedicarboxylic acid	264	64	13[326]	(123)
C_{15}	1,13-Tridecanedicarboxylic acid	247	93	13[326]	(114)
C_{16}	1,14-Tetradecanedicarboxylic acid	264	....	13[327]	(126), 163An
			Alicyclic Dicarboxylic Acids		
C_5	1,1-Cyclopropanedicarboxylic acid	265	....	13[328]	(134)
C_6	1,1-Cyclobutanedicarboxylic acid	264	23	13[131]	(158), 277Am *
	Cyclopropylmalonic acid	249	83	13[281]	(175)
C_7	cis-1,3-Cyclopentanedicarboxylic acid	254	20	13[330]	(122), 226Am *
	trans-1,2-Cyclopentanedicarboxylic acid	264	30	13[329]	(161)
	trans-1,1-Dimethylcyclopropane-2,3-dicarboxylic acid	249	80	13[331]	(213)
C_8	trans-1,2-Cyclohexanedicarboxylic acid	270	44	13[632]	(228)
		254	....	13[333]	(222)
	cis-1,3-Cyclohexanedicarboxylic acid	270	30	13[632]	(168)
	1-Carboxycyclopentane-1-acetic acid	247	81	13[300]	(156)
	Cyclopentylmalonic acid	265	100	13[300]	(165)
	trans-2,2-Dimethylcyclobutane-1,3-dicarboxylic acid	264	100	13[332]	
C_9	1-Carboxycyclohexane-1-acetic acid	247	86	13[300]	(134)
	cis-o-Carboxycyclohexaneacetic acid	254	....	13[333]	(147)
	Cyclohexylmalonic acid	265	100	13[300]	(178)

For explanations and symbols see pp. xi–xii.

TABLE 43 (*continued*)

C_n	Compound	Method	Yield (%)	Chapter[ref.]	B.p./mm., n_D^t, (M.p.), Deriv.
Alicyclic Dicarboxylic Acids (*continued*)				

C_n	Compound	Method	Yield (%)	Chapter[ref.]	B.p./mm., n_D^t, (M.p.), Deriv.
	Alicyclic Dicarboxylic Acids (continued)				
C_9	Cyclopentane-1,1-diacetic acid	275	55 †	13[309]	(177)
C_{10}	Cycloheptylmalonic acid	265	....	13[300]	(165)
	1-Carboxycycloheptane-1-acetic acid	247	86	13[300]	(159)
	Cyclohexane-1,1-diacetic acid	275	73 †	13[309]	(181)
	cis-Cyclohexane-1,2-diacetic acid	254	30	13[334]	(160)
		254	40	13[335]	(164)
	trans-Cyclohexane-1,2-diacetic acid	254	47	13[336]	(162)
		254	59	13[334]	(167)
C_{13}	*trans*-Decahydronaphthyl-malonic acid	265	100	13[300]	(122)
	Aromatic Dicarboxylic Acids				
C_8	Terephthalic acid	257	88	13[339]	
C_9	Phenylmalonic acid	262	65	13[341]	(153)*, 233Am *
		262	60 †	13[342]	
	o-Carboxyphenylacetic (homophthalic) acid	247	75	13[343]	(181)
		247	70	13[347]	(185), 228Am
		255	77	13[490]	(181)
		269	85	13[345]	(180)
		269	100	13[346]	(181)
		....	58	13[344]	(180)
	1,3,5-Benzenetricarboxylic acid	260	94	13[580]	(375)
C_{10}	Phenylsuccinic acid	247	70	13[166]	(166)
		264	95	13[348]	(166), 210Am *
	1,2,4,5-Benzenetetracarboxylic acid	....	....	13[604]	(271)
C_{11}	β-Phenylglutaric acid	264	85	13[56]	(140)*
	Benzylsuccinic acid	264	91	13[352]	(161)
		266	80	13[627]	(160)
	o-Phenyleneaceticpro-pionic acid	248	67	13[353]	(140)
C_{12}	α-Phenyladipic acid	264	43 †	13[354]	(133)
	β-Phenyladipic acid	247	33 †	13[56]	(146)
	4-*t*-Butylphthalic acid	257	35	13[506]	(154)
C_{14}	Biphenyl-2,2′-dicarboxylic (diphenic) acid	254	70	13[355]	(227), 212Am *
		254	85	13[356]	(228)
		254	51	13[357]	(228)
		254	35	13[358]	

TABLE 44. OLEFINIC ACIDS   451

TABLE 43 (continued)

C_n	Compound	Method	Yield (%)	Chapter[ref.]	B.p./mm., n_D^t, (M.p.), Deriv.
			Aromatic Dicarboxylic Acids (continued)		
C_{14}	Biphenyl-2,2′-dicar-	....	84 †	13[359]	(228)
	boxylic (diphenic) acid	....	21 †	13[360]	(233)
	(continued)				
	Biphenyl-4,4′-dicar-	247	95	13[361]	
	boxylic acid				
C_{16}	α,β-Diphenylsuccinic	247	86	13[362]	(220)
	acid				

For explanations and symbols see pp. xi–xii.

TABLE 44. OLEFINIC ACIDS

C_n	Compound	Method	Yield (%)	Chapter[ref.]	B.p./mm., n_D^t, (M.p.), Deriv.
			Aliphatic Olefinic Acids		
C_3	Acrylic acid	24	75	13[603]	70/50
		247	74	13[363]	104An *
		297	78	13[603]	55/25
C_4	cis-2-Butenoic (isocro-	7	48	13[607]	55/5, 1.4450, (14)
	tonic) acid				
	trans-Crotonic acid	20	75	2[156]	
		37	86	2[323]	(72), 157Am
	Vinylacetic acid	247	66	13[364]	78/19, 73Am *
		247	82	13[365]	70/12, 58An *
	Methacrylic acid	247	67	13[173]	104/92
		248	91	13[367]	
		249	87	13[173]	92/52
		260	41	13[366]	63/10, 1.429, 106Am *
	Fumaric acid	....	58	13[286]	(284), 270Am *
C_5	2-Pentenoic acid	37	55	2[324]	(9)
	3-Pentenoic acid	247	70	13[370]	93/14, 1.4362
		267	60	13[369]	98/19, 75An
	Allylacetic acid	264	70	13[371]	92/18, 1.4283, 94Am *
	cis-2-Methyl-2-butenoic	19	17	2[83]	95/12, (64) *, 77An *
	(tiglic) acid	247	53	13[372]	(64)
	trans-2-Methyl-2-butenoic	7	61	13[372]	(46)
	(angelic) acid	19	25	2[83]	86/12, (46) *, 126An *
	2-Methyl-3-butenoic acid	262	70	13[374]	102/50, 1.4233
	3-Methyl-3-butenoic acid	262	40 †	13[616]	69/5, 1.4308, (21)
	β,β-Dimethylacrylic acid	260	44	13[376]	(67)
		260	44	13[375]	106/20, (67), 108Am *
	Mesaconic acid	250	52	13[295]	(205), 176Am *
	Citraconic acid	250	94	13[294]	(93), 187Am *

For explanations and symbols see pp. xi–xii.

TABLE 44 (continued)

C_n	Compound	Method	Yield (%)	Chapter[ref.]	B.p./mm., n_D^t, (M.p.), Deriv.
				Aliphatic Olefinic Acids (continued)	
C_5	Vinylacrylic acid	37	60	2[336]	(72), 47Di
C_6	2-Hexenoic acid	37	76	2[326]	(32), 110An
	3-Hexenoic acid	31	11	2[510]	108/15, 1.4397[14], 75An
		37	42	2[327]	110/15, (12), 1.4391
	cis-3-Hexenoic acid	262	56	13[610]	111/20, 1.4400, 62An
	trans-3-Hexenoic acid	37	....	13[610]	109/19, 1.4387, 87An
	4-Hexenoic acid	262	65	13[611]	118/24, 1.4380
		264	75	13[377]	112/20, 1.4367[19], 87An
		267	19	13[378]	107/16, 1.4385, 103To
	5-Hexenoic acid	247	89	13[142]	104/13, 1.4318[25]
		264	....	13[379]	107/17, 1.4343
		264	96	13[380]	103/12, 1.4337, 58To
	cis-α-Methyl-β-ethylacrylic acid	19	30	2[84]	94/10, 1.4488[25], 46pP
	trans-α-Methyl-β-ethylacrylic acid	19	20	2[84]	107/10, 1.4578, (24), 91pP
		253	60	13[369]	112/12, (23), 80Am
	4-Methyl-2-pentenoic acid	37	66	2[328]	113/20, 119An
		264	21 †	13[381]	115/18, 1.4466[25]
	4-Methyl-3-pentenoic acid	31	75	2[510]	99/10, 104An
	2,4-Hexadienoic (sorbic) acid	37	32	2[337]	(134)
	4-Methyl-2,4-pentadienoic acid	37	50	2[338]	(57)
	Muconic acid	20	43	2[154]	(297)
	1,2,3-Propenetricarboxylic acid	19	44	2[81]	(199)
C_7	4-Heptenoic acid	247	79	13[382]	109/5
		262	68	13[611]	124/20, 1.4407
		264	52 †	13[382]	117/14
	6-Heptenoic acid	30	81	2[462]	82/1, 1.4355[27], 58To
		264	67	13[318]	125/15, 1.4404[15]
	4-Methyl-2-hexenoic acid	37	80	2[329]	125/13, 1.4526, 110An
	4-Methyl-3-hexenoic acid	37	40	2[329]	118/12, 1.4512[17]
	5-Methyl-4-hexenoic acid	264	52	13[371]	95/1, 1.4461
	3-Ethyl-2-pentenoic acid	19	72	2[419]	116/10, 1.4689[14], 80To
	3-Ethyl-3-pentenoic acid	249	56	13[383]	115/13, 1.4547[14], 95To
	γ-Butenylmalonic acid	264	64 †	13[380]	(92)
C_8	2-Octenoic acid	37	75	2[330]	102/5, 1.4588, 93pB
	7-Octenoic acid	30	78	2[462]	91/1, 1.4340[27], 57To

TABLE 44. OLEFINIC ACIDS 453

TABLE 44 (*continued*)

C_n	Compound	Method	Yield (%)	Chapter[ref.]	B.p./mm., n_D^t, (M.p.), Deriv.
	Aliphatic Olefinic Acids (*continued*)				
C_8	2-Ethyl-2-hexenoic acid	253	53	13[384]	108/3, 1.4590
	2-Ethyl-3-hexenoic acid	253	74	13[385]	132/19, 80Am
	3,4,4-Trimethyl-2-pentenoic acid	19	85	2[161]	(85)
	4-Pentenylmalonic acid	264	63 †	13[318]	(87)
C_9	2-Nonenoic acid	37	85	2[372]	131/2
	8-Nonenoic acid	264	83	13[318]	118/1, 1.4492[15]
C_{10}	3-Methyl-2-nonenoic acid	19	63	2[171]	121/1, 1.4636[25]
	3-Methyl-3-nonenoic acid	19	90	2[171]	104/0.3, 1.4512[25]
C_{11}	ω-Undecylenic acid	....	10	13[386]	145/3, (24)
	Alicyclic Olefinic Acids				
C_6	1-Cyclopentenylcarboxylic acid	253	65	13[389]	(121), 126An *
		247	90	13[390]	(121), 122To *
	2-Cyclopentenylcarboxylic acid	247	35	13[391]	(118)
C_7	2-Cyclopentenylacetic acid	264	99	13[394]	95/3, 1.4682
	1-Cyclohexenylcarboxylic acid	247	79	13[392]	107/3, (38), 128Am *
	3-Cyclohexenylcarboxylic acid	253	63	13[393]	126/13
C_8	Cyclohexenylacetic acid	19	80	2[86]	82/2
	Cyclohexylideneacetic acid	19	68	2[86]	(92)
	4-Methyl-1-cyclohexenecarboxylic acid	19	37	2[80]	(132)
	2-Cyclopentenylmalonic acid	264	85 †	13[394]	(149)
C_9	β-Cyclohexylacrylic acid	37	86	2[332]	154/11, (60), 159Am
	β-Cyclohexylidenepropionic acid	37	36	2[331]	158/16, (48)
	2,3,3-Trimethyl-1-cyclopentene-1-carboxylic acid	....	65	13[395]	(134)
C_{10}	γ-Cyclohexylcrotonic acid	37	88	2[333]	(55), 144Am
	Aromatic Olefinic Acids				
C_9	Cinnamic acid	38	60	2[384]	(132)
		247	55	13[400]	(134), 147Am *
	p-Vinylbenzoic acid	247	67	13[401]	(144)

For explanations and symbols see pp. xi-xii.

TABLE 44 (*continued*)

C_n	Compound	Method	Table (%)	Chapter[ref.]	B.p./mm., n_D^t, (M.p.), Deriv.
		Aromatic Olefinic Acids (*continued*)			
C_{10}	α-Methylcinnamic acid	38	70	2[384]	(74), (81)
		260	93	13[402]	(81), 128Am *
	trans-β-Methylcinnamic acid	19	27	2[408]	136/1, (99)
		249	41	13[403]	136/1
	4-Phenyl-3-butenoic acid	37	60	2[350]	(87)
	o-Methylcinnamic acid	37	75	2[341]	(169)
	p-Methylcinnamic acid	37	75	2[341]	(199)
	o-Carboxycinnamic acid	254	71	13[349]	(205)
C_{11}	4-Phenyl-3-pentenoic acid	19	75 †	2[82]	(76)
	Cinnamalacetic acid	259	90	13[404]	(166)
		260	70 †	13[176]	(163)
	α-Vinylcinnamic acid	38	40	2[389]	(92)
C_{12}	α-*n*-Propylcinnamic acid	260	80	13[405]	(93)
C_{13}	α-Naphthylacrylic acid	37	56	2[344]	(208)
C_{15}	α-Phenylcinnamic acid	38	56	2[388]	(172)
	o-Carboxystilbene	19	100	2[85]	(160)
C_{16}	Stilbene-2-acetic acid	247	67	13[406]	(106)
C_{17}	β-(1-Phenanthryl)-acrylic acid	37	100	2[351]	(262)
	β-(2-Phenanthryl)-acrylic acid	37	100	2[351]	(246)
	β-(3-Phenanthryl)-acrylic acid	37	100	2[351]	(274)
	β-(10-Phenanthryl)-acrylic acid	37	100	2[351]	(233)
		Heterocyclic Olefinic Acids			
C_7	2-Furylacrylic acid	37	92	2[354]	(141)
		38	70	2[390]	(139)
	2-Thienylacrylic acid	37	85	2[352]	(144)
C_8	3-Pyridylacrylic acid	37	73	2[353]	(233), 148Am
C_9	α-Ethylfurylacrylic acid	38	80	2[402]	(97)
C_{13}	α-Phenyl-β-furylacrylic acid	38	80	2[391]	(144)

For explanations and symbols see pp. xi–xii.

TABLE 46. HALO ACIDS   455

TABLE 45. ACETYLENIC ACIDS

C_n	Compound	Method	Yield (%)	Chapter[ref.]	B.p./mm., n_D^t, (M.p.), Deriv.
C_3	Propiolic acid	264	90	13[407]	70/13, 62Am *
C_4	2-Butynoic (tetrolic) acid	262	65	13[609]	(76)
	Ethynylacetic acid	253	28	13[409]	(83), 153Sb
	Acetylenedicarboxylic	43	88	3[51]	(176)
	acid	253	23	13[409]	(177)
C_5	2-Pentynoic (ethyl-propiolic) acid	262	49 †	13[408]	100/10, (50), 146Am
	3-Pentynoic acid	43	15	3[53]	80/1, (53)
	4-Pentynoic acid	43	40	3[53]	102/17, (58)
C_6	2-Hexynoic acid	262	42 †	13[408]	110/10, (25), 82Am
		262	48 †	13[408]	122/10, 1.4619, 69Am
		262	72 †	13[410]	128/12, 1.4633[16]
C_7	3-Heptynoic acid	262	16	13[618]	102/2, 1.4635[25], (14), 67Am
	6-Heptynoic acid	247	63	13[62]	94/1, 1.4495[25], 85To
C_8	2-Octynoic acid	262	40 †	13[408]	133/10, 1.4595, 90Am
		247	52	13[62]	97/1, 1.4506[25], 60An
C_9	Phenylpropiolic acid	43	80	3[52]	(137)
C_{11}	6-Hendecynoic acid	247	38 †	13[411]	125/0.2, 1.4566[25]
C_{13}	α-Naphthylpropiolic acid	43	85	3[54]	(139)
C_{18}	Stearolic acid	43	42	3[50]	(46)

For explanations and symbols see pp. xi–xii.

TABLE 46. HALO ACIDS

C_n	Compound	Method	Yield (%)	Chapter[ref.]	B.p./mm., n_D^t, (M.p.), Deriv.
	Aliphatic and Alicyclic Halo Acids				
C_2	Fluoroacetic acid	249	90 †	13[239]	168, (32)
	Dichloroacetic acid	62	80	4[406]	102/20
		....	92	13[412]	104/23, 118An *
	Trifluoroacetic acid	255	87	13[413]	72*
	Bromoacetic acid	67	85	4[544]	110/30
C_3	α-Fluoropropionic acid	248	67	13[200]	60/8, 76Am
	β-Fluoropropionic acid	253	80	13[463]	79/12
	β-Chloropropionic acid	247	75	13[95]	116/32
		253	65 †	13[414]	107/20, (40)
		253	81	13[415]	115/25
		253	56	13[416]	127/35
		309	91	13[244]	(42)
	β-Bromopropionic acid	309	58	13[244]	88/0.5, (62)
		247	83	13[417]	(63)
	β-Iodopropionic acid	309	62	13[244]	(83)

For explanations and symbols see pp. xi–xii.

TABLE 46 (continued)

C_n	Compound	Method	Yield (%)	Chapter[ref.]	B.p./mm., n_D^t, (M.p.), Deriv.
			Aliphatic and Alicyclic Halo Acids (continued)		
C_3	α,β-Dichloropropionic	249	65	13[418]	133/26, (50)
	acid	253	85 †	13[419]	118/15, (50)
		253	70	13[420]	115/12, (50)
	α,β-Dibromopropionic	249	72	13[418]	(60)
	acid	253	76	13[421]	160/20, 130Am *
	α-Chloroacrylic acid	20	62	2[158]	(65)
	α-Bromoacrylic acid	20	70	2[158]	(72)
C_4	α-Chlorobutyric acid	264	100	13[623]	98/14, 1.435[25]
	α-Bromo-n-butyric acid	67	90	4[531]	110/14
	γ-Bromobutyric acid	54	70	4[371]	127/7
	2-Iodoisobutyric acid	62	50	4[408]	(39)
	α,β-Dibromosuccinic acid	74	84	4[434]	
C_5	δ-Bromovaleric acid	51	18 †	4[68]	119/3
		54	64	4[372]	145/13, (39)
	5-Iodopentanoic acid	54	68	4[374]	(56)
	α-Bromoisovaleric acid	67	89	4[528]	110–125/15
		264	66 †	13[423]	153/40, 133Am *
	α,β-Dibromovaleric acid	74	41	4[622]	90/0.02, 1.5272[17]
	2,5-Dibromopentanoic acid	67	91	4[540]	152/5, 1.5347[25]
	α,α'Dibromoglutaric acid	67	54	4[541]	(134), (174)
C_6	α-Chlorocaproic acid	264	100	13[623]	122/12, 1.441[25]
	α-Bromo-n-caproic acid	67	89	4[530]	128–131/10
		264	71 †	13[425]	153/30
	β-Chlorohexanoic acid	73	80	4[199]	98/4
	6-Bromohexanoic acid	54	62	4[372]	168/18, (35)
		253	91	13[427]	130/5
	2-Bromo-3-methylpentanoic acid	67	54	4[532]	100/23
		264	67 †	13[426]	140/20
	α-Bromoisocaproic acid	67	66	4[529]	125–131/12
	α-Ethyl-β-iodobutyric acid	73	60	4[200]	(30)
	α-Bromo-t-butylacetic acid	67	81	4[534]	102–109/2, (73)
	γ-Bromo-β,β-dimethylbutyric acid	309	19	13[599]	127/12
	2,6-Dibromohexanoic acid	54	87	4[591]	146/2
		67	80	4[372]	160/4, 1.5245[21]
	α,α'-Dibromoadipic acid	67	70	4[542]	(139), (191)
C_7	7-Bromoheptanoic acid	51	60 †	4[572]	142/1.5, (29)
C_8	2-Bromoöctanoic acid	67	76	4[533]	140/25
	8-Iodoöctanoic acid	54	71	4[604]	(44)
	α,α'-Dibromosuberic acid	67	66	4[543]	(121), (170)
	α-Bromo-α-carboxycyclopentaneacetic acid	67	92	4[538]	(135)

TABLE 46. HALO ACIDS 457

TABLE 46 (continued)

C_n	Compound	Method	Yield (%)	Chapter[ref.]	B.p./mm., n_D^t, (M.p.), Deriv.

Aliphatic and Alicyclic Halo Acids (continued)

C_n	Compound	Method	Yield (%)	Chapter[ref.]	B.p./mm., n_D^t, (M.p.), Deriv.
C_9	α-Bromo-α-carboxycyclo-hexaneacetic acid,	67	88	4[538]	(142)
C_{10}	α-Bromohexahydrobenzyl-malonic acid	67	92	4[535]	(138)
C_{11}	ω-Bromoundecanoic acid	73	70	4[201]	(50)

Aromatic Halo Acids

C_n	Compound	Method	Yield (%)	Chapter[ref.]	B.p./mm., n_D^t, (M.p.), Deriv.
C_7	o-Chlorobenzoic acid	257	58	13[259]	(141)
		257	78	13[429]	(140), 139Am *
	o-Bromobenzoic acid	14	34	13[25]	(150)*
	o-Iodobenzoic acid	261	88	13[563]	(167), 184Am *
	m-Chlorobenzoic acid	257	48	13[259]	(157)
		261	88	13[563]	(157), 134Am *
	m-Bromobenzoic acid	14	32	13[25]	
		261	89	13[563]	(155), 155Am *
	m-Iodobenzoic acid	14	47 ‡	13[431]	(188), 147pP *
		64	75	4[593]	(186)
	p-Fluorobenzoic acid	56	69	4[328]	(186)
		262	41 †	13[428]	(182), 154Am *
	p-Chlorobenzoic acid	257	44	13[259]	(243)
		260	93	13[145]	(236), 179Am *
	p-Bromobenzoic acid	260	91	13[145]	(251), 189Am *
	p-Iodobenzoic acid	59	81	4[361]	(267)
		247	60	13[433]	(270)
		257	50	13[432]	(270), 217Am *
		261	84	13[563]	147pB *
	2,4-Dibromobenzoic acid	247	90	13[430]	(174), 198Am *
C_8	o-Chlorophenylacetic acid	248	63	13[147]	(95), 138An *
	o-Bromophenylacetic acid	64	30	4[286]	(109)
		271	63 †	13[215]	(105), 187Am *
	m-Chlorophenylacetic acid	259	57	13[434]	(74)
	p-Fluorophenylacetic acid	247	60	13[196]	(85)
	p-Chlorophenylacetic acid	248	59	13[147]	(100), 175Am *
	p-Iodophenylacetic acid	64	45	4[285]	(135)
	p-Chloromethylbenzoic acid	247	78	13[435]	(202), 173Am *
	p-Bromomethylbenzoic acid	247	73	13[435]	(224)
C_9	α-Bromo-β-phenylpro-pionic acid	264	....	13[437]	(52) *

For explanations and symbols see pp. xi-xii.

TABLE 46 (*continued*)

C$_n$	Compound	Method	Yield (%)	Chapter[ref.]	B.p./mm., n_D^t, (M.p.), Deriv.
		Aromatic Halo Acids (*continued*)			
C$_9$	α-Iodo-β-chloro-β-phenyl-propionic acid	74	92	4[433]	(126)
	p-Chlorocinnamic acid	20		2[157]	(241)
C$_{10}$	o-Chlorophenylsuccinic acid	264	53 †	13[350]	(174)
	α-Bromobenzylmalonic acid	67	90	4[536]	(110)
C$_{11}$	α-Bromo-βphenylethyl-malonic acid	67	90	4[539]	(158)
C$_{15}$	2,2-Diphenyl-3-chloro-propionic acid	273	65	13[596]	(203)

For explanations and symbols see pp. xi–xii.

TABLE 47. HYDROXY ACIDS

C$_n$	Compound	Method	Yield (%)	Chapter[ref.]	B.p./mm., n_D^t, (M.p.), Deriv.
		Aliphatic and Alicyclic Hydroxy Acids			
C$_2$	Hydroxyacetic (glycolic) acid	249	88	13[287]	(79)
		96	89	5[556]	(78)
C$_3$	β-Hydroxypropionic acid	247	80	13[442]	
C$_4$	γ-Hydroxybutyric acid	250	40	13[443]	
	dl-threo-2,3-Dihydroxy-butyric acid	107	70	5[602]	(75)
	dl-erythro-2,3-Dihydroxy-butyric acid	107	80	5[602]	(81), 124Phz
C$_5$	δ-Hydroxyvaleric acid	250	47	13[443]	56Am *
	α-Hydroxy-α-methylbutyric acid	247	65	13[444]	(72)
	β-Hydroxyisovaleric acid	260	9	13[376]	
	2,3-Dihydroxypentanoic acid	107	75	5[608]	(106), 119Phz
		107	80	5[608]	(75), 141Phz
C$_6$	α-Hydroxycaproic acid	95	....	5[526]	(60)
		96	60	5[554]	(62)
	ε-Hydroxycaproic acid	250	20	13[443]	
	α-Hydroxy-α-methyl-valeric acid	247	60 †	13[445]	(54)
	β,β,β-Trimethyllactic acid	276	93	13[446]	(87)
	2,3-Dihydroxyhexanoic acid	107	46	5[608]	(100), 121Phz
		107	86	5[608]	(109), 142Phz

TABLE 47. HYDROXY ACIDS 459

TABLE 47 (*continued*)

C_n	Compound	Method	Yield (%)	Chapter[ref.]	B.p./mm., n_D^t, (M.p.), Deriv.
		Aliphatic and Alicyclic Hydroxy Acids (*continued*)			
C_7	Methyl-*n*-butylglycolic acid	247	80 †	13[447]	(33), 58Am
	4-Hydroxycyclohexane-carboxylic acid	270	49	13[448]	(104)
	trans-Cyclopentanol-2-acetic acid	264	80	13[449]	(54)
C_8	α-Hydroxycaprylic acid	95	80	5[526]	163/10, (70)
	Methyl-*n*-amylglycolic acid	247	80 †	13[447]	(45), 65Am
	Methylneopentylglycolic acid	247	80 †	13[447]	(109), 116Am
	trans-Cyclohexanol-2-acetic acid	250	98	13[450]	(106)
	1-Hydroxy-4-methylcyclohexanecarboxylic acid	247	79 †	13[451]	(130)
C_9	Methyl-*n*-hexylglycolic acid	247	80 †	13[447]	(40), 59Am
	2,3-Dihydroxynonanoic acid	107	51	5[599]	(118)
		Aromatic Hydroxy Acids			
C_7	*o*-Hydroxybenzoic (salicyclic) acid	257	80	13[453]	(158), 140*p*B *
		274	85	13[452]	(158), 139Am *
	m-Hydroxybenzoic acid	92	91	5[720]	(200)
		93	87	5[494]	(200)
		274	40	13[452]	(201), 170Am *
	p-Hydroxybenzoic acid	93	82	5[495]	(212)
		263	80	13[454]	(212), 162Am *
		274	98	13[452]	(213), 202An *
	2,4-Dihydroxybenzoic (β-resorcylic) acid	263	60	13[455]	(217), 222Am *
	2,5-Dihydroxybenzoic acid	96	72	5[718]	(205)
		97	65	5[712]	(191)
	3,4-Dihydroxybenzoic (protocatechuic) acid	261	75	13[593]	(200)
C_8	α-Hydroxyphenylacetic (mandelic) acid	247	52 †	13[457]	(118), 133Am *
		247	50 †	13[458]	(118)
		276	90	13[456]	(117), 151An *
	o-Hydroxyphenylacetic acid	97	75	5[539]	(149)
		248	81	13[459]	(147), 118Am *
		248	59	13[147]	(141)
		259	34	13[646]	(146)
	m-Hydroxyphenylacetic acid	97	72	5[540]	(134)
		248	72	13[636]	(134)

For explanations and symbols see pp. xi–xii.

TABLE 47 (*continued*)

C_n	Compound	Method	Yield (%)	Chapter[ref.]	B.p./mm., n_D^t, (M.p.), Deriv.
		Aromatic Hydroxy Acids (*continued*)			
C_8	p-Hydroxyphenylacetic	93	100	5[496]	(148)
	acid	248	50	13[147]	(148)
		248	62	13[459]	(147), 175Am
	p-Hydroxymethylbenzoic acid	247	90	13[460]	(180)
C_9	β-Phenyl-α-hydroxy-	247	60 †	13[458]	(97)
	propionic acid	247	32 †	13[461]	(96), 112Am *
	p-Methylmandelic acid	264	58	13[462]	(145)
C_{10}	Phenylethylglycolic acid	89	83	5[400]	(131)
	β-Phenyl-α-hydroxy- butyric acid	247	20 †	13[458]	(122)
	γ-Phenyl-α-hydroxy- butyric acid	247	50 †	13[458]	(105)
	γ-(o-Hydroxyphenyl)- butyric acid	269	96	13[464]	(67)
C_{11}	Phenyl-n-propylglycolic acid	247	80 †	13[447]	(94), 132Am
	4-Hydroxy-4-phenyl- pentanoic acid	249	95	13[264]	(104)
C_{12}	α-Naphthylglycolic acid	88	50	5[335]	(99)
		251	50	13[396]	(99), 135Am
C_{14}	Benzilic acid	276	90	13[467]	(150), 154Am *
	p-Xenylhydroxyacetic	79	97	5[159]	(203)
	acid	247	63	13[468]	(192)
	9-Hydroxyfluorene-9- carboxylic acid	276	60	13[469]	(166)
C_{15}	α,α-Diphenyl-β-hydroxy- propionic acid	249	83	13[387]	(158)
C_{16}	Ethyl-p-xenylhydroxy- acetic acid	89	71	5[159]	(177)

For explanations and symbols see pp. xi–xii.

TABLE 48. ALKOXY AND ARYLOXY ACIDS

C_n	Compound	Method	Yield (%)	Chapter[ref.]	B.p./mm., n_D^t, (M.p.), Deriv.
		Aliphatic Alkoxy Acids			
C_4	α-Methoxypropionic acid	249	79	13[471]	89/10, 81Am *
	Ethoxyacetic acid	115	74	6[53]	111/18
	Dimethoxyacetic acid	249	86	13[299]	

TABLE 48. ALKOXY AND ARYLOXY ACIDS 461

TABLE 48 (continued)

C_n	Compound	Method	Yield (%)	Chapter[ref.]	B.p./mm., n_D^t, (M.p.), Deriv.
		Aliphatic Alkoxy Acids (continued)			
C_5	β-Methoxybutyric acid	253	25	13[438]	108/13
	γ-Methoxybutyric acid	264	26 †	13[472]	105/7, 1.4251
	β-Methoxyisobutyric acid	264	82	13[616]	83/3, 1.4192
	α-Ethoxypropionic acid	115	77	6[57]	93/10
	β-Ethoxypropionic acid	247	86 †	13[473]	120/17, 1.4216, 51Am *
	β-(Methoxyethoxy)-acetic acid	115	44	6[55]	149/18
C_6	γ-Methoxy-α-methyl-butyric acid	264	85 †	13[474]	120/11
	β-Methoxyisovaleric acid	260	38	13[588]	88/2, 1.4348[22], 55pP
	α-Ethoxyisobutyric acid	251	70	13[475]	97/19
	β-(Ethoxyethoxy)-acetic acid	115	55	6[55]	155/18
C_7	6-Methoxycaproic acid	247	82	13[476]	132/6, 1.4347
C_9	n-Heptyloxyacetic acid	115	60	6[54]	157/18, 1.4362
		Aromatic Alkoxy and Aryloxy Acids			
C_9	α-Methoxyphenylacetic acid	116	42 †	6[162]	(71)
	o-Methoxyphenylacetic acid	248	70	13[147]	(121)
		268	90	13[480]	(124)
	m-Methoxyphenylacetic acid	248	82	13[147]	(69)
		248	60	13[481]	
	p-Methoxyphenylacetic acid	248	36	13[147]	(84)
		248	85	13[483]	(87), 189Am
		268	90	13[161]	(86)
	o-Ethoxybenzoic acid	115	63	6[98]	216–229/90
	m-Ethoxybenzoic acid	115	90	6[98]	(135)
	β-Phenoxypropionic acid	253	45	13[479]	(98), 119Am
C_{10}	γ-Phenoxybutyric acid	247	61	13[443]	197/18, 80Am
	3,4,5-Trimethoxybenzoic acid	116	78	6[99]	(165)
C_{11}	α-Isopropoxyphenyl-acetic acid	277	57	13[492]	(59), 115pP
	δ-Phenoxyvaleric acid	264	90	13[322]	(56)
		264	93 †	13[487]	175/4, (66)
	γ-Phenoxy-α-methyl-butyric acid	266	87	13[488]	(80)
C_{12}	6-Phenoxycaproic acid	264	91	13[493]	(69)
C_{13}	7-Phenoxyheptoic acid	264	72	13[495]	(55)
C_{14}	Diphenoxyacetic acid	115	62	6[56]	(91)

For explanations and symbols see pp. xi-xii.

TABLE 49. ALDO AND KETO ACIDS

C_n	Compound	Method	Yield (%)	Chapter[ref.]	B.p./mm., n_D^t, (M.p.), Deriv.
		Aliphatic and Alicyclic Aldo and Keto Acids			
C_2	Glyoxylic acid	157	54	9[185]	135-Ox
C_3	Pyruvic acid	184	55	10[294]	80/25, 218Dn *
		247	73	13[496]	108/126, 1.4138, 145Am *
C_4	α-Ketobutyric acid	184	65	10[366]	(31), 194pN
		247	....	13[496]	78/25, 1.3972, 117Am *
C_5	α-Ketovaleric acid	184	85	10[295]	66/6, 145-Ox *
	γ-Ketovaleric (levulinic) acid	....	42	13[499]	108/2, 108Am *
	α-Ketoglutaric acid	184	65	10[299]	(109)
	β-Ketoglutaric acid	....	90	10[671]	
	α,γ-Diketovaleric acid	249	70	13[500]	(98), 132Am *
C_6	α-Ketocaproic acid	184	70	10[295]	102/20, 140-Ox *
	4-Ketohexanoic (homolevulinic) acid	179	80	10[216]	89/0.4, (40), 176Se
	5-Ketocaproic acid	283	68	13[605]	141-149/2
	α-Methyl-γ-ketovaleric acid	184	67	10[296]	141/11
	β-Methyllevulinic acid	264	40 †	13[501]	118/3, 197Se *
	γ-Acetylbutyric acid	184	75	10[672]	155/12
	γ-Acetobutyric acid	184	85	10[625]	109/5
	Methylethylpyruvic acid	193	20 †	10[450]	80/12, (30)
	Trimethylpyruvic acid	257	40	13[502]	85/20, 157Ph
C_7	2-Ketoheptanoic acid	184	65	10[295]	111/17, (30), 127-Ox
	6-Ketoheptanoic acid	185	50	10[579]	167/9, (33), 146Se *
		254	85	13[485]	
		254	55	13[652]	123/1, (35)
		283	57	13[605]	156/2, 144Se
	α,β-Dimethyllevulinic acid	264	83 †	13[501]	122/4
	Cyclopentanone-2-acetic acid	266	87	13[504]	(53)
C_8	α-Ketocaprylic acid	184		10[295]	104/6, (33)
	7-Ketoöctanoic acid	284	60	13[606]	161/4
	α-n-Propyl-γ-keto valeric acid	184	48	10[296]	165/15
	β-Pivalylpropionic acid	264	80	13[624]	(69), 141-Ox
	2-Ketocyclohexylacetic acid	179	32	10[217]	(74)
	1-Methylcyclopentyl-glyoxylic acid	257	30	13[507]	114/10, 168Se
C_9	8-Ketononoic acid	184	68	10[297]	148/0.8, (40)
	5-Methyl-7-ketoöctanoic acid	184	75	10[298]	114/0.1, 1.4528, 147Se

TABLE 49. ALDO AND KETO ACIDS 463

TABLE 49 (*continued*)

C_n	Compound	Method	Yield (%)	Chapter ref.	B.p./mm., n_D^t, (M.p.), Deriv.
			Aliphatic and Alicyclic Aldo and Keto Acids (continued)		
C_9	3-Heptanone-1,5-dicarboxylic acid	249	92	13^{268}	(84)
	β-(2-Cyclohexanone)-propionic acid	184	90	10^{300}	(55)
C_{30}	12-Ketotriacontanoic acid	189	79 †	10^{407}	(102)
			Aromatic and Heterocyclic Aldo and Keto Acids		
C_6	α-Thienylglyoxylic acid	249	70	13^{503}	(91), 88Am *
C_8	o-Carboxybenzaldehyde	155	22 †	9^{252}	(99.5)
		170	41	9^{166}	(95)
		170	65 †	9^{165}	(97)
		249	68	13^{505}	(96)
		....	83	9^{193}	(96)
	Benzoylformic acid	179	67	10^{214}	(61), 197Dn *
		247	77	13^{508}	(66)
		249	90	13^{510}	105/0.1, (65), 164Ph
		255	55	13^{509}	(61)
	3-(α-Thenoyl)-propionic acid	178	75	10^{147}	(121)
C_9	2-(β-Carboxyethyl)-2-ethylbutanal	247	89	13^{511}	142/3, 1.4550^{25}
	8-Carboxyoctanal	160	64	9^{147}	197/15, (42), 162Se
	Phenylpyruvic acid	210	94	10^{610}	(154), 159-Ox *
	m-Chlorophenylpyruvic acid	210	77	10^{611}	(145)
	o-Nitrophenylpyruvic acid	210	83	10^{613}	(120)
	o-Acetobenzoic acid	188	62	10^{392}	(115), 159-Ox
		....	49	10^{582}	(115), 186Dn
	p-Acetobenzoic acid	247	40	13^{513}	(205), 269Se *
	o-Carboxyphenylglyoxylic (phthalonic) acid	183	80	10^{574}	
		254	82	13^{346}	
		254	85	13^{512}	
C_{10}	β-Benzoylpropionic acid	178	84 †	10^{147}	(114), 150An *
		178	95	10^{135}	(115)
		179	83	10^{216}	(115)
	o-Propionylbenzoic acid	188	67	10^{392}	(88), 117-Ox
	2-Methoxyphenylpyruvic acid	210	90	10^{612}	(161)
C_{11}	α-Keto-δ-phenylvaleric acid	184	63 †	10^{301}	(69.5)

For explanations and symbols see pp. xi–xii.

TABLE 49 (*continued*)

C_n	Compound	Method	Yield (%)	Chapter[ref.]	B.p./mm., n_D^t, (M.p.), Deriv.
	Aromatic and Heterocyclic Aldo and Keto Acids (*continued*)				
C_{11}	α-Phenyl-γ-ketovaleric acid	184	83	10^{296}	(127)
	γ-Benzoyl-*n*-butyric acid	178	85	10^{135}	(126)
		178	83	10^{148}	(132), 110-Ox *
	α-Methyl-β-benzoylpropionic acid	178	60	10^{81}	(140)
C_{12}	δ-Benzoylvaleric acid	178	78 †	10^{147}	(71)
		178	75	10^{140}	(71)
	α,α-Dimethyl-β-benzoylpropionic acid	178	60	10^{149}	(171)
	α-Naphthylglyoxylic acid	249	96	13^{203}	(113), 151Am *
	β-Naphthylglyoxylic acid	257	40	13^{517}	(171), 230Se
C_{14}	o-Benzoylbenzoic acid monohydrate	188	64	10^{392}	(91), 127-Ox
	Fluorenone-2-carboxylic acid	254	74	13^{478}	(341)
		260	60	13^{589}	(335)
C_{16}	α-Phenyl-β-benzoylpropionic acid	247	90	13^{232}	(151)

For explanations and symbols see pp. xi–xii.

REFERENCES FOR CHAPTER 13

[1] Bergmann et al., *J. Am. Chem. Soc.*, **70**, 1612 (1948).

[2] Osman and Cope, *J. Am. Chem. Soc.*, **66**, 885 (1944).

[3] Boyd and Robson, *Biochem. J.*, **29**, 542 (1935).

[4] Smith, Alderman, and Nadig, *J. Am. Chem. Soc.*, **67**, 272 (1945).

[5] Martin in *Organic Reactions*, Vol. 1, John Wiley & Sons, New York, 1942, pp. 160, 166, 167.

[6] Fischer and Flatau, *Ber.*, **42**, 2983 (1909).

[7] Marshall, *J. Chem. Soc.*, 2754 (1930).

[8] Norris and Tucker, *J. Am. Chem. Soc.*, **55**, 4697 (1933).

[9] Chargaff, *Ber.*, **65**, 745 (1932).

[10] Conant and Aston, *J. Am. Chem. Soc.*, **50**, 2783 (1928).

[11] Calloway, *Chem. Revs.*, **17**, 356 (1935).

[12] Burton, *Am. Chem. J.*, **3**, 385 (1882).

[13] Gränacher, *Helv. Chim. Acta*, **5**, 610 (1922); **6**, 458 (1923).

[14] Rydon, *J. Chem. Soc.*, 1444 (1936); Bond and Sprankling, *ibid.*, **75**, 839 (1899).

[15] Whitmore and Laughlin, *J. Am. Chem. Soc.*, **56**, 1128 (1934); Whitmore and Wilson, *ibid.*, **56**, 1397 (1934).

[16] Long, *Chem. Revs.*, **27**, 437 (1940).

[17] Gilman and Harris, *Rec. trav. chim.*, **50**, 1055 (1931).

[18] Waters, *Chem. Revs.*, **41**, 585 (1947).

[19] Leuchs, *Ber.*, **44**, 1507 (1911).

[20] Adams and Kamm, *Org. Syntheses*, Coll. Vol. I, 250 (1941).

[21] Kinney and Mayhue, *J. Am. Chem. Soc.*, **53**, 190 (1931).

[22] Rosenmund and Schindler, *Arch. Pharm.*, **266**, 281 (1928).

[23] Butlerow, *Ann.*, **170**, 158 (1873).

[24] Morton, LeFevre, and Heckenbleikner, *J. Am. Chem. Soc.*, **58**, 1024 (1936).

[25] Kornblum in *Organic Reactions*, Vol. 2, John Wiley & Sons, New York, 1944, p. 313.

[26] Wallach, *Ann.*, **414**, 296 (1918); **437**, 166 (1924).

[27] Burrows and Bentley, *J. Chem. Soc.*, **67**, 511 (1895).

[28] Hessler, *J. Am. Chem. Soc.*, **35**, 990 (1913).

[29] Alexander, *J. Am. Chem. Soc.*, **69**, 289 (1947).

[30] Wheeler and Hoffman, *Am. Chem. J.*, **45**, 369 (1911).

[31] Djerassi, *Chem. Revs.*, **43**, 271, 276 (1948).

[32] Johnson in *Organic Reactions*, Vol. 1, John Wiley & Sons, New York, 1942, pp. 210, 231, 232.

[33] Block, *Chem. Revs.*, **38**, 526–533 (1946).

[34] Fischer, *Ber.*, **34**, 445 (1901); Morsch, *Monatsh.*, **60**, 61–68 (1932).

[35] Bouveault, *Bull. soc. chim. France*, **15**, 1017 (1896).

[36] Greenwood, *J. Org. Chem.*, **10**, 414 (1945).

[37] Hass and Riley, *Chem. Revs.*, **32**, 395 (1943).

[38] Whitmore and Langlois, *J. Am. Chem. Soc.*, **54**, 3438 (1932).

[39] Herbst and Shemin, *Org. Syntheses*, Coll. Vol. II, 1 (1943).

[40] Cohen, Marshall, and Woodman, *J. Chem. Soc.*, 895–896 (1915).

[41] Asinger, *Ber.*, **75**, 656 (1942).

[42] Kon and Thorpe, *J. Chem. Soc.*, 686 (1919).

[43] Dakin, *J. Biol. Chem.*, **154**, 549 (1944).

[44] Albertson and Tullar, *J. Am. Chem. Soc.*, **67**, 502 (1945); Ehrhart, *Ber.*, **82**, 60 (1949).

[45] Lock, *Ber.*, **66**, 1527 (1933); **68**, 1505 (1935).

[46] Rodionow and Postovskaja, *J. Am. Chem. Soc.*, **51**, 841 (1929).

[47] Eistert in *Newer Methods of Preparative Organic Chemistry*, Interscience Publishers, London, 1948, p. 513.

[48] Farmer and Galley, *J. Chem. Soc.*, 687 (1933).

[49] Bachmann and Struve in *Organic Reactions*, Vol. 1, John Wiley & Sons, New York, 1942, p. 38.

[50] Nicolet and Jurist, *J. Am. Chem. Soc.*, **44**, 1136 (1922).

[51] Abderhalden and Heyns, *Ber.*, **67**, 530 (1934).

[52] Greenstein and Wyman, *J. Am. Chem. Soc.*, **60**, 2341 (1938).

[53] Redemann and Dunn, *J. Biol. Chem.*, **130**, 341 (1939).

[54] Gilman and Van Ess, *J. Am. Chem. Soc.*, **55**, 1258 (1933).

[55] Anslow and King, *J. Chem. Soc.*, 2463 (1929).

[56] Manske, *J. Am. Chem. Soc.*, **53**, 1106 (1931).

[57] Hess and Haber, *Ber.*, **70**, 2205 (1937).

[58] Winstein, Hanson, and Grunwald, *J. Am. Chem. Soc.*, **70**, 815 (1948).

[59] Beckurts and Otto, *Ber.*, **10**, 262 (1877).

[60] Lippincott and Hass, *Ind. Eng. Chem.*, **31**, 118 (1939).

[61] Pierre and Puchot, *Ann. chim.*, (4) **28**, 75 (1873).

[62] Taylor and Strong, *J. Am. Chem. Soc.*, **72**, 4264 (1950); Newman and Wotiz, *ibid.*, **71**, 1292 (1949).

[63] Fournier, *Bull. soc. chim. France*, **7**, 25 (1910)

[64] Fournier, *Bull. soc. chim. France*, (4) **5**, 920 (1909).

[65] Adams and Marvel, *J. Am. Chem. Soc.*, **42**, 310 (1920).

[66] Gilman and Parker, *J. Am. Chem. Soc.*, **46**, 2816 (1924).

[67] Gilman and Kirby, *Org. Syntheses*, Coll. Vol. I, 361 (1941).

[68] Marvel, Blomquist, and Vaughn, *J. Am. Chem. Soc.*, **50**, 2810 (1928).

[69] Levene and Bass, *J. Biol. Chem.*, **70**, 211 (1926).

[70] Cumming, Hopper, and Wheeler, *Systematic Organic Chemistry*, 2nd ed., D. Van Nostrand Co., New York, 1931, p. 194.

[71] Mosher and Whitmore, *J. Am. Chem. Soc.*, **70**, 2544 (1948).

[72] Puntambeker and Zoellner, *Org. Syntheses*, Coll. Vol. I, 524 (1941).

[73] Sandborn and Bousquet, *Org. Syntheses*, Coll. Vol. I, 526 (1941).

[74] Hass and Marshall, *Ind. Eng. Chem.*, **23**, 352 (1931).

[75] Drake and Riemenschneider, *J. Am. Chem. Soc.*, **52**, 5005 (1930).

[76] Bergmann and Hartrott, *J. Chem. Soc.*, 1218 (1935).

[77] Olivier, *Rec. trav. chim.*, **55**, 1030 (1936).

[78] Vliet, Marvel, and Hsueh, *Org. Syntheses*, Coll. Vol. II, 416 (1943).

[79] Bohnsack, *Ber.*, **74**, 1583 (1941).

[80] Bentley and Perkin, *J. Chem. Soc.*, **73**, 48 (1898).

[81] Noyes, *J. Am. Chem. Soc.*, **23**, 393 (1901).

[82] Schuerch and Huntress, *J. Am. Chem. Soc.*, **70**, 2824 (1948); Corson, Thomas, and Waugh, *ibid.*, **51**, 1950 (1929).

[83] Reichstein, Rosenberg, and Eberhardt, *Helv. Chim. Acta*, **18**, 721 (1935).

[84] Nenitzescu and Chicos, *Ber.*, **68**, 1587 (1935).

[85] Homeyer, Whitmore, and Wallingford, *J. Am. Chem. Soc.*, **55**, 4211 (1933).

[86] Darapsky and Engels, *J. prakt. Chem.*, **146**, 238 (1936).

[87] Ruhoff, *Org. Syntheses*, Coll. Vol. II, 315 (1943).

[88] Hecht, *Ann.*, **209**, 313 (1881).

[89] Levene and Marker, *J. Biol. Chem.*, **91**, 687 (1931).

[90] Levene and Marker, *J. Biol. Chem.*, **95**, 1, 153 (1932).

[91] Paal and Hoffmann, *Ber.*, **23**, 1498 (1890).

[92] Curtius, *J. prakt. Chem.*, **125**, 157 (1930).

[93] Henne and Hill, *J. Am. Chem. Soc.*, **65**, 753 (1943).

[94] Levene and Marker, *J. Biol. Chem.*, **91**, 405 (1931).

[95] Barnes, Kraft, and Gordon, *J. Am. Chem. Soc.*, **71**, 3525 (1949).

[96] Whitmore and Badertscher, *J. Am. Chem. Soc.*, **55**, 1566 (1933).

[97] Shivers, Hudson, and Hauser, *J. Am. Chem. Soc.*, **66**, 309 (1944).

[98] Crossley and LeSueur, *J. Chem. Soc.*, **77**, 89 (1900); Drischerl and Nahm, *Ber.*, **76**, 639 (1943).

[99] Karrer et al., *Helv. Chim. Acta*, **13**, 1297 (1930).

[100] Carter and Slater, *J. Chem. Soc.*, **131** (1946).

[101] Levene and Marker, *J. Biol. Chem.*, **111**, 299 (1935).

[102] Kenyon and Platt, *J. Chem. Soc.*, **636** (1939).

[103] Levene, Rothen, and Meyer, *J. Biol. Chem.*, **115**, 401 (1936).

[104] Whitmore et al., *J. Am. Chem. Soc.*, **63**, 2028 (1941).

[105] Newman and Rosher, *J. Org. Chem.*, **9**, 221 (1944).

[106] Curtius and Nadenheim, *J. prakt. Chem.*, (2) **125**, 171 (1930).

[107] Kroll, Pfeiffer, and Rosenberg, *Ber.*, **69**, 465 (1936).

[108] Fisher et al., *Ber.*, **45**, 253, 256 (1912).

[109] v. Braun and Fisher, *Ber.*, **66**, 101 (1933).

[110] Reid and Ruhoff, *Org. Syntheses*, Coll. Vol. II, 474 (1943).

[111] Cason, *J. Am. Chem. Soc.*, **64**, 1108 (1942).

[112] Kögl and Boar, *Rec. trav. chim.*, (4) 54, 793 (1935).

[113] Smith and Rouault, *J. Am. Chem. Soc.*, **65**, 747 (1943).

[114] Cope and McElvain, *J. Am. Chem. Soc.*, **54**, 4319 (1932).

[115] Smith and Horwitz, *J. Am. Chem. Soc.*, **71**, 3418 (1949); Cragoe, Robb, and Sprague, *J. Org. Chem.*, **15**, 381 (1950); cf. ref. 300.

[116] Jones and Pyman, *J. Chem. Soc.*, **127**, 2597 (1922).

[117] Whitmore, Wheeler, and Surmatis, *J. Am. Chem. Soc.*, **63**, 3237 (1941).

[118] Whitmore, Marker, and Plambeck, *J. Am. Chem. Soc.*, **63**, 1628 (1941).

[119] Kao and Ma, *J. Chem. Soc.*, **2047** (1931).

[120] Fierz-David and Kuster, *Helv. Chim. Acta*, **22**, 87 (1939).

[121] Strating and Backer, *Rec. trav. chim.*, **55**, 904 (1936).

[122] Polgar and Robinson, *J. Chem. Soc.*, **393** (1945).

[123] Bartlett, Fraser, and Woodward, *J. Am. Chem. Soc.*, **63**, 495 (1941).

[124] Beal, *Org. Syntheses*, Coll. Vol. I, 379 (1941).

[125] Dauben, *J. Am. Chem. Soc.*, **70**, 1376 (1948).

[126] Backer and Strating, *Rec. trav. chim.*, **59**, 938, 939 (1940).

[127] Bleyberg and Ulrich, *Ber.*, **64**, 2504 (1931).

[128] McCloskey and Coleman, *Org. Syntheses*, **24**, 36 (1944).

[129] Jones and Scott, *J. Am. Chem. Soc.*, **44**, 413 (1922).

[130] Schlatter, *J. Am. Chem. Soc.*, **63**, 1735 (1941).

[131] Cason and Allen, *J. Org. Chem.*, **14**, 1036 (1949); Heisig and Stodola, *Org. Syntheses*, **23**, 16 (1943).

[132] Jackman, Bergman, and Archer, *J. Am. Chem. Soc.*, **70**, 497 (1948).

[133] Neunhoeffer, *Ann.*, **509**, 125 (1934).

[134] Nenitzescu and Ionescu, *Ann.*, **491**, 207 (1931).

[135] Delepine and Badoche, *Ann. chim.*, (11) 17, 180 (1942).

[136] Kindler, *Ber.*, **74**, 315 (1941).

[137] Clarke and Taylor, *Org. Syntheses*, Coll. Vol. II, 588 (1943).

[138] King, *J. Chem. Soc.*, **984** (1935).

[139] Cairns, Joyce, and Schreiber, *J. Am. Chem. Soc.,* 70, 1689 (1948).

[140] Coleman, Callen, and Dornfeld, *J. Am. Chem. Soc.,* 68, 1102 (1946).

[141] Tsatsas, *Ann. chim.,* (11) 19, 262 (1944).

[142] LaForge, Green, and Gersdorff, *J. Am. Chem. Soc.,* 70, 3709 (1948).

[143] Blicke and Sheetz, *J. Am. Chem. Soc.,* 71, 2856 (1949).

[144] Rueggeberg, Frantz, and Ginsburg, *Ind. Eng. Chem.,* 38, 624 (1946).

[145] VanArendonk and Cupery, *J. Am. Chem. Soc.,* 53, 3184 (1931).

[146] Kindler and Kwok, *Ann.,* 554, 9 (1943).

[147] King and McMillan, *J. Am. Chem. Soc.,* 68, 2335 (1946).

[148] Adams and Thal, *Org. Syntheses,* Coll. Vol. I, 436 (1941); Wenner, *J. Org. Chem.,* 15, 548 (1950).

[149] Zaugg and Rapala, *Org. Syntheses,* 27, 84 (1947).

[150] Tomisek et al., *J. Am. Chem. Soc.,* 68, 1588 (1946).

[151] Senseman and Stubbs, *Ind. Eng. Chem.,* 23, 1129 (1931).

[152] Tuley and Marvel, *Org. Syntheses,* 27, 86 (1947).

[153] Coulson, *J. Chem. Soc.,* 1408 (1934).

[154] Larsen et al., *J. Am. Chem. Soc.,* 71, 532 (1949).

[155] Adkins and Connor, *J. Am. Chem. Soc.,* 53, 1091 (1931).

[156] Miescher and Billeter, *Helv. Chim. Acta,* 22, 606, 607 (1939).

[157] Ingersoll, *Org. Syntheses,* Coll. Vol. I, 311 (1941).

[158] Julian et al., *J. Am. Chem. Soc.,* 70, 180 (1948).

[159] Hill and Short, *J. Chem. Soc.,* 1125 (1935).

[160] Lewis and Elderfield, *J. Org. Chem.,* 5, 290 (1940).

[161] Kindler and Gehlhaar, *Arch. Pharm.,* 274, 377 (1936).

[162] Morgan and Coulson, *J. Chem. Soc.,* 2326 (1931).

[163] Snyder, Adams, and McIntosh, *J. Am. Chem. Soc.,* 63, 3281 (1941).

[164] Chu and Marvel, *J. Am. Chem. Soc.,* 55, 2842 (1933).

[165] Wegler, *Ann.,* 510, 80 (1934).

[166] Allen and Johnson, *Org. Syntheses,* 30, 83 (1950).

[167] Woodruff and Pierson, *J. Am. Chem. Soc.,* 60, 1076 (1938).

[168] Martin, *J. Am. Chem. Soc.,* 58, 1438 (1936); Fieser et al., *ibid.,* 70, 3200 (1948).

[169] Martin, *Org. Syntheses,* Coll. Vol. II, 499 (1943).

[170] Litvan and Robinson, *J. Chem. Soc.,* 1999 (1938).

[171] Horne and Shriner, *J. Am. Chem. Soc.,* 55, 4652 (1933).

[172] Bogert and Stamatoff, *Rec. trav. chim.,* 52, 586 (1933).

[173] Heyboer and Staverman, *Rec. trav. chim.,* 69, 790 (1950).

[174] Knowles, Kuck, and Elderfield, *J. Org. Chem.,* 7, 374 (1942).

[175] Kloetzel, *J. Am. Chem. Soc.,* 62, 1708 (1940).

[176] Plati, Strain, and Warren, *J. Am. Chem. Soc.,* 65, 1273 (1943).

[177] Wallis and Bowman, *J. Org. Chem.,* 1, 389 (1936).

[178] Fuson and Rabjohn, *Org. Syntheses,* 25, 65 (1945); Lutz and Hinkley, *J. Am. Chem. Soc.,* 72, 4091 (1950).

[179] Zaki and Fahim, *J. Chem. Soc.,* 307 (1942).

[180] Marvel, Frank, and Prill, *J. Am. Chem. Soc.,* 65, 1649 (1943).

[181] Marvel et al., *J. Am. Chem. Soc.,* 66, 915 (1944).

[182] Hanby, Waley, and Watson, *J. Chem. Soc.,* 3243 (1950).

[183] Gilman, St. John, and Schulze, *Org. Syntheses,* Coll. Vol. II, 425 (1943).

[184] Jacobs et al., *J. Org. Chem.,* 11, 229 (1946).

[185] Whitmore and Fox, *J. Am. Chem. Soc.,* 51, 3363 (1929); Bassilios, *Bull. soc. chim. France,* (5) 17, 757 (1950).

[186] Price et al., *J. Am. Chem. Soc.*, 63, 1857 (1941).
[187] King, *J. Am. Chem. Soc.*, 66, 894 (1944).
[188] Newman and Holmes, *Org. Syntheses*, Coll. Vol. II, 428 (1943).
[189] Gilman and St. John, *Rec. trav. chim.*, 48, 743 (1929).
[190] Colver and Noyes, *J. Am. Chem. Soc.*, 43, 902 (1921).
[191] Papa, Schwenk, and Hankin, *J. Am. Chem. Soc.*, 69, 3021 (1947).
[192] Berger and Olivier, *Rec. trav. chim.*, 46, 600 (1927).
[193] Johnson and Jones, *J. Am. Chem. Soc.*, 69, 793 (1947).
[194] Sengupta, *J. prakt. Chem.*, 151, 88 (1938).
[195] Arndt and Eistert, *Ber.*, 68, 200 (1935).
[196] Pattison and Saunders, *J. Chem. Soc.*, 2748 (1949).
[197] Olivier and Wit, *Rec. trav. chim.*, 56, 857 (1937).
[198] Newman, *J. Org. Chem.*, 9, 518 (1944).
[199] Clement, *Bull. soc. chim. France*, (5) 5, 1013 (1938).
[200] Gryszkiewicz-Trochimowski, *Bull. soc. chim. France*, (5) 16, 929 (1949).
[201] Fusier, *Ann. chim.*, (12) 5, 887 (1950).
[202] Fieser and Gates, *J. Am. Chem. Soc.*, 62, 2338 (1940).
[203] Blicke and Feldkamp, *J. Am. Chem. Soc.*, 66, 1087 (1944).
[204] Gutsche and Johnson, *J. Am. Chem. Soc.*, 68, 2242 (1946).
[205] Sörensen, *Z. physiol. Chem.*, 44, 448 (1905); *Bull. soc. chim. France*, (3) 33, 1042, 1052 (1905).
[206] Thompson and Cromwell, *J. Am. Chem. Soc.*, 61, 1375 (1939).
[207] Fuson and Corse, *J. Am. Chem. Soc.*, 60, 2065 (1938).
[208] Fieser and Cason, *J. Am. Chem. Soc.*, 61, 1742 (1939).
[209] Fieser and Novello, *J. Am. Chem. Soc.*, 62, 1857 (1940).
[210] Schönberg and Warren, *J. Chem. Soc.*, 1840 (1939).
[211] Schwenk and Papa, *J. Org. Chem.*, 11, 798 (1946).
[212] Blicke and Grier, *J. Am. Chem. Soc.*, 65, 1726 (1943).
[213] Marvel, Hager, and Caudle, *Org. Syntheses*, Coll. Vol. I, 224 (1941).
[214] Yost and Hauser, *J. Am. Chem. Soc.*, 69, 2326 (1947).
[215] Fieser and Kilmer, *J. Am. Chem. Soc.*, 62, 1354 (1940).
[216] Bachmann and Sheehan, *J. Am. Chem. Soc.*, 63, 204 (1941).
[217] Snyder and Pilgrim, *J. Am. Chem. Soc.*, 70, 3770 (1948).
[218] Wegmann and Dahn, *Helv. Chim. Acta*, 29, 425 (1946).
[219] Bateman and Marvel, *J. Am. Chem. Soc.*, 49, 2917 (1927).
[220] Bachmann and Sheehan, *J. Am. Chem. Soc.*, 62, 2687 (1940).
[221] Latham, May, and Mosettig, *J. Am. Chem. Soc.*, 70, 1079 (1948).
[222] Bachmann and Kloetzel, *J. Org. Chem.*, 3, 60 (1938).
[223] Burtner and Cusic, *J. Am. Chem. Soc.*, 65, 265 (1943).
[224] Burtner and Cusic, *J. Am. Chem. Soc.*, 65, 1582 (1943).
[225] Bachmann and Boatner, *J. Am. Chem. Soc.*, 58, 2101 (1936).
[226] Mosettig and van de Kamp, *J. Am. Chem. Soc.*, 52, 3708 (1930).
[227] Shoppee, *J. Chem. Soc.*, 40 (1933).
[228] Goldberg, Ordas, and Carsch, *J. Am. Chem. Soc.*, 69, 261 (1947).
[229] Mosettig and van de Kamp, *J. Am. Chem. Soc.*, 54, 3334 (1932).
[230] Plentl and Bogert, *J. Am. Chem. Soc.*, 63, 994 (1941).
[231] Newman, *J. Am. Chem. Soc.*, 62, 872 (1940).
[232] Baker and Jenkins, *J. Am. Chem. Soc.*, 68, 2102 (1946).
[233] Koelsch, Hochmann, and Le Claire, *J. Am. Chem. Soc.*, 65, 59 (1943).
[234] Breslow, Baumgarten and Hauser, *J. Am. Chem. Soc.*, 66, 1287 (1944).
[235] Fieser, Leffler, et al., *J. Am. Chem. Soc.*, 70, 3208 (1948).

[236] Mitz, Axelrod, and Hofmann, *J. Am. Chem. Soc.,* **72,** 1231 (1950).
[237] Bachmann and Carmack, *J. Am. Chem. Soc.,* **63,** 2499 (1941).
[238] Hellerman, *J. Am. Chem. Soc.,* **49,** 1737 (1927).
[239] Saunders and Stacey, *J. Chem. Soc.,* 1777 (1948).
[240] Hurd, Garrett, and Osborne, *J. Am. Chem. Soc.,* **55,** 1082 (1933).
[241] Wilson, *Org. Syntheses,* Coll. Vol. I, 276 (1941).
[242] Gilman and Burtner, *J. Am. Chem. Soc.,* **55,** 2903 (1933).
[243] Schick and Hartough, *J. Am. Chem. Soc.,* **70,** 286 (1948).
[244] Gresham et al., *J. Am. Chem. Soc.,* **70,** 999, 1003 (1948); **72,** 72 (1950).
[245] Campaigne and LeSuer, *J. Am. Chem. Soc.,* **70,** 1555 (1948).
[246] Steinkopf and Schmitt, *Ann.,* **533,** 267 (1938).
[247] Rinkes, *Rec. trav. chim.,* **55,** 992 (1936).
[248] Plucker and Amstutz, *J. Am. Chem. Soc.,* **62,** 1512 (1940).
[249] Singer and McElvain, *Org. Syntheses,* **20,** 79 (1940); Black, Depp, and Corson, *J. Org. Chem.,* **14,** 14 (1949).
[250] Gilman and Spatz, *J. Am. Chem. Soc.,* **62,** 446 (1940).
[251] McElvain, *Org Syntheses,* Coll. Vol. I, 385 (1941); cf. refs. 249 and 252.
[252] Woodward, Badgett, and Kaufman, *Ind. Eng. Chem.,* **36,** 544 (1944); Rohrlich, *Arch. Pharm.,* **283,** 122 (1950).
[253] McElvain and Goese, *J. Am. Chem. Soc.,* **63,** 2283 (1941).
[254] Barnes and Adams, *J. Am. Chem. Soc.,* **49,** 1309 (1927).
[255] Burrus and Powell, *J. Am. Chem. Soc.,* **67,** 1468 (1945).
[256] Leis and Curran, *J. Am. Chem. Soc.,* **67,** 79 (1945).
[257] Koelsch, *J. Am. Chem. Soc.,* **65,** 2464 (1943); Malan and Dean, *ibid.,* **69,** 1797 (1947); cf. refs. 249, 255–258.
[258] Wibaut and Arens, *Rec. trav. chim.,* **60,** 137 (1941).
[259] Emerson, Lucas, and Heimsch, *J. Am. Chem. Soc.,* **71,** 1742 (1949).
[260] Amstutz and Plucker, *J. Am. Chem. Soc.,* **63,** 206 (1941).
[261] Kirner and Richter, *J. Am. Chem. Soc.,* **51,** 3131 (1929).
[262] Barger, Robinson, and Smith, *J. Chem. Soc.,* 718 (1937).
[263] Barger and Easson, *J. Chem. Soc.,* 2103 (1938).
[264] Arnold and Buckley, *J. Am. Chem. Soc.,* **71,** 1782 (1949).
[265] Southwick and Seivard, *J. Am. Chem. Soc.,* **71,** 2536 (1949).
[266] Fieser and Kennelly, *J. Am. Chem. Soc.,* **57,** 1615 (1935); Buu-Hoi et al., *J. Org. Chem.,* **14,** 807 (1949).
[267] Hofmann, *J. Am. Chem. Soc.,* **66,** 51 (1944).
[268] Carter, *J. Am. Chem. Soc.,* **50,** 2299 (1928).
[269] Fuson, Kneisley, and Kaiser, *Org. Syntheses,* **24,** 33 (1944).
[270] Schönberg, Petersen, and Kaltschmitt, *Ber.,* **66,** 235 (1933).
[271] Blicke and Sheets, *J. Am. Chem. Soc.,* **70,** 3768 (1948); Crook and Davies, *J. Chem. Soc.,* 1698 (1937).
[272] Komppa and Weckman, *J. prakt. Chem.,* **138,** 116 (1933).
[273] Doering and Wiberg, *J. Am. Chem. Soc.,* **72,** 2608 (1950).
[274] Gilman and Spatz, *J. Am. Chem. Soc.,* **63,** 1553 (1941).
[275] Koelsch, *J. Org. Chem.,* **10,** 34 (1945).
[276] Tyson, *J. Am. Chem. Soc.,* **61,** 183 (1939).
[277] Gilman, Wallis, and Swislowsky, *J. Am. Chem. Soc.,* **61,** 1372 (1939).
[278] Dunlop and Tucker, *J. Chem. Soc.,* 1953 (1939).
[279] Gilman and Avakian, *J. Am. Chem. Soc.,* **68,** 2104 (1946).
[280] Gilman et al., *J. Am. Chem. Soc.,* **61,** 2844 (1939).
[281] Smith and McKenzie, *J. Org. Chem.,* **15,** 74 (1950).

[282] Clarke and Davis, *Org. Syntheses,* Coll. Vol. I, 421 (1941).
[283] Hultman, Davis, and Clarke, *J. Am. Chem. Soc.,* 43, 368 (1921).
[284] Weiner, *Org. Syntheses,* Coll. Vol. II, 376 (1943).
[285] Allen, Wyatt, and Henze, *J. Am. Chem. Soc.,* 61, 843 (1939).
[286] Milas, *Org. Syntheses,* Coll. Vol. II, 302 (1943).
[287] Sporzynski, Kocay, and Briscoe, *Rec. trav. chim.,* 68, 614 (1949).
[288] Vogel, *J. Chem. Soc.,* 336 (1934).
[289] Marvel and Tuley, *Org. Syntheses,* Coll. Vol. I, 289 (1941).
[290] Allen and Ball, *Org. Syntheses,* Coll. Vol. I, 290 (1941).
[291] Otterbacher, *Org. Syntheses,* Coll. Vol. I, 290 (1941).
[292] Brown, *Org. Syntheses,* 26, 54 (1946).
[293] Linstead, Noble, and Wright, *J. Chem. Soc.,* 915 (1937).
[294] Shriner, Ford, and Roll, *Org. Syntheses,* Coll. Vol. II, 140 (1943).
[295] Shriner, Ford, and Roll, *Org. Syntheses,* Coll. Vol. II, 382 (1943).
[296] Ellis, *Org. Syntheses,* Coll. Vol. I, 18 (1941).
[297] Kent and McElvain, *Org. Syntheses,* 23, 60 (1943).
[298] Day and Thorpe, *J. Chem. Soc.,* 1465 (1920).
[299] Scheibler, Schmidt, and Kenntnis, *Ber.,* 69B, 14 (1936).
[300] Vogel, *J. Chem. Soc.,* 2010 (1928).
[301] Theilacker and Wendtland, *Ann.,* 570, 50 (1950).
[302] Meyer, *Helv. Chim. Acta,* 16, 1293 (1933).
[303] Snyder, Brooks, and Shapiro, *Org. Syntheses,* Coll. Vol. II, 531 (1943).
[304] Müller, *Org. Syntheses,* Coll. Vol. II, 535 (1943).
[305] Cason, Wallcave, and Whiteside, *J. Org. Chem.,* 14, 41 (1949).
[306] Altman, *Rec. trav. chim.,* 57, 950 (1938).
[307] Godchot, Cauquil, and Calas, *Bull. soc. chim. France,* (5) 6, 1355 (1939).
[308] Vogel, *J. Chem. Soc.,* 911 (1931); Desai, *ibid.,* 1218 (1931).
[309] Vogel, *J. Chem. Soc.,* 1758 (1934).
[310] Alder, Pascher, and Schmitz, *Ber.,* 76, 45 (1943).
[311] Bush, *J. Am. Chem. Soc.,* 61, 637 (1939).
[312] Müller and Bleier, *Monatsh.,* 56, 397 (1930).
[313] Vogel, *J. Chem. Soc.,* 2033 (1928); Baker and Ingold, *ibid.,* 123, 122 (1923).
[314] Walker, *J. Chem. Soc.,* 1306 (1940).
[315] Rydon, *J. Chem. Soc.,* 1340 (1937).
[316] Franke and Kroupa, *Monatsh.,* 69, 182 (1936).
[317] Rydon, *J. Chem. Soc.,* 593 (1936).
[318] Gaubert, Linstead, and Rydon, *J. Chem. Soc.,* 1971 (1937).
[319] Grunfeld, *Ann. chim.,* (10) 20, 338 (1933).
[320] Hill and McEwen, *Org. Syntheses,* Coll. Vol. II, 53 (1943).
[321] Arbusow and Schapschinskaja, *Ber.,* 68, 440 (1935).
[322] Carter, *J. Am. Chem. Soc.,* 50, 1967 (1928).
[323] Dox, *J. Am. Chem. Soc.,* 46, 1707 (1924).
[324] Bernhard and Lincke, *Helv. Chim. Acta,* 29, 1462 (1946).
[325] Franke, Kroupa, and Hadzidimitriu, *Monatsh.,* 62, 125 (1933).
[326] Jones, *J. Am. Chem. Soc.,* 69, 2350 (1947).
[327] Schmid and Kemeny, *Monatsh.,* 66, 3 (1936).
[328] Jones and Scott, *J. Am. Chem. Soc.,* 44, 413 (1922).
[329] Fuson and Cole, *J. Am. Chem. Soc.,* 60, 1237 (1938).
[330] Ingold and Mohrhenn, *J. Chem. Soc.,* 950 (1935).
[331] Guha and Sankaran, *Ber.,* 70, 1688 (1937).
[332] Guha and Ganapathi, *Ber.,* 69, 1189 (1936).

[333] Kon and Khuda, *J. Chem. Soc.*, 3071 (1926).
[334] Kandiah, *J. Chem. Soc.*, 935, 947 (1931).
[335] Thakur, *J. Chem. Soc.*, 2151 (1932).
[336] Tudor and Vogel, *J. Chem. Soc.*, 1251 (1934).
[337] Wagner and Tome, *J. Am. Chem. Soc.*, 72, 3477 (1950).
[338] Ivanoff, *Bull. soc. chim. France*, (5) 15, 661 (1948).
[339] Koelsch, *Org. Syntheses*, 26, 95 (1946).
[340] Huntress, Shloss, and Ehrlich, *Org. Syntheses*, Coll. Vol. II, 457 (1943).
[341] Ivanoff and Spassoff, *Bull. soc. chim. France*, 49, 19 (1931).
[342] Morton, Fallwell, and Palmer, *J. Am. Chem. Soc.*, 60, 1426 (1938).
[343] Price, *Org. Syntheses*, 22, 61 (1942).
[344] Whitmore and Cooney, *J. Am. Chem. Soc.*, 66, 1239 (1944).
[345] Miescher and Billeter, *Helv. Chim. Acta*, 22, 601 (1939).
[346] Davies and Poole, *J. Chem. Soc.*, 1617 (1928).
[347] Komppa et al., *Ann.*, 521, 247 (1935).
[348] Lapworth and Baker, *Org. Syntheses*, Coll. Vol. I, 452 (1941).
[349] Greenspan, *Ind. Eng. Chem.*, 39, 847 (1947).
[350] Naps and Johns, *J. Am. Chem. Soc.*, 62, 2450 (1940).
[351] Wood and Cox, *Org. Syntheses*, 26, 24 (1946).
[352] Weizmann, *J. Org. Chem.*, 8, 285 (1943).
[353] Fry and Fieser, *J. Am. Chem. Soc.*, 62, 3490 (1940).
[354] Case, *J. Am. Chem. Soc.*, 55, 2927 (1933).
[355] Underwood and Kochmann, *J. Am. Chem. Soc.*, 46, 2071 (1924).
[356] Bischoff and Adkins, *J. Am. Chem. Soc.*, 45, 1031 (1923).
[357] Roberts and Johnson, *J. Am. Chem. Soc.*, 47, 1399 (1925).
[358] Bell and Briggs, *J. Chem. Soc.*, 1563 (1938).
[359] Atkinson and Lawler, *Org. Syntheses*, Coll. Vol. I, 222 (1941).
[360] Linstead and Doering, *J. Am. Chem. Soc.*, 64, 1998 (1942).
[361] Work, *J. Chem. Soc.*, 1317 (1940).
[362] Wawzonek, *J. Am. Chem. Soc.*, 62, 747 (1940).
[363] Kaszuba, *J. Am. Chem. Soc.*, 67, 1227 (1945).
[364] Jeffery and Vogel, *J. Chem. Soc.*, 661 (1948).
[365] Rietz, *Org. Syntheses*, 24, 96 (1944).
[366] White, *J. Chem. Soc.*, 238 (1943).
[367] Crawford, *J. Soc. Chem. Ind. (London)*, 64, 231 (1945).
[368] Glattfeld and Lee, *J. Am. Chem. Soc.*, 62, 354 (1940).
[369] Goldberg and Linstead, *J. Chem. Soc.*, 2343 (1928).
[370] Lane, Fentress, and Sherwood, *J. Am. Chem. Soc.*, 66, 547 (1944).
[371] Linstead and Rydon, *J. Chem. Soc.*, 580 (1933).
[372] Buckles and Mock, *J. Org. Chem.*, 15, 680 (1950).
[373] Lane, Roberts, and Young, *J. Am. Chem. Soc.*, 66, 543 (1944).
[374] Roberts and Young, *J. Am. Chem. Soc.*, 67, 148 (1945); cf. ref. 373.
[375] Smith, Prichard, and Spillane, *Org. Syntheses*, 23, 27 (1943).
[376] Pressman and Lucas, *J. Am. Chem. Soc.*, 62, 2069 (1940).
[377] Eccott and Linstead, *J. Chem. Soc.*, 2163 (1929).
[378] Letch and Linstead, *J. Chem. Soc.*, 1994 (1934).
[379] Michael and Mason, *J. Am. Chem. Soc.*, 65, 683 (1943).
[380] Linstead and Rydon, *J. Chem. Soc.*, 1998 (1934).
[381] Foreman and McElvain, *J. Am. Chem. Soc.*, 62, 1439 (1940).
[382] Hunsdiecker, *Ber.*, 75, 460 (1942).
[383] Colonge and Joly, *Ann. chim.*, (11) 18, 312 (1943).

[384] Lichtenberger and Naftali, *Bull. soc. chim. France,* (5) 4, 332 (1937).
[385] Mannich and Kniss, *Ber.,* 74, 1641 (1941).
[386] Oskerko, *Ber.,* 70, 56 (1937).
[387] Zaugg, *J. Am. Chem. Soc.,* 72, 3002 (1950).
[388] Moser and Gompf, *J. Org. Chem.,* 15, 585 (1950).
[389] Urion, *Ann. chim.,* (11) 1, 45 (1934).
[390] Cook and Linstead, *J. Chem. Soc.,* 959 (1934).
[391] David, Dupont, and Paquot, *Bull. soc. chim. France,* (5) 11, 563 (1944).
[392] Boorman and Linstead, *J. Chem. Soc.,* 258 (1935).
[393] Fiesselmann, *Ber.,* 75, 889 (1942).
[394] Noller and Adams, *J. Am. Chem. Soc.,* 48, 2447 (1926).
[395] Shive, Horeczy, and Lochte, *J. Am. Chem. Soc.,* 62, 2744 (1940).
[396] McKenzie and Dennler, *J. Chem. Soc.,* 1600 (1926).
[397] Heath and Rose, *J. Chem. Soc.,* 1485 (1947).
[398] English and Dayan, *Org. Syntheses,* 30, 38 (1950).
[399] Crombie and Harper, *J. Chem. Soc.,* 2688 (1950).
[400] Koelsch, *J. Am. Chem. Soc.,* 65, 57 (1943).
[401] Marvel and Overberger, *J. Am. Chem. Soc.,* 67, 2250 (1945).
[402] Woodruff and Conger, *J. Am. Chem. Soc.,* 60, 465 (1938).
[403] Lipkin and Stewart, *J. Am. Chem. Soc.,* 61, 3295 (1939).
[404] Friedmann and Mai, *Helv. Chim. Acta,* 14, 1213 (1931).
[405] Bogert and Davidson, *J. Am. Chem. Soc.,* 54, 334 (1932).
[406] Natelson and Gottfried, *J. Am. Chem. Soc.,* 64, 2962 (1942).
[407] Alder and Stein, *Ann.,* 525, 209 (1936); Owen and Sultanbawa, *J. Chem. Soc.,* 3111 (1949).
[408] Zoss and Hennion, *J. Am. Chem. Soc.,* 63, 1151 (1941).
[409] Heilbron, Jones, and Sondheimer, *J. Chem. Soc.,* 606 (1949).
[410] Haynes and Jones, *J. Chem. Soc.,* 504 (1946).
[411] Ahmad and Strong, *J. Am. Chem. Soc.,* 70, 1699 (1948).
[412] Cope, Clark, and Connor, *Org. Syntheses,* Coll. Vol. II, 181 (1943).
[413] Henne and Trott, *J. Am. Chem. Soc.,* 69, 1820 (1947).
[414] Moureu and Chaux, *Org. Syntheses,* Coll. Vol. I, 166 (1941).
[415] Fieser and Seligman, *J. Am. Chem. Soc.,* 58, 2484 (1936).
[416] Powell, *J. Am. Chem. Soc.,* 46, 2879 (1924).
[417] Kendall and McKenzie, *Org. Syntheses,* Coll. Vol. I, 131 (1941).
[418] Marvel et al., *J. Am. Chem. Soc.,* 62, 3495 (1940).
[419] Yarnall and Wallis, *J. Org. Chem.,* 4, 287 (1939).
[420] Koelsch, *J. Am. Chem. Soc.,* 52, 3364 (1930).
[421] Davis, *J. Am. Chem. Soc.,* 63, 1677 (1941); Kohler, *Am. Chem. J.,* 42, 382 (1909).
[422] Carter and West, *Org. Syntheses,* 20, 81 (1940).
[423] Marvel and du Vigneaud, *Org. Syntheses,* Coll. Vol. II, 93 (1943).
[424] Carter and Ney, *J. Am. Chem. Soc.,* 64, 1223 (1942).
[425] Adams and Marvel, *J. Am. Chem. Soc.,* 42, 310 (1920).
[426] Marvel, *Org. Syntheses,* 21, 60 (1941).
[427] Degering and Boatright, *J. Am. Chem. Soc.,* 72, 5138 (1950).
[428] Fosdick and Campaigne, *J. Am. Chem. Soc.,* 63, 974 (1941).
[429] Clarke and Taylor, *Org. Syntheses,* Coll. Vol. II, 135 (1943).
[430] Olivier, *Rec. trav. chim.,* 48, 568 (1929).
[431] Wallingford and Krueger, *Org. Syntheses,* Coll. Vol. II, 353 (1943).

[432] Sah and Hsu, *Rec. trav. chim.*, **59**, 351 (1940); Gaudemaris and Dubois, *Bull. soc. chim. France*, (5) **17**, 64 (1950).

[433] Sah and Wang, *Rec. trav. chim.*, **59**, 365 (1940).

[434] Buck and Ide, *J. Am. Chem. Soc.*, **54**, 3308 (1932).

[435] Case, *J. Am. Chem. Soc.*, **47**, 3004 (1925).

[436] Snyder and Brewster, *J. Am. Chem. Soc.*, **71**, 1062 (19491.

[437] Marvel, *Org. Syntheses*, **21**, 99 (1941).

[438] Krausz, *Ann. Chim.*, (12) **4**, 820 (1949).

[439] Foreman and McElvain, *J. Am. Chem. Soc.*, **62**, 1435 (1940); Blicke and Lilienfeld, *ibid.*, **65**, 2283 (1943).

[440] Fieser and Seligman, *J. Am. Chem. Soc.*, **60**, 170 (1938).

[441] Grummitt, Buck, and Egan, *Org. Syntheses*, **26**, 21 (1946).

[442] Read, *Org. Syntheses*, Coll. Vol. I, 321 (1941).

[443] Marvel and Birkhimer, *J. Am. Chem. Soc.*, **51**, 260 (1929).

[444] Young, Dillon, and Lucas, *J. Am. Chem. Soc.*, **51**, 2528 (1929).

[445] Lucas and Prater, *J. Am. Chem. Soc.*, **59**, 1682 (1937).

[446] Fuson, Gray, and Gouza, *J. Am. Chem. Soc.*, **61**, 1937 (1939).

[447] Stoughton, *J. Am. Chem. Soc.*, **63**, 2376 (1941).

[448] Levin and Pendergrass, *J. Am. Chem. Soc.*, **69**, 2436 (1947); cf. Campbell and Hunt, *J. Chem. Soc.*, 1379 (1950).

[449] Grigsby et al., *J. Am. Chem. Soc.*, **64**, 2606 (1942).

[450] Newman and Vanderwerf, *J. Am. Chem. Soc.*, **67**, 233 (1945).

[451] Bardhan and Banerji, *J. Chem. Soc.*, 477 (1935).

[452] King, McWhirter, and Barton, *J. Am. Chem. Soc.*, **67**, 2089 (1945).

[453] Lock and Stitz, *Ber.*, **72**, 80 (1939).

[454] Buehler and Cate, *Org. Syntheses*, Coll. Vol. II, 341 (1943).

[455] Nierenstein and Clibbens, *Org. Syntheses*, Coll. Vol. II, 557 (1943).

[456] Aston, Newkirk, Jenkins, and Dorsky, *Org. Syntheses*, **23**, 48 (1943).

[457] Corson et al., *Org. Syntheses*, Coll. Vol. I, 336 (1941).

[458] Biquard, *Ann. chim.*, (10) **20**, 135–150 (1933).

[459] Ott, Mattano, and Coleman, *J. Am. Chem. Soc.*, **68**, 2633 (1946).

[460] Case, *J. Am. Chem. Soc.*, **47**, 1145 (1925).

[461] Blicke and Kaplan, *J. Am. Chem. Soc.*, **65**, 1969 (1943).

[462] Riebsomer, Irvine, and Andrews, *J. Am. Chem. Soc.*, **60**, 1015 (1938); Riebsomer et al., *ibid.*, **60**, 2974 (1938).

[463] Gryszkiewicz-Trochimowski, *Rec. trav. chim.*, **66**, 430 (1947).

[464] Fieser, Gates, and Kilmer, *J. Am. Chem. Soc.*, **62**, 2966 (1940).

[465] Peacock and Menon, *J. Chem. Soc.*, 1299 (1934).

[466] Arnold and Sprung, *J. Am. Chem. Soc.*, **60**, 1163 (1938).

[467] Ballard and Dehn, *Org. Syntheses*, Coll. Vol. I, 89 (1941).

[468] Riebsomer et al., *J. Am. Chem. Soc.*, **64**, 2080 (1942).

[469] Staudinger, *Ber.*, **39**, 3062 (1906).

[470] Rohrmann, Jones, and Shonle, *J. Am. Chem. Soc.*, **66**, 1856 (1944).

[471] Niemann, Benson, and Mead, *J. Org. Chem.*, **8**, 401 (1943).

[472] Palomaa and Kenetti, *Ber.*, **64**, 800 (1931).

[473] Christian and Hixon, *J. Am. Chem. Soc.*, **70**, 1333 (1948); Leslie and Henze, *ibid.*, **71**, 3480 (1949).

[474] Prelog and Zalan, *Helv. Chim. Acta*, **27**, 534 (1944).

[475] Weizmann, Sulzbacher, and Bergmann, *J. Am. Chem. Soc.*, **70**, 1153 (1948).

[476] Palomaa, *Ber.*, **74**, 297 (1941).

[477] Swern, *Chem. Revs.*, **45**, 38 (1949).

[478] Rieveschl and Ray, *Org. Syntheses,* **28**, 63 (1948).
[479] Powell, *J. Am. Chem. Soc.,* **45**, 2710 (1923).
[480] Levine, Eble, and Fischbach, *J. Am. Chem. Soc.,* **70**, 1930 (1948).
[481] Kornfeld, *J. Am. Chem. Soc.,* **70**, 1373 (1948).
[482] Weidlich and Meyer-Delius, *Ber.,* **73**, 327 (1940).
[483] Burger and Avakian, *J. Org. Chem.,* **5**, 606 (1940).
[484] Tschudi and Schinz, *Helv. Chim. Acta,* **33**, 1868 (1950).
[485] Ruzicka et al., *Helv. Chim. Acta,* **31**, 427 (1948).
[486] Buck and Ide, *Org. Syntheses,* Coll. Vol. II, 333 (1943).
[487] Merchant, Wickert, and Marvel, *J. Am. Chem. Soc.,* **49**, 1829 (1927).
[488] King and Robinson, *J. Chem. Soc.,* 272 (1933).
[489] Hardegger, Redlich, and Gal, *Helv. Chim. Acta,* **28**, 632 (1945).
[490] Grummitt, Egan, and Buck, *Org. Syntheses,* **29**, 49 (1949).
[491] Haworth and Sheldrick, *J. Chem. Soc.,* 1951 (1934).
[492] Fuson and Rachlin, *J. Am. Chem. Soc.,* **64**, 1567 (1942).
[493] Marvel et al., *J. Am. Chem. Soc.,* **46**, 2841 (1924).
[494] Brown, *J. Soc. Chem. Ind. (London),* **66**, 168 (1947).
[495] Gaubert, Linstead, and Rydon, *J. Chem. Soc.,* 1976 (1937).
[496] Tschelinzeff and Schmidt, *Ber.,* **62**, 2210 (1929).
[497] Sah and Ma, *J. Am. Chem. Soc.,* **52**, 4880 (1930).
[498] McKenzie, *Org. Syntheses,* Coll. Vol. I, 335 (1941).
[499] Thomas and Schuette, *J. Am. Chem. Soc.,* **53**, 2324 (1931).
[500] Lehninger and Witzemann, *J. Am. Chem. Soc.,* **64**, 874 (1942).
[501] Adams and Long, *J. Am. Chem. Soc.,* **62**, 2289 (1940).
[502] Berger, *J. prakt. Chem.,* **152**, 322 (1939).
[503] Blicke and Tsao, *J. Am. Chem. Soc.,* **66**, 1645 (1944).
[504] Linstead and Meade, *J. Chem. Soc.,* 940 (1934).
[505] Shriner and Wolf, *Org. Syntheses,* **23**, 74 (1943).
[506] Contractor and Peters, *J. Chem. Soc.,* 1314 (1949).
[507] Nenitzescu and Curcaneanu, *Ber.,* **71**, 2064 (1938).
[508] Oakwood and Weisgerber, *Org. Syntheses,* **24**, 14, 16 (1944).
[509] Hurd, McNamee, and Green, *J. Am. Chem. Soc.,* **61**, 2979 (1939).
[510] Baer and Kates, *J. Am. Chem. Soc.,* **67**, 1482 (1945).
[511] Bruson and Riener, *J. Am. Chem. Soc.,* **66**, 56 (1944).
[512] Fuson, *J. Am. Chem. Soc.,* **48**, 1095 (1926).
[513] Langenbeck and Baltes, *Ber.,* **67**, 1207 (1934).
[514] Campbell and Tucker, *J. Chem. Soc.,* 2624 (1949).
[515] Short and Wang, *J. Chem. Soc.,* 992 (1950).
[516] Buu-Hoi and Nguyen-Hoàn, *Rec. trav. chim.,* **68**, 19 (1949).
[517] Popovici, *Ann. chim.,* (10), **18**, 198 (1932).
[518] Anslow and King, *Org. Syntheses,* Coll. Vol. I, 298 (1941).
[519] Cocker and Lapworth, *J. Chem. Soc.,* 1391 (1931).
[520] Kendall and McKenzie, *Org. Syntheses,* Coll. Vol. I, 21 (1941).
[521] Buc, Ford, and Wise, *J. Am. Chem. Soc.,* **67**, 92 (1945).
[522] Ford, *J. Am. Chem. Soc.,* **67**, 876 (1945).
[523] Ford, *Org. Syntheses,* **27**, 1 (1947).
[524] Galat, *J. Am. Chem. Soc.,* **67**, 1414 (1945).
[525] Chodroff, Kapp, and Beckmann, *J. Am. Chem. Soc.,* **69**, 256 (1947).
[526] Billman and Parker, *J. Am. Chem. Soc.,* **65**, 2455 (1943).
[527] Wegand, *Ber.,* **74**, 257 (1941).
[528] Redemann and Icke, *J. Org. Chem.,* **8**, 159 (1934).

[529] Billman and Parker, *J. Am. Chem. Soc.*, **66**, 538 (1944).
[530] Jacobson, *J. Am. Chem. Soc.*, **68**, 2628 (1946).
[531] Clarke and Bean, *Org. Syntheses*, Coll. Vol. II, 29 (1943).
[532] Galat, *J. Am. Chem. Soc.*, **69**, 965 (1947).
[533] Fox, Dunn, and Stoddard, *J. Org. Chem.*, **6**, 410 (1941).
[534] Schniepp and Marvel, *J. Am. Chem. Soc.*, **57**, 1557 (1935).
[535] Marvel and Stoddard, *J. Org. Chem.*, **3**, 198 (1938).
[536] King, *Org. Syntheses*, Coll. Vol. I, 286 (1941).
[537] Steiger, *Helv. Chim. Acta*, **17**, 559 (1934); Gabriel, *Ber.*, **46**, 1355 (1913).
[538] Goldsmith and Tishler, *J. Am. Chem. Soc.*, **68**, 144 (1946).
[539] Booth, Burnop, and Jones, *J. Chem. Soc.*, 666 (1944).
[540] Galat and Mallin, *J. Am. Chem. Soc.*, **68**, 2729 (1946).
[541] Eck, *Org. Syntheses*, Coll. Vol. II, 28 (1943).
[542] Albertson and Archer, *J. Am. Chem. Soc.*, **67**, 308 (1945).
[543] Steiger, *Org. Syntheses*, **22**, 13 (1942).
[544] Foster and Shemin, *Org. Syntheses*, Coll. Vol. II, 330 (1943).
[545] Gortner and Hoffman, *Org. Syntheses*, Coll. Vol. I, 194 (1941).
[546] Merrill, *J. Am. Chem. Soc.*, **43**, 2692 (1921).
[547] Brand and Sandberg, *Org. Syntheses*, Coll. Vol. II, 49 (1943).
[548] Albertson, *J. Am. Chem. Soc.*, **68**, 450 (1946).
[549] Kobayashi, *Ann.*, **536**, 158 (1938).
[550] Marvel and Noyes, *J. Am. Chem. Soc.*, **42**, 2275 (1920).
[551] Steiger, *Org. Syntheses*, **22**, 23 (1942).
[552] Johnson, *J. Am. Chem. Soc.*, **61**, 2485 (1939).
[553] Steiger, *Org. Syntheses*, **24**, 9 (1944).
[554] Johnson and Livak, *J. Am. Chem. Soc.*, **58**, 299 (1936).
[555] Scudi, *J. Am. Chem. Soc.*, **57**, 1279 (1935).
[556] Gillespie and Snyder, *Org. Syntheses*, Coll. Vol. II, 489 (1943).
[557] Snyder, Shekleton, and Lewis, *J. Am. Chem. Soc.*, **67**, 310 (1945).
[558] Blicke and Lilienfeld, *J. Am. Chem. Soc.*, **65**, 2377 (1943).
[559] Painter, *J. Am. Chem. Soc.*, **69**, 232 (1947).
[560] Snyder and Smith, *J. Am. Chem. Soc.*, **66**, 350 (1944).
[561] Albertson, Archer, and Suter, *J. Am. Chem. Soc.*, **67**, 36 (1945).
[562] Sah and Yin, *Rec. trav. chim.*, **59**, 240 (1940).
[563] Lock, *Ber.*, **63**, 855 (1930).
[564] Kamm and Segur, *Org. Syntheses*, Coll. Vol. I, 391 (1941).
[565] Wacek and Bezard, *Ber.*, **74**, 857 (1941).
[566] Kamm and Matthews, *Org. Syntheses*, Coll. Vol. I, 392 (1941).
[567] Storrie, *J. Chem. Soc.*, 1746 (1937).
[568] May and Mosettig, *J. Org. Chem.*, **11**, 435 (1946).
[569] Yabroff and Porter, *J. Am. Chem. Soc.*, **54**, 1199 (1932).
[570] Robertson, *Org. Syntheses*, Coll. Vol. I, 406 (1941); Lewis et al., *J. Am. Chem. Soc.*, **71**, 3751 (1949).
[571] Morton and Heckenbleikner, *J. Am. Chem. Soc.*, **58**, 754 (1936).
[572] Whitmore and Randall, *J. Am. Chem. Soc.*, **64**, 1246 (1942); Whitmore and Lester, *ibid.*, **64**, 1251 (1942).
[573] Baumgarten, Levine, and Hauser, *J. Am. Chem. Soc.*, **66**, 862 (1944).
[574] Neunhoeffer and Schlüter, *Ann.*, **526**, 70 (1936).
[575] Jeffery and Vogel, *J. Chem. Soc.*, 447 (1939).
[576] Varrentrapp, *Ann.*, **35**, 196 (1840).

[577] Ralston, *Fatty Acids and Their Derivatives,* John Wiley & Sons, New York, 1948, p. 474.

[578] Hilditch, *The Chemical Constitution of Natural Fats,* John Wiley & Sons, New York, 1947.

[579] Markley, *Fatty Acids,* Interscience Publishers, New York, 1947.

[580] Mowry and Ringwald, *J. Am. Chem. Soc.,* **72,** 2038 (1950).

[581] Wislicenus and Eble, *Ber.,* **50,** 253 (1917).

[582] Geissman in *Organic Reactions,* Vol. 2, John Wiley & Sons, New York, 1944, p. 94; Kharasch and Snyder, *J. Org. Chem.,* **14,** 819 (1949).

[583] Lock, *Ber.,* **62,** 1177 (1929).

[584] Dunn, *Ann. Rev. Biochem.,* **10,** 91 (1941).

[585] Clarke in Gilman's *Organic Chemistry,* Vol. 2, John Wiley & Sons, New York, 1943, p. 1079.

[586] Carter and Hooper in Sahyun's *Amino Acids and Proteins,* Reinhold Publishing Corp., New York, 1944, p. 94.

[587] Dunn in Schmidt's *Amino Acids and Proteins,* 2nd ed., Charles C. Thomas, Springfield, Ill., 1944., p. 21.

[588] Tarbell and Noble, *J. Am. Chem. Soc.,* **72,** 2660 (1950).

[589] Schiessler and Eldred, *J. Am. Chem. Soc.,* **70,** 3958 (1948).

[590] Jeffery and Vogel, J. *Chem. Soc.,* 1805 (1948); cf. ref. 281.

[591] Levine et al., *J. Am. Chem. Soc.,* **71,** 1496 (1949), **72,** 1642 (1950).

[592] Colonge and Pichat, *Bull. soc. chim. France,* (5) **16,** 180 (1949).

[593] Pearl, *Org. Syntheses,* **29,** 85 (1949).

[594] Ogata and Ishiguro, *J. Am. Chem. Soc.,* **72,** 4302 (1950).

[595] Arnold, Parham, and Dodson, *J. Am. Chem. Soc.,* **71,** 2439 (1949).

[596] Zaugg and Horrom, *J. Am. Chem. Soc.,* **72,** 3006 (1950).

[597] Sperger, Papa, and Schwenk, *J. Am. Chem. Soc.,* **70,** 3091 (1948).

[598] McElvain and Vozza, *J. Am. Chem. Soc.,* **71,** 897 (1949).

[599] Pattison and Saunders, *J. Chem. Soc.,* 2747 (1949).

[600] Berswerth et al., *J. Org. Chem.,* **14,** 355 (1949), **15,** 46, 255 (1950).

[601] Adkins and Rosenthal, *J. Am. Chem. Soc.,* **72,** 4550 (1950); Ford, Jacobson, and McGrew, *ibid.,* **70,** 3793 (1948); Newitt and Momen, *J. Chem. Soc.,* 2945 (1949).

[602] Hickinbottom, *Reactions of Organic Compounds,* 2nd ed., Longmans, Green & Co., New York, 1948, p. 378.

[603] Ratchford, *Org. Syntheses,* **29,** 2 (1949); Rehberg, *ibid.,* **29,** 5 (1949).

[604] Philippi and Thelen, *Org. Syntheses,* Coll. Vol. II, 551 (1943).

[605] Fieser and Szmuszkovicz, *J. Am. Chem. Soc.,* **70,** 3352 (1948); Adkins and Roebuck, *ibid.,* **70,** 4044 (1948).

[606] Hauser, Swamer, and Ringler, *J. Am. Chem. Soc.,* **70,** 4023 (1948).

[607] Hatch and Nesbitt, *J. Am. Chem. Soc.,* **72,** 730 (1950).

[608] Gaudry, *Can. J. Research,* **27B,** 21 (1949).

[609] Henbest, Jones, and Walls, *J. Chem. Soc.,* 3650 (1950).

[610] Crombie and Harper, *J. Chem. Soc.,* 1157 (1950).

[611] Crombie and Harper, *J. Chem. Soc.,* 1720, 1721 (1950).

[612] Sherman and Amstutz, *J. Am. Chem. Soc.,* **72,** 2195 (1950).

[613] Moser and Sause, *J. Org. Chem.,* **15,** 631 (1950).

[614] Barnes, *Org. Syntheses,* **21,** 77 (1941).

[615] Lester and Proffitt, *J. Am. Chem. Soc.,* **71,** 1878 (1949).

[616] Wagner, *J. Am. Chem. Soc.,* **71,** 3216 (1949).

617 Wagner and Moore, *J. Am. Chem. Soc.*, 72, 975 (1950).
618 Wotiz, J. *Am. Chem. Soc.*, 72, 1639 (1950).
619 Breslow, J. *Am. Chem. Soc.*, 72, 4245 (1950).
620 Kepner, Winstein, and Young, *J. Am. Chem. Soc.*, 71, 118 (1949).
621 Roberts and Shaw, *J. Chem. Soc.*, 2842 (1950).
622 Ansell and Hey, *J. Chem. Soc.*, 1683 (1950).
623 Horn, Miller, and Slater, *J. Chem. Soc.*, 2900 (1950).
624 Hill, Salvin, and O'Brien, *J. Am. Chem. Soc.*, 59, 2385 (1937).
625 Renfrow and Walker, *J. Am. Chem. Soc.*, 70, 3957 (1948).
626 Sayles and Degering, *J. Am. Chem. Soc.*, 71, 3163 (1949).
627 Beech and Legg, *J. Chem. Soc.*, 1888 (1949).
628 Owen and Nord, *J. Org. Chem.*, 15, 991 (1950).
629 Levin, Papa, and Schwenk, *J. Am. Chem. Soc.*, 69, 1830 (1947).
630 Freedman and Doak, *J. Am. Chem. Soc.*, 71, 779 (1949).
631 Horning and Reisner, *J. Am. Chem. Soc.*, 71, 1036 (1949); Alexander and Mudrak, *ibid.*, 72, 3195 (1950).
632 Smith and Byrne, *J. Am. Chem. Soc.*, 72, 4406 (1950).
633 Smith and Schmehl, *J. Org. Chem.*, 13, 859 (1948).
634 Newman and Mangham, *J. Am. Chem. Soc.*, 71, 3343 (1942).
635 Arnold, Murai, and Dodson, *J. Am. Chem. Soc.*, 72, 4194 (1950).
636 Kornfeld, *J. Am. Chem. Soc.*, 70, 1375 (1948).
637 Bachmann and Cortes, *J. Am. Chem. Soc.*, 65, 1332 (1943).
638 Jones et al., *J. Am. Chem. Soc.*, 70, 2846 (1948).
639 Malan and Dean, *J. Am. Chem. Soc.*, 69, 1797 (1947).
640 Turner, *J. Am. Chem. Soc.*, 72, 3823 (1950).
641 Crowe and Nord, *J. Org. Chem.*, 15, 86 (1950).
642 Barger and Weichselbaum, *Org. Syntheses*, Coll. Vol. II, 384 (1943); cf. refs. 538 and 539.
643 Dunn and Smart, *Org. Syntheses*, 30, 7 (1950); cf. ref. 532.
644 Atkinson and Scott, *J. Chem. Soc.*, 1041 (1949).
645 Galat, *J. Am. Chem. Soc.*, 72, 4438 (1950).
646 Offe and Jatzkewitz, *Chem. Ber.*, 80, 472 (1947).
647 Boekelheide and Schramm, *J. Org. Chem.*, 14, 298 (1949).
648 Elks, Hems, and Ryman, *J. Chem. Soc.*, 1386 (1948).
649 Rogers et al., *J. Am. Chem. Soc.*, 71, 1837 (1949).
650 Ware, *Chem. Revs.*, 46, 403 (1950).
651 Smith and McLoed, *Org. Syntheses*, 31, 40 (1951).
652 Scheaffer and Snoddy, *Org. Syntheses*, 31, 3 (1951).

14

Carboxylic Esters

CONTENTS *(continued)*

285. Esterification of Carboxylic Acids by Hydroxy Compounds

$$RCO_2H + R'OH \rightleftharpoons RCO_2R' + H_2O$$

This method is applicable to the preparation of esters from most acids and primary alcohols. Over one hundred of the simpler aliphatic esters of mono- and di-basic acids have been made in this way for a study of their physical properties.[26] The yields of esters from secondary alcohols are only fair. Tertiary alcohols and phenols do not react to an appreciable extent.

Esterification is usually effected by refluxing the acid and alcohol with a small amount of sulfuric acid, hydrogen chloride, or arylsulfonic acid. The equilibrium is shifted to the right by an excess of one of the reactants or by removal of water either by azeotropic distillation or by means of a suitable drying agent. The necessity for continuous drying is eliminated when methylene or ethylene chlorides are used as solvents for the reaction.[19] A small amount of an acid chloride such as thionyl chloride, acetyl chloride, or stearoyl chloride has proved superior to hydrogen chloride as a catalyst for certain esterifications at room temperature.[21] No catalysts are necessary for the preparation of esters of benzyl alcohol[14] or formic acid.[26]

The use of boron trifluoride as an esterification catalyst is increasing.[2,4,5] This substance is particularly useful in the preparation of esters of substituted benzoic acids. The time of refluxing and ratio of catalyst to reactants have been studied. Yields are in the range of 55% to 100% for esters of primary alcohols and benzoic acids containing such groups as *p*-nitro, *o*-amino, *o*-hydroxy, and *o*-chloro.[1] A modification of this catalytic process employs the amide in place of the acid as the acylating agent. Yields are somewhat lower than with the corresponding acids.[4]

t-Butyl alcohol and phenol are converted to their acetates in 38% and 50% yields, respectively.[3] Alcohols and amino alcohols are quantitatively converted to the corresponding acetates by a solution of boron trifluoride in glacial acetic acid.[5] Trifluoroacetic anhydride has found use as an esterification catalyst. It is particularly suited to esterifications of phenols and glycosides.[397] Oxidation of primary alcohols in acid media is often accompanied by esterification. By the use of the proper proportions of reactants, fair yields of esters may be obtained directly from the alcohols; e.g., n-butyl n-butyrate (47%) by chromic acid oxidation of n-butyl alcohol.[10] Aqueous acid chlorate solutions in the presence of vanadium pentoxide have been used for this purpose.[13]

Substituents in the *ortho* positions of aromatic acids generally retard esterification. Such sterically hindered acids may be esterified by dissolving in 100% sulfuric acid and pouring the solutions into the desired alcohol. This reaction is limited to those acids which dissociate in sulfuric acid to give a positive acyl ion, RCO^{+}[18] (cf. method 314).

By the above procedures, esterifications have been accomplished for long-chain aliphatic acids,[11,23,24] polybasic acids,[12,15,19,33-39] heterocyclic acids,[27-32] and acids containing the following groups: double bonds;[40-42,401] triple bonds;[44] halogen atoms in the *alpha*,[4,6,16,50] *beta*,[47,49,51,52] and *omega*[229,288] positions; hydroxyl groups in the *alpha* and *beta* positions[20,43,45,54-56] and on the aromatic nucleus;[57,58] alkoxyl groups;[59-64,66] keto groups in the *alpha*,[19,67,69,71] *beta*,[68] and *gamma*[70] positions; and cyano,[77] amino,[1,7,72-74] dialkylamino,[290,291] and nitro groups.[1,19,75,76]

High yields of esters of straight-chain acids and glycol or glycerol may be obtained by heating the fatty acids and polyhydric alcohols at 200° in the presence of zinc dust, which acts as a catalyst.[106] More specialized methods are required to make mono- and di-glycerides.[397]

286. Action of Acyl Halides on Hydroxy Compounds

$$RCOCl + R'OH \rightarrow RCO_2R' + HCl$$

This reaction has wide application for the preparation of esters. The difficulties encountered in method 285 because of a reversible reaction are avoided. Esters of tertiary alcohols and phenols are best prepared in this way. The formation of tertiary halides from tertiary alcohols is prevented by carrying out the reaction in the presence of powdered magnesium[80] or dimethylaniline[79] which react with the hydrogen chloride as it is formed. The esterification of phenols is effected in the same manner. Magnesium[88] or pyridine[78] is added to combine with the hydrogen halide. Pyridine has replaced aqueous alkali formerly used for this purpose

(Schotten-Baumann).[87] The acylation of phenols without a basic solvent is promoted by small amounts of sulfuric acid[83] or stannic chloride.[86,89] Care must be exercised to prevent rearrangement of the phenolic ester to a phenolic ketone (Fries reaction, method 209).

A variety of *other functional groups* may be present in both the acyl halide and the alcohol. Olefinic acyl chlorides,[93,94] α- and β-acetoxy-acyl halides,[90,91] halomethylbenzoyl chlorides,[97,98,102] and 2-furanacrylyl chloride[95] are converted to esters by this method. The α-halo acyl halides from the Hell-Volhard-Zelinsky reaction (method 67) give α-halo esters. Glycerol and palmityl chloride in pyridine give glyceryl tripalmitate (76%).[92] Esters containing hydroxyl[104] and halo[96,99-101] groups in the alcoholic portion of the molecule may be made by the action of acyl halides on diols and halohydrins, respectively. Cyanomethyl esters, RCO_2CH_2CN, are formed by the action of the acyl halide on an aqueous solution of formaldehyde and sodium cyanide; glycolonitrile, $HOCH_2CN$, is formed and acylated immediately by a typical Schotten-Baumann reaction.[105]

Esters of the enolic forms of β-keto esters and β-diketones are prepared from the corresponding carbonyl compounds and acyl halides in pyridine solution. In this manner, the enol acetate of benzoylacetone, $C_6H_5COCH=C(OCOCH_3)CH_3$, is formed in 70% yield.[103]

287. Action of Anhydrides on Hydroxy Compounds

$$(RCO)_2O + R'OH \rightarrow RCO_2R' + RCO_2H$$

All types of alcohols and phenols are acylated by anhydrides. The reaction is catalyzed by a small amount of sulfuric acid,[115,117] zinc chloride,[116,118] acetyl chloride,[121] sodium acetate,[113,114] or pyridine. t-Butyl alcohol gives t-butyl acetate in 60% yield.[116] Acetylation of phenols may be accomplished in an aqueous alkaline solution, the acylation proceeding more rapidly than the hydrolysis of the anhydride. The yields are above 90%. Phenol, dihydroxybenzenes, naphthols, and phenols carrying nitro, amino, halo, carboxyl, or carbomethoxyl groups are acetylated by this procedure.[119,132]

Cyclic anhydrides of dibasic acids are cleaved by alcohols to mono-acid esters.[122,128,129] Similarly, the anhydride ring is opened by alkali-metal and halomagnesium alkoxides to give the corresponding salts of the acid esters.[111,126]

$$\begin{array}{ccc}
RCH-CO & & RCH-CO_2H \\
| \quad \backslash & R'OH & | \\
\quad O & \longrightarrow & \\
| \quad / & & | \\
RCH-CO & & RCH-CO_2R'
\end{array}$$

Anhydrides have been used in the acylation of hydroxy compounds containing halo,[112,119] aldehyde,[124] keto,[112,123] and nitro[125,133] groups.

288. Action of Ketenes on Hydroxy Compounds

$$H_2C=C=O + ROH \xrightarrow{H^+} CH_3CO_2R$$

Acetylation of alcohols and phenols by ketene has limited use.[134] Unless apparatus for the preparation of ketene is readily available, less troublesome methods can usually be found. Worthy of mention, however, are the acetylations of lactic esters in 94-98% yields[136] and of tertiary alcohols and phenols in 89-96% yields.[137,139] Catalysts are necessary even to convert a high percentage of n-butyl alcohol to n-butyl acetate.[135] Sulfuric and p-toluenesulfonic acids are commonly used. Certain aldehydes and ketones are attacked by ketene.[137,138] Acetates of enol forms of ketones may be made in this way.[140] Under certain conditions β-lactones are formed (cf. method 327).

An important method for the preparation of β-keto esters is by the action of alcohols on ketene dimers in the presence of acid catalysts. Diketene and alcohols give acetoacetic esters in 60-80% yields.[141,143] Dimers of higher ketenes are made by dehydrohalogenation of acyl halides and are converted to β-keto esters in one operation[142] (cf. method 245).

$$RCH_2COCl \xrightarrow{R_3'N} (RCH=C=O) \rightarrow RCH_2COC(R)=C=O \xrightarrow{R'OH}$$

$$RCH_2COCHRCO_2R''$$

289. Action of Phosgene on Hydroxy Compounds

$$COCl_2 \xrightarrow[\text{Amines}]{ROH} ROCOCl \xrightarrow[\text{Base}]{R'OH} (RO)(R'O)CO$$

The reaction of phosgene with alcohols or phenols gives *chlorocarbonates* (chloroformates) or *carbonates*, depending upon the experimental conditions. The reaction can be stopped at the chlorocarbonate stage in good yield if carried out at about 0-15°.[360,362] Benzene, toluene, and ether have been used as solvents. The reaction is catalyzed by tertiary amines such as dimethylaniline[361,371] and quinoline.[365] The hydroxy compound may contain various other functional groups including the double bond[361] and halo,[370] alkoxyl,[364] and nitro[361] groups. *t*-Butyl chloroformate decomposes at 10°. It is prepared from sodium *t*-butoxide and phosgene in butane solution at -60°.[363] Chloroformic esters of phenols are formed to protect the phenolic hydroxyl group in certain reactions.[373]

The preparation of a carbonate is usually accomplished by treating phosgene or a chloroformate with an alcohol dissolved in a tertiary amine[368,373] or with a sodium[363,366] or halomagnesium[367] alkoxide or phenoxide.[369,373] The disadvantages of phosgene are circumvented in the preparation of diphenyl carbonate from phenol and carbon tetrachloride.[372]

$$2C_6H_5OH + CCl_4 \xrightarrow[ZnO]{ZnCl_2} (C_6H_5O)_2CCl_2 \xrightarrow{H_2O} (C_6H_5O)_2CO$$

290. Action of Halides on Salts of Carboxylic Acids

$$RCO_2Na + R'X \rightarrow RCO_2R' + NaX$$

Reactive halogen compounds such as benzyl chloride,[192] 2-thenyl chloride,[406] 2-bromoacetylthiophene, $(C_4H_3S)COCH_2Br$[191], and 2-chloromethylthianaphthene $(C_8H_5S)CH_2Cl$[189] are readily converted to esters by treatment with the sodium salts of carboxylic acids. A small amount of triethylamine has proved to be an effective catalyst.[189,192] Acetates are oftentimes made by heating halides with fused sodium acetate in glacial acetic acid,[191] e.g., p-ethylbenzyl acetate (93%).[188] The reaction is of little value for the preparation of simple aliphatic esters. Secondary and tertiary halides give increasing amounts of olefin by dehydrohalogenation.

1,2-Diacyloxy compounds are intermediates in the conversion of olefins and 1,2-dihalides to glycols (method 95). Although the *diesters* are seldom isolated, yields are good where their isolation has been attempted.[195,200]

The well-known reaction of an alkyl halide with a silver salt of an acid is used infrequently. It is sometimes valuable in making esters from acids which isomerize during direct esterification.[26,194,401] Thus, the labile double bond of 3-methyl-3-butenoic acid is unaffected by conversion to the methyl ester by this method.[190]

A number of 1-alkoxyalkyl esters (*acylals*) such as 1-methoxyethylacetate, $CH_3CO_2CH(OCH_3)CH_3$, have been made from 1-alkoxyalkyl chlorides and sodium salts of carboxylic acids.[199]

Ether,[196,198] keto,[198] ester,[193] and nitro[197] groups have been present in the halogen compounds during ester formation by this method.

291. Action of Alkyl Chlorosulfites or Alkyl Sulfates on Salts of Carboxylic Acids

$$RCO_2Na + R'OSOCl \rightarrow RCO_2R' + SO_2 + NaCl$$

This reaction has been developed as a new method of esterification. The chlorosulfites are prepared from the corresponding alcohols and thionyl chloride. A vigorous exothermic reaction occurs between the chlorosulfites and the acid salts. Further heating to 100–150° results in the evolution of sulfur dioxide and the formation of the esters in 61–82% yields. Aliphatic and aromatic acids including the hindered 2,4,6-trialkylbenzoic acids have been esterified.[396]

Di-(β-chloroethyl) sulfate, $(ClCH_2CH_2O)_2SO_2$, reacts with sodium salts of acids to give β-chloroethyl esters.[393]

292. Action of Diazomethane on Carboxylic Acids

$$RCO_2H + CH_2N_2 \rightarrow RCO_2CH_3 + N_2$$

This reaction for the preparation of methyl esters takes place in ethereal solution at room temperature. The completion of the reaction is noted by the cessation of the evolution of nitrogen and a permanent yellow color of excess diazomethane. The method is excellent for the conversion of small amounts of expensive acids to their methyl esters. The relatively unstable β-keto acids are converted to the corresponding methyl esters by this reagent.[322] The reaction of diazomethane with various types of acidic hydrogen atoms has been reviewed.[302] α-Amino acids and diazomethane give betaines, $(CH_3)_3\overset{+}{N}CH(R)CO_2^-$, in addition to amino esters, $RCH(NH_2)CO_2CH_3$.[301] Certain conjugated olefinic esters add diazomethane to give pyrazolines which are pyrolyzed to cyclopropyl-carboxylic esters.[413]

293. Alcoholysis of Nitriles

$$RCH_2CN \xrightarrow[HX]{R'OH} RCH_2C(OR')=NH \cdot HX \xrightarrow{H_2O} RCH_2CO_2R'$$

Nitriles are directly converted to esters by heating with an alcohol and sulfuric or hydrochloric acid.[150] When water is absent, the imino ester salt is readily isolated (method 402). Aliphatic,[151] aromatic,[144,147] and heterocyclic[146,148,405] cyano compounds react in this manner. Most of the aromatic compounds contain a cyanomethyl group although the cyanide radical may be attached directly to the aromatic nucleus.[153] Monosubstituted malonic esters free from unsubstituted and disubstituted malonic esters are made from the corresponding α-cyano esters by this method.[154,155] Malonic ester[158] and disubstituted malonic esters have been similarly prepared.[156]

No isomerization of the double bond is reported in the conversion of 3-pentenonitrile to the olefinic ester, methyl 3-pentenoate, by hydrogen chloride in methanol.[49]

Aliphatic and aromatic halo groups are unaffected by the alcoholysis, as in the preparations of methyl γ-chlorobutyrate[51] and various halo-phenylacetates.[65]

α-*Hydroxy* and α-*acetoxy* groups are common in esters made by this method because the cyanohydrins are readily available from aldehydes.[159,162,163] For example, the combination of acrolein and hydrogen cyanide followed by treatment with alcoholic hydrogen chloride gives ethyl vinylglycolate, $CH_2=CHCH(OH)CO_2C_2H_5$, in 61% over-all yield.[164] Both halogen and hydroxyl groups are present during the conversion of 2-hydroxy-3-halobutyronitrile to the corresponding ester.[165] Alkoxy[167] and phenoxy[166] esters have been prepared in a similar manner.

Both α-[169] and β-[168,170,172,173,176] keto cyanides undergo alcoholysis leading to *keto* esters. The β-keto cyanides are formed by the acylation of nitriles (method 216), thus providing a convenient route to the formation of β-keto esters.

The ethyl ester of glycine is obtained by alcoholysis and hydrolysis of methyleneaminoacetonitrile.[171]

$$H_2C=NCH_2CN \xrightarrow[HCl]{C_2H_5OH,\ H_2O} Cl^- \overset{+}{N}H_3CH_2CO_2C_2H_5$$

The nitrile is readily formed from formaldehyde, sodium cyanide, and ammonium chloride (method 391). Other *amino esters* such as those containing β-[175] and γ-[174] dialkylamino groups are formed from the corresponding dialkylamino cyanides by alcoholysis.

294. Alcoholysis of Esters

$$RCO_2R' + R''OH \underset{}{\overset{H^+\ or\ OH^-}{\rightleftharpoons}} RCO_2R'' + R'OH$$

The interchange of ester components occurs in acid[180,181] or alkaline[8,185,187] medium. The reaction is reversible, and the equilibrium is shifted in the desired direction by removing the lower-boiling alcohol or by employing an excess of one component. The relative replacing power of a large number of primary and secondary alcohols in this reaction has been determined.[186] Solutions of potassium alkoxides in the corresponding alcohols at room temperature convert methyl benzoate and certain *p*-substituted derivatives to a variety of esters. This conversion fails with secondary and tertiary alcohols.[185] Ethyl esters of oxalic, malonic, succinic, and terephthalic acids are prepared from the corresponding methyl esters. Dimethyl phthalate does not react. Esters of higher-molecular-weight fatty acids are best obtained from natural fats, waxes, and oils by this method.[179,180]

Esters of acids that are unstable in an acidic medium are conveniently prepared by this reaction. Alkyl *acrylates* having two to sixteen carbon atoms in the alkyl group are made in high yields by the alcoholysis of methyl acrylate over acid catalysts.[181] Halomagnesium alkoxides of primary and secondary alcohols undergo a similar interconversion with esters. A series of acrylates and *carbonates* have been obtained in fair yields in this manner.[182] Ester interchange is the most convenient of four

$$RCO_2R' + R''OMgX \longrightarrow RCO_2R'' + R'OMgX$$

$$\begin{array}{c} \underline{\quad}CO\underline{\quad} \\ | \qquad | \end{array}$$

methods for the preparation of ethylene carbonate, OCH_2CH_2O. Ethylene glycol, diethyl carbonate, and a small amount of potassium carbonate are heated until the theoretical amount of ethanol distils.[183] Higher cyclic glycol esters of carbonic acid are prepared in a similar manner.[184]

This reaction furnishes the best method for the preparation of nineteen esters of γ-diethylamino-α-phenylbutyric acid.[174]

295. Alcoholysis and Rearrangement of Diazoketones (Arndt-Eistert)

$$RCOCl \xrightarrow{CH_2N_2} RCOCHN_2 \xrightarrow[Ag_2O]{R'OH} RCH_2CO_2R'$$

This rearrangement leads to carboxylic acids (method 271), their esters, or amides (method 360), depending upon the manner in which the diazo-ketone is decomposed. The carbon chain is lengthened by one carbon atom. The esters are prepared by adding silver oxide catalyst to a hot solution of the diazoketone in anhydrous alcohol. The progress of the reaction is followed by measuring the amount of nitrogen evolved. Ethyl α-thienylacetate is prepared in 68% over-all yield from α-thenoyl chloride.[205] A survey of the literature to November, 1941, lists only seven esters prepared by this method although more than half of the rearrangements have been carried out *via* the ester as the primary product.[201] The several additional examples since then include the methyl and ethyl esters of thianaphthene-2-acetic acid[204] and benzofuran-2-acetic acid.[408]

The Arndt-Eistert synthesis has been extended to the preparation of disubstituted acetic acids and derivatives through the use of higher diazo hydrocarbons.

Improved procedures for the rearrangement of diazo ketones have been developed. In one of these, the readily hydrolyzable benzyl ester is formed by heating the diazo ketone with benzyl alcohol in the presence of a tertiary amine.[203]

$$RCOCl \xrightarrow{R'CHN_2} RCOCR'N_2 \xrightarrow[C_6H_5N(CH_3)_2]{C_6H_5CH_2OH} RR'CHCO_2CH_2C_6H_5$$

Another modification employs silver benzoate catalyst in a homogeneous reaction medium containing the alcohol and triethylamine.[407]

296. Alcoholysis of Trihalo Ketones (Haloform Reaction)

$$RCOCH_3 \xrightarrow[CH_3OH, KOH]{Ca(OCl)_2} RCOCCl_3 \xrightarrow[KOH]{CH_3OH} RCO_2CH_3 + CHCl_3$$

An 80% yield of a methyl ester has been obtained directly by the haloform reaction on an acetyltetralin, $ArCOCH_3$, in aqueous methanolic solvent.[379] The intermediate trihalo ketone apparently reacts more rapidly with methanol than with water. Another example is the cleavage of α,α,α-trichloroacetophenone, $C_6H_5COCCl_3$, by alcoholic sodium ethoxide solution to give ethyl benzoate (85%).[382]

297. Acidolysis of Esters

$$C_2H_5O_2C(CH_2)_nCO_2C_2H_5 + HO_2C(CH_2)_nCO_2H \overset{H^+}{\rightleftharpoons} C_2H_5O_2C(CH_2)_nCO_2H$$

The acid-catalyzed equilibrium of a dibasic acid with its mono- and di-esters furnishes a means of preparation of alkyl hydrogen esters of most aliphatic α,ω-dibasic acids.[356,358] A mixture of the acid and its dialkyl ester is refluxed with concentrated hydrochloric acid and dibutyl ether, and the acid ester is isolated by fractional distillation or extraction techniques. Excellent directions are given for the acid esters of adipic,[357] sebacic,[355] and azelaic[417] acids.

298. Carbethoxylation of Compounds Containing an Active Hydrogen Atom

$$RCOCH_2R' \xrightarrow{NaH} (RCOCHR')^-Na^+ \xrightarrow[CH_3CO_2H]{CO(OC_2H_5)_2;} RCOCH(R')CO_2C_2H_5$$

This is an excellent general method for the introduction of a carbethoxyl group in place of an active hydrogen atom in a molecule. Most ketones give moderate yields of *β-keto esters* by heating with sodium ethoxide in a large excess of dialkyl carbonate.[325] The stronger bases, sodium triphenylmethide[322] and sodium amide,[320,329] are useful in carbethoxylations of certain less reactive ketones. Sodium hydride has been employed extensively in this reaction.[326,327,336] An excess of basic reagent gives improved yields. An olefinic ketone, 5-hepten-2-one, has been converted to ethyl 3-oxo-6-octenoate in 85% yield by the action of sodium hydride and ethyl carbonate.[328]

The enolates of simple esters add to diethyl carbonate to give *malonic esters*.[321,324,336] The reaction is valuable in the preparation of "mixed" malonic esters.[323]

$$RCH_2CO_2R' \xrightarrow[(C_2H_5O)_2CO]{NaC(C_6H_5)_3;} RCH(CO_2R')CO_2C_2H_5$$

Excess diethyl carbonate acts as an alkylating agent under certain conditions, thus replacing the remaining active hydrogen of the malonic ester by an ethyl group.[334]

α-Cyano esters are synthesized by this method from nitriles. Phenylacetonitrile, $C_6H_5CH_2CN$, is carboxylated in 79% yield by diethyl carbonate and sodium ethoxide or sodium amide.[331] Simple aliphatic nitriles give lower yields of the corresponding α-cyano esters.[333,335]

Methyl groups in the *alpha* and *gamma* positions on the pyridine and quinoline nuclei are carbethoxylated in low yield by sodium amide and diethyl carbonate.[330]

1-Acetylenes condense with diethyl carbonate in the presence of sodium ethoxide to substitute a carbethoxyl group in place of the acetylenic hydrogen atom. The condensation is followed, however, by the addition of alcohol to the triple bond.[332]

Carbethoxylations of esters[217,337] and nitriles[338] are also effected by treating their enolates with ethyl chlorocarbonate (ethyl chloroformate), $ClCO_2C_2H_5$. In this manner, triethyl methanetricarboxylate, $CH(CO_2C_2H_5)_3$, is prepared from malonic ester through the magnesium enolate.[339,431]

299. Alkylation of Esters

$$R_2CHCO_2C_2H_5 \xrightarrow[R'x]{(C_6H_5)_3CNa} R_2R'CCO_2C_2H_5$$

Alkylation of disubstituted acetic esters has become an important new route to trisubstituted acetic acids and their derivatives. Sodium triphenylmethide[216,217] or potassium triphenylmethide[215] is used to convert the ester to its enolate ion, which, in turn, is allowed to react with an alkyl iodide to form the trialkylated ester. The yields are in the range of 42-61%. Potassium hydroxide in acetal solvents serves as basic reagent in the alkylation of certain esters by reactive halides.[409] An interesting preparation of diethyl tetramethylsuccinate involves alkylation of ethyl isobutyrate with ethyl α-bromoisobutyrate. The yield is 30%.[217]

Esters having two α-hydrogen atoms give poor yields of alkylated product partly because of their greater tendency for self-condensation to β-keto esters (method 211). Ethyl isovalerate, however, has been ethylated in 33% yield by treatment with sodium triphenylmethide and ethyl benzenesulfonate.[217]

Monoalkylation of malonic ester proceeds much more readily than alkylation of simple esters. The enolate is formed from diethyl malonate and alcoholic sodium ethoxide solution. Alkylation is effected in good yield by the use of primary bromides,[233,235] diethyl sulfate,[236] or ethyl *p*-toluenesulfonate.[239] In addition to the simpler primary alkylmalonates listed in Table 51, many higher members have been prepared. The list includes substituted malonates made from diethyl malonate and the following halides in the yields stated: s-butyl (84%),[234,238] n-amyl (80%),[240] isoamyl (54%),[238] n-hexyl (73%),[237] cyclopentyl (56%),[238,252] cyclohexyl (44%),[251] γ-cyclopentylpropyl (83%),[249] benzyl (57%),[241] β-phenylethyl (65%),[253] α-naphthylmethyl (82%),[242] furfuryl (76%),[244] tetrahydrofurfuryl (70%),[32] and 2-pyridyl (19%).[243]

Dialkylation of malonic ester proceeds in most cases almost as readily as monoalkylation. Diethyl ethylmalonate is alkylated equally well by s-octyl[247] and n-butyl[254] halides. Di-n-propylmalonic ester is prepared in one step from malonic ester and n-propyl bromide.[248] Methylmalonic ester is alkylated by β-phenylethyl bromide,[246] and even α-naphthyl-malonic ester may be further alkylated by n-alkyl iodides.[147] Difficulty is encountered, however, in introducing two s-alkyl groups into malonic ester. A 23% yield of diisopropylmalonic ester is obtained from iso-propylmalonic ester, sodium triphenylmethide, and isopropyl iodide.[245]

Alkylation of malonic ester with an equimolar portion of ethylene bromide or trimethylene bromide produces ring closure to give diethyl esters of 1,1-cyclopropane- and 1,1-cyclobutane-dicarboxylic acids, respectively.[257,259] Five- and six-membered rings also have been formed in this manner.[260]

$$CH_2(CO_2C_2H_5)_2 \xrightarrow[Br(CH_2)_3Br]{NaOC_2H_5;} \begin{array}{c} H_2C-CH_2 \\ | \quad\quad | \\ H_2C-C(CO_2C_2H_5)_2 \end{array}$$

The yields are low because of a competing reaction between two molecules of malonic ester and one molecule of the dihalide to give open-chain tetra-carboxylic esters, $(C_2H_5O_2C)_2CH(CH_2)_nCH(CO_2C_2H_5)_2$. The latter esters may be made in fair yields by using an excess of malonic ester in the reaction.[262] Unique ring closures are produced by further alkylation re-actions of these open-chain esters.[261,262]

$$(C_2H_5O_2C)_2CH(CH_2)_2CH(CO_2C_2H_5)_2 \xrightarrow[CH_2Br_2]{NaOC_2H_5;}$$

$$(C_2H_5O_2C)_2CH(CH_2)_3CH(CO_2C_2H_5)_2 \xrightarrow[COBr_2]{Na;}$$

An improved yield of diethyl 1,1-cyclobutanedicarboxylate is obtained by preparing the intermediate haloalkylmalonic ester, $Br(CH_2)_3CH(CO_2C_2H_5)_2$, by the "reverse" addition of hydrogen bromide to allylmalonic ester. Cyclization is then effected by sodium ethoxide.[258]

Alkylation of malonic esters by halo esters leads to tricarboxylic esters. The halogen atom of the alkylating halo ester has been in the *alpha*,[282,284] *beta*,[285] and *delta*[274] positions.

Olefinic malonic esters are obtained directly by alkylation with olefinic halides[252,255] or by alkylation of alkylidenemalonic esters obtained from the Knoevenagel condensation[256] (method 37).

$$RCH_2CH = C(CO_2C_2H_5)_2 \xrightarrow[R'X]{NaOC_2H_5;} RCH = CHC(R') (CO_2C_2H_5)_2$$

An interesting preparation of 2-cyclohexenylmalonates involves alkylation of malonic esters with 1,2-dibromocyclohexane. Dehydrohalogenation accompanies alkylation to give the olefinic malonates in 55–65% yields.[250,307]

Fair yields of *halomalonic esters* are obtained by alkylation of malonic esters with ethylene bromide,[263,266] o-chlorobenzyl halides,[264] and 1-bromo-4-chlorobutane.[265]

Other groups which may be present in the alkylating agent include *alkoxyl, keto, cyano, diethylamino,* and *nitro.* Many alkylations have been made with halo ethers in which the ether group is in the *alpha*,[267,272,275] *beta*,[273,276] *gamma*,[274] *delta*,[279] or *epsilon*[277] positions of an aliphatic chain or on an aromatic nucleus.[278] Similarly, α-halo ketones such as chloroacetone,[269] bromopinacolone,[271] and α-bromoethyl methyl ketone[270] give good yields of γ-ketomalonic esters. α-Bromoisobutyraldehyde also has been used as an alkylating agent,[268] as have p-nitrobenzyl chloride,[283] diethylaminopropyl bromide hydrobromide,[281] δ-bromovaleronitrile,[280] and 2-chloro-2-nitropropane.[410]

300. Addition of Carboxylic Acids to Unsaturated Compounds

$$(CH_3)_2C = CH_2 + RCO_2H \rightleftharpoons RCO_2C(CH_3)_3$$

Several acids have been esterified by reaction with propene,[306] isobutylene, and trimethylethylene.[303] The reaction is reversible and catalyzed by sulfuric acid or boron trifluoride. The optimum conditions for maximum conversion are low reaction temperature, large quantity of catalyst, and anhydrous conditions.[303] By this method, the *keto ester, t*-butyl o-benzoyl benzoate,[303] and the *halo esters, t*-butyl and isopropyl trichloroacetates,[304,306] have been prepared.

The addition of carboxylic acids to acetylenes leads to *alkenyl esters* in 30–68% yields.[305]

$$RCO_2H + R'C \equiv CH \rightarrow RCO_2C(R') = CH_2$$

Reaction takes place at $0-30°$ in the presence of boron trifluoride and mercuric oxide. The reaction is reversible in the presence of mercury salts and allows the preparation of vinyl esters from vinyl acetate and higher-molecular-weight carboxylic acids.[418]

301. Addition of Compounds Containing an Active Hydrogen Atom to Olefinic Compounds (Michael)

$$C_6H_5COCH = CHC_6H_5 + CH_2(CO_2C_2H_5)_2 \xrightarrow{\text{Base}}$$

$$C_6H_5COCH_2CH(C_6H_5)CH(CO_2C_2H_5)_2$$

The addition of malonic ester to benzalacetophenone is an illustration of a very general base-catalyzed condensation. The olefinic compound taking part in the reaction may be one in which the double bond is in the *alpha* position of an aldehyde,[311] ketone,[308,312,315,316,416] ester,[308-310,317-319,415] cyanide (method 388), sulfone,[340] or nitro compound.[414] The vinyl group in the *alpha* or *gamma* positions on the pyridine nucleus also undergoes this type of addition.[314] The activity of the labilizing group is transmitted to the terminal double bond of a vinylogous system. Thus, methyl vinylacrylate reacts with malonic ester as follows:[313]

$$CH_2 = CHCH = CHCO_2CH_3 + CH_2(CO_2CH_3)_2 \rightarrow$$

$$CH_2[CH(CO_2CH_3)_2] \ CH = CHCH_2CO_2CH_3$$

In addition to malonic, acetoacetic, and cyanoacetic esters, compounds furnishing the active hydrogen atom are nitro paraffins,[310,414-416] benzyl cyanide,[318] malononitrile,[316] cyanoacetamide,[316] sulfones,[312] methylpyridines,[319] and ketones.[315]

Five experimental procedures employing sodium alkoxide or piperidine catalysts are compared for a number of varied condensations.[308] Secondary amines are mild catalysts which seldom lead to by-products but which do not always effect condensation. Sodium ethoxide catalyst sometimes gives rearranged products.[315] Potassium hydroxide in acetal solvents is the most convenient reagent for a number of condensations.[409]

302. Addition of Grignard Reagents to Olefinic Esters

$$\begin{array}{c} CHCO_2C_2H_5 \\ \| \\ CHCO_2C_2H_5 \end{array} \xrightarrow[\text{H}_2\text{O}]{\text{R}_2\text{CHMgX};} \begin{array}{c} R_2CHCHCO_2C_2H_5 \\ | \\ CH_2CO_2C_2H_5 \end{array}$$

Organometallic reagents react with olefinic esters by both 1,2 and 1,4 addition. The latter process leads to saturated esters and is exhibited by diethyl fumarate and to a greater extent by ethylenetetracarboxylic ester, $(C_2H_5O_2C)_2C = C(CO_2C_2H_5)_2$. These substances are starting materials for the synthesis of alkyl- and aryl-substituted succinic esters.[421,422]

This reaction serves as an indirect method for the introduction of a tertiary alkyl group into malonic and cyanoacetic esters. The yields are 42-75%.[420]

$$R_2C = C(CN)CO_2C_2H_5 \xrightarrow[H_2O]{R'MgX;} R_2R'CCH(CN)CO_2C_2H_5$$

Direct alkylation of these esters by tertiary halides is unsatisfactory because the halides undergo dehydrohalogenation.

303. Reduction of Olefinic Esters

$$RCH = CHCO_2C_2H_5 \xrightarrow[Pt]{H_2} RCH_2CH_2CO_2C_2H_5$$

Olefinic esters are quantitatively hydrogenated over platinum catalysts.[231,293,296] Palladium catalysts have been used with equal success in the hydrogenation of substituted cinnamic esters.[297]

Catalytic hydrogenation of the olefinic esters obtained in the Knoevenagel and Stobbe condensations (method 37) is valuable for the preparation of alkylmalonates and alkylsuccinates, particularly for those having branching in the alkyl group.

$$R_2C = C(CO_2C_2H_5)_2 \xrightarrow[Ni]{H_2} R_2CHCH(CO_2C_2H_5)_2$$

Hydrogenation is effected over Raney nickel at 100-130 atm.[292] Low-pressure hydrogenation over palladium catalysts has also been used for the succinates.[294]

304. Reduction of Aromatic Esters

$$C_6H_5CO_2C_2H_5 \xrightarrow[Ni \text{ or } Pt]{H_2} C_6H_{11}CO_2C_2H_5$$

Ester groups in compounds containing an aromatic nucleus are stable during the catalytic hydrogenation of the nucleus over platinum catalysts at low temperatures and pressures or over nickel catalysts at high temperatures and pressures (method 4). Cyclohexanecarboxylic ester[218,219] and cyclohexanedicarboxylic esters[220,221] are made in this manner. Phenolic esters are best reduced by Raney nickel catalysts in alcoholic solution containing sodium ethoxide[224] (method 86).

305. Direct Oxidation of Aldehydes and Ketones

$$RCOR' \xrightarrow{C_6H_5 CO_3H} RCO_2R'$$

An unusual oxidation of certain aldehydes and ketones occurs with *per*acids. A carbon-to-carbon linkage of the carbonyl compound is broken and an oxygen atom introduced between the two resulting fragments. Esters have been prepared in 63–73% yields from several simple cycloalkyl and aryl alkyl ketones by reaction at room temperature with perbenzoic acid.[374] The larger radical of the ketone appears as the alcohol fragment of the ester. Cyclic ketones are oxidized by potassium persulfate and sulfuric acid to esters from which ω-hydroxy aliphatic esters are obtained upon hydrolysis and reesterification.[375] Peracetic acid in acetic anhydride converts salicylaldehyde to o-hydroxyphenyl formate (88%).[376]

306. Intermolecular Oxidation-Reduction of Aldehydes (Tischenko)

$$2RCHO \xrightarrow{Al(OC_2H_5)_3} RCO_2CH_2R$$

This dismutation resembles the Cannizzaro reaction (cf. method 81) but is applicable to aldehydes which also contain an α-hydrogen atom. Aluminum alkoxides are the most effective catalysts for the reaction; only a few mole per cent is required. The yields of esters from aliphatic aldehydes containing two to eight carbon atoms are in the range of 69–100%.[208,209] With more basic catalysts such as $Mg(OC_2H_5)_2$ or $Mg[Al(OC_2H_5)_4]_2$ aldol condensation occurs followed by a crossed Tischenko reaction between and the aldol and the original aldehyde. The products are mono esters of 1,3-diols, $RCH_2CHOHCHRCH_2O_2CCH_2R$.[208] The highly basic sodium alkoxides produce only aldol-condensation products with these aldehydes. However, with benzaldehyde, which does not have an α-hydrogen atom, dismutation to benzyl benzoate occurs in 93% yield.[207] Similarly, furfural is condensed to furfuryl furoate in 78% yield.[214]

307. Cleavage of α-Keto Esters

$$RCH(CO_2C_2H_5)COCO_2C_2H_5 \xrightarrow{160-175^\circ} RCH(CO_2C_2H_5)_2 + CO$$

The Claisen condensation of diethyl oxalate with esters of fatty acids (cf. method 211) produces α-ethoxalyl esters which are thermally decarbonylated to *alkylmalonic* esters. The over-all yields range from 78% to 91% for the conversion of fatty esters up to ethyl stearate.[346] Phenylmalonic ester is made in 85% yield.[341] Powdered glass is sometimes used as a catalyst for the decarbonylation.[147,345] α-Furylacetates[28] and α-thienylacetates[345] undergo the condensation and thermal cleavage to give the corresponding malonates in 34–38% yields.

Acylation of ketones by diethyl oxalate (cf. method 203) gives α,γ-diketo esters from which *β-keto esters* are obtained by pyrolysis at 175° over powdered glass and powdered iron.[343,344]

$$RCOCH_2COCO_2C_2H_5 \xrightarrow[\text{and iron, }175°]{\text{Powdered glass}} RCOCH_2CO_2C_2H_5 + CO$$

308. Cleavage of β-Keto Esters

$$RCOCH_2CO_2C_2H_5 \xrightarrow[XCH_2CO_2C_2H_5]{NaOC_2H_5;} \begin{array}{c} RCOCHCO_2C_2H_5 \\ | \\ CH_2CO_2C_2H_5 \end{array} \xrightarrow[C_2H_5OH,\ H^+]{H_2O,\ H^+;}$$

$$RCOCH_2CH_2CO_2C_2H_5$$

The introduction of an ester group by the acetoacetic ester synthesis (cf. methods 184 and 213) is possible by alkylation of β-keto esters with halo esters.[347,348] Cleavage of the alkylated products by mineral acids furnishes an important route to *γ-keto* acids and *esters.*[349,350]

α,α-Dialkylacetoacetic esters are cleaved to esters by a hot solution of sodium ethoxide in absolute ethanol.

$$CH_3COCRR'CO_2C_2H_5 \xrightarrow[C_2H_5OH]{NaOC_2H_5} RR'CHCO_2C_2H_5$$

The yields of *dialkylacetates* are 74–82% when R and R' are combinations of n-, iso-, and s-butyl groups.[353] This interesting cleavage has been used to prepare *ethoxy esters* from ethoxy halides of the type $C_2H_5O(CH_2)_nX$[351,352] as well as α-methyladipic ester from the corresponding cyclic β-keto ester (83%).[354]

309. Cleavage of Lactones

$$RCH(CH_2)_nCO \xrightarrow[H^+]{C_2H_5OH} RCHOH(CH_2)_nCO_2C_2H_5$$

Alcoholysis of lactones leads to *hydroxy esters*. The reaction is well illustrated by the conversion of α-ethyl-γ-butyrolactone to ethyl α-ethyl-γ-hydroxybutyrate (84%).[225] The lactone is allowed to stand with ethanol saturated with dry hydrogen chloride. By treating the appropriate lactones with ethanolic hydrogen bromide, *halo esters* having bromine in the gamma,[226] delta,[227] or epsilon[228] positions are obtained. Phosphorus pentabromide is sometimes used for this purpose; bromoacyl bromides are formed, and are esterified by mixing with alcohol.[226,230] Chlorine is substituted for tertiary hydroxyl groups when ethanolic hydrogen chloride is used to open the lactone ring. Chloro esters having a tertiary γ-chlorine atom are best prepared, however, by treating the lactones with thionyl chloride in refluxing benzene followed by stirring with alcoholic hydrogen chloride.[231]

β-Propiolactone, CH_2CH_2CO, is an important source of β-substituted

propionic acids and esters,[232] Aqueous solutions of sodium halides give β-halo acids, and aqueous sodium acetate gives β-acetoxypropionic acid. Alcohols open this lactone ring in either of two ways, depending upon the nature of the catalyst; β-hydroxypropionic esters are formed by basic catalysts and β-alkoxypropionic acids by acid catalysts.

310. Decarboxylation of Alkyl Hydrogen Malonates and Dialkyl Malonates

$$RCHO + CH_2(CO_2H)CO_2C_2H_5 \xrightarrow[C_5H_5N]{-CO_2} RCH=CHCO_2C_2H_5$$

Olefinic esters are obtained directly by the Knoevenagel condensation (cf. method 37) of ethyl hydrogen malonate with an aliphatic[289] or aromatic[286] aldehyde.

Certain dialkylmalonates may be partially saponified to the acid esters, which decarboxylate to esters upon heating.[245] Decarbethoxylation of dialkylmalonic esters may also be effected by heating at 220–230° with sodium ethoxide.

$$R_2C(CO_2C_2H_5)_2 \xrightarrow[220-230°]{NaOC_2H_5} R_2CHCO_2C_2H_5$$

This method is illustrated by the preparation of ethyl diethylacetate (67%).[287] A similar modification involves the treatment of the disubstituted malonic ester with metallic sodium or potassium in ether. In this way di-n-propylacetic ester is obtained in 61% yield.[299]

311. Action of Carboxylic Acids on Diazoketones

$$RCOCHN_2 + R'CO_2H \rightarrow RCOCH_2O_2CR' + N_2$$

Esters of α-hydroxymethyl ketones are formed by heating diazoketones with organic acids.[202,388] The crude diazoketones prepared from acyl halides and diazomethane may be used. The over-all yields of acetoxy ketones, $ArCOCH_2O_2CCH_3$, from benzoyl and β-naphthoyl chlorides are 55% and 72%, respectively.[388]

312. Action of Organometallic Reagents on Alkyl Carbonates

$$CO(OC_2H_5)_2 \xrightarrow[H_2O]{RMgX;} RCO_2C_2H_5$$

This reaction has been used infrequently for the preparation of esters. Simultaneous reaction of the Grignard reagent with the ester formed leads to tertiary alcohols (method 91). However, if the organometallic reagent is relatively unreactive[210,213] or if it is added to an excess of ethyl carbonate,[211,212] esters may be isolated. A typical example is the preparation of ethyl α-naphthoate (73%).[210]

313. Rearrangement of α-Halo Ketones (Favorsky)

$$R_2CBrCOR' + NaOR' \rightarrow R_3CCO_2R' + NaBr$$

Certain α-halo ketones undergo rearrangement with sodium alkoxides in anhydrous ether to form esters.[329,390,419] Methyl α-bromoisopropyl ketone and sodium ethoxide give ethyl trimethylacetate (61%).[391] Ring contraction occurs with α-chlorocyclohexanone to give cyclopentanecarboxylic ester (53%).[329]

When α,α'-dibromo ketones are treated under the same conditions, rearrangement and dehydrohalogenation take place; α,β-olefinic esters are formed in 46–84% yield.[389]

$$RR'CBrCOCHBrR'' \xrightarrow{NaOCH_3} RR'C=CR''CO_2CH_3$$

Similarly, α,β-dibromo ketones yield β,γ-olefinic esters in most cases.[392]

$$RCHBrC(CH_3)BrCOCH_3 \xrightarrow{NaOCH_3} RCH=C(CH_3)CH_2CO_2CH_3$$

Action of other basic reagents on the halo ketones is complicated by accompanying metathetical reactions.[394,395]

314. Pyrolysis of Tetramethylammonium Salts

$$ArC\bar{O}_2\overset{+}{N}(CH_3)_4 \xrightarrow{250°} ArCO_2CH_3$$

Methyl esters of sterically hindered ortho substituted benzoic acids are prepared in 63–90% yields by this reaction[426] (cf. method 285).

315. Addition of Acyl Halides or Anhydrides to Aldehydes

$$RCHO + (R'CO)_2O \xrightarrow{BF_3} RCH(OCOCH_3)_2$$

Acylals are formed by the addition of simple anhydrides to aliphatic or aromatic aldehydes.[199] The reaction occurs at 0–5° in the presence of boron trifluoride etherate. Yields are in the range of 65% to 81%.[383] A similar addition of acyl chlorides to aldehydes produces α-*haloalkyl esters* in 40–70% yield.[384,385]

$$RCHO + R'COCl \xrightarrow{ZnCl_2} R'CO_2CHClR$$

316. Cleavage of Ethers by Acyl Halides[424]

$$ROR \xrightarrow[BF_3]{R'COCl} R'CO_2R$$

317. Electrolysis of Acid Esters[425]

$$RCO_2H + HO_2C(CH_2)_nCO_2CH_3 \longrightarrow \begin{cases} R(CH_2)_nCO_2CH_3 \\ CH_3O_2C(CH_2)_{2n}CO_2CH_3 \end{cases}$$

318. Addition of Diazoacetic Ester to Unsaturated Compounds[386,387]

$$C_6H_5CH = CH_2 \xrightarrow{N_2CHCO_2C_2H_5} C_6H_5CH \overset{\displaystyle CH_2}{\underset{}{\diagdown\!\!\diagup}} CHCO_2C_2H_5$$

319. Decomposition of Diazonium Salts by Carboxylic Acids (cf. method 93)

$$Ar\overset{+}{N}_2Cl^- \xrightarrow{HBF_4} ArN_2^+BF_4^- \xrightarrow{CH_3CO_2H} ArO_2CCH_3$$

320. Reduction of α- and β-Keto Esters[427]

$$RCOCH_2CO_2C_2H_5 \xrightarrow[ZnCl_2]{CH_3SH} RC(SCH_3)_2CH_2CO_2C_2H_5 \xrightarrow[Ni]{C_2H_5OH} RCH_2CH_2CO_2C_2H_5$$

321. Alcoholysis of Benzotrihalides[428]

$$ArCX_3 \xrightarrow[H_2SO_4]{ROH} ArCO_2R \quad (52\text{--}90\%)$$

322. Reduction of Arylchloromalonates[430]

$$CO(CO_2C_2H_5)_2 \xrightarrow[H_2O]{ArMgX;} ArCOH(CO_2C_2H_5)_2 \xrightarrow[H_2,\ Pd]{SOCl_2;} ArCH(CO_2C_2H_5)_2$$

TABLE 50. MONOCARBOXYLIC ESTERS

C_n	Compound	Method	Yield (%)	Chapter[ref.]	B.p./mm., n_D^t, (M.p.), Deriv.
		Aliphatic Monocarboxylic Esters			
C_3	Ethyl formate	285	70	14[402]	55
C_4	Ethyl acetate	285	85	14[22]	78
	n-Propyl formate	285	84	14[402]	80-83
C_6	Methyl trimethylacetate	286	50	14[82]	100/731, 1.3895
	n-Butyl acetate	285	90	14[50]	125/756
	t-Butyl acetate	286	68	14[79]	97
		286	55	14[80]	96/740
		287	60	14[116]	96
		288	89	14[137]	95
		300	85	14[303]	97/766, 1.3842[26]
C_7	Ethyl n-valerate	293	90	14[151]	142-146
	Methyl dimethylethylacetate	313	57	14[391]	126/730, 1.4021, 106Am
	Methyl t-butylacetate	286	94	14[82]	128/735, 1.3997
	Ethyl trimethylacetate	299	55	14[216]	117, 153Am
		313	61	14[391]	116/725, 1.3912, 154Am
	t-Butyl propionate	286	61	14[79]	118
	t-Amyl acetate	288	89	14[137]	124
C_8	Methyl methyl-t-butylacetate	313	73	14[390]	95/150, 1.4116
	Ethyl diethylacetate	310	67	14[287]	149
	Ethyl dimethylethylacetate	286	63	14[81]	141/744, 1.4025
		299	58	14[215]	141, 102Am
	n-Butyl n-butyrate	285	47†	14[10]	162-166
		306	82	14[208]	
	t-Butyl isobutyrate	286	71	14[79]	128
	2-Ethylbutyl acetate	287	80	14[120]	161/750, 1.4119[17]
C_9	Ethyl α-ethylisovalerate	299	33	14[217]	165
	Ethyl methyldiethylacetate	286	64	14[81]	73/35, 1.4130
	t-Butyl isovalerate	286	26	14[79]	156
C_{15}	Methyl myristate	294	....	14[180]	160/10, 1.4353[25]
C_{17}	Methyl palmitate	294	....	14[180]	181/10, (30)
		Alicyclic Monocarboxylic Esters			
C_6	Methyl cyclopropylacetate	292	79	14[412]	132/745, 1.4175[23]
	Cyclopentyl formate	285	46	14[25]	138/762, 1.4321
C_7	Cyclohexyl formate	285	60	14[25]	160/757, 1.4431
C_8	Ethyl cyclopentanecarboxylate	312	49	14[211]	89/45, 1.4360
	Cyclohexyl acetate	285	53	14[25]	172/752, 1.4417
		305	67	14[374]	76/23, 1.4401[25]

TABLE 50. MONOCARBOXYLIC ESTERS   501

TABLE 50 *(continued)*

C_n	Compound	Method	Yield (%)	Chapter[ref.]	B.p./mm., n_D^t, (M.p.), Deriv.
		Alicyclic Monocarboxylic Esters *(continued)*			
C_9	Methyl cyclohexylacetate	285	93	14[19]	65/18, 1.4450[25]
	Methyl 1-methyl-1-cyclo-hexanecarboxylate	313	79	14[419]	35/3, 1.4456
	Ethyl cyclohexanecarboxylate (ethyl hexahydrobenzoate)	304	100	14[218]	85/16
C_{11}	Ethyl β-cyclohexylpropionate	304	97	14[222]	110/11
		Aromatic Monocarboxylic Esters			
C_8	Methyl benzoate	285	90	14[20]	83/12
		285	85	14[1]	196
		285	95	14[19]	1.5155[25]
		321	90	14[428]	200
	Phenyl acetate	286	92	14[88]	76/8
		287	99	14[119]	195/764
		288	89	14[137]	191
		305	63	14[374]	93/22, 1.5200[25]
C_9	Methyl phenylacetate	285	90	14[4]	220, 102Am
	Phenyl propionate	286	92	14[88]	100/16
		305	73	14[374]	99/18, 1.5003
C_{10}	Ethyl phenylacetate	293	87	14[144]	125/18
	n-Propyl benzoate	321	81	14[428]	230
	Isopropyl benzoate	285	60	14[1]	208
		300	88	14[306]	216/747, 1.4890[25]
	Phenyl n-butyrate	286	98	14[88]	107/13
	Phenyl isobutyrate	286	83	14[86]	211/707
	p-Ethylphenyl acetate	287	92	14[113]	121/20, 1.4970[25]
C_{11}	Methyl α-phenylbutyrate	293	90	14[150]	226
	Methyl 2,4,6-trimethylbenzoate	285	78	14[18]	115/7, 1.5083
	Ethyl p-ethylbenzoate	285	96	14[380]	127/16, 1.5065[25]
	n-Butyl benzoate	285	87	14[1]	248
	s-Butyl benzoate	285	27	14[1]	232
	Isobutyl benzoate	285	81	14[1]	235
	t-Butyl benzoate	286	80	14[78]	112/18, 1.4896[25]
		300	35	14[303]	79/3, 1.4893[23]
	p-Ethylbenzyl acetate	290	93	14[188]	131/15, 1.5042[25]
C_{12}	Ethyl 2-phenylcyclopropanecarboxylate	318	68	14[386]	131/10
	α-Naphthyl acetate	286	96	14[88]	(47)
		287	99	14[119]	(49)

For explanations and symbols see pp. xi–xii.

TABLE 50 *(continued)*

C_n	Compound	Method	Yield (%)	Chapter[ref.]	B.p./mm., n_D^t, (M.p.), Deriv.

Aromatic Monocarboxylic Esters *(continued)*

C_n	Compound	Method	Yield (%)	Chapter[ref.]	B.p./mm., n_D^t, (M.p.), Deriv.
C_{12}	β-Naphthyl acetate	286	96	14[88]	(70)
		287	100	14[119]	(72)
		305	67	14[374]	(68)
C_{13}	Ethyl p-isopropylphenyl-acetate	293	56	14[152]	135/12
	Ethyl α-Naphthoate	312	73	14[210]	144/3
	Phenyl benzoate	286	93	14[88]	(70)
		321	83	14[428]	(70)
	α-Naphthyl propionate	286	95	14[83]	135/2, 1.5811[25]
C_{14}	Ethyl p-t-butylphenyl-acetate	285	18[†]	14[65]	95/0.5
	Ethyl α-naphthylacetate	293	67	14[147]	181/15
		295	82	14[206]	177/11
	Phenyl phenylacetate	286	93	14[88]	(40)
	Benzyl benzoate	306	93	14[207]	185/15
	4-Acetoxybiphenyl	287	100	14[110]	(88)
C_{16}	Methyl diphenylmethyl-acetate	286	70	14[85]	150/3, 1.5691
	Ethyl diphenylacetate	310	81	14[287]	187/20, (61)
		312	52	14[213]	(59)
	Ethyl 2-biphenylacetate	293	100	14[145]	180-185/15
	1-Acetoxyphenanthrene	287	100	14[109]	(134)
	4-Acetoxyphenanthrene	287	100	14[109]	(60)

Heterocyclic Monocarboxylic Esters

C_n	Compound	Method	Yield (%)	Chapter[ref.]	B.p./mm., n_D^t, (M.p.), Deriv.
C_6	Methyl furoate	285	73	14[29]	76/20, 1.4875
C_7	Methyl α-furylacetate	285	80	14[28]	75/11
	Ethyl tetrahydrofuran-2-carboxylate	554	97	39[95]	82/11, 1.4445[18]*, 80 Am*
	Furfuryl acetate	287	93	14[114]	70/7
	2 Thenyl-acetate	290	56	14[406]	97/12, 1.5140[25]
	N-Carbethoxypyrrole	558	88	39[171]	180
	Methyl nicotinate	285	60	14[31]	72/3
C_8	Ethyl 2-methyl-3-furoate	562	60	39[42]	85-89/25
	Ethyl 2-thienylacetate	293	66	14[146]	120/23
		295	68	14[205]	124-129/26
	Ethyl α-pyrroleacetate	318	16	14[387]	129/15, 1.4963[19]
	Ethyl picolinate	285	30	14[27]	95/5
		293	40	14[405]	126/15, 1.5108
	Ethyl nicotinate	285	61	14[27]	84/5
		286	90	14[84]	104/5
	Ethyl isonicotinate	285	30	14[27]	79/5, (23)
		....	20[†]	14[377]	107-113/16

TABLE 51. DICARBOXYLIC ESTERS   503

TABLE 50 *(continued)*

C_n	Compound	Method	Yield (%)	Chapter[ref.]	B.p./mm., n_D^t, (M.p.), Deriv.
		Heterocyclic Monocarboxylic Esters *(continued)*			
C_8	3-Carbethoxypiperidine	554	80	39^{95}	85/5
C_9	Ethyl β-(tetrahydrofuryl)-propionate	285	69	14^{32}	105/11, 1.4425^{15}
	Ethyl 2-(α-tetrahydrofuryl)-propanoate	554	92	39^{98}	106/10
	Ethyl α-(1-pyrrolidyl)-propionate	436	92	24^{169}	84/12, 1.4450^{25}
	Ethyl 2-pyridylacetate	285	40 †	14^{399}	136/28, 1.4979^{25}
		298	25	14^{330}	130/21
	Ethyl β-piperidylacetate	293	30	14^{149}	102/6, 1.4643^{25}
	Ethyl piperidinoacetate	554	100	39^{116}	212/736
C_{10}	Furfuryl furoate	306	78	14^{214}	121/1.5, 1.5280
C_{11}	Ethyl 5-(α-furyl)-valerate	285	90	14^{30}	133/16
	Ethyl 5-(α-tetrahydrofuryl)-valerate	554	90	39^{98}	131/10
	Methyl thianaphthene-2-acetate	295	65	14^{204}	112/0.01
	Ethyl indole-2-carboxylate	572	80	39^{65}	(123)
C_{12}	Ethyl 2-benzofurylacetate	295	64	14^{408}	148/8, 1.5400, (18), 164Am
C_{13}	Ethyl α-quinolylacetate	298	36	14^{330}	176/10, 153Pi
	Ethyl 8-quinolineacetate	293	91	14^{148}	159/3
C_{15}	1-Carbethoxycarbazole	557	75	39^{158}	(107)

For explanations and symbols see pp. xi–xii.

TABLE 51. DICARBOXYLIC ESTERS

C_n	Compound	Method	Yield (%)	Chapter[ref.]	B.p./mm., n_D^t, (M.p.)
		Aliphatic Dicarboxylic Esters			
C_3	Ethylene carbonate	294	55	14^{183}	
C_4	Dimethyl oxalate	285	76	14^{34}	(53)
	Trimethylene carbonate	294	65	14^{184}	135/4, (48)
C_5	Tetramethylene carbonate	294	54	14^{184}	(59)
C_6	Diethyl oxalate	285	83	14^{33}	107/25
		285	95	14^{15}	106/25
	Methyl α-acetoxypropionate	287	82	14^{117}	77/12, 1.4111
		288	96	14^{136}	68–73/14
	Ethylidene diacetate	315	65	14^{383}	55/10
	Glycol diacetate	290	73	14^{195}	186
	Pentamethylene carbonate	294	63	14^{184}	(46)

For explanations and symbols see pp. xi–xii.

TABLE 51 (continued)

C_n	Compound	Method	Yield (%)	Chapter[ref.]	B.p./mm., n_D^t, (M.p.)
				Aliphatic Dicarboxylic Esters (continued)	
C_6	Methyl α-carbomethoxyethyl carbonate	289	73	14^{368}	92/12, 1.4102
C_7	Diethyl malonate	293	62	14^{158}	195
	Methyl α-acetoxyisobutyrate	286	90	14^{90}	77/18, 1.413
	Ethyl α-acetoxypropionate	288	98	14^{136}	75/11
	Ethyl β-acetoxypropionate	286	....	14^{91}	34/0.3, 1.4163
	Propylidene diacetate	315	73	14^{383}	69/12
	Hexamethylene carbonate	294	67	14^{184}	(60)
	Tricarbomethoxymethane	298	42	14^{432}	(45)
C_8	Dimethyl adipate	285	87	14^{19}	113/13, 1.4265^{25}
	Diethyl methylmalonate	293	93	14^{155}	105/27
		299	83	14^{235}	96/16
		303	95	14^{292}	198
	Isopropyl α-acetoxypropionate	288	97	14^{136}	76/9
	Isobutylidene diacetate	315	80	14^{383}	75/10
	Tetramethylene acetate	290	95	14^{200}	106–112
C_9	Diethyl methylsuccinate	303	98	14^{292}	109/16
	Diethyl ethylmalonate	298	48	14^{336}	95/10
		298	45	14^{324}	95/13, 1.4170
		299	88	14^{236}	98/12, 1.4171
		299	61	14^{409}	200
		303	93	14^{292}	207
		307	78	14^{346}	89/10, 1.4157^{25}
	Diethyl dimethylmalonate	298	75	14^{217}	88/15
	Ethyl t-butyl malonate	298	54	14^{323}	94/17
	Di-s-butyl carbonate	294	30	14^{182}	75/18, 1.4039
	Di-t-butyl carbonate	289	41	14^{363}	158/767, (41)
	Methyl α-acetoxyhexoate	290	100	14^{193}	90–95/6
	1,4-Diacetoxy-2-methylbutane	303	100	14^{298}	116/17, 1.4330
	Propylidene dipropionate	315	73	14^{383}	111/10
C_{10}	Diethyl adipate	285	97	14^{35}	138/20
	Diethyl β-methylglutarate	285	92	14^{37}	122/16
	Diethyl isopropylmalonate	298	29	14^{336}	105/15
		299	56	14^{245}	218
	Ethyl t-butyl α-methylmalonate	298	72	14^{323}	95/14
	Di-n-butyl oxalate	285	95	14^{39}	100/2
	Tricarbethoxymethane	298	93	14^{431}	132/10, (29)
		298	90	14^{339}	137/12
C_{11}	Diethyl pimelate	285	38 †	14^{36}	152/22
	Diethyl α-methyladipate	308	83	14^{354}	134/18
	Ethyl α,α-dimethylglutarate	285	54	14^{38}	113/9, 1.4249^{32}
	Diethyl isopropylsuccinate	302	30	14^{421}	124/20, 1.4284
		303	97	14^{292}	111/8, 1.4237^{25}

TABLE 51. DICARBOXYLIC ESTERS 505

TABLE 51 (continued)

C_n	Compound	Method	Yield (%)	Chapter[ref.]	B.p./mm., n_D^t, (M.p.)
	Aliphatic Dicarboxylic Esters (continued)				
C_{11}	Diethyl n-butylmalonate	298	26	14[324]	137/21, 1.425
		299	90	14[233]	130–135/20
		303	95	14[292]	129/17
		307	91	14[346]	132/17, 1.4218[25]
	Diethyl s-butylmalonate	299	84	14[234]	110–120/18–20
	Diethyl diethylmalonate	298	36	14[334]	103/11, 1.4240
C_{12}	Diethyl tetramethylsuccinate	299	30	14[217]	120/15
	Alicyclic Dicarboxylic Esters				
C_9	Dimethyl cis-cyclopentane-1,2-dicarboxylate	290	80	14[194]	117/12
	Diethyl 1,1-cyclopropanedicarboxylate	299	40	14[259]	114/22, 1.4331
C_{10}	Dimethyl 1,3-cyclohexanedicarboxylate	304	90	14[221]	
	Dimethyl 1,4-cyclohexanedicarboxylate	304	95	14[220]	133/13
	Diethyl 1,1-cyclobutanedicarboxylate	299	74	14[258]	119–126/23, 1.433[26]
		299	42	14[257.]	102/11, 1.4359
	Diethyl cyclopropylmalonate	288	43	14[404]	78/3, 1.4315[24]
C_{12}	Diethyl cyclohexane-1,1-dicarboxylate	303	94	14[295]	112/5, 1.4438[25]
	cis-Diethyl hexahydrophthalate	287	70	14[108]	131/9, 1.4543[17]
	Aromatic and Heterocyclic Dicarboxylic Esters				
C_{10}	Methyl acetylsalicylate	287	95	14[107]	(49)
	o-Diacetoxybenzene (o-phenylene diacetate)	287	100	14[119]	(65)
	m-Diacetoxybenzene (m-phenylene diacetate)	286	92	14[88]	154/12
		287	95	14[119]	279/753
	p-Diacetoxybenzene	286	95	14[88]	(120)
		287	98	14[115]	(122)
C_{11}	Dimethyl phenylmalonate	307	61	14[341]	(49)
	Benzylidene diacetate	315	80	14[383]	135/10, (44)
	Diethyl α-thienylmalonate	307	38	14[345]	147/5
	2,3-Dicarbethoxypiperidine	554	77	39[95]	121/3
	2,6-Dicarbethoxypiperidine	554	66	39[95]	156/11
C_{12}	Ethyl α-acetoxyphenylacetate	293	85	14[159]	160/28
	2,4-Dimethyl-3,5-dicarbethoxypyrrole	563	64	39[38]	(137)

For explanations and symbols see pp. xi–xii.

TABLE 51 (continued)

C_n	Compound	Method	Yield (%)	Chapter[ref.]	B.p./mm., n_D^t, (M.p.)
Aromatic and Heterocyclic Dicarboxylic Esters (continued)					
C_{13}	Diethyl phenylmalonate	293	78	14^{154}	165/18
		298	64	14^{321}	129/2
		307	85	14^{341}	160/10
	Diphenyl carbonate	289	66	14^{367}	(81)
C_{14}	Diethyl m-phenylenediacetate	293	81	14^{157}	175–182/10
	Diethyl p-phenylenediacetate	293	73	14^{157}	(57)
C_{15}	Dimethyl α-naphthylmalonate	307	33	14^{342}	(104)
C_{17}	Diethyl α-naphthylmalonate	307	69	14^{147}	182/3, (62)
C_{19}	Diethyl diphenylmalonate	....	17	14^{287}	193/5, (63)

For explanations and symbols see pp. xi–xii.

TABLE 52. OLEFINIC ESTERS

C_n	Compound	Method	Yield (%)	Chapter[ref.]	B.p./mm., n_D^t, (M.p.), Deriv.
Aliphatic Olefinic Esters					
C_4	Methyl acrylate	24	84	2^{235}	80*
		35	79	2^{527}	
C_5	Methyl methacrylate	285	99	14^{400}	97–101
	Ethyl acrylate	24	33	2^{234}	
		294	99	14^{181}	43/103, 1.4068
	2-Acetoxy-1-propene	300	30	14^{305}	93/736, 1.4033
C_6	Methyl 3-pentenoate	293	73	14^{49}	128/625, 1.4217
	Methyl tiglate	285	65	14^{401}	138/757, 1.4371
	Methyl angelate	290	63	14^{401}	128/745, 1.4330
	Methyl 3-methyl-3-butenoate	290	47	14^{190}	41/27, 1.4168
	Methyl β,β-dimethylacrylate	313	58	14^{389}	60/50, 1.4382, 131An
	Ethyl methacrylate	23	90	2^{503}	120/760
	Allyl acrylate	24	43	2^{237}	122/760, 1.4295
	Dimethyl maleate	287	92	14^{121}	205
C_7	Methyl 2-hexenoate	285	98	14^{41}	57/13
	Ethyl α-methylcrotonate	20	78	2^{155}	56/15, 1.4347[17]
	(ethyl tiglate)	285	80	14^{401}	155/760, 1.4347
	Methyl 3-methyl-2-pentenoate (cis)	313	29	14^{389}	74/50, 1.4420, 82Am
	Methyl 3-methyl-2-pentenoate (trans)	313	22	14^{389}	79/50, 1.4446, 98Am

TABLE 52. OLEFINIC ESTERS 507

TABLE 52 (continued)

C_n	Compound	Method	Yield (%)	Chapter[ref.]	B.p./mm., n_D^t, (M.p.), Deriv.
		Aliphatic Olefinic Esters (continued)			
C_7	Methyl trans-3-methyl-3-pentenoate	313	55	14^{392}	74/50, 1.4306, 131Am
	Methyl β-methyl-β-ethylacrylate	20	80	2^{159}	49.5/11
	Allyl methacrylate	23	90	2^{503}	82/17
C_8	Methyl β-methyl-β-propylacrylate	20	90	2^{159}	57/12
	Ethyl 2-hexenoate	285	94	14^{41}	73/15
	Methyl β,β-diethylacrylate	20	87	2^{159}	57/11
	Ethyl 3-methyl-2-pentenoate	19	77	2^{89}	62/13
	Ethyl 4-methyl-2-pentenoate	285	79	14^{42}	60/13, 1.4341^{17}
		285	84	14^{40}	172, 1.4301^{25}
	Ethyl 3-methyl-3-pentenoate	19	43	2^{421}	58–63/14
	Ethyl α-ethylcrotonate	20	80	2^{155}	63/12, 1.4339^{17}
	Ethyl 2,3-dimethyl-2-butenoate	19	19	2^{420}	99/82, 1.4430
	Ethyl 2,3-dimethyl-3-butenoate	19	25	2^{420}	85/83, 1.4210
	t-Butyl methacrylate	286	48	14^{403}	74/96
	Vinyl caproate	300	40	14^{418}	99/100, 1.4159^{30}
	2-Acetoxy-1-hexene	300	31	14^{305}	75/39, 1.4176^{26}
	Methyl β-methylsorbate	19	57	2^{415}	82/12, 1.5010^{18}
	Diethyl methylenemalonate	37	45	2^{360}	210/760, 1.432^{25}
C_9	Methyl-2-octenoate	292	91	14^{300}	97/18
	Ethyl 2-heptenoate	37	78	2^{362}	59/3, 1.4355^{25}
		310	78	14^{289}	58/3, 1.4355^{25}
	Ethyl 3-ethyl-3-pentenoate	19	75	2^{419}	80/16, 1.4350
	Ethyl 3-methyl-2-ethyl-2-butenoate	19	33	2^{94}	67/13, 1.4430
	Ethyl 3-methyl-2-ethyl-3-butenoate	19	31	2^{94}	57/13, 1.4250
	2-Acetoxy-1-heptene	300	34	14^{305}	93/40, 1.4217^{25}
C_{10}	Diethyl propylidene-malonate	37	46	2^{357}	120/15, 1.4402^{25}
	Diethyl isopropylidene-malonate	37	52	2^{370}	112/9, 1.4478^{25}
C_{11}	Diethyl isopropylidene-succinate	37	41	2^{358}	115–122/7
	Diethyl butylidene-malonate	37	59	2^{357}	123/10, 1.4425^{25}

For explanations and symbols see pp. xi–xii.

TABLE 52 (continued)

C_n	Compound	Method	Yield (%)	Chapter[ref.]	B.p./mm., n_D^t, (M.p.), Deriv.
		Aliphatic Olefinic Esters (continued)			
C_{11}	Diethyl isobutylidene-malonate	37	92	2^{357}	136/27, 1.4398[25]
	Diethyl (1-methylpropyl-idene)-malonate	37	19	2^{405}	120/9, 1.4479[25]
	Diethyl ethylvinyl-malonate	....	54	14^{381}	123/30, 1.4341
		Alicyclic Olefinic Esters			
C_8	Ethyl 1-cyclopentenyl-carboxylate	19 293	85 75	2^{91} 14^{160}	92/25 92/25
C_9	Methyl cyclohexyl-ideneacetate	313	46	14^{389}	78/5, 1.4838
	Ethyl 1-cyclohexene-carboxylate	286	90	14^{94}	96/15, 1.4716[16]
	4-Carbomethoxy-4-methylcyclohexene	34	84	2^{497}	65/10, 1.4600
	Ethyl 1-cyclopentenyl-acetate	19	82	2^{90}	
C_{10}	Ethyl 1-cyclohexenyl-acetate	19	90	2^{92}	
C_{12}	Diethyl 3-cyclohexene-1,1-dicarboxylate	34	67	2^{498}	107/3, 1.4540[25]
		Aromatic Olefinic Esters			
C_9	Phenyl acrylate	24	80	2^{236}	64/2, 1.5210
	Ethyl β-(2-furyl)-acrylate	37	81	2^{406}	115/10
	Ethyl β-(2-thienyl)-acrylate	37	49	2^{352}	110–116/3.5
C_{10}	Methyl p-vinylbenzoate	19	49	2^{96}	90/2, (36)
	p-Vinylphenyl acetate	19	45	2^{97}	105/4, 1.5356[25]
C_{11}	Ethyl cinnamate	37	74	2^{394}	130/6
	Methyl p-methyl-cinnamate	37	65	2^{395}	157/22, (58)
	o-Allylphenyl acetate	288	74	14^{139}	110/11
C_{12}	Ethyl β methylcinnamate	19	70	2^{411}	140/13, 1.5451*
C_{13}	Ethyl α,β-dimethyl-cinnamate	19	55	2^{410}	130/12
	Ethyl 4,β-dimethyl-cinnamate	19	94	2^{416}	152/10, 1.5458
	t-Butyl cinnamate	286	58	14^{79}	144/8

TABLE 53. HALO ESTERS 509

TABLE 52 *(continued)*

C_n	Compound	Method	Yield (%)	Chapter[ref.]	B.p./mm., n_D^t, (M.p.), Deriv.
	Aromatic Olefinic Esters *(continued)*				
C_{14}	Ethyl 2-phenylcyclo-hexenylacetate	19	77	2^{95}	153/3
	Ethyl benzalmalonate	37	91	2^{355}	141/4
C_{15}	Phenyl cinnamate	286	75	14^{93}	(76)
C_{16}	4-Carbomethoxystilbene	28	52	2^{272}	(159)
C_{17}	4-Carboethoxystilbene	28	36	2^{272}	(106)
C_{20}	Diethyl 4,4'-stilbene-dicarboxylate	293	67	14^{153}	(131)

For explanations and symbols see pp. xi–xii.

TABLE 53. HALO ESTERS

C_n	Compound	Method	Yield (%)	Chapter[ref.]	B.p./mm., n_D^t, (M.p.), Deriv.
	Aliphatic and Alicyclic Halo Esters				
C_2	Methyl fluoroformate	55	40	4^{380}	38
C_3	Methyl fluoroacetate	55	90	4^{380}	105, 1.3679
	Methyl chloroacetate	285	64	14^4	131, 118Am
	Methyl dichloroacetate	285	71	14^4	143, 98Am
	Methyl trichloroacetate	285	88	14^4	153, 141Am
C_4	Methyl α-fluoropropionate	55	50	4^{380}	108
	Methyl α-chloropropionate	53	71	4^{169}	130/748
	Methyl α-bromopropionate	52	50	4^{131}	56.5/21
	Methyl β-bromopropionate	73	84	4^{202}	66/18
		285	76	14^{51}	83/40, 1.4542
	Methyl α,β-dichloropro-pionate	74	85	4^{435}	75/21
	Methyl α,β-dibromopro-pionate	74	88	4^{435}	98/22
	Methyl α-chloroacrylate	20	73	2^{162}	58/55, 1.4400
	Methyl α-bromoacrylate	20	82	2^{162}	74/78, 1.4840
	Ethyl fluoroacetate	55	75	4^{380}	118
	Ethyl bromoacetate	285	70	14^{16}	155/759
	Ethyl difluoroacetate	....	60	14^{378}	100
	Ethyl trifluoroacetate	285	90	14^6	61, 75Am
		....	93	14^{429}	62
	1-Chloro-2-acetoxyethane	285	53	14^{48}	142/738, 1.4235
	(β-chloroethyl acetate)	286	82	14^{100}	144
		291	96	14^{394}	145
	β-Bromoethyl chloro-acetate	286	90	14^{96}	113/22

For explanations and symbols see pp. xi–xii.

TABLE 53 *(continued)*

C_n	Compound	Method	Yield (%)	Chapter[ref.]	B.p./mm., n_D^t, (M.p.), Deriv.
				Aliphatic and Alicyclic Halo Esters *(continued)*	
C_4	β-Methoxyethyl chloroformate	289	93	14[364]	59/13, 1.4163[25]
	Allyl chloroformate	289	90	14[361]	56/97, 1.4223
	Isopropyl chloroformate	289	83	14[361]	47/100, 1.3981
	γ-Chloropropyl chloroformate	289	80	14[370]	177, 1.4456
	Ethylene-*bis*-chloroformate	289	77	14[361]	113/25, 1.4498
C_5	Methyl γ-chlorobutyrate	54	84	4[605]	174/749
		293	80	14[51]	90/45, 1.4319
	Methyl α-bromoisobutyrate	67	84	4[546]	55/21, 1.4410*
	Methyl β-bromoisobutyrate	73	100	4[203]	67/17, 1.4551
	Ethyl α-bromopropionate	67	70	4[545]	70/25
	Ethyl β-chloropropionate	285	59	14[52]	161
	Ethyl β-bromopropionate	73	90	4[202]	79/19
		285	87	14[47]	65/15
	Ethyl β-Iodopropionate	55	80	4[387]	85/13
	Ethyl α-bromoacrylate	39	77	2[147]	25/1.5, 1.4660[25]
	Isopropyl chloroacetate	300	34	14[306]	150/747, 1.4175[25]
	γ-Chloropropyl acetate	285	95	14[46]	168, 1.4295[22]
		286	80	14[101]	166
	γ-Bromopropyl acetate	286	90	14[101]	89/22
	γ-Iodopropyl acetate	285	88	14[101]	99/15
	1-Chloro-2-acetoxypropane	77	72	4[629]	149/745, 1.4223
		285	72	14[48]	148/745, 1.4223
	n-Butyl chloroformate	289	85	14[362]	36/13
	s-Butyl chloroformate	289	70	14[365]	25/13, 1.4093[19]
	t-Butyl chloroformate	289	20	14[363]	4/1
	β-Ethoxyethyl chloroformate	289	77	14[364]	67/14, 1.4169[25]
C_6	Methyl 5-bromopentanoate	61	68	4[393]	80/4
		285	71	14[51]	96/13, 1.4618
	Methyl 3,4-dibromopentanoate	285	94	14[49]	123/17, 1.5105
	Ethyl γ-bromobutyrate	285	72†	14[161]	105/28, 1.4539[25]
		309	74†	14[411]	84/13, 1.4545[25]
	Ethyl α,β-dibromo-*n*-butyrate	74	95	4[437]	104/17
	Ethyl β-bromocrotonate	52	51	4[134]	84.5/6
	Ethyl γ-chlorocrotonate	20	65	2[160]	72-80/10
	Ethyl γ-bromocrotonate	20	60	2[160]	78-82/2
	n-Butyl chloroacetate	285	97	14[50]	94/38
	t-Butyl chloroacetate	286	63	14[79]	49/11, 1.4260
	t-Butyl bromoacetate	286	70	14[79]	74/25
	t-Butyl trichloroacetate	300	80	14[304]	37/1, 1.4398[25]

TABLE 53. HALO ESTERS 511

TABLE 53 *(continued)*

C_n	Compound	Method	Yield (%)	Chapter[ref.]	B.p./mm., n_D^t, (M.p.), Deriv.
		Aliphatic and Alicyclic Halo Esters *(continued)*			
C_6	α-Chloro-*n*-butyl acetate	315	68	14[384]	52/10, 1.4198
	4-Chlorobutyl acetate	54	76	4[416]	79/15, 1.4344
	Neopentyl chloroformate	289	83	14[361]	52/27, 1.4091
	Ethyl δ-chlorovalerate	285	58	14[288]	84/8, 1.4355
	Ethyl δ-bromovalerate	51	52†	4[207]	103/12, 1.4577
	Ethyl δ-iodovalerate	55	85	4[609]	125/17, 1.4970
	Ethyl methylethylbromoacetate	286	86	14[94]	75/14
	Methyl β-methyl-β-ethyl-β-chloropropionate	52	42	4[132]	48/16
	1-Chloro-4-acetoxypentane	287	82	14[112]	102–106/30, 1.4309[25]
	5-Chloroamyl acetate	54	88	4[566]	112/24
	2-Chloro-3-acetoxypentane	285	65	14[48]	74/20, 1.4299
	2-Methyl-2-acetoxy-3-chlorobutane	285	22	14[48]	100/100, 1.4320
	2,2-Dimethyl-1-bromo-3-acetoxypropane	285	84	14[53]	90/16
	Diethyl bromomalonate	67	75	4[551]	121–125/16
	Ethyl α-bromo-β,β-dimethylacrylate	20	80	2[164]	89/13
C_8	Methyl 7-bromoheptanoate	61	69	4[392]	112/5
	Ethyl ζ-chlorohexoate	53	80	4[168]	106/14, 1.4398[18]
	Ethyl ζ-Bromohexoate	52	80	4[168]	125/12
		309	55†	14[228]	120–125/14, 1.4566[21]
	Ethyl α,δ-dibromocaproate	285	96	14[229]	136/11
	Methyl α-bromoisoheptylate	67	70	4[548]	90/10
	Ethyl 2-bromocyclohexanoate	52	50	4[135]	76/0.1, 1.4909[25]
	Ethyl β-bromoisocaproate	73	87	4[135]	64/0.1, 1.4557[25]
	Ethyl α-ethyl-γ-bromobutyrate	52	78	4[133]	93/8
	Methyl β-methyl-β-*n*-propyl-β-chloropropionate	52	60	4[132]	59/13
	Methyl β,β-diethyl-β-chloropropionate	52	59	4[132]	58/11
	3-Chloro-4-acetoxyhexane	285	59	14[48]	125/100, 1.4340
	Dimethyl α,α'-dibromoadipate	67	93	4[549]	163/3
	Diethyl iodosuccinate	55	100	4[389]	144/18

For explanations and symbols see pp. xi–xii.

TABLE 53 *(continued)*

C_n	Compound	Method	Yield (%)	Chapter[ref.]	B.p./mm., n_D^t, (M.p.), Deriv.

Aliphatic and Alicyclic Halo Esters *(continued)*

C_n	Compound	Method	Yield (%)	Chapter[ref.]	B.p./mm., n_D^t, (M.p.), Deriv.
C_8	Ethyl α-bromo-β-isopropylacrylate	39	86	2^{147}	31/0.1, 1.4688[25]
C_9	Methyl 8-bromoöctanoate	61	70	4^{392}	124/6
	Ethyl γ,γ-dimethyl-β-bromovalerate	73	75	4^{135}	66/0.1, 1.4588[25]
	Ethyl δ-bromo-β,β-dimethylvalerate	309	93	14^{227}	90/1.8
	Ethyl β,β-diethyl-β-chloropropionate	52	62	4^{132}	68/12
	1-Chloro-2-acetoxyheptane	285	56	14^{48}	120/20, 1.4367
	Ethyl-2-bromocyclopentylacetate	309	73	14^{226}	125/15
	Diethyl α-bromoglutarate	67	92	4^{550}	124/2
C_{10}	Methyl 9-bromononanoate	61	75	4^{392}	131/2
	Ethyl α-bromocyclohexylacetate	67	98	4^{550}	98/1, 1.4708[25]*
	Ethyl α-chloroadipate	67	90	4^{550}	121/5
	Ethyl α-bromoadipate	67	90	4^{550}	135/5
	Diethyl γ-bromopropylmalonate	73	79	4^{586}	140/5, 1.455[28]
	Diethyl methyl-β-bromoethylmalonate	299	32	14^{266}	136/12
C_{11}	Methyl 10-bromodecanoate	61	71	4^{392}	165/12
	Diethyl 4-chlorobutylmalonate	299	65	14^{265}	147/10
C_{12}	Ethyl γ-bromocaprate	75	57	4^{559}	94/0.2, 1.4599

Aromatic Halo Esters

C_n	Compound	Method	Yield (%)	Chapter[ref.]	B.p./mm., n_D^t, (M.p.), Deriv.
C_7	Phenyl chloroformate	289	58	14^{361}	75/13, 1.5131
C_8	Benzyl chloroformate	289	94	14^{360}	119/19
	Methyl o-chlorobenzoate	285	70	14^1	119/19
	Methyl p-chlorobenzoate	321	78	14^{428}	(43)
	Methyl p-bromobenzoate	294	93	14^{185}	(74)
	Chloromethyl benzoate	315	60	14^{385}	115/8
	Bromomethyl benzoate	315	50	14^{385}	136/18
C_9	Methyl phenylchloroacetate	52	62	4^{136}	130/15
	Ethyl p-bromobenzoate	294	82	14^{185}	262
	Ethyl 4-iodobenzoate	56	69	4^{327}	135/5, 1.5854[25]
	m-Carbomethoxybenzyl bromide	64	65	4^{288}	114/3, (47)
	m-Carbomethoxybenzyl iodide	55	78	4^{288}	(53)

TABLE 54. HYDROXY ESTERS 513

TABLE 53 (continued)

C_n	Compound	Method	Yield (%)	Chapter[ref.]	B.p./mm., n_D^t, (M.p.), Deriv.
		Aromatic Halo Esters (continued)			
C_9	p-Carbomethoxybenzyl bromide	64	65	4[288]	117/3, (55)
		286	60	14[97]	116/3, (55)
	p-Carbomethoxybenzyl iodide	55	80	4[288]	(77)
	α-Chloroethyl benzoate	315	60	14[385]	120/8
	β-Chloroethyl benzoate	291	62	14[393]	125-130/14
		286	91	14[99]	103/2, 1.5298[19]
	2-Iodoethyl benzoate	55	81	4[608]	136/2.5, 1.5820[15]
C_{10}	Methyl α-iodo-β-chloro-β-phenylpropionate	74	77	4[433]	(98)
	Ethyl α-chlorophenylacetate	67	92	4[550]	132/8
	Ethyl α-bromophenylacetate	67	96	4[550]	113/1.5
	Ethyl o-fluorophenylacetate	293	52†	14[65]	124/24
	Ethyl m-fluorophenylacetate	293	22†	14[65]	128/28
	Ethyl p-fluorophenylacetate	293	48†	14[65]	129/31, 1.4776[25]
	Ethyl p-(chloromethyl)benzoate	286	90	14[98]	140-150/15
	Ethyl m-(chloromethyl)benzoate	286	89	14[102]	140-150/12
	γ-Chloropropyl benzoate	286	84	14[99]	134/2
C_{11}	Ethyl α-bromo-β-phenylpropionate	67	80	4[552]	159/15, 1.5180[25]
		67	77†	4[536]	152/13
	Ethyl α,β-dibromo-β-phenylpropionate	74	85	4[436]	(75)
C_{16}	Ethyl diphenyl-α-fluoroacetate	55	63	4[388]	116/0.1, (34)

For explanations and symbols see pp. xi-xii.

TABLE 54. HYDROXY ESTERS

C_n	Compound	Method	Yield (%)	Chapter[ref.]	B.p./mm., n_D^t, (M.p.)
		Aliphatic Hydroxy Esters			
C_4	Methyl lactate	285	88	14[56]	
		285	69	14[20]	144
	Methyl β-hydroxypropionate	309	85	14[232]	71/13, 1.4225

For explanations and symbols see pp. xi-xii.

TABLE 54 *(continued)*

C_n	Compound	Method	Yield (%)	Chapter[ref.]	B.p./mm., n_D^t, (M.p.)
		Aliphatic Hydroxy Esters *(continued)*			
C_5	Methyl α,β-dihydroxybutyrate	285	72	14^{43}	109/10
	Ethyl β-hydroxypropionate	309	80	14^{232}	75/8, 1.4222
C_6	Ethyl β-hydroxybutyrate	79	97	5^{165}	78/15
		79	100	5^{111}	78/15, 1.4200^{25}
		79	100	5^{99}	
	Ethyl 2,3-dihydroxybutyrate	107	56	5^{604}	124/18
		285	79	14^{43}	113/10
	Methyl 2,3-dihydroxy-3-methylbutyrate	107	61	5^{606}	59/0.2
	Isopropyl lactate	285	68	14^{54}	75-80/32
C_7	Ethyl γ-hydroxyvalerate	79	85	5^{137}	85/3
	Ethyl α-methyl-β-hydroxybutyrate	79	71	5^{165}	86/22
	Methyl 3-methyl-3-ethyl-3-hydroxypropionate	103	60	5^{233}	67/10
	Ethyl 2-ethyl-3-hydroxypropionate	103	46	5^{235}	100/16
	1-Acetoxy-4-pentanol	79	70	5^{164}	119/18, 1.4314
C_8	Ethyl 6-hydroxyhexoate	305	45	14^{375}	134/15
	Ethyl α-methyl-β-hydroxyvalerate	79	100	5^{99}	
	Ethyl 3-methyl-3-hydroxypentanoate	103	42	5^{227}	84/16
	Ethyl α-ethyl-γ-hydroxybutyrate	309	84	14^{225}	79/3
	Ethyl 2,2-dimethyl-3-hydroxybutanoate	103	70	5^{236}	98/20
	Ethyl 3-methyl-2-(hydroxymethyl)-butyrate	103	41	5^{235}	112/20
	Methyl 3,3-diethyl-3-hydroxypropionate	103	59	5^{233}	80/11
	Methyl 3-methyl-3-propyl-3-hydroxypropionate	103	60	5^{233}	81/12
	Ethyl 2-propyl-3-hydroxypropionate	103	67	5^{235}	121/22
C_9	Ethyl 2-(hydroxymethyl)-hexanoate	103	52	5^{235}	120/10
	Methyl 3-hydroxy-3,4,4-trimethylpentanoate	103	66	5^{757}	89/14
	Ethyl 3-ethyl-3-hydroxypentanoate	103	76	5^{228}	102/18, 1.4336^{17}
	Ethyl 2,3-dimethyl-3-hydroxypentanoate	103	75	5^{231}	90/13, 1.4319

TABLE 54. HYDROXY ESTERS 515

TABLE 54 (continued)

C_n	Compound	Method	Yield (%)	Chapter[ref.]	B.p./mm., n_D^t, (M.p.)
	Aliphatic Hydroxy Esters (continued)				
C_9	Ethyl 3-hydroxy-2-ethyl-3-methylbutanoate	103	31	5[223]	77/3, 1.4310
	Ethyl β-hydroxyglutarate	79	76	5[161]	133/8, 1.4381
	Diethyl β-methylmalate	79	92	5[163]	123/10, 1.4335
	Alicyclic Hydroxy Esters				
C_8	Methyl cis-2-cyclohexanol-1-carboxylate	79	80	5[671]	105/14
	Methyl trans-2-cyclohexanol-1-carboxylate				115/14
C_9	Ethyl 2-hydroxycyclohexanecarboxylate	304	85	14[224]	99/7, 1.4625
	Ethyl 3-hydroxycyclohexanecarboxylate	304	75	14[224]	133-138/9, 1.4665
	Ethyl 4-hydroxycyclohexanecarboxylate	304	87	14[223]	136/8, 1.4698
	Ethyl cyclopentanol-1-acetate	103	55	5[224]	91/4
C_{10}	Ethyl cyclohexanol-1-acetate	103	70	5[224]	90/3
	Ethyl 4-hydroxycyclohexyl-acetate	304	89	14[224]	140/7, 1.4705
	Aromatic Hydroxy Esters				
C_7	o-Hydroxyphenyl formate	305	88	14[376]	125/12
C_8	Methyl o-Hydroxybenzoate	285	55	14[1]	224
		285	92	14[19]	105/14, 1.5360[25]
	Methyl p-hydroxybenzoate	285	84	14[58]	(128)
C_9	Methyl α-hydroxyphenylacetate (methyl mandelate)	285	87	14[55]	100/0.01, (56)
	Ethyl p-hydroxybenzoate	285	81	14[58]	(115)
C_{11}	Ethyl β-phenyl-β-hydroxy-propionate	103	64	5[226]	154/12
	Ethyl p-(α-hydroxyethyl)-benzoate	79	63	5[160]	113/3, 1.5240[25]
	3-Hydroxybutyl benzoate	286	52	14[104]	133/3, 1.5130

For explanations and symbols see pp. xi–xii.

TABLE 55. ALKOXY AND ARYLOXY ESTERS

C_n	Compound	Method	Yield (%)	Chapter[ref.]	B.p./mm., n_D^t, (M.p.)
		Aliphatic Alkoxy Esters			
C_5	Methyl α-methoxypropionate	115	63	6[59]	129/747
	Methyl β-methoxypropionate	121	91	6[113]	55/23, 1.4022
	1-Methoxyethyl acetate	290	51	14[199]	25/15, 1.3870
C_6	Methyl α-methoxyisobutyrate	285	80	14[59]	135
	Methyl β-ethoxypropionate	121	91	6[113]	60/20, 1.4050
	Ethyl α-methoxypropionate	285	54	14[60]	141/760
	Ethyl β-methoxypropionate	121	27	6[113]	60/20, 1.4049
	Ethyl ethoxyacetate	285	72	14[66]	154
	Methyl diglycolate $(CH_3O_2CCH_2OCH_2CO_2CH_3)$	285	76	14[63]	120/13, (38)
C_7	Ethyl α-ethoxypropionate	115	65	6[58]	68/27
	Ethyl β-ethoxypropionate	121	84	6[113]	67/17, 1.4070
C_8	Ethyl α-ethoxy-n-butyrate	115	65	6[58]	68/16
	Ethyl α-ethoxyisobutyrate	285	88	14[59]	55/13
C_9	Ethyl β,β-diethoxypropionate	121	84	6[114]	65/2, 1.4108[25]
C_{10}	Ethyl α-methyl-δ-ethoxyvalerate	308	54	14[351]	97/13
	Ethyl α-ethyl-γ-ethoxybutyrate	308	30	14[352]	94/15
	Diethyl methoxymethylmethylmalonate	299	50	14[267]	116/16, 1.4220
		Aromatic Alkoxy and Aryloxy Esters			
C_8	o-Methoxyphenyl formate	305	99	14[376]	109/12
C_9	Methyl o-methoxybenzoate	116	71	6[100]	133/15
C_{10}	Methyl β-phenoxypropionate	121	59	6[164]	85/0.4, 1.5071
	Ethyl γ-phenoxycrotonate	20	20	2[153]	183/12
	p-Methoxybenzyl acetate (anisyl acetate)	290	54†	14[196]	115-120/4
C_{11}	Ethyl β-phenoxypropionate	121	53	6[164]	92/0.7, 1.5002
		285	90	14[62]	170/40
	Ethyl m-methoxyphenylacetate	285	86	14[64]	142/12
C_{12}	Ethyl γ-phenoxybutyrate	293	80	14[166]	160-165/25
	Ethyl α-ethoxyphenylacetate	115	60	6[58]	157/26
	Ethyl p-ethoxyphenylacetate	285	81†	14[61]	130/3
C_{16}	Ethyl α-phenoxyphenylacetate	115	68	6[60]	156/0.8, 1.5452

For explanations and symbols see pp. xi–xii.

TABLE 57. KETO ESTERS 517

TABLE 56. ALDO ESTERS

C_n	Compound	Method	Yield (%)	Chapter[ref.]	B.p./mm., n_D^t, (M.p.), Deriv.
C_4	Ethyl glyoxylate	....	50	9^{200}	138, 131Ph, 218Se
C_5	β-Carbomethoxypropionaldehyde	162	65	9^{56}	70/14
C_6	Methyl γ-formylbutyrate	162	52	9^{68}	106Dn
	γ-Acetoxybutyraldehyde	145	84	9^{190}	60/1, 1.4245^{25}, 181Dn
	β-Carbethoxypropion-	145	71	9^{190}	69/7, 1.4212^{25}, 137Se
	aldehyde	....	50	9^{201}	87/10, 1.425^{14}
C_7	Ethyl β-formylbutyrate	145	65	9^{190}	59/0.01, 1.4236^{25}, 88Dn
C_8	DL-erythro-α,β-Diace-toxybutyric aldehyde	162	87	9^{69}	87/4
C_9	Methyl m-formylbenzoate	164	84	9^{53}	153/15, (58)
	Methyl p-formylbenzoate	148	72	9^{261}	(63), 144Ph
		164	90	9^{53}	135/12, (60)
	p-Acetoxybenzaldehyde	288	91	14^{138}	120/6, 241Dn
	Methyl phthalaldehydate	162	84	9^{233}	138/13, 1.5411, 195Se
	Methyl terephthaldehydate	147	53	9^{85}	97/2, (62)
C_{10}	Methyl 8-aldehydoöctanoate	156	60	9^{116}	112/3, 1.4384, 105Se
	γ,γ-Dicarbethoxybutyraldehyde	301	50	14^{311}	78/0.06, 1.4340^{25}, 76Dn
	Ethyl m-formylbenzoate	164	86	9^{53}	164/13
	Ethyl p-formylbenzoate	164	86	9^{53}	142/13
C_{11}	Methyl 9-aldehydononanoate	156	60	9^{116}	121/3, 1.4410, 100Se
C_{13}	Methyl 11-aldehydoundecanoate	145	74	9^{190}	147/0.1, 1.4432^{25}, 70Dn
C_{14}	Methyl 12-aldehydododecanoate	156	60	9^{116}	153/3, 1.4469, 118Se

For explanations and symbols see pp. xi–xii.

TABLE 57. KETO ESTERS

C_n	Compound	Method	Yield (%)	Chapter[ref.]	B.p./mm., n_D^t, (M.p.), Deriv.
	Aliphatic Keto Esters				
C_4	Methyl pyruvate	285	73	14^{19}	136–140, 1.4046^{25}
		285	71	14^{67}	136–140
C_5	Ethyl pyruvate	285	59	14^{71}	146–150
		179	54	10^{692}	57/20, 1.4053
	Methyl acetoacetate	211	50	10^{616}	74/12*, 152Se*
C_6	Methyl γ-ketovalerate (methyl levulinate)	285	85	14^{70}	1.4223

For explanations and symbols see pp. xi–xii.

TABLE 57 *(continued)*

C_n	Compound	Method	Yield (%)	Chapter[ref.]	B.p./mm., n_D^t, (M.p.), Deriv.
				Aliphatic Keto Esters (continued)	
C_6	Ethyl acetoacetate	211	29	10^{621}	80/18, 129Se*
		211	68	10^{148}	80/16
	Methyl acetopyruvate	203	70	10^{555}	97/12, (63), 132Am*
	Ethyl a,β-diketo-butyrate	183	35	10^{573}	68/9, (148)
C_7	Methyl a-propionyl-propionate	211	71	10^{616}	76/10, 1.4211[25], 82Am*
	Ethyl a-ketovalerate	184	88†	10^{366}	72/11, 1.4170[18], 116Dn
	Ethyl propionylacetate	187	58	10^{386}	77/8.5, 149Cu
		211	44	10^{620}	92/17
		214	60	10^{651}	93/17
	Ethyl γ-ketovalerate (ethyl levulinate)	285	81	14^{70}	94/18, 1.4212
	Ethyl a-methylaceto-acetate	213	71	10^{644}	76/15, 73Am*
	Butyl pyruvate	179	70	10^{218}	71/11
	1-Acetoxy-4-pentanone	287	55	14^{112}	107/18, 1.4259
	2-Acetoxy-2-methyl-3-butanone	200	49	10^{657}	93/50, 1.4180
	Diethyl oxomalonate	183	32	10^{572}	(57)
		183	76	10^{575}	108/15
	Methyl propionopyruvate	203	42	10^{555}	95/4
C_8	Ethyl n-butyrylacetate	212	39	10^{386}	94/15
		293	64	14^{170}	95/15, 125Cu
		298	60	14^{327}	95/14, 126Cu*
	Ethyl β-propionyl-propionate	....	23	14^{423}	103/15, 1.4311[21]
		184	82	10^{302}	107/12, 106Se*
	Methyl β-oxo-γ,γ-dimethylvalerate	203	80	10^{653}	93/20
		307	80	14^{343}	92/20
	Ethyl a-propionyl-propionate	211	81	10^{148}	90/12
		211	76	10^{622}	92/19, 82Am*
		288	65	14^{142}	86/11
		298	20	14^{325}	105/32, 1.419[24]
	Ethyl isobutyrylacetate	293	81	14^{173}	92/16, 1.4245[25]
		298	37	14^{327}	85/16
	Ethyl 2,2-dimethyl-acetoacetate	213	54	10^{644}	73/14, 187Se*
		215	51	10^{623}	76/15
	t-Butyl acetoacetate	211	66	10^{255}	82/15
	Methyl butyropyruvate	203	52	10^{555}	112/8
	Ethyl diacetylacetate	212	52	10^{638}	97/12
C_9	Methyl 3-oxoöctoate	212	88	10^{635}	116/14, 1.4315[26], 114Cu*
	Methyl 4-oxoöctoate	189	80	10^{401}	117/14
	Ethyl 6-oxoheptanoate	189	59	10^{425}	123/13, 107Se*

TABLE 57. KETO ESTERS 519

TABLE 57 *(continued)*

C_n	Compound	Method	Yield (%)	Chapter[ref.]	B.p./mm., n_D^t, (M.p.), Deriv.
		Aliphatic Keto Esters *(continued)*			
C_9	Ethyl isovalerylacetate	298	64	14^{320}	98/14, 122Cu
		298	60	14^{325}	97/14, 1.4270^{24}
	Ethyl γ,γ,γ-trimethyl-acetylacetate	298	45	14^{336}	98/15
	Ethyl α-isopropylaceto-acetate	213	42	10^{646}	203
		213	67	10^{647}	98/20
	Methyl isovaleropyruvate	203	84	10^{555}	103/4
	Methyl pivalopyruvate	203	75	10^{555}	113/11, 1.4720
	Ethyl α-ethoxalyl-propionate	211	70	10^{618}	116/10, 78/2, 1.4313
	Dimethyl β-keto-α-methyladipate	212	50	10^{640}	94/0.1, 1.4458^{16}
	Diethyl β-oxoglutarate	285	43	14^{68}	146/17
	Diethyl acetylmalonate	215	86	10^{654}	120/12
C_{10}	Methyl 4-keto-5-methyl-octanoate	189	22	10^{426}	131/21
	Methyl 4-keto-6-methyl-octanoate	189	60	10^{426}	134/16
	Methyl 4-keto-7-methyl-octanoate	189	75	10^{426}	137/20
	Ethyl caproylacetate	200	80	10^{580}	112/10
	Ethyl α-n-butyryl-n-butyrate	211	76	10^{148}	105/12
	Ethyl α-isobutyryl-isobutyrate	211	55	10^{626}	94/15
		215	55	10^{653}	95/18
	Ethyl n-butyryldi-methylacetate	215	58	10^{623}	111/29
	Ethyl α-n-butylaceto-acetate	213	72	10^{645}	117/16, 1.4283*
		213	79	10^{642}	113/17
	Ethyl α-isobutylaceto-acetate	213	66	10^{642}	102/13
		213	69	10^{656}	112/21
	Ethyl α-s-butylaceto-acetate	213	62	10^{642}	109/18.5
	Ethyl α-ethoxalyl-n-butyrate	211	80	10^{295}	85/0.7, 99Dn
	Ethyl α-ethoxalyliso-butyrate	211	61	10^{623}	123/15, 97Se
	Diethyl β-ketoadipate	214	40	10^{652}	126/0.5
	Diethyl acetosuccinate	308	62	14^{347}	123/5
	Diethyl acetonylmalonate	299	61	14^{269}	111/3
C_{11}	Ethyl α-isoamylaceto-acetate	213	58	10^{649}	86/5, 1.4289^{21}
	Ethyl α-methyl-α-iso-butylacetoacetate	213	72	10^{656}	117/21, 1.4309^{25}

For explanations and symbols see pp. xi–xii.

TABLE 57 (continued)

C_n	Compound	Method	Yield (%)	Chapter[ref.]	B.p./mm., n_D^t, (M.p.), Deriv.
			Aliphatic Keto Esters (continued)		
C_{11}	Ethyl α-ethoxalyl-n-valerate	211	85	10[295]	86Dn
	Diethyl β-ketopimelate	215	30	10[655]	121/0.15
	Diethyl α-acetoglutarate	308	52	14[348]	133/4
C_{12}	Ethyl α-ethoxalyl-succinate	211	83	10[624]	115/1
			Alicyclic Keto Esters		
C_8	3-Acetoxycyclohexanone	179	45	10[215]	118/11.5
	2-Carbethoxycyclopentanone	211	81	10[627]	88/5, 1.4526[25]*, 143Se*
		288	40	14[142]	104/11, 144Se
	Ethyl β-cyclopropyl-β-ketopropionate	298	57	14[329]	100/11
C_9	2-Carbethoxycyclohexanone	298	37	14[336]	106/11
		307	62†	14[344]	
	α-Methyl-α-carbethoxycyclopentanone	213	70	10[266]	106/14
		213	82	10[268]	107/17, 1.4464*, 153Se
		213	80	10[643]	112/16, 1.4461
	Ethyl β-cyclobutyl-β-ketopropionate	212	19	10[633]	115/19
	Ethyl γ-cyclopropyl-α,γ-diketobutryate	203	55	10[558]	149/23
C_{10}	2-Methyl-2-carbethoxycyclohexanone	213	90	10[641]	100/4, 1.4491[26]
	α-Ethyl-α-carbethoxycyclopentanone	213	74	10[268]	100/7, 149Se
	Ethyl β-cyclopentyl-β-ketopropionate	212	36	10[633]	94/1.8
	Ethyl 2-cyclohexanone-glyoxalate	203	67	10[557]	105-165/10-15
C_{11}	α-Isopropyl-α-carbethoxycyclopentanone	213	59	10[268]	137/34, 142Se
			Aromatic Keto Esters		
C_9	Methyl phenylglyoxylate	179	85	10[213]	111/6, 88Ph
C_{10}	Methyl benzoylacetate	211	45	10[616]	122/2.5, 1.5355[22], 113Am*
	p-Acetylphenyl acetate	183	79	10[239]	162/13
	Ethyl benzoylformate	285	40	14[69]	118/5
	Methyl p-acetylbenzoate	183	54	10[246]	145/4, (95.4)
	ω-Acetoxyacetophenone	311	55†	14[388]	120/0.7, (49)
C_{11}	Methyl α-benzoylpropionate	211	61	10[616]	127/0.3, 1.5206[25], 146Am*

TABLE 57. KETO ESTERS 521

TABLE 57 *(continued)*

C_n	Compound	Method	Yield (%)	Chapter[ref.]	B.p./mm., n_D^t, (M.p.), Deriv.
		Aromatic Keto Esters *(continued)*			
C_{11}	Methyl β-benzoyl-propionate	189	51	10^{678}	120/0.4, 1.5260^{18}
	Ethyl benzoylacetate	212	78	10^{632}	137/4
		212	55	10^{636}	106/1
		214	44	10^{652}	145/3, 182Cu
		293	72	14^{176}	119/1
		298	81	14^{336}	151/12, 1.526^{24*}, 180Cu
	p-Acetylbenzyl acetate	183	55	10^{247}	163/11, 1.5225^{25}, 167Se
	Ethyl p-acetylbenzoate	183	41	10^{246}	168/13, (49)
C_{12}	Methyl α-benzoylbutyrate	211	41	10^{616}	129/3.0, 1.5215^{25}, 149Am*
		211	65	10^{545}	134/4
	Ethyl α-phenylacetoacetate	293	81	14^{168}	141/12
	Ethyl α-methylbenzoyl-acetate	293	64	14^{176}	129/1
	Ethyl m-acetylphenyl-acetate	178	40	10^{153}	118/0.5, 1.5185
	Ethyl p-acetylphenyl-acetate	178	40	10^{153}	(68)
C_{13}	Ethyl benzoyldimethyl-acetate	215	55	10^{653}	135/9
		215	65	10^{623}	148/15
		234	52	10^{658}	135/9
	Ethyl benzylacetoacetate	213	61	10^{674}	160/13
	Ethyl α-benzoylaceto-acetate	212	75	10^{632}	148/6
C_{14}	Ethyl benzoylmethyl-ethylacetate	215	52	10^{623}	164/18
	β-Naphthyl acetoxymethyl ketone	311	72†	14^{388}	(80)
	Ethyl α-naphthylgly-oxylate	178	46	10^{151}	167/3
	Diethyl benzoylmalonate	215	95	10^{654}	190/12
C_{15}	Ethyl β-naphthoylacetate	298	25	14^{325}	(34)
C_{16}	Ethyl p-biphenylylgly-oxylate	178	70	10^{152}	205/5, (39)
	Benzoin acetate	287	90	14^{123}	(82)
C_{17}	Ethyl α-phenylbenzoyl-acetate	293	63	14^{172}	(90)
		Heterocyclic Keto Esters			
C_8	Methyl 2-furoylacetate	211	50	10^{628}	145/20
	Ethyl α-thienylglyoxylate	178	50	10^{150}	120/3

For explanations and symbols see pp. xi–xii.

TABLE 57 *(continued)*

C_n	Compound	Method	Yield (%)	Chapter[ref.]	B.p./mm., n_D^t, (M.p.), Deriv.
		Heterocyclic Keto Esters *(continued)*			
C_9	Ethyl 2-furoylacetate	211	98	10^{629}	114/1, 132-Ox*
		214	70	10^{651}	139/10
	Ethyl picolinoylacetate	211	70	10^{630}	120/0.4, 1.5184
C_{10}	Ethyl β-pyridoylacetate	211	67	10^{630}	123/0.4, 138/3
		211	70	10^{280}	157HCl
	Ethyl γ-pyridoylacetate	211	85	10^{630}	120/0.4, (55)
C_{12}	Ethyl indole-3-glyoxylate	203	50	10^{559}	(178)

For explanations and symbols see pp. xi–xii.

TABLE 58. CARBOXY ESTERS

C_n	Compound	Method	Yield (%)	Chapter[ref.]	B.p./mm., n_D^t, (M.p.)
C_5	Methyl hydrogen succinate	287	96	14^{122}	(58)
	Potassium ethyl malonate	249	82	13^{234}	
	α-Acetoxypropionic acid	285	78	14^9	90/1
	β-Acetoxypropionic acid	309	73	14^{232}	84/0.4, 1.4311^{25}
C_6	Methyl hydrogen glutarate	287	92	14^{127}	158–165/23
C_7	Methyl hydrogen adipate	297	70	14^{359}	178/30, (9)
	Ethyl hydrogen glutarate	287	86	14^{130}	159–165/17
C_8	Ethyl hydrogen adipate	297	84	14^{357}	140–145/2, (29)
	Ethyl α,β-dimethylhydrogen succinate	287	88	14^{129}	116/3, 1.4345
C_9	Methyl hydrogen phthalate	287	83	14^{128}	(83)
	p-Acetoxybenzoic acid	287	91	14^{132}	(186)
C_{11}	Ethyl hydrogen azelate	297	63	14^{417}	170/1, (29)
	Ethyl 1-carboxycyclohexane-1-acetate	287	84	14^{131}	175–180/11

For explanations and symbols see pp. xi–xii.

REFERENCES FOR CHAPTER 14

[1] Sowa and Nieuwland, *J. Am. Chem. Soc.*, **58**, 271 (1936).

[2] Hinton and Nieuwland, *J. Am. Chem. Soc.*, **54**, 2017 (1932).

[3] Sowa and Nieuwland, *J. Am. Chem. Soc.*, **55**, 5052 (1933).

[4] Toole and Sowa, *J. Am. Chem. Soc.*, **59**, 1971 (1937).

[5] Smith, Mitchell, and Hawkins, *J. Am. Chem. Soc.*, **66**, 715 (1944).

[6] Reid, *J. Am. Chem. Soc.*, **69**, 2069 (1947); Gilman and Jones, *ibid.*, **65**, 1458 (1943).

[7] Brewer and Herbst, *J. Org. Chem.*, **6**, 870 (1941).

[8] Reid, *Ind. Eng. Chem.*, **29**, 1344 (1937).

[9] Filachione and Fisher, *Ind. Eng. Chem.*, **36**, 472 (1944).

[10] Robertson, *Org. Syntheses*, Coll. Vol. I, 138 (1941).

[11] Ruhoff, *Org. Syntheses*, Coll. Vol. II, 292 (1943).

[12] Mitchovitch, *Bull. soc. chim. France*, (5) **4**, 1661 (1937).

[13] Milas, *J. Am. Chem. Soc.*, **50**, 493 (1928); Wagner, *ibid.*, **50**, 1233 (1928).

[14] Thompson and Leuck, *J. Am. Chem. Soc.*, **44**, 2894 (1922).

[15] Hultman, Davis, and Clarke, *J. Am. Chem. Soc.*, **43**, 366 (1921).

[16] Natelson and Gottfried, *Org. Syntheses*, **23**, 37 (1943).

[17] Zaganiaris and Varvoglis, *Ber.*, **69B**, 2277 (1936).

[18] Newman, *J. Am. Chem. Soc.*, **63**, 2431 (1941).

[19] Clinton and Laskowski, *J. Am. Chem. Soc.*, **70**, 3135 (1948).

[20] Rinderknecht and Niemann, *J. Am. Chem. Soc.*, **70**, 2605 (1948).

[21] Freudenberg and Jakob, *Ber.*, **74**, 1001 (1941).

[22] Gattermann and Wieland, *Laboratory Methods of Organic Chemistry*, The Macmillan Co., New York, 1938, p. 141.

[23] Barkovsky, *Ann. chim.*, (11) **19**, 489 (1944).

[24] Backer and Strating, *Rec. trav. chim.*, **55**, 903–912 (1936); **59**, 936–939 (1940).

[25] Vogel, *J. Chem. Soc.*, 1811 (1948).

[26] Vogel, *J. Chem. Soc.*, 624, 644, 654 (1948); Jeffery and Vogel, *ibid.*, 658, 674 (1948).

[27] Burrus and Powell, *J. Am. Chem. Soc.*, **67**, 1469 (1945); Gilman and Broadbent, *ibid.*, **70**, 2757 (1948); LaForge, *ibid.*, **50**, 2479 (1928).

[28] Reichstein and Morsman, *Helv. Chim. Acta*, **17**, 1123 (1934).

[29] Price et al., *J. Am. Chem. Soc.*, **63**, 1859 (1941).

[30] Hofmann, *J. Am. Chem. Soc.*, **67**, 421 (1945).

[31] Kaufman, *J. Am. Chem. Soc.*, **67**, 497 (1945).

[32] Barger, Robinson, and Smith, *J. Chem. Soc.*, 719, 720 (1937).

[33] Clarke and Davis, *Org. Syntheses*, Coll. Vol. I, 261 (1941); Jewel and Butts, *J. Am. Chem. Soc.*, **53**, 3560 (1931).

[34] Bowden, *Org. Syntheses*, Coll. Vol. II, 414 (1943).

[35] Mićović, *Org. Syntheses*, Coll. Vol. II, 264 (1943).

[36] Müller, *Org. Syntheses*, Coll. Vol. II, 536 (1943).

[37] Karrer and Lee, *Helv. Chim. Acta*, **17**, 544 (1934).

[38] Bardhan, Banerji, and Bose, *J. Chem. Soc.*, 1127 (1935).

[39] Skinner, *J. Am. Chem. Soc.*, **55**, 2038 (1933).

[40] Foreman and McElvain, *J. Am. Chem. Soc.*, **62**, 1439 (1940).

[41] Baker et al., *J. Org. Chem.*, **12**, 144 (1947).

[42] Linstead, *J. Chem. Soc.*, 2505 (1929).

[43] Glattfeld and Straitiff, *J. Am. Chem. Soc.*, **60**, 1386 (1938).

[44] Lindstrom and McPhee, *J. Am. Chem. Soc.*, **65**, 2387 (1943).

[45] Rehberg, *Org. Syntheses*, 26, 4 (1946).
[46] Allen and Spangler, *Org. Syntheses*, 29, 33 (1949).
[47] Kendall and McKenzie, *Org. Syntheses*, Coll. Vol. I, 246 (1941).
[48] Irwin and Hennion, *J. Am. Chem. Soc.*, 63, 858 (1941).
[49] Goering, Cristol, and Dittmer, *J. Am. Chem. Soc.*, 70, 3314 (1948).
[50] Liston and Dehn, *J. Am. Chem. Soc.*, 60, 1264 (1938).
[51] Campbell and Campbell, *J. Am. Chem. Soc.*, 60, 1372 (1938).
[52] Conant and Kirner, *J. Am. Chem. Soc.*, 46, 243 (1924).
[53] Fourneau, Benoit, and Firmenich, *Bull. soc. chim. France*, 47, 875 (1930).
[54] McDermott, *Org. Syntheses*, Coll. Vol. II, 365 (1943).
[55] Baer and Kates, *J. Am. Chem. Soc.*, 67, 1483 (1945).
[56] Filachione, Lengel, and Fisher, *Ind. Eng. Chem.*, 37, 388 (1945).
[57] Ault et al., *J. Am. Chem. Soc.*, 69, 2003 (1947).
[58] Cavill and Vincent, *J. Soc. Chem. Ind. (London)*, 66, 175 (1947); Rohmann and Koch, *Arch. Pharm.*, 276, 161 (1938).
[59] Weismann, Sulzbacher, and Bergmann, *J. Am. Chem. Soc.*, 70, 1154, 1156 (1948).
[60] Reeve and Sadle, *J. Am. Chem. Soc.*, 72, 1253 (1950).
[61] Carter and Hey, *J. Chem. Soc.*, 152 (1948).
[62] Powell, *J. Am. Chem. Soc.*, 45, 2710 (1923).
[63] Backer and Stevens, *Rec. trav. chim.*, 59, 426 (1940).
[64] Hunter and Hogg, *J. Am. Chem. Soc.*, 71, 1923 (1949).
[65] Corse et al., *J. Am. Chem. Soc.*, 70, 2840 (1948).
[66] Fuson and Wojcik, *Org. Syntheses*, Coll. Vol. II, 261 (1943).
[67] Weissberger and Kibler, *Org. Syntheses*, 24, 72 (1944); cf. ref. 71.
[68] Adams and Chiles, *Org. Syntheses*, Coll. Vol. I, 237 (1941); cf. ref. 71.
[69] Corson et al., *Org. Syntheses*, Coll. Vol. I, 241 (1941).
[70] Schuette and Cowley, *J. Am. Chem. Soc.*, 53, 3485 (1931); Frank et al., *ibid.*, 66, 4 (1944).
[71] Archer and Pratt, *J. Am. Chem. Soc.*, 66, 1656 (1944).
[72] Jacobson, *J. Am. Chem. Soc.*, 68, 2628 (1946).
[73] McElvain and Pryde, *J. Am. Chem. Soc.*, 71, 326 (1949).
[74] Marvel and Noyes, *J. Am. Chem. Soc.*, 42, 2265 (1920); cf. ref. 7.
[75] Shriner and Cross, *J. Am. Chem. Soc.*, 60, 2339 (1938).
[76] Tindall, *Ind. Eng. Chem.*, 33, 65 (1941).
[77] Inglis, *Org. Syntheses*, Coll. Vol. I, 254 (1941).
[78] Cohen and Schneider, *J. Am. Chem. Soc.*, 63, 3386 (1941).
[79] Hauser et al., *Org. Syntheses*, 24, 19 (1944); Abramovitch et al., *J. Am. Chem. Soc.*, 65, 986 (1943).
[80] Spassow, *Org. Syntheses*, 20, 21 (1940); *Ber.*, 70, 1926 (1937).
[81] Whitmore and Lewis, *J. Am. Chem. Soc.*, 64, 2964 (1942).
[82] Whitmore and Forster, *J. Am. Chem. Soc.*, 64, 2967 (1942).
[83] Stoughton, *J. Am. Chem. Soc.*, 57, 203 (1935).
[84] Huber, Boehme, and Laskowski, *J. Am. Chem. Soc.*, 68, 189 (1946); McElvain and Adams, *ibid.*, 45, 2744 (1923).
[85] Bateman and Marvel, *J. Am. Chem. Soc.*, 49, 2917 (1927).
[86] Huber and Brunner, *Monatsh.*, 56, 325 (1930).
[87] Menalda, *Rec. trav. chim.*, 49, 967 (1930).
[88] Spassow, *Ber.*, 75, 779, 780 (1942).
[89] Adickes, Brunnert, and Lücher, *J. prakt. Chem.*, 130, 163 (1931).
[90] Burns, Jones, and Ritchie, *J. Chem. Soc.*, 714 (1935).

[91] Gresham, Jansen, and Shaver, *J. Am. Chem. Soc.*, **70**, 1003 (1948).

[92] Dauben, *J. Am. Chem. Soc.*, **70**, 1377 (1948).

[93] Womack and McWhirter, *Org. Syntheses*, **20**, 77 (1940).

[94] Gardner and Rydon, *J. Chem. Soc.*, **52**, 53 (1938).

[95] Bartlett and Ross, *J. Am. Chem. Soc.*, **69**, 460 (1947).

[96] Work, *J. Chem. Soc.*, 191 (1941).

[97] Fuson and Cooke, *J. Am. Chem. Soc.*, **62**, 1180 (1940).

[98] Blicke and Lilienfeld, *J. Am. Chem. Soc.*, **65**, 2282 (1943).

[99] Kirner, *J. Am. Chem. Soc.*, **48**, 2751 (1926); Ford-Moore, *Org. Syntheses*, **30**, 11 (1950).

[100] Blicke and Blake, *J. Am. Chem. Soc.*, **53**, 1018 (1931); cf. ref. 101.

[101] Bogert and Slocum, *J. Am. Chem. Soc.*, **46**, 766 (1924).

[102] Morgan and Porter, *J. Chem. Soc.*, 1258 (1926).

[103] Roll and Adams, *J. Am. Chem. Soc.*, **53**, 3469 (1931).

[104] McElvain and Carney, *J. Am. Chem. Soc.*, **68**, 2599 (1946).

[105] Mowry, *J. Am. Chem. Soc.*, **66**, 371 (1944).

[106] Verkade, Van der Lee, and Meerburg, *Rec. trav. chim.*, **51**, 850 (1932); Flaschenträger and Allemann, *Ann.*, **552**, 106 (1942).

[107] Stahmann, Wolff, and Link, *J. Am. Chem. Soc.*, **65**, 2287 (1943); cf. ref. 119.

[108] Price and Schwarcz, *J. Am. Chem. Soc.*, **62**, 2894 (1940).

[109] Duvall and Mosettig, *J. Am. Chem. Soc.*, **60**, 2411 (1938).

[110] Cheetham and Hey, *J. Chem. Soc.*, 771 (1937); Hazlet and Kornberg, *J. Am. Chem. Soc.*, **61**, 3037 (1939).

[111] Auwers, *Ann.*, **292**, 178, 179 (1896); Fessler and Shriner, *J. Am. Chem. Soc.*, **58**, 1384 (1936).

[112] Elderfield et al., *J. Am. Chem. Soc.*, **68**, 1579 (1946).

[113] Emerson et al., *J. Am. Chem. Soc.*, **68**, 1665 (1946).

[114] The Miner Laboratories, *Org. Syntheses*, Coll. Vol. I, 285 (1941).

[115] Prichard, *Org. Syntheses*, **28**, 68 (1948); cf. ref. 119.

[116] Baker and Bordwell, *Org. Syntheses*, **24**, 18 (1944).

[117] Burns, Jones, and Ritchie, *J. Chem. Soc.*, 403 (1935).

[118] Perkin and Simonsen, *J. Chem. Soc.*, 858 (1905).

[119] Chattaway, *J. Chem. Soc.*, 2495 (1931).

[120] Colonge, *Bull. soc. chim. France*, (5) 9, 731 (1942).

[121] Adickes, *J. prakt. Chem.*, **161**, 275 (1943); Clemo and Graham, *J. Chem. Soc.*, 215 (1930).

[122] Cason, *Org. Syntheses*, **25**, 19 (1945).

[123] Corson and Saliani, *Org. Syntheses*, Coll. Vol. II, 69 (1943).

[124] Malkin and Nierenstein, *J. Am. Chem. Soc.*, **53**, 241 (1931); Slotta and Lauersen, *J. prakt. Chem.*, **139**, 224 (1934).

[125] Hurd, Drake, and Fancher, *J. Am. Chem. Soc.*, **68**, 789 (1946).

[126] Lavine and Herkness, *J. Am. Chem. Soc.*, **70**, 3951 (1948); Anderson and Kenyon, *ibid.*, **70**, 3952 (1948).

[127] Harris et al., *J. Am. Chem. Soc.*, **67**, 2098 (1945).

[128] Eliel and Burgstahler, *J. Am. Chem. Soc.*, **71**, 2252 (1949).

[129] Adams and Wilkinson, *J. Am. Chem. Soc.*, **65**, 2207 (1943).

[130] Bachmann, Kushner, and Stevenson, *J. Am. Chem. Soc.*, **64**, 977 (1942).

[131] Rothstein and Thorpe, *J. Chem. Soc.*, 2015 (1926).

[132] Marshall, Kuck, and Elderfield, *J. Org. Chem.*, **7**, 450 (1942); cf. ref. 119.

[133] Galatis, *J. Am. Chem. Soc.*, **69**, 2062 (1947).

[134] Rice, Greenberg, Waters, and Vollrath, *J. Am. Chem. Soc.*, **56**, 1764 (1934).

[135] Morey, *Ind. Eng. Chem.*, **31**, 1132 (1939).
[136] Claborn and Smith, *J. Am. Chem. Soc.*, **61**, 2727 (1939).
[137] Hurd and Roe, *J. Am. Chem. Soc.*, **61**, 3357 (1939).
[138] Williams and Sadle, *J. Am. Chem. Soc.*, **62**, 2801 (1940).
[139] Hurd and Hoffman, *J. Org. Chem.*, **5**, 217 (1940).
[140] Gwynn and Degering, *J. Am. Chem. Soc.*, **64**, 2216 (1942).
[141] Kimel and Cope, *J. Am. Chem. Soc.*, **65**, 1995 (1943).
[142] Sauer, *J. Am. Chem. Soc.*, **69**, 2444 (1947).
[143] Boese, *Ind. Eng. Chem.*, **32**, 16 (1940).
[144] Adams and Thal, *Org. Syntheses*, Coll. Vol. I, 270 (1941).
[145] Geissman and Tess, *J. Am. Chem. Soc.*, **62**, 515 (1940).
[146] Blicke and Leonard, *J. Am. Chem. Soc.*, **68**, 1934 (1946).
[147] Blicke and Feldkamp, *J. Am. Chem. Soc,*, **66**, 1087 (1944).
[148] Jones et al., *J. Am. Chem. Soc.*, **70**, 2846 (1948).
[149] Merchant and Marvel, *J. Am. Chem. Soc.*, **50**, 1199 (1928).
[150] Rising and Zee, *J. Am. Chem. Soc.*, **50**, 1211 (1928).
[151] Adams and Marvel, *J. Am. Chem. Soc.*, **42**, 310 (1920).
[152] Slater, *J. Chem. Soc.*, **69** (1941).
[153] Hager, Van Arendonk, and Shonle, *J. Am. Chem. Soc.*, **66**, 1982 (1944).
[154] Nelson and Cretcher, *J. Am. Chem. Soc.*, **50**, 2758 (1928).
[155] Steele, *J. Am. Chem. Soc.*, **53**, 286 (1931).
[156] Rising and Zee, *J. Am. Chem. Soc.*, **49**, 541 (1927).
[157] Ruggli, Bussemaker, and Müller, *Helv. Chim. Acta*, **18**, 617, 620 (1935).
[158] Gattermann and Wieland, *Laboratory Methods of Organic Chemistry*, The Macmillan Co., New York, 1938, p. 254.
[159] Kindler, *Ber.*, **74**, 316 (1941).
[160] Cook and Linstead, *J. Chem. Soc.*, 959 (1934).
[161] Prill and McElvain, *J. Am. Chem. Soc.*, **55**, 1237 (1933).
[162] Fosdick and Wessinger, *J. Am. Chem. Soc.*, **60**, 1466 (1938).
[163] Ladenburg, Folkers, and Major, *J. Am. Chem. Soc.*, **58**, 1294 (1936).
[164] Glattfeld and Lee, *J. Am. Chem. Soc.*, **62**, 355 (1940).
[165] Braun, *J. Am. Chem. Soc.*, **52**, 3170, 3173 (1930).
[166] Marvel and Tanenbaum, *J. Am. Chem. Soc.*, **44**, 2647 (1922).
[167] Bennett and Hock, *J. Chem. Soc.*, 475 (1927).
[168] Kimball, Jefferson, and Pike, *Org. Syntheses*, Coll. Vol. II, 284 (1943); Kimball, *J. Am. Chem. Soc.*, **58**, 1968 (1936).
[169] Smith et al., *J. Am. Chem. Soc.*, **71**, 3772 (1949).
[170] Abramovitch and Hauser, *J. Am. Chem. Soc.*, **64**, 2721 (1942).
[171] Marvel, *Org. Syntheses*, Coll. Vol. II, 310 (1943).
[172] Howk and McElvain, *J. Am. Chem. Soc.*, **54**, 286 (1932).
[173] Kroeker and McElvain, *J. Am. Chem. Soc.*, **56**, 1172 (1934).
[174] Billman, Smith, and Rendall, *J. Am. Chem. Soc.*, **69**, 2059 (1947).
[175] Weisel, Taylor, Mosher, and Whitmore, *J. Am. Chem. Soc.*, **67**, 1071 (1945).
[176] Dorsch and McElvain, *J. Am. Chem. Soc.*, **54**, 2963 (1932).
[177] Ferber and Bendix, *Ber.*, **72**, 841 (1939); Ferber and Leonhardt, *ibid.*, **67**, 245 (1934).
[178] McElvain and Schroeder, *J. Am. Chem. Soc.*, **71**, 43 (1949).
[179] Reid et al., *Org. Syntheses*, Coll. Vol. II, 469 (1943).
[180] Sauer, Hain, and Boutwell, *Org. Syntheses*, **20**, 67, 69 (1940).
[181] Rehberg, *Org. Syntheses*, **26**, 18 (1946); Rehberg and Fisher, *J. Am. Chem. Soc.*, **66**, 1203 (1944).

[182] Frank et al., *J. Am. Chem. Soc.*, **66**, 1509 (1944).

[183] Carlson and Cretcher, *J. Am. Chem. Soc.*, **69**, 1954 (1947); Morgan and Cretcher, *ibid.*, **68**, 783 (1946).

[184] Carothers and Van Natta, *J. Am. Chem. Soc.*, **52**, 322 (1930).

[185] Reimer and Downes, *J. Am. Chem. Soc.*, **43**, 945 (1921).

[186] Hatch and Adkins, *J. Am. Chem. Soc.*, **59**, 1694 (1937); Fehlandt and Adkins, *ibid.*, **57**, 193 (1935).

[187] Fischer, *Ber.*, **53**, 1634 (1920).

[188] Emerson et al., *J. Am. Chem. Soc.*, **69**, 1906 (1947).

[189] Blicke and Sheets, *J. Am. Chem. Soc.*, **71**, 2857 (1949).

[190] Wagner, *J. Am. Chem. Soc.*, **71**, 3214 (1949).

[191] Kipnis, Soloway, and Omfelt, *J. Am. Chem. Soc.*, **71**, 10 (1949).

[192] Tharp, Herr, et al., *Ind. Eng. Chem.*, **39**, 1300 (1947); Rueggeberg, Ginsburg, and Frantz, *ibid.*, **38**, 207 (1946).

[193] Guest, *J. Am. Chem. Soc.*, **69**, 301 (1947).

[194] Ingold and Mohrhenn, *J. Chem. Soc.*, 1484 (1935).

[195] Gattermann and Wieland, *Laboratory Methods of Organic Chemistry*, The Macmillan Co., New York, 1938, p. 114.

[196] Ofner, *Helv. Chim. Acta*, **18**, 955 (1935).

[197] Hartman and Rahrs, *Org. Syntheses*, **24**, 79 (1944).

[198] Kindler and Blaas, *Ber.*, **77**, 589, 590 (1944).

[199] Hurd and Green, *J. Am. Chem. Soc.*, **63**, 2201 (1941).

[200] Hill and Hibbert, *J. Am. Chem. Soc.*, **45**, 3130 (1923).

[201] Bachmann and Struve in *Organic Reactions*, Vol. 1, John Wiley & Sons, New York, 1942, pp. 38, 52.

[202] Plattner and Heusser, *Helv. Chim. Acta*, **28**, 1047 (1945); Ruggli and Knecht, *ibid.*, **27**, 1113 (1944).

[203] Wilds and Meader, *J. Org. Chem.*, **13**, 763 (1948).

[204] Blicke and Sheets, *J. Am. Chem. Soc.*, **70**, 3769 (1948).

[205] Blicke and Zienty, *J. Am. Chem. Soc.*, **63**, 2945 (1941).

[206] Arndt and Eistert, *Ber.*, **68B**, 204 (1935); cf. ref. 201.

[207] Kamm and Kamm, *Org. Syntheses*, Coll. Vol. I, 104 (1941).

[208] Villani and Nord, *J. Am. Chem. Soc.*, **69**, 2605 (1947); Kulpinski and Nord, *J. Org. Chem.*, **8**, 256 (1943).

[209] Child and Adkins, *J. Am. Chem. Soc.*, **45**, 3013 (1923); **47**, 798 (1925).

[210] Loder and Whitmore, *J. Am. Chem. Soc.*, **57**, 2727 (1935); *Org. Syntheses*, Coll. Vol. II, 282 (1943).

[211] Whitmore et al., *J. Am. Chem. Soc.*, **64**, 1802 (1942).

[212] Haynes and Jones, *J. Chem. Soc.*, 505 (1946).

[213] Yost and Hauser, *J. Am. Chem. Soc.*, **69**, 2326 (1947).

[214] Nielsen, *J. Am. Chem. Soc.*, **66**, 1230 (1944).

[215] Levine, Baumgarten, and Hauser, *J. Am. Chem. Soc.*, **66**, 1231 (1944); cf. ref. 216.

[216] Hudson and Hauser, *J. Am. Chem. Soc.*, **62**, 2457 (1940).

[217] Hudson and Hauser, *J. Am. Chem. Soc.*, **63**, 3161 (1941).

[218] Covert, Connor, and Adkins, *J. Am. Chem. Soc.*, **54**, 1659 (1932); Adkins and Cramer, *ibid.*, **52**, 4355 (1930); cf. ref. 219.

[219] Gray and Marvel, *J. Am. Chem. Soc.*, **47**, 2799 (1925).

[220] Fichter and Holbro, *Helv. Chim. Acta*, **21**, 141 (1938).

[221] Skita and Rössler, *Ber.*, **72**, 269 (1939).

[222] Kindler and Blaas, *Ber.*, **76**, 1215 (1943).

[223] Owen and Robins, *J. Chem. Soc.*, 330 (1949); cf. ref. 224.

[224] Ungnade and Morriss, *J. Am. Chem. Soc.*, **70**, 1898 (1948).

[225] Meincke and McElvain, *J. Am. Chem. Soc.*, **57**, 1444 (1935).

[226] Linstead and Meade, *J. Chem. Soc.*, 943 (1934).

[227] Rydon, *J. Chem. Soc.*, 1341 (1937).

[228] Brown and Partridge, *J. Am. Chem. Soc.*, **66**, 839 (1944).

[229] Winterfeld and Rönsberg, *Arch. Pharm.*, **274**, 44 (1936).

[230] Jones and Tattersall, *J. Chem. Soc.*, **85**, 1693 (1904).

[231] Cason et al., *J. Am. Chem. Soc.*, **66**, 1764 (1944).

[232] Gresham et al., *J. Am. Chem. Soc.*, **70**, 999–1004 (1948); **72**, 72 (1950).

[233] Adams and Kamm, *Org. Syntheses*, Coll. Vol. I, 250 (1941); cf. ref. 151.

[234] Marvel, *Org. Syntheses*, **21**, 60 (1941).

[235] Weiner, *Org. Syntheses*, Coll. Vol. II, 279 (1943).

[236] Hurd, Jones, and Blunck, *J. Am. Chem. Soc.*, **57**, 2034 (1935).

[237] Dox, *J. Am. Chem. Soc.*, **46**, 1708 (1924).

[238] Shonle, Keltch, and Swanson, *J. Am. Chem. Soc.*, **52**, 2445 (1930).

[239] Peacock and Tha, *J. Chem. Soc.*, 2304 (1928).

[240] Karrer et al., *Helv. Chim. Acta*, **13**, 1296 (1930).

[241] Marvel, *Org. Syntheses*, **21**, 99 (1941).

[242] Fieser and Gates, *J. Am. Chem. Soc.*, **62**, 2338 (1940).

[243] Walter and McElvain, *J. Am. Chem. Soc.*, **57**, 1891 (1935).

[244] Kirner and Richter, *J. Am. Chem. Soc.*, **51**, 3132 (1929); cf. ref. 32.

[245] Shivers, Hudson, and Hauser, *J. Am. Chem. Soc.*, **66**, 309 (1944); Marshall, *J. Chem. Soc.*, 2336 (1931).

[246] Adkins and Davis, *J. Am. Chem. Soc.*, **71**, 2957 (1949).

[247] Hsueh and Marvel, *J. Am. Chem. Soc.*, **50**, 858 (1928).

[248] Koller and Kandler, *Monatsh.*, **58**, 233 (1931).

[249] Coleman, Callen, and Dornfeld, *J. Am. Chem. Soc.*, **68**, 1102 (1946).

[250] Kolloff et al., *J. Am. Chem. Soc.*, **70**, 3862 (1948).

[251] Hiers and Adams, *J. Am. Chem. Soc.*, **48**, 2390 (1936).

[252] Yohe and Adams, *J. Am. Chem. Soc.*, **50**, 1507 (1928); Arvin and Adams, *ibid.*, **50**, 1793 (1928); **49**, 2941 (1927).

[253] Levy, *Ann. chim.*, (11) **9**, 66 (1938); Cohen, Marshall, and Woodman, *J. Chem. Soc.*, 895, 896 (1915).

[254] Berger, *J. prakt. Chem.*, **152**, 302 (1939).

[255] Linstead et al., *J. Chem. Soc.*, 580 (1933); 1971 (1937); 1998 (1934); 2163 (1929); Noller and Adams, *J. Am. Chem. Soc.*, **48**, 2446 (1926).

[256] Cope et al., *J. Am. Chem. Soc.*, **62**, 314 (1940); **60**, 2645 (1938).

[257] Heisig and Stodola, *Org. Syntheses*, **23**, 16 (1943); Jeffery and Vogel, *J. Chem. Soc.*, 1805, 1806 (1948); Dox and Yoder, *J. Am. Chem. Soc.*, **43**, 680 (1921).

[258] Walborsky, *J. Am. Chem. Soc.*, **71**, 2941 (1949).

[259] Dox and Yoder, *J. Am. Chem. Soc.*, **43**, 2097 (1921); Cason and Allen, *J. Org. Chem.*, **14**, 1036 (1949); cf. ref. 257.

[260] Dox and Yoder, *J. Am. Chem. Soc.*, **43**, 1368 (1921); Jacobs and Florsheim, *ibid.*, **72**, 258 (1950); Skinner, Limperos, and Pettebone, *ibid.*, **72**, 1649 (1950).

[261] Guha and Ranganathan, *Ber.*, **69**, 1202 (1936).

[262] Guha and Seshadriengar, *Ber.*, **69**, 1215 (1936); Arbusow and Schapschinskaja, *ibid.*, **68**, 440 (1935); Altman, *Rec. trav. chim.*, **57**, 950 (1938).

[263] Rosenberg, Kneeland, and Skinner, *J. Am. Chem. Soc.*, **56**, 1340 (1934).

[264] Barnes and Gordon, *J. Am. Chem. Soc.*, **71**, 2646 (1949).

[265] Sayles and Degering, *J. Am. Chem. Soc.*, 71, 3162 (1949).

[266] Kobayashi, *Ann.*, 536, 156, 157 (1938).

[267] Wagner, *J. Am. Chem. Soc.*, 71, 3217 (1949); Elks, Elliott, and Hems, *J. Chem. Soc.*, 627 (1944); cf. ref. 275.

[268] Franke and Groeger, *Monatsh.*, 43, 55 (1922).

[269] Hurd and McAuley, *J. Am. Chem. Soc.*, 70, 1651 (1948).

[270] Adams and Long, *J. Am. Chem. Soc.*, 62, 2291 (1940).

[271] Hill, Salvin, and O'Brien, *J. Am. Chem. Soc.*, 59, 2385 (1937).

[272] McElvain and Burkett, *J. Am. Chem. Soc.*, 64, 1831 (1942).

[273] Work, *J. Chem. Soc.*, 198 (1946).

[274] Carter, *J. Am. Chem. Soc.*, 50, 1968, 1969 (1928).

[275] Hill and Keach, *J. Am. Chem. Soc.*, 48, 257 (1926).

[276] Swallen and Boord, *J. Am. Chem. Soc.*, 52, 658 (1930); Palomaa and Kenetti, *Ber.*, 64, 800 (1931); Prelog and Zalan, *Helv. Chim. Acta*, 27, 534 (1944).

[277] Prelog et al., *Ann.*, 545, 257 (1940); Gaubert, Linstead, and Rydon, *J. Chem. Soc.*, 1976 (1937).

[278] Hardegger, Redlich, and Gal, *Helv. Chim. Acta*, 28, 632 (1945).

[279] Marvel et al., *J. Am. Chem. Soc.*, 46, 2840 (1924).

[280] Karrer, Keller, and Usteri, *Helv. Chim. Acta*, 27, 239 (1944).

[281] Marvel, Zartman, and Bluthardt, *J. Am. Chem. Soc.*, 49, 2302 (1927).

[282] Curtius and Sandhaas, *J. prakt. Chem.*, 125, 95 (1930); Weizmann, *J. Org. Chem.*, 8, 287 (1943).

[283] Curtius, *J. prakt. Chem.*, 125, 291 (1930).

[284] Bernhard and Lincke, *Helv. Chim. Acta*, 29, 1462 (1946); Rydon, *J. Chem. Soc.*, 1444 (1936).

[285] Rydon, *J. Chem. Soc.*, 595 (1936).

[286] Galat, *J. Am. Chem. Soc.*, 68, 376 (1946).

[287] Cope and McElvain, *J. Am. Chem. Soc.*, 54, 4323 (1932).

[288] Cheney and Piening, *J. Am. Chem. Soc.*, 67, 733 (1945).

[289] Martin, Schepartz, and Daubert, *J. Am. Chem. Soc.*, 70, 2601 (1948).

[290] Kobayashi, *Ann.*, 536, 158 (1938).

[291] Magidson and Strukow, *Arch. Pharm.*, 271, 573, 575 (1933).

[292] Wojcik and Adkins, *J. Am. Chem. Soc.*, 56, 2424 (1934); Marvel, Myers, and Saunders, *ibid.*, 70, 1695 (1948); cf. ref. 294.

[293] Baker and Dodson, *J. Am. Chem. Soc.*, 68, 1284 (1946).

[294] Overberger and Roberts, *J. Am. Chem. Soc.*, 71, 3618 (1949).

[295] Cope, Kovacic, and Burg, *J. Am. Chem. Soc.*, 71, 3659 (1949).

[296] Cymerman, Heilbron, and Jones, *J. Chem. Soc.*, 147 (1944).

[297] Robinson and Walker, *J. Chem. Soc.*, 193 (1936); van der Zanden, *Rec. trav. chim.*, 57, 245 (1938).

[298] Shepard and Johnson, *J. Am. Chem. Soc.*, 54, 4389 (1932).

[299] Krollpfeiffer and Rosenberg, *Ber.*, 69, 465 (1936).

[300] Anker and Cook, *J. Chem. Soc.*, 312 (1945).

[301] Kuhn and Brydowna, *Ber.*, 70, 1333 (1937); Weinstock and May, *J. Am. Chem. Soc.*, 62, 3266 (1940).

[302] Eistert in *Newer Methods of Preparative Organic Chemistry*, Interscience Publishers, New York, 1948, p. 518.

[303] Johnson, McCloskey, and Dunnigan, *J. Am. Chem. Soc.*, 72, 516 (1950); Altschul, *ibid.*, 68, 2605 (1946).

[304] Scovill, Burk, and Lankelma, *J. Am. Chem. Soc.*, 66, 1039 (1944).

[305] Hennion and Nieuwland, *J. Am. Chem. Soc.*, 56, 1802 (1934).

[306] Dorris, Sowa, and Nieuwland, *J. Am. Chem. Soc.*, **56**, 2689 (1934).

[307] Moffett, Hart, and Hoehn, *J. Am. Chem. Soc.*, **69**, 1855 (1947); Buu-Hoi and Cagniant, *Bull. soc. chim. France*, (5) **9**, 102 (1942).

[308] Connor and McClellan, *J. Org. Chem.*, **3**, 570 (1939); Michael and Ross, *J. Am. Chem. Soc.*, **55**, 1632 (1933).

[309] Michael and Ross, *J. Am. Chem. Soc.*, **53**, 1150 (1931); **52**, 4598 (1930).

[310] Kloetzel, *J. Am. Chem. Soc.*, **70**, 3571 (1948); Leonard and Beck, *ibid.*, **70**, 2506 (1948).

[311] Warner and Moe, *J. Am. Chem. Soc.*, **70**, 3470 (1948); **71**, 2586 (1949).

[312] Connor, Fleming, and Clayton, *J. Am. Chem. Soc.*, **58**, 1386 (1936).

[313] Kohler and Butler, *J. Am. Chem. Soc.*, **48**, 1040 (1926).

[314] Doering and Weil, *J. Am. Chem. Soc.*, **69**, 2461 (1947); Boekelheide and Rothchild, *ibid.*, **71**, 882 (1949).

[315] Connor and Andrews, *J. Am. Chem. Soc.*, **56**, 2713 (1934); Bartlett and Woods, *ibid.*, **62**, 2937 (1940); Mannich and Koch, *Ber.*, **75**, 803 (1942); Dey and Linstead, *J. Chem. Soc.*, 1065 (1935); Kohler, *J. Am. Chem. Soc.*, **44**, 843 (1922); Holden and Lapworth, *J. Chem. Soc.*, 2368 (1931).

[316] Kohler, Graustein, and Merrill, *J. Am. Chem. Soc.*, **44**, 2536 (1922); Kohler and Souther, *ibid.*, **44**, 2903 (1922).

[317] Lin et al., *J. Chem. Soc.*, 72 (1937); Rapson and Robinson, *ibid.*, 1538 (1935); Cook and Linstead, *ibid.*, 959 (1934).

[318] Koelsch, *J. Am. Chem. Soc.*, **65**, 437 (1943).

[319] Weiss and Hauser, *J. Am. Chem. Soc.*, **71**, 2026 (1949).

[320] Levine and Hauser, *J. Am. Chem. Soc.*, **66**, 1768 (1944); cf. ref. 327.

[321] Walker et al., *J. Am. Chem. Soc.*, **68**, 672 (1946).

[322] Baumgarten, Levine, and Hauser, *J. Am. Chem. Soc.*, **66**, 862 (1944).

[323] Hauser, Abramovitch, and Adams, *J. Am. Chem. Soc.*, **64**, 2714 (1942).

[324] Wallingford, Homeyer, and Jones, *J. Am. Chem. Soc.*, **63**, 2056 (1941).

[325] Wallingford, Homeyer, and Jones, *J. Am. Chem. Soc.*, **63**, 2252 (1941).

[326] Soloway and LaForge, *J. Am. Chem. Soc.*, **69**, 2677 (1947); Green and La-Forge, *ibid.*, **70**, 2287 (1948).

[327] Jackman et al., *J. Am. Chem. Soc.*, **70**, 2885 (1948); cf. ref. 320.

[328] LaForge, Green, and Gersdorff, *J. Am. Chem. Soc.*, **70**, 3708 (1948).

[329] Jackman, Bergman, and Archer, *J. Am. Chem. Soc.*, **70**, 499 (1948).

[330] Weiss and Hauser, *J. Am. Chem. Soc.*, **71**, 2023 (1949).

[331] Horning and Finelli, *Org. Syntheses*, **30**, 43 (1950); *J. Am. Chem. Soc.*, **71**, 3204 (1949); Chamberlain et al., *ibid.*, **57**, 353 (1935); cf. refs. 154 and 333.

[332] Croxall and Schneider, *J. Am. Chem. Soc.*, **71**, 1257, 1261 (1949).

[333] Wallingford, Jones, and Homeyer, *J. Am. Chem. Soc.*, **64**, 576 (1942).

[334] Wallingford and Jones, *J. Am. Chem. Soc.*, **64**, 578 (1942).

[335] Levine and Hauser, *J. Am. Chem. Soc.*, **68**, 760 (1946).

[336] Swamer and Hauser, *J. Am. Chem. Soc.*, **72**, 1352 (1950).

[337] Rising and Zee, *J. Am. Chem. Soc.*, **50**, 1212 (1928).

[338] Rising and Zee, *J. Am. Chem. Soc.*, **49**, 544 (1927); Flürscheim and Holmes, *J. Chem. Soc.*, 2237 (1928).

[339] Lund, *Ber.*, **67**, 938 (1934).

[340] Buckley, Charlish, and Rose, *J. Chem. Soc.*, 1514 (1947); Kohler and Potter, *J. Am. Chem. Soc.*, **57**, 1318 (1935).

[341] Levene and Meyer, *Org. Syntheses*, Coll. Vol. II, 288 (1943); Souther, *J. Am. Chem. Soc.*, **46**, 1303 (1924).

[342] Keach, *J. Am. Chem. Soc.*, **55**, 3440 (1933); cf. ref. 147.

[343] Dessert and Halverstadt, *J. Am. Chem. Soc.*, **70**, 2595 (1948).
[344] Snyder, Brooks, and Shapiro, *Org. Syntheses*, Coll. Vol. II, 531 (1943).
[345] Blicke and Zienty, *J. Am. Chem. Soc.*, **63**, 2946 (1941).
[346] Floyd and Miller, *J. Am. Chem. Soc.*, **69**, 2354 (1947).
[347] Adkins, Isbell, and Wojcik, *Org. Syntheses*, Coll. Vol. II, 262 (1943); *J. Am. Chem. Soc.*, **54**, 3685 (1932).
[348] Linstead and Rydon, *J. Chem. Soc.*, 2000 (1934); Clemo and Welch, *ibid.*, 2626 (1928); cf. ref. 347.
[349] Chuang and Ma, *Ber.*, **68**, 872 (1935).
[350] Franke and Kroupa, *Monatsh.*, **69**, 192 (1936).
[351] Finkelstein and Elderfield, *J. Org. Chem.*, **4**, 371 (1939).
[352] Elderfield, Pitt, and Wempen, *J. Am. Chem. Soc.*, **72**, 1344 (1950).
[353] Renfrow and Walker, *J. Am. Chem. Soc.*, **70**, 3957 (1948).
[354] Cornubert and Borrel, *Bull. soc. chim. France*, **47**, 305 (1930).
[355] Swann, Oehler, and Buswell, *Org. Syntheses*, Coll. Vol. II, 276 (1943).
[356] Jones, *J. Am. Chem. Soc.*, **69**, 2352 (1947).
[357] Brown, Baker, et al., *J. Org. Chem.*, **12**, 163 (1947); cf. ref. 71.
[358] Fourneau and Sabetay, *Bull. soc. chim. France*, **43**, 859 (1928), 45, 834 (1929).
[359] Morgan and Walton, *J. Chem. Soc.*, 91 (1933).
[360] Carter, Frank, and Johnston, *Org. Syntheses*, **23**, 13 (1943); Farthing, *J. Chem. Soc.*, 3215 (1950).
[361] Strain et al., *J. Am. Chem. Soc.*, **72**, 1254 (1950).
[362] Slimowicz and Degering, *J. Am. Chem. Soc.*, **71**, 1044 (1949).
[363] Choppin and Rogers, *J. Am. Chem. Soc.*, **70**, 2967 (1948).
[364] Ashburn, Collett, and Lazzell, *J. Am. Chem. Soc.*, **60**, 2933 (1938).
[365] Kenyon, Phillips, and Pittman, *J. Chem. Soc.*, 1079 (1935).
[366] Bowden and Butler, *J. Chem. Soc.*, 78 (1939).
[367] Bowden and John, *J. Chem. Soc.*, 317 (1939); cf. ref. 372.
[368] Ritchie, *J. Chem. Soc.*, 1054 (1935).
[369] Robinson and Smith, *J. Chem. Soc.*, 394 (1926).
[370] Pierce and Adams, *J. Am. Chem. Soc.*, **45**, 791 (1923).
[371] Oesper, Broker, and Cook, *J. Am. Chem. Soc.*, **47**, 2609 (1925).
[372] Gomberg and Snow, *J. Am. Chem. Soc.*, **47**, 201 (1925).
[373] Hickinbottom, *Reactions of Organic Compounds*, 2nd ed., Longmans, Green and Co., New York, 1948, p. 99.
[374] Friess, *J. Am. Chem. Soc.*, **71**, 14 (1949).
[375] Robinson and Smith, *J. Chem. Soc.*, 373 (1937).
[376] von Wacek and von Bezard, *Ber.*, **74**, 845 (1941).
[377] Van Dorp and Arens, *Rec. trav. chim.*, **66**, 189 (1947).
[378] Young and Tarrant, *J. Am. Chem. Soc.*, **72**, 1860 (1950).
[379] Arnold, Buckles, and Stoltenberg, *J. Am. Chem. Soc.*, **66**, 208 (1944).
[380] Emerson et al., *J. Am. Chem. Soc.*, **68**, 674 (1946).
[381] Cope and McElvain, *J. Am. Chem. Soc.*, **54**, 4315 (1932).
[382] Houben and Fischer, *Ber.*, **64**, 244 (1931).
[383] Man, Sanderson, and Hauser, *J. Am. Chem. Soc.*, **72**, 847 (1950).
[384] Späth and Schmid, *Ber.*, **73**, 248 (1940); cf. ref. 385.
[385] Ulich and Adams, *J. Am. Chem. Soc.*, **43**, 660 (1921).
[386] Burger and Yost, *J. Am. Chem. Soc.*, **70**, 2198 (1948).
[387] Clemo and Metcalfe, *J. Chem. Soc.*, 607 (1936); Nenitzescu and Solomonica, *Ber.*, **64**, 1927 (1931).

[388] Linville and Elderfield, *J. Org. Chem.*, 6, 271 (1941).
[389] Wagner and Moore, *J. Am. Chem. Soc.*, 72, 974 (1950); cf. ref. 392.
[390] Aston et al., *J. Am. Chem. Soc.*, 64, 301 (1942).
[391] Aston and Greenburg, *J. Am. Chem. Soc.*, 62, 2590 (1940).
[392] Wagner, *J. Am. Chem. Soc.*, 71, 3214 (1949).
[393] Suter and Evans, *J. Am. Chem. Soc.*, 60, 537 (1938).
[394] Wagner and Moore, *J. Am. Chem. Soc.*, 72, 1873 (1950).
[395] Faworsky, *J. prakt. Chem.*, 88, 641 (1913).
[396] Newman and Fones, *J. Am. Chem. Soc.*, 69, 1046 (1947).
[397] Bourne et al., *J. Chem. Soc.*, 2976 (1949).
[398] Feuer, Hass, and Warren, *J. Am. Chem. Soc.*, 71, 3078 (1949).
[399] Woodward and Kornfeld, *Org. Syntheses*, 29, 44 (1949).
[400] Church and Lynn, *Ind. Eng. Chem.*, 42, 772 (1950).
[401] Buckles and Mock, *J. Org. Chem.*, 15, 680 (1950).
[402] Wagner, *J. Chem. Education*, 27, 245 (1950).
[403] Heyboer and Staverman, *Rec. trav. chim.*, 69, 794 (1950).
[404] Smith and McKenzie, *J. Org. Chem.*, 15, 74 (1950).
[405] Frank and Reiner, *J. Am. Chem. Soc.*, 72, 4183 (1950).
[406] Emerson and Patrick, *J. Org. Chem.*, 14, 792 (1949).
[407] Newman and Beal, *J. Am. Chem. Soc.*, 72, 5163 (1950).
[408] Wagner and Tome, *J. Am. Chem. Soc.*, 72, 3477 (1950).
[409] Weizmann, Bergmann, and Sulzbacher, *J. Org. Chem.*, 15, 919 (1950).
[410] van Tamelen and Van Zyl, *J. Am. Chem. Soc.*, 72, 2979 (1950).
[411] Avison and Morrison, *J. Chem. Soc.*, 1473 (1950).
[412] Smith and McKenzie, *J. Org. Chem.*, 15, 78 (1950).
[413] Siegel and Bergstrom, *J. Am. Chem. Soc.*, 72, 3816 (1950).
[414] Bahner and Kite, *J. Am. Chem. Soc.*, 71, 3597 (1949).
[415] Leonard and Felley, *J. Am. Chem. Soc.*, 71, 1758, 1760 (1949); 72, 2542 (1950).
[416] Smith and Engelhardt, *J. Am. Chem. Soc.*, 71, 2678 (1949); Kloetzel, *ibid.*, 69, 2272 (1947).
[417] Schmidt and Shirley, *J. Am. Chem. Soc.*, 71, 3804 (1949).
[418] Adelman, *J. Org. Chem.*, 14, 1057 (1949); Swern and Jordan, *Org. Syntheses*, 30, 106 (1950).
[419] Wagner and Moore, *J. Am. Chem. Soc.*, 72, 2887 (1950).
[420] Alexander, McCollum, and Paul, *J. Am. Chem. Soc.*, 72, 4791 (1950).
[421] Marvel, Myers, and Saunders, *J. Am. Chem. Soc.*, 70, 1695 (1948).
[422] Hsing and Li, *J. Am. Chem. Soc.*, 71, 774 (1949).
[423] Moffatt, Newbery, and Webster, *J. Chem. Soc.*, 452 (1946).
[424] Hennion, Hinton, and Nieuwland, *J. Am. Chem. Soc.*, 55, 2858 (1933).
[425] Linstead et al., *J. Chem. Soc.*, 3326–3335 (1950); Swann, Oehler, and Pinkney, *Org. Syntheses*, 21, 48 (1941); Fichter and Holbro, *Helv. Chim. Acta*, 21, 141 (1938).
[426] Fuson, Corse, and Horning, *J. Am. Chem. Soc.*, 61, 1290 (1939).
[427] Newman and Walborsky, *J. Am. Chem. Soc.*, 72, 4296 (1950).
[428] Le Fave and Scheurer, *J. Am. Chem. Soc.*, 72, 2464 (1950).
[429] Norton, *J. Am. Chem. Soc.*, 72, 3527 (1950).
[430] Cope and Field, *J. Org. Chem.*, 14, 856 (1949).
[431] Lund and Voigt, *Org. Syntheses*, Coll. Vol. II, 594 (1943).
[432] Corson and Sayre, *Org. Syntheses*, Coll. Vol. II, 596 (1943).

15

Lactones

CONTENTS

323. Intramolecular Esterification of Hydroxy Acids

$$RCH(OH)CH_2CH_2CO_2H \underset{}{\overset{H^+}{\rightleftharpoons}} R\underset{\underset{O}{\rule{1.2cm}{0.4pt}}}{C}HCH_2CH_2CO + H_2O$$

The equilibrium between a hydroxy acid and its lactone is catalyzed by hydrogen ion. This equilibrium favors lactone formation from γ- and δ-hydroxy acids; removal of the water formed completes the reaction. β-Lactones are not obtained directly by this method. Under forced conditions γ-lactones are formed from certain β-hydroxy acids, presumably by dehydration of the latter to olefinic acids followed by lactonization according to method 324.[19, 20] Direct lactonization of hydroxy acids having the hydroxyl group in the *epsilon* or a more remote position in the chain is difficult. Competing interesterification reactions occur which lead to dimers and polyesters. Under certain conditions, however, ϵ-caprolactone has been obtained in 63% yield.[11]

Many of the methods listed for the preparation of hydroxy acids (Table 47) have been used to prepare lactones directly. Reduction of levulinic acid, $CH_3COCH_2CH_2CO_2H$, by sodium and alcohol or by catalytic hydrogenation over Raney nickel leads to γ-valerolactone.[1] δ-Caprolactone is prepared in a similar manner from γ-acetobutyric acid.[5] Other δ-lactones have been formed by catalytic hydrogenation of the corresponding aldehydo acids.[22] A number of γ-substituted-γ-lactones are best made by the action of Grignard reagents on levulinic esters followed by acid hydrolysis.[2-4, 6]

$$CH_3COCH_2CH_2CO_2R \xrightarrow{R'MgX} CH_3C(R')(OMgX)CH_2CH_2CO_2R \xrightarrow[H^+]{H_2O}$$

$$CH_3\underset{\underset{O}{\rule{3cm}{0.4pt}}}{CR'CH_2CH_2C}O$$

Sodiomalonic esters behave like organometalic reagents toward alkene oxides. Acid hydrolysis of the adduct accompanied by decarboxylation and lactonization furnishes α-substituted lactones in high yields.[12, 30] γ-Substituted γ-butyrolactones result from sodiomalonic ester and substituted ethylene oxides.[13, 15, 17, 29]

$$RCH(CO_2C_2H_5)_2 \xrightarrow[\underset{O}{\overset{R'CH-CH_2}{\diagdown\diagup}}]{NaOC_2H_5;} NaOCHR'CH_2CR(CO_2C_2H_5)_2 \xrightarrow[H^+]{H_2O}$$

$$\underset{\underset{O}{\rule{3cm}{0.4pt}}}{CHR'CH_2CHRC}O$$

Cyanoacetic ester may be used in place of malonic ester. The intermediate α-cyano lactones are isolated in good yields.[16]

Other functional groups can be present in the molecule during lactonization. Thus, *olefinic*,[13, 24] *halo*,[17] *hydroxy*,[8-10, 27] and *carboxy*[7] lactones have been prepared by this method.

324. Cyclization of Olefinic Acids

$$RCH=CHCH_2CO_2H \rightarrow \underset{\underset{O}{\rule{2.5cm}{0.4pt}}}{RCHCH_2CH_2C}O$$

β,γ-Olefinic acids are readily converted to γ-lactones by the action of boiling 50% sulfuric acid.[23, 34-36] Branching on the γ-carbon atom greatly increases the ease of lactonization. The same lactones are obtained from the more readily available α,β-olefinic acids, which are isomerized and lactonized under the same conditions.

Vinylacetic acid, $CH_2=CHCH_2CO_2H$, is converted mainly to its α,β-isomer rather than to γ-butyrolactone.[23]

The lactonization of allylacetic acid, $CH_2=CHCH_2CH_2CO_2H$, gives γ-valerolactone free from the δ-isomer, whereas lactonization of γ,δ-isoheptenoic acid, $(CH_3)_2C=CHCH_2CH_2CO_2H$, involves six-membered ring formation to give the corresponding δ-lactone. In the latter case the lactonization is an equilibrium reaction above $200°$.[38]

325. Cyclization of Halo Acids

$$XCH_2CH_2CH_2CO_2H \xrightarrow{NaOC_2H_5} \underset{\underset{O}{\rule{2.5cm}{0.5pt}}}{CH_2CH_2CH_2CO}$$

Several variations of this reaction are possible. The halo acid is boiled with a solution of sodium in absolute alcohol as in the formation of γ-butyrolactone (67%),[39] or the dry sodium salt of a halo acid is heated under vacuum as in the preparation of δ-valerolactone (30%).[38] The corresponding esters are sometimes refluxed with alcoholic potassium hydroxide[39] or decomposed thermally at $150–180°$ whereby a molecule of an alkyl halide is eliminated.[42] The latter process is valuable in making α-alkyl-γ-lactones of higher-molecular-weight acids since the γ-bromo esters are available by the free-radical addition of α-bromo esters to 1-olefins.

$$R_2CBrCO_2CH_3 \xrightarrow{R'CH=CH_2} R'CHBrCH_2CR_2CO_2CH_3 \xrightarrow{180°} \underset{\underset{O}{\rule{2.5cm}{0.5pt}}}{R'CHCH_2CR_2CO}$$

The α-bromine atom is stable during lactone formation from α,γ-dibromobutyryl bromide; the yield of α-bromo lactone is 94%.[25] Under similar conditions the β-bromine atom of β,γ-dibromohexanoic acid is eliminated as hydrogen bromide to give the lactone of 4-hydroxy-2-hexenoic acid.[26]

Cyclization of alkali salts of 15-bromopentadecanoic acid has been studied using various solvents and concentrations. Best yields of the ω-lactone are obtained from the potassium salt in methyl ethyl ketone.[41]

A related reaction which probably involves silver salts of ω-halo acids as intermediates is useful in the preparation of β-substituted-γ-lactones (cf. method 61). The silver salts of β-substituted glutaric acids are treated with iodine at $100–150°$, whereby the lactones are produced in 30–50% yields.[40]

326. Reduction of Anhydrides

$$
\begin{array}{ccc}
\overset{\displaystyle CO}{\diagup\quad\diagdown} & & \overset{\displaystyle CH_2}{\diagup\quad\diagdown} \\
(CH_2)_3\;\;\;O & \xrightarrow[C_2H_5OH]{Na} & (CH_2)_3\;\;\;O \\
\diagdown\quad\diagup & & \diagdown\quad\diagup \\
\underset{\displaystyle CO}{} & & \underset{\displaystyle CO}{}
\end{array}
$$

Substituted δ-valerolactones are formed by reduction of the corresponding glutaric anhydrides by sodium in absolute ethanol. Most of the product is hydrolyzed during the isolation procedure, but the resulting hydroxy acid is lactonized by refluxing with mineral acid. In general, the yields are poor (25–50%), although β,β-dimethyl-δ-valerolactone is reported in 76% yield by this method.[44]

The dihydroxy lactone from L-threonic acid is prepared from L-dibenzoyl tartaric anhydride by catalytic hydrogenation over palladium.[43] The substituted anhydride is formed from tartaric acid and benzoyl chloride.

327. Condensation of Ketene with Carbonyl Compounds

$$CH_3CHO + CH_2 = C = O \xrightarrow{ZnCl_2} CH_3\underset{\underset{O}{\big|\_\_\_\_\big|}}{C}HCH_2CO$$

In the presence of suitable catalysts, β-lactones are formed by the action of ketene on aldehydes and ketones. Many catalysts have been used; those preferred for aldehydes include boric acid, triacetyl borate, zinc thiocyanate, and zinc chloride. Ketones require stronger catalysts such as boron trifluoride etherate. The reactions are conducted at low temperatures (0–10°) to minimize polymerization of the product. Yields of β-lactones from formaldehyde and acetaldehyde are 85%.[47] The β-lactones formed from conjugated olefinic ketones decompose to dienoic acids which isomerize to olefinic δ-lactones.[48]

$$RCH = CH\underset{\underset{O}{\big|\_\_\_\_\big|}}{C}(CH_3)CH_2CO \rightarrow RCH = CHC(CH_3) = CHCO_2H \rightleftharpoons$$

$$R\underset{\underset{O}{\big|_____\big|}}{C}HCH = C(CH_3)CH_2CO$$

328. Dehydrogenation of Diols

$$CH_3CH(OH)CH_2CH_2CH_2CH_2OH \xrightarrow{CuCrO} CH_3\underset{\underset{O}{\big|_____\big|}}{C}HCH_2CH_2CH_2CO$$

Aliphatic glycols having one primary hydroxyl group and a second hydroxyl group in the 4- or 5-position dehydrogenate to γ- and δ-lactones, respectively. Loss of hydrogen occurs at 200–210° over copper chromite catalyst. γ-Butyrolactone and γ- and δ-valerolactones have been prepared by this procedure.[28,32] The reaction may go through the lactole form of the hydroxy aldehyde since δ-valerolactone is readily prepared by air oxidation of the corresponding hydroxy aldehyde.[33]

329. Olefinic Lactones by Pyrolysis of γ-Keto Acids [49]

$$CH_3COCH_2CH_2CO_2H \cdots \rightarrow CH_3\underset{\underset{O}{\Big\lfloor}}{C}{=}CHCH_2\underset{}{C}O + H_2O$$

330. Keto Lactones by Condensation Reactions [50]

(1) $\quad RCHO + CH_3COCH_2COCO_2C_2H_5 \xrightarrow{\text{Base}} R\underset{\underset{O}{\Big\lfloor}}{C}HCH(COCH_3)\underset{}{C}O\underset{}{C}O$

(2) $\quad CH_3CH_2CO_2C_2H_5 \xrightarrow[\text{NaOCH}_3]{(CO_2C_2H_5)_2} CH_3CH(CO_2C_2H_5)COCO_2C_2H_5 \xrightarrow[\text{HCl}]{\text{HCHO;}}$

$$\underset{\underset{O}{\Big\lfloor}}{C}H_2CH(CH_3)\underset{}{C}O\underset{}{C}O + CO_2 + C_2H_5OH$$

TABLE 59. LACTONES

C_n	Compound	Method	Yield (%)	Chapter[ref.]	B.p./mm., n_D^t, (M.p.)
C_3	Propionolactone	327	84	15[47]	28/3, 1.4135
C_4	β-Butyrolactone	327	85	15[47]	61/10
	γ-Butyrolactone	323	72†	15[31]	201-205
		325	67	15[39]	202-206, 1.4343[27]
		325	30†	15[23]	84/12
	Isocrotonolactone	19	53	15[10]	80-86/7
	α-Bromo-γ-butyrolactone	67	82	15[45]	131/8, 1.5094[25]
		325	94	15[25]	130-135/20
	β-Hydroxybutyrolactone	323	35	15[10]	148/4
	α-Amino-γ-butyrolactone hydrobromide		55	15[25]	(218)
C_5	γ-Valerolactone	79	81	5[2]	1.4319[25]
		323	94	15[1]	90/10, 1.4301[25]
		328	87	15[28]	91/16, 1.4290[26]
	δ-Valerolactone	323	100	15[14]	133/7, (53)
		328	71	15[32]	105/8, 1.4553[25]
	β-Methyl-γ-butyrolactone	325	35	15[40]	88/12
	δ-Chloro-γ-valerolactone	323	67†	15[17]	134
	4-Hydroxy-2-pentenoic acid lactone	323	68†	15[24]	84/10, 1.4532[21]
	5-Hydroxy-2-pentenoic acid lactone	323	61†	15[24]	103/10, 1.4827[17]
	α-Hydroxy-γ-valerolactone	323	45	15[9]	89/0.2
	α-Hydroxy-δ-valerolactone	323	64	15[9]	124/10
	α-Keto-β-methyl-γ-butyrolactone	330	83	15[50]	129/12, (92)
C_6	γ-Caprolactone	324	74	15[34]	86/10, 1.4387
	δ-Caprolactone	323	50†	15[5]	230
	ε-Caprolactone	323	63	15[11]	99/2, 1.4608[24]
	α-Methyl-γ-valerolactone	324	81	15[36]	81/10, 1.4289
	β-Methyl-δ-valerolactone	326	25	15[40]	90/12
	α-Ethyl-γ-butyrolactone	323	88†	15[12]	214/740
	β-Ethyl-γ butyrolactone	325	40	15[40]	99/12
	α,α-Dimethylbutyrolactone	323	55†	15[18]	196
	β,β-Dimethyl-γ-butyrolactone	325	30	15[40]	89/12, (56)
	γ,γ-Dimethylbutyrolactone	323	62†	15[6]	201-206/760
	4-Hydroxy-2-hexenoic acid lactone	325	20†	15[26]	95/11, 1.462[21]
	4-Hydroxy-4-methyl-2-pentenoic acid lactone	323	60†	15[24]	80/10, 1.4470[18]
	γ-Vinyl-γ-butyrolactone	323	64†	15[13]	75/2, 1.4603[25]
	α-Hydroxy-β,β-dimethyl-γ-butyrolactone	323	81	15[8]	120/15
	α-Amino-γ,γ-dimethyl-γ-butyrolactone	324	85	15[37]	(209)
	α-Cyano-γ-valerolactone	323	61†	15[16]	109/0.35, 1.4558[25]

TABLE 59. LACTONES 539

TABLE 59 *(continued)*

C_n	Compound	Method	Yield (%)	Chapter[ref.]	B.p./mm., n_D^t, (M.p.)
C_7	γ-Pimelolactone	323	96	15[7]	174/13
	β-Ethyl-δ-valerolactone	326	28	15[40]	104/13
	β,β-Dimethyl-δ-valerolactone	326	76	15[44]	119/20, (29)
	α-n-Propyl-γ-butyrolactone	323	70 †	15[30]	107/15, 1.4410
	β-Methyl-β-ethyl-γ-butyrolactone	325	40	15[40]	98/10
	γ-Methyl-γ-ethylbutyrolactone	323	65 †	15[4]	103/15, 1.4412
	Cyclopentanol-2-acetic acid lactone	324	78	15[35]	124/17
	β-Methyl-β,γ-hexeno-δ-lactone	327	95	15[48]	85/5, 1.4640[30]
	4-Hydroxy-2-heptenoic acid lactone	323	82 †	15[24]	73/0.05, 1.4596[18]
	α-Hydroxy-β-methyl-β-ethyl-γ-butyrolactone	323	76 †	15[27]	140/20
	δ-Ethoxy-γ-valerolactone	115	90	15[17]	128/14
	α-Cyano-γ-isocaprolactone	323	82 †	15[16]	131/1.4, 1.4515[25]
C_8	γ-Caprylolactone	323	70 †	15[29]	127/16, 1.4451[19]
	β-Methyl-β-ethyl-δ-valerolactone	326	30	15[40]	122/10
	β-t-Butyl-γ-butyrolactone	323	94	15[20]	117/22, (100)
	γ-Methyl-γ-propylbutyrolactone	323	73 †	15[3]	129/25
	β,β-Diethyl-γ-butyrolactone	325	50	15[40]	117/12
	trans-Cyclohexanol-2-acetic acid lactone	323	77 †	15[15]	119/6
	3-Methyl-3-hydroxycyclohexanecarboxylic acid lactone	324	77	15[36]	(44)
	Phthalide	323	71 †	15[21]	(73)
C_9	β,β-Diethyl-δ-valerolactone	326	50	15[40]	144/15
	γ,γ-Diethyl-δ-valerolactone	323	80 †	15[22]	101/2.5, 1.4634[25]
	γ-Methyl-γ-n-butylbutyrolactone	323	60 †	15[4]	86/2, 1.4452
C_{10}	γ-Decanolactone	325	48	15[42]	84/0.2, 1.4489
	β-Cyclohexylbutyrolactone	323	79	15[19]	125/1.2, 1.4794[25]
	γ-Phenyl-γ-butyrolactone	323	72 †	15[13]	130/1.5, (46)
C_{11}	γ-Methyl-γ-phenylbutyrolactone	323	50 †	15[2]	129/3, 1.5310
C_{15}	ω-Pentadecanolactone	325	85	15[41]	122/0.1, (37)
	α,α-Diphenyl-β-propiolactone	325	61	15[52]	178/15, (92)
	Benzylphthalide	....	100	15[46]	190–200/5, (61)

For explanations and symbols see pp. xi–xii.

REFERENCES FOR CHAPTER 15

[1] Schuette and Sah, *J. Am. Chem. Soc.*, 48, 3163 (1926); Christian, Brown, and Hixon, *ibid.*, 69, 1961 (1947).

[2] Arnold and Buckley, *J. Am. Chem. Soc.*, 71, 1782 (1949).

[3] Cason et al., *J. Am. Chem. Soc.*, 66, 1765 (1944).

[4] Frank et al., *J. Am. Chem. Soc.*, 70, 1380 (1948).

[5] Winterfield and Rönsberg, *Arch. Pharm.*, 274, 44 (1936).

[6] Arnold, Buckley, and Richter, *J. Am. Chem. Soc.*, 69, 2323 (1947).

[7] Tchitchibabine, *Bull. soc. chim. France*, (5) 8, 672 (1941.

[8] Carter and Ney, *J. Am. Chem. Soc.*, 63, 313 (1941); Stiller et al., *ibid.*, 62, 1787 (1940); cf. ref. 9.

[9] Reichstein and Grüssner, *Helv. Chim. Acta*, 23, 650 (1940).

[10] Glattfeld and Rietz, *J. Am. Chem. Soc.*, 62, 974 (1940).

[11] Van Natta, Hill, and Carothers, *J. Am. Chem. Soc.*, 56, 455 (1934); 58, 183, (1936); Stoll and Rouve, *Helv. Chim. Acta*, 18, 1087 (1935).

[12] Meincke and McElvain, *J. Am. Chem. Soc.*, 57, 1444 (1935).

[13] Russell and Vanderwerf, *J. Am. Chem. Soc.*, 69, 11 (1947).

[14] Guest, *J. Am. Chem. Soc.*, 69, 301 (1947).

[15] Newman and Vanderwerf, *J. Am. Chem. Soc.*, 67, 235 (1945).

[16] Glickman and Cope, *J. Am. Chem. Soc.*, 67, 1012 (1945).

[17] Winterfeld and Holschneider, *Arch. Pharm.*, 277, 227 (1939).

[18] Hudson and Hauser, *J. Am. Chem. Soc.*, 63, 3162 (1941).

[19] Blout and Elderfield, *J. Org. Chem.*, 8, 29 (1943).

[20] Newman and Rosher, *J. Org. Chem.*, 9, 221 (1944).

[21] Gardner and Naylor, *Org. Syntheses*, Coll. Vol. II, 526 (1943).

[22] Bruson and Riener, *J. Am. Chem. Soc.*, 66, 58 (1944).

[23] Boorman and Linstead, *J. Chem. Soc.*, 578 (1933).

[24] Haynes and Jones, *J. Chem. Soc.*, 954 (1946).

[25] Plieninger, *Chem. Ber.*, 83, 267 (1950); cf. ref. 45.

[26] Kuhn and Jerchel, *Ber.*, 76, 417 (1943).

[27] Wieland and Möller, *Chem. Ber.*, 81, 321 (1948).

[28] Kyrides and Zienty, *J. Am. Chem. Soc.*, 68, 1385 (1946).

[29] Rothstein, *Bull. soc. chim. France*, (5) 2, 1940 (1935).

[30] Rothstein, *Bull. soc. chim. France*, (5) 2, 85 (1935).

[31] Nelson and Cretcher, *J. Am. Chem. Soc.*, 52, 3703 (1930).

[32] Schniepp and Geller, *J. Am. Chem. Soc.*, 69, 1545 (1947).

[33] Bremmer, Jones, and Taylor, U. S. pat. 2,429,799 (1947); *C. A.* 42, 923 (1948)

[34] Linstead, *J. Chem. Soc.*, 115 (1932).

[35] Linstead and Meade, *J. Chem. Soc.*, 942 (1934).

[36] Boorman and Linstead, *J. Chem. Soc.*, 258 (1935).

[37] Fillman and Albertson, *J. Am. Chem. Soc.*, 70, 171 (1948).

[38] Linstead and Rydon, *J. Chem. Soc.*, 580 (1933).

[39] Marvel and Birkhimer, *J. Am. Chem. Soc.*, 51, 261 (1929); Blicke, Wright, and Zienty, *ibid.*, 63, 2488 (1941).

[40] Sircar, *J. Chem. Soc.*, 898 (1928); Pattison and Saunders, *ibid.*, 2747 (1949).

[41] Stoll, *Helv. Chim. Acta*, 30, 1393 (1947).

[42] Kharasch, Skell, and Fisher, *J. Am. Chem. Soc.*, 70, 1059 (1948).

[43] Micheel and Peschke, *Ber.*, 75, 1603 (1942).

[44] Rydon, *J. Chem. Soc.*, 595 (1936).

[45] Livak et al., *J. Am. Chem. Soc.*, 67, 2219 (1945); cf. ref. 25.

[46] Natelson and Gottfried, *J. Am. Chem. Soc.*, **58**, 1434 (1936); Weiss, *Org. Syntheses*, Coll. Vol. II, 61 (1943).
[47] Hagemeyer, *Ind. Eng. Chem.*, **41**, 765 (1949).
[48] Young, *J. Am. Chem. Soc.*, **71**, 1346 (1949).
[49] Thiele, *Ann.*. 319. 144 (1901).
[50] Nield, *J. Am. Chem. Soc.*, **67**, 1147 (1945); Fleck et al., *Helv. Chim. Acta*, **33**, 130 (1950); Puetzer, Nield, and Barry, *J. Am. Chem. Soc.*, **67**, 832 (1945).
[51] Cavallito, Fruehauf, and Bailey, *J. Am. Chem. Soc.*, **70**, 3724 (1948).
[52] Zaugg, *J. Am. Chem. Soc.*, **72**, 2999 (1950).

16

Ortho Esters

The chemistry of aliphatic ortho esters has been reviewed to 1943, and their preparation by the following four methods, as well as several lesser used reactions, has been treated in detail.[19]

331. Alcoholysis of Orthothioformates

$$HC(SC_2H_5)_3 + 3ROH \underset{}{\overset{ZnCl_2}{\rightleftharpoons}} HC(OR)_3 + 3C_2H_5SH$$

This interchange reaction is a convenient process for making orthoformates.[1] The equilibrium is shifted to the right by removal of the volatile mercaptan to give high yields of the ortho esters. The reaction is catalyzed by Friedel-Crafts type catalysts. The ethyl orthothioformate is available in nearly quantitative yield from ethyl formate and ethyl mercaptan.

332. Alcoholysis of Imino Ester Hydrochlorides

$$RCN \xrightarrow[HCl]{R'OH} RC(OR')=NH \cdot HCl \xrightarrow{R''OH} RC(OR')(OR'')_2$$

This is the best reaction for the preparation of ortho esters. The imino ester hydrochlorides are available in excellent yields by partial alcoholysis of nitriles (method 402). In early procedures, the hydrochlorides and excess alcohol were allowed to stand at room temperature for 5 to 40 days.[13] The time of reaction can be reduced to 6 to 28 hours by carrying out the alcoholysis in refluxing ether solution.[6] Good yields are common for both steps in the process.[17] The principal side reaction is the thermal

542

decomposition of the imino ester hydrochloride to an amide and an alkyl chloride.[10,12] This reaction may be minimized by keeping the temperature of alcoholysis below 40°. Imino esters of the type $C_6H_5CHRC(OCH_3){=}NH \cdot HCl$ undergo alcoholysis with methanol to give dimethyl ether and esters, $C_6H_5CHRCO_2CH_3$, in addition to orther esters.[12] Ortho esters with chloro[9] or ethoxyl[7] groups in the *alpha* position or a cyano group in the *alpha* or *beta* position have been made. A variation in the procedure allows the preparation of a diortho ester from succinonitrile.[5]

333. Interaction of Trihalides and Sodium Alkoxides

$$CHCl_3 + 3NaOR \longrightarrow CH(OR)_3 + 3NaCl$$

This reaction is similar to the Williamson synthesis of ethers (method 115). Orthoformates in which the alkyl group is methyl, ethyl, n-propyl, isopropyl, n-butyl, isobutyl, and isoamyl have been prepared from chloroform.[2] The yield of ethyl orthoformate is 45%.[3] Mixed esters are obtained from a mixture of sodium alkoxides and chloroform.[4] Benzotrichloride, $C_6H_5CCl_3$, is converted to methyl orthobenzoate in 86% yield by sodium methoxide in methanol.[18]

334. Halogenation of Ortho Esters

$$RCH_2C(OR')_3 \xrightarrow[C_5H_5N]{Br_2} RCHBrC(OR')_3$$

Ortho esters may be brominated in pyridine solution. The reaction takes place rapidly at 10–30° to give good yields of α-bromoörtho esters.[9,14] Higher yields are obtained when a mixture of carbon tetrachloride and pyridine is used as solvent.[11] The reaction fails for ethyl orthoisobutyrate.[16] Two α-hydrogen atoms of ethyl orthoacetate have been replaced by bromine atoms to give ethyl orthodibromoacetate (53%).[7] Bromine is replaced by iodine when an orthobromo ester is heated with sodium iodide in absolute alcohol.[9] (cf. method 55).

TABLE 60. ORTHO ESTERS

C_n	Compound	Method	Yield %	Chapter[ref.]	B.p./mm., n_D^t, (M.p.)
C_5	Methyl orthobromoacetate	334	70	16^{15}	75/17, 1.4501[25]
C_6	Methyl orthopropionate	332	69	16^{13}	127
	Methyl ortho-β,β,β-trichloropropionate	332	84	16^5	92/4, 1.4578[25]
	Methyl orthocyanoacetate	332	65	16^5	100/13, 1.4215[25]
C_7	Methyl orthoisobutyrate	332	43	16^{18}	136, 1.4003[25]
	Methyl ortho-β-cyanopropionate	332	77	16^5	74/0.5, 1.4269[25]
	Ethyl orthoformate	331	66	16^1	145, 1.3917[24]
		333	45	16^3	
C_8	Methyl orthovalerate	332	79	16^{11}	165, 1.4090[24]
	Methyl ortho-α-bromovalerate	334	79	16^{11}	95/14, 1.4507[25]
	Methyl ortho-β-carbomethoxypropionate	332	63	16^5	65/1, 1.4230[25]
	Ethyl orthoacetate	332	78	16^6	145/740
	Ethyl orthochloroacetate	332	73	16^6	69/10
		332	15	16^9	75/13, 1.4199[25]
	Ethyl orthobromoacetate	334	74	16^9	78/9, 1.4393[25]
	Ethyl orthodibromoacetate	334	53	16^7	103/8, 1.4691[25]
	Ethyl orthoiodoacetate	55	60	16^9	97/10, 1.4660[25]
C_9	Ethyl orthopropionate	332	78	16^6	71/32
		332	48	16^8	44/9, 1.4000
	Ethyl ortho-α-bromopropionate	334	67	16^8	73/8, 1.4338[25]
	Ethyl orthocyanoacetate	332	62	16^5	84/2, 1.4189[25]
C_{10}	Ethyl orthoethoxyacetate	332	47	16^7	70/10, 1.4055[25]
	Methyl orthobenzoate	333	86	16^{18}	115/25, 1.4858[25]
C_{11}	Ethyl ortho-α-bromoisovalerate	334	67	16^{14}	64/1.3, 1.4408[25]
	Ethyl orthocarboethoxyacetate	332	82	16^5	121/18, 1.4220[25]
	Methyl orthophenylacetate	332	46	16^{18}	74/0.5
C_{12}	Methyl α-phenylorthopropionate	332	21	16^{12}	71/0.5, 1.4928[25]
	Phenyl diethyl orthochloroacetate	332	69	16^{10}	79/10, 1.4988
	Phenyl diethyl orthobromoacetate	332	54	16^{10}	85/2, 1.5048

For explanations and symbols see pp. xi–xii.

REFERENCES FOR CHAPTER 16

[1] Mochel, Agre, and Hanford, *J. Am. Chem. Soc.*, **70**, 2268 (1948).
[2] Sah and Ma, *J. Am. Chem. Soc.*, **54**, 2964 (1932).
[3] Kaufmann and Dreger, *Org. Syntheses*, Coll. Vol. I, 258 (1941).
[4] Post and Erickson, *J. Am. Chem. Soc.*, **55**, 3851 (1933).
[5] McElvain and Schroeder, *J. Am. Chem. Soc.*, **71**, 40 (1949).
[6] McElvain and Nelson, *J. Am. Chem. Soc.*, **64**, 1825 (1942).
[7] McElvain and Walters, *J. Am. Chem. Soc.*, **64**, 1963 (1942).
[8] Walters and McElvain, *J. Am. Chem. Soc.*, **62**, 1483 (1940).
[9] Beyerstedt and McElvain, *J. Am. Chem. Soc.*, **59**, 1273 (1937).
[10] McElvain and Fajardo-Pinzon, *J. Am. Chem. Soc.*, **67**, 690 (1945).
[11] McElvain, Kent, and Stevens, *J. Am. Chem. Soc.*, **68**, 1922 (1946).
[12] McElvain and Stevens, *J. Am. Chem. Soc.*, **69**, 2663 (1947).
[13] Sah, *J. Am. Chem. Soc.*, **50**, 516 (1928); Brooker and White, *ibid.*, **57**, 2485 (1935).
[14] McElvain, Clarke, and Jones, *J. Am. Chem. Soc.*, **64**, 1969 (1942).
[15] McElvain, Anthes, and Shapiro, *J. Am. Chem. Soc.*, **64**, 2529 (1942).
[16] McElvain and Stevens, *J. Am. Chem. Soc.*, **69**, 2667 (1947).
[17] McElvain, *Chem. Revs.*, **45**, 463 (1949).
[18] McElvain and Venerable, *J. Am. Chem. Soc.*, **72**, 1661 (1950).
[19] Post, *Aliphatic Orthoesters*, Reinhold Publishing Corp., New York, 1943, pp. 11-44.

17

Acyl Halides

CONTENTS

335. Interaction of Carboxylic Acids and Inorganic Acid Halides

$$RCO_2H \xrightarrow{\ SOCl_2,\ PX_3,\ etc.\ } RCOX$$

The conversion of a carboxylic acid to its halide is usually accomplished by thionyl chloride or phosphorus halides. Phosphorus trichloride and glacial acetic acid give acetyl chloride (67%).[15] The other product is phosphorus acid. Phosphorus pentachloride is converted to phosphorus oxychloride (b.p. 105°), from which the acyl halide is sometimes separated with difficulty. This reagent, however, finds use in the preparation of certain higher-molecular-weight halides.[53,65,79] Most acyl bromides are made from phosphorus tribromide.[56,57]

The most convenient reagent for the preparation of acyl chlorides is thionyl chloride. The halides are formed in excellent yields at room temperature or upon refluxing gently for a short time. The other products of the reaction are the gases hydrogen chloride and sulfur dioxide. Good directions are given for the preparations of benzoyl chloride (91%),[15] ethylphenylacetyl chloride (94%),[3] and mesitoyl chloride (97%).[1] Benzene is used as a solvent,[9,14,24] and sometimes a few drops of pyridine are added.[6] Thionyl chloride has been used to prepare aliphatic acyl halides containing eleven to nineteen carbon atoms.[21,25]

Acyl halides free from traces of phosphorus or sulfur compounds may be made from carboxylic acids and silicon tetrachloride[58] or oxalyl halides (method 339).

Oxalyl chloride is the simplest *diacyl halide*. It is obtained in 55% yield from oxalic acid and phosphorus pentachloride.[68] Other diacyl halides are made in good yields by the thionyl chloride procedure.[22,27] Succinic and glutaric acids, however, give anhydrides, which are then converted to the halides by method 337.

Olefinic acyl halides are made from the corresponding acids by treatment with thionyl chloride[28-30,32] or phosphorus pentachloride.[63,67]

A variety of *halo acyl halides* have been made by use of the above reagents. Table 61 includes examples of compounds containing halogen atoms in *alpha, beta, gamma,* and *delta* positions of an aliphatic carbon chain as well as on the aromatic nucleus. All four halogen elements are represented.

Alkoxy and *phenoxy*[10,39] *acyl halides* in which the ether group is on an aromatic nucleus[10] or an aliphatic chain[19,36,41] are made with thionyl chloride.

Carboalkoxy acyl halides are made from mono esters of dibasic acids and thionyl chloride or phosphorus pentachloride. Examples are numerous.[46,47,52,62] Halides with the ester group in the *beta* position are unstable to prolonged heating. Alkyl halide is eliminated with the formation of an anhydride.[46,54] Under certain conditions a "rearrangement" occurs in the preparation of ester acid chlorides. The product obtained is a mixture of the expected compound and its isomer in which the ester and acid chloride groups are interchanged, viz., $RO_2CCHR'(CH_2)_nCO_2H \rightarrow RO_2C(CH_2)_nCHR'COCl$. The cyclic anhydride is a likely intermediate.[48,69]

Nitro[4,45,59] and *cyano*[64] groups may be present in the carboxylic acid during its conversion to the halide.

336. Action of Inorganic Acid Halides on Carboxylic Esters or Salts

$$RCO_2Na \xrightarrow[\text{SOCl}_2, \text{ etc.}]{\text{PCl}_3, \text{ PCl}_5, \text{ POCl}_3,} RCOCl$$

In this procedure no possibility of the formation of water exists at any stage of the reaction. The method has been used for the preparation of several α,β-*olefinic acyl halides* from phosphorus oxychloride,[73] although the procedure is said to be less satisfactory than treatment of the free acid with phosphorus trichloride (method 335).[67]

The method is applied to the greatest extent in making *fluoro acyl halides* such as fluoroacetyl chloride from sodium fluoroacetate and phosphorus pentachloride.[75] The products are distilled from a mixture of the dry reagents, usually without a solvent. Phosphorus trichloride[74] and phosphorus oxychloride[76] have also been used for the preparation of compounds of this type.

Ethoxalyl chloride, $C_2H_5O_2CCOCl$, is made either by the action of phosphorus pentachloride on ethyl oxalate or from thionyl chloride and potassium ethyl oxalate. The former procedure gives almost quantitative yields,[72] but the latter gives a better product.[77]

Acetyl chloride adds to β-propiolactone in the presence of sulfuric acid to give β-acetoxypropionyl chloride, $CH_3CO_2CH_2CH_2COCl$ (67%).[70] The lactone ring is also opened by thionyl chloride to give β-chloropropionyl chloride, from which acrylyl chloride may be obtained by heating with anhydrous barium chloride.

Ethyl acetoacetate and phosphorus pentachloride give β-chlorocrotonyl chloride (84%).[71]

337. Action of Inorganic Acid Halides on Anhydrides

$$(RCO)_2O \xrightarrow{SOCl_2} 2RCOCl + SO_2$$

This reaction has limited value because most anhydrides are obtained from acyl halides. Acetyl chloride[81] and acetyl bromide[57] have been made in this way from the corresponding phosphorus trihalides.

Several *dibasic acid halides* are best prepared by this method from the readily available anhydrides. Thionyl chloride in the presence of a small amount of zinc chloride converts succinic and phthalic anhydrides to succinyl chloride (74%)[80] and phthalyl chloride (86%),[82] respectively. Phosphorus halides are used in similar preparations of phthalyl bromide (83%)[83] and diphenic acid chloride (71%).[85]

Phthalyl chloride is obtained in almost quantitative yield by passing dry chlorine gas into molten thiophthalic anhydride, $C_6H_4(CO)_2S$, at 245° until sulfur monochloride no longer distils. Thioanhydrides are made from the oxygen analogs and sodium sulfide.[84]

338. Action of Hydrogen Halide or Metallic Halides on Acyl Halides

$$RCOCl + HX \longrightarrow RCOX + HCl$$

Interchange of halogen is a means of synthesis of certain acyl halides which cannot be conveniently prepared by other methods. Acetyl fluoride is made from acetyl chloride and sodium hydrogen fluoride in acetic anhydride solution.[86] By passing a stream of hydrogen bromide through oxalyl chloride an 85% yield of oxalyl bromide, $(COBr)_2$, is obtained.[87] The bromide cannot be made by the action of phosphorus pentabromide on oxalic acid. The method has also been applied to the preparation of acetyl bromide and iodide and other acyl iodides.[88, 89]

339. Interaction of Carboxylic Acids and Acyl Halides

$$C_6H_5COCl + RCO_2H \rightarrow RCOCl + C_6H_5CO_2H$$

Exchange of acyl groups on a halogen atom has frequently been applied to the synthesis of acyl halides. An excellent procedure for the preparation of volatile acyl halides involves their distillation from a reacting mixture consisting of a higher-boiling acyl halide and a carboxylic acid. Benzoyl chloride has been employed in this procedure to make a variety of aliphatic acyl halides including olefinic, halo, and methoxy acyl halides.[4,90]

Oxalyl chloride, $(COCl)_2$, and oxalyl bromide are similarly used to make acyl chlorides and bromides in excellent yield. The only other products of these reactions are the gases hydrogen halide, carbon monoxide, and carbon dioxide.[60] For the preparation of acyl bromides, sodium salts rather than the free acids have been treated with oxalyl bromide. This procedure requires a smaller excess of reagent.

Oxalyl chloride is recommended as the best reagent for the preparation of high-molecular-weight *olefinic acyl chlorides*.[55,79]

Phthalyl chloride, $C_6H_4(COCl)_2$, converts butyric acid to butyryl chloride (92%)[82] and maleic anhydride to fumaryl chloride (95%).[91]

340. Chlorination of Aldehydes[97]

$$ArCHO + Cl_2 \rightarrow ArCOCl + HCl$$

TABLE 61. ACYL HALIDES

C_n	Compound	Method	Yield %	Chapter[ref]	B.p./mm., n_D^t, (M.p.)
		Aliphatic and Alicyclic Acyl Halides			
C_2	Acetyl fluoride	338	66	17[86]	20–23
	Acetyl chloride	335	85	17[58]	
		335	67	17[15]	51
		337	89	17[81]	52
		339	85	17[90]	50
	Acetyl bromide	335	80	17[57]	75/740
		337	82	17[57]	75/740
		338	80	17[88]	84
	Acetyl iodide	338	70	17[88]	105/735, 1.5491
C_3	Propionyl chloride	339	89	17[90]	78
C_4	n-Butyryl chloride	335	85	17[2]	101/730, 1.4117*
		339	87	17[90]	102
		339	92	17[82]	
	Isobutyryl chloride	335	75	17[12]	91, 1.4070
		339	88	17[90]	92
	Cyclopropanecarbonyl chloride	335	95	17[5]	119/763
C_5	n-Valeryl chloride	339	84	17[90]	126
		339	95	17[60]	109/756
	Isovaleryl chloride	339	84	17[90]	115
	Trimethylacetyl chloride	339	92	17[90]	104
		335	80	17[12]	71/250, 1.4118
	Cyclobutanecarbonyl chloride	335	90	17[5]	137/762
C_6	Caproyl chloride	335	95	17[21]	152/725
		339	80	17[90]	153
	Diethylacetyl chloride	335	80	17[4]	140, 1.4234
	t-Butylacetyl chloride	335	86	17[13]	68/100, 1.4226
C_7	Heptanoyl chloride	335	99	17[21]	60/11
C_8	Octanoyl chloride	335	96	17[21]	75/11
		335	82	17[65]	83/15
	Methyl-n-amylacetyl chloride	335	84	17[20]	180/727
	Cyclohexylacetyl chloride	335	59	17[99]	96/21
C_9	Nonanoyl chloride	335	94	17[21]	95/11
	3,3,4,4-Tetramethylpentanoyl chloride	335	80	17[14]	88/20, 1.4557
C_{18}	Stearyl chloride	335	70	17[53]	182/3, (23)
		Aromatic and Heterocyclic Acyl Halides			
C_5	Furoyl chloride	335	90	17[24]	60/7
	α-Thienoyl chloride	335	60	17[10]	85/14
C_6	2-Thienylacetyl chloride	335	70	17[4]	64/3
	Nicotinyl chloride	335	91	17[26]	
		335	84	17[4]	90/15

TABLE 61. ACYL HALIDES 551

TABLE 61 (*continued*)

C_n	Compound	Method	Yield %	Chapter ref.	B.p./mm., n_D^t, (M.p.)
	Aromatic and Heterocyclic Acyl Halides (*continued*)				
C_7	Benzoyl chloride	335	91	17^{15}	194
		339	98	17^{60}	93/20
	Benzoyl bromide	339	90	17^{60}	219/739
	Benzoyl iodide	338	95	17^{88}	109/10
C_8	Phenylacetyl chloride	335	95	17^8	95/12
		339	74	17^{60}	100/12
	Phenylacetyl bromide	339	90	17^{60}	153/50
	o-Methylbenzoyl bromide	339	90	17^{60}	135/37
	m-Methylbenzoyl bromide	339	90	17^{60}	137/52
	p-Methylbenzoyl chloride	335	92	17^7	119/24
	p-Methylbenzoyl bromide	339	90	17^{60}	147/42
		335	66	17^{56}	173/113
C_9	β-Phenylpropionyl chloride	335	85	17^{11}	118/17
		339	98	17^{60}	116/15
	3,4-Dimethylbenzoyl chloride	335	86	17^{16}	185/126
C_{10}	Ethylphenylacetyl chloride	335	94	17^3	114/15
	p-Isopropylbenzoyl chloride	335	87	17^{10}	121/10
	Mesitoyl chloride	335	97	17^1	146/60
C_{11}	p-Isopropylphenylacetyl chloride	335	91	17^4	128/15
	p-s-Butylbenzoyl chloride	335	89	17^6	136/15
C_{15}	2-Phenanthroyl chloride	335	100	17^{18}	(101)
	3-Phenanthroyl chloride	335	100	17^{18}	(117)
	9-Phenanthroyl chloride	335	91	17^9	(104)
	Diacyl Halides				
C_2	Oxalyl chloride	335	55	17^{68}	64/763
	Oxalyl bromide	338	85	17^{87}	17/10
C_4	Succinyl chloride	337	74	17^{80}	74/9
C_6	Adipyl chloride	335	90	17^{27}	85/2
C_8	cis-1,4-Cyclohexanedicarbonyl chloride	335	73	17^{22}	97/0.5, 1.5026
	trans-1,4-Cyclohexanedicarbonyl chloride	335	49	17^{22}	(67)
	Phthalyl chloride	337	86	17^{82}	122/5
	Phthalyl bromide	337	83	17^{83}	185–193/24, (80)
	Isophthaloyl chloride	335	92	17^{23}	136/11, (43)
C_{14}	Diphenic acid chloride	337	71	17^{85}	(94)
	Olefinic Acyl Halides				
C_3	Acrylyl chloride	20	74	17^{70}	73, 1.4337
		335	66	17^{67}	75, 1.4343
		336	60	17^{73}	77

For explanations and symbols see pp. xi–xii.

TABLE 61 (continued)

C_n	Compound	Method	Yield %	Chapter[ref.]	B.p./mm., n_D^t, (M.p.)
			Olefinic Acyl Halides (continued)		
C_3	Acrylyl chloride	339	72	17[4]	74
	(continued)	339	72	17[95]	73/740
C_4	Crotonyl chloride	335	86	17[32]	125
		339	80	17[90]	122
	Vinylacetyl chloride	335	76	17[29]	99/774
	Methacrylyl chloride	335	80	17[67]	96, 1.4435
		336	64	17[73]	95
	Fumaryl chloride	339	95	17[90]	63/13
C_5	β,β-Dimethylacryloyl chloride	335	81	17[28]	60/30
C_6	cis-3-Hexenoyl chloride	335	97	17[98]	52/28, 1.4496
	4-Methyl-2-pentenoyl chloride	335	89	17[31]	59/18
	Dimethylfumaryl chloride	335	92	17[63]	80/22
C_9	Cinnamoyl chloride	335	94	17[10]	137/10
	Cinnamoyl bromide	339	90	17[60]	182/40, (48)
C_{11}	Undecenoyl chloride	335	76	17[30]	128/13
C_{18}	Oleyl chloride	339	90	17[55]	163/2
			Halo Acyl Halides		
C_2	Fluoroacetyl chloride	335	68	17[61]	72/760
		336	52	17[75]	71/755, 1.3835[27]
	Difluoroacetyl chloride	336	69	17[76]	32-35
	Trifluoroacetyl chloride	336	53	17[74]	−27
		336	90	17[76]	
	Chlorodifluoroacetyl chloride	336	80	17[76]	
	Chloroacetyl chloride	335	55	17[17]	
		339	80	17[60]	105/750
		339	76	17[90]	106
	Dichloroacetyl chloride	339	73	17[90]	106
	Trichloroacetyl chloride	335	60	17[19]	118/754, 1.4695
		339	56	17[90]	118
	Trifluoroacetyl bromide	336	59	17[74]	−5
	Bromoacetyl bromide	67	68	17[92]	147
	Chloroacetyl iodide	338	68	17[88]	37/4, 1.5903
	Dichloroacetyl iodide	338	58	17[88]	55/15, 1.5754
	Trichloroacetyl iodide	338	72	17[88]	74/30, 1.5711
C_3	α-Chloropropionyl chloride	67	34	17[93]	53/100, 1.440
	β-Chloropropionyl chloride	67	42	17[93]	83/100, 1.454
		335	96	17[34]	53/23
		336	87	17[70]	80/100, 1.4566
	β-Iodopropionyl chloride	335	90	17[38]	71-75/11
	α,β-Dichloropropionyl chloride	335	53†	17[37]	53/16
	α,β-Dibromopropionyl chloride	335	77†	17[37]	83/18
C_4	γ-Chlorobutyryl chloride	335	82	17[36]	61/12
	γ-Bromobutyryl chloride	335	60	17[10]	101/37

TABLE 61. ACYL HALIDES 553

TABLE 61 (*continued*)

C_n	Compound	Method	Yield %	Chapter[ref.]	B.p./mm., n_D^t, (M.p.)

Halo Acyl Halides (*continued*)

C_n	Compound	Method	Yield %	Chapter[ref.]	B.p./mm., n_D^t, (M.p.)
C_4	α-Bromoisobutyryl chloride	335	90	17[96]	52/30, 1.4750[23]
	β-Chlorocrotyl chloride	336	84	17[71]	122–140
C_5	5-Bromopentanoyl chloride	335	80	17[33]	103/15, 1.4879[26]
	β-Chlorotrimethylacetyl chloride	67	80	17[93]	86/60, 1.4539
C_6	α-Bromocaproyl chloride	335	67	17[35]	102–105/30
C_7	α-Bromocyclohexanecarbonyl bromide	67	93	4[648]	125/20, 1.5429
	o-Chlorobenzoyl chloride	340	72	17[97]	94/10
	o-Bromobenzoyl chloride	339	93	17[60]	125/20
	o-Chlorobenzoyl bromide	339	90	17[60]	144/37
	o-Bromobenzoyl bromide	339	90	17[60]	167/18
	m-Chlorobenzoyl chloride	335	91	17[4]	105/14
	m-Chlorobenzoyl bromide	339	90	17[60]	145/40
	p-Chlorobenzoyl chloride	335	76	17[10]	107/10
	p-Bromobenzoyl chloride	335	95	17[10]	155/12
		339	94	17[60]	182/125, (42)
	p-Chlorobenzoyl bromide	339	90	17[60]	142/27
	p-Bromobenzoyl bromide	339	90	17[60]	136/18
	p-Iodobenzoyl bromide	339	90	17[60]	(55)
C_8	p-(Chloromethyl)-benzoyl chloride	67	89	17[7]	155–160/35
C_9	α-Bromo-β-phenylpropionyl chloride	67	69	17[11]	114/5, 1.5768
C_{10}	α-Bromo-α-phenylbutyryl chloride	67	74	17[94]	152/22
C_{14}	α-Chlorodiphenylacetyl chloride	335	75	17[66]	(49)

Alkoxy and Aryloxy Acyl Halides

C_n	Compound	Method	Yield %	Chapter[ref.]	B.p./mm., n_D^t, (M.p.)
C_3	Methoxyacetyl chloride	335	45	17[19]	51/69, 1.4195
		339	57	17[4]	113
C_4	β-Methoxypropionyl chloride	335	85	17[41]	64/44
		335	60	17[19]	27/3, 1.4237
C_5	γ-Methoxybutyryl chloride	335	30	17[19]	47/7, 1.4299
		335	81	17[36]	47/7
	β-Methoxyisobutyryl chloride	335	90	17[40]	48–59/15
	β-Ethoxypropionyl chloride	335	96	17[41]	78/52
C_8	Phenoxyacetyl chloride	335	89	17[10]	112/10
	o-Methoxybenzoyl chloride	335	90	17[10]	133/10
	p-Methoxybenzoyl chloride	335	92	17[10]	143/13
		335	99	17[43]	128/4
	p-Methoxybenzoyl bromide	339	90	17[60]	185/27

For explanations and symbols see pp. xi–xii.

TABLE 61 (*continued*)

C_n	Compound	Method	Yield %	Chapter[ref.]	B.p./mm., n_D^t, (M.p.)
		Alkoxy and Aryloxy Acyl Halides (*continued*)			
C_9	*p*-Ethoxybenzoyl chloride	335	90	17^{10}	144/10
C_{10}	γ-Phenoxybutyryl chloride	335	75	17^{39}	155/20
	β-Methoxy-β-phenylpropionyl chloride	....	70	17^{89}	101/3
	3,4,5-Trimethoxybenzoyl	335	84	17^{42}	130/2, (78)
		Carbalkoxy and Acyloxy Acyl Halides			
C_3	Methoxalyl chloride	336	65	17^{77}	119
C_4	Ethoxalyl chloride (ethyl	336	100	17^{72}	40/18
	chloroglyoxalate)	336	70	17^{78}	
		336	59	17^{77}	134
C_5	β-Carbomethoxypropionyl chloride	335	93	17^{46}	87/13
	β-Acetoxypropionyl chloride	....	67	17^{70}	80/12, 1.4365
C_7	γ-Carboethoxybutyryl chloride	335	75	17^{44}	52-57/1
C_8	γ-Carbethoxyvaleryl chloride	335	86	17^{50}	140/16
	ω-Carbethoxyvaleryl chloride	335	98	17^{52}	121/13
	α-Carbethoxyisovaleryl chloride	335	29	17^{62}	72/8
	β-Carbethoxy-α,β-dimethyl-propionyl chloride	335	52	17^{54}	97/15, 1.4462
	α,β-Diacetoxybutyryl chloride	335	97	17^{51}	79/3
C_{11}	ω-Carbethoxyoctanoyl chloride	335	84	17^{47}	155/14
		Cyano and Nitro Acyl Halides			
C_3	Cyanoacetyl chloride	335	54	17^{64}	57/0.5
C_7	*o*-Nitrobenzoyl chloride	335	....	17^{45}	Explosive
	m-Nitrobenzoyl bromide	339	90	17^{60}	166/18, (43)
	p-Nitrobenzoyl chloride	335	96	17^{59}	155/20, (73)
	p-Nitrobenzoyl bromide	339	90	17^{60}	(64)
	3,5-Dinitrobenzoyl bromide	339	90	17^{60}	(60)
C_8	*p*-Nitrophenylacetyl chloride	335	54	17^{4}	(48)

For explanations and symbols see pp. xi–xii.

REFERENCES FOR CHAPTER 17

[1] Barnes, *Org. Syntheses,* **21**, 77 (1941).
[2] Helferich and Schaefer, *Org. Syntheses,* Coll. Vol. I, 147 (1941).
[3] Pierce, Haden, and Gano, *J. Am. Chem. Soc.,* **67**, 408 (1945).
[4] Miller, Dessert, and Anderson, *J. Am. Chem. Soc.,* **70**, 502 (1948).
[5] Jeffery and Vogel, *J. Chem. Soc.,* 1804 (1948).
[6] Marvel, Frank, and Prill, *J. Am. Chem. Soc.,* **65**, 1650 (1943).
[7] Blicke and Lilienfeld, *J. Am. Chem. Soc.,* **65**, 2282 (1943); cf. ref. 10.
[8] Truitt, Mark, Long, and Jeanes, *J. Am. Chem. Soc.,* **70**, 4214 (1948).
[9] Goldberg, Ordas, and Carsch, *J. Am. Chem. Soc.,* **69**, 261 (1947).
[10] McElvain and Carney, *J. Am. Chem. Soc.,* **68**, 2599 (1946).
[11] Shriner and Damschroder, *J. Am. Chem. Soc.,* **60**, 895 (1938).
[12] Greenwood, Whitmore, and Crooks, *J. Am. Chem. Soc.,* **60**, 2028 (1938).
[13] Whitmore et al., *J. Am. Chem. Soc.,* **60**, 2462 (1938).
[14] Whitmore, Marker, and Plambeck, *J. Am. Chem. Soc.,* **63**, 1628 (1941).
[15] Gattermann and Wieland, *Laboratory Methods of Organic Chemistry,* The Macmillan Co., New York, 1938, p. 121.
[16] Morgan and Coulson, *J. Chem. Soc.,* 2326 (1931).
[17] McMaster and Ahmann, *J. Am. Chem. Soc.,* **50**, 145 (1928).
[18] Mosettig and van de Kamp, *J. Am. Chem. Soc.,* **55**, 2995 (1933).
[19] Leimu, *Ber.,* **70B**, 1049 (1937).
[20] Karrer et al., *Helv. Chim. Acta,* **13**, 1298 (1930).
[21] Fierz-David and Kuster, *Helv. Chim. Acta,* **22**, 86, 89 (1939).
[22] Malachowski et al., *Ber.,* **71B**, 761 (1938).
[23] Ruggli and Knecht, *Helv. Chim. Acta,* **27**, 1111 (1944).
[24] Hartman and Dickey, *Ind. Eng. Chem.,* **24**, 151 (1932); Douglass and Dains, *J. Am. Chem. Soc.,* **56**, 720 (1934).
[25] Ralston, Segerbrecht, and Bauer, *J. Org. Chem.,* **4**, 503 (1939).
[26] Ingersoll and Robbins, *J. Am. Chem. Soc.,* **48**, 245 (1926).
[27] Lieser and Macura, *Ann.,* **548**, 243 (1941).
[28] Smith and Engelhardt, *J. Am. Chem. Soc.,* **71**, 2672 (1949).
[29] Jeffery and Vogel, *J. Chem. Soc.,* 661 (1948).
[30] Kapp and Knoll, *J. Am. Chem. Soc.,* **65**, 2063 (1943).
[31] Linstead, *J. Chem. Soc.,* 2505 (1929).
[32] Fuson, Christ, and Whitman, *J. Am. Chem. Soc.,* **58**, 2450 (1936).
[33] Merchant, Wickert, and Marvel, *J. Am. Chem. Soc.,* **49**, 1830 (1927).
[34] Fieser and Seligman, *J. Am. Chem. Soc.,* **58**, 2484 (1936).
[35] Marvel and Noyes, *J. Am. Chem. Soc.,* **42**, 2273 (1920).
[36] Blicke, Wright, and Zienty, *J. Am. Chem. Soc.,* **63**, 2488 (1941).
[37] Marvel et al., *J. Am. Chem. Soc.,* **62**, 3496 (1940).
[38] Karrer and Schmid, *Helv. Chim. Acta,* **27**, 119 (1944).
[39] Hanford and Adams, *J. Am. Chem. Soc.,* **57**, 922 (1935).
[40] Wagner, *J. Am. Chem. Soc.,* **71**, 3217 (1949).
[41] Leslie and Henze, *J. Am. Chem. Soc.,* **71**, 3481 (1949).
[42] Reeve and Sterling, *J. Am. Chem. Soc.,* **71**, 3657 (1949).
[43] Nauta and Mulder, *Rec. trav. chim.,* **58**, 1064 (1939).
[44] Clark et al., *J. Am. Chem. Soc.,* **68**, 99 (1946); Harris et al., *ibid.,* **67**, 2098 (1945).
[45] Bonner and Hurd, *J. Am. Chem. Soc.,* **68**, 344 (1946).
[46] Cason, *Org. Syntheses,* **25**, 20 (1945); *J. Am. Chem. Soc.,* **64**, 1107 (1942).

[47] Schmidt and Shirley, *J. Am. Chem. Soc.*, **71**, 3805 (1949).
[48] Ställberg-Stenhagen, *J. Am. Chem. Soc.*, **69**, 2568 (1947).
[49] Papa, Schwenk, and Hankin, *J. Am. Chem. Soc.*, **69**, 3021 (1947).
[50] Lin et al., *J. Chem. Soc.*, **72** (1937).
[51] Glattfeld and Straitiff, *J. Am. Chem. Soc.*, **60**, 1386 (1938).
[52] Duschinsky and Dolan, *J. Am. Chem. Soc.*, **67**, 2082 (1945); cf. ref. 49.
[53] Sherk, Augur, and Soffer, *J. Am. Chem. Soc.*, **67**, 2239 (1945).
[54] Adams and Wilkinson, *J. Am. Chem. Soc.*, **65**, 2207 (1943).
[55] Daubert, Fricke, and Longenecker, *J. Am. Chem. Soc.*, **65**, 2143 (1943).
[56] Coulson, *J. Chem. Soc.*, 1409 (1934).
[57] Burton and Degering, *J. Am. Chem. Soc.*, **62**, 227 (1940).
[58] Montonna, *J. Am. Chem. Soc.*, **49**, 2115 (1927).
[59] Adams and Jenkins, *Org. Syntheses*, Coll. Vol. I, 394 (1941).
[60] Adams and Ulich, *J. Am. Chem. Soc.*, **42**, 599 (1920).
[61] Saunders and Stacey, *J. Chem. Soc.*, 1773 (1948).
[62] Brown and Ferger, *J. Am. Chem. Soc.*, **68**, 1507 (1946).
[63] Lutz and Taylor, *J. Am. Chem. Soc.*, **55**, 1589 (1933).
[64] Weissberger and Porter, *J. Am. Chem. Soc.*, **65**, 52 (1943).
[65] Paquette, Lingafelter, and Tartar, *J. Am. Chem. Soc.*, **65**, 686 (1943).
[66] Billman and Hidy, *J. Am. Chem. Soc.*, **65**, 760 (1943).
[67] Rehberg, Dixon, and Fisher, *J. Am. Chem. Soc.*, **67**, 209 (1945).
[68] Staudinger, *Ber.*, **41**, 3563 (1908).
[69] Cason, *J. Am. Chem. Soc.*, **69**, 1548 (1947).
[70] Gresham, Jansen, and Shaver, *J. Am. Chem. Soc.*, **72**, 72 (1950).
[71] Shriner and Keyser, *J. Am. Chem. Soc.*, **60**, 287 (1938).
[72] Kindler, Metzendorf, and Dschi-yin-Kwok, *Ber.*, **76B**, 310, 311 (1943);
Weygand, *Organic Preparations*, Interscience Publishers, New York, 1945, p. 105.
[73] Haworth, Gregory, and Wiggins, *J. Chem. Soc.*, 490 (1946); cf. ref. 67.
[74] Simons and Ramler, *J. Am. Chem. Soc.*, **65**, 389 (1943); cf. ref. 76.
[75] Truce, *J. Am. Chem. Soc.*, **70**, 2828 (1948).
[76] Cohen, Wolosinski, and Scheuer, *J. Am. Chem. Soc.*, **71**, 3439 (1949).
[77] Southwick and Seivard, *J. Am. Chem. Soc.*, **71**, 2535 (1949).
[78] Adickes, Brunnert, and Lücker, *J. prakt. Chem.*, **130**, 168 (1931).
[79] Bauer, *Oil & Soap*, **23**, 1 (1946).
[80] Ruggli and Maeder, *Helv. Chim. Acta*, **26**, 1486 (1943).
[81] Hurd and Thomas, *J. Am. Chem. Soc.*, **55**, 279 (1933).
[82] Kyrides, *J. Am. Chem. Soc.*, **59**, 206 (1937).
[83] Davies, Hambly, and Semmens, *J. Chem. Soc.*, 1312 (1933).
[84] Ott, Langenohl, and Zerweck, *Ber.*, **70B**, 2360 (1937).
[85] Roberts and Johnson, *J. Am. Chem. Soc.*, **47**, 1399 (1925).
[86] Calloway, *J. Am. Chem. Soc.*, **59**, 1476 (1937); Nesmejanow and Kahn,
Ber., **67B**, 370 (1934).
[87] Staudinger and Anthes, *Ber.*, **46**, 1431 (1913).
[88] Gustus and Stevens, *J. Am. Chem. Soc.*, **55**, 374 (1933); Staudinger and
Anthes, *Ber.*, **46**, 1417 (1913).
[89] Blomquist, Holley, and Sweeting, *J. Am. Chem. Soc.*, **69**, 2357 (1947).
[90] Brown, *J. Am. Chem. Soc.*, **60**, 1325 (1938).
[91] Kyrides, *Org. Syntheses*, **20**, 51 (1940); cf. ref. 82.
[92] Arens and van Dorp, *Rec. trav. chim.*, **66**, 409 (1947).
[93] Kharasch and Brown, *J. Am. Chem. Soc.*, **62**, 925 (1940).
[94] Phillips, *J. Chem. Soc.*, 222 (1942).

[95] Stempel et al., *J. Am. Chem. Soc.*, **72**, 2299 (1950).
[96] Tarbell and Noble, *J. Am. Chem. Soc.*, **72**, 2659 (1950).
[97] Clark and Taylor, *Org. Syntheses*, Coll. Vol. I, 155 (1941).
[98] Crombie and Harper, *J. Chem. Soc.*, 1158 (1950).
[99] Mihina and Herbst, *J. Org. Chem.*, **15**, 1086 (1950).

18

Anhydrides

CONTENTS

341. Acylation of Carboxylic Acids by Acyl Halides

$$RCO_2H + R'COCl \xrightarrow{C_5H_5N} (RCO)(R'CO)O$$

This is the best procedure for the preparation of simple[1,3] and mixed[5] anhydrides. Benzoic anhydride is prepared simply by heating an equimolar mixture of benzoic acid and benzoyl chloride.[6] The reaction is general when carried out in the presence of pyridine. The acyl halides react with pyridine to give pyridinium salts, which are powerful acylating agents. The pyridinium salt formed from the acyl halide and pyridine in the absence of a carboxylic acid is able to diacylate water and hydrogen sulfide at −20° to give simple anhydrides and diacyl sulfides, respectively.[2]

$$2C_6H_5COCl \cdot C_5H_5N + H_2O \longrightarrow (C_6H_5CO)_2O + 2C_5H_5NHCl$$

By means of these procedures anhydrides of aromatic acids containing nuclear halo, methoxyl, and nitro groups have been made.

342. Interaction of Acyl Halides and Salts of Carboxylic Acids

$$RCO_2Na + R'COCl \rightarrow (RCO)(R'CO)O + NaCl$$

Although this is the classical method of anhydride formation it has been replaced to a large extent by the acylation of free carboxylic acids (method 341). The conditions employed and the solvents used in this reaction vary widely. Excellent directions are given for the preparations of nicotinic anhydride (89%)[32] and acetic propionic anhydride (60%)[30] from the respective potassium and sodium salts of the carboxylic acids. Silver salts of acids have also been used.[33] The reaction has been extended to the preparation of mixed anhydrides of short- and long-chain fatty acids[31] but has failed in the preparation of mixed anhydrides of substituted benzoic acids.[26]

343. Dehydration of Carboxylic Acids

$$2RCO_2H \xrightarrow{-H_2O} (RCO)_2O$$

The formation of cyclic anhydrides from dibasic acids is often possible by means of simple distillation. Water is removed as an azeotrope with tetrachloroethane in the preparation of maleic anhydride (90%).[15] Vacuum distillation of 1-carboxycyclohexane-1-acetic acid gives the corresponding five-membered anhydride in 76% yield.[16] More often, dehydration is accomplished by heating the dibasic acid with acetyl chloride,[8-14] phosphorus oxychloride,[8,9] or acetic anhydride.[18-20, 24, 49] The cyclic anhydrides having five- and six-membered rings are very stable compounds, whereas those with larger rings polymerize readily at low temperatures.[25] This method has been applied with somewhat less success to the synthesis of simple and mixed[28] anhydrides from aliphatic[21, 27, 29] and aromatic[17, 22, 23, 26] acids.

344. Addition of Carboxylic Acids to Ketenes

$$2RCO_2H + H_2C = C = O \rightarrow (RCO)(CH_3CO)O$$

Acetic acid is quantitatively converted to acetic anhydride by reaction with ketene.[46] Mixed anhydrides are formed when homologs of acetic acid or aromatic acids are used in the reaction. Upon distillation at atmospheric pressure, the mixed anhydrides disproportionate into acetic anhydride and the symmetrical anhydride corresponding to the carboxylic acid. Yields of propionic, n-butyric, and n-caproic anhydrides prepared by this method are in the range of 80% to 87%.[45]

345. Addition of Cyclic Olefinic Anhydrides to Dienes (Diels-Alder)

Maleic anhydride and several related derivatives have been added to a large number of dienes. Reaction of butadiene with maleic anhydride occurs at 50° in benzene solution to give 1,2,3,6-tetrahydrophthalic anhydride (97%).[39, 41] This method furnishes many important partially hydrogenated aromatic anhydrides, most of which are outside the scope of this book. An excellent discussion of the reaction and survey of the literature to 1945 has been made[38] (cf. method 34).

346. Interaction of Acyl Halides and Esters[34]

$$ArCO_2C_2H_5 + ArCOCl \xrightarrow[270-290°]{ZnCl_2} (ArCO)_2O + C_2H_5Cl$$

347. Interaction of Acyl Halides and Anhydrides[44]

$$(CH_3CO)_2O + 2C_6H_5COCl \rightarrow (C_6H_5CO)_2O + 2CH_3COCl$$

TABLE 62. ANHYDRIDES 561

TABLE 62. ANHYDRIDES

C_n	Compound	Method	Yield (%)	Chapter[ref.]	B.p./mm., n_D^t, (M.p.)
C_3	Formic acetic anhydride	343	....	18^{28}	29/17
C_4	Succinic anhydride	343	95	18^8	(119)
	Maleic anhydride	343	90	18^{15}	198, 83/15
	Trifluoroacetic anhydride	343	74	18^{47}	39
C_5	Acetic propionic anhydride	342	60	18^{30}	154/760, 70-75/40
	Glutaric anhydride	343	93	18^{14}	165-170/20, (55)
	Methylmaleic (citraconic) anhydride	....	66	18^{35}	105-110/22, (8)
C_6	Propionic anhydride	344	87	18^{45}	169 *
	a,a-Dimethylsuccinic anhydride	343	82	18^9	223
	a,β-Dimethylsuccinic anhydride	343	79	18^{12}	233, (88)
	Dimethylmaleic anhydride	343	20 †	18^{37}	(96)
C_7	a-Ethylglutaric anhydride	343	51 †	18^{13}	164/13
C_8	n-Butyric anhydride	344	87	18^{45}	198 *
	a,β-Diethylsuccinic anhydride	343	91	18^{11}	101/1
	cis-Cyclohexanedicarboxylic anhydride	....	93	18^{40}	162/25, (31)
	trans-Cyclohexanedicarboxylic anhydride	343	70	18^{40}	(142)
	1,2,3,6-Tetrahydrophthalic anhydride	345	90	18^{39}	(104)
	Phthalic anhydride	....	76	18^{42}	(131) *
	4-Bromophthalic anhydride	343	80	18^{43}	305-309, (107)
	3-Nitrophthalic anhydride	343	93	18^{24}	(164)
C_9	a-n-Butylglutaric anhydride	343	76	18^{49}	171/12
	Anhydride of 1-carboxy-1-cyclohexaneacetic acid	343	76	18^{16}	(55)
	Homophthalic anhydride	343	88	18^{18}	(141)
C_{10}	Phenylsuccinic anhydride	343	80	18^{10}	192/6, (54)
	Furoic anhydride	341	64	18^2	(73)
C_{11}	a-Phenylglutaric anhydride	343	86	18^{19}	(96)
	Benzylsuccinic anhydride	343	95	18^{48}	185/2
C_{12}	n-Caproic anhydride	344	87	18^{45}	120/6
	Nicotinic anhydride	342	89	18^{32}	(123)
C_{13}	β-Naphthoic acetic anhydride	341	83	18^5	(51)
C_{14}	Heptoic anhydride	341	83	18^1	172/15
	Benzoic anhydride	341	85	18^6	215-219
		341	85	18^2	(42)
		343	74	18^{17}	(43)
		347	80	18^{44}	(40)
	Mono-p-chlorobenzoic anhydride	341	69	18^5	(70)
	p-Chlorobenzoic anhydride	341	90	18^1	(193)

For explanations and symbols see pp. xi–xii.

TABLE 62 (*continued*)

C $_n$	Compound	Method	Yield (%)	Chapter[ref.]	B.p./mm., n_D^t, (M.p.)
C $_{14}$	Mono-*p*-bromobenzoic anhydride	341	80	18[5]	(83)
	p-Bromobenzoic anhydride	343	82	18[26]	(218)
	Mono-*o*-nitrobenzoic anhydride	341	75	18[5]	(65)
	Mono-*m*-nitrobenzoic anhydride	341	75	18[5]	(103)
	m-Nitrobenzoic anhydride	343	90	18[26]	(160)
	Mono-*p*-nitrobenzoic anhydride	341	65	18[5]	(130)
	Diphenic anhydride	343	97	18[20]	(217)
C $_{15}$	Mono-*o*-methoxybenzoic anhydride	341	77	18[5]	(77)
C $_{16}$	Phenylacetic anhydride	343	70	18[23]	(72)
	o-Toluic anhydride	343	60	18[26]	(39)
	m-Toluic anhydride	343	65	18[26]	(71)
	p-Toluic anhydride	343	96	18[26]	(95)
	p-Methoxybenzoic anhydride	341	98	18[7]	(99)
C $_{18}$	Acetic palmitic anhydride	342	70	18[31]	(63)
	α-Naphthoic benzoic anhydride	341	69	18[5]	(90)
	p-Ethoxybenzoic anhydride	343	80	18[26]	(108)
C $_{22}$	α-Naphthoic anhydride	341	80	18[4]	(146)
C $_{24}$	Lauric anhydride	343	75	18[21]	(44)
C $_{28}$	Diphenylacetic anhydride	343	92	18[22]	182/3, (98)

For explanations and symbols see pp. xi–xii.

REFERENCES FOR CHAPTER 18

[1] Allen et al., *Org. Syntheses*, 26, 1 (1946).
[2] Adkins and Thompson, *J. Am. Chem. Soc.*, 71, 2242 (1949).
[3] Lewis and Archer, *J. Am. Chem. Soc.*, 71, 3753 (1949).
[4] Blicke, *J. Am. Chem. Soc.*, 49, 2848 (1927).
[5] Zeavin and Fisher, *J. Am. Chem. Soc.*, 54, 3739, 3740 (1932).
[6] Böeseken, Tellegen, and Plusje, *Rec. trav. chim.*, 57, 75 (1938).
[7] Heap and Robinson, *J. Chem. Soc.*, 69 (1929).
[8] Fieser and Martin, *Org. Syntheses*, Coll. Vol. II, 560 (1943).
[9] Conn et al., *J. Am. Chem. Soc.*, 64, 1749 (1942).
[10] Price and Tomisek, *J. Am. Chem. Soc.*, 65, 440 (1943).
[11] Baker, *J. Am. Chem. Soc.*, 65, 1577 (1943).
[12] Fieser and Daudt, *J. Am. Chem. Soc.*, 63, 784 (1941); cf. ref. 9.
[13] Kornfeld, Jones, and Parke, *J. Am. Chem. Soc.*, 71, 158 (1949).
[14] Bachmann, Kushner, and Stevenson, *J. Am. Chem. Soc.*, 64, 977 (1942).
[15] Mason, *J. Chem. Soc.*, 701 (1930).
[16] Rothstein and Thorpe, *J. Chem. Soc.*, 2015 (1926).
[17] Clarke and Rahrs, *Org. Syntheses*, Coll. Vol. I, 91 (1941); cf. ref. 26.
[18] Grummitt, Egan, and Buck, *Org. Syntheses*, 29, 49 (1949).
[19] Horning and Finelli, *J. Am. Chem. Soc.*, 71, 3205 (1949); *Org. Syntheses*, 30, 81 (1950).
[20] Roberts and Johnson, *J. Am. Chem. Soc.*, 47, 1399 (1925).
[21] Mannich and Nadelmann, *Ber.*, 63, 797 (1930).
[22] Hurd, Christ, and Thomas, *J. Am. Chem. Soc.*, 55, 2591 (1933).
[23] Heilbron, Hey, and Lythgoe, *J. Chem. Soc.*, 297 (1936); cf. ref. 26.
[24] Nicolet and Bender, *Org. Syntheses*, Coll. Vol. I, 410 (1941).
[25] Hill, *J. Am. Chem. Soc.*, 52, 4113 (1930); Hill and Carothers, *ibid.*, 55, 5023 (1933).
[26] Autenrieth and Thomae, *Ber.*, 57, 423 (1924).
[27] Fournier, *Bull. soc. chim. France*, (4) 5, 922 (1909).
[28] Béhal, *Ann. chim.*, (7) 20, 411 (1900).
[29] Wallace and Copenhaver, *J. Am. Chem. Soc.*, 63, 699 (1941).
[30] Polya and Spotswood, *J. Am. Chem. Soc.*, 71, 2938 (1949).
[31] Ralston and Reck, *J. Org. Chem.*, 11, 624 (1946).
[32] Badgett, *J. Am. Chem. Soc.*, 69, 2231 (1947).
[33] Whitby, *J. Chem. Soc.*, 1462 (1926).
[34] Kyrides and Dvornikoff, *J. Am. Chem. Soc.*, 55, 4630 (1933).
[35] Shriner, Ford, and Roll, *Org. Syntheses*, Coll. Vol. II, 140 (1943).
[36] Hershberg and Fieser, *Org. Syntheses*, Coll. Vol. II, 423 (1943).
[37] Tarbell and Bartlett, *J. Am. Chem. Soc.*, 59, 409 (1937); Ott, *Ber.*, 61, 2131 (1928).
[38] Kloetzel, *Organic Reactions*, Vol. 4, John Wiley & Sons, New York, 1948, pp. 1, 41.
[39] Diels and Alder, *Ann.*, 460, 113 (1928); Fieser and Novello, *J. Am. Chem. Soc.*, 64, 806 (1942); cf. refs. 40 and 41.
[40] Kohler and Jansen, *J. Am. Chem. Soc.*, 60, 2144, 2145 (1938).
[41] Cope and Herrick, *J. Am. Chem. Soc.*, 72, 984 (1950); *Org. Syntheses*, 30, 93 (1950).
[42] Shreve and Welborn, *Ind. Eng. Chem.*, 35, 279 (1943).
[43] Waldmann, *J. prakt. Chem.*, 126, 66 (1930).

[44] Zetzsche et al., *Helv. Chim. Acta,* 9, 181 (1926).
[45] Williams and Krynitsky, *Org. Syntheses,* 21, 13 (1941), note 5.
[46] Hurd and Dull, *J. Am. Chem. Soc.,* 54, 3427 (1932).
[47] Bourne et al., *J. Chem. Soc.,* 2977 (1949).
[48] Beech and Legg, *J. Chem. Soc.,* 1888 (1949).
[49] Roberts and Shaw, *J. Chem. Soc.,* 2844 (1950).

19

Amides, Imides, Hydrazides, Hydroxamic Acids, and Azides

CONTENTS

348. Acylation of Ammonia or Amines by Acyl Halides

$$\text{RCOCl} \begin{array}{c} \xrightarrow{\text{NH}_3} \text{RCONH}_2 \\ \xrightarrow{\text{R}'\text{NH}_2} \text{RCONHR}' \end{array}$$

This reaction represents the best general method for amide preparation. Cold, concentrated aqueous ammonia is used as in the preparation of iso-butyramide (83%),[38] or the reaction may be carried out by passing dry ammonia into a solution of the acyl halide in anhydrous ether as in the formation of cyclopropanecarboxamide (91%).[43] Separation of the amide from ammonium chloride is usually accomplished by extraction of the amide by organic solvents. Aqueous sodium hydroxide is employed to take up the hydrogen chloride when amine hydrochlorides are used in place of the free amines as in the preparation of N-methylisobutyramide (75%).[41] When phosphorus trichloride is added to a mixture of an amine and a carboxylic acid, phosphazo compounds, RN=PNHR, rather than acyl halides, are believed to be intermediates. These compounds have been shown to react with carboxylic acids to give amides.[7]

$$\text{RN} = \text{PNHR} + 2\text{R}'\text{CO}_2\text{H} \rightarrow 2\text{R}'\text{CONHR} + \text{HPO}_2$$

Olefinic amides have been made by this method.[39] The best laboratory preparation of oleamide consists in the reaction of oleyl chloride with aqueous ammonia.[3]

α-Halo acyl halides are treated with concentrated ammonium hydroxide at 0-10° to give α-*halo* amides.[48, 50, 52, 55] In another procedure the appropriate primary or secondary amine and the acyl halide are allowed to react in carbon tetrachloride,[48, 53] ethylene dichloride,[45, 46, 49] or ether[51] solution. In general, the yields are exceptionally good.

Acyl chlorides of various phenolic carboxylic acids are converted to the corresponding *hydroxy* N,N-diethylamides with diethylamine.[60]

The reaction of ammonia with the acyl chloride grouping is much more rapid than with a methyl ester, as is shown in the preparation of methyl sebacamate, $\text{NH}_2\text{CO}(\text{CH}_2)_8\text{CO}_2\text{CH}_3$, in 95% yield from ω-carbomethoxy-pelargonyl chloride.[58]

Benzoylation of α-amino acids is carried out in aqueous sodium hydroxide solution, which neutralizes the hydrogen chloride formed.[56, 57] The literature of this reaction has been reviewed and an improved procedure described.[59]

$$\text{RCH(NH}_2\text{)CO}_2\text{H} + \text{C}_6\text{H}_5\text{COCl} + 2\text{NaOH} \rightarrow \text{C}_6\text{H}_5\text{CONHCH(R)CO}_2\text{Na} + \text{NaCl}$$

Hydroxamic acids may sometimes be prepared from acyl halides and hydroxylamine.[184]

349. Acylation of Ammonia or Amines by Carboxylic Acids

$$RNH_2 + R'CO_2H \rightleftharpoons R'CONHR + H_2O$$

The pyrolysis of an ammonium or an amine salt of a carboxylic acid is an equilibrium reaction. Good yields of amides and N-substituted amides are obtained by using an excess of one of the reactants and distilling water from the mixture during the heating period. Acetamide is prepared in 90% yield by heating ammonium acetate in excess glacial acetic acid at 110°.[1] Higher-molecular-weight aliphatic amides are formed by passing excess ammonia or amine through the molten acid at 160-210°.[17, 18] Water and aniline are distilled from a mixture of benzoic acid and aniline at 180-190° to give benzanilide, $C_6H_5CONHC_6H_5$, in 84% yield.[2] Water is removed as an azeotrope with toluene in the preparation of N-methylformanilide, $HCON(CH_3)C_6H_5$, from formic acid and methylaniline.[12] The cyclic amide, phenanthridone, is formed spontaneously from the corresponding amino acid prepared by the Hofmann degradation[19] (cf. method 446).

Internal oxidation-reduction of chloral hydrate is accompanied by amide formation when the hydrate is treated with ammonium hydroxide in the presence of potassium cyanide. The yield of α,α-dichloroacetamide is 78%.[10] Distillation of ammonium succinate gives the cyclic *imide*, succinimide, in 83% yield.[5]

350. Acylation of Ammonia or Amines by Anhydrides

$$RNH_2 + (R'CO)_2O \rightarrow RNHCOR' + R'CO_2H$$

This method has been used chiefly for the preparation of acyl derivatives of aromatic primary and secondary amines. The anhydride and amine are heated together, sometimes with a small amount of sulfuric acid as in the preparation of o-nitro-N-methylacetanilide (73%).[130] Catalytic hydrogenation of nitriles in acetic anhydride solvent leads to high yields of acetyl derivatives of primary amines.[174] N-Acylcarbazoles are obtained by refluxing a mixture of carbazole and the anhydride for 24 hours.[126]

Cyclic anhydrides of dibasic acids react with ammonia and certain amines to give cyclic *imides*, such as phthalimide (97%)[123] and α-ethylglutarimide (85%).[135] Aqueous ammonia, ammonium carbonate, and dry ammonia gas have been used. 2-Aminopyridine and phthalic anhydride react at 180° to yield N-(2-pyridyl)-phthalimide (76%).[127] *t*-Butylphthalimide is made by the action of phthalic anhydride on *t*-butylurea at 200–240°.[14] The use of alkylureas in this reaction is general.[138]

Acetylation of α-amino acids with acetic anhydride takes place in aqueous solution at room temperature.[124]

$$RCH(NH_2)CO_2H + (CH_3CO)_2O \rightarrow RCH(NHCOCH_3)CO_2H + CH_3CO_2H$$

In the presence of pyridine or sodium acetate, carbon dioxide is evolved and two acyl groups are introduced, one attached to the nitrogen and one to the α-carbon atom. The products are α-acylamido ketones.[136, 139]

$$RCH(NH_2)CO_2H + (R'CO)_2O \xrightarrow{C_5H_5N} R\underset{\underset{COR'}{|}}{C}HNHCOR'$$

351. Acylation of Amines by Amides

$$RNH_2 + R'CONH_2 \rightarrow R'CONHR + NH_3$$

By heating methylamine hydrochloride and acetamide for a few minutes, ammonium chloride is precipitated and N-methylacetamide is obtained in 75% yield.[13] The reaction has been extended to the preparation of N-alkyl-amides of higher-molecular-weight mono- and di-basic acids.[6] The free amine and amide are heated to 150–200° until the evolution of ammonia ceases. A series of mono- and di-alkylamides have been obtained by this process in the presence of boron trifluoride, which removes the ammonia as monoamminoboron trifluoride, $NH_3 \cdot BF_3$.[9]

352. Reaction of Esters with Ammonia and Its Derivatives

$$RCO_2C_2H_5 + NH_3 \rightarrow RCO_2NH_2 + C_2H_5OH$$

The conversion of esters to the corresponding amides is usually carried out by shaking with concentrated ammonium hydroxide, as in the preparations of chloroacetamide (67%),[30] cyanoacetamide (88%),[31] and nicotinamide (78%).[25] The reaction is catalyzed by water and other hydroxylated solvents.[21] Malonic ester gives a practically quantitative yield of the corresponding *diamide* by heating for 2 days with 20% ammonium hydroxide.[24] Malonmonoamide is prepared similarly from the potassium salt of monomethyl malonate.[4] Monoalkylmalonic esters are best converted to diamides by the action of ammonia in methanol.[23] This reaction is catalyzed by sodium methoxide. Dialkylmalonic esters do not react to an appreciable extent.

Lactic esters are converted to α-*hydroxy* amides by liquid ammonia[22] or amines.[28] Hydroxyl groups may be present also on aromatic nuclei (salicylamides)[26] and on the alkyl groups of the amine (ethanolamides).[27]

Acetal esters such as diethoxyacetic ester and β,β-diethoxypropionic ester are readily converted to amides with concentrated ammonium hydroxide.[29] The former ester gives an N,N-dimethylamide by reaction with dimethylamine.[33]

Ethyl benzoylacetate, $C_6H_5COCH_2CO_2C_2H_5$, reacts with concentrated ammonium hydroxide in the cold or with aniline in xylene at 150° to give the corresponding β-*keto* amides, benzoylacetamide (81%)[32] and benzoylacetanilide (76%),[34] respectively.

Esters of α-amino acids undergo ammonolysis by methanolic ammonia to give good yields of *amino* acid amides.[35] This procedure represents an improvement over the bomb reaction using liquid ammonia.

The following is the most important method for the preparation of hydrazides:

$$RCO_2C_2H_5 + NH_2NH_2 \longrightarrow RCONHNH_2 + C_2H_5OH$$

The reaction is carried out by heating the ester with 40% aqueous hydrazine hydrate solution. The yields of hydrazides are usually excellent from aliphatic and aromatic esters.[112, 113, 116] The procedure is well illustrated by the conversion of methyl *p*-nitrophenylacetate to *p*-nitrophenylacethydrazide (97%).[36] Mono- and di-hydrazides of dibasic acids also have been made.[115]

Interaction of an ester with hydroxylamine is the most general synthetic route to hydroxamic acids.[110, 120]

$$RCO_2C_2H_5 \xrightarrow[\text{Base}]{NH_2OH \cdot HCl} RCO_2NHOH$$

353. Acidolysis of Amides

$$RCONH_2 + R'CO_2H \rightleftharpoons RCO_2H + R'CO_2NH_2$$

This little-used exchange reaction presents certain possibilities. Equilibrium is shifted to the right at 230° by removal of formic acid from a reacting mixture of oleic acid and formamide. Oleamide is isolated in 50% yield.[3] The reaction likewise goes to completion when urea is employed as the amide.

$$RCO_2H + NH_2CONH_2 \longrightarrow RCONH_2 + CO_2 + NH_3$$

Thus, formamide, acetamide, benzamide, and nicotinamide have been made in 60-95% yields,[20] and adipamide and sebacamide in better than 85% yields.[6, 15]

354. Hydrolysis of Nitriles

$$RCN + H_2O \longrightarrow RCONH_2$$

Hydrolysis of a nitrile oftentimes can be stopped at the amide stage. A series of trisubstituted acetamides have been made by hydrolysis at 100° with 80% sulfuric acid.[68] Vigorous stirring with aqueous concentrated hydrochloric acid at low temperatures converts arylacetonitriles to arylacetamides.[171] Nicotinonitrile is hydrolyzed to nicotinamide in 90% yield by boiling with basic IRA-400 resin and in 73% yield by the action of concentrated ammonium hydroxide at 108°.[71] Optimum conditions have been determined for the dehydration and partial hydrolysis of acetone cyanohydrin to the *olefinic* amide, methacrylamide (70%).[69] Several cyanides containing *alkylamino* groups have been hydrolyzed by dissolving in concentrated sulfuric acid and, after a time, pouring the resulting solutions onto ice.[72, 73, 169]

Hydrogen peroxide reacts with aliphatic and aromatic nitriles in alkaline solution at 50° to give amides in 50-95% yields.

$$2RCN + 2H_2O_2 \xrightarrow{\text{NaOH}} 2RCONH_2 + O_2$$

The reaction is exothermic and may be followed by the evolution of oxygen. The hydrogen peroxide is used in concentrations varying from 3% to 30%.[66, 67] o-Substituted benzonitriles which are difficult to hydrolyze require the higher concentrations. Partial hydrolysis of adiponitrile and sabaconitrile to the corresponding ω-cyanocarboxamides has been achieved in 6-31% yields by this procedure.[170] Certain olefinic nitriles are converted to *glycidamides* by this reagent (cf. method 126).[70]

$$RCH = C(C_6H_5)CN \xrightarrow[\text{NaOH}]{H_2O_2} RCH - C(C_6H_5)CONH_2$$
$$\diagdown O \diagup$$

355. Addition of Olefins to Nitriles

$$(CH_3)_2C = CH_2 \xrightarrow[H_2SO_4]{RCN} R\underset{\underset{OSO_3H}{|}}{C} = NC(CH_3)_3 \xrightarrow{H_2O} RCONHC(CH_3)_3$$

This is a new reaction for the preparation of N-alkyl amides.[100] Nitriles and various substituted cyano compounds are treated with active olefins in the presence of sulfuric acid. Reaction occurs at room temperature in glacial acetic acid or dibutyl ether solution. The use of hydrogen cyanide in the reaction leads to the formation of N-alkylformamides. t-Butyl alcohol and sodium cyanide are used in place of the olefin and hydrogen cyanide in the preparation of N-t-butylformamide (50%).[100] The reaction has been extended to the synthesis of N-alkyl diamides from dinitriles and olefins or alcohols.[99]

356. Addition of Amines to Ketenes

$$CH_3COCH = C = O + RNH_2 \rightarrow CH_3COCH_2CONHR$$

This reaction has found greatest use in the preparation of N-aryl-β-ketoamides from diketene and arylamines. Acetoacetanilide is formed in 74% yield from diketene and aniline in benzene solution.[94] N-Alkyl-acetoacetanilides are similarly prepared when an alkylaniline is substituted for aniline in the reaction.[95]

A series of N,N-dialkylmalonamides have been made by the addition of amines to carbon suboxide.[96]

$$O = C = C = C = O + 2RNH_2 \rightarrow CH_2(CONHR)_2$$

357. Addition of Grignard Reagents to Isocyanates

$$RNCO \xrightarrow{R'MgX} RNC(R')OMgX \xrightarrow{H_2O} R'CONHR$$

Anilides, toluides, and α-naphthalides are prepared from phenyl, p-tolyl, and α-naphthyl isocyanates, respectively, by reaction with a Grignard reagent. The reaction is valuable for the identification of halogen compounds of the type that form organometallic derivatives.[105] The reaction occurs in ether solution at room temperature. In general, the yields of N-arylamides are excellent. This method has been used in the preparation of N-(α-furyl)-propionamide (89%).[97]

358. Alkylation of Amides and Imides

$$RCONHAr \xrightarrow[CH_3I]{Na;} RCON(CH_3)Ar$$

N-Methylacetanilide is obtained in 96% yield by the action of methyl iodide or dimethyl sulfate on the sodium salt of acetanilide.[137] The last compound is prepared from acetanilide and sodium wire in hot benzene. The reaction has been extended to other aliphatic and aromatic N-substituted amides. Sodium hydride serves to convert the amide to its salt, and a variety of simple halides have been successfully employed as alkylating agents.[175]

Alkylation of phthalimide is the first step in the Gabriel synthesis of primary amines. The scope of this alkylation is discussed in method 452 because the phthalimides are often hydrolyzed directly, without purification, to primary amines.

359. Rearrangement of Oximes (Beckmann)

$$R_2C = N - OH \xrightarrow{PCl_5} RCONHR$$

The rearrangement of oximes is of importance in establishing the geometrical configurations of these compounds. Ketoximes are rearranged by acidic reagents such as benzenesulfonyl chlorides, phosphorus pentachloride, or sulfuric acid. The R group which is *trans* to the hydroxyl group migrates in the reaction.

The preparative value of this reaction is limited to a few special cases. Oximes of cyclopentanone[62] and cyclohexanone[56, 61] are rearranged by concentrated sulfuric acid to cyclic amides of ω-amino acids (cf. method 248).

$$(CH_2)_5 C = NOH \xrightarrow{H_2SO_4} \overline{NH(CH_2)_5 CO}$$

The oxime of 2-acetyldibenzothiophene rearranges in the presence of phosphorus pentachloride to give 2-acetamidodibenzothiophene in 70% yield.[63] The rearrangement also serves as a preparative method for the acetyl derivatives of 1-, 2-, 3-, and 9-aminophenanthrenes.[168]

Aldoximes are rearranged to amides at 100–150° under the catalytic influence of Raney nickel.[65] The yields of amides from the oximes of acetaldehyde, heptaldehyde, benzaldehyde, and furfural are good (75–96%), although the reactions are carried out on a small scale only.

$$RCH = NOH \xrightarrow{Raney\ Ni} RCONH_2$$

360. Ammonolysis and Rearrangement of Diazoketones (Arndt-Eistert)

$$\text{RCOCl} \xrightarrow{\text{CH}_2\text{N}_2} \text{RCOCHN}_2 \xrightarrow{\text{NH}_3} \text{RCH}_2\text{CONH}_2$$

Preparation of diazoketones and their rearrangements during hydrolysis (method 271) and alcoholysis (method 295) are discussed elsewhere. Ammonolysis of diazoketones leads to amides of acids containing one more carbon atom than the original acyl halide.[91] Halogen atoms may be present in a remote position on an aliphatic chain.[117] The reaction is carried out by heating the diazoketone in alcohol[93, 103] or dioxane[102] solution with aqueous ammonia in the presence of silver oxide or silver nitrate catalysts. Substituted acetanilides are formed when aniline is used in place of ammonia.[93, 104]

$$\text{RCOCHN}_2 \xrightarrow[180°]{\text{C}_6\text{H}_5\text{NH}_2} \text{RCH}_2\text{CONHC}_6\text{H}_5$$

361. Willgerodt Reaction

$$\left.\begin{array}{l} \text{RCOCH}_3 \\ \text{RCH}=\text{CH}_2 \\ \text{RC}\equiv\text{CH} \end{array}\right\} \xrightarrow{(\text{NH}_4)_2\text{S}_x} \text{RCH}_2\text{CONH}_2$$

From a preparative standpoint this reaction is most useful in the synthesis of arylacetic acids and amides from substituted methyl aryl ketones or vinyl aromatic compounds. The conversion is effected by heating the aromatic compounds under pressure at 160-200° with aqueous ammonium polysulfide.[77] Several modifications of this process have found more general application. Higher yields and purer products result at lower temperatures when dioxane is used as a solvent.[76, 86, 87] A combination of sulfur, ammonium hydroxide, and pyridine has given equal success.[74, 75] In the Kindler modification, the ketone or styrene is refluxed with a mixture of sulfur and an amine, usually morpholine, to give a thioamide, $\text{ArCH}_2\text{CSNR}_2$.[75, 82, 83, 85] The *terminal* methyl group is always oxidized at the expense of the double bond or carbonyl group regardless of their position in the carbon chain.

$$\text{RCO(CH}_2)_n\text{CH}_3 \rightarrow \text{R(CH}_2)_{n+1}\text{CONH}_2$$

Thus, β-phenylpropionamide, γ-phenylbutyramide, and δ-phenylvaleramide are formed in decreasing yields from the homologs of acetophenone, where

$n = 1$, 2, and 3, respectively.[74] Carbon-skeleton rearrangement does not take place during the reaction.[75, 81]

Willgerodt reactions have been carried out on aromatic compounds containing halo,[82, 83, 85, 89] hydroxyl,[77, 82, 85] alkoxyl,[82, 83, 85, 90] amino,[82, 85] acetamido,[82] methylmercapto,[89] and nitro[82] groups on the aromatic nucleus. Several heterocyclic compounds including acetyl or vinyl derivatives of dibenzofuran,[76] pyridine,[75, 85, 88] and quinoline[85] also have been used.

Simple aliphatic aldehydes, ketones, alcohols, olefins, thiols, and acetylenes react in the same manner as the related aryl derivatives, but the yields of products are usually very low.[78, 79] α,β-Olefinic acids are decarboxylated during the process to give amides with one less carbon atom.[84]

$$RCH = CHCO_2H \rightarrow RCH_2CONH_2$$

The literature of the Willgerodt reaction to 1946 has been reviewed.[80]

362. Action of Hydrazoic Acid on Ketones (Schmidt)

$$RCOR + HN_3 \xrightarrow{\text{H}^+} RCONHR + N_2$$

Ketones react with hydrazoic acid at room temperature in the presence of acid catalysts.[150] The products are N-substituted amides. Hydrazoic acid is prepared in benzene or chloroform solution from sodium azide. A modification involves the addition of sodium azide to a solution of acid catalyst and ketone. Improved experimental procedures have been based on a study of the reaction mechanism.[151] Several series of alkyl and N-aryl amides have been prepared from symmetrical and methyl ketones.[64, 151, 169] Higher alkyl and aryl groups migrate more readily than methyl groups to the nitrogen atom. In the presence of large amounts of alcohol, imino esters are formed instead of amides (cf. method 410). Hydrazoic acid attacks the keto group of keto esters to give amido esters from which amino acids are obtained upon hydrolysis (method 449).

363. Cleavage of Ketones by Sodium Amide

$$C_6H_5COCR_3 \xrightarrow{\text{NaNH}_2} C_6H_6 + R_3CONHNa$$

Cleavage by sodium amide is a general reaction of diaryl ketones, hexaalkylacetones, and t-alkyl aryl ketones.[140] The reaction has found preparative value in the cleavage of trialkylacetophenones to amides of trialkylacetic acids (method 248).[141] Fission occurs when the ketones are refluxed with sodium amide in benzene, toluene, or xylene solutions.

The synthesis has been extended to higher-molecular-weight compounds but fails for the preparation of trialkylacetamides containing more than twelve carbon atoms unless two of the alkyl groups are methyl.[142]

364. Acyl Azides by the Action of Nitrous Acid on Hydrazides

$$RCONHNH_2 \xrightarrow[\text{HCl}]{\text{NaNO}_2} RCON_3$$

This reaction is carried out in the same manner as the diazotization of primary amines. Most azides are relatively unstable compounds and explode upon heating. Hydrazides of all types of acids have been converted to azides.[112, 113, 115] Halo alkoxyl, and nitro groups on an aromatic nucleus do not interfere. The reaction is illustrated by the preparations of p-nitrophenylacetyl azide (84%)[36] and 6-methylnicotinyl azide (70%).[107]

365. Acyl Azides by Interaction of Sodium Azide and Acyl Halides

$$RCOCl + NaN_3 \rightarrow RCON_3 + NaCl$$

Acyl azides are conveniently prepared by treating an acetone, ether, or dioxane solution of the corresponding acyl halides with an aqueous solution of sodium azide.[121] The reaction is rapid at 0–25°, and, in general, the azides are isolated in excellent yields. Many types of acyl halides have been used.[106, 119, 122]

366. Condensation of Carbonyl Compounds with α-Halo Amides (Reformatsky)

$$RCOR + R'CHBrCONR''_2 \xrightarrow[\text{H}_2\text{O}]{\text{Zn};} R_2C(OH)CH(R')CONR''_2$$

N,N-Dialkyl-α-halo amides may be substituted for α-halo esters in the Reformatsky reaction.[51] The yields of N,N-dialkyl-β-hydroxyamides compare favorably with those of the corresponding hydroxy esters (cf. method 103).

367. Condensation of Aldehydes with Amides and Imides

$$RCONH_2 + HCHO \xrightarrow{\text{K}_2\text{CO}_3} RCONHCH_2OH$$

$$CH_3CONH_2 + RCHO \xrightarrow{\text{CH}_3\text{CO}_2\text{H}} RCH(NHCOCH_3)_2$$

N-Methylol derivatives of amides and cyclic imides are obtained by heating these compounds with formaldehyde and a basic catalyst.[146, 152, 176]

The yields are exceptionally good. In the presence of acetic acid two molecules of acetamide and one molecule of aldehyde condense to alkylidenediacetamides in poor yields.[148]

368. Condensation of Aldehydes with Malonmonoamide [4, 147] (cf. method 37)

$$RCHO + CH_2(CO_2H)(CONH_2) \xrightarrow{C_5H_5N} RCH=CHCONH_2 + CO_2$$

369. Condensation of Amides [149]

$$2CH_3CON(C_6H_5)_2 \xrightarrow{Na} CH_3COCH_2CON(C_6H_5)_2 + (C_6H_5)_2NNa$$

370. Coupling of Diethylaminocarbonyl Chloride with Organometallic Compounds [101]

$$RMgX + ClCON(C_2H_5)_2 \rightarrow RCON(C_2H_5)_2$$

371. Pyrolysis of Imino Ester Hydrochlorides [43]

$$RC(OC_2H_5)=NH \cdot HCl \xrightarrow{150^\circ} RCONH_2 + C_2H_5Cl$$

372. Acylation of Amides [159]

$$RCONH_2 \xrightarrow[(R'CO)_2O]{R'COCl\ or} RCONHCOR'$$

373. Action of Diazomethane on Isocyanates [180]

$$C_6H_5NCO + 2CH_2N_2 \rightarrow C_6H_5N-CO + 2N_2$$
$$||$$
$$CH_2-CH_2$$

374. Action of Ammonia or Amines on Lactones [184]

$$CH_2(CH_2)_nCO \xrightarrow[280^\circ]{RNH_2} CH_2(CH_2)_nCO + H_2O$$
$$|\underline{O}| |\underline{NR}|$$

375. Hydroxamic Acids by Oxidation of Aldoximes [111, 164]

$$RCHO + NH_2OH + H_2O_2 \rightarrow RCONHOH + 2H_2O$$

376. Hydroxamic Acids by Rearrangement of Nitroparaffins [111, 183] (cf. method 252)

$$CH_3CH_2CH_2NO_2 \xrightarrow[60^\circ]{H_2SO_4} CH_3CH_2CONHOH \quad (44\%)$$

377. Hydroxamic Acids by Interaction of Aldehydes and Sodium Nitro-
hydroxamate [111]

$$RCHO + Na_2N_2O_3 \rightarrow RC(OH){=}NONa + NaNO_2$$

TABLE 63. AMIDES

C_n	Compound	Method	Yield (%)	Chapter[ref.]	B.p./mm., n_D^t, (M.p.)
		Aliphatic and Alicyclic Amides			
C_1	Formamide	353	84	19[20]	113/20
C_2	Acetamide	349	90	19[1]	(81)
		353	95	19[20]	223
C_3	Propionamide	349	95	19[17]	(81)
	N-Methylacetamide	351	75	19[13]	202–206
	N,N-Dimethylformamide	349	73	19[17]	153/760, 1.4269[25]
C_4	Butyramide	349	88	19[17]	(115)
	Isobutyramide	348	83	19[38]	(129)
	N,N-Dimethylacetamide	349	78	19[8]	165/758, 1.4351[25]
		358	69	19[175]	(167)
	Cyclopropanecarboxamide	348	91	19[43]	(125)
C_5	Valeramide	349	82	19[17]	(106)
	N-Methylisobutyramide	348	75	19[41]	121/27, 1.4350
	N,N-Dimethylpropionamide	349	78	19[17]	176/765, 1.4371[25]
	Trimethylacetamide	363	100	19[141]	(156)
	N-t-Butylformamide	355	50	19[100]	202
C_6	Caproamide	349	75	19[17]	(101)
	Dimethylethylacetamide	363	100	19[141]	(104)
	β,β-Dimethylbutyramide	361	58	19[79]	(134)
	N,N-Dimethylbutyramide	349	84	19[17]	125/100, 1.4391[25]
	N-n-Butylacetamide	351	37	19[9]	229
	N-t-Butylacetamide	355	85	19[100]	194, (98)
C_7	Heptamide	349	75	19[17]	(97)
		361	46	19[79]	(97)
	γ,γ-Dimethylvaleramide	361	30	19[79]	(141)
	N,N-Dimethylvaleramide	349	87	19[17]	141/100, 1.4419[25]
	N-Isoamylacetamide	351	64	19[9]	234
C_8	Caprylamide	349	80	19[17]	(106)
	Dimethyl-n-butylacetamide	363	56	19[142]	(89)
	N,N-Dimethylcaproamide	349	88	19[17]	158/100, 1.4430[25]
	Cyclohexylacetamide	361	40	19[79]	(165)
		348	40	19[167]	(171)
C_9	N,N-Dimethylheptamide	349	81	19[17]	173/100, 1.4450[25]
	3,3,4,4-Tetramethylvaleramide	348	77	19[42]	(138)
	β-Cyclohexylpropionamide	361	27	19[79]	(120)
		Aromatic Amides			
C_7	Benzamide	349	50	19[16]	(130)*
C_8	Phenylacetamide	360	70	19[93]	(156)
		361	80	19[74]	(158)
	o-Toluamide	354	92	19[66]	(141)

TABLE 63. AMIDES 579

TABLE 63 (continued)

C_n	Compound	Method	Yield (%)	Chapter[ref.]	B.p./mm., n_D^t, (M.p.)
		Aromatic Amides (continued)			
C_8	N-Phenylacetamide	350	85	19[128]	(115)
	(acetanilide)	351	99	19[9]	(114)
	N-Methylformanilide	349	97	19[12]	131/22, (14), 1.554[29]
	($C_6H_5 N(CH_3)CHO$)				
C_9	β-Phenylpropionamide	361	82	19[74]	(99)
	N-Phenylpropionamide	351	97	19[9]	221, (103)
	o-Methylacetanilide	350	82	19[128]	(111)
	p-Methylacetanilide	350	100	19[128]	(155)
	N-Methylacetanilide	351	54	19[9]	255, (98)
		358	89	19[175]	(101)
		358	98	19[137]	(98)
C_{10}	α-Phenylbutyramide	348	97	19[40]	(85)
	γ-Phenylbutyramide	361	42	19[74]	(84)
C_{11}	δ-Phenylvaleramide	361	29	19[74]	(108)
	N-n-Butylbenzamide	348	45	19[7]	(42)
	N-t-Butylbenzamide	355	90	19[100]	(135)
	α-Naphthamide	354	100	19[67]	(202)
C_{12}	α-Naphthylacetamide	360	80	19[93]	(181)
	β-Naphthylacetamide	348	96	19[44]	(204)
	2-Acetamidonaphthalene	350	97	19[129]	(132)
		362	95	19[151]	(134)
	N-α-Naphthylacetamide	351	45	19[9]	(159)
C_{13}	Benzanilide	349	84	19[2]	(161)
C_{14}	N-Methylbenzanilide	358	62	19[175]	(59)
	4-Biphenylacetamide	361	84	19[74]	(243)
	2-Acetamidobiphenyl	350	93	19[132]	(121)
C_{15}	2-Fluoreneacetamide	361	70	19[87]	(266)
C_{16}	2-Phenanthrylacetamide	361	82	19[74]	(248)
	3-Phenanthrylacetamide	361	81	19[86]	(172-176)
C_{17}	β-(2-Phenanthryl)-propionamide	361	66	19[74]	(189)
C_{19}	γ-(3-Phenanthryl)-valeramide	360	72	19[103]	(139)
		Lactams			
C_4	2-Pyrrolidone (γ-Butyrolactam)	374	64	19[182]	103/1, (24)
C_5	1-Methyl-2-pyrrolidone	374	93	19[182]	202
	5-Methyl-2-pyrrolidone (γ-valerolactam)	374	74	19[182]	(44)
C_6	2-Ketohexamethyleneimine	359	65	19[61]	127-133/7, (68)
	(ϵ-caprolactam)	362	63	19[151]	(64)
	1,5-Dimethyl-2-pyrrolidone (N-methyl-γ-valerolactam)	349	77	19[181]	85/13, 1.4611[25]

For explanations and symbols see pp. xi–xii.

TABLE 63 *(continued)*

C_n	Compound	Method	Yield (%)	Chapter[ref.]	B.p./mm., n_D^t, (M.p.)

Lactams *(continued)*

C_n	Compound	Method	Yield (%)	Chapter[ref.]	B.p./mm., n_D^t, (M.p.)
C_9	N-Phenyl-β-propiolactam	373	20	19[180]	(79)
C_{11}	5-Phenyl-2-piperidone	574	88	39[106]	228/20, (128)
C_{13}	Phenanthridone	349	83	19[19]	(293)

Heterocyclic Amides

C_6	2-Thienylacetamide	354	35	19[172]	(148)
	Nicotinamide	352	78	19[25]	(132)
		353	85	19[20]	(122)
		354	86	19[71]	(130)
C_7	N-(α-Furyl)-propionamide	357	89	19[97]	134/12, (81)
	2-Pyridineacetamide	361	31	19[75]	(121)
C_{13}	N,N-Diethylindole-3-carboxamide	370	44	19[101]	(152)
	N,N-Diethylthianaphthene-3-carboxamide	370	21	19[101]	220/11
C_{14}	2-Dibenzofurylacetamide	361	70	19[76]	(210)
	4-Dibenzofurylacetamide	360	67	19[92]	(212)
	2-Acetamidodibenzothiophene	359	70	19[63]	(178)
	N-Acetylcarbazole	350	83	19[126]	(69)

Amides of Dicarboxylic Acids

C_3	Malonamide (malondiamide)	352	99	19[24]	(169)
C_5	Ethylmalondiamide	352	91	19[23]	(215)
	N,N'-Dimethylmalonamide	356	70	19[96]	(133)
	Methylenediacetamide	367	54	19[148]	(198)
C_6	Ethylidenediacetamide	367	44	19[148]	(180)
C_7	n-Butylmalondiamide	352	87	19[23]	(198)
	N,N'-Diethylmalonamide	356	63	19[96]	(147)
C_8	N-Mono-t-butylsuccinamide	355	25	19[99]	(149)
	Phthalamide	....	90	19[154]	(220)
C_9	N,N'-Diisopropylmalonamide	355	40	19[99]	(115)
C_{10}	Benzylmalondiamide	352	96	19[23]	(226)
	Diacetyl-o-phenylenediamine	350	80	19[130]	(188)

Olefinic Amides

C_4	Vinylacetamide	354	80	19[70]	(72)
	Methacrylamide	352	75	19[177]	(111)
		354	70	19[69]	(110)
C_5	N-Methylmethacrylamide	348	87	19[166]	85/4
C_6	β-Isopropylacrylamide	368	70	19[147]	(86)

TABLE 63. AMIDES 581

TABLE 63 (continued)

C_n	Compound	Method	Yield (%)	Chapter[ref.]	B.p./mm., n_D^t, (M.p.)
		Olefinic Amides (continued)			
C_8	N-t-Butylmethacrylamide	355	88	19[166]	94/20, (59)
C_9	Cinnamamide	368	57	19[4]	(147)
C_{11}	α-Allylphenylacetamide	348	82	19[39]	(54)
	N-Allylacetanilide	358	73	19[175]	101/2
		Halo Amides			
C_2	Fluoroacetamide	348	73	19[47]	(108)
		352	100	19[109]	(108)
	γ-Chloroacetamide	352	67	19[30]	(120)
	α,α-Dichloroacetamide	349	78	19[10]	(99)
	Trichloroacetamide	348	54	19[54]	(141)
	N-Bromoacetamide	68	60	4[691]	
		68	51	4[695]	(105)
C_3	N-Methylfluoroacetamide	352	75	19[109]	(64)
	N-Methyl-α,α-dichloroacetamide	348	72	19[49]	98/8, 79
	N-Methyl-α-bromoacetamide	348	61	19[45]	61/0.6, (45)
C_4	α-Chloroisobutyramide	348	70	19[50]	(118)
	N-Methyl-α-bromopropionamide	348	89	19[46]	81/2, (40)
	N-Ethyl-α,α-dichloroacetamide	348	77	19[49]	104/8, (59)
	N,N-Dimethyl-α,α-dichloroacetamide	348	76	19[49]	97/9, 1.4931[25]
	N,N-Dimethyl-α-bromoacetamide	348	32	19[45]	116/18, 1.5097
	N-Ethyl-α-bromoacetamide	348	82	19[45]	121/17, (47)
	N-Bromosuccinimide	68	81	4[687]	
C_5	α-Bromo-n-valeramide	348	60	19[55]	(79)
	N-Ethyl-α-bromopropionamide	348	89	19[46]	82/2, (62)
	N,N-Dimethyl-α-bromopropionamide	348	85	19[46]	75/3, 1.4979
C_6	α-Bromo-t-butylacetamide	348	71	19[52]	(138)
	N,N-Diethyl-α,α-dichloroacetamide	348	85	19[49]	100/4, 1.4813[25]
	N,N-Diethyl-α-bromoacetamide	348	67	19[45]	82/0.6, 1.4963
C_7	N,N-Diethyl-α-bromopropionamide	348	79	19[46]	84/1.6, 1.4862
	N-Bromobenzamide	68	55	4[690]	
C_8	α-Bromophenylacetamide	348	92	19[48]	(148)
	N-Chloroacetanilide	68	83	4[689]	
	4-Iodoacetanilide	....	92	19[163]	(184)

For explanations and symbols see pp. xi–xii.

TABLE 63 *(continued)*

C_n	Compound	Method	Yield (%)	Chapter[ref.]	B.p./mm., n_D^t, (M.p.)
		Halo Amides *(continued)*			
C_9	N-Methyl-α-bromophenyl-acetamide	348	68	19^{48}	(74)
	N-Methyl-p-chloroacetanilide	358	72	19^{175}	(93)
C_{13}	o-Iodobenzanilide	348	74	19^{53}	(143)
C_{14}	N-Phenyl-α-bromophenyl-acetamide	348	40	19^{48}	(123)
		Hydroxy Amides			
C_3	Lactamide	352	74	19^{22}	(75)
C_4	N-Methyllactamide	352	91	19^{28}	(72)
C_5	N,N-Dimethyllactamide	352	86	19^{28}	57/0.6, 1.4588
C_6	N-Hydroxymethylisovaleramide	367	65	19^{152}	(79)
C_8	α-Hydroxyphenylacetamide (mandelamide)	349 352	62 81	19^{11} 19^{21}	(132)
	p-Hydroxyphenylacetamide	361	68	19^{77}	(174)
	p-Acetamidophenol	350	56	19^{178}	(168)
C_9	N-Hydroxymethylphenyl-acetamide	367	82	19^{176}	(78)
C_{13}	o-Hydroxybenzanilide	352	70	19^{26}	(132)
		Alkoxy Amides			
C_5	α-Methoxyisobutyramide	352	86	19^{165}	(118)
C_6	Diethoxyacetamide	352	84	19^{29}	(78)
C_7	β,β-Diethoxypropionamide	352	80	19^{29}	(55)
C_8	N,N-Dimethyldiethoxy-acetamide	352	51	19^{33}	105/12
C_9	m-Methoxyphenylacetamide	361	53	19^{82}	(126)
	p-Methoxyphenylacetamide (p-homoanisamide)	360	81	19^{102}	(189)
	p-Methoxyacetanilide (p-acetoanisidide)	350 350	96 95	19^{131} 19^{137}	(128) (128)
C_{10}	N-Methyl-p-methoxyacetanilide	358	96	19^{137}	(57)
		Keto Amides			
C_8	Isatin	....	78	19^{153}	(197)
C_9	Benzoylacetamide	352	81	19^{32}	(113)
C_{10}	α-Benzoylpropionamide	352	67	19^{32}	(153)
	Acetoacetanilide	356	74	19^{94}	(85)
	p-Acetaminoacetophenone	178	82	19^{158}	(167)
C_{11}	α-Benzoylbutyramide	352	42	19^{32}	(155)
	N-Methylacetoacetanilide	356	69	19^{95}	131/4
C_{15}	Benzoylacetanilide	352	76	19^{34}	(106)

TABLE 64. IMIDES 583

TABLE 63 (continued)

C_n	Compound	Method	Yield (%)	Chapter[ref.]	B.p./mm., n_D^t, (M.p.)
		Carboxy Amides			
C_3	Malon-monoamide	352	61	19[4]	(110–115)
C_4	Acetylglycine	350	92	19[124]	(208)
C_8	Diethyl formylaminomalonate	....	55	19[156]	(49)
C_9	Benzoylaminoacetic (hippuric) acid	348	68	19[57]	(187)
C_{11}	N-Benzoyl-α-aminoisobutyric acid	348	88	19[59]	(202)
C_{15}	N-Benzoyl-α-aminophenylacetic acid	348	97	19[59]	(178)
		Amino Amides			
C_2	α-Aminoacetamide	352	56	19[35]	(68)
C_3	D-α-Aminopropionamide	352	84	19[35]	(72)
	Methylaminoacetamide	354	90	19[169]	(72)
C_4	Dimethylaminoacetamide	354	76	19[72]	(96)
C_8	o-Aminoacetanilide	425	90	19[179]	(133)
C_{13}	p-Aminobenzanilide	425	90	19[162]	(136)
		Cyano Amides			
C_3	Cyanoacetamide	352	88	19[31]	(120)
C_4	α-Cyanopropionamide	352	41 †	19[160]	
C_8	o-Cyanobenzamide	384	65	20[374]	(171)
		Nitro Amides			
C_8	o-Nitrophenylacetamide	360	55	19[93]	(161)
	o-Nitroacetanilide	350	97	19[130]	(93)
	p-Nitroacetanilide	350	100	19[128]	(216)
		486	95	28[63]	(207)
C_9	o-Nitro-N-methylacetanilide	350	73	19[130]	(71)

For explanations and symbols see pp. xi–xii.

TABLE 64. IMIDES

C_n	Compound	Method	Yield (%)	Chapter[ref.]	(M.p.)
C_4	Succinimide	349	83	19[5]	(125)
C_5	Glutarimide	350	....	19[135]	(165)
C_6	α-Methylglutarimide	350	80	19[134]	(91)
C_7	α-Ethylglutarimide	350	85	19[135]	(108)
C_8	Phthalimide	350	97	19[123]	(235)
	N-Bromophthalimide	68	80	4[688]	
	4-Nitrophthalimide	486	53	19[157]	(198)

For explanations and symbols see pp. xi–xii.

TABLE 64 (continued)

C_n	Compound	Method	Yield (%)	Chapter[ref.]	(M.p.)
C_9	N-Methylphthalimide	358	90	19[145]	(134)
	N-Bromomethylphthalimide	51	70	19[146]	(148)
	N-Hydroxymethylphthalimide	367	94	19[146]	(140)
C_{10}	Succinanil (N-phenylsuccinimide)	349	75	19[133]	(158)
	β-Bromoethylphthalimide	358	79	19[143]	(83)
C_{12}	N-n-Butylphthalimide	358	74	19[145]	(37)
	N-t-Butylphthalimide	350	76	19[14]	(60)
C_{13}	2-Pyridylphthalimide	350	76	19[127]	(225)
C_{15}	N-Benzylphthalimide	358	63	19[125]	(116)
	Diethyl phthalimidomalonate	358	71	19[144]	(74)

For explanations and symbols see pp. xi–xii.

TABLE 65. HYDRAZIDES AND AZIDES

C_n	Compound	Method	Yield (%)	Chapter[ref.]	(M.p.)
C_5	Betaine hydrazide hydrochloride (Girard's reagent)	352	90	19[108]	(175–180)
	2-Furoyl azide	365	92	19[119]	
C_6	Nicotinyl azide	364	88	19[173]	(48)
C_7	Benzhydrazide	352	80	19[116]	(112)
	Benzoyl azide	364	70	19[118]	(28)
		365	54	19[121]	(32)
		365	50	19[118]	(28)
	p-Iodobenzoyl azide	364	90	19[112]	(56)
	2,4-Dinitrobenzoyl azide	365	91	19[122]	(68)
	6-Methylnicotinyl azide	364	70	19[107]	(45)
C_8	Ethylisobutylacethydrazide	352	76	19[114]	(74)
	p-Methoxybenzhydrazide	352	95	19[113]	(136)
	p-Nitrophenylacethydrazide	352	97	19[36]	(167)
	p-Nitrophenylacetyl azide	364	84	19[36]	(45)
C_9	p-Ethoxybenzhydrazide	352	95	19[113]	(127)
	p-Ethoxybenzoyl azide	352	95	19[113]	(31)
C_{15}	9-Phenanthroyl azide	365	98	19[106]	(95), Explodes

For explanations and symbols see pp. xi–xii.

REFERENCES FOR CHAPTER 19

[1] Coleman and Alvarado, *Org. Syntheses,* Coll. Vol. I, 3 (1941); cf. ref. 17.
[2] Webb, *Org. Syntheses,* Coll. Vol. I, 82 (1941); cf. refs. 7 and 9.
[3] Roe, Scanlan, and Swern, *J. Am. Chem. Soc.,* 71, 2217 (1949).
[4] Galat, *J. Am. Chem. Soc.,* 70, 2596 (1948).
[5] Clarke and Behr, *Org. Syntheses,* Coll. Vol. II, 562 (1943).
[6] MacGregor and Ward, *J. Soc. Chem. Ind. (London),* 66, 344 (1947).
[7] Grimmel, Guenther, and Morgan, *J. Am. Chem. Soc.,* 68, 539 (1946).
[8] Ruhoff and Reid, *J. Am. Chem. Soc.,* 59, 401 (1937); cf. ref. 17.
[9] Sowa and Nieuwland, *J. Am. Chem. Soc.,* 59, 1203 (1937).
[10] Clarke, Shibe, and Connor, *Org. Syntheses,* 20, 37 (1940).
[11] Audrieth and Sveda, *Org. Syntheses,* 20, 62 (1940).
[12] Fieser and Jones, *Org. Syntheses,* 20, 66 (1940).
[13] Galat and Elion, *J. Am. Chem. Soc.,* 65, 1566 (1943).
[14] Smith and Emerson, *J. Am. Chem. Soc.,* 67, 1862 (1945); *Org. Syntheses,* 29, 19 (1949).
[15] Biggs and Bishop, *Org. Syntheses,* 25, 97 (1945), note 6.
[16] Kao and Ma, *J. Chem. Soc.,* 2788 (1930); 443 (1931).
[17] Mitchell and Reid, *J. Am. Chem. Soc.,* 53, 1879 (1931); cf. ref. 8.
[18] Ralston, Hoerr, and Pool, *J. Org. Chem.,* 8, 473 (1943).
[19] Oyster and Adkins, *J. Am. Chem. Soc.,* 43, 208 (1921); Moore and Huntress, *ibid.,* 49, 1332 (1927).
[20] Cherbuliez and Landolt, *Helv. Chim. Acta,* 29, 1438 (1946).
[21] Gordon, Miller, and Day, *J. Am. Chem. Soc.,* 71, 1245 (1949).
[22] Audrieth and Kleinberg, *J. Org. Chem.,* 3, 312 (1938); *Org. Syntheses,* 21, 71 (1941).
[23] Russell, *J. Am. Chem. Soc.,* 72, 1853 (1950).
[24] Röhrs and Lang, *J. prakt. Chem.,* 158, 112 (1941).
[25] Karrer et al., *Helv. Chim. Acta,* 20, 65 (1937); LaForge, *J. Am. Chem. Soc.,* 50, 2480 (1928).
[26] Allen and VanAllan, *Org. Syntheses,* 26, 92 (1946), note 5.
[27] Phillips and Baltzly, *J. Am. Chem. Soc.,* 69, 200 (1947).
[28] Ratchford and Fisher, *J. Org. Chem.,* 15, 317, 326 (1950); *J. Am. Chem. Soc.,* 69, 1913 (1947).
[29] McElvain and Clarke, *J. Am. Chem. Soc.,* 69, 2659, 2662 (1947).
[30] Jacobs and Heidelberger, *Org. Syntheses,* Coll. Vol. I, 153 (1941).
[31] Corson, Scott, and Vose, *Org. Syntheses,* Coll. Vol. I, 179 (1941).
[32] Abrams and Kipping, *J. Chem. Soc.,* 1990 (1934).
[33] Scheibler et al., *Ber.,* 67, 1509 (1934).
[34] Kibler and Weissberger, *Org. Syntheses,* 25, 7 (1945).
[35] Yang and Rising, *J. Am. Chem. Soc.,* 53, 3183 (1931); cf. ref. 37.
[36] Shriner and Cross, *J. Am. Chem. Soc.,* 60, 2339 (1938).
[37] Jones, *J. Am. Chem. Soc.,* 71, 79 (1949).
[38] Kent and McElvain, *Org. Syntheses,* 25, 58 (1945).
[39] Horowitz and Geissman, *J. Am. Chem. Soc.,* 72, 1519 (1950).
[40] McElvain and Stevens, *J. Am. Chem. Soc.,* 69, 2665 (1947).
[41] McElvain and Stevens, *J. Am. Chem. Soc.,* 69, 2668 (1947).
[42] Whitmore, Marker, and Plambeck, *J. Am. Chem. Soc.,* 63, 1628 (1941).
[43] Schlatter, *J. Am. Chem. Soc.,* 63, 1735 (1941).
[44] Newman, *J. Org. Chem.,* 9, 518 (1944).

[45] Weaver and Whaley, *J. Am. Chem. Soc.*, **69**, 516 (1947); cf. ref. 51.
[46] Weaver and Whaley, *J. Am. Chem. Soc.*, **69**, 1144 (1947).
[47] Truce, *J. Am. Chem. Soc.*, **70**, 2828 (1948).
[48] Truitt et al., *J. Am. Chem. Soc.*, **71**, 3480 (1949).
[49] Swensen and Weaver, *J. Am. Chem. Soc.*, **70**, 4060 (1948).
[50] Stevens, *J. Am. Chem. Soc.*, **70**, 166 (1948).
[51] Drake, Eaker, and Shenk, *J. Am. Chem. Soc.*, **70**, 677 (1948).
[52] Homeyer, Whitmore, and Wallingford, *J. Am. Chem. Soc.*, **55**, 4213 (1933).
[53] Rapson and Shuttleworth, *J. Chem. Soc.*, 488 (1941).
[54] Tarbell and Weaver, *J. Am. Chem. Soc.*, **63**, 2942 (1941).
[55] Pomerantz and Connor, *J. Am. Chem. Soc.*, **61**, 3386 (1939).
[56] Eck and Marvel, *Org. Syntheses*, Coll. Vol. II, 76 (1943).
[57] Ingersoll and Babcock, *Org. Syntheses*, Coll. Vol. II, 328 (1943).
[58] Bishop, *Org. Syntheses*, **25**, 71 (1945).
[59] Steiger, *J. Org. Chem.*, **9**, 396 (1944).
[60] Couturier, *Ann. chim.*, (11) **10**, 563 (1938).
[61] Marvel and Eck, *Org. Syntheses*, Coll. Vol. II, 371 (1943).
[62] Fox, Dunn, and Stoddard, *J. Org. Chem.*, **6**, 410 (1941).
[63] Gilman and Jacoby, *J. Org. Chem.*, **3**, 116 (1938).
[64] Sanford, *J. Am. Chem. Soc.*, **67**, 1942 (1945).
[65] Paul, *Bull. soc. chim. France*, (5) **4**, 1115 (1937); *Compt. rend.*, **204**, 363 (1937).
[66] Noller, *Org. Syntheses*, Coll. Vol. II, 586 (1943).
[67] West, *J. Am. Chem. Soc.*, **42**, 1662 (1920).
[68] Sperber, Papa, and Schwenk, *J. Am. Chem. Soc.*, **70**, 3091 (1948).
[69] Wiley and Waddey, *Org. Syntheses*, **29**, 61 (1949); *J. Org. Chem.*, **13**, 421 (1948).
[70] Murray and Cloke, *J. Am. Chem. Soc.*, **56**, 2749 (1934).
[71] Galat, *J. Am. Chem. Soc.*, **70**, 3945 (1948); Krewson and Couch, *ibid.*, **65**, 2256 (1943).
[72] Turner, *J. Am. Chem. Soc.*, **68**, 1607 (1946).
[73] Jenkins, Bigelow, and Buck, *J. Am. Chem. Soc.*, **52**, 5202 (1930).
[74] DeTar and Carmack, *J. Am. Chem. Soc.*, **68**, 2025 (1946).
[75] Carmack and DeTar, *J. Am. Chem. Soc.*, **68**, 2029, 2033 (1946).
[76] Gilman and Avakian, *J. Am. Chem. Soc.*, **68**, 2105 (1946).
[77] Ott, Mattano, and Coleman, *J. Am. Chem. Soc.*, **68**, 2633 (1946).
[78] King and McMillan, *J. Am. Chem. Soc.*, **68**, 1369 (1946).
[79] Cavalieri, Pattison, and Carmack, *J. Am. Chem. Soc.*, **67**, 1783 (1945).
[80] Carmack and Spielman in *Organic Reactions*, Vol. 3, John Wiley & Sons, New York, 1946, pp. 83 and 95–98.
[81] Shantz and Rittenberg, *J. Am. Chem. Soc.*, **68**, 2109 (1946); King and McMillan, *ibid.*, **68**, 632 (1946); Campaigne and Rutan, *ibid.*, **69**, 1211 (1947).
[82] King and McMillan, *J. Am. Chem. Soc.*, **68**, 2335 (1946).
[83] Kindler and Li, *Ber.*, **74**, 321 (1941).
[84] Davis and Carmack, *J. Org. Chem.*, **12**, 76 (1947).
[85] Schwenk and Bloch, *J. Am. Chem. Soc.*, **64**, 3051 (1942); Schwenk and Papa, *J. Org. Chem.*, **11**, 798 (1946).
[86] Bachmann and Cortes, *J. Am. Chem. Soc.*, **65**, 1332 (1943).
[87] Bachmann and Sheehan, *J. Am. Chem. Soc.*, **62**, 2688 (1940).
[88] Hartmann and Bosshard, *Helv. Chim. Acta*, **24**, 28E (1941).
[89] Corse et al., *J. Am. Chem. Soc.*, **70**, 2841 (1948).

[90] Solmssen and Wenis, *J. Am. Chem. Soc.,* **70,** 4200 (1948).

[91] Bachmann and Struve in *Organic Reactions,* Vol. 1, John Wiley & Sons, New York, 1942, p. 38.

[92] Gilman et al., *J. Am. Chem. Soc.,* **61,** 2844 (1939).

[93] Arndt and Eistert, *Ber.,* **68,** 204 (1935).

[94] Williams and Krynitsky, *Org. Syntheses,* **21,** 4 (1941).

[95] Kaslow and Cook, *J. Am. Chem. Soc.,* **67,** 1969 (1945).

[96] Pauw, *Rec. trav. chim.,* **55,** 218 (1936).

[97] Singleton and Edwards, *J. Am. Chem. Soc.,* **60,** 543 (1938).

[98] Gilman and Kirby, *J. Am. Chem. Soc.,* **51,** 3477 (1929).

[99] Benson and Ritter, *J. Am. Chem. Soc.,* **71,** 4128 (1949).

[100] Ritter and Minieri, *J. Am. Chem. Soc.,* **70,** 4045 (1948); Ritter and Kalish, *ibid.,* **70,** 4048 (1948).

[101] Wegler and Binder, *Arch. Pharm.,* **275,** 511 (1937).

[102] Burger and Avakian, *J. Org. Chem.,* **5,** 606 (1940).

[103] Bachmann and Chemerda, *J. Org. Chem.;* **6,** 40 (1941).

[104] Wilds and Meader, *J. Org. Chem.,* **13,** 763, 774 (1948).

[105] Schwartz and Johnson, *J. Am. Chem. Soc.,* **53,** 1063 (1931); Underwood and Gale, *ibid.,* **56,** 2117 (1934); Gilman and Furry, *ibid.,* **50,** 1214 (1928).

[106] Goldberg, Ordas, and Carsch, *J. Am. Chem. Soc.,* **69,** 261 (1947).

[107] Graf, *J. prakt. Chem.,* **133,** 25 (1932).

[108] Girard, *Org. Syntheses,* Coll. Vol. II, 85 (1943); Girard and Sandulesco, *Helv. Chim. Acta,* **19,** 1103 (1936).

[109] Buckle, Heap, and Saunders, *J. Chem. Soc.,* 912 (1949); Bacon et al., *J. Am. Chem. Soc.,* **70,** 2654 (1948).

[110] Bright and Hauser, *J. Am. Chem. Soc.,* **61,** 627 (1939); Renfrow and Hauser, *ibid.,* **59,** 2312 (1937).

[111] Yale, *Chem. Revs.* **33,** 225-231 (1943).

[112] Sah et al., *Rec. trav. chim.,* **58,** 9, 14, 596, 1014 (1939); **59,** 238, 349, 357 (1940).

[113] Sah and Chang, *Ber.,* **69,** 2763 (1936); Curtius and Ulmer, *J. prakt. Chem.,* **125,** 54 (1930).

[114] Curtius and Nadenheim, *J. prakt. Chem.,* **125,** 170, 172 (1930).

[115] Curtius et al., *J. prakt. Chem.,* **125,** 63, 77, 90, 152, 170, 182, 200, 211 (1930).

[116] Gatterman and Wieland, *Laboratory Methods of Organic Chemistry,* The Macmillan Co., New York, 1938, p. 153.

[117] Buckle, Pattison, and Saunders, *J. Chem. Soc.,* 1478 (1949).

[118] Newman, Lee, and Garrett, *J. Am. Chem. Soc.,* **69,** 113 (1947); cf. ref. 116.

[119] Singleton and Edwards, *J. Am. Chem. Soc.,* **60,** 541 (1938).

[120] Jones and Neuffer, *J. Am. Chem. Soc.,* **39,** 659 (1917).

[121] Barrett and Porter, *J. Am. Chem. Soc.,* **63,** 3434 (1941); cf. ref. 118.

[122] Naegeli, Tyabji, and Conrad, *Helv. Chim. Acta,* **21,** 1138 (1938).

[123] Noyes and Porter, *Org. Syntheses,* Coll. Vol. I, 457 (1941).

[124] Herbst and Shemin, *Org. Syntheses,* Coll. Vol. II, 11 (1943).

[125] Manske, *Org. Syntheses,* Coll. Vol. II, 83 (1943); Ing and Manske, *J. Chem. Soc.,* 2348 (1926).

[126] Hurd and Dull, *J. Am. Chem. Soc.,* **54,** 2432 (1932).

[127] Feist and Schultz, *Arch. Pharm.,* **272,** 789 (1934).

[128] Kaufmann, *Ber.,* **42,** 3480 (1909).

[129] Brown et al., *J. Org. Chem.,* **11,** 166 (1946); cf. ref. 128.

[130] Roeder and Day, *J. Org. Chem.*, 6, 25 (1941).
[131] Lauer et al., *J. Am. Chem. Soc.*, 68, 1546 (1946).
[132] Popkin, *J. Am. Chem. Soc.*, 65, 2043 (1943).
[133] Adams, Long, and Jeanes, *J. Am. Chem. Soc.*, 61, 2347 (1939).
[134] Crouch and Lochte, *J. Am. Chem. Soc.*, 65, 271 (1943).
[135] Kornfeld, Jones, and Parke, *J. Am. Chem. Soc.*, 71, 158, 159 (1949).
[136] Cleland and Niemann, *J. Am. Chem. Soc.*, 71, 841 (1949).
[137] Thielepape, *Ber.*, 68, 752 (1935).
[138] Tingle and Brenton, *J. Am. Chem. Soc.*, 32, 116 (1910); Manske, *ibid.*, 51, 1202 (1929).
[139] Dakin and West, *J. Biol. Chem.*, 78, 91, 757 (1928).
[140] Bergstrom and Fernelius, *Chem. Revs.*, 12, 122 (1933); 20, 449 (1937).
[141] Haller and Bauer, *Ann. chim.*, (9) 1, 5 (1914); Mentzer, Buu-Hoi, and Cagniant, *Bull. soc. chim. France*, (5) 9, 816 (1942).
[142] Carter and Slater, *J. Chem. Soc.*, 130 (1946); Buu-Hoi and Cagniant, *Rec. trav. chim.*, 65, 248 (1946).
[143] Salzberg and Supniewski, *Org. Syntheses*, Coll. Vol. I, 119 (1941).
[144] Osterberg, *Org. Syntheses*, Coll. Vol. I, 271 (1941).
[145] Sakellarios, *Helv. Chim. Acta*, 29, 1675 (1946).
[146] Buc, *J. Am. Chem. Soc.*, 69, 254 (1947); Pucher and Johnson, *ibid.*, 44, 820 (1922).
[147] Ross and Burnett, *J. Am. Chem. Soc.*, 71, 3562 (1949).
[148] Noyes and Forman, *J. Am. Chem. Soc.*, 55, 3493 (1933).
[149] Tschelinzew et al., *Ber.*, 69, 374, 2024 (1936).
[150] Wolff in *Organic Reactions*, Vol. 3, John Wiley & Sons, New York, 1946, pp. 315, 335, 336.
[151] Smith, *J. Am. Chem. Soc.*, 70, 320 (1948); Smith and Horwitz, *ibid.*, 72, 3718 (1950).
[152] Einhorn et al., *Ann.* 343, 207–310 (1905).
[153] Marvel and Hiers, *Org. Syntheses*, Coll. Vol. I, 327 (1941).
[154] Byrne, Linstead, and Lowe, *J. Chem. Soc.*, 1019 (1934).
[155] Adams and Jones, *J. Am. Chem. Soc.*, 69, 1804 (1947).
[156] Galat, *J. Am. Chem. Soc.*, 69, 965 (1947).
[157] Huntress and Shriner, *Org. Syntheses*, Coll. Vol. II, 459 (1943).
[158] Ferber and Brückner, *Ber.*, 72, 999 (1939).
[159] Polya and Spotswood, *Rec. trav. chim.*, 67, 927 (1948); Hurd and Dull, *J. Am. Chem. Soc.*, 54, 2436 (1932).
[160] Strack and Schwaneberg, *Ber.*, 67, 41 (1934).
[161] Briggs, Ath, and Ellis, *J. Chem. Soc.*, 61 (1942).
[162] Chu, *J. Am. Chem. Soc.*, 67, 1862 (1945); Rivier and Kunz, *Helv. Chim. Acta*, 15, 377 (1932).
[163] Shepherd and Fellows, *J. Am. Chem. Soc.*, 70, 159 (1948).
[164] Oddo and Deleo, *Ber.*, 69, 287 (1936).
[165] Tarbell and Noble, *J. Am. Chem. Soc.*, 72, 2659 (1950).
[166] Heyboer and Staverman, *Rec. trav. chim.*, 69, 787 (1950).
[167] Mihina and Herbst, *J. Org. Chem.*, 15, 1087 (1950).
[168] Bachmann and Boatner, *J. Am. Chem. Soc.*, 58, 2097 (1936); Mosettig and Krueger, *J. Org. Chem.*, 3, 328 (1938); 5, 313 (1940).
[169] Cook and Cox, *J. Chem. Soc.*, 2336 (1949).
[170] Wiley and Morgan, *J. Org. Chem.*, 15, 800 (1950).
[171] Wenner, *J. Org. Chem.*, 15, 548 (1950).

[172] Crowe and Nord, *J. Org. Chem.*, **15**, 87 (1950).
[173] Breslow, *J. Am. Chem. Soc.*, **72**, 4245 (1950).
[174] Carothers and Jones, *J. Am. Chem. Soc.*, **47**, 3051 (1925).
[175] Fones, *J. Org. Chem.*, **14**, 1099 (1949).
[176] Haworth, MacGillivray, and Peacock, *J. Chem. Soc.*, 1496 (1950).
[177] Arcus, *J. Chem. Soc.*, 2735 (1949).
[178] Burckhalter et al., *J. Am. Chem. Soc.*, **70**, 1364 (1948).
[179] Fieser and Martin, *J. Am. Chem. Soc.*, **57**, 1838 (1935); cf. ref. 130
[180] Sheehan and Izzo, *J. Am. Chem. Soc.*, **70**, 1985 (1948).
[181] Frank, Schmitz, and Zeidman, *Org. Syntheses*, **27**, 28 (1947).
[182] Späth and Lintner, *Ber.*, **69**, 2727 (1936); McElvain and Vozza, *J. Am. Chem. Soc.*, **71**, 897 (1949).
[183] Lippincott and Hass, *Ind. Eng. Chem.*, **31**, 119 (1939).
[184] Scott and Kearse, *J. Org. Chem.*, **5**, 598 (1940); Jones et al., *J. Am. Chem. Soc.*, **48**, 181 (1926); **49**, 2528 (1927).

20

Cyanides

CONTENTS

In this chapter are gathered twenty-four methods for the preparation of cyanides. An excellent review of methods for the introduction of cyano groups appeared in 1948.[36] In addition, a monograph on the chemistry of organic cyanogen compounds has been published.[397]

378. Interaction of Metallic Cyanides and Halogen Compounds

$$RX + NaCN \xrightarrow{C_2H_5OH} RCN + NaX$$

The alkali cyanides react with alkyl halides to furnish predominantly nitriles. Primary aliphatic nitriles, including those of high-molecular weight, are readily formed in high yields.[5,6,43] Secondary alkyl halides give poor yields (30%), and tertiary alkyl halides give little or no nitrile. The reactivity of the different halides in this reaction is in the increasing order of chloride, bromide, and iodide. This is illustrated by the formation of the chloronitrile from trimethylene chlorobromide in 70% yield.[70] Often the reaction of an alkyl chloride can be facilitated by the addition of sodium iodide, which rapidly forms the faster-acting alkyl iodide (cf. method 55).[2] Sometimes alkyl sulfates and sulfonates are used in place of alkyl halides.[162-164] Small amounts of isocyanides formed in these reactions can be removed by washing the crude products with warm 50% sulfuric acid[9] or cold concentrated hydrochloric acid.[4]

Benzyl-type chlorides are converted to the corresponding cyanides much more rapidly (85-90%). Ring substituents include alkyl,[9-12] halo,[363] carbethoxy[1,364] and nitro[365] groups. The more reactive benzyl halides, particularly the p-methoxy derivatives, are subject to extensive alcoholysis when ethanol is employed as the solvent.[17,41] The successful use of acetone,[17] acetonitrile,[54] and phenylacetonitrile[55] as solvents has been described. Conversion by cuprous cyanide and pyridine has been successfully applied to benzyl chloride[10] as well as to di-o-tolylchloromethane.[53] It is interesting to find that treatment of α-chloroethylbenzene, $C_6H_5CH(Cl)CH_3$, with cuprous cyanide gives 1,3-diphenyl-1-butene, $C_6H_5CH{=}CH{-}CH(CH_3)C_6H_5$, instead of the anticipated nitrile.[366]

The replacement of an aryl halogen atom by the cyano group can be accomplished by the action of anhydrous cuprous cyanide at 150-250° with or without an organic base (usually pyridine) as a promoter or solvent (Rosenmund-von Braun nitrile synthesis). The reaction is autocatalytic and may be accelerated by the addition of small amounts of a nitrile and copper sulfate.[21] Typical laboratory procedures are found in the syntheses of α-naphthonitrile (90%)[25] and 9-cyanophenanthrene (87%).[26] The adaptation of the process to commercial practice has been discussed.[42]

For the most part, the cyanides of heterocyclic compounds are similarly prepared by the action of alkali cyanides or cuprous cyanide on sidechain or nuclear halogen atoms, respectively. Several notable exceptions are found in the furan series. Thus, the product from the reaction of furfuryl chloride is mainly 5-methyl-2-furonitrile instead of the expected 2-furanacetonitrile.[30]

$$
\begin{array}{ccc}
\text{HC---CH} & & \text{HC---CH} \\
\| \quad \| & \overset{\sim}{\longrightarrow} & \| \quad \| \\
\text{HC} \quad \text{CCH}_2\text{Cl} + \text{KCN} & & \text{CH}_3\text{C} \quad \text{CCN} \\
\diagdown\diagup & & \diagdown\diagup \\
\text{O} & & \text{O}
\end{array}
$$

A similar rearrangement occurs with α-(1-chloroethyl)-furan; 5-ethylfuryl cyanide is formed.[52] Also, 3-furylmethyl chloride and aqueous potassium cyanide furnish an isomeric mixture of nitriles, a 9:1 ratio of 3-furylacetonitrile and 3-methyl-2-furonitrile.[361] Tetrahydrofurfuryl chloride behaves normally although its halogen is more firmly held.[29] As expected, the halides of pyridine,[34] quinoline,[37] and isoquinoline[39] react satisfactorily without a solvent-promoter.

Polymethylene *dicyanides* are readily prepared from the corresponding dibromides,[49] as illustrated by the preparation of trimethylene cyanide, $CN(CH_2)_3CN$ (86%).[45] The o- and p-ω,ω'-dibromoxylenes react rapidly to give only the corresponding phenylenediacetonitriles (70–90%); with the *meta* isomer, the reaction may be controlled to yield the bromonitrile (90%).[12,50,51]

The formation of *olefinic nitriles* from allylic halides is best accomplished with dry, powdered cuprous cyanide rather than with alcoholic alkali cyanides, with which side reactions such as isomerization and alcoholysis of the double bond are particularly bothersome.[57] With cuprous cyanide the yields in the synthesis of allyl cyanide[56] and methallyl cyanide[58] are 84% and 86%, respectively. Higher allylic halides are subject to allylic rearrangements; thus cuprous cyanide acts on crotyl halide $(CH_3CH=CHCH_2X)$ and methylvinylcarbinyl halide $(CH_3CHXCH=CH_2)$ to produce the same mixture of isomeric nitriles (9:1) regardless of which halide is treated.[59] Numerous cyanides of the allylic type (C_5-C_{14}) have been prepared, although the possibility of an isomerization has not been considered.[60] A similar isomerization has been observed in the reaction of sorbyl chloride and potassium cyanide.[62]

$$
CH_3CH=CH-CH=CHCH_2Cl \xrightarrow{\text{KCN}} CH_3CH(CN)CH=CH-CH=CH_2
$$

For the most part, vinyl halides are unreactive; however, a few have been converted to vinyl-type cyanides under conditions employed for aromatic halogen compounds. Thus, *sym*-diiodoethylene has been converted by cuprous cyanide with an amine promoter to fumaronitrile (74%).[65] The halogen atom in certain triarylvinyl bromides has also been replaced by the cyano group under these conditions.[66]

Acetylenic nitriles are best prepared by heating the corresponding iodides with alkali cyanides in aqueous acetone or with cuprous cyanide in xylene.[68] With methanolic potassium cyanide, 1-chloro-1-heptyne yields a cyanovinyl ether of the structure $C_5H_{11}C(OCH_3)$=CHCN which results from the addition of methanol to the triple bond.[69]

Halo nitriles are prepared from the corresponding dihalides or from mixed halides by taking advantage of the different reactivities of two dissimilar halogen atoms.[70,72]

Hydroxy nitriles are obtained from halo alcohols as illustrated by the preparation of ethylene cyanohydrin from ethylene chlorohydrin (80%).[74] In the reaction of the next higher homolog, 2-chloropropanol, with alcoholic potassium cyanide, a 60% yield of the secondary alcohol ($CH_3CHOHCH_2CN$) is obtained instead of the expected 2-cyanopropanol.[77] Other chlorohydrins containing a third functional group have been converted to valuable synthetic starting materials, e.g., β-hydroxy-γ-methoxybutyronitrile[76] and 1-cyano-3-buten-2-ol.[78]

Treatment of α-halo ethers with metallic cyanides such as cuprous, mercuric, or silver cyanides gives the corresponding *cyano ethers;* the alkali cyanides are without effect.[80,88,89] Very little of the corresponding isonitriles are encountered despite the fact that these compounds often result from the interaction of heavy-metal cyanides and alkyl halides. Generally, cuprous cyanide, the most commonly used reagent, is suspended in dry anhydrous ether or dry benzene and treated with the halo ether under gentle reflux (55–80%).

More often than not, a halogen atom on the carbon *beta* to the ether linkage is unreactive. For example, the comparative reactivities of α- and β-halogens may be illustrated by the reaction of ethers containing both these groups.[84,89] In each case, the β-halogen is retained. On the other hand, the bromine atom in β-ethoxyethyl bromide, $C_2H_5OCH_2CH_2Br$, is readily replaced by the cyano group from sodium cyanide (58%).[86] It is interesting to note that aqueous potassium cyanide effects a cleavage of the carbon-oxygen bond in α,β-dichloroethyl ether, giving the cyanohydrin of chloroacetaldehyde, $CH_2ClCHOHCN$ (40%).[91]

The formation of *cyano ketones* by this method is illustrated by the conversion of phenacyl halides to the corresponding nitriles.[98, 99] Ring closure to cyclopropane derivatives is a side reaction which has been encountered with γ-halo ketones. Benzalacetophenone dibromide is converted by alcoholic potassium cyanide to the β-cyano ketone, the α-halogen atom being reduced.[102] Several α-chloro ketones have been found to yield α-cyano epoxides.[103,104]

Cyano acids are prepared by first neutralizing the corresponding halo acids with sodium carbonate and then treating the aqueous solutions with

sodium cyanide. The organic acid is liberated with concentrated hydrochloric acid.[108,109,211] Sometimes the halogen atom in a halo ester is replaced by cyanide and the ester group is then preferentially hydrolyzed
with cold alcoholic potassium hydroxide.[110]

γ-Diethylaminobutyronitrile is prepared in 50% yield from trimethylene
chlorobromide by successive treatment with diethylamine and potassium
cyanide. This is almost twice the yield reported for the more common
procedure of introducing the cyanide group first.[113]

379. Fusion of Alkali Cyanides and Sulfonic Acid Salts

$$ArSO_3K + KCN \xrightarrow{Heat} ArCN$$

The fusion of alkali arylsulfonates with potassium cyanide forms aromatic nitriles by a replacement of the sulfo group. For the most part,
the yields are low, although the reaction has been applied successfully
in the preparation of naphthonitriles[165,166] and cyanopyridines.[171,172]
Sometimes potassium ferrocyanide is substituted for the alkali cyanide
with better results.[167] Ten isomeric cyanonaphthalenesulfonates have
been converted to the dinitriles by fusion with this reagent in yields
ranging from 8% to 75%.[168] Migration of the cyano group from the beta
to the *alpha* position has been observed in the formation of these
compounds.[169]

380. Replacement of the Diazonium Group by Cyanide

$$ArNH_2 \xrightarrow[NaNO_2]{HCl} ArN_2^+ Cl^- \xrightarrow{CuCN} ArCN$$

The replacement of aromatic amino groups by cyanide is easily accomplished by the action of cuprous cyanide on the diazonium compound
(Sandmeyer). The procedure is illustrated by the preparation of o- and
p-tolunitriles; each is obtained in 64% to 70% yield.[218] Several features
are noteworthy. The diazonium solution is neutralized with sodium
carbonate before treatment with cuprous cyanide solution so that the
liberation of hydrogen cyanide is avoided. Also, vigorous stirring in
the presence of an inert solvent is required during the addition of the
cold neutralized diazonium solution to the cold cuprous cyanide solution
so that the decomposition proceeds without violence.[221] Methods for the
preparation of cuprous cyanide have been described.[218,220]

In the preparation of α-naphthonitrile, somewhat better yields are obtained by substituting nickel cyanide for the usual cuprous cyanide
reagent (55% vs. 78%).[224] 5-Cyanoquinoline is prepared satisfactorily
by the Sandmeyer reaction, but the 8-isomer could not be obtained by this
procedure.[226]

The diazonium group may be replaced in the presence of other nuclear groups including halogen,[227] hydroxyl,[228] alkoxyl,[229] acyl,[107] carboxyl,[230,232] carbomethoxyl,[233] and nitro.[234]

381. Replacement of Halogen in Acyl Halides by the Cyano Group

$$RCOBr + CuCN \longrightarrow RCOCN + CuBr$$

The conversion of aliphatic and aromatic acyl halides to α-keto nitriles has been effected by heating the halides with dry metallic cyanides, of which cuprous cyanide has given the most satisfactory results (60–87%). The acyl bromides rather than the chlorides are preferred, at least in the formation of aliphatic compounds.[295] Thus, pyruvonitrile is prepared in 77% yield from acetyl bromide and cuprous cyanide whereas no product is obtained if acetyl chloride is employed.[296] Benzoyl cyanide is made in 65% yield by heating the corresponding acyl chloride with cuprous cyanide.[297]

Another procedure consists in slowly adding pyridine to an ethereal solution of an acyl chloride and anhydrous hydrogen cyanide. This order of addition of the reactants is important in order to retard the formation of acyl cyanide dimers. In this manner, certain benzoyl cyanides[298] as well as furoyl cyanide[299] have been prepared (40–80%).

382. β-Keto Cyanides by Interaction of Alkali Cyanides and β-Keto Amines

$$ArCOCH_2CH_2N(CH_3)_2 \xrightarrow[H_2O]{KCN} ArCOCH_2CH_2CN + (CH_3)_2NH$$

Certain β-dialkylaminoethyl aryl ketones, readily prepared by the Mannich reaction (method 444), are converted to β-aroylpropionitriles in good yields by the action of hot aqueous potassium cyanide.[393] β-Benzoylpropionitrile is made in this way in 67% yield. The reaction has been successfully applied to the formation of β-2-furoylpropionitrile (57%) and β-2-thienoylpropionitrile (67%).

383. Cyanogenation of Aromatic Compounds

$$ArH + CCl_3CN \xrightarrow{AlCl_3} Ar\overset{\overset{\displaystyle NH \cdot HCl}{\|}}{C}CCl_3 \xrightarrow{NaOH} ArCN + CHCl_3$$

The introduction of a cyano group into an aromatic nucleus has been accomplished by the action of trichloroacetonitrile in the presence of anhydrous aluminum chloride followed by degradation of the intermediate ketimine. It is not necessary to isolate the trichloromethyl ketimine.

Instead, in a single process, the latter is liberated from its hydrochloride by the addition of dry ammonia and then degraded by the action of dry, powdered sodium hydroxide. Dry hydrogen chloride is a more satisfactory condensing agent than aluminum chloride for the cyanogenation of phenols and aromatic ethers. Typical aromatic nitriles obtained by this procedure include benzonitrile (69%), 2,4-, 3,4-, and 2,5-dimethylbenzonitriles from the corresponding xylenes (82–86%), 2,4,6-trimethylbenzonitrile from mesitylene (68%), 2-methoxy-5-methylbenzonitrile from the methyl ether of p-cresol (67%), and 3-cyano-2-methylindole (95%).[329]

Cyanogenation of aromatic compounds can also be carried out directly by the action of cyanogen bromide and aluminum chloride in carbon disulfide.

$$\text{ArH} + \text{BrCN} \xrightarrow[\text{CS}_2]{\text{AlCl}_3} \text{ArCN} + \text{HBr}$$

The success of the reaction depends largely on the use of finely ground aluminum chloride and freshly prepared cyanogen bromide. Aromatic hydrocarbons—benzene, toluene, anthracene, and acenaphthene—and phenolic ethers respond favorably.[330] However, phenanthrene gives none of the anticipated nitrile.[331] As might be expected, a by-product is the aryl bromide.[334] Indeed, thiophene[332] and furan[333] are converted largely to the α-bromo derivatives.

384. Dehydration of Amides

$$\text{RCONH}_2 \xrightarrow{-\text{H}_2\text{O}} \text{RCN}$$

The preparation of nitriles by the removal of water from amides can be accomplished in high yields by numerous dehydrating agents including phosphorus pentoxide, phosphorus oxychloride, and thionyl chloride. A commonly used procedure for the preparation of simple aliphatic nitriles, e.g., isobutyronitrile (86%), consists in heating an intimate mixture of the dry, powdered amide and phosphorus pentoxide at 100–220° and distilling the product as it is formed, sometimes under diminished pressure.[114] Thionyl chloride is frequently the reagent of choice for the dehydration of higher-molecular-weight amides, since the secondary products are gaseous and the nitrile is more readily purified.[119] Oftentimes, the higher fatty acids are converted to the nitriles in a single operation via the intermediate ammonium salts and amides. For this purpose, dry ammonia gas is passed into the molten acids at 290–300°; the yields of nitriles are excellent (80–85%).[117, 118] A small amount of 85% phosphoric acid appreciably reduces the reaction time.[157] Another procedure consists in passing the acid vapors mixed with ammonia over silica gel at 500°. This technique is particularly successful for lower aliphatic acids (C_2–C_6) and certain aryl-substituted acids such as phenylacetic and β-phenylpropionic acids (80–95%); it is less satisfactory for long-chain fatty acids.[158] Boron trifluoride has been used to effect the dismutation of an amide to an acid and a nitrile, viz.,[355]

$$2RCONH_2 + BF_3 \xrightarrow{CH_3COOH} RCN + RCO_2H + BF_3 \cdot NH_3$$

Aromatic nitriles are also prepared by heating amides with phosphorus pentoxide,[130] phosphorus oxychloride,[123] phosphorus pentachloride,[128] thionyl chloride,[124] and ammonium sulfamate.[367] In addition, the action of a double salt of aluminum and sodium chlorides, $NaCl \cdot AlCl_3$, gives excellent yields of nitriles from both aliphatic and aromatic amides.[120] Heating an amide with phthalic anhydride causes dehydration.[131] A novel synthesis consists in treating a mixture of an aromatic acid and p-toluenesulfonamide with phosphorus pentachloride; the yields of nitriles range from 63% to 79%.[136,156]

$$ArCO_2H + CH_3C_6H_4SO_2NH_2 + 2PCl_5 \rightarrow ArCN + CH_3C_6H_4SO_2Cl +$$

$$2POCl_3 + 3HCl$$

Pyridinecarboxamides are dehydrated with phosphorus pentoxide.[133]

Preparation of malonitrile, the simplest *dinitrile,* has been extensively studied. A convenient and rapid synthesis is brought about by the action of phosphorus pentachloride on cyanoacetamide in ethylene dichloride solution.[135] The simplest unsaturated dinitriles—fumaronitrile (90%), maleonitrile (39%), and acetylene dicarbonitrile (37%)—are prepared by the rapid heating of the corresponding diamides with phosphorus pentoxide.[138,372] The chief by-products in the above reactions are probably the cyclic imides. Similarly, o-diamides are deaminated as well as dehydrated to give a mixture of products. An interesting synthesis of sebaconitrile consists in heating the corresponding dicarboxylic acid with urea to form the intermediate diamide, $H_2NCO(CH_2)_8CONH_2$. Stronger heating gives the dinitrile, $NC(CH_2)_8CN$, and ω-cyanopelargonic acid, $NC(CH_2)_8COOH$, in 49% and 34% yields, respectively.[139]

Unsaturated nitriles prepared by the dehydration of amides include 1-cyano-1-alkynes, e.g. 1-cyano-1-heptyne (85%),[142] and 1-cyano-1-alkenes, e.g. β-isopropylacrylonitrile (80%).[143] Some dehydrating agents such as phosphorus pentachloride may lead to the formation of halogen-containing products; phosphorus pentoxide is preferred in these cases.[144] In a comparison of methods for preparing olefinic nitriles, it has been shown that dehydration of α,β- and β,γ-unsaturated amides can be accomplished without noticeable migration of the double bond.[144]

The dehydration of an amide containing an acid-sensitive acetal group to a cyano acetal like β,β-diethoxypropionitrile has been carried out with phosphorus pentoxide in the presence of triethylamine.[353]

Other functional groups which may be present in the amide are halo,[146–1?] alkoxyl,[152, 153, 156] carbalkoxyl,[154] and nitro.[156]

385. Dehydration of Oximes

$$RCH = NOH \xrightarrow[\text{anhydride}]{\text{Acetic}} RCN$$

The conversion of an aldoxime to a cyanide by the removal of water has been successfully applied in many instances. Hot acetic anhydride is the most common dehydrating agent. The reaction is important in sugar chemistry as a step in the degradation of an aldose to the next homolog.[237] Oximes of aromatic aldehydes respond particularly well to this treatment, giving nitriles in good yields, e.g., α-methylbenzyl cyanide (90%),[189] 9-cyanoanthracene (98%),[235] and 3,4-dimethoxybenzonitrile (76%).[240] Oximes of unsaturated aldehydes like the α-alkylacroleins, $H_2C = C(R)CHO$, undergo dehydration without apparent migration of the double bond to furnish α-alkylacrylonitriles.[272, 378]

Nitriles are also formed in excellent yields by the decarboxylation and dehydration of oximino acids with warm acetic anhydride. A good route for obtaining the starting materials consists in the condensation of aldehydes with rhodanine followed by cleavage of the product with alkali and treatment with hydroxylamine.

Yields in each step are in the range of 80% to 97%. The facile preparation of rhodanine in large quantity has been described along with improved directions for each step.[241,243] Aliphatic, aromatic, and heterocyclic aldehydes undergo the initial condensation;[242] however, only products from the last two series are frequently carried to the final step, for example, 3,4-dimethoxyphenylacetonitrile (90% over-all),[241] 2-furanacetonitrile (80% over-all),[236] and 2-thienylacetonitrile (74% over-all).[380] The rhodanine synthesis has been extended to the preparation of phenylacetonitriles having chlorine or bromine atoms in the o-, m-, or p-position (38-62% over-all).[243] Oximino acids are also obtained from the corresponding α-keto acids, which are readily available by the azlactone synthesis (method 210). This route has been found satisfactory for the preparation of certain alkoxyphenylacetonitriles.[244,245]

A closely related reaction involves the conversion of α-oximino ketones to nitriles by pyrolysis or by the action of thionyl chloride (75%). This reaction constitutes a step in a series for the synthesis of aliphatic acids from valeric to lauric acids.[274]

$$\text{RCH}_2\text{COCl} \xrightarrow[\text{AlCl}_3]{\text{C}_6\text{H}_6} \text{RCH}_2\text{COC}_6\text{H}_5 \xrightarrow{\text{NH}_4\text{NO}_3} \overset{\overset{\displaystyle \text{NOH}}{\|}}{\text{RCCOC}_6\text{H}_5} \xrightarrow{210^\circ} \text{RCN} + \text{C}_6\text{H}_5\text{COOH}$$

386. Alkylation of Cyano Compounds

$$\text{RCH}_2\text{CN} + \text{R}'\text{X} + \text{NaNH}_2 \rightarrow \text{RR}'\text{CHCN} + \text{NaX} + \text{NH}_3$$

The alkylation of nitriles has been developed as a general method for the preparation of substituted acetonitriles.[173] An excellent discussion of the literature to 1937 has been given.[176] The procedure consists in treating a nitrile in an inert solvent with finely divided sodium amide and the halogenated compound, followed by careful hydrolysis with water. Common solvents are ether, benzene, toluene, or liquid ammonia. Mono-, di-, and tri-alkylated products are possible, as shown by the alkylation of acetonitrile with ethyl bromide;[175] however, the mixtures can often be separated by fractional distillation.

The degree of alkylation has been controlled in certain instances. Straight-chain nitriles and equimolar quantities of low-molecular-weight bromides react in boiling ether solution to give mainly monoalkylated products. Nitriles prepared in this manner include capronitrile from the action of n-butyl bromide on acetonitrile (60%), diethylacetonitrile from ethyl bromide on butyronitrile (77%), and α-isopropylbutyronitrile from isopropyl bromide on butyronitrile (71%).[173] Higher temperatures, obtained with refluxing benzene or toluene solutions, favor the formation of trialkylacetonitriles when excess alkylating agent is used. The higher temperatures are necessary for alkylation with high-molecular-weight halides, e.g., n-decyl bromide on propionitrile.[178]

The versatility of the reaction is illustrated by the preparation of tri-n-butylacetonitrile from n-butyl bromide on either capronitrile (88%) or acetonitrile (80%).[177] In most preparations, the alkylating agents are bromides rather than chlorides, since bromides react more smoothly and at a lower temperature.[173,177]

Alicyclic nitriles are prepared by the intramolecular alkylation of halo nitriles. For example, cyclopropyl cyanide is obtained in 75–90% yield by the action of sodium amide on γ-chlorobutyronitrile in ether or liquid ammonia.[186]

$$ClCH_2CH_2CH_2CN + NaNH_2 \rightarrow CH_2{-}CHCN + NaCl + NH_3$$

Among the aryl-aliphatic nitriles subject to alkylation, phenylaceto-nitrile, $C_6H_5CH_2CN$, is especially reactive and its methylene hydrogens are readily replaced by one or two alkyl groups. Alkylation of this sub-stance has been performed with alkyl halides or dialkyl sulfates.[180–182] It unites with both halogens in polymethylene halides (two equivalents of sodium amide are required) to form 1-phenylcycloalkyl cyanides.[121,187,188] The action of substituted alkyl halides on phenylacetonitrile and its homologs furnishes valuable intermediates for syntheses.[191]

$$C_6H_5CH_2CN + Z(CH_2)_nBr \xrightarrow{NaNH_2} C_6H_5CH(CH_2)_nZ \quad (CN)$$

where Z = CN, X, HO, RO, or NH_2. In this manner, cyano,[189] halo,[180] hydroxyl,[187] alkoxyl,[173] and amino[173,177,190] groups have been introduced. The yields are good.

Certain *unsaturated* nitriles are prepared by the alkylation of reactive olefinic nitriles like vinylacetonitrile, 1-cyclohexenylacetonitrile, and 3-ethyl-2-pentenonitrile.[192]

$$H_2C=CHCH_2CN + 2RX \xrightarrow[\text{Liquid NH}_3]{NaNH_2} H_2C=CHC(R_2)CN$$

Other olefinic nitriles may be obtained by the alkylation of malonitrile with unsaturated halides.[193]

Ethyl cyanoacetate is readily alkylated under the usual conditions employed for the malonic and acetoacetic ester syntheses (methods 299 and 213) to yield mono- and di-substituted *cyano acetates.* These sub-stances may then be hydrolyzed and decarboxylated to furnish mono-carboxylic acids (method 265). In many instances, it is difficult to avoid the formation of the dialkylated ester; the yields may be low.[194,195] Several disubstituted cyano esters such as diisopropyl- and alkylphenyl-cyanoacetic esters are valuable intermediates in the synthesis of other-wise difficultly obtained acids.[195, 198]

Certain unsaturated cyanoacetic esters, $RCH=C(R')CH(CN)CO_2C_2H_5$, derived in excellent yields by the condensation of ketones, RCH_2COR', with cyanoacetic ester are alkylated to produce (dialkylvinyl)-alkyl-cyanoacetic esters, $RCH=C(R')C(R'')(CN)COOC_2H_5$. The yields are highest when sodium isopropoxide in isopropyl alcohol is employed as the condensing agent.[208,217]

The cyanoacetic ester synthesis of certain alicyclic compounds is pre-ferred to the malonic ester synthesis. Thus, cyclopropane-1,1-cyano-carboxylate is readily obtained by the condensation of ethylene bromide and ethyl cyanoacetate in the presence of two equivalents of sodium ethoxide (76%).[199] A second procedure for synthesizing alicyclic com-pounds consists in treating α,α'-dibromodicarboxylic esters with alcoholic cyanide, whereby simultaneous replacement and ring closure occurs.[200]

$$
\begin{array}{ccccc}
 & \underset{|}{CO_2C_2H_5} & & \underset{|}{CO_2C_2H_5} & \\
CH_2\!-\!CHBr & & CH_2\!-\!CHCN & & CH_2\!-\!C(CN)CO_2C_2H_5 \\
| & \xrightarrow{\;NaCN\;} & | & \xrightarrow{\;-HBr\;} & | \qquad\qquad\quad | \\
CH_2\!-\!CHBr & & CH_2\!-\!CHBr & & CH_2\!-\!CHCO_2C_2H_5 \\
 & \underset{|}{CO_2C_2H_5} & & \underset{|}{CO_2C_2H_5} &
\end{array}
$$

The cyano ester ring closure has been applied to the synthesis of four-, five-, and six-membered rings.[202]

α-Cyanosuccinic esters are readily obtained by alkylating ethyl cyano-acetate with α-bromo esters.[203,206] These compounds may then be further alkylated to form α,β-dialkyl-α-cyanosuccinates.

$$
NCCH_2CO_2C_2H_5 + RCHBrCO_2C_2H_5 \xrightarrow{\;C_2H_5ONa\;} \begin{array}{c} RCHCO_2C_2H_5 \\ | \\ NCCHCO_2C_2H_5 \end{array}
$$

387. Decarboxylation of Cyano Acids

$$
RCHO + H_2C(CN)CO_2Na \xrightarrow[\text{HCl}]{\text{KOH;}} RCH=C(CN)CO_2H \xrightarrow{\text{Heat}} RCH=CHCN
$$

Cyanoacetic acid reacts readily with aliphatic and aromatic carbonyl compounds to form α-cyanoacrylic acids, which can be decarboxylated by heating to give β-substituted acrylonitriles.[144]

The over-all synthesis is carried out in several ways. One very satis-factory procedure employs ammonium acetate as the condensing agent

and benzene as solvent. The liberated water is removed by means of a
water separator. The crude unsaturated cyano acid is decarboxylated
directly by heat.[192] Aqueous alkali has been used as the condensing
agent,[143,210] and various organic bases such as pyridine and piperidine
are also effective.[144, 212] By proper choice of the base, the reaction can
be controlled to yield either the cyano acid or the unsaturated nitrile.
Copper-bronze powder and quinoline with copper oxide have been used
for the decarboxylation.[143,209]

An interesting reaction for the preparation of α,β-disubstituted acrylonitriles consists in the cleavage of (dialkylvinyl)-alkylcyanoacetic esters
by sodium alkoxides.[217] Although an equilibrium mixture of α,β- and
β,γ-olefinic nitriles is possible,[144] the products are predominantly the
α,β-isomers. The yields are about 90%.

$$R''CH=C(R')\underset{\underset{R}{|}}{C}(CN)CO_2C_2H_5 \xrightarrow[C_2H_5OH]{C_2H_5ONa} R''CH_2\underset{\underset{R}{|}}{C}(R')=C-CN + CO(OC_2H_5)$$

Simple saturated nitriles are seldom prepared by the decarboxylation of
cyano acids derived from the cyanoacetic ester synthesis (cf. method 265)
However, difunctional compounds are frequently obtained by this route, as
in the preparation of α-methyl-γ-phenoxybutyronitrile from β-phenoxy-
ethyl bromide and ethyl methylcyanoacetate (52% over-all).[214]

$$C_6H_5OCH_2CH_2-\underset{\underset{CH_3}{|}}{C}(CN)CO_2C_2H_5 \xrightarrow[-CO_2]{KOH;H^+} C_6H_5OCH_2CH_2-\underset{\underset{CH_3}{|}}{C}HCN$$

This synthesis has been adopted for obtaining 4-dialkylaminobutyro-
nitriles.[215]

388. Cyanoethylation

(a) $ROH + H_2C=CHCN \xrightarrow{KOH} ROCH_2CH_2CN$

(b) $CH_3COCH_3 + 3H_2C=CHCN \xrightarrow{KOH} CH_3COC(CH_2CH_2CN)_3$

Compounds possessing labile hydrogen atoms add readily to acrylonitrile, thereby placing a β-cyanoethyl group at the location of the reactive hydrogen atom. The hydrogen atom may be attached to nitrogen,
oxygen, or sulfur atoms like those present in amines,[247,249] alcohols,[254]
phenols,[256] mercaptans, etc.; or it may be present in reactive $-CH_2-$
or $-CH-$ groups contained in aldehydes,[258] ketones,[259] nitroparaffins,[383]
haloforms, malonic esters,[255,261] acetoacetic esters,[259,381] and cyanoacetic

esters.[382] The reaction is a form of the Michael condensation (cf. method 301). It is base-catalyzed and requires a solvent such as benzene, dioxane, pyridine, or acetonitrile. This versatile and convenient reaction results in the formation of a large number of polyfunctional nitriles. The scope, limitations, and experimental procedures along with many examples of cyanoethylation reactions have been presented.[246]

389. Addition of Hydrogen Cyanide to Unsaturated Compounds

$$HC \equiv CH \xrightarrow{HCN} H_2C = CHCN \xrightarrow{HCN} CNCH_2CH_2CN$$

The addition of hydrogen cyanide to olefins and acetylenes has been the subject of many patents.[36] An important application is the addition of hydrogen cyanide to acetylene under special catalytic conditions leading to acrylonitrile or succinonitrile, as illustrated above.

Important laboratory applications involve the addition of hydrogen cyanide to an olefinic linkage which is activated by another group such as carbonyl,[304] carbalkoxyl,[306] cyano,[246] or nitro[307] on the adjacent carbon; β-cyano compounds are formed. The reaction is related to the Michael condensation (method 301). For the most part, the additions are base-catalyzed and are carried out by treating the unsaturated compound with an alkali cyanide in aqueous or aqueous-alcoholic solution.

The reaction of α,β-unsaturated ketones with alkali cyanides may be complicated by side reactions. Cyanohydrin formation may occur, and also, since alkali hydroxide is generated during the reaction, hydrolysis of the γ-keto cyanide to a γ-keto acid may take place.[304]

$$(CH_3)_2C = CHCOCH_3 \xrightarrow[H_2O]{KCN} (CH_3)_2C(CN)CH_2COCH_3 \xrightarrow[H_2O]{KOH}$$

$$(CH_3)_2C(CO_2H)CH_2COCH_3$$

This difficulty may be overcome by partial neutralization with acetic acid. In this manner, α-phenyl-β-benzoylpropionitrile has been prepared from benzalacetophenone and alcoholic potassium cyanide (96%).[303]

If two activating groups are attached to the α-carbon atom, then the double bond is especially susceptible to hydrogen cyanide addition. Thus, unsaturated cyanoacetic acids[211] or esters,[294, 308] $RCH = C(CN)CO_2C_2H_5$, unsaturated malonitriles,[302] $RCH = C(CN)_2$, and unsaturated malonic esters,[309, 310, 387] $RCH = C(CO_2C_2H_5)_2$, add hydrogen cyanide in good yield. The products are readily converted by hydrolysis and decarboxylation to substituted succinic acids, thus affording a good synthesis for these sub-

stances (cf. method 247). Oftentimes, the intermediate addition products
are not isolated but are hydrolyzed directly.[305,387]

$$\underset{\displaystyle RCH=\overset{\displaystyle CN}{\overset{\displaystyle |}{C}}CO_2C_2H_5}{} \overset{HCN}{\longrightarrow} \underset{\displaystyle RCH\overset{\displaystyle CN\;CN}{\overset{\displaystyle |\;\;|}{C}}HCO_2C_2H_5}{} \overset{H^+}{\underset{H_2O}{\longrightarrow}} \underset{\displaystyle RCHCH_2COOH}{\overset{\displaystyle COOH}{\overset{\displaystyle |}{}}}$$

Sometimes, the alkaline condition of the addition reaction is sufficiently
strong to cause hydrolysis of the ester group but not of the cyano groups.
Decarboxylation then occurs to give a dicyanide, as in the preparation of
phenylsuccinonitrile from ethyl α-cyanocinnamate.[301]

$$C_6H_5CH=\overset{CN}{\overset{|}{C}}CO_2C_2H_5 + NaCN + 2H_2O \rightarrow C_6H_5\overset{CN}{\overset{|}{C}}HCH_2CN +$$

$$NaHCO_3 + C_2H_5OH$$

A convenient procedure has been developed for the synthesis of α,β-
dicyano esters whereby an unsaturated cyano ester is prepared and treated
with hydrogen cyanide in a single operation.[308] For this purpose, a hot
mixture of the carbonyl compound, cyanoacetic ester, and pyridyl acetate
is treated with ethanol and potassium cyanide.

$$R_2C=O + CH_2(CN)CO_2C_2H_5 \underset{\displaystyle \rightleftharpoons}{\overset{C_5H_5N-CH_3COOH}{\Longrightarrow}} R_2C=C(CN)CO_2C_2H_5 + H_2O$$

The condensation equilibrium is displaced to the right by removing the
unsaturated cyano ester as it is formed by the addition of hydrogen cyanide.
The effect is analogous to the single-step formation and hydrogenation of
α,β-unsaturated cyanoacetic esters (method 394). The yields are good
with most aliphatic ketones and aldehydes (49–75%), but poor results are
obtained with aromatic carbonyl compounds and diisopropyl ketone.

390. Addition of Hydrogen Cyanide to Carbonyl Compounds

$$RCHO + HCN \rightleftharpoons RCHOHCN$$

The addition of hydrogen cyanide to carbonyl compounds gives α-hydroxy
cyanides (cyanohydrin synthesis). The reaction is reversible, and the
extent of the cyanohydrin formation depends upon the structure of the
carbonyl compound. The equilibrium highly favors the formation of aliphatic and alicyclic cyanohydrins; however, aryl alkyl ketones react to
a lesser extent, and diaryl ketones, not at all.[265,280] The reaction may
be accomplished by mixing the carbonyl compound with liquid hydrogen
cyanide in the presence of a basic catalyst.[265,266,275,287] The equilibrium

is quickly reached, and the product is stabilized by acidification before processing. More conveniently, hydrogen cyanide can be generated in the reaction mixture by the action of sulfuric,[263] nitric,[288] phosphoric,[267] or acetic[270] acid on an alkali cyanide. Oftentimes, the bisulfite addition product is first prepared and then treated directly with an alkali cyanide.

$$R_2CO \xrightarrow{NaHSO_3} R_2C(OH)SO_3Na \xrightarrow{NaCN} R_2C(OH)CN$$

These procedures are illustrated by the preparation of acetone cyanohydrin (78%).[263,264]

Quite often, the bisulfite product is isolated and purified before the treatment with alkali cyanide, particularly in the conversion of aromatic aldehydes since their bisulfite compounds are easily manipulated. The preparation of aromatic cyanohydrins from their bisulfite products is advantageous since benzoin formation, which is catalyzed by alkali cyanides, is largely avoided. Furthermore, because of the basic environment, hydrogen cyanide fumes are curtailed.

The simplest aldehyde cyanohydrin, glycolonitrile, has been prepared by a cyanohydrin interchange between formalin and methyl ethyl ketone cyanohydrin.[276]

$$CH_2O + C_2H_5(CH_3)C(OH)CN \rightleftharpoons HOCH_2CN + C_2H_5COCH_3$$

Under acidic conditions, acetal formation may occur between the cyanohydrin and the unreacted carbonyl compounds.[265]

Other carbonyl compounds carrying a second functional group undergo this reaction, e.g., acrolein,[279] chloroacetone,[275] p-hydroxybenzaldehyde,[284] acetoacetic ester,[278] and p-dimethylaminobenzaldehyde.[285] The method is important in the synthesis of sugars (Kiliani cyanohydrin synthesis).[281]

391. Cyanoaminolysis of Carbonyl Compounds

$$R_2CO + NaCN + NH_4Cl \rightarrow R_2C(NH_2)CN + NaCl + H_2O$$

α-Aminonitriles are prepared by replacing the carbonyl oxygen in aldehydes and ketones with amino and cyano groups (Strecker synthesis). The reaction is valuable as the initial step in a practical laboratory synthesis of α-amino acids (method 247).

Many modifications of the original procedure have been developed, furnishing the aminonitriles over a wide range of yields. A convenient procedure consists in adding an alcoholic solution of the carbonyl compound to an aqueous solution of sodium cyanide and ammonium chloride. Both aliphatic and aromatic carbonyl compounds react, e.g., diethyl ketone, acetophenone, and benzaldehyde.[311] Similar treatment of formaldehyde is more complicated; methylene aminoacetonitrile (molecular formula, $C_9H_{12}N_6$) is formed.[312]

$$2HCHO + NaCN + NH_4Cl \rightarrow H_2C=NCH_2CN + NaCl + 2H_2O$$

Certain N-alkylamino nitriles have been made by replacing the ammonium chloride with a primary or a secondary amine hydrochloride. An aqueous solution of amine hydrochloride, alkali cyanide, and aldehyde (or ketone) is shaken at room temperature for 2 to 48 hours (39–78%).[319] A variation of this procedure consists in adding concentrated hydrochloric acid to an aqueous solution of amine, aldehyde, and sodium cyanide. In this manner, dimethylaminoacetonitrile is prepared by the condensation of dimethylamine and formaldehyde in 73–83% yield.[313] Acetic acid serves as a solvent for the reaction of less soluble aromatic compounds.[320]

Another procedure replaces the above combination of ammonium chloride and alkali cyanide with ammonium cyanide. This reagent and the carbonyl compound in alcoholic solution are allowed to react at room temperature for several days. Aliphatic[317,318] and alkyl aryl[314-316] ketones, but not diaryl ketones, give products in 20% to 90% yield.

The sodium bisulfite addition products of aldehydes have been converted by the action of potassium cyanide and an amine to α-alkylamino cyanides. The procedure is best suited for obtaining amino nitriles derived from formaldehyde and simple amines[319] and is illustrated in the preparation of diethylaminoacetonitrile (90%).[322]

$$H_2C(OH)SO_3Na \xrightarrow{R_2NH} H_2C(NR_2)SO_3Na \xrightarrow{KCN} R_2NCH_2CN$$

Higher homologs have been prepared by employing other amines[319,390] or aldehydes.[324,390] The yields are improved in the reaction of hindered amines by the addition of a dispersing agent.[325] The procedure is of little importance for the conversion of ketones.

Still another variation consists in the treatment of cyanohydrins with ammonia or amines. This procedure has given very successful results in the conversion of acetone cyanohydrin to the corresponding amino cyanides by the action of ammonia (80%), dimethylamine (88%), diethylamine (59%), aniline (93%), or piperidine (71%).[327] Methylaminoacetonitrile is made in the same way in 93% yield.[390]

392. Addition of Hydrogen Cyanide to Carbon-Nitrogen Double Bonds

Hydrogen cyanide adds to the carbon-nitrogen double bonds present in various aldehyde and ketone derivatives, like those in imines, hydrazones, oximes, and Schiff bases.[338] In each instance, a new carbon-carbon linkage is formed. Thus, the reaction of dry hydrogen cyanide with an imine gives an α-amino cyanide.[391] The procedure is illustrated by the treatment of benzophenoneimine in alcohol solution to form α-aminodiphenylacetonitrile (77%).[339] Ether has also been employed as a solvent.[340]

$$(C_6H_5)_2C=NH + HCN \longrightarrow (C_6H_5)_2C(NH_2)CN$$

The addition of dry hydrogen cyanide to the trimer of methyleneaminoacetonitrile, $CH_2=NCH_2CN$, in the presence of hydrochloric acid yields iminodiacetonitrile, $NH(CH_2CN)_2$.[341]

Oximes add hydrogen cyanide to form α-hydroxylaminonitriles.[343] The yields are greatly improved by substituting a sodium cyanide-phosphate buffer for liquid hydrocyanic acid, as in the preparation of α-hydroxylaminoisobutyronitrile (67%) from acetoxime.[342]

$$(CH_3)_2C=NOH + NaCN \xrightarrow{KH_2PO_4} (CH_3)_2C(NHOH)CN$$

Aqueous hydrogen cyanide in the presence of pyridine has also been proved a successful reagent.[344]

Aldonitrones, prepared by the condensation of aromatic aldehydes and phenylhydroxylamine, are converted by the action of aqueous potassium cyanide to substituted anils of aroyl cyanides.[345]

$$ArCH=N(O)C_6H_5 \xrightarrow{HCN} [ArCH(CN)N(OH)C_6H_5] \xrightarrow{-H_2O} ArC(CN)=NC_6H_5$$

The interaction of acyl chlorides, hydrocyanic acid, and quinoline in absolute benzene forms 1-acyl-1,2-dihydroquinaldonitriles.[346]

Treatment of the 1-benzoyl derivative with phosphorus pentachloride in chloroform solution regenerates benzoyl chloride and forms 2-cyanoquinoline in an over-all yield of 50–63%.[347] Isoquinoline behaves in a similar manner to give 1-cyanoisoquinoline.

393. Addition of Hydrogen Cyanide to Lactones

The heating of lactones with powdered alkali cyanides leads to salts of cyano acids. The procedure is illustrated (above equation) by the synthesis of o-carboxybenzyl cyanide from phthalide and potassium cyanide (67–83%).[349] In another instance, the reaction of potassium cyanide with γ-anisyl-γ-butyrolactone involves a rearrangement thereby forming a β-cyano acid instead of the anticipated γ-cyano acid.[350]

$$p\text{-}CH_3OC_6H_4\overset{\displaystyle\lceil\text{----}O\text{----}\rceil}{CH\text{---}CH_2CH_2CO} \longrightarrow p\text{-}CH_3OC_6H_4CH_2\overset{\displaystyle\overset{CN}{|}}{CH}CH_2CO_2K$$

A similar rearrangement has been observed in the treatment of γ-methyl-γ-valerolactone with potassium cyanide whereby γ-methyl-β-cyanovaleric acid is formed instead of the expected γ-cyano acid.[351]

394. Reduction of Unsaturated Cyano Compounds

$$RCH = CHCN + H_2 \overset{Pd}{\longrightarrow} RCH_2CH_2CN$$

Unsaturated nitriles are converted smoothly to the saturated compounds by selective hydrogenation over palladinized charcoal[217, 291] or by chemical reduction.[290] The reaction is of special value in the preparation of a variety of substituted cyano compounds from the olefinic nitriles obtained in cyanoacetic ester condensations (method 387).

Conditions have been found whereby the condensation and hydrogenation steps are carried out as a single operation.[292] In this procedure, a solution of carbonyl compound and ethyl cyanoacetate in glacial acetic acid is shaken with hydrogen in the presence of palladium-on-carbon and a condensing agent, such as ammonium acetate or piperidine. The yields are excellent for the conversion of aldehydes and simple ketones (63–98%). The condensation-reduction of aromatic ketones like acetophenone and propiophenone gives mixtures, apparently because of incomplete hydrogenation of the condensation products. The procedure is given in detail for the synthesis of ethyl n-butylcyanoacetate (96%).[293]

395. Reduction of α-Halo Cyanides

$$C_6H_5CH(Cl)CN \overset{(H)}{\longrightarrow} C_6H_5CH_2CN$$

A synthesis of nitriles from the cyanohydrins of aromatic aldehydes via the reduction of the corresponding α-halo cyanides has been proposed. As an example, benzaldehyde cyanohydrin is converted by the action of thionyl chloride to phenylchloroacetonitrile (80%). This substance is reduced with zinc in acetic acid to phenylacetonitrile (70%).[335]

396. Action of Hydrazoic Acid on Aldehydes

$$RCHO + HN_3 \xrightarrow{H^+} RCN + H_2O + N_2$$

The reaction between equimolar quantities of hydrazoic acid and aldehydes in the presence of strong mineral acid yields nitriles and, to a lesser extent, N-substituted formyl derivatives, RNHCHO (Schmidt reaction). A number of aldehydes, including acetaldehyde, benzaldehyde, m-nitrobenzaldehyde, and vanillin, have been converted to the nitriles in yields of 64% to 83%.[336,337]

397. Hydrogenolysis of α-Benzoyloxy Cyanides[396]

$$ArCHO \xrightarrow[KCN]{C_6H_5COCl} ArCH(O_2CC_6H_5)CN \xrightarrow[Pd]{H_2} ArCH_2CN \quad (70\% \text{ over-all})$$

398. Dehydrogenation of Amines[352,392]

$$RCH_2NH_2 \xrightarrow[Heat]{Catalyst} RCN + 2H_2$$

399. Action of Metallic Thiocyanates on Salts of Carboxylic Acids[354]

$$(RCOO)_2Zn + Pb(CNS)_2 \rightarrow 2RCN + PbS + ZnS + 2CO_2$$

400. Addition of Hydrogen Cyanide to Oxides[348]

$$\overset{O}{\overset{/\backslash}{CH_2CH_2CH_2Cl}} + HCN \xrightarrow{NaCN} CH_2ClCH_2OHCH_2CN \quad (85\%)$$

401. Coupling of Diazonium Salts with Acrylonitrile[356] (cf. method 28)

$$ArN_2^+Cl^- + H_2C{=}CHCN \xrightarrow{CuCl_2} ArCH_2CHClCN$$

TABLE 66. CYANIDES

C_n	Compound	Method	Yield (%)	Chapter[ref.]	B.p./mm., n_D^t, (M.p.), Deriv.
		Aliphatic Cyanides			
C_2	Methyl cyanide (aceto-	378	100	20[161]	76-82
	nitrile)	378	63	20[162]	
		384	50	20[4]	81/757, 1.3441
		384	91	20[120]	82
		396	64	20[336]	
C_3	Ethyl cyanide	378	50	20[4]	97/758, 1.3658
		384	83	20[158]	97
C_4	n-Propyl cyanide	378	36	20[4]	118/757, 1.3842
		384	94	20[158]	
	Isopropyl cyanide (iso-	384	86	20[114]	101-103/740, 1.3713[25]
	butyronitrile)				
C_5	n-Butyl cyanide	378	80	20[1]	141/764, 1.3969
	Isobutyl cyanide (iso-	384	80	20[115]	129
	valeronitrile)				
	t-Butyl cyanide (tri-	384	73	20[398]	104/738, 1.3792
	methylacetonitrile)				
C_6	n-Amyl cyanide	378	90	20[2]	162/777, 1.4069
	(capronitrile)	384	63	20[120]	159
		386	60	20[173]	162
	Isoamyl cyanide	378	82	20[3]	154/756, 1.4059
	Methyl-n-propyl-	386	65	20[173]	146
	acetonitrile				
	Diethylacetonitrile	386	77	20[173]	145
		387	60 †	20[182]	142-146
	Neopentyl cyanide (t-	384	90	20[116]	136/737, (32.5)
	butylacetonitrile)				
C_7	n-Hexyl cyanide	378	72	20[4]	182/757, 1.4141
	Ethylisopropylace-	386	71	20[173]	158
	tonitrile				
C_8	Ethyl-n-butylacetonitrile	386	68	20[173]	70/12
C_9	2-Ethyl-3-methylhexano-	394	67	20[217]	72/7, 1.4232[25]
	nitrile				
C_{10}	Diethyl-n-butylacetonitrile	386	78	20[173]	86/11
C_{11}	n-Decyl cyanide	378	95	20[5]	125-129/11
	Tri-n-propylacetonitrile	386	76	20[177]	70/2
C_{12}	Lauronitrile	384	85	20[118]	160/30, (4)
C_{13}	n-Dodecyl cyanide	378	88	20[6]	168/21, 1.4389
C_{14}	Myristonitrile	384	80	20[118]	168/12, (19)
C_{16}	Palmitonitrile	384	80	20[118]	173/7, (31)
C_{17}	Cetyl cyanide	378	86	20[163]	(30)
		378	68	20[15]	200/13
C_{18}	Stearonitrile	384	95	20[119]	173/1.5, (42)
		384	85	20[117]	358, (43)

TABLE 66. CYANIDES 611

TABLE 66 (continued)

C_n	Compound	Method	Yield (%)	Chapter[ref.]	B.p./mm., n_D^t, (M.p.), Deriv.
		Alicyclic Cyanides			
C_4	Cyclopropyl cyanide	386	60	20^{186}	93–96/26
C_5	2-Methylcyclopropane-carbonitrile	386	60	20^{71}	146, 1.4259
C_6	Cyclopentyl cyanide	378	27	20^8	75/30, 1.4404^{25}
C_7	Cyclohexyl cyanide	384	93	20^{121}	80–84/18
C_{10}	δ-Cyclopentylbutyl cyanide	378	85	20^7	126/17, 1.4542
C_{12}	Dicyclopentylacetonitrile	384	100	20^{127}	90/0.3, (35)
		Aromatic Cyanides			
C_7	Benzonitrile	383	69	20^{329}	79/17
		384	80	20^{122}	190
		384	97	20^{120}	191
		396	70	20^{336}	
C_8	Benzyl cyanide	378	90	20^9	135–140/38
		384	87	20^{158}	129/31
		395	70	20^{335}	234
	o-Tolunitrile	380	70	20^{218}	96/20
	m-Tolunitrile	380	59	20^{219}	100/20
	p-Tolunitrile	380	70	20^{218}	106/20, (27)
		384	89	20^{120}	220
C_9	α-Methylbenzyl cyanide	385	90	20^{189}	107–110/11
		386	66	20^{179}	94/6, 1.5084^{25}
	β-Phenylethyl cyanide	384	81	20^{158}	142/25
		386	49	20^{173}	125/11
	o-Methylbenzyl cyanide	378	89	20^{11}	84/14
	m-Methylbenzyl cyanide	378	85	20^{12}	133/15
	2,3-Dimethylbenzonitrile	380	40	20^{222}	107/11
	2,4-Dimethylbenzonitrile	383	87	20^{329}	(111)
	2,5-Dimethylbenzonitrile	383	82	20^{329}	109/17
	3,4-Dimethylbenzonitrile	383	86	20^{329}	118-122/15, (69)
C_{10}	α-Phenylbutyronitrile	384	78	20^{124}	112/9, 1.5075
		386	87	20^{181}	115/16
	1-Phenylcyclopropyl cyanide	386	44	20^{187}	253/751, 1.5386
	p-Ethylbenzyl cyanide	378	82	20^{13}	127–130/14
	α,α-Dimethylbenzyl cyanide	386	78	20^{184}	82/2.2, $1.5043–55^{25}$
	2,5-Dimethylbenzyl cyanide	378	73	20^{14}	118/6, 143/19

For explanations and symbols see pp. xi–xii.

TABLE 66 *(continued)*

C_n	Compound	Method	Yield (%)	Chapter[ref.]	B.p./mm., n_D^t, (M.p.), Deriv.
		Aromatic Cyanides *(continued)*			
C_{10}	2,4,6-Trimethylbenzonitrile	383	73	20[329]	125/16, (55)
C_{11}	p-Isopropylphenylacetonitrile	378	78	20[358]	104–110/1.5
	p-s-Butylbenzonitrile	378	84	20[24]	80/4, 1.5310
	Mesitylacetonitrile	378	100	20[16]	160–165/22
	α-Naphthonitrile	378	90	20[25]	174/27
		379	86	20[165]	(38)
		380	78	20[224]	148/12
		384	100	20[128]	
	β-Naphthonitrile	379	50	20[166]	
		380	60	20[225]	160–170/20, (62)
		384	80	20[120]	(66)
	β-Cyanotetralin	383	65	20[329]	155–158/14
C_{12}	β-Ethyl-γ-phenylpropyl cyanide	378	90	20[19]	142/13
	1-Cyanomethyl-2,3,4,6-tetramethylbenzene	378	74	20[18]	135/5, (75)
	1-Cyanomethyl-2,3,4,5-tetramethylbenzene	378	95	20[17]	184/25
	1-Phenylcyclopentyl cyanide	386	85	20[121]	148–153/20
	α-Naphthylacetonitrile	378	87	20[20]	182–186/12, (33), 1.6173[25]
	β-Naphthylacetonitrile	384	77	20[129]	(86)
C_{13}	2,4,6-Triethylbenzonitrile	378	64	20[22]	151/24, 1.5201
	2-Cyanobiphenyl	384	86	20[369]	172/15, 166/8
	4-Cyanobiphenyl	380	50	20[385]	(86)
C_{14}	Diphenylacetonitrile	1	60 †	20[375]	(75)
		384	90	20[123]	(73)
	α-Cyclohexylphenylacetonitrile	386	77	20[188]	176/13, 1.5330[26]
	o-Benzylbenzonitrile	378	54	20[23]	160–164/4
C_{15}	1-Cyanophenanthrene	379	40	20[170]	(128)
		384	96	20[130]	
	2-Cyanophenanthrene	384	77	20[159]	(109)
	3-Cyanophenanthrene	384	62	20[159]	(102)
	9-Cyanophenanthrene	378	87	20[26]	(107)
	9-Cyano-1,2,3,4-tetrahydrophenanthrene	378	81	20[28]	(125)
	1-Cyanoanthracene	384	60	20[131]	(144.5)
	9-Cyanoanthracene	378	87	20[27]	(175)
		385	98	20[235]	(179)

TABLE 66. CYANIDES 613

TABLE 66 (continued)

C_n	Compound	Method	Yield (%)	Chapter[ref]	B.p./mm., n_D^t, (M.p.), Deriv.
		Aromatic Cyanides (continued)			
C_{16}	α,α-Diphenylbutyronitrile	386	88	20^{185}	147/0.3, 1.5660[25]
	α,γ-Diphenylbutyronitrile	386	63	20^{183}	147–151/0.5–1
	Dibenzylacetonitrile	386	40	20^{173}	200–215
	Di-o-tolylacetonitrile	378	54	20^{53}	(115)
C_{21}	α,α,β-Triphenylpropionitrile	386	67	20^{376}	(126)
	β,β,β-Triphenylpropionitrile	384	89	20^{125}	(140)
		Heterocyclic Cyanides			
C_5	α-Cyanotetrahydrofuran	385	76	20^{273}	82/23, 1.4351[25]
C_6	2-Furylacetonitrile	384	15†	20^{394}	80/20, 1.4715[25]
		385	88	20^{236}	84/17, 1.4691[25]
	5-Methyl-2-furonitrile	385	67	20^{239}	67/15, 1.4848
	α-Tetrahydrofurylacetonitrile	378	52	20^{29}	92/13, 1.4476[13]
		378	36	20^{164}	45/2, 1.4625
	2-Thienylacetonitrile	385	74†	20^{380}	90/3, 1.5041[30]
		378	81	20^{31}	115–120/22
	2-Cyanopyridine	378	74	20^{35}	120/25
	3-Cyanopyridine (nicotinonitrile)	378	50	20^{34}	(50)
		379	46	20^{171}	(50)
		380	50	20^{271}	
		384	100	20^{133}	201/760
	4-Cyanopyridine	384	55	20^{134}	(79)
C_7	N-(β-Cyanoethyl)pyrrole	388	86	20^{253}	135–150/8–10
	3-Pyridylacetonitrile	384	34	20^{370}	108/0.5, 161Pi
	4-Pyridylacetonitrile	384	55	20^{371}	(79), 230Pi
	3-Cyano-4-methylpyridine	379	33	20^{172}	64/1–2, 185Pi
	3-Cyano-5-methylpyridine	379	35	20^{171}	(84)
	N-Cyanomethylpiperidine	391	94	20^{319}	83/9
C_8	N-(β-Cyanoethyl)piperidine	388	93	20^{253}	130/30, 1.4697
C_9	γ-Piperidinobutyronitrile	436	87	24^{193}	129/25, 1.4653, 117Pi
	α-Piperidinoisobutyronitrile	391	71	20^{327}	94/14
C_{10}	2-Cyanomethylbenzothiophene	378	51	20^{32}	126/0.2, (67)
	3-Cyanomethylbenzothiophene	378	53	20^{33}	140/2, (67)
	3-Cyano-2-methylindole	383	95	20^{329}	208

For explanations and symbols see pp. xi–xii.

TABLE 66 *(continued)*

C_n	Compound	Method	Yield (%)	Chapter[ref.]	B.p./mm., n_D^t, (M.p.), Deriv.

Heterocyclic Cyanides *(continued)*

C_n	Compound	Method	Yield (%)	Chapter[ref.]	B.p./mm., n_D^t, (M.p.), Deriv.
C_{10}	2-Cyanoquinoline	378	63	20[38]	(94)
		392	63†	20[347]	(94)
	5-Cyanoquinoline	380	51	20[226]	147/8, (88)
	8-Cyanoquinoline	378	67	20[226]	(83.5)
	1-Cyanoisoquinoline	392	85	20[347]	(74)
	3-Cyanoquinoline	378	92	20[37]	(108)
	4-Cyanoisoquinoline	378	88	20[39]	(104)
	5-Cyanoisoquinoline	378	81	20[39]	(139)
	6-Cyanoisoquinoline	378	25	20[39]	(152)
	8-Cyanoisoquinoline	378	53	20[39]	(133)
C_{11}	8-Cyanomethylquinoline	378	78	20[40]	(87)
C_{15}	N-(β-Cyanoethyl)-carbazole	388	85	20[250]	(155.5)

For explanations and symbols see pp. xi–xii.

TABLE 67. DICYANIDES

C_n	Compound	Method	Yield (%)	Chapter[ref.]	B.p./mm., n_D^t, (M.p.)
C_3	Malononitrile	384	66	20[135]	113–118/25, 94/8
C_4	Succinonitrile	388	93	20[246]	160/20
		378	80	20[44]	147/10
	Methylmalononitrile	384	78	20[136]	198, (26)*
C_5	Trimethylene cyanide	378	86	20[45]	134/10, 1.4295*
C_8	Hexamethylene cyanide	378	80	20[47]	180/12
		386	50	20[377]	172/11, 1.4448[22]
	2-Methyl-1,3-dicyanopentane	378	42	20[46]	189–193/12
	1-Methylbutylmalononitrile	394	67	20[289]	100/8, 1.4324[25]
	cis-1,4-Dicyanocyclohexane	384	77	20[140]	(65)
	trans-1,4-Dicyanocyclohexane	384	69	20[140]	(140)
	Phthalonitrile	384	75	20[141]	(141)
C_9	Heptamethylene cyanide	378	80	20[48]	183/11
		384	78	20[368]	160/3, 1.4426[25]
		386	69	20[377]	176/11, 1.4518[19]
	Phenylmalononitrile	384	60	20[137]	(69)
C_{10}	Sebaconitrile	384	49	20[139]	201–203/16
	Phenylsuccinonitrile	389	64	20[301]	(68)
	m-Phenylenediacetonitrile	378	91	20[12]	231/20, (27)
	p-Phenylenediacetonitrile	378	70	20[12]	(96)
C_{11}	α-Phenyl-α,β-β-tricyanoethane	389	90	20[302]	(125)
C_{12}	α-Phenylglutaronitrile	388	33	20[262]	200/12

TABLE 68. OLEFINIC CYANIDES   615

TABLE 67 (continued)

C_n	Compound	Method	Yield (%)	Chapter[ref.]	B.p./mm., n_D^t, (M.p.)
C_{13}	α-Methyl-α-phenyladiponitrile	386	88	20^{189}	150–160/1
C_{14}	Biphenyl-4,4-dicyanide	380	45	20^{223}	(233)

For explanations and symbols see pp. xi–xii.

TABLE 68. OLEFINIC CYANIDES

C_n	Compound	Method	Yield (%)	Chapter[ref.]	B.p./mm., n_D^t, (M.p.)
	Aliphatic Olefinic Cyanides				
C_3	Acrylonitrile	19	80	2^{442}	78
		24	63	2^{239}	77/760
		398	85	20^{392}	
C_4	trans-2-Butenonitrile (crotononitrile)	384	40	20^{144}	119, 1.4217
	Allyl cyanide	378	84	20^{56}	119/753, 1.4034
		378	75	20^{360}	116–121, 1.4060
	α-Methylacrylonitrile	19	50	2^{102}	
		19	34	2^{100}	90
		384	85	20^{272}	91, 1.3999^{25}
		385	76	20^{272}	91, 1.3977^{25}
		398	90	20^{392}	90/760, 1.4001
	Maleonitrile	384	39	20^{138}	(31)
	Fumaronitrile	378	74	20^{65}	(96)
		384	80	20^{372}	(96)
C_5	2-Pentenonitrile (β-ethylacrylonitrile)	384	45	20^{143}	72/72, 1.4301
	3-Pentenonitrile	378	92	20^{59}	146, 1.4228
	4-Pentenonitrile	384	60	20^{160}	145, 1.4213^{14}
	Methallyl cyanide	378	86	20^{58}	136, 1.4180
	1-Cyano-1,3-butadiene (cis and trans)	24	70	2^{238}	50/31, 1.4852 57/31, 1.4960
		378	20	20^{64}	68/58, 1.4880
	α-Ethylacrylonitrile	385	30	20^{378}	111, 1.4132
C_6	2-Hexenonitrile	384	60	20^{144}	50/10, 1.4379
	3-Hexenonitrile	378	77	20^{60}	99/90, 1.4289^{19}
		384	40	20^{144}	58/15, 1.4301
		387	48	20^{209}	59/12
	5-Hexenonitrile	378	88	20^{359}	162, 59/16, 1.4268^{25}
	3-Methyl-2-pentenonitrile	384	36	20^{145}	63/20, 1.4447
	4-Methyl-2-pentenonitrile	384	80	20^{143}	68/34, 1.4329
	3-Methyl-3-pentenonitrile	384	80	20^{145}	60/19, 1.4367^{21}
	4-Methyl-3-pentenonitrile	387	60	20^{144}	66/24, 1.4352

For explanations and symbols see pp. xi–xii.

TABLE 68 *(continued)*

C_n	Compound	Method	Yield (%)	Chapter[ref.]	B.p./mm., n_D^t, (M.p.)
		Aliphatic Olefinic Cyanides *(continued)*			
C_7	3-Heptenonitrile	378	76	20^{60}	68.5/11, 1.4323^{21}
	4-Heptenonitrile	378	79	20^{61}	50/5, 1.4367^{15}
	3-Ethyl-3-pentenonitrile	387	72†	20^{192}	105/72, 1.4394^{25}
	2,3-Dimethyl-2-pentenonitrile	387	90	20^{217}	64/17, 1.4469^{25}
	β-t-Butylacrylonitrile	387	70	20^{143}	60/28, 1.4344
C_8	3-Octenonitrile	378	70	20^{60}	95/19, 1.4350^{25}
	2,3-Dimethyl-2-hexenonitrile	387	90	20^{217}	73-77/14-16, 1.4491^{25}
	3-Ethyl-2-methyl-2-pentenonitrile	387	90	20^{217}	76/17, 1.4500^{25}
C_9	2-Ethyl-3-methyl-2-hexenonitrile	387	90	20^{217}	78/8, 1.4512^{25}
	2,3,5-Trimethyl-2-hexenonitrile	387	89	20^{217}	76/9, 1.4503^{25}
	Diethylallylacetonitrile	386	90	20^{173}	79/14
		Alicyclic Olefinic Cyanides			
C_6	1-Cyano-1-cyclopentene	19	75	2^{98}	69/15
		19	50	2^{91}	69/15
	3-Cyano-1-cyclopentene	378	76	20^{63}	50/15
		389	24	20^{300}	56/15, 1.4669^{15}
C_7	Cyclopentylideneacetonitrile	384	55	20^{145}	98/24, 1.4805^{18}
	1-Cyclopentenylacetonitrile	384	62	20^{145}	92/19, 1.4683^{18}
	2-Methyl-1-cyano-1-cyclopentene	19	80	20^{101}	69/14
C_8	Cyclohexylideneacetonitrile	384	58	20^{145}	108/22, 1.4928^{15}
	1-Cyclohexenylacetonitrile	384	56	20^{145}	105/22, 1.4843^{19}
		387	79†	20^{192}	99/15, 1.4769^{25}
		387	91	20^{399}	111/25, 1.4769^{25}
C_9	Cyclohexylidenemalononitrile	37	30	2^{381}	(174)
		Aromatic Olefinic Cyanides			
C_9	Cinnamonitrile *(trans)*	20	33	2^{275}	118/12, (20)
		385	84	20^{272}	137/16, 1.6005^{25}, (23)
		387	60	20^{212}	139/30, (22), 1.6031
	(cis)	387			152/30, (−4.4), 1.5843
	o-Cyanostyrene	27	29	2^{256}	53/0.15, 1.5756
	m-Cyanostyrene	27	51	2^{257}	83/3.5, 1.5630
	p-Cyanostyrene	19	71	2^{166}	89/1.5, 1.5750^{25}
		24	76	2^{492}	93/3, 1.5772
C_{10}	α-Phenylcrotononitrile	37	36	2^{383}	102/1, 1.555
	4-Phenyl-3-butenonitrile	384	62	20^{145}	(60)
	Benzalmalononitrile	37	96	20^{381}	(84)

TABLE 70. HALO CYANIDES   617

TABLE 68 *(continued)*

C_n	Compound	Method	Yield (%)	Chapter[ref.]	B.p./mm., n_D^t, (M.p.)
	Aromatic Olefinic Cyanides *(continued)*				
C_{11}	Cinnamylidenacetonitrile	387	78	20^{213}	160/11, (41.5)
	α-Methylbenzalmalononitrile	37	70	20^{380}	123/2, (94)
C_{12}	α-Phenyl-β-*n*-propylacrylonitrile	37	54	2^{379}	118.5/3.5, 1.5404
C_{15}	α-Phenylcinnamonitrile	37	91	2^{485}	(88)
C_{16}	Stilbene-2-acetonitrile	378	63	20^{67}	(82)
C_{21}	Triphenylacrylonitrile	378	100	20^{66}	(165)

For explanations and symbols see pp. xi–xii.

TABLE 69. ACETYLENIC CYANIDES

C_n	Compound	Method	Yield (%)	Chapter[ref.]	B.p./mm., n_D^t, (M.p.)
C_4	Acetylenedicarbonitrile	384	37	20^{138}	
C_8	1-Cyano-1-heptyne	384	85	20^{142}	81/13, 1.4551[25]
	1-Cyano-2-heptyne	378	92	20^{68}	124/56, 1.4475[25]
	1-Cyano-3-heptyne	384	50	20^{68}	71/3, 1.4492[25]
	1-Cyano-4-heptyne	378	82	20^{68}	111/29, 1.4514[25]
	1-Cyano-5-heptyne	378	75†	20^{68}	79/2, 1.4530[25]
	1-Cyano-6-heptyne	378	74	20^{68}	80/3, 1.4460[25]
C_9	1-Cyano-1-octyne	384	80	20^{142}	96/13, 1.4564[14]
	Cyclohexylpropiolonitrile	50	67	3^{67}	96/21, 1.4947[11]

For explanations and symbols see pp. xi–xii.

TABLE 70. HALO CYANIDES

C_n	Compound	Method	Yield (%)	Chapter[ref.]	B.p./mm., n_D^t, (M.p.)
	Aliphatic Halo Cyanides				
C_2	Fluoroacetonitrile	384	65	20^{373}	80/760
	Chloroacetonitrile	384	70	20^{146}	124, 61/100
	Trifluoroacetonitrile	384	74	20^{149}	−64/743
	Trichloroacetonitrile	384	80	20^{150}	86
C_3	β-Chloropropionitrile	73	80	4^{206}	71/16
	β-Bromopropionitrile	52	43	4^{139}	69/7, 1.4789[25]
C_4	γ-Chlorobutyronitrile	378	70	20^{70}	93–96/26
	γ-Iodobutyronitrile	55	96	4^{390}	74/1

For explanations and symbols see pp. xi–xii.

TABLE 70 *(continued)*

C_n	Compound	Method	Yield (%)	Chapter[ref.]	B.p./mm., n_D^t, (M.p.)
		Aliphatic Halo Cyanides *(continued)*			
C_4	α-Chloroisobutyronitrile	52	38	4[140]	100/60, 1.4310
		384	84	20[147]	116, 1.4045[25]
	α-Bromoisobutyronitrile	384	86	20[147]	139, 1.4460[25]
		....	76	4[205]	140, 1.4447[25]
	β-Chloroisobutyronitrile	73	79	4[205]	52/6, 1.4323[25]
	β-Bromoisobutyronitrile	73	72	4[205]	62/5, 1.4680[25]
C_5	δ-Chlorovaleronitrile	378	52	20[72]	102/17, 1.4441[25]
	δ-Bromovaleronitrile	378	43	20[73]	111/11, 1.4781
	β-Methyl-γ-chlorobutyronitrile	378	26	20[71]	83/16, 1.4426
C_6	ε-Bromocapronitrile	378	26	20[362]	134/15, 1.4754[24]
		384	76	20[148]	117/6
		Aromatic Halo Cyanides			
C_7	o-Chlorobenzonitrile	384	93	20[120]	(44)
	o-Bromobenzonitrile	384	79	20[156]	(53)*
	p-Bromobenzonitrile	380	70	20[221]	(113)*
	p-Iodobenzonitrile	380	70	20[227]	(114)
C_8	o-Chlorophenylacetonitrile	385	64	20[243]	125/11
	o-Bromophenylacetonitrile	385	88	20[243]	141/13
	m-Chlorophenylacetonitrile	385	55	20[243]	136/10
	m-Bromophenylacetonitrile	385	70	20[243]	147/10
	p-Fluorophenylacetonitrile	378	72	20[363]	116/16
	p-Chlorophenylacetonitrile	385	80	20[243]	139/12, (32)
	p-Bromophenylacetonitrile	385	72	20[243]	156/12, (48)
	o-Cyanobenzyl bromide	64	57	4[292]	(72.5)
	o-Cyanobenzyl iodide	55	97	4[292]	(78)
	o-Cyanobenzal bromide	64	40	4[294]	(65)
	p-Cyanobenzyl bromide	64	47	4[293]	(116)
	Phenylchloroacetonitrile	53	80	4[179]	131/13
C_9	α-Chlorohydrocinnamonitrile	401	34	20[356]	140/15, (21)
	m-Bromomethylphenylacetonitrile	378	90	20[51]	141/18
	p-(β-Bromoethyl)-benzonitrile	384	68	20[151]	151/5, (50)
C_{10}	α-Phenyl-γ-chlorobutyronitrile	53	30	4[180]	129/4, 1.5327
C_{12}	γ-Chloro-α-ethyl-α-phenyl-butyronitrile	386	53	20[180]	106/1.5

For explanations and symbols see pp. xi–xii.

TABLE 72. CYANO ETHERS 619

TABLE 71. HYDROXY CYANIDES

C_n	Compound	Method	Yield (%)	Chapter[ref.]	B.p./mm., n_D^t, (M.p.)
C_2	Formaldehyde cyanohydrin	390	80	20[277]	88/8
	(glycolonitrile)	390	40	20[276]	100/17, 1.4090[25]
C_3	Ethylene cyanohydrin	378	80	20[74]	107–109/12
C_4	Acetone cyanohydrin	390	78	20[263]	78–82/15
	Chloroacetone cyanohydrin	390	90	20[275]	110/20, 1.4520
	4-Chloro-3-hydroxybutyronitrile	400	85	20[348]	135/15, 1.4735[15]
	β-Hydroxybutyronitrile	378	60	20[77]	215
	Acrolein cyanohydrin	390	96	20[279]	
C_5	Methyl ethyl ketone cyanohydrin	390	100	20[266]	
	β-Hydroxy-γ-methoxybutyronitrile	378	85	20[76]	133/18
	Butadiene cyanohydrin	378	74	20[78]	133/30, 1.4559
C_6	Diethyl ketone cyanohydrin	390	75	20[267]	93/13
	Cyclopentanone cyanohydrin	390	87	20[268]	114/14
C_7	α-Methyl-α-hydroxycapronitrile	378	70	20[75]	113/10
	Cyclohexanone cyanohydrin	390	98	20[269]	120/10, (26)
	p-Hydroxybenzonitrile	380	70	20[228]	148/1
	Acetoacetic ester cyanohydrin	390	85	20[278]	120–124/13, 1.4298[25]
C_8	Mandelonitrile	390	86	20[283]	170d*
	2-Hydroxymandelonitrile	390	90	20[284]	
	4-Hydroxymandelonitrile	390	90	20[284]	(102)
	p-Cyanobenzyl alcohol	96	85	5[549]	203/53, (42)
	p-Hydroxybenzyl cyanide	93	71	5[492]	(70)
	Phenylacetaldehyde cyanohydrin	390	67	20[286]	(55)
C_9	p-Cyanophenylmethylcarbinol	80	88	5[179]	157/6, 1.5474
		378	36	20[79]	136–140/5, 1.5477
C_{10}	α-Phenyl-γ-hydroxybutyronitrile	386	40	20[187]	146–149/1.5–2.0
	p-Dimethylaminobenzaldehyde cyanohydrin	390	59	20[285]	(113)
C_{13}	2-Phenylcyclohexanone cyanohydrin	390	89	20[270]	(117)

For explanations and symbols see pp. xi–xii.

TABLE 72. CYANO ETHERS

C_n	Compound	Method	Yield (%)	Chapter[ref.]	B.p./mm., n_D^t, (M.p.)
	Aliphatic Cyano Ethers				
C_3	Methoxyacetonitrile	116	77	6[102]	118–122
		378	74	20[80]	121/759, 1.3831
C_4	α-Methoxypropionitrile	378	36	20[87]	118/740, 1.3818
	β-Methoxypropionitrile	121	89	6[116]	85/49, 1.4032
		388	89	20[254]	85/49, 1.4032

For explanations and symbols see pp. xi–xii.

TABLE 72 (*continued*)

C_n	Compound	Method	Yield (%)	Chapter[ref.]	B.p./mm., n_D^t, (M.p.)
		Aliphatic Cyano Ethers (continued)			
C_4	Ethoxyacetonitrile	378	83	20[81]	135/755, 1.3898
		384	60	20[152]	134, 1.3888[25]
C_5	1-Methoxybutyronitrile	378	52	20[88]	133/746, 1.4025
	β-Methoxyisobutyronitrile	121	28	6[157]	162, 1.4038
	α-Ethoxypropionitrile	378	51	20[85]	130/751, 1.3890[22]
	β-Ethoxypropionitrile	121	89	6[115]	173, 78/25, 1.4068*
		378	58	20[86]	169–174
		388	78	20[254]	78/25, 1.4068
	n-Propoxyacetonitrile	378	55	20[82]	56/40, 152/751, 1.4001
	Isopropoxyacetonitrile	378	72	20[83]	74/53, 146/748, 1.3960
	γ-Methoxycrotononitrile	19	70	2[99]	182
C_6	β-n-Propoxypropionitrile	121	84	6[117]	84/19, 1.4131
	β-Isopropoxypropionitrile	121	69	6[116]	82/25, 1.4089
		388	69	20[254]	83/25, 1.4089
	Methoxyethoxypropionitrile	388	87	20[254]	100/9
	bis-(β-Cyanoethyl) ether	388	91	20[255]	162/5, 1.4407[25]
C_7	α,α-Dimethyl-γ-methoxy-butyronitrile	386	54	20[173]	67/14
	β-n-Butoxypropionitrile	388	86	20[254]	98/20, 1.4180
C_8	1,2-bis-(β-Cyanoethoxy)-ethane	388	83	20[255]	158/2
	α-Ethyl-γ-ethoxybutyronitrile	387	54	20[216]	216/750
		Aromatic Cyano Ethers			
C_8	Phenoxyacetonitrile	115	75	6[155]	123/12, 1.5243
		384	40 †	20[153]	128/17, 1.5246
	m-Methoxybenzonitrile	384	79	20[156]	
		385	70	20[238]	116–120/13
C_9	β-Phenoxypropionitrile	388	68	20[256]	(60)
	o-Methoxybenzyl cyanide	378	37	20[95]	
	m-Methoxybenzyl cyanide	378	88	20[94]	165/20
	p-Methoxybenzyl cyanide	116	88	6[103]	154/15
		378	43	20[96]	131–134/9
		397	70	20[396]	153/16
	p-Cyanobenzyl methyl ether	115	84	6[62]	102/4, 1.5266
	p-Ethoxybenzonitrile	380	65	20[229]	(65)
	3,4-Dimethoxybenzonitrile (veratronitrile)	385	76	20[240]	(67)
C_{10}	γ-Phenoxypropyl cyanide	378	96	20[92]	162–166/22
	3-Ethoxyphenylacetonitrile	385	80	20[244]	141/8
	3,4-Dimethoxyphenylacetonitrile	378	52	20[97]	(68)
		385	90 †	20[241]	(65)
		397	70	20[396]	(68)

TABLE 73. CYANO ALDEHYDES AND KETONES 621

TABLE 72 *(continued)*

C_n	Compound	Method	Yield (%)	Chapter[ref.]	B.p./mm., n_D^t, (M.p.)
	Aromatic Cyano Ethers *(continued)*				
C_{10}	*p*-Propoxyphenyl cyanide	115	54	6[156]	122/3, (47)
C_{11}	α-Methyl-γ-phenoxybutyronitrile	387	64	20[214]	165-170/19, 1.5060[24]
	γ-Benzyloxypropyl cyanide	378	57	20[93]	157/12
	2-Ethoxy-3-methoxyphenylacetonitrile	385	80	20[244]	133/2.0
	3-Methoxy-4-ethoxyphenylacetonitrile	385	53	20[245]	158/0.4, (54)
	3-Ethoxy-4-methoxyphenylacetonitrile	385	80	20[244]	151/2.5
C_{13}	β-(2-Naphthoxy)-propionitrile	388	79	20[257]	(107)

For explanations and symbols see pp. xi–xii.

TABLE 73. CYANO ALDEHYDES AND KETONES

C_n	Compound	Method	Yield (%)	Chapter[ref.]	B.p./mm., n_D^t, (M.p.)
	Aliphatic Cyano Aldehydes and Ketones				
C_3	Acetyl cyanide (pyruvonitrile)	381	87	20[295]	93, 1.3743
C_4	Propionyl cyanide	381	60	20[295]	110, 1.3225
C_5	Isobutyryl cyanide	381	60	20[295]	118
C_6	*n*-Butyrylacetonitrile	216	52	20[663]	105/11
	5-Oxocapronitrile	184	71	20[381]	86.5/5.2, 1.4790[25]
	Isobutyrylacetonitrile	216	44	10[664]	104/13
		381	78	20[295]	149
	Trimethylacetyl cyanide	381	87	20[386]	122, 1.3940[27]
C_7	2,4-Dimethyl-3-ketovaleronitrile	216	40	10[661]	96/24, 1.4213[25]
	Trimethylacetylacetonitrile	378	80	20[101]	(68)
	2-Cyanocyclohexanone	378	64	20[105]	131/15
C_8	α-Butyrylbutyronitrile	216	60	10[659]	135/3
C_9	2-(β-Cyanoethyl)-2-ethylbutyraldehyde	388	77	20[258]	128/4, 1.4500[25]
C_{11}	2-(β-Cyanoethyl)-2-ethylhexanal	388	80	20[258]	142/5, 1.4515[25]
C_{12}	1,1,1-*tris*-(β-Cyanoethyl)-acetone	388	80	20[259]	(154)
	Aromatic Cyano Aldehydes and Ketones				
C_8	*o*-Cyanobenzaldehyde	155	29 †	9[152]	(104)
	m-Cyanobenzaldehyde	151	45	9[138]	(77)
	p-Cyanobenzaldehyde	147	70	9[110]	(100)
		148	70	9[261]	(96)

For explanations and symbols see pp. xi–xii.

TABLE 73 (continued)

C_n	Compound	Method	Yield (%)	Chapter[ref.]	B.p./mm., n_D^t, (M.p.)
	Aromatic Cyano Aldehydes and Ketones (continued)				
C_8	p-Cyanobenzaldehyde (continued)	155	15[†]	9[251]	(76)
		158	90	9[13]	(95)
	Benzoyl cyanide	381	65	20[297]	209/745, (33)
C_9	Benzoylacetonitrile	216	56	10[659]	(81)
		216	70	10[662]	(81)
		235	42[†]	10[682]	(81)
		378	60	20[100]	
	o-Cyanoacetophenone	378	80	20[107]	148/12
	p-Cyanoacetophenone	378	70	20[106]	(56)
C_{10}	α-Phenylacetoacetonitrile	216	60	10[660]	(89)
	α-Benzoylpropionitrile	216	53	10[659]	130/3
	β-Benzoylpropionitrile	382	67	20[393]	(76)
	4-Methylbenzoylacetonitrile	378	67	20[98]	(99)
C_{11}	4-Benzoylbutyronitrile	184	52	20[381]	125/0.1, 1.5326[25]
C_{13}	α-Cyanopropiomesitylene	178	19	10[156]	(128)
C_{15}	4,4'-Dicyanobenzophenone	380	60	20[228]	(162)
C_{16}	α-Phenyl-β-benzoylpropionitrile	389	96	20[303]	(127)
	Heterocyclic Cyano Ketones				
C_6	Furoyl cyanide	381	60	20[299]	32/0.15, (25)
C_7	α-Furoylacetonitrile	216	31	10[662]	(79)
	α-Thienoylacetonitrile	216	50	10[662]	(135)
C_8	β-2-Furoylpropionitrile	382	57	20[393]	(76)
	β-2-Thienoylpropionitrile	382	67	20[393]	(66)

For explanations and symbols see pp. xi–xii.

TABLE 74. CYANO ACIDS

C_n	Compound	Method	Yield (%)	Chapter[ref.]	B.p./mm., n_D^t, (M.p.)
C_3	Cyanoacetic acid	378	89	20[108]	(65)
C_7	6-Cyanocaproic acid	378	56	20[109]	160/3
C_8	m-Cyanobenzoic acid	380	61	20[232]	(217)
	p-Cyanobenzoic acid	380	45	20[231]	(210)
C_9	o-Carboxyphenylacetonitrile	393	83	20[349]	(115)
	p-Cyanophenylacetic acid	380	50	20[230]	(152)
C_{10}	ω-Cyanopelargonic acid	384	34	20[139]	(49)

For explanations and symbols see pp. xi–xii.

TABLE 75. CYANO ESTERS 623

TABLE 75. CYANO ESTERS

C_n	Compound	Method	Yield (%)	Chapter[ref]	B.p./mm., n_D^t, (M.p.)
C_5	Ethyl cyanoacetate	285	80	14[77]	97/16
		298	40	14[335]	107/22
		378	50	20[112]	107/27*, 1.4179*
	Methyl β-cyanopropionate	293	75	14[178]	96/8
C_6	Ethyl α-cyanopropionate	378	20	20[111]	77/9.5, 1.4104[29]
	Ethyl β-cyanopropionate	378	82	20[110]	106/11, 1.4233
C_7	Ethyl ethylcyanoacetate	298	40	14[333]	110/24, 1.418
		394	85†	20[292]	85/7, 1.4163[25]
	Ethyl γ-cyanobutyrate	378	78	20[110]	122/18
	Ethyl cyclopropane-1-cyano-1-carboxylate	386	76	20[199]	212–216
C_8	Ethyl n-propylcyanoacetate	386	45	20[194]	108–110/14–15
		394	94†	20[292]	96/8, 1.4200[25]
	Ethyl isopropylcyanoacetate	298	47	14[333]	112/22, 1.422
		386	65	20[197]	116/25
		394	93†	20[292]	91/8, 1.4203[25]
C_9	Ethyl n-butylcyanoacetate	298	54	14[333]	129/23, 1.426
		394	96†	20[293]	109/9, 1.4242[25]
	Ethyl isobutylcyanoacetate	394	98†	20[292]	99/7, 1.4232[25]
		386	34	20[194]	111–115/12
	Ethyl s-butylcyanoacetate	394	81†	20[292]	100/7, 1.4267[25]
	Ethyl t-butylcyanoacetate	302	75	14[420]	88/5, 1.4278
	Ethyl α,β-dicyano-β-methylbutyrate	389	70	20[308]	136–141/9
	Ethyl (2-cyanoethyl)-acetoacetate	388	63	20[381]	121/2, 1.4446[25]
	Methyl o-cyanobenzoate	380	65	20[233]	154/15, (51)
C_{10}	Ethyl isoamylcyanoacetate	386	76	20[194]	128–135/18
		394	95†	20[292]	114/7, 1.4279[25]
	Ethyl 1-methylbutylcyanoacetate	394	63†	20[292]	112/8, 1.4300[25]
	Ethyl cyclopentylcyanoacetate	394	77	20[294]	129/13, 1.4536[19]
	Ethyl α,β-dicyanocaproate	389	53	20[308]	160/12
	Ethyl α,β-dicyano-β-methylvalerate	389	49	20[308]	146/10
	Diethyl α-cyano-β-methylsuccinate	386	70	20[205]	160–165/17
	Ethyl α-carboethoxy-γ-cyanobutyrate	388	45	20[260]	175–180/25
C_{11}	Ethyl diisopropylcyanoacetate	386	40	20[195]	238–241
	Methyl ω-cyanopelargonate	384	71	20[154]	121–124/1, 170/14
	Ethyl 1,3-dimethylbutylcyanoacetate	394	63†	20[292]	119/8, 1.4316[25]
	Ethyl n-propylisopropylcyanoacetate	386	76	20[197]	116–119/13

For explanations and symbols see pp. xi–xii.

TABLE 75 *(continued)*

C_n	Compound	Method	Yield (%)	Chapter[ref.]	B.p./mm., n_D^t, (M.p.)
C_{11}	γ-Carboethoxy-γ-cyanopimelo-nitrile	388	97	20[255]	(37)
	Ethyl α,β-dicyano-δ-methyl-caproate	389	67	20[308]	151-155/10
	Ethyl β,β-diethyl-α,β-dicyano-propionate	389	40	20[395]	165/15
	Diethyl α-cyano-β-ethylsuccinate	386	67	20[203]	164/21
	Diethyl α-cyano-α,β-dimethyl-succinate	386	75	20[204]	159-162/15-20
	Ethyl α-carboethoxy-β-cyanovalerate	389	62	20[309]	130-140/2.5
	Methyl α,α-di-(2-cyanoethyl)-acetoacetate	388	50	20[259]	(154)
	Ethyl cyclohexylcyanoacetate	394	98 †	20[292]	139/8, 1.4574[25]
	Ethyl phenylcyanoacetate	298	79	14[331]	135/5, 1.5015[25]
	o-Carbethoxyphenylacetonitrile	378	76†	20[364]	170/16, 1.5172
C_{12}	Ethyl n-heptylcyanoacetate	394	71†	20[292]	113/1, 1.4337[25]
	Ethyl benzylcyanoacetate	394	63†	20[292]	118-122/0.4, 1.5033[25]
	Ethyl β-cyano-β-phenyl-propionate	389	82	20[387]	164/8
C_{13}	Ethyl ethylphenylcyanoacetate	386	76	20[198]	147/11
	Diethyl α-cyano-α,β-diethyl-succinate	386	79	20[203]	167-170/18
	Dimethyl β-cyanobenzylmalonate	389	100	20[310]	(48.5)
	γ,γ-Dicarboethoxypimelonitrile	388	83	20[255]	(62)
C_{14}	α-Phenyl-α-carbethoxyglutaro-nitrile	388	83	20[382]	167/1, 1.5103[25]

For explanations and symbols see pp. xi-xii.

REFERENCES FOR CHAPTER 20

[1] Adams and Marvel, *J. Am. Chem. Soc.*, **42**, 310 (1920); ref. 4.
[2] Hass and Marshall, *Ind. Eng. Chem.*, **23**, 352 (1931); ref. 4.
[3] Noyes, *J. Am. Chem. Soc.*, **23**, 393 (1901); ref. 4.
[4] Jeffery and Vogel, *J. Chem. Soc.*, 674 (1948).
[5] Fierz and Kuster, *Helv. Chim. Acta*, **22**, 82 (1939).
[6] Suida and Drahowzal, *Ber.*, **75**, 991 (1942); Ruhoff, *Org. Syntheses*, Coll. Vol. II, 292 (1943).
[7] Yohe and Adams, *J. Am. Chem. Soc.*, **50**, 1503 (1928).
[8] Rogers and Roberts, *J. Am. Chem. Soc.*, **68**, 843 (1946).
[9] Adams and Thal, *Org. Syntheses*, Coll. Vol. I, 107 (1941).
[10] Wawzonek and Hsu, *J. Am. Chem. Soc.*, **68**, 2741 (1946).
[11] Newman, *J. Am. Chem. Soc.*, **62**, 2295 (1940).
[12] Titley, *J. Chem. Soc.*, 514 (1926).
[13] Baker, Dippy, and Page, *J. Chem. Soc.*, 1777 (1937).
[14] Akin, Stamatoff, and Bogert, *J. Am. Chem. Soc.*, **59**, 1271 (1937); Bardhan and Sengupta, *J. Chem. Soc.*, 2525 (1932).
[15] v. Braun and Sobecki, *Ber.*, **44**, 1472 (1911).
[16] Fuson, Corse, and McKeever, *J. Am. Chem. Soc.*, **62**, 3250 (1940).
[17] Hewett and Martin, *J. Chem. Soc.*, 1396 (1940).
[18] Fuson and Sperati, *J. Am. Chem. Soc.*, **63**, 2643 (1941).
[19] Lévy, *Ann. chim.*, (11) 9, 73 (1938).
[20] Cloke and Leary, *J. Am. Chem. Soc.*, **67**, 1249 (1945); Briggs and Wilson, *J. Chem. Soc.*, 500 (1941); Gaylord and Becker, *J. Org. Chem.*, **15**, 313 (1950).
[21] Koelsch and Whitney, *J. Org. Chem.*, **6**, 795 (1941).
[22] Fuson et al., *J. Am. Chem. Soc.*, **68**, 533 (1946).
[23] Bradsher, *J. Am. Chem. Soc.*, **62**, 486 (1940).
[24] Marvel, Frank, and Prill, *J. Am. Chem. Soc.*, **65**, 1647 (1943); cf. ref. 25.
[25] Newman, *Org. Syntheses*, **21**, 89 (1941).
[26] Callen, Dornfeld, and Coleman, *Org. Syntheses*, **28**, 34 (1948).
[27] Bachmann and Kloetzel, *J. Org. Chem.*, **3**, 55 (1938).
[28] Bachmann and Cronyn, *J. Org. Chem.*, **8**, 456 (1943).
[29] Barger, Robinson, and Smith, *J. Chem. Soc.*, 720 (1937).
[30] Johnson et al., *J. Am. Chem. Soc.*, **52**, 1284 (1930); Reichstein, *Ber.*, **63**, 749 (1930).
[31] Blicke and Leonard, *J. Am. Chem. Soc.*, **68**, 1934 (1946).
[32] Blicke and Sheets, *J. Am. Chem. Soc.*, **71**, 2856 (1949); Avakian et al., *ibid.*, **70**, 3075 (1948).
[33] Blicke and Sheets, *J. Am. Chem. Soc.*, **70**, 3768 (1948).
[34] McElvain and Goese, *J. Am. Chem. Soc.*, **63**, 2283 (1941).
[35] Craig, *J. Am. Chem. Soc.*, **56**, 231 (1934).
[36] Mowry, *Chem. Revs.*, **42**, 189 (1948).
[37] Gilman and Spatz, *J. Am. Chem. Soc.*, **63**, 1553 (1941).
[38] Jansen and Wibaut, *Rec. trav. chim.*, **56**, 709 (1937).
[39] Tyson, *J. Am. Chem. Soc.*, **61**, 183 (1939).
[40] Jones et al., *J. Am. Chem. Soc.*, **70**, 2846 (1948).
[41] Quelet, *Bull. soc. chim. France*, (5) 7, 205 (1940).
[42] Braun, U. S. Dept. of Commerce, Office Technical Services, P.B. Report 626 (1946).
[43] Levene and Taylor, *J. Biol. Chem.*, **59**, 905 (1924).

[44]Fauconnier, *Bull. soc. chim. France,* (2) **50**, 214 (1888).
[45]Marvel and McColm, *Org. Syntheses,* Coll. Vol. I, 536 (1941); ref. 4.
[46]Montmollin and Martenet, *Helv. Chim. Acta,* **12**, 604 (1929).
[47]Müller and Bleier, *Monatsh.,* **56**, 396 (1930).
[48]Braun and Danziger, *Ber.,* **45**, 1970 (1912).
[49]Chuit, *Helv. Chim. Acta,* **9**, 264 (1926); Ziegler and Hechelhammer, *Ann.,* **528**, 114 (1937).
[50]Ruggli, Bussemaker, and Müller, *Helv. Chim. Acta,* **18**, 613 (1935).
[51]Gough and Thorpe, *J. Chem. Soc.,* 1155 (1919).
[52]Reichstein and Zschokke, *Helv. Chim. Acta,* **15**, 1124 (1932).
[53]Fuson and Rachlin, *J. Am. Chem. Soc.,* **64**, 1571 (1942).
[54]Wittig and Petri, *Ann.,* **513**, 39 (1934).
[55]Hewett, *J. Chem. Soc.,* 293 (1940).
[56]Rietz, *Org. Syntheses,* **24**, 96 (1944); Supniewski and Salzberg, *ibid.,* Coll. Vol. I, 46 (1941); cf. ref. 4.
[57] Tamele et al., *Ind. Eng. Chem.,* **33**, 115 (1941); v. Auwers, *Ber.,* **56**, 1172 (1923).
[58]Cheldelin and Schink, *J. Am. Chem. Soc.,* **69**, 2625 (1947); Fuson and Southwick, *ibid.,* **66**, 679 (1944).
[59]Lane, Fentress, and Sherwood, *J. Am. Chem. Soc.,* **66**, 545 (1944).
[60]Delaby and Lecomte, *Bull. soc. chim. France,* (5) **4**, 749 (1937); cf. ref. 59.
[61]Treff and Werner, *Ber.,* **68**, 642 (1935); Hunsdiecker, *ibid.,* **75**, 465 (1942).
[62]Reichstein and Trivelli, *Helv. Chim. Acta,* **15**, 254 (1932).
[63]Buu-Hoi and Cagniant, *Bull. soc. chim. France.,* (5) **12**, 978 (1945).
[64]Coffman, *J. Am. Chem. Soc.,* **57**, 1981 (1935).
[65]Hochwalt, U.S. Pat. 2,399,349 (1946); *C. A.,* **40**, 4744 (1946).
[66]Koelsch, *J. Am. Chem. Soc.,* **58**, 1328 (1936).
[67]Natelson and Gottfried, *J. Am. Chem. Soc.,* **64**, 2962 (1942).
[68]Newman and Wotiz, *J. Am. Chem. Soc.,* **71**, 1292 (1949).
[69]McCusker and Vogt, *J. Am. Chem. Soc.,* **59**, 1307 (1937).
[70]Allen, *Org. Syntheses,* Coll. Vol. I, 156 (1941).
[71]Cloke et al., *J. Am. Chem. Soc.,* **67**, 1587 (1945).
[72]Horning, Horning, and Platt, *J. Am. Chem. Soc.,* **69**, 2929 (1947); Starr and Dixon, *ibid.,* **56**, 1595 (1934); Leonard and Barthel, *ibid.,* **71**, 3098 (1949).
[73]Cloke and Ayers, *J. Am. Chem. Soc.,* **56**, 2144 (1934); Leonard and Wildman, *ibid.,* **71**, 3100 (1949).
[74]Kendall and McKenzie, *Org. Syntheses,* Coll. Vol. I, 256 (1941); Hands and Walker, *J. Soc. Chem. Ind. (London),* **67**, 458 (1948).
[75]Festraete, *Bull. soc. chim. Belg.,* **41**, 327 (1932).
[76]Koelsch, *J. Am. Chem. Soc.,* **65**, 2460 (1943).
[77]Dewael, *Bull. soc. chim. Belg.,* **33**, 504 (1924).
[78]Bissinger et al., *J. Am. Chem. Soc.,* **69**, 2960 (1947).
[79]Marvel and Overberger, *J. Am. Chem. Soc.,* **67**, 2250 (1945).
[80]Henze and Rigler, *J. Am. Chem. Soc.,* **56**, 1350 (1934).
[81]Rigler and Henze, *J. Am. Chem. Soc.,* **58**, 474 (1936).
[82]Henze et al., *J. Am. Chem. Soc.,* **64**, 1222 (1942).
[83]Barnes and Budde, *J. Am. Chem. Soc.,* **68**, 2339 (1946); cf. ref. 82.
[84]Lingo and Henze, *J. Am. Chem. Soc.,* **61**, 1574 (1939).
[85]Henze and Thompson, *J. Am. Chem. Soc.,* **65**, 1422 (1943).
[86]Harrison and Diehl, *Org. Syntheses,* **23**, 33 (1943).

[87]Wallace and Henze, *J. Am. Chem. Soc.*, **64**, 2882 (1942); Niemann, Benson, and Mead, *J. Org. Chem.*, **8**, 401 (1943).

[88]Henze, Benz, and Sutherland, *J. Am. Chem. Soc.*, **71**, 2122 (1949).

[89]Spurlock and Henze, *J. Org. Chem.*, **4**, 234 (1939).

[90]Baker, *J. Chem. Soc.*, 520 (1942); Price, Coyner, and DeTar, *J. Am. Chem. Soc.*, **63**, 2796 (1941).

[91]Houben and Pfankuch, *Ber.*, **59**, 2400 (1926).

[92]Marvel and Tanenbaum, *J. Am. Chem. Soc.*, **44**, 2645 (1922).

[93]Bennett and Hock, *J. Chem. Soc.*, 474 (1927).

[94]Woodward, *J. Am. Chem. Soc.*, **62**, 1478 (1940); Rapson and Robinson, *J. Chem. Soc.*, 1537 (1935).

[95]Niederl and Roth, *J. Am. Chem. Soc.*, **60**, 2140 (1938).

[96]Shriner and Hull, *J. Org. Chem.*, **10**, 230 (1945); cf. ref. 10.

[97]Kindler and Gehlhaar, *Arch. Pharm.*, **274**, 386 (1936).

[98]Long, *J. Am. Chem. Soc.*, **69**, 990 (1947).

[99]Rabcewicz-Zubkowski and Kaflinska, *Roczniki Chem.*, **10**, 541 (1930); *C. A.*, **25**, 505 (1931).

[100]Gabriel and Eschenbach, *Ber.*, **30**, 1126 (1897).

[101]Widman and Wahlberg, *Ber.*, **44**, 2065 (1911).

[102]Hidayetulla, Shah, and Wheeler, *J. Chem. Soc.*, 111 (1941).

[103]Kohler and Brown, *J. Am. Chem. Soc.*, **55**, 4299 (1933).

[104]Delbaere, *Bull. soc. chim. Belg.*, **51**, 1 (1942); Justoni, *Gazz. chim. ital.*, **69**, 378 (1939); *C. A.*, **33**, 8574 (1939).

[105]Meyer, *Helv. Chim. Acta.*, **16**, 1291 (1933).

[106]Mowry, Renoll, and Huber, *J. Am. Chem. Soc.*, **68**, 1108 (1946).

[107]Helberger and von Rebay, *Ann.*, **531**, 279 (1937).

[108]Ruggli and Businger, *Helv. Chim. Acta*, **25**, 35 (1942); Lapworth and Baker, *Org. Syntheses*, Coll. Vol. I, 181 (1941).

[109]Schultz, *J. Am. Chem. Soc.*, **69**, 1056 (1947).

[110]Ives and Sames, *J. Chem. Soc.*, 513 (1943).

[111]Pollack, *J. Am. Chem. Soc.*, **65**, 1335 (1943); cf. ref. 136.

[112]Noyes, *J. Am. Chem. Soc.*, **26**, 1545 (1904); Goldschmidt and Gräfinger, *Ber.*, **68**, 282 (1935).

[113]Humphlett, Weiss, and Hauser, *J. Am. Chem. Soc.*, **70**, 4020 (1948).

[114]Kent and McElvain, *Org. Syntheses*, **25**, 61 (1945).

[115]McElvain, Clarke, and Jones, *J. Am. Chem. Soc.*, **64**, 1968 (1942).

[116]Homeyer, Whitmore, and Wallingford, *J. Am. Chem. Soc.*, **55**, 4212 (1933).

[117]Ralston, Harwood, and Pool, *J. Am. Chem. Soc.*, **59**, 986 (1937).

[118]Whitmore, Sutherland, and Cosby, *J. Am. Chem. Soc.*, **64**, 1360 (1942).

[119]Sherk, Augur, and Soffer, *J. Am. Chem. Soc.*, **67**, 2239 (1945).

[120]Norris and Klemka, *J. Am. Chem. Soc.*, **62**, 1432 (1940).

[121]Tilford, Van Campen, and Shelton, *J. Am. Chem. Soc.*, **69**, 2902 (1947).

[122]Michaelis and Siebert, *Ann.*, **274**, 312 (1893).

[123]Reid and Hunter, *J. Am. Chem. Soc.*, **70**, 3515 (1948); cf. ref. 126.

[124]McElvain and Stevens, *J. Am. Chem. Soc.*, **69**, 2663 (1947).

[125]Hellerman and Garner, *J. Am. Chem. Soc.*, **68**, 819 (1946).

[126]Freeman, Ringk, and Spoerri, *J. Am. Chem. Soc.*, **69**, 858 (1947).

[127]Kuhn and Wagner-Jauregg, *Ber.*, **67**, 1770 (1934).

[128]Blicke, *J. Am. Chem. Soc.*, **49**, 2848 (1927); ref. 120.

[129]Newman, *J. Org. Chem.*, **9**, 522 (1944).

[130]Bachmann and Boatner, *J. Am. Chem. Soc.*, **58**, 2097 (1936).
[131]Waldmann and Oblath, *Ber.*, **71**, 366 (1938).
[132]Oxley et al., *J. Chem. Soc.*, 763 (1946).
[133]LaForge, *J. Am. Chem. Soc.*, **50**, 2480 (1928); ref. 134.
[134]Camps, *Arch. Pharm.*, **240**, 368 (1902).
[135]Corson, Scott, and Vose, *Org. Syntheses*, Coll. Vol. II, 379 (1943); Surrey, *ibid.*, **25**, 63 (1945).
[136]Strack and Schwaneberg, *Ber.*, **67**, 41 (1934).
[137]Hessler, *Am. Chem. J.*, **32**, 123 (1904).
[138]Blomquist and Winslow, *J. Org. Chem.*, **10**, 149 (1945).
[139]Biggs and Bishop, *Org. Syntheses*, **25**, 95 (1945).
[140]Malachowski, Wasoska, and Jozkiewicz, *Ber.*, **71**, 759 (1938).
[141]Linstead and Lowe, *J. Chem. Soc.*, 1022 (1934).
[142]Moureu and Lazennec, *Bull. soc. chim. France*, (3) **35**, 524 (1903); cf. ref. 68.
[143]Ross and Burnett, *J. Am. Chem. Soc.*, **71**, 3562 (1949).
[144]Letch and Linstead, *J. Chem. Soc.*, 443 (1932).
[145]Kandiah and Linstead, *J. Chem. Soc.*, 2139 (1929).
[146]Reisner and Horning, *Org. Syntheses*, **30**, 22 (1950).
[147]Stevens, *J. Am. Chem. Soc.*, **70**, 165 (1948).
[148]Breslow and Hauser, *J. Am. Chem. Soc.*, **67**, 686 (1945).
[149]Gilman and Jones, *J. Am. Chem. Soc.*, **65**, 1458 (1943).
[150]Dunlop and Tucker, *J. Chem. Soc.*, 1953 (1939).
[151]Blicke and Lilienfeld, *J. Am. Chem. Soc.*, **65**, 2283 (1943); Foreman and McElvain, *ibid.*, **62**, 1436 (1940).
[152]McElvain and Walters, *J. Am. Chem. Soc.*, **64**, 1965 (1942).
[153]Whitney and Henze, *J. Am. Chem. Soc.*, **60**, 1148 (1938); Powell and Adams, *ibid.*, **42**, 655 (1920).
[154]Bishop, *Org. Syntheses*, **25**, 69 (1945).
[155]Bennett and Wain, *J. Chem. Soc.*, 1108 (1936).
[156]Miller, *Org. Syntheses*, **29**, 75 (1949).
[157]Schiessler, Rytina, and Whitmore, *J. Am. Chem. Soc.*, **70**, 529 (1948), footnote 12.
[158]Mitchell and Reid, *J. Am. Chem. Soc.*, **53**, 321 (1931).
[159]Bachmann, *J. Am. Chem. Soc.*, **57**, 558 (1935).
[160]Paul and Cottin, *Bull. soc. chim. France*, (5) **4**, 933 (1937).
[161]Walden, *Ber.*, **40**, 3214 (1907); cf. ref. 4.
[162]Rodionow, *Bull. soc. chim. France*, **39**, 324 (1926).
[163]Sekera and Marvel, *J. Am. Chem. Soc.*, **55**, 345 (1933).
[164]Zief, Fletcher, and Kirshen, *J. Am. Chem. Soc.*, **68**, 2743 (1946).
[165]Whitmore and Fox, *J. Am. Chem. Soc.*, **51**, 3363 (1929); West, *ibid.*, **42**, 1661 (1920).
[166]Colver and Noyes, *J. Am. Chem. Soc.*, **43**, 898 (1921).
[167]Wahl, Goedkoop, and Heberlein, *Bull. soc. chim. France*, (5) **6**, 533 (1939).
[168]Bradbrook and Linstead, *J. Chem. Soc.*, 1739 (1936).
[169]King and Wright, *J. Chem. Soc.*, 253 (1939).
[170]Fieser, *J. Am. Chem. Soc.*, **54**, 4110 (1932).
[171]McElvain and Goese, *J. Am. Chem. Soc.*, **65**, 2233 (1943).
[172]Webb and Corwin, *J. Am. Chem. Soc.*, **66**, 1456 (1944).
[173]Ziegler and Ohlinger, *Ann.*, **495**, 84 (1932).
[174]Bergstrom and Agostinho, *J. Am. Chem. Soc.*, **67**, 2152 (1945); Baldinger and Nieuwland, *ibid.*, **55**, 2851 (1933).

[175]Schuerch and Huntress, *J. Am. Chem. Soc.*, **70**, 2824 (1948).

[176]Bergstrom and Fernelius, *Chem. Revs.*, **12**, 135 (1933); **20**, 451 (1937).

[177]Sperber, Papa, and Schwenk, *J. Am. Chem. Soc.*, **70**, 3091 (1948).

[178]Birch and Robinson, *J. Chem. Soc.*, 493 (1942).

[179]Crawford, *J. Am. Chem. Soc.*, **56**, 140 (1934); ref. 124.

[180]Murray and Cloke, *J. Am. Chem. Soc.*, **68**, 126 (1946).

[181]Rising and Zee, *J. Am. Chem. Soc.*, **49**, 541 (1927); refs. 180 and 182.

[182]Bowden, *J. Am. Chem. Soc.*, **60**, 131 (1938).

[183]Newman, *J. Am. Chem. Soc.*, **62**, 870 (1940).

[184]Cope, Foster, and Towle, *J. Am. Chem. Soc.*, **71**, 3932 (1949).

[185]Larsen et al., *J. Am. Chem. Soc.*, **71**, 532 (1949).

[186]Schlatter, *Org. Syntheses*, **23**, 20 (1943); Cloke et al., *J. Am. Chem. Soc.*, **53**, 2791 (1931).

[187]Knowles and Cloke, *J. Am. Chem. Soc.*, **54**, 2028 (1932); cf. ref. 71.

[188]Hancock and Coke, *Org. Syntheses*, **25**, 25 (1945); Weston, *J. Am. Chem. Soc.*, **68**, 2345 (1946).

[189]Newman and Closson, *J. Am. Chem. Soc.*, **66**, 1553 (1944).

[190]Billman, Smith, and Rendall, *J. Am. Chem. Soc.*, **69**, 2058 (1947).

[191]Ziegler, U.S. Pat. 1,958,653; *C. A.*, **28**, 4435 (1934).

[192]Whyte and Cope, *J. Am. Chem. Soc.*, **65**, 1999 (1943).

[193]Cope, Hoyle, and Heyl, *J. Am. Chem. Soc.*, **63**, 1843 (1941).

[194]Darapsky, *J. prakt. Chem.*, **146**, 250 (1936).

[195]Marshall, *J. Chem. Soc.*, 2754 (1930).

[196]Hessler, *J. Am. Chem. Soc.*, **35**, 990 (1913).

[197]Fischer and Flatau, *Ber.*, **42**, 2981 (1909).

[198]Chamberlain et al., *J. Am. Chem. Soc.*, **57**, 352 (1935).

[199]Jones and Scott, *J. Am. Chem. Soc.*, **44**, 413 (1922).

[200]Fuson and Kao, *J. Am. Chem. Soc.*, **51**, 1536 (1929).

[201]Fuson, Kreimeier, and Nimmo, *J. Am. Chem. Soc.*, **52**, 4074 (1930).

[202]Fuson and Cole, *J. Am. Chem. Soc.*, **60**, 1237 (1938).

[203]Wren and Haller, *J. Chem. Soc.*, 230 (1937).

[204]Bone and Sprankling, *J. Chem. Soc.*, **75**, 839 (1899).

[205]Linstead, Noble, and Wright, *J. Chem. Soc.*, 915 (1937); cf. ref. 204.

[206]Bone and Sprankling, *J. Chem. Soc.*, 654, 1298 (1900).

[207]Hessler and Lamb, *J. Am. Chem. Soc.*, **43**, 205 (1921).

[208]Cope and Hancock, *J. Am. Chem. Soc.*, **60**, 2903 (1938).

[209]Baker et al., *J. Org. Chem.*, **12**, 143 (1947); cf. ref. 144.

[210]Lapworth and Baker, *Org. Syntheses*, Coll. Vol. I, 181 (1941).

[211]Lapworth and McRae, *J. Chem. Soc.*, **121**, 1699 (1922).

[212]Ghosez, *Bull. soc. chim. Belg.*, **41**, 477 (1932); Kistiakowsky and Smith, *J. Am. Chem. Soc.*, **58**, 2428 (1936).

[213]Wittig and Kethur, *Ber.*, **69**, 2078 (1936).

[214]Adams and Rogers, *J. Am. Chem. Soc.*, **63**, 228 (1941).

[215]Huber et al., *J. Am. Chem. Soc.*, **67**, 1618 (1945).

[216]Work, *J. Chem. Soc.*, 197 (1946).

[217]Osman and Cope, *J. Am. Chem. Soc.*, **66**, 881 (1944).

[218]Clarke and Read, *Org. Syntheses*, Coll. Vol. I, 514 (1941).

[219]Tomisek et al., *J. Am. Chem. Soc.*, **68**, 1587 (1946).

[220]Barber, *J. Chem. Soc.*, 79 (1943).

[221]Clarke and Read, *J. Am. Chem. Soc.*, **46**, 1001 (1924).

[222]Fieser and Cason, *J. Am. Chem. Soc.*, **61**, 1744 (1939).

[223] Work, *J. Chem. Soc.*, 1315 (1940); DeMilt and Sartor, *J. Am. Chem. Soc.*, **62**, 1954 (1940); ref. 228.

[224] Rupe and Brentano, *Helv. Chim. Acta*, **19**, 581 (1936); McRae, *J. Am. Chem. Soc.*, **52**, 4550 (1930).

[225] Goldstein and Chastellain, *Helv. Chim. Acta*, **17**, 1481 (1934).

[226] Fieser and Hershberg, *J. Am. Chem. Soc.*, **62**, 1644 (1940).

[227] Sah and Wang, *Rec. trav. chim.*, **59**, 364 (1940).

[228] Ashley et al., *J. Chem. Soc.*, 103 (1942).

[229] Wertheim, *J. Am. Chem. Soc.*, **57**, 545 (1935).

[230] Jaeger and Robinson, *J. Chem. Soc.*, 744 (1941).

[231] Valby and Lucas, *J. Am. Chem. Soc.*, **51**, 2718 (1929).

[232] Curtius and Hess, *J. prakt. Chem.*, **125**, 40 (1930).

[233] Boyd and Ladhams, *J. Chem. Soc.*, 2089 (1928).

[234] Storrie, *J. Chem. Soc.*, 1746 (1937).

[235] Fieser and Hartwell, *J. Am. Chem. Soc.*, **60**, 2555 (1938).

[236] Plucker and Amstutz, *J. Am. Chem. Soc.*, **62**, 1512 (1940).

[237] Clarke and Nagy, *Org. Syntheses*, **20**, 74 (1940).

[238] Curd and Raison, *J. Chem. Soc.*, 160 (1947).

[239] Scott and Johnson, *J. Am. Chem. Soc.*, **54**, 2549 (1932).

[240] Buck and Ide, *Org. Syntheses*, Coll. Vol. II, 622 (1943).

[241] Julian and Sturgis, *J. Am. Chem. Soc.*, **57**, 1126 (1935).

[242] Gränacher et al., *Helv. Chim. Acta*, **5**, 610 (1922); **6**, 458 (1923).

[243] Campbell and McKail, *J. Chem. Soc.*, 1251 (1948).

[244] Buck, Baltzly, and Ide, *J. Am. Chem. Soc.*, **60**, 1789 (1938).

[245] Haworth and Robinson, *J. Chem. Soc.*, 120 (1935).

[246] Bruson in *Organic Reactions*, Vol. 5, John Wiley & Sons, New York, 1949, p. 79.

[247] Buc, *Org. Syntheses*, 27, 3 (1947).

[248] Cook and Reed, *J. Chem. Soc.*, 399 (1945); cf. ref. 249.

[249] Tarbell et al., *J. Am. Chem. Soc.*, **68**, 1217 (1946).

[250] Whitmore et al., *J. Am. Chem. Soc.*, **66**, 725 (1944).

[251] Pearson, Jones, and Cope, *J. Am. Chem. Soc.*, **68**, 1225 (1946).

[252] King and McMillan, *J. Am. Chem. Soc.*, **68**, 1468 (1946).

[253] Corse, Bryant, and Shonle, *J. Am. Chem. Soc.*, **68**, 1911 (1946).

[254] Utermohlen, *J. Am. Chem. Soc.*, **67**, 1505 (1945); MacGregor and Pugh, *J. Chem. Soc.*, 535 (1945).

[255] Bruson and Riener, *J. Am. Chem. Soc.*, **65**, 23 (1943).

[256] Bachman and Levine, *J. Am. Chem. Soc.*, **70**, 599 (1948).

[257] Bachman and Levine, *J. Am. Chem. Soc.*, **69**, 2341 (1947).

[258] Bruson and Riener, *J. Am. Chem. Soc.*, **66**, 56 (1944).

[259] Bruson and Riener, *J. Am. Chem. Soc.*, **64**, 2850 (1942); also ref. 246.

[260] Koelsch, *J. Am. Chem. Soc.*, **65**, 2458 (1943).

[261] Floyd, *J. Am. Chem. Soc.*, **71**, 1746 (1949).

[262] Koelsch, *J. Am. Chem. Soc.*, **65**, 437 (1943).

[263] Cox and Stormont, *Org. Syntheses*, Coll. Vol. II, 7 (1941); cf. ref. 264.

[264] Wagner and Baizer, *Org. Syntheses*, **20**, 43 (1940), note 1.

[265] Ultee, *Rec. trav. chim.*, **28**, 1, 248 (1909).

[266] Jacobson, *J. Am. Chem. Soc.*, **68**, 2628 (1946); cf. ref. 265.

[267] Colonge and Joly, *Ann. chim.*, (11) **18**, 303 (1943); cf. ref. 265.

[268] Cook and Linstead, *J. Chem. Soc.*, 958 (1934).

[269]van Coillie, *Bull. soc. chim. Belg.*, **42**, 419 (1933); Frank et al., *J. Am. Chem. Soc.*, **71**, 3889 (1949).

[270]Boekelheide and Schilling, *J. Am. Chem. Soc.*, **72**, 712 (1950).

[271]Räth, *Ann.*, **486**, 102 (1931).

[272]Mowry and Morner, *J. Am. Chem. Soc.*, **69**, 1831 (1947).

[273]Williams, *Ber.*, **60**, 2512 (1927).

[274]Darzens and Mentzer, *Compt. rend.*, **213**, 268 (1941).

[275]Hurd and Rector, *J. Org. Chem.*, **10**, 441 (1945).

[276]Mowry, *J. Am. Chem. Soc.*, **66**, 371 (1944).

[277]Gaudry, *Org. Syntheses*, **27**, 41 (1947).

[278]Mowry and Rossow, *J. Am. Chem. Soc.*, **67**, 926 (1945).

[279]Glattfeld and Hoen, *J. Am. Chem. Soc.*, **57**, 1405 (1935).

[280]Lapworth and Manske, *J. Chem. Soc.*, 2533 (1928); 1976 (1930).

[281]Hudson, *Advances in Carbohydrate Chemistry*, Academic Press, New York, 1945, Vol. I, pp. 1-36.

[282]Corson et al., *Org. Syntheses*, Coll. Vol. I, 336 (1941).

[283]Ruskin and Pfalz, *J. Am. Chem. Soc.*, **60**, 1471 (1938); cf. ref. 282.

[284]Ladenburg, Folkers, and Major, *J. Am. Chem. Soc.*, **58**, 1292 (1936).

[285]Jenkins, Bigelow, and Buck, *J. Am. Chem. Soc.*, **52**, 5198 (1930).

[286]Ruggli and Hegedüs, *Helv. Chim. Acta*, **25**, 1292 (1942).

[287]Stoughton, *J. Am. Chem. Soc.*, **63**, 2376 (1941).

[288]Lucas and Prater, *J. Am. Chem. Soc.*, **59**, 1682 (1937).

[289]Heyl and Cope, *J. Am. Chem. Soc.*, **65**, 669 (1943).

[290]Vogel et al., *J. Chem. Soc.*, 1528 (1940); 768 (1930); 2010 (1928).

[291]Cope et al., *J. Am. Chem. Soc.*, **63**, 3452 (1941).

[292]Alexander and Cope, *J. Am. Chem. Soc.*, **66**, 886 (1944); cf. ref. 293.

[293]Alexander and Cope, *Org. Syntheses*, **26**, 31 (1946); cf. ref. 292.

[294]Vogel, *J. Chem. Soc.*, 2010 (1928).

[295]Tschelinzeff and Schmidt, *Ber.*, **62**, 2210 (1929).

[296]Hurd, Edwards, and Roach, *J. Am. Chem. Soc.*, **66**, 2013 (1944).

[297]Oakwood and Weisgerber, *Org. Syntheses*, **24**, 14 (1944).

[298]Claisen, *Ber.*, **31**, 1023 (1898); Mauthner, *ibid.*, **42**, 188 (1909).

[299]Fisher and Brauns, *Ber.*, **46**, 892 (1913).

[300]David, Dupont, and Paquot, *Bull. soc. chim. France*, (5) **11**, 563 (1944).

[301]Mowry, *J. Am. Chem. Soc.*, **68**, 2108 (1946).

[302]Corson and Stoughton, *J. Am. Chem. Soc.*, **50**, 2825 (1928).

[303]Allen and Kimball, *Org. Syntheses*, Coll. Vol. II, 498 (1943).

[304]Lapworth, *J. Chem. Soc.*, **85**, 1214 (1904).

[305]Lapworth and Baker, *Org. Syntheses*, Coll. Vol. I, 451 (1941).

[306]Higginbotham and Lapworth, *J. Chem. Soc.*, **121**, 49 (1922).

[307]Buckley, Heath, and Rose, *J. Chem. Soc.*, 1500 (1947).

[308]Smith and Horwitz, *J. Am. Chem. Soc.*, **71**, 3418 (1949).

[309]Koelsch and Stratton, *J. Am. Chem. Soc.*, **66**, 1883 (1944).

[310]Michael and Weiner, *J. Am. Chem. Soc.*, **59**, 744 (1937).

[311]Steiger, *Org. Syntheses*, **22**, 13, 23 (1942); **24**, 9 (1944).

[312]Adams and Langley, *Org. Syntheses*, Coll. Vol. I, 355 (1941).

[313]Turner, *J. Am. Chem. Soc.*, **68**, 1607 (1946).

[314]Read, *J. Am. Chem. Soc.*, **44**, 1746 (1922).

[315]Herbst and Johnson, *J. Am. Chem. Soc.*, **54**, 2463 (1932).

[316]Jawelow, *Ber.*, **39**, 1195 (1906).

[317]Gulewitsch and Wasmus, *Ber.*, **39**, 1181 (1906).
[318]Cocker and Lapworth, *J. Chem. Soc.*, 1391 (1931).
[319]Luten, *J. Org. Chem.*, **3**, 588 (1938–1939).
[320]Walther and Hübner, *J. prakt. Chem.*, **93**, 119 (1916).
[321]Immendörfer, *Ber.*, **48**, 605 (1915); cf. ref. 388.
[322]Allen and VanAllen, *Org. Syntheses*, **27**, 20 (1947).
[323]Stewart and Cook, *J. Am. Chem. Soc.*, **50**, 1973 (1928); cf. ref. 324.
[324]Knoevenagel and Mercklin, *Ber.*, **37**, 4087 (1904).
[325]Corse, Bryant, and Shonle, *J. Am. Chem. Soc.*, **68**, 1905 (1946).
[326]Bloom, Breslow, and Hauser, *J. Am. Chem. Soc.*, **67**, 539 (1945).
[327]Jacobson, *J. Am. Chem. Soc.*, **67**, 1996 (1945); **68**, 2628 (1946).
[328]Menge, *J. Am. Chem. Soc.*, **56**, 2197 (1934).
[329]Houben and Fischer, *Ber.*, **66**, 339 (1933).
[330]Karrer, Rebmann, and Zeller, *Helv. Chim. Acta*, **3**, 261 (1920); **2**, 482 (1919).
[331]Mosettig and van de Kamp, *J. Am. Chem. Soc.*, **54**, 3328 (1932).
[332]Steinkopf, *Ann.*, **430**, 78 (1923).
[333]Klopp and Wright, *J. Org. Chem.*, **4**, 142 (1939).
[334]Bargellini and Madesani, *Gazz. chim. ital.*, **61**, 684 (1931); *C. A.*, **26**, 1264 (1932).
[335]Hignett and Kay, *J. Soc. Chem. Ind. (London)*, **54**, 98T (1935).
[336]Wolff in *Organic Reactions*, Vol. 3, John Wiley & Sons, New York, 1946, pp. 307, 335.
[337]Schuerch, *J. Am. Chem. Soc.*, **70**, 2293 (1948).
[338]Miller and Plöchl, *Ber.*, **25**, 2020 (1892); **26**, 1545 (1893).
[339]Smith and Bergstrom, *J. Am. Chem. Soc.*, **56**, 2095 (1934).
[340]Harris, Harriman, and Wheeler, *J. Am. Chem. Soc.*, **68**, 846 (1946).
[341]Bailey and Lochte, *J. Am. Chem. Soc.*, **39**, 2443 (1917); **37**, 935 (1915).
[342]Lillevik et al., *J. Org. Chem.*, **7**, 164 (1942); Porter and Hellerman, *J. Am. Chem. Soc.*, **61**, 754 (1939); cf. ref. 344.
[343]Porter and Hellerman, *J. Am. Chem. Soc.*, **66**, 1652 (1944).
[344]Adickes, *J. prakt. Chem.*, **161**, 279 (1943).
[345]Bellavita, *Gazz. chim. ital.*, **70**, 584 (1940); *C. A.*, **35**, 2127 (1941).
[346]Grosheintz and Fischer, *J. Am. Chem. Soc.*, **63**, 2021 (1941).
[347]Kaufmann and Dändliker, *Ber.*, **46**, 2924 (1913).
[348]Rambaud, *Bull. soc. chim. France*, (5) **3**, 138 (1936).
[349]Price and Rogers, *Org. Syntheses*, **22**, 30 (1942).
[350]Price and Kaplan, *J. Am. Chem. Soc.*, **66**, 477 (1944).
[351]Blaise, *Compt. rend.*, **124**, 89 (1897).
[352]Mailhe, *Ann. chim.*, (9) **13**, 183 (1920); *Bull. soc. chim. France*, (4) **25**, 588 (1919); **27**, 229 (1920).
[353]McElvain and Clarke, *J. Am. Chem. Soc.*, **69**, 2657, 2661 (1947).
[354]Van Epps and Reid, *J. Am. Chem. Soc.*, **38**, 2120 (1916).
[355]Sowa and Nieuwland, *J. Am. Chem. Soc.*, **59**, 1202 (1937).
[356]Koelsch, *J. Am. Chem. Soc.*, **65**, 57 (1943).
[357]Johnson and Shelberg, *J. Am. Chem. Soc.*, **67**, 1745 (1945).
[358]Horning, Horning, and Platt, *J. Am. Chem. Soc.*, **72**, 2731 (1950).
[359]LaForge, Green, and Gersdorff, *J. Am. Chem. Soc.*, **70**, 3709 (1948).
[360]Price and Krishnamurti, *J. Am. Chem. Soc.*, **72**, 5334 (1950).
[361]Sherman and Amstutz, *J. Am. Chem. Soc.*, **72**, 2195 (1950).
[362]Cason, Wallcave, and Whiteside, *J. Org. Chem.*, **14**, 37 (1949).

[363] Pattison and Saunders, *J. Chem. Soc.,* 2748 (1949).
[364] Price, Lewis, and Meister, *J. Am. Chem. Soc.,* **61,** 2760 (1939).
[365] Bader, Downer, and Driver, *J. Chem. Soc.,* 2779 (1950).
[366] Goerner and Hines, *J. Am. Chem. Soc.,* **70,** 3511 (1948).
[367] Boivin, *Can. J. Research,* **28,** 671B (1950).
[368] Mowry and Ringwald, *J. Am. Chem. Soc.,* **72,** 4439 (1950).
[369] Goldschmidt and Veer, *Rec. trac. chim.,* **67,** 502 (1948).
[370] Burger and Walter, *J. Am. Chem. Soc.,* **72,** 1988 (1950).
[371] Prijs, Lutz, and Erlenmeyer, *Helv. Chim. Acta,* **31,** 571 (1948).
[372] Mowry and Butler, *Org. Syntheses,* **30,** 46 (1950).
[373] Buckle, Heap, and Saunders, *J. Chem. Soc.,* 914 (1949).
[374] Byrne, Linstead, and Lowe, *J. Chem. Soc.,* 1019 (1934).
[375] Robb and Schultz, *Org. Syntheses,* **28,** 55 (1948).
[376] Sisido, Nozaki, and Kurihara, *J. Am. Chem. Soc.,* **72,** 2270 (1950).
[377] Paul and Tchelitcheff, *Bull. soc. chim. France,* (5) **16,** 470 (1949).
[378] Marvel, Miller, and Chou, *J. Am. Chem. Soc.,* **72,** 5408 (1950).
[379] Rousseau and Lindwall, *J. Am. Chem. Soc.,* **72,** 3047 (1950).
[380] Crowe and Nord, *J. Org. Chem.,* **15,** 81 (1950).
[381] Albertson, *J. Am. Chem. Soc.,* **72,** 2594 (1950).
[382] Horning and Finelli, *Org. Syntheses,* **30,** 80 (1950).
[383] Buckley et al., *J. Chem. Soc.,* 1505 (1947).
[384] Bader, Downer, and Driver, *J. Chem. Soc.,* 2779 (1950).
[385] Bauer and Cymerman, *J. Chem. Soc.,* 2078 (1950).
[386] Sperber and Fricano, *J. Am. Chem. Soc.,* **72,** 2792 (1950).
[387] Allen and Johnson, *Org. Syntheses,* **30,** 83 (1950).
[388] Leonard and Barthel, *J. Am. Chem. Soc.,* **72,** 3632 (1950).
[389] Asscher, *Rec. trav. chim.,* **68,** 963 (1949).
[390] Cook and Cox, *J. Chem. Soc.,* 2334 (1949).
[391] Tiollais, *Bull. soc. chim. France,* (5) **14,** 966 (1947).
[392] Peters et al., *Ind. Eng. Chem.,* **40,** 2046 (1948).
[393] Knott, *J. Chem. Soc.,* 1190 (1947).
[394] Runde, Scott, and Johnson, *J. Am. Chem. Soc.,* **52,** 1286 (1930).
[395] Verkade and Hartman, *Rec. trav. chim.,* **52,** 952 (1933).
[396] Kindler and Peschke, *Arch. Pharm.,* **271,** 431 (1933).
[397] Migrdichian, *The Chemistry of Organic Cyanogen Compounds,* Reinhold Publishing Corp., New York, 1947.
[398] Whitmore, Noll, and Meunier, *J. Am. Chem. Soc.,* **61,** 683 (1939).
[399] Cope et al., *Org. Syntheses,* **31,** 25 (1951).

21

Imino Esters (Imino Ethers) and Amidines

CONTENTS

The relationship of imino esters, $RC(OR')$=NH, and amidines, $RC(NH_2)$=NH, to esters and amides, respectively, suggests analogous methods of preparation. For example, amidines are obtained by the action of ammonia on imino esters (method 403). The chemistry of the amidines to 1944 has been reviewed. In addition to the methods discussed here, many lesser used reactions for their preparation are listed.[23]

402. Imino Esters by the Addition of Alcohols to Nitriles

$$RCN \xrightarrow[\text{HCl}]{R'OH} RC(OR')\text{=}NH \cdot HCl \xrightarrow{Na_2CO_3} RC(OR')\text{=}NH$$

Aliphatic and aromatic imino ester hydrochlorides are most easily obtained by passing dry hydrogen chloride into an equimolar mixture of a nitrile and an alcohol in ether solution.[1, 2, 9, 11] Strictly anhydrous conditions are essential for successful conversions. The time of reaction is greatly reduced by refluxing the ether solution.[8] Dioxane is superior as a solvent in certain cases.[12] At temperatures above 60–80°, decomposition of the imino ester hydrochloride to an alkyl chloride and an amide occurs. The free imino esters are obtained by neutralization of the hydrochlorides with sodium bicarbonate[1] or potassium carbonate[2, 11, 12] under ether.

Imino esters containing halo,[7, 10, 11] hydroxyl,[6] carbalkoxyl,[5, 11] and cyano[11] groups have been prepared.

This method, along with several other lesser used reactions for the preparation of imino esters, has been discussed in more detail.[22]

403. Ammonolysis of Imino Esters

$$RC(OR') \!\!=\!\! NH \cdot HCl \xrightarrow{NH_3} RC(NH_2) \!\!=\!\! NH \cdot HCl$$

Excellent examples of this reaction are found in the preparations of acetamidine (91%)[13] and nicotinamidine (60%).[14] The conversion is accomplished by treatment of the imino ester hydrochloride with alcoholic ammonia or by the action of ammonium chloride on the free imino ester. The amidines are frequently isolated as salts such as the sulfates or picrates.[6] N-Substituted amidines result when amines are used in place of ammonia.[29]

404. Addition of Ammonia or Amines to Nitriles

$$RCN \xrightarrow[AlCl_3]{NH_3} RC(NH_2) \!\!=\!\! NH$$

The addition of ammonia or ammonium chloride to nitriles does not occur readily.[15, 20] Some success has been achieved by condensing these substances in the presence of aluminum chloride or catalysts of similar nature.[27]

Certain nitriles add amines to form N-substituted amidines. This reaction has been modified and extended through the use of ammonia and alkyl- or aryl-ammonium salts of sulfonic acids. Many amidines have been prepared in yields ranging from 13% to 86%.[15] Some amidines are obtained in better yields by heating a cyanide with ammonium thiocyanate or an alkylammonium thiocyanate.[24]

405. Condensation of Amines with Amides

$$RCONHR' + R''NH_2 \xrightarrow{PCl_3} RC(NHR'') \!\!=\!\! NR'$$

A number of aromatic amidines have been readily obtained by boiling a primary or secondary amine with a substituted amide in a solution of phosphorus trichloride.[16] Several aliphatic amides undergo a similar condensation with amines and phosphorus oxychloride.[17] An imino chloride, $RC(Cl) \!\!=\!\! NR'$, is an intermediate in this process. N-Phenylbenzamidine, $C_6H_5C(NHC_6H_5) \!\!=\!\! NH$, is obtained by the action of methanolic ammonia on the corresponding imino chloride.[19] Also, amidines are formed in the Beckmann rearrangement of ketoximes in which imino chlorides are sometimes intermediates.[18]

406. Addition of Dialkylaminomagnesium Halides to Nitriles [30]

$$R'CN \xrightarrow[H_2O]{R_2NMgBr;} R'C(NR_2)=NH \quad (45\text{--}83\%)$$

407. Amination of Nitriles by Sodium Amide [25]

$$R_3CCN \xrightarrow{NaNH_2} R_3CC(NH_2)=NNa \left.\begin{array}{l} \xrightarrow{R'X} R_3CC(NH_2)=NR' \\ \xrightarrow{H_2O} R_3CC(NH_2)=NH \end{array}\right.$$

408. Ammonolysis of N-Arylamidinium Salts [26]

$$RC(NHAr)=NH_2{}^+X^- \xrightarrow{NH_3} RC(NH_2)=NH_2{}^+X^-$$

409. Interaction of Arylamines and Orthoformates [28]

$$2ArNH_2 + HC(OC_2H_5)_3 \rightarrow HC(NHAr)=NAr$$

410. Imino Esters by the Action of Hydrazoic Acid on Ketones [21]

$$CH_3COCH_3 + HN_3 + C_2H_5OH \xrightarrow{HCl} CH_3C(OC_2H_5)=NCH_3 \cdot HCl$$

TABLE 76. IMINO ESTERS (IMINO ETHERS)   637

TABLE 76. IMINO ESTERS (IMINO ETHERS)

C_n	Compound	Method	Yield (%)	Chapter[ref.]	B.p./mm., n_D^t, (M.p.), Deriv.
C_4	Ethyl iminoacetate	402	22	21[2]	90/765, 1.4025[25]
		402	95	21[8]	
	Ethyl chloroiminoacetate	402	90	21[8]	
	Methyl cyanoiminoacetate	402	87	21[11]	
C_5	Ethyl iminopropionate	402	95	21[8]	
	Ethyl N-methylacetimidate	410	50	21[21]	100
	Methyl γ,γ,γ-trichloro-iminobutyrate	402	92	21[11]	
	Methyl β-cyanoiminopropionate	402	80	21[11]	
	Ethyl cyanoiminoacetate	402	97	21[11]	103/10, (79)
C_6	Methyl iminovalerate	402	79	21[4]	
	Ethyl iminobutyrate	402	63	21[8]	
	Ethyl iminoisobutyrate	402	80	21[8]	
	Methyl β-carbomethoxy-iminopropionate	402	93	21[11]	
C_7	Ethyl iminovalerate	402	75	21[8]	
	Ethyl iminoisovalerate	402	40	21[8]	
	Diethyl iminomalonate	402	44	21[11]	63/0.4, 1.4530[25]
	Ethyl carboethoxyimino-acetate	402	93	21[11]	
C_8	Phenyl iminoacetate	402	27	21[7]	113HCl
	Phenyl chloroiminoacetate	402	79	21[7]	97HCl
C_9	Ethyl o-hydroxyimino-benzoate	402	41	21[6]	151HCl
	Ethyl m-hydroxyimino-benzoate	402	93	21[6]	164HCl
C_{10}	Methyl α-phenyliminopropionate	402	73	21[12]	73/1, 1.5185[25]
	Ethyl phenyliminoacetate	402	73	21[1]	99/2, 1.5126
	Ethyl p-hydroxyphenyl-iminoacetate	402	97	21[6]	148HCl
C_{11}	Methyl α-phenylimino-butyrate	402	77	21[9]	92HCl

For explanations and symbols see pp. xi–xii.

TABLE 77. AMIDINES

C_n	Compound	Method	Yield (%)	Chapter[ref.]	B.p./mm., n_D^t, (M.p.), Deriv.
C_2	Acetamidine hydrochloride	403	91	21[13]	(166)
C_5	n-Valeramidine	408	96	21[26]	
	1,3-Diamidinopropane (glutaramidine)	404	50	21[15]	235Pi
C_6	2-Amidinopyridine	404	49	21[15]	208Pi
	3-Amidinopyridine (nicotinamidine) hydrochloride	403	60	21[14]	(190)
C_7	Benzamidine	404	57	21[27]	240Pi
		404	66	21[15]	239Pi
		404	50	21[24]	240Pi
		408	91	21[26]	
	Benzamidine hydrochloride	403	95	21[3]	(73)
	p-Chlorobenzamidine	404	61	21[15]	256Pi
	p-Bromobenzamidine	404	52	21[15]	(159), 265HCl
	o-Nitrobenzamidine	404	13	21[15]	233Pi
	m-Nitrobenzamidine	404	35	21[15]	
	p-Nitrobenzamidine	404	44	21[15]	240Pi
C_8	Phenylacetamidine	404	55	21[15]	
		408	93	21[26]	
	p-Hydroxyphenylacetamidine hydrochloride	403	87	21[6]	(254)
	p-Methoxybenzamidine	404	18	21[15]	(119), 213Pi
C_9	N,N'-Dimethylbenzamidine	....	82	21[15]	128/11, (81)
	p-Hydroxyphenyl-N-methylacetamidine hydrochloride	403	60	21[6]	(230)
C_{10}	N-Phenylbutyramidine	405	16	21[17]	(65)
C_{11}	α-Naphthamidine	404	29	21[15]	(154), 227Pi
	β-Naphthamidine	404	25	21[15]	(136), 247Pi
C_{13}	N-Phenylbenzamidine	404	82	21[15]	(116), 231HCl
		405	75	21[19]	(117)
	N,N'-Diphenylformamidine	409	80	21[28]	(139), 245HCl
C_{14}	Tributylacetamidine	407	88	21[25]	135/0.5, 142HCl
	N-Phenyl-N-methylbenzamidine	404	100	21[27]	(86), 187Pi
C_{15}	N,N-Dibutylbenzamidine	406	82	21[30]	121/1, 174HCl
C_{16}	N,N-Diphenylbutyramidine	405	61	21[17]	(104), 154HCl
C_{19}	N,N-Diphenylbenzamidine	404	29	21[15]	(113)
	N,N'-Dimethylbenzamidine	405	80	21[31]	(145)

For explanations and symbols see pp. xi–xii.

REFERENCES FOR CHAPTER 21

[1] McElvain and Stevens, *J. Am. Chem. Soc.*, 68, 1919 (1946).
[2] Glickman and Cope, *J. Am. Chem. Soc.*, 67, 1019 (1945); Sah, *ibid.*, 50, 516 (1928).
[3] Ronzio and Ekeley, *Org. Syntheses*, Coll. Vol. I, 6, 7 (1941).
[4] McElvain, Kent, and Stevens, *J. Am. Chem. Soc.*, 68, 1922 (1946).
[5] Rising and Zee, *J. Am. Chem. Soc.*, 49, 544 (1927).
[6] Easson and Pyman, *J. Chem. Soc.*, 2991 (1931).
[7] McElvain and Fajardo-Pinzon, *J. Am. Chem. Soc.*, 67, 691 (1945).
[8] McElvain and Nelson, *J. Am. Chem. Soc.*, 64, 1827 (1942).
[9] Rising and Zee, *J. Am. Chem. Soc.*, 50, 1210 (1928); cf. ref. 12.
[10] Steinkopf and Malinowski, *Ber.*, 44, 2898 (1911).
[11] McElvain and Schroeder, *J. Am. Chem. Soc.*, 71, 43 (1949).
[12] McElvain and Stevens, *J. Am. Chem. Soc.*, 69, 2663 (1947).
[13] Dox, *Org. Syntheses*, Coll. Vol. I, 5 (1941).
[14] Barber and Slack, *J. Am. Chem. Soc.*, 66, 1607 (1944); cf. ref. 15.
[15] Short et al., *J. Chem. Soc.*, 147, 763 (1946); 382 (1947); 703, 2097 (1949).
[16] Sen and Ray, *J. Chem. Soc.*, 646 (1926).
[17] Drozdov and Bekhli, *J. Gen. Chem. (U.S.S.R.)*, 14, 472 (1944).
[18] Stephen and Bleloch, *J. Chem. Soc.*, 886 (1931).
[19] Ghadiali and Shah, *J. Univ. Bombay*, 6, 127 (1937); *C. A.*, 32, 3761 (1938).
[20] Krewson and Couch, *J. Am. Chem. Soc.*, 65, 2256 (1943).
[21] Wolff in *Organic Reactions*, Vol. 3, John Wiley & Sons, New York, 1946, pp. 318, 330.
[22] Migrdichian, *Organic Cyanogen Compounds*, Reinhold Publishing Corp., New York, 1947, pp. 64–66, 84–90.
[23] Shriner and Neumann, *Chem. Revs.*, 35, 351 (1944).
[24] Partridge and Short, *J. Chem. Soc.*, 390 (1947).
[25] Newbery and Webster, *J. Chem. Soc.*, 738 (1947); Sperber, Papa, and Schwenk, *J. Am. Chem. Soc.*, 70, 3092 (1948).
[26] Oxley and Short, *J. Chem. Soc.*, 449 (1949).
[27] Oxley, Partridge, and Short, *J. Chem. Soc.*, 1110 (1947).
[28] Backer and Wanmaker, *Rec. trav. chim.*, 67, 257 (1948); Dains, Malleis, and Meyers, *J. Am. Chem. Soc.*, 35, 970 (1913); Price, Leonard, and Herbrandson, *ibid.*, 68, 1252 (1946).
[29] Djerassi and Scholz, *J. Am. Chem. Soc.*, 69, 1691 (1947).
[30] Lorz and Baltzly, *J. Am. Chem. Soc.*, 70, 1904 (1948); Hullin, Miller, and Short, *J. Chem. Soc.*, 394 (1947).
[31] Hontz and Wagner, *Org. Syntheses*, 31, 48 (1951).

22

Isocyanates

CONTENTS

411. Action of Phosgene on Amines

$$RNH_2 \xrightarrow{COCl_2} RNHCOCl \xrightarrow{-HCl} RNCO$$

Simple isocyanates containing up to twelve carbon atoms are best prepared by a vapor-phase reaction of phosgene and a primary amine reported in 1950.[2] The reaction occurs without a catalyst at 240–350° to form carbamyl chlorides from which the isocyanates are obtained by refluxing in an inert solvent or by treating with a tertiary amine. Over-all yields range from 58% to 88%. Secondary amines are converted to disubstituted carbamyl chlorides, R_2NCOCl.[2, 28]

Higher-molecular-weight amines are treated in the liquid phase usually in solvents like ethyl acetate,[1] toluene,[3, 5, 6] chlorobenzene,[4, 8] or chloronaphthalene.[8] This process is illustrated by the preparation of *p*-nitrophenyl isocyanate (95%).[1] Amine hydrochlorides or carbamic acids are sometimes used in place of the free amine.[8]

412. Pyrolysis of Acyl Azides (Curtius)

$$RCON_3 \rightarrow RNCO + N_2$$

Pyrolysis of acid azides results in the loss of nitrogen gas and intramolecular rearrangement of an R radical from carbon to nitrogen. Degradation to the isocyanate is best carried out by warming the azide in a solution of benzene,[9] toluene,[14, 15, 29] or diphenyl ether.[13] Kinetic studies have been made in thirteen solvents.[12] Yields of isocyanates are usually in the range of 75–95%. In the preparation of methyl isocyanate by this method, acetic anhydride rather than acetyl chloride is best employed in the preparation of the azide from sodium azide. Otherwise, the isocyanate is contaminated with acetyl chloride.[16] Azides are also prepared by diazotization of hydrazides (method 364).

The conversion of azides to amines is discussed elsewhere (method 447). The related Hofmann and Lossen rearrangements (methods 446 and 448) are inferior for the preparation of isocyanates.

413. Alkylation of Metallic Cyanates

$$\text{KNCO} + \text{R}_2\text{SO}_4 \xrightarrow{\text{Na}_2\text{CO}_3} \text{RNCO} + \text{ROSO}_3\text{K}$$

Alkyl isocyanates where R is methyl and ethyl have been prepared by this reaction in yields of 43% and 95%, respectively.[24] Diphenylmethyl bromide also serves as an alkylating agent to give diphenylmethyl isocyanate (80%).[30]

414. α-Keto Isocyanates by Acylation of Silver Cyanate

$$\text{RCOCl} + \text{AgOCN} \rightarrow \text{RCONCO} + \text{AgCl}$$

Ten α-keto isocyanates have been prepared in 40–90% yields by refluxing ethereal solutions of the corresponding acyl halides with a suspension of silver cyanate.[25] Adipyl isocyanate has been made in this way, but the yield is not stated.[26]

415. Action of Phosphorus Pentachloride on Urethanes [27]

$$\text{RNHCO}_2\text{R} \xrightarrow{\text{PCl}_5} \text{RNCO}$$

TABLE 78. ISOCYANATES

C_n	Compound	Method	Yield (%)	Chapter[ref.]	B.p./mm., n_D^t, (M.p.)
C_2	Methyl isocyanate	411	88	22[2]	38
		412	60 †	22[14]	
		412	78	22[16]	36–39
		413	43	22[24]	42–45
	Chloromethyl isocyanate	412	65	22[21]	81
C_3	Ethyl isocyanate	411	71	22[2]	58–61, 1.3801*
		412	65 †	22[14]	
	β-Chloroethyl isocyanate	411	87	22[8]	42/16
		415	49	22[27]	
C_4	n-Propyl isocyanate	411	76	22[2]	87
		412	53 †	22[14]	
	Isopropyl isocyanate	411	82	22[2]	70–75, 1.3886
		412	83 †	22[14]	
	Ethylene isocyanate	412	65	22[22]	75/25
	γ-Chloropropyl isocyanate	411	81	22[8]	55/16
C_5	n-Butyl isocyanate	411	70	22[2]	115, 1.4060
		412	96 †	22[14]	
	Isobutyl isocyanate	411	78	22[2]	102
		412	84 †	22[14]	
	t-Butyl isocyanate	412	94	22[11]	85
	Carboethoxymethyl isocyanate	411	85	22[8]	68/11
	2-Furyl isocyanate	412	73	22[13]	54/40
		412	75	22[17]	111/740
C_6	Cyclopentyl isocyanate	411	94	22[8]	135/12
C_7	Diethylacetyl isocyanate	414	90	22[25]	60/31
	Phenyl isocyanate	411	86	22[2]	160
		412	87	22[20]	55/13
	o-Nitrophenyl isocyanate	411	95	22[6]	(41)
	m-Nitrophenyl isocyanate	411	95	22[6]	(51)
		412	100	22[18]	(50)
	p-Nitrophenyl isocyanate	411	95	22[1]	161/18, (57)
		412	90	22[15]	163/20, (57)
C_8	Hexamethylenediisocyanate	411	95	22[8]	132/15
		411	95	22[31]	110/5, 1.4585
	p-Methoxyphenyl isocyanate	412	80	22[19]	106/8
	Benzoyl isocyanate	414	50	22[25]	90/20
C_9	Phenacetyl isocyanate	414	40	22[25]	118/20
	1,3,5-Benzenetriisocyanate	411	50	22[4]	(85)
	p-Ethoxyphenyl isocyanate	412	81	22[23]	110/11
	p-Carbomethoxyphenyl isocyanate	411	86	22[8]	123/11, (49)
	p-Dimethylaminophenyl isocyanate	412	56	22[29]	104/2, (39)*
C_{12}	Undecyl isocyanate	412	86	22[9]	103/3

TABLE 78. ISOCYANATES 643

TABLE 78 (*continued*)

C$_n$	Compound	Method	Yield (%)	Chapter[ref.]	B.p./mm., n_D^t, (M.p.)
C$_{13}$	4-Biphenylyl isocyanate	411	90	22[5]	(57)
C$_{14}$	Diphenylmethyl isocyanate	413	80	22[30]	148/4
	2-Fluoryl isocyanate	411	89	22[3]	(70)

For explanations and symbols see pp. xi–xii.

REFERENCES FOR CHAPTER 22

[1] Shriner, Horne, and Cox, *Org. Syntheses,* Coll. Vol. II, 453 (1943).
[2] Slocombe, Hardy, Saunders, and Jenkins, *J. Am. Chem. Soc.,* 72, 1888 (1950).
[3] Ray and Rieveschl, *J. Am. Chem. Soc.,* 60, 2676 (1938).
[4] Gill, MacGillivray, and Munro, *J. Chem. Soc.,* 1753 (1949).
[5] Gelderen, *Rec. trav. chim.,* 52, 970 (1933).
[6] Hoeke, *Rec. trav. chim.,* 54, 506 (1935).
[7] Saunders and Slocombe, *Chem. Revs.,* 43, 203 (1948).
[8] Siefken, *Ann.,* 562, 76, 111 (1948).
[9] Allen and Bell, *Org. Syntheses,* 24, 94 (1944).
[10] Smith in *Organic Reactions,* Vol. 3, John Wiley & Sons, New York, 1946, pp. 337, 376, 392.
[11] Bühler and Fierz-David, *Helv. Chim. Acta,* 26, 2133 (1943).
[12] Newman, Lee, and Garrett, *J. Am. Chem. Soc.,* 69, 113 (1947).
[13] Singleton and Edwards, *J. Am. Chem. Soc.,* 60, 542 (1938).
[14] Boehmer, *Rec. trav. chim.,* 55, 379 (1936).
[15] Sah, *Rec. trav. chim.,* 59, 233 (1940).
[16] Colucci, *Can. J. Research,* 23B, 111 (1945).
[17] Stevenson and Johnson, *J. Am. Chem. Soc.,* 59, 2529 (1937).
[18] Sah and Woo, *Rec. trav. chim.,* 58, 1014 (1939).
[19] Brunner and Wöhrl, *Monatsh.,* 63, 376 (1934).
[20] Schroeter, *Ber.,* 42, 2339 (1909).
[21] Schroeter, *Ber.,* 42, 3358 (1909).
[22] Curtius and Hechtenberg, *J. prakt. Chem.,* 105, 316 (1923).
[23] Curtius and Ulmer, *J. prakt. Chem.,* 125, 59 (1930).
[24] Slotta and Lorenz, *Ber.,* 58, 1320 (1925).
[25] Hill and Degnan, *J. Am. Chem. Soc.,* 62, 1595 (1940).
[26] Lieser and Macura, *Ann.,* 548, 243 (1941).
[27] Wenker, *J. Am. Chem. Soc.,* 58, 2608 (1936).
[28] Raiford and Alexander, *J. Org. Chem.,* 5, 306 (1940).
[29] Breslow, *J. Am. Chem. Soc.,* 72, 4246 (1950).
[30] Donleavy and English, *J. Am. Chem. Soc.,* 62, 218 (1940).
[31] Farlow, *Org. Syntheses,* 31, 62 (1951).

23

Carbamates (Urethanes), Semicarbazides, and Ureas

CONTENTS

416. Action of Amines, Hydrazines, or Alcohols on Isocyanates

$$RNCO \quad \begin{array}{l} \xrightarrow{R'NH_2} RNHCONHR' \\ \xrightarrow{R'NHNH_2} RNHCONHNHR' + RNHCON(R')NH_2 \\ \xrightarrow{R'OH} RNHCO_2R' \end{array}$$

These reactions indicate the relationship of ureas, urethanes, and semicarbazides to each other but are not generally used for the preparation of these compounds. Isocyanates are formed in the Hofmann[5] and Curtius[6] rearrangements (methods 446 and 447) and may be converted directly to urethanes[2,9] and symmetrically substituted ureas[1] by modifications of these reactions. For example, N-bromoamides are rearranged directly to urethanes by a solution of sodium methoxide in methyl alcohol.[3,4] Hydrazines can react with isocyanates to give either 1,4- or 2,4-disubstituted semicarbazides.[7] Alkylhydrazines produce only 2,4-dialkylsemicarbazides, $RNHCON(R)NH_2$. A general method of preparation of arylureas involves treatment of an arylamine with aqueous sodium cyanate and acetic acid, viz., $ArNH_2 + HNCO \rightarrow ArNHCONH_2$ (54–95%).[41]

645

417. Action of Amines on Urea or Nitrourea

$$RNH_2 + CO(NH_2)_2 \rightarrow CO(NH_2)NHR + NH_3$$

Symmetrical dialkyl- and diaryl-ureas are formed in 43–78% yields by heating primary amines and ureas in the dry state at $160°$[14] or by boiling an aqueous solution of the amine hydrochloride and urea.[15, 42] Urea is converted to ammonium cyanate, which reacts with the amine to give a monosubstituted urea. This compound, in turn, breaks down into an alkylisocyanate from which the sym-dialkylurea is obtained by the action of more primary amine. By interrupting this process from time to time, phenylurea can be made from aniline and urea in 55% yield. The remainder of the product is sym-diphenylurea.[10]

Nitrourea is decomposed quantitatively into cyanic acid and nitrous oxide when heated in aqueous solution. If primary or secondary amines are present, the products are alkylureas or N,N-dialkylureas, respectively.[11, 12] Alcohol is used as a solvent for amines which are only slightly soluble in water.[16, 18] The yields in general are excellent (70–98%), and the reaction is preferred to the exchange with urea described above. Alkanolamines give hydroxyalkylureas in 85–95% yields.[13] Nitrourea is conveniently prepared in 90% yield from urea nitrate.[11]

A similar exchange reaction occurs between arylureas and hydrazine hydrate in boiling alcohol solution; arylsemicarbazides are formed in fair yields.[23]

418. Action of Ammonia or Amines on Chloroformates

$$RNH_2 + ClCO_2R' \xrightarrow{\text{Base}} RNHCO_2R' + (HCl)$$

The acylation of ammonia or primary and secondary amines by chloroformic esters (chlorocarbonates) is the most general method for the synthesis of urethanes. Chloroformates are obtained by the action of phosgene on alcohols (method 289) and, without purification, are converted to carbamates by cold concentrated ammonium hydroxide. Over-all yields from primary and secondary alcohols range from 55% to 94%.[20, 24] N-substituted carbamates result in similar yields when primary[19] or secondary[25] amines are substituted from ammonia in the reaction. Aqueous sodium hydroxide is sometimes used to neutralize the acid formed.[19]

In the presence of sodium, further acylation of ethyl carbamate by chloroformic ester gives ethyl N-tricarboxylate, $N(CO_2C_2H_5)_3$, in 57% yield.[21]

Chlorohydrins,[26] hydroxy ethers,[28] and dialkylaminoalkylamines[27] furnish urethanes containing an additional functional group in yields ranging from 60% to 93%.

419. Action of Alcohols on Urea and Urethanes

$$ROH + NH_2CONH_2 \rightarrow NH_2CO_2R + NH_3$$

Primary alcohols when heated to 175-190° with urea give 43-60% yields of urethanes.[29, 30] Alcohols below n-butyl require pressure. The reaction probably goes through the intermediate cyanic acid obtained by decomposition of the urea. The reversible reaction $HNCO + ROH \rightleftharpoons NH_2CO_2R$ is well known, and urethanes are sometimes prepared by the exchange reaction of an alcohol and another urethane.[32]

In concentrated sulfuric acid solution at 20-25° urea is alkylated by tertiary alcohols to give t-alkylureas in 33-58% yields.[33]

420. Action of Carbamyl Chlorides on Alcohols, Ammonia, or Hydrazines

$$R_2NCOCl + NH_3 \rightarrow R_2NCONH_2$$

Asymmetric ureas,[35] N,N-dialkylurethanes,[36] and 4,4-dialkylsemicarbazides[7] are available by this method. In general, the yields are excellent. Carbamyl chlorides are prepared by the action of phosgene on secondary amines (cf. method 411).

421. Acylation of Ureas

$$NH_2CONH_2 \xrightarrow{RCOCl} RCONHCONH_2 \xrightarrow{R'COCl} RCONHCONHCOR'$$

Both straight-chain and branched acyl halides successfully acylate urea to the mono- and di-acyl derivatives. Yields of 75-85% of either derivative may be obtained.[37] A review of four additional methods for the preparation of acylureas has been made.[37]

422. Reaction of Amides with Isocyanates[34]

$$RCONH_2 + R'NCO \rightarrow RCONHCONHR'$$

423. Urea and Alkylisoureas from Cyanamides[38, 39]

$$NH_2CN \xrightarrow[H^+]{H_2O} NH_2CONH_2$$

$$RNH_2 \xrightarrow{\text{BrCN}} RNHCN \xrightarrow[\text{H}^+]{\text{CH}_3\text{OH}} RNHC(OCH_3)=NH$$

$$RR'NHCN \xrightarrow[\text{CH}_3\text{OH}]{\text{NaOCH}_3} RR'NC(OCH_3)=NH$$

424. Reduction of Nitro- or Nitroso-ureas [7, 31]

$$NH_2CONHNO_2 \xrightarrow{\text{(H)}} NH_2CONHNH_2$$

TABLE 80. SEMICARBAZIDES AND UREAS 649

TABLE 79. CARBAMATES (URETHANES)

C_n	Compound	Method	Yield (%)	Chapter[ref.]	B.p./mm., n_D^t, (M.p.)
C_4	n-Propyl carbamate	418	68	23[24]	(53), (60)
	Isopropyl carbamate	418	68	23[24]	(92)
	Ethyl methylcarbamate	418	90	23[19]	55–60/12
C_5	n-Butyl carbamate	418	65	23[24]	(54)
		419	76	23[30]	109/14, (54)
	Isobutyl carbamate	419	42	23[29]	117/25, (66)
		418	72	23[24]	(62)
	s-Butyl carbamate	418	57	23[24]	(94)
	Methyl n-propylcarbamate	416	77	23[3]	76/20
	Methyl cyclopropylcarbamate	416	78	23[4]	85/11, (31)
C_6	n-Amyl carbamate	418	76	23[24]	(56)
C_7	Ethyl s-butylcarbamate	418	75	23[25]	88/14
C_8	Benzyl carbamate	418	94 †	23[20]	(87)
		419	86	23[32]	(87)
C_9	Methyl n-heptylcarbamate	416	81	23[3]	130/14
	Ethyl N-tricarboxylate	418	57	23[21]	147/12
C_{12}	Diethyl 1,3-cyclohexanedicarbamate	416	79	23[9]	(150)

For explanations and symbols see pp. xi–xii.

TABLE 80. SEMICARBAZIDES AND UREAS

C_n	Compound	Method	Yield (%)	Chapter[ref.]	B.p./mm., (M.p.)
C_1	Semicarbazide (carbamic acid hydrazide)	416	60	23[8]	(96) *
	Semicarbazide sulfate	424	69	23[31]	(145)
	Urea	423	95	23[39]	(133)
	Nitrourea	....	87	23[22]	(156) *
C_2	2-Methylsemicarbazide	424	40	23[7]	(115)
	4-Methylsemicarbazide	416	60	23[7]	(117)
	Methylurea	417	85	23[11]	(102)
C_3	2,4-Dimethylsemicarbazide	424	28	23[7]	(150)
	4,4-Dimethylsemicarbazide	420	77	23[7]	(83)
	Ethylurea	417	90	23[12]	(92)
	sym-Dimethylurea	417	78	23[15]	(100)
	unsym-Dimethylurea	417	88	23[11]	(182)
	Ethyleneurea	417	98	23[17]	187/10, (134)
	β-Hydroxyethylurea	417	90	23[13]	(95)
	Acetylurea	421	80	23[37]	(217)

For explanations and symbols see pp. xi–xii.

TABLE 80 (*continued*)

C_n	Compound	Method	Yield (%)	Chapter[ref.]	B.p./mm., (M.p.)
C_4	β-Hydroxy-*n*-propylurea	417	88	23 [13]	(119)
	Propionylurea	421	78	23 [37]	(211)
	N-Acetyl-N-methylurea	422	75	23 [40]	
C_5	*sym*-Diethylurea	417	43	23 [15]	(112)
	unsym-Diethylurea	417	65	23 [11]	(76)
	n-Butylurea	417	91	23 [11]	(96)
	t-Butylurea	419	33	23 [33]	(182)
	n-Butyrylurea	421	80	23 [37]	(174)
	Isobutyrylurea	421	80	23 [37]	(176)
	sym-Diacetylurea	421	80	23 [37]	(155)
C_6	N-Acetyl-N'-propionylurea	421	80	23 [37]	(113)
C_7	Phenylurea	417	98	23 [11]	(147)
		417	55	23 [10]	(147)
	p-Bromophenylurea	416	92	23 [41]	(227)
	1-Butyryl-3-ethylurea	422	25	23 [34]	(100)
C_8	*unsym*-Methylphenylurea	417	72	23 [11]	(82)
	p-Methoxyphenylurea	416	85	23 [1]	(165)
		417	85	23 [42]	
C_9	*unsym*-Ethylphenylurea	417	76	23 [11]	(63)
		420	100	23 [35]	(60)
	p-Ethoxyphenylurea	417	90	23 [42]	(174)
	1-Acetyl-3-phenylurea	422	89	23 [34]	
C_{10}	1-Benzoyl-3-ethylurea	422	38	23 [34]	(114)
C_{13}	*p*-Biphenylylsemicarbazide	417	71	23 [23]	(276)
	sym-Diphenylurea	417	40	23 [10]	(235)
	p-Biphenylylurea (*p*-xenylurea)	417	100	23 [16]	(196)
C_{14}	1-Benzoyl-3-phenylurea	422	82	23 [34]	(204)
C_{15}	*sym*-Di-*o*-tolylurea	417	78	23 [14]	(248)
	sym-Di-*p*-tolylurea	417	53	23 [14]	(264)
C_{21}	*sym*-Di-α-naphthylurea	417	75	23 [14]	(286)
	sym-Di-β-naphthylurea	417	46	23 [14]	(296)

For explanations and symbols see pp. xi–xii.

REFERENCES FOR CHAPTER 23

[1] Sah and Chang, *Ber.*, 69, 2764 (1936); Curtius et al., *J. prakt. Chem.*, 125, 60, 167 (1930); Manske, *J. Am. Chem. Soc.*, 51, 1202 (1929).

[2] Shriner and Cross, *J. Am. Chem. Soc.*, 60, 2338 (1938); Donleavy and English, *ibid.*, 62, 218 (1940).

[3] Montagne, *Bull. soc. chim. France*, (5) 14, 125 (1947).

[4] Schlatter, *J. Am. Chem. Soc.*, 63, 1735 (1941); Lipp, Buchkremer, and Seeles, *Ann.*, 499, 13 (1932).

[5] Wallis and Lane in *Organic Reactions*, Vol. 3, John Wiley & Sons, New York, 1946, p. 267.

[6] Smith in *Organic Reactions*, Vol. 3, John Wiley & Sons, New York, 1946, p. 377.

[7] Vogelesang, *Rec. trav. chim.*, 62, 5 (1943); Gelderen, *ibid.*, 52, 979 (1933).

[8] Gattermann and Wieland, *Laboratory Methods of Organic Chemistry*, The Macmillan Co., New York, 1938, p. 134; Thiele and Strange, *Ber.*, 27, 31 (1894).

[9] Skita and Rössler, *Ber.*, 72, 465 (1939).

[10] Davis and Blanchard, *Org. Syntheses*, Coll. Vol. I, 453 (1941).

[11] Davis and Blanchard, *J. Am. Chem. Soc.*, 51, 1790 (1929).

[12] Biilmann and Klit, *Ber.*, 63, 2205 (1930); cf. ref. 11.

[13] Charlton and Day, *J. Org. Chem.*, 1, 552 (1937).

[14] Davis and Underwood, *J. Am. Chem. Soc.*, 44, 2601 (1922).

[15] Davis and Blanchard, *J. Am. Chem. Soc.*, 45, 1817 (1923).

[16] Sah and Kao, *Rec. trav. chim.*, 58, 460 (1939).

[17] Schweitzer, *J. Org. Chem.*, 15, 471, 475 (1950).

[18] Buck and Ferry, *J. Am. Chem. Soc.*, 58, 854 (1936); Buck, Ide, and Baltzly, *ibid.*, 64, 2233 (1942).

[19] Hartman and Brethen, *Org. Syntheses*, Coll. Vol. II, 278 (1943).

[20] Carter, Frank, and Johnston, *Org. Syntheses*, 23, 14 (1943).

[21] Allen and Bell, *Org. Syntheses*, 24, 60 (1944).

[22] Ingersoll and Armendt, *Org. Syntheses*, Coll. Vol. I, 417 (1941).

[23] Sah and Kao, *Rec. trav. chim.*, 58, 461 (1939); Wheeler, *J. Am. Chem. Soc.*, 51, 3654 (1929).

[24] Kraft and Herbst, *J. Org. Chem.*, 10, 483, 484, 490 (1945).

[25] Marvel and Noyes, *J. Am. Chem. Soc.*, 42, 2276 (1920).

[26] Pierce, *J. Am. Chem. Soc.*, 50, 242 (1928); Pierce and Adams, *ibid.*, 45, 792 (1923).

[27] Shriner and Hickey, *J. Am. Chem. Soc.*, 61, 889 (1939).

[28] Ashburn, Collett, and Lazzell, *J. Am. Chem. Soc.*, 60, 2933 (1938).

[29] Jacobson, *J. Am. Chem. Soc.*, 60, 1742 (1938).

[30] Davis and Lane, *Org. Syntheses*, Coll. Vol. I, 140 (1941).

[31] Ingersoll, Bircher, and Brubaker, *Org. Syntheses*, Coll. Vol. I, 485 (1941).

[32] Kraft, *J. Am. Chem. Soc.*, 70, 3570 (1948).

[33] Smith and Emerson, *Org. Syntheses*, 29, 18 (1949); Harvey and Caplan, U. S. pat. 2,247,495; *C. A.* 35, 6267 (1941).

[34] Wiley, *J. Am. Chem. Soc.*, 71, 1310 (1949).

[35] Abrahart, *J. Chem. Soc.*, 1273 (1936).

[36] Raiford and Alexander, *J. Org. Chem.*, 5, 300 (1940).

[37] Stoughton, *J. Org. Chem.*, 2, 514 (1938); Stoughton, Dickison, and Fitzhugh, *J. Am. Chem. Soc.*, 61, 408 (1939).

[38] Curd, Davey, and Richardson, *J. Chem. Soc.*, 1732, 1745 (1949).

[39] Murray and Ronzio, *J. Am. Chem. Soc.*, **71**, 2245 (1949).
[40] Lamchen, *J. Chem. Soc.*, 748 (1950).
[41] Kurzer, *Org. Syntheses*, **31**, 8 (1951) including note 5.
[42] Kurzer, *Org. Syntheses*, **31**, 11 (1951) including note 5.

24

Amines

CONTENTS

CONTENTS *(continued)*

425. Reduction of Nitro Compounds

$$ArNO_2 \xrightarrow{(H)} ArNH_2$$

This method has had limited application for making aliphatic amines[2] although it assumes increasing importance in view of the commercial availability of the nitroparaffins and the development of processes for their ready conversion to nitro olefins,[31, 487, 518] nitro alcohols,[1] nitro ethers,[518] nitro amines,[487] and nitro cyanides,[519] all of which have been reduced to the corresponding amino compounds.

Aromatic primary amines are commonly prepared from nitro compounds by the action of one of several reducing agents; the reaction has been discussed.[535] Reduction with a metal-acid combination like granulated iron and a small quantity of acid gives excellent results. By this procedure, many aromatic amines have been prepared, including aniline (86%), o-toluidine (73%), 4-aminobiphenyl (93%), and α-naphthylamine (96%).[4, 6] Another common combination is tin and hydrochloric acid, but reduction may be accompanied by nuclear halogenation, particularly in the treatment of o-substituted nitrobenzenes. The action of zinc dust and aqueous alcohol in the presence of calcium chloride, essentially neutral conditions, is sufficient to convert 2-nitrofluorene to 2-aminofluorene (82%).[21] Aluminum amalgam and aqueous alcohol, still another neutral combination, has been successfully applied in the formation of 3-aminoacenaphthene (85%)[22] and the isomeric aminoacridines (70–75%).[30] Lithium aluminum hydride is an effective reductant for certain nitroölefins in the thiophene series.[31, 559]

Catalytic hydrogenation is performed in alcohol solution over Raney nickel at 25° to 100° and 30 atm.[14] or over platinum oxide at room temperature and 1 to 2 atm.[16] The reaction is highly exothermic; therefore, precautions should be taken against excessive reaction temperatures. Typical illustrations are found in the preparations of 2-amino-p-cymene (90%)[15] and 3,4-diethylaniline (90%).[13] Heterocyclic nitro compounds in the quinoline[25] and dibenzothiophene[35] series also respond favorably to catalytic hydrogenation.

In addition to these procedures, electrolytic reduction of the nitro group has been accomplished, as illustrated by the preparation of o-aminocyclohexylbenzene (85%); however, the procedure is rarely employed. An apparatus for large-scale runs has been described,[17] and a comprehensive review of electrolytic reactions has been given.[201]

Often under the non-acidic conditions, the reduction stops at the hydroxylamine stage.[26, 526] Thus phenylhydroxylamine, C_6H_5NHOH, is synthesized in 68% yield by the action of zinc dust and water on nitrobenzene.[527]

Certain aliphatic *diamines* have been prepared by reduction of nitro amines with hydrogen[40, 487] or aluminum amalgam.[39] The starting materials are readily obtained by the reaction of nitroparaffins with formaldehyde and amines (method 444).

Aromatic diamines and other polyfunctional aromatic amino compounds are prepared by the above general procedures. In the hydrogenation of polynitro compounds in the presence of Raney nickel catalyst, ethyl acetate has been found to be a better solvent than aliphatic alcohols.[42] The synthesis of 2,4-diaminotoluene is accomplished by reduction of the corresponding dinitro compound with iron filings and hydrochloric acid (89%).[43] Alkaline reducing agents, including ammonium sulfide, sodium sulfide, zinc and alcoholic alkali, etc., have also been employed. For example, o-phenylenediamine is synthesized in 85% to 90% yield by reducing o-nitroaniline with zinc and alcoholic alkali.[41]

Certain *unsaturated amino* compounds like the *cis*- and *trans*-p,p'-diaminostilbenes and p,p'-diaminotolane are prepared by selective hydrogenation of the corresponding dinitro compounds using Raney nickel catalyst (60–89%).[45, 47] The reduction has also been accomplished with hydrazine hydrate in the presence of alkali.[46]

Haloanilines are obtained from halonitrobenzenes preferably by the iron-acid reduction procedure.[4, 51] Nuclear halogenation occurs during the reduction of nitrobenzene by stannous chloride in the presence of acetic anhydride; a quantitative yield of p-chloroacetanilide is obtained.[49] Hydrogenation of halonitrobenzenes over Raney nickel catalyst is possible provided that the temperature is kept below 150°, at which point dehalogenation occurs.[50, 52] The iodine atom is the most susceptible of the halogens to replacement during catalytic hydrogenation of the nitro group; however reduction by stannous chloride and hydrochloric acid has been successful, e.g., m-iodoaniline (83%).[53]

Aliphatic nitro alcohols, conveniently derived by the condensation of nitroparaffins with aldehydes,[54] are reduced to *amino alcohols* in almost quantitative yields by the action of iron powder and mineral acid.[1] Best results are obtained when an excess of acid is present. The procedure is illustrated by the synthesis of 2-amino-1-butanol (90%).[1]

$$CH_3CH_2CH_2NO_2 + H_2CO \xrightarrow{OH^-} CH_3CH_2CH(NO_2)CH_2OH \xrightarrow[Ca(OH)_2]{Fe - H_2SO_4;}$$

$$CH_3CH_2CH(NH_2)CH_2OH$$

This same reducing agent has been successfully employed in the synthesis of 2-amino-1-phenyl-1-propanol (70%).[55] The formation of amino alcohols by catalytic hydrogenation over Raney nickel catalyst has been accomplished. However, because of the instability of the nitro alcohols in basic media, lower amines are also formed.

$$RCHOHCH(NO_2)CH_3 \rightleftharpoons RCHO + C_2H_5NO_2$$

$$C_2H_5NO_2 + H_2 \xrightarrow{Ni} C_2H_5NH_2$$

$$RCHO + C_2H_5NH_2 + H_2 \xrightarrow{Ni} RCH_2NHC_2H_5$$

These by-products are suppressed by hydrogenating in an acid medium, e.g., in the presence of carbonic, acetic, or oxalic acids.[55, 56, 529]

The acid-sensitive *amino phenols* can be obtained by the reduction of nitro phenols with sodium sulfide or sodium hydrogen sulfite[58] or by treatment of the p-tolylsulfonic esters with iron and acetic acid.[59] Also, hydrogenation over Raney nickel at 100° gives excellent results.[14]

Aromatic nitro alcohols are converted by hydrogenation[60] or by the action of metals and acids. Various combinations have been compared in the preparation of β-(4-aminophenyl)-ethanol.[62]

Other functional groups may be present during reduction. Aromatic *amino ethers* are prepared by the same general procedures described above, e.g., m-aminoanisole (80%)[63] and 2-aminodiphenyl ether (94%).[65] The reduction of o-nitrobenzaldehyde to the sensitive *o-aminobenzaldehyde* is successfully accomplished by the action of ferrous sulfate and ammonia (75%).[67] m-Dimethylaminobenzaldehyde is formed by reduction of the nitro acetal in aqueous solution with sodium sulfide followed by methylation (74% over-all)[68] or by catalytic reduction of m-nitrobenzaldehyde in the presence of formaldehyde (27%)[530] (cf. method 431). Reduction of the nitroacetophenones has been accomplished by metal-acid combinations and by selective hydrogenations over Raney nickel and platinum oxide catalysts; a comparison of these procedures has been made in the preparation of o- and m-aminoacetophenones.[69, 70] Other methods of preparation for o-amino ketones have been summarized.[72] p-Aminophenylacetic acid is best obtained by reduction of the nitro compound with ammonium sulfide (84%).[73] Amino esters are readily obtained by catalytic reduction of nitro esters over platinum oxide, e.g., ethyl p-aminobenzoate (100%).[75] A novel synthesis of ethyl m-aminophenylacetate from m-nitrobenzaldehyde consists in converting this substance to m-nitro-O-benzoylmandelonitrile by the action of benzoyl chloride and sodium cyanide, followed by alcoholysis and hydrogenation with simultaneous hydrogenolysis (69% over-all).[77]

3-Aminobenzonitrile is prepared by reduction of 3-nitrobenzonitrile by sodium disulfide in aqueous suspension (63%). This reagent causes some hydrolysis of the cyano group.[79] A selective hydrogenation of the more reactive nitro group in the presence of the cyano group can also be done, e.g., in the preparation of p-aminobenzyl cyanide (79%).[78]

Partial reduction of aromatic polynitro compounds leads to nitro amines. The most successful reagents are the alkali metal or ammonium sulfides in aqueous alcohol.[80] In some instances, sodium bicarbonate combined with sodium sulfide gives better results because of the formation of sodium hydrosulfide, which is believed to be the main reducing agent. Also, aqueous methanol is preferred to aqueous ethanol.[81] Nitro compounds that are sparingly soluble in alcohol solutions may be reduced by hydrogen sulfide in pyridine solution.[82]

Very often reduction of an aromatic nitro compound is carried out in the presence of acetic anhydride, whereby the corresponding acetamido compound is formed.[49] Amino amides are prepared by catalytic hydrogenation of nitro amides, e.g., 2-aminoacetanilide (90%).[83]

426. Reduction of Oximes

$$R_2C = NOH \xrightarrow{(H)} R_2CHNH_2$$

Reduction of oximes to primary amines proceeds readily and can be accomplished with hydrogen and Raney nickel catalyst with or without high pressures (50–90%).[174, 206, 308, 346—349] Primary amines formed from aldoximes are accompanied by secondary amines, $(RCH_2)_2NH$. The reduction may also be carried out with sodium and absolute ethanol, as illustrated by the synthesis of n-heptylamine (73%).[350] The action of zinc dust and acetic acid is effective in the formation of 9-fluorylamine (74%).[351] Lithium aluminum hydride is a good reagent, as shown by the reduction of 2,2-diphenylcyclohexanone oxime to 2,2-diphenylcyclohexylamine (80%).[545]

Aliphatic *diamines* are made by reduction of amino oximes by these same general procedures.[352, 353] Sometimes catalytic hydrogenation gives low-boiling cleavage products.[219]

The reduction of isonitroso ketones with hydrogen and platinum in the presence of hydrochloric acid gives *amino ketones* or *amino alcohols,* e.g., 1-phenyl-2-amino-1-propanol (98%)[356] and α-aminopropiophenone (88%).[357]

The reduction of α-oximino acids to α-*amino acids* is accomplished by catalytic hydrogenation with a Raney nickel[361] or palladium-charcoal[362, 363] catalyst or by the action of sodium or aluminum amalgam.[314, 364—367]

Several procedures involving the formation of α-oximino acid intermediates for the synthesis of α-amino acids have been described[103, 360] (cf. method 385). One outstanding synthesis consists in the production of α-oximino acids or esters by the action of a nitrite on a substituted acetoacetic or malonic ester.[360, 361]

$$\left.\begin{array}{l} CH_3COCH(R)CO_2R' \\ \\ RCH(CO_2R')_2 \end{array}\right\rangle \xrightarrow[\text{Acid or Base}]{(HONO)} HON = C(R)COOH \xrightarrow{(H)} RCH(NH_2)COOH$$

Oximes carrying a second group like a hydroxyl, carbonyl, or carbalkoxyl may form cyclic products, such as pyrazines from α-keto oximes and pyrrolidones from γ-oximino esters, upon reduction.[341]

427. Reduction of Nitriles

$$RCN + H_2 \xrightarrow{Ni} RCH = NH \xrightarrow{H_2} RCH_2NH_2$$

$$RCH = NH + RCH_2NH_2 \rightarrow RCH(NH_2)NHCH_2R \xrightarrow{H_2} (RCH_2)_2NH + NH_3$$

Catalytic hydrogenation of aliphatic and aromatic nitriles yields primary and secondary amines.[215, 309] Formation of the secondary products can be suppressed (1) by carrying out the reduction in acetic anhydride, which acetylates the primary amine and prevents its reaction with the intermediate aldimine (platinum catalyst);[307] (2) by reducing in the presence of ammonia (nickel catalyst);[203, 310] or (3) by simply hydrogenating as rapidly as possible with a relatively large amount of catalyst.[14] Temperatures above 150° during hydrogenation favor the formation of the secondary amine by the elimination of ammonia from the primary amine, viz., $2RNH_2 \rightarrow R_2NH + NH_3$.[215] A typical procedure employing high-pressure equipment and ammonia is illustrated by the synthesis of β-phenylethylamine (87%).[310] If hydrogenation of the nitrile is performed in the presence of an amine like methylamine or dimethylamine, then the corresponding N-mono- or N,N-di-alkylamine is formed.[342] A Raney nickel catalyst that is useful for hydrogenation at room temperature and low pressure has been described.[308]

Reduction may also be brought about by sodium and alcohol, although extensive cleavage of the cyanide group may occur, viz., $RCN \rightarrow RH + NaCN$.[303-306] Lithium aluminum hydride has been successfully employed for the reduction of aliphatic and aromatic nitriles [302, 559] as well as several cyanides in the thiophene series.[314, 544]

A large number of aliphatic *diamines* have been made by the reduction of amino nitriles. Dialkylaminoacetonitriles, R_2NCH_2CN, are reduced with hydrogen in the presence of ammonia (Raney nickel catalyst)[316, 317, 320] or with sodium and alcohol (40-80%).[304, 320] Unsubstituted α-amino nitriles lose hydrogen cyanide on attempted hydrogenation and poison the catalyst; consequently, the stable acetyl derivatives are reduced in acetic anhydride to give the diacetyl diamine.[318] Also, the acetamido nitriles may be converted to 1,2-diamines through the dihydroimidazoles with subsequent hydrolysis, as illustrated by the preparation of 2-methyl-1,2-diaminobutane (53% over-all).[322]

The addition of primary or secondary amines to acrylonitriles, followed by catalytic reduction of the β-amino cyanides, constitutes a good synthesis of γ-aminopropylamines. The yields in the first step are usually in the range of 60% to 95% and in the second about 50% to 75%.[195, 319, 320]

$$RNH_2 + H_2C = CHCN \rightarrow RNHCH_2CH_2CN \xrightarrow[Ni]{H_2, NH_3} RNH(CH_2)_3NH_2$$

In a similar manner, higher amino nitriles are reduced.[321]

Amines containing *other functional groups* have been prepared. Amino ethers are readily made by catalytic hydrogenation or sodium-alcohol reduction of the corresponding cyanides.[328-331] β-Hydroxy amines may be prepared by reduction of α-hydroxy or α-keto nitriles. Best results are obtained when the reduction is carried out with hydrogen and platinum or palladium catalyst in the presence of mineral acid. In this manner, substituted mandelonitriles, ArCHOHCN,[332] and aroyl cyanides, ArCOCN,[333] yield β-hydroxy-β-arylethylamines (24-94%). Reduction of β-keto nitriles gives keto amines or amino alcohols; however, the yields are poor.[334] Amino acids and amino esters are similarly prepared in good yields.[336-340]

Cyanides bearing a second group in a suitable position may undergo ring closure on hydrogenation, as illustrated by the formation of piperidine from trimethylene cyanide and pyrrolidines from β-cyano esters[341] (cf. method 574).

428. Reduction of Amides

$$RCONH_2 \xrightarrow{(H)} RCH_2NH_2$$

Catalytic hydrogenation of amides to amines requires drastic conditions: in general, a temperature of 250° to 265° and a pressure of 200 to 300 atm. over copper-chromium oxide catalyst using dioxane as the solvent.[14] The yields of primary amines from unsubstituted amides are lowered mainly by the formation of secondary amines, viz., $2RNH_2 \rightarrow R_2NH + NH_3$. N-Mono- and di-substituted amides yield secondary and tertiary amines, respectively; however, considerable cleavage of the carbon-nitrogen bonds occurs.[343]

Amides are more conveniently reduced with lithium aluminum hydride in ether solution to yield amines with the same carbon content, e.g., triethylamine from N,N-diethylacetamide (50%) and ethyl-*n*-propylamine from N-ethylpropionamide (53%).[330, 344, 559] The same conversion has been accomplished by an electrolytic reduction.[201, 345]

429. Reduction of Schiff Bases

$$RCH = NR' \xrightarrow[Catalyst]{H_2} RCH_2NHR'$$

Unsymmetrical secondary amines are readily prepared in good yields by the catalytic reduction of Schiff bases at moderate temperatures in high- or low-pressure equipment. Many examples have been cited.[202] The intermediate imines are prepared from primary amines and aldehydes—very seldom from ketones—and may be used without isolation (cf. method 431). For the preparation of aliphatic amines, e.g., ethyl-n-propylamine and n-butylisoamylamine, a prereduced platinum oxide catalyst is preferred with alcohol as the solvent.[368, 369] Schiff bases from the condensation of aromatic aldehydes with either aromatic[215, 372] or aliphatic[138, 373] amines are more readily prepared and are reduced over a nickel catalyst. In this manner, a large number of N-alkylbenzylamines having halo,[138] hydroxyl,[374] or methoxyl[138, 374] groups on the nucleus have been made. Reductions by means of sodium and alcohol[370] and lithium aluminum hydride[302, 559] have also been described.

430. Reduction of Aromatic Amines

$$C_6H_5NH_2 \xrightarrow{(H)} C_6H_{11}NH_2$$

Certain amines are readily prepared by the reduction of aromatic, aryl aliphatic, and heterocyclic amines. For example, aniline is reduced to cyclohexylamine by high-pressure hydrogenation in the presence of Raney nickel catalyst or a cobalt oxide-calcium oxide catalyst. The reaction occurs at a temperature above 200°, where condensation of the primary amine also takes place, viz., $2C_6H_{11}NH_2 \rightarrow (C_6H_{11})_2NH + NH_3$. If this side reaction is repressed by the presence of dicyclohexylamine at the start of the reaction, a 94% yield of cyclohexylamine is obtained.[377] Hydrogenation of aryl aliphatic amines proceeds more readily, occurring at moderate temperatures and pressures over platinum catalyst in glacial acetic acid.[378, 379] Other reductions using this catalyst are best performed on the amines in the form of their hydrochlorides.[523]

The reduction of N-alkyl-p-nitroanilines to the corresponding cyclo-hexanediamines has been carried out with hydrogen over cobalt-on-alumina and ruthenium catalysts.[198] Sometimes a nuclear-substituted aniline is acetylated before reduction in order to avoid side reactions. Thus, catalytic hydrogenation of p-acetaminophenol[381] and ethyl p-acetaminophenylacetate[382] has been successfully accomplished with platinum catalyst at 50–60° in the presence of acetic acid.

Other conditions for the reduction of the aromatic nucleus are discussed in method 4. The hydrogenation of heterocyclic nuclei is treated in method 554.

431. Reductive Alkylation (or Reductive Amination)

$$RCOR' + NH_3 + H_2 \xrightarrow{Ni} RR'CHNH_2 + H_2O \quad (R' = H \text{ or alkyl})$$

Alkyl groups may be introduced into ammonia, a primary amine, or a secondary amine by means of an aldehyde or ketone in the presence of a reducing agent, such as molecular hydrogen and a catalyst, active metals and acids, or formic acid or one of its derivatives. When the reducing agent is formic acid or a derivative, the reaction is known as the Leuckart reaction and is discussed elsewhere (method 432). An excellent review of the preparation of amines by reductive alkylation has been presented. This article includes a discussion of the scope and utility of the reaction, a selection of experimental conditions, illustrative preparations, and a tabulation of primary, secondary, and tertiary amines prepared thereby.[202]

Reductive alkylation of ammonia has been proved an effective and highly versatile method for obtaining *primary amines*. The most satisfactory conditions have been catalytic hydrogenation (Raney nickel) of the carbonyl compound in an ethanolic solution of ammonia under pressure ranging from 20 to 150 atm. and at temperatures in the range of 40° to 150°.[203–206] Typical amines prepared in this manner include benzylamine (89%)[204] and 2-aminoheptane (80%).[206] With liquid ammonia and no solvent, a higher pressure (330 atm.) at the higher temperature (150°) is required, as illustrated by the synthesis of α-phenylethylamine from acetophenone (52%).[208] More recently, improved procedures for hydrogenation at lower pressures over platinum oxide or Raney nickel have been described.[205, 207] Treatment of benzalacetone and furfuralacetone under these conditions leads to saturation of the α,β-olefinic linkage as well as to reductive alkylation.[205] In general, the method is particularly successful for obtaining aliphatic amines having five or more carbon atoms. In all these reactions for making a primary amine, ammonia is present in excess to minimize the formation of a secondary amine.

Secondary amines are prepared by several procedures of reductive alkylation. A procedure similar to that described for primary amines may be employed; the ratio of reactants must be changed to at least two moles of the carbonyl compound to one of ammonia. The procedure leads to symmetrical secondary amines and is most successful starting with aromatic aldehydes, as in the formation of dibenzylamine (67%).[204]

$$2ArCHO + NH_3 + H_2 \xrightarrow{Ni} ArCH_2NHCH_2Ar + 2H_2O$$

Symmetrical and unsymmetrical secondary amines are made by substituting a primary amine for the ammonia. In this reduction, the higher aliphatic aldehydes (above C_3) and simple ketones [215] respond best, usually over a platinum catalyst.

$$RCOR' + R''NH_2 + H_2 \xrightarrow{Pt} RR'CHNHR'' + H_2O$$

Aromatic amines like aniline, α- and β-naphthylamines, etc., are readily converted to the N-alkylamines by using aldehydes in the presence of Raney nickel, hydrogen, and sodium acetate (24–88%).[210,213] Since many aromatic amines are prepared under similar conditions by the reduction of nitro compounds, it is possible to combine both reductions in a single operation and convert nitro compounds to secondary amines (31–96%).[211]

Tertiary amines are formed if the reduction of the nitro compound and aldehyde is carried out with hydrogen and platinum in the presence of acetic acid. Nitroparaffins as well as aromatic nitro compounds react (34–92%).[212] Reductive dimethylation of amines of the type $ArCH(CH_3)CH_2NH_2$ and $ArCH_2CH(CH_3)NH_2$ with formaldehyde and hydrogen over Raney nickel catalyst occurs in 48–97% yields.[214] N-Monoalkylated anilines are methylated in good yields by the action of formaldehyde in the presence of zinc and mineral acid.[217] Many tertiary aliphatic amines have been prepared by reductive alkylation of secondary amines with aldehydes and ketones, the aldehydes giving better results.[216]

Difunctional compounds are formed by these procedures. Diamines are prepared by reductive amination of amino ketones [205] or by reductive alkylation of diamines.[219] A few aromatic halo amines [50, 221] and amino ethers [213] have been made. Hydroxy amines are conveniently formed by the reductive alkylation of amino alcohols [160, 222–227] as illustrated by the synthesis of 2-isopropylaminoethanol (95%).[223] N-Alkyl derivatives of 5-amino-1-pentanol are readily obtained by the reductive amination of 5-hydroxypentanal.[228–230] Several α-diketones have been treated under these conditions giving amino ketones or amino alcohols, only one carbonyl group undergoing reductive amination and the other being unaffected or reduced to a hydroxyl group.[231] Aliphatic and aromatic amino acids can be converted to their N,N-dimethyl derivatives in excellent yields with formaldehyde and hydrogen over palladium-charcoal catalyst.[232] Aromatic nitro acids may be reduced and methylated in one operation. Reductive amination of α-keto acids yields α-amino acids.[233] Sometimes a considerable quantity of the corresponding hydroxy acid is also formed; β- and γ-keto acids give little or no amino acids.[233]

432. Reductive Alkylation of Amines (Leuckart)

$$R_2CO \xrightarrow[Heat]{HCO_2NH_4} R_2CHNHCHO \xrightarrow{H_2O} R_2CHNH_2$$

Reductive amination of carbonyl compounds with ammonia or amines in the presence of a reducing agent has been discussed (method 431). When the reducing agent is formic acid or a derivative, the products are the formyl derivatives of primary or secondary amines or the formates of tertiary amines. These intermediates readily furnish the amines. A critical discussion of the reaction along with experimental conditions and procedures and a tabular survey of compounds has been presented.[397]

Many water-insoluble ketones, aliphatic, aryl aliphatic, and hetero-cyclic, respond favorably to treatment with ammonium formate or formamide to form with subsequent hydrolysis the primary amines. A typical procedure for the synthesis of α-phenylethylamine (66%) from acetophenone and ammonium formate has been applied to many other ketones (65-84%).[399] Nuclear alkoxyl, halo, and nitro groups are not disturbed.[399, 401] The reaction with formamide as the reducing agent is catalyzed by ammonium formate, ammonium sulfate, or magnesium chloride.[405]

If the ammonium formate is substituted by N-alkylformamide, then the formyl derivative of a secondary amine is formed.

$$R_2CO + 2HCONHR' \xrightarrow{\text{Heat}} R_2CHN(R')CHO + R'NH_2$$

In a similar manner, treatment with an N,N-dialkylformamide leads to tertiary amines; moreover, magnesium chloride, or better still calcium chloride, catalyzes the reaction.[402] Other factors have been studied.[403]

The method is employed extensively for the methylation of primary and secondary to the corresponding tertiary amines by the action of formaldehyde and formic acid.

$$RNH_2 + 2CH_2O + 2HCO_2H \xrightarrow{\text{Heat}} RN(CH_3)_2 + 2CO_2 + 2H_2O$$

In this manner, N,N-dimethyl-n-butylamine[123] and N,N-dimethylphenethylamine[400] are obtained in yields over 80% from the corresponding primary amines. Higher aliphatic aldehydes do not respond as satisfactorily as formaldehyde.

By means of a modification of the procedure, aromatic aldehydes may be converted by the action of ammonium formate to primary amines, e.g., benzylamine (60%) and p-methoxybenzylamine (23%).[547]

Methylation of *diamines* with formaldehyde and formic acid yields the tetramethyl derivatives, e.g., tetramethyldiaminobutane (92%).[123] In most instances, alkylation of *amino acids* by this same combination gives complex products, although α-dimethylaminobutyric acid can be made from the corresponding α-amino acid in 80% yield.[123] Reaction of the readily available *amino alcohols* like N-methylethanolamine and 2-isopropylaminoethanol gives the N,N-dialkyl derivatives.[408]

433. Reductive Cleavage of Azo Compounds

$$HOC_6H_4N = NC_6H_4SO_3Na \xrightarrow{Na_2S_2O_4} HOC_6H_4NH_2$$

The introduction of amino groups into phenols and ethers can be accomplished by the formation and reductive cleavage of their azo compounds. The diazotizing agent may be prepared from sulfanilic acid, and the reduction can be performed with sodium hydrosulfite. Excellent examples are found in the synthesis of 1-amino-2-naphthol (85%) and 4-amino-1-naphthol (75%).[554]

434. Catalytic Debenzylation of N-Benzyldialkylamines

$$C_6H_5CH_2NR_2 \xrightarrow[Catalyst]{H_2} R_2NH + C_6H_5CH_3$$

The reductive debenzylation of N-benzyldialkylamines with hydrogen in the presence of a platinum or palladium catalyst affords an excellent synthesis for symmetrical and unsymmetrical secondary amines.[122, 125, 444] The starting materials are readily available by dialkylation of benzylamine or by the monoalkylation of alkylbenzylamines, which in turn are prepared by the reduction of Schiff bases (method 429). The method has been extended to the formation of hydroxy amines,[446] amino esters,[447] and amino acids.[447]

435. Ammonolysis of Halogen Compounds

$$RCl + NH_3 \rightarrow RNH_2 \cdot HCl$$

The direct conversion of halides to primary amines is discussed here. However, it is usually much more desirable to use one of the indirect methods such as method 437 or 452.

The reaction of ammonia with primary alkyl halides generally forms a mixture of primary, secondary, and tertiary amines and even a certain amount of the quaternary ammonium halide. Still, the method may be profitable for obtaining primary amines if the halogen compound is above C_3 and excess ammonia is employed, for then polyalkylation is less likely and the products, having widely different boiling points, are more readily separated. Thus n-butyl bromide and a large excess of ammonia in alcohol solution at room temperature give a 47% yield of n-butylamine.[84] In general, primary alkyl halides react better than secondary; tertiary halides undergo dehydrohalogenation. High-molecular-weight alkyl halides are slow to react and must be heated with alcoholic ammonia.[85] Anhydrous liquid ammonia favors the formation of primary amines.[96] Aryl-substituted aliphatic halides such as the arylchloropropanes give 21–51% yields of the corresponding amines.[86]

Aryl halides react to form largely primary amines. High-pressure ammonolysis at an elevated temperature (100–200°) in the presence of a copper catalyst is required.[87, 88] The 9-halofluorenes take an anomalous course.[89] Heterocyclic amines are quite often prepared by ammonolysis of the halides over a copper catalyst.[90–94] The halogen atom in 9-chloro-acridine is easily replaced by an amino group by heating to 120° with ammonium carbonate and phenol.[92] Similarly, 2-chlorolepidine is converted to 2-aminolepidine (2-amino-4-methylquinoline) (78%).[95] Aryl halides in which the halogen atom is activated by nitro groups are easily converted to the amines without catalyst, as in the preparation of 2,4-dinitroaniline (76%).[113]

Preparation of the simplest *diamine*, ethylene diamine, by ammonolysis of the dihalide is accompanied by the formation of diethylenediamine and triethylenetetramine;[98] other methods for its preparation are more suitable. Only the higher homologs of β-dialkylaminoethyl bromide respond favorably to this treatment. Thus, di-*n*-butylaminoethyl bromide is converted to the diamine in 55% yield whereas the dimethylaminoethyl bromide undergoes extensive dimerization.[97] Trimethylene bromide reacts with liquid ammonia to form trimethylenediamine (50%);[96] however, experimental details are lacking. When the two halogens in the dihalide approach one another in space as in tetra- and penta-methylene dibromides, then nitrogen spiranes are the main products.[96]

$$Br(CH_2)_5Br \xrightarrow{NH_3} \left[CH_2 \begin{array}{c} \diagup CH_2CH_2 \diagdown \\ \\ \diagdown CH_2CH_2 \end{array} N \begin{array}{c} \diagup CH_2CH_2 \diagdown \\ \\ \diagdown CH_2CH_2 \end{array} CH_2 \right]^+ \quad \bar{Br}$$

The exchange of halogen for the amino group is important in the formation of other polyfunctional compounds, particularly the *amino acids*. In several of these transformations with aqueous or liquid ammonia, it has been shown that the presence of ammonium salts minimizes the formation of secondary and tertiary amines.[100, 102] Excellent directions for the synthesis of α-amino acids (C_2-C_6) from α-halo acids and ammonia are given.[104–110] The methods have been reviewed.[102, 103] Long-chain amino acids are prepared by this and other procedures.[112]

Other aspects of the ammonolysis process have been discussed.[536, 555]

436. Alkylation of Amines

$$RNH_2 \xrightarrow{R'X} RR'NH \xrightarrow{R'X} RR'_2N \cdot HX$$

The direct alkylation of a primary amine with an alkyl halide results in the formation of secondary and tertiary amines in varying amounts, depending on the conditions of the reaction. Quite often, these products are accompanied by unchanged amine and quaternary ammonium salt. As in the ammonolysis of halides, formation of a particular product is favored by employing a large excess of one reactant: excess alkylating agent for the tertiary amine or excess amine for the secondary amine. The reaction is important in the synthesis of aromatic secondary and tertiary amines as well as some aliphatic tertiary amines. Thus, in the synthesis of N-phenylbenzylamine, an unusually high yield of this secondary amine (96%) is obtained with a 4 : 1 molar ratio of aniline to benzyl chloride.[114] Other N-monoalkylated anilines are obtained in a similar manner (75–85%).[119] Also, certain β-arylethylamines, $ArCH_2CH_2NHR$, are prepared from β-arylethyl bromides and primary amines by using a large excess of the latter.[118] Very often, alkylations of this nature which are carried out in aqueous ethanol are accompanied by hydrolysis and alcoholysis of the halide.[86] Some N-alkylated aryl amines like N-ethyl-m-toluidine may be synthesized in fair yields from reactants which are present in equimolar quantities (66%).[115] Conditions for the exclusive formation of N-methylaniline from chlorobenzene and methylamine have been found.[117]

$$C_6H_5Cl + 2CH_3NH_2 \xrightarrow[\text{Heat}]{\text{Cu}} C_6H_5NHCH_3 + CH_3NH_2 \cdot HCl$$

Such a process parallels that for making aniline from chlorobenzene and ammonia and involves a copper catalyst which promotes the reaction of the aryl halogen atom.

Sometimes the degree of alkylation can be controlled more carefully by employing other alkylating agents. Thus, primary amines may be alkylated to secondary amines free from tertiary amines by the action of aluminum alkoxides at 250–350° in a sealed tube. The procedure is illustrated by the treatment of aniline with aluminum ethoxide at 275° to form N-ethylaniline (94%).[116] On the other hand, alkylation with alkyl phosphates leads to tertiary amines, e.g., N,N-diethylaniline (99%) and N,N-di-n-butylaniline (79%).[131, 132] These reagents afford a simple and convenient procedure furnishing yields in the range of 53% to 95%. Other alkylating agents for the formation of dialkylarylamines include the esters of sulfuric, sulfurous, and p-toluenesulfonic acids.[131] It has been noted that pyridine acts as a catalyst in the production of N,N-dimethyl-α-naphthylamine from α-naphthylamine and dimethyl sulfate.[134]

Commercial processes for obtaining the N-alkylated anilines are based on the reaction of aniline salts with alcohol in an autoclave at about 200°. A laboratory adaptation of this application of an alcohol as the alkylating agent consists in heating the alcohol and aniline with a small amount of iodine in an autoclave for 10 hours at 220° to 230°. In this manner, either mono- or di-alkylated anilines are prepared (60-90%).[135] Other catalysts include copper and sodium halides.[200] The mono- and di-alkylated amines may be separated by treatment with acetic anhydride and distillation.[395]

Aliphatic tertiary amines are prepared by the interaction of secondary amines and alkyl bromides. Equimolar quantities of the reactants are treated in alcohol solution in the presence of an inorganic base for 2 to 6 days at room temperature or more quickly in an autoclave at a higher temperature. Many compounds have been characterized; however, the yields are not always stated.[121, 124] N-Alkylated benzylamines are commonly prepared by this procedure;[122, 125, 138] these compounds are important intermediates in the synthesis of pure secondary amines (method 434). Alkylation of diethylamine with isopropyl bromide has been accomplished, after many unsuccessful attempts, by heating the reactants under reflux in glycerol solution for 72 hours (60%).[126]

Preparation of aromatic secondary and tertiary amines like diphenyl- and triphenyl-amine is catalyzed by copper powder.[136]

Further alkylation of tertiary amines yields quaternary ammonium salts. These compounds are numerous and are readily prepared by heating the alkyl halide and tertiary amine in the absence of a solvent or in the presence of alcohol.[139-141] Methylation of tertiary amines to quaternary ammonium salts can be accomplished with methyl halides[142, 537] or dimethyl sulfate.[143]

Monoalkylation of *ethylenediamine* with high-molecular-weight alkyl chlorides and bromides (C_8 to C_{18}) can be successfully carried out when a highly concentrated solution (95%) of the diamine is employed. The yields are in the range of 83% to 98%.[144] N,N-Dialkylethylenediamines, $R_2NCH_2CH_2NH_2$, are prepared by other methods (methods 427, 435, and 452). *sym*-N,N'-Dialkylethylenediamines, $RNHCH_2CH_2NHR$, may be obtained either by the treatment of ethylenediamine with two moles of halide (84-90%)[145] or by the reaction of ethylene chloride with an excess of the primary amine in an autoclave, as in the preparation of N,N'-di-*n*-butylethylenediamine (50%).[146] Other alkylated diamines are formed by the amination of dialkylaminoethyl chloride.[147, 148] In some instances, a copper-bronze catalyst has been employed;[148, 149] the yield of diethyl-aminoethylaniline from the alkylation of aniline by diethylaminoethyl chloride is increased from 72% to 88% with this catalyst.[149] A copper-bronze or cuprous chloride catalyst is more frequently employed in the condensation of aryl halides with amines.[150]

Alkylation with allyl halides gives *olefinic amines*.[151]

Halo amines are formed by these procedures. Partial amination of trimethylene chlorobromide with diethylamine yields 1-diethylamino-3-

chloropropane (70%) accompanied by the formation of diethylamine hydrobromide.[153] Halo anilines respond to the usual treatment with dimethyl sulfate,[130, 155] alkyl halides,[154] or alkyl phosphates.[132]

Amino alcohols are commonly made by the amination of halo alcohols or by alkylation of amino alcohols. Thus β-diethylaminoethyl alcohol is synthesized from diethylamine and ethylene chlorohydrin (70%).[156] Higher amino alcohols are made in a similar manner.[152, 165-168] No isomerization through the formation of an ethylene oxide intermediate occurs during the reaction of a 1,2-chlorohydrin.[165] Several series of alkylaminoalkylcarbinols, $RNHCH_2(CH_2)_nOH$, have been prepared by alkylations of ethanolamine (16-53%),[157] 2-amino-2-methyl-1-propanol, and 2-amino-1-butanol.[162] For the preparation of mixed N,N-dialkyl derivatives, better yields are obtained when the larger alkyl group is introduced first.[160, 161] Aliphatic tertiary amino alcohols of the type $(CH_3)_2COH(CH_2)_nN(CH_3)_2$, $n = 1$ to 4, have been prepared by amination of the corresponding bromohydrins (52%).[163] The latter compounds are readily obtained by the action of methylmagnesium bromide on bromo esters (method 91). The alkylation of 2-amino-2-methylpropanol with tetramethylene bromide leads to 2-(1-pyrrolidyl)-2-methylpropanol (76%).[169]

$$Br(CH_2)_4Br + (CH_3)_2C(NH_2)CH_2OH \rightarrow \begin{array}{c} H_2C - CH_2 \\ | \qquad | \\ H_2C \qquad CH_2 \\ \diagdown \diagup \\ NC(CH_3)_2CH_2OH \end{array}$$

Amino ethers are obtained by the same reactions employed for amino alcohols.[152, 170-174]

Aliphatic and aryl aliphatic *amino ketones* are made by the amination of the halogenated carbonyl compounds,[178-185] e.g., dimethylaminoacetone (74%),[178] 1-diethylamino-2-pentanone (79%),[538] and α-methylaminopropiophenone (57%).[185] It is noteworthy that this system may undergo a rearrangement, viz., $ArCOCH_2Br + (C_2H_5)_2NH \rightarrow ArCH_2CON(C_2H_5)_2$ (45%).[539] The reaction of α-halo ketones with arylamines is even more complex.[540] Examples of the formation of α-aminoaldehydes by this method are few.[175] However, the same results may be achieved by the amination of the halo acetals with subsequent hydrolysis.[68, 176, 177]

Amination of halogenated *acids* or *esters* is possible.[187-191] When circumstances are favorable, dehydrohalogenation occurs, as in the treatment of ethyl α-bromoisovalerate with diethylamine; the product is predominantly the α,β-unsaturated ester.[191] The amination of aliphatic chloro and bromo *nitriles* is facilitated by the presence of potassium iodide.[193-196] Halogen atoms in the o- and p-nitrohalobenzenes are readily replaced by the dialkylamino group, as in the preparation of *p-nitrodi-methylaniline* (97%).[197, 198]

437. Interaction of Hexamine and Halogen Compounds

$$RX + (CH_2)_6N_4 \rightarrow (CH_2)_6N_4 \cdot RX \xrightarrow{HCl} RNH_2 \cdot HCl + NH_4Cl$$

The interaction of alkyl halides, preferably iodides or bromides, with hexamine in chloroform or alcohol solution forms quaternary ammonium salts which on heating with hydrochloric acid are readily converted to primary amines.[234, 235, 237] The procedure has been employed successfully in the reaction of primary, but not secondary or tertiary, aliphatic halides,[235, 236] certain benzyl halides,[234, 237] halo ketones,[238] halo acids,[239, 240] and halo esters.[240, 241] The yields range from 40% to 85%.

Certain quaternary ammonium salts, particularly the hexaminebenzyl halides, form aldehydes when heated with water (method 147).

438. Replacement of Hydroxyl Groups by Amino Groups

$$C_{10}H_7OH + NH_3 \overset{(NH_4)_2SO_3}{\rightleftharpoons} C_{10}H_7NH_2 + H_2O$$

This equilibrium reaction in the presence of sulfites is important for the preparation of certain polyfunctional benzenes and naphthalene derivatives bearing hydroxyl or amino groups (cf. method 94) (Bucherer). A review of the literature to 1942 has been made.[389] The hydroxy compounds are converted to the corresponding primary amines by treatment with aqueous ammonia and ammonium sulfite at 90–150°, good mixing being essential, as illustrated by the preparation of 2-naphthylamine (96%) and 7-methyl-1-naphthylamine (90%).[389] In a similar manner, resorcinol and its alkylated derivatives have been changed to the corresponding amino phenols (50–80%).[390, 391] Benzene derivatives containing one hydroxyl or one amino group are much less reactive. Hydroxyquinolines undergo this reaction (65–88%).[392, 393, 546]

Sometimes, replacement can be effected by heating with ammonia under pressure in the presence of zinc chloride, e.g., 3-amino-2-naphthoic acid from 3-hydroxy-2-naphthoic acid (70%).[524]

439. Amination of Aromatic Nuclei

Certain aromatic and heterocyclic compounds having reactive nuclear positions undergo direct amination. Thus α-nitronaphthalene on treatment with hydroxylamine in methanolic potassium hydroxide yields 4-nitro-1-naphthylamine (60%),[507] following the rules of orientation for substitution by a nucleophilic reagent rather than an electrophilic reagent.

The amination of heterocyclic bases such as pyridine, quinoline, and their derivatives by alkali amides furnishes a good method for obtaining the 2-amino compounds (50–100%). The scope and limitations of the reaction have been reviewed; the procedure is illustrated by the preparation of 2-aminopyridine (76%).[508]

440. Rearrangement of N-Alkylanilines

$$C_6H_5NHR \xrightarrow[\text{Heat}]{CoCl_2} p\text{-}RC_6H_4NH_2$$

Treatment of N-monoalkylanilines with anhydrous cobalt chloride at about 220° for 13 hours causes a nitrogen-to-carbon rearrangement to form p-alkylanilines.[359, 396] Normal alkyl groups migrate without apparent isomerization within the group to give good yields (60–85%); however, s- and t-alkylanilines undergo extensive decomposition to give olefins and aniline. Similar treatment of the aniline salts gives the rearrangement, viz., N-isobutylaniline · HCl → p-amino-t-butylbenzene. In this case, isomerization occurs within the alkyl group.

441. Amination of Cyclic Imines

$$\begin{array}{c} CH_2 \\ | \quad \diagdown \\ \quad \quad NH + R_2NH \xrightarrow{AlCl_3} \\ | \quad \diagup \\ CH_2 \end{array} \begin{array}{c} CH_2NR_2 \\ | \\ CH_2NH_2 \end{array}$$

N-Alkyl- and N,N-dialkyl-ethylenediamines are prepared in a single step (cf. methods 427, 435, and 452) by the addition of gaseous ethylenimine to primary or secondary amines in the presence of anhydrous aluminum chloride (77–89%).[451] Primary amines react at about 90° with benzene as solvent, whereas secondary amines react at 180° with tetralin or biphenyl as solvent. In a similar manner, homologs of ethylenimine and ammonia (or amines) react in high-pressure equipment at 100° in the presence of ammonium chloride.[452]

442. Amination of Oxides

$$CH_2 \overset{O}{\underset{\diagup\ \diagdown}{-}} CH_2 + R_2NH \rightarrow R_2NCH_2CH_2OH$$

Ammonia and amines open oxide rings to form amino alcohols;[461-469] the yields are markedly higher when amines are employed (55-90% vs. 18-40%).[464,467,468] The ready availability of ethylene and propylene oxides makes this procedure attractive for preparing 2-dialkylaminoethanols[461] and 1-dialkylamino-2-propanols.[464] Thus β-diethylaminoethanol is conveniently prepared by the addition of ethylene oxide to diethylamine in methanol at 45° to 60° or by a combination of the two reactants in an autoclave at 100° (81%).[461] Isopropylamine reacts with ethylene oxide in the presence of water and a small amount of hydrochloric acid to form β-isopropylaminoethanol (76%).[463] The reaction is general and is shown by higher oxides like isobutylene oxide,[465] styrene oxide,[468] and stilbene oxide.[469]

443. Amination of Unsaturated Compounds

$$HC\equiv CH \xrightarrow[\text{Catalyst}]{R_2NH} [R_2NCH=CH_2] \xrightarrow{HC\equiv CH} R_2NCH(CH_3)C\equiv CH$$

Acetylene and either primary or secondary aliphatic amines react under pressure at 80° to 100° in the presence of a copper catalyst to form N-mono- and N-di-substituted 3-aminobutynes, e.g., 3-diethylamino-1-butyne (65%).[472] Although benzylamine responds favorably, aniline and acetylene furnish only a 25% yield of 3-anilino-1-butyne.

The treatment of allyl alcohol with amines in the presence of an equimolar quantity of alkali in an autoclave at about 115° represents a general method for the preparation of N-alkyl-3-aminopropanols, e.g., 3-dimethylamino-1-propanol (65%).[473]

$$CH_2=CHCH_2OH \xrightarrow[\text{NaOH}]{R_2NH} R_2NCH_2CH_2CH_2OH$$

Ammonia and amines add more easily to a double bond which is conjugated with a carbonyl or carbalkoxyl group to form β-amino compounds. Thus, mesityl oxide and aqueous ammonia react under mild conditions to form diacetonamine (70%).[474]

$$CH_3COCH=C(CH_3)_2 \xrightarrow{NH_3} CH_3COCH_2C(CH_3)_2NH_2$$

The addition of aliphatic and aromatic amines to other unsaturated ketones has been discussed.[475] α,β-Unsaturated aldehydes like acrolein and crotonaldehyde combine with two moles of amine to form unsaturated 1,3-diamines, $RCH(NR_2)CH=CHNR_2$.[453] The addition of primary or secondary amines to acrylic esters has provided a good route to the N-alkyl-β-aminopropionic esters.[477-480] The product may add a second molecule of ester to furnish alkyl di-(carbalkoxyethyl)-amines;[481] however, the course of the reaction can be controlled in many instances to provide largely the secondary or tertiary amine.

$$RNH_2 \xrightarrow{\text{CH}_2=\text{CHCO}_2\text{R}'} RNHCH_2CH_2CO_2R' \xrightarrow{\text{CH}_2=\text{CHCO}_2\text{R}'}$$

$$RN(CH_2CH_2CO_2R')_2$$

Other α,β-unsaturated esters including methyl methacrylate,[169] ethyl crotonate,[482] and ethyl cinnamate[483] respond to this treatment. Ammonia adds to ethyl crotonate to form a 55% yield of ethyl β-aminobutyrate; on the other hand, the interaction of ammonia and ethyl acrylate produces only di- and tri-substituted products.[484]

Amination of α,β-unsaturated acids is brought about by treatment with two moles of hydroxylamine in alcohol solution, as illustrated by the synthesis of dl-β-amino-β-phenylpropionic acid (34%).[485,486]

$$C_6H_5CH=CHCO_2H \xrightarrow{\text{NH}_2\text{OH}} C_6H_5CH(NHOH)CH_2CO_2H \xrightarrow{\text{NH}_2\text{OH}}$$

$$C_6H_5CH(NH_2)CH_2CO_2H$$

The interaction of ammonia or amines with α-nitro olefins, $RCH=CHNO_2$, in alcoholic solution at $0°$ forms nitroamines, e.g., 1-nitro-2-aminopropane (55%) and 2-nitro-3-aminobutane (60%). The reaction is general and is applied to numerous nitro olefins readily obtained by the dehydration of aldehyde-nitroparaffin condensation products.[487,488]

$$RCH=CHNO_2 + NH_3 \rightarrow RCH(NH_2)CH_2NO_2$$

444. Aminomethylation (Mannich)

$$RCOCH_3 + CH_2O + (CH_3)_2NH \cdot HCl \xrightarrow{-H_2O} RCOCH_2CH_2N(CH_3)_2 \cdot HCl$$

Compounds possessing labile hydrogen atoms readily condense with formaldehyde and an amine (primary or secondary) or ammonia, thereby placing an aminomethyl or substituted aminomethyl group at the location of the reactive hydrogen atom. The reactive hydrogen may be present in the *alpha* position of an aldehyde,[416] ketone,[417-423] acid,[424] ester, or nitro-paraffin;[39,40,425,426] or it may be in the *ortho* or *para* position of a phenol[415] or in certain heterocyclic compounds.[409-412]

Secondary products are often formed by the replacement of a second active hydrogen with an aminomethyl group.

$$RCOCH_2CH_2N(CH_3)_2 \cdot HCl \xrightarrow[\text{(CH}_3)_2\text{NH} \cdot \text{HCl}]{\text{CH}_2\text{O}} RCOCH[CH_2N(CH_3)_2 \cdot HCl]_2$$

Also, Mannich bases which are themselves primary or secondary amines may undergo further condensation to yield tertiary amines.

$$RCOCH_2CH_2NHR \cdot HCl \xrightarrow[\text{RCOCH}_3]{\text{CH}_2\text{O}} (RCOCH_2CH_2)_2NR \cdot HCl + H_2O$$

The literature of this reaction to 1942 has been reviewed.[427] Later observations have been made.[414,422,514] The synthesis of β-dimethylamino-propiophenone (72%) exhibits a typical procedure.[420]

445. Aminomethylation of Alcohols

$$R_2NH + CH_2O + R'OH \longrightarrow R_2NCH_2OR'$$

The interaction of paraformaldehyde, a secondary amine, and an alcohol occurs vigorously to form in good yields an aminomethyl alkyl ether. The method is general and has been applied to the formation of many amino ethers.[513]

446. Degradation of Amides (Hofmann)

$$RCONH_2 \xrightarrow{\text{NaOBr}} RNCO \xrightarrow{\text{H}_2\text{O}} RNH_2$$

Amides react with alkaline hypochlorite or hypobromite solutions to form primary amines having one less carbon atom. The reaction involves the hydrolysis of an isocyanate, which is seldom isolated. Isocyanates are also intermediates in the Curtius and Lossen rearrangements (methods 447 and 448). Although these methods have a common mechanism and intermediate, they involve three separate and distinct types of starting materials and are, therefore, treated individually. A comparison of these reactions has been made.[270] A detailed discussion of the Hofmann reaction, which includes conditions, typical procedures, and compounds prepared thereby, has been presented.[244]

The method has been used for the preparation of aliphatic, aryl aliphatic,[254-258] aromatic,[252,253] and heterocyclic[24,260,261,522,542] amines. Yields for the lower aliphatic amines (C_1–C_8) are about 70-90% but are poor for the higher amines because of the formation of the corresponding nitriles and acyl alkyl ureas.[245–248] In order to overcome this difficulty, the high-molecular-weight aliphatic amides are treated with bromine and sodium methoxide with subsequent hydrolysis of the resulting urethanes.[349]

$$RCONH_2 + Br_2 + 2NaOCH_3 \rightarrow RNHCO_2CH_3 + 2NaBr + CH_3OH$$

Alicyclic amines have been produced by the same modification.[250,251] A few diamides have been converted to diamines.[220,262,263] For the most part, the conversion of unsaturated amides is unsatisfactory; however, α-allylphenylacetamide is transformed to α-allylbenzylamine in a 90% yield.[264] Aromatic amides having free or methylated phenolic groups are treated preferably with sodium hypochlorite rather than hypobromite in order to avoid excessive ring halogenation.[256,265,266] Certain amino acids like anthranilic acid and β-alanine have been synthesized from the appropriate imides.[268]

$$
\begin{array}{c}
CH_2CO \\
\quad \diagdown \\
\qquad \diagdown NH \xrightarrow{KOBr} \\
\quad \diagup \\
CH_2CO
\end{array}
\quad
\begin{array}{c}
CH_2NH_2 \\
\\
CH_2CO_2H
\end{array}
\quad (45\% \text{ yield})
$$

447. Degradation of Acyl Azides (Curtius)

$$
RCON_3 \xrightarrow{\triangle} RNCO
\begin{cases}
\xrightarrow{C_2H_5OH} RNHCO_2C_2H_5 \\
\xrightarrow{H_2O} RNH_2 \xleftarrow{H_2O} \\
\xrightarrow{H_2O} (RNH)_2CO
\end{cases}
$$

The conversion of an acid to an amine of one less carbon may be conveniently accomplished by way of the azide and rearrangement to the isocyanate. The azide may be obtained either from the acyl chloride and sodium azide or from an ester by treatment with hydrazine and subsequent diazotization. An excellent review including scope and limitations of the reactions, selection of experimental conditions and procedures, and a tabulation of compounds prepared thereby has been presented.[270]

The acyl azide undergoes a rearrangement similar to the Hofmann rearrangement (method 446) and to the Lossen rearrangement (method 448). This step is carried out in inert solvents like benzene and chloroform to give the isocyanate directly or in solvents like alcohol and water which will react with the isocyanate to form urethanes and ureas.

The amines are obtained by hydrolysis of any of these three intermediates. When hydrolysis is impracticable, the alkylureas or urethanes may be converted with phthalic anhydride to alkylphthalimides which are formed in excellent yields. These compounds are then readily decomposed by hydrazine according to the usual Gabriel synthesis (method 452).[272]

$$2\left[\begin{array}{c}\text{CO}\\\text{O}\\\text{CO}\end{array}\right] + (RNH)_2CO \rightarrow 2\left[\begin{array}{c}\text{CO}\\\text{NR}\\\text{CO}\end{array}\right] + CO_2 + H_2O$$

The Curtius reaction can be performed on aliphatic,[271] alicyclic,[273,278,279] aromatic,[274-278] or heterocyclic[281-283] azides.

The application of the procedure to azides containing *other functional groups* has also been described.[270] Diamines (from dicarboxylic acids),[278-280] arylhaloamines,[285,286] and nitroarylamines[285,286] have been successfully prepared, whereas certain groups like the double bond, hydroxyl, carbonyl, and amino often cause the formation of products other than the anticipated amine. For the synthesis of α-amino acids, the readily accessible alkylcyanoacetic esters may be employed as starting materials. Their azides rearrange to cyano isocyanates, which can be easily hydrolyzed.[287,288]

$$NCCH(R)CON_3 \xrightarrow{\sim} NCCH(R)NCO \xrightarrow{H_2O} HOOCCH(R)NH_2$$

α-Amino acids may also be obtained by applying the Curtius reaction to substituted malonic acid esters as in the preparation of β-phenylalanine (44% over-all).[278,289,290]

$$C_6H_5CH_2CH\begin{array}{c}CO_2K\\CO_2C_2H_5\end{array} \xrightarrow{99\%} C_6H_5CH_2CH\begin{array}{c}CO_2K\\CONNH_2\end{array} \xrightarrow[H^+]{NaNO_2} C_6H_5CH_2CH\begin{array}{c}CO_2H\\CON_3\end{array} \xrightarrow{44\%}$$

$$C_6H_5CH_2CH\begin{array}{c}CO\\O\\CO\end{array}NH \xrightarrow{100\%} C_6H_5CH_2CH(NH_2)CO_2H$$

448. Degradation of Hydroxamic Acids (Lossen)

$$RCONHOH \xrightarrow[\text{Heat}]{KOH} RNCO \xrightarrow{H_2O} RNH_2 + CO_2$$

Alkali salts of hydroxamic acids and their derivatives undergo a rearrangement to give isocyanates. The method has had little synthetic application; it has been reviewed.[291]

449. Interaction of Hydrazoic Acid and Carbonyl Compounds (Schmidt)

(a) $RCO_2H + HN_3 \xrightarrow{H_2SO_4} RNH_2 + CO_2 + N_2$

(b) $RCOR + HN_3 \xrightarrow{H_2SO_4} RCONHR \rightarrow RNH_2$

The reaction of equimolar quantities of hydrazoic acid with an acid or ketone affords a convenient method for preparing certain amines. The reaction is carried out by treating the organic compound in an inert solvent in the presence of sulfuric acid with gaseous hydrogen azide,[299] hydrazoic acid in solution, or sodium azide directly.[292] An excess of hydrazoic acid should be avoided in the reaction of ketones, for then tetrazoles are formed. It should be recalled that hydrazoic acid is toxic and explosive. A discussion of the method including scope and limitations, experimental conditions and procedures, and compounds prepared thereby has been presented.[292]

Aliphatic,[293] alicyclic,[294] and aromatic acids[294-298] which are stable to concentrated sulfuric acid undergo the reaction in good yields, although detailed directions are frequently lacking. Amines prepared by this single-step process are often obtained in higher yields than when prepared by either the Hofmann or Curtius degradation.*

Benzoic acids substituted with alkyl, halo, hydroxyl, alkoxyl, cyano, or nitro groups react to give the corresponding substituted anilines in 41-80% yields.[295] The carboxyl group in an α-amino acid does not react with hydrazoic acid; the reaction proceeds, however, if the amino group is further removed. This difference in reactivity is shown by the conversion of α-aminoadipic acid to dl-ornithine (75%).[300]

$$HO_2C(CH_2)_3CH(NH_2)CO_2H + HN_3 \xrightarrow{H_2SO_4} H_2N(CH_2)_3CH(NH_2)CO_2H$$

The conversion of ketones to amides by the Schmidt reaction has been mentioned elsewhere (method 362). Since the hydrolysis of the amides so obtained proceeds readily, the two steps provide a convenient synthesis of amines from ketones. The yields are often higher than those obtained from the Beckmann rearrangement with subsequent hydrolysis (method

*For a comparison of the Schmidt, Hofmann, and Curtius reactions, see ref. 270, p. 363.

451).[297-299] The procedure is convenient for the synthesis of α-amino acids from mono- or di-substituted acetoacetic esters (80–98%).[301]

$$CH_3COC(R)_2CO_2C_2H_5 + HN_3 \xrightarrow[C_6H_6]{H_2SO_4} CH_3CONHC(R)_2CO_2C_2H_5 \xrightarrow{H_2O}$$

$$H_2NCR_2CO_2H + C_2H_5OH + CH_3CO_2H$$

450. Hydrolysis of Isocyanates, Isothiocyanates, Urethanes, and Ureas

$$RNCO + H_2O \rightarrow RNH_2 + CO_2$$

Many important amines have been obtained by the hydrolysis of one of these substances. Thus, t-butylamine is formed by alkaline hydrolysis of t-butylurea (78%)[454] or by treatment of t-butylisothiocyanate with formic acid (79%).[455] Allylamine is synthesized by hydrolysis of allyl isocyanate with dilute hydrochloric acid (73%).[456] The hydrolysis of isocyanates, urethanes, and ureas, which occur as intermediates in the degradation of amides and azides, has been discussed under methods 446 and 447, where many examples have been cited.

β-Arylaminoethanols are made by the condensation of arylamines with chloroethyl chloroformate followed by treatment of the resulting carbamates with excess alkali. The reaction proceeds by way of an intermediate oxazolidone which need not be isolated.[458]

$$ArNH_2 \xrightarrow[80\%]{ClCO_2CH_2CH_2Cl} ArNHCO_2CH_2CH_2Cl \rightarrow ArNCO_2CH_2CH_2$$

$$\downarrow \begin{array}{c} KOH \\ (80\%-100\%) \end{array}$$

$$ArNHCH_2CH_2OH$$

In a similar manner, γ-chloropropyl arylcarbamates formed from aromatic amines and γ-chloropropyl chloroformate are converted to γ-arylamino-propanols.[459]

451. Hydrolysis of N-Substituted Amides

$$RCONHR \xrightarrow[Na]{R'X} RCONRR' \xrightarrow{H_2O} RR'NH$$

The N-alkylation of amides followed by hydrolysis furnishes a good route for making secondary amines. The formyl,[494] acetyl,[375] and aryl-sulfonyl[492,550] derivatives of amines are best suited for alkylation (method 358). Hydrolysis is accomplished by refluxing concentrated hydrochloric acid alone[35,375,494,497] or in acetic acid.[492,502,503] N-Alkyl-formamides prepared by the addition of olefins to nitriles (method 355) are hydrolyzed with aqueous alkali.[506] Similar hydrolytic procedures have been employed for obtaining diamines,[387,497] unsaturated amines,[495,496] and amino acids.[498-500] The deacylation of p- and o-nitroacetanilides is carried out with sodium ethoxide in boiling alcohol.[501]

Certain amines are conveniently prepared by the hydrolysis of N-substituted amides which are made by the Beckmann rearrangement (method 359) and the Schmidt reaction (method 362).

452. Hydrolysis of N-Substituted Phthalimides (Gabriel)

The facile alkylation of phthalimide and subsequent hydrolysis of the N-substituted derivatives furnishes a convenient synthesis for primary amines. The substituted phthalimide was originally prepared by heating a mixture of phthalimide, potassium carbonate, and organic halide in a non-polar solvent for 2 to 24 hours at $100°$ to $150°$.[428] An improved procedure consists in performing this initial step in a polar solvent like dimethylformamide, in which potassium phthalimide is appreciably soluble; the reaction occurs at room temperature within 10 minutes.[429] Various esters of p-toluenesulfonic acid may be substituted for the organic halides as alkylating agents.[437]

Tertiary alkyl halides lose hydrogen halide in their reaction with potassium phthalimide. However, the t-alkylphthalimides are readily prepared by heating the corresponding t-alkylureas and phthalic anhydride to $200°$ to $240°$.[430]

Hydrolysis may be carried out directly by refluxing the alkylated phthalimide in basic or acidic solutions or by the action of hydrazine hydrate followed by acidification.[428] This procedure is illustrated by the synthesis of t-butylamine (67% over-all).[430]

Alkylation with organic halides carrying a second functional group affords a good synthesis of some difficultly obtained difunctional compounds including diamines,[353,432-436] amino halides,[438] hydroxy amines,[556] amino ketones,[429,440] amino acids,[429,441-443] amino cyanides,[441,445] and nitro amines.[428] Also the stability of the N-substituted phthalimide allows further changes to be made, for example, (a) amination of γ-bromopropyl-phthalimide with various secondary amines (60–80%),[433] (b) catalytic reduction of N-(m-nitrobenzyl)-phthalimide,[38] (c) oxidation of β-hydroxy-ethylphthalimide,[443] and (d) the action of halogen acids on epihydrin-phthalimide.[439]

453. Hydrolysis of Nitrosoanilines

$$C_6H_5NRR' \xrightarrow{\text{(HONO)}} p\text{-}RR'NC_6H_4NO \xrightarrow{H_2O} RR'NH + p\text{-}HOC_6H_4NO$$

This classical method for preparing secondary amines is rarely used. It has been applied in the preparation of some α-dialkylamino-ω-methyl-aminoalkanes (65–70%).[158] Higher yields have been obtained by hydro-lyzing with sodium bisulfite rather than with sodium hydroxide, which is the common reagent.

454. Hydrolysis of Quaternary Imine Salts

$$ArCH = NR \xrightarrow{R'X} [ArCH = NRR']^+ X^- \xrightarrow{H_2O} RRNH$$

The alkylation of Schiff bases and hydrolysis of the resulting quater-nary salts is an excellent method for obtaining certain secondary amines, RR'NH, particularly where $R' = CH_3$.[214] The procedure is less satisfactory for the introduction of large alkyl groups. The Schiff base is usually a derivative of benzaldehyde. It is readily prepared, and, without isolation, is alkylated; furthermore, the salt is seldom isolated. An example is the treatment of the Schiff base from allylamine and benzaldehyde. Methyla-tion is accomplished by the action of methyl iodide at 80° for 16 hours; subsequent hydrolysis furnishes methylallylamine in 71% yield.[553]

455. Hydrolysis of Cyanamides

$$2RBr \xrightarrow{Na_2NCN} R_2NCN \xrightarrow{H_2O} R_2NH + CO_2 + NH_3$$

Examples include the synthesis of diallylamine (88%) and di-n-butyl-amine (75%).[460]

456. Ring Dehydrogenation

Azines of certain carbonyl compounds like 3-methyl-5-alkyl-2-cyclo-hexen-1-ones and the alkylated 1-tetralones have been aromatized to the corresponding 3-methyl-5-alkylanilines and 1-aminonaphthalenes by boiling with a palladium-carbon catalyst in triethylbenzene.[449] The yields in the first step are in the range 24% to 74% and in the second 20% to 55%.

The nuclear amino group is stable during the sulfur dehydrogenation of 2-amino-9,10-dihydrophenanthrene (cf. method 2).[450] In another instance, it is protected by acetylation before dehydrogenation.[491]

457. Condensation of Grignard Reagents and O-Methylhydroxylamine

$$CH_3ONH_2 \xrightarrow{2RMgX} RNHMgX \xrightarrow{H_2O} RNH_2$$

A general method for the preparation of primary amines, free from secondary and tertiary amines, involves the interaction of Grignard reagents and O-methylhydroxylamine. The yields range from 45% to 90% for many amines including ethylamine (81%), t-butylamine (70%), n-amylamine (65%), and β-phenylethylamine (68%).[512]

Grignard reagents which have been prepared from polymethylene halides and magnesium *in the presence of 0.1% water in the ether* react readily with O-methylhydroxylamine to form the corresponding polymethylene diamines (50–68%).[512]

458. Addition of Grignard Reagents to Schiff Bases

$$ArCHO \xrightarrow{RNH_2} ArCH=NR \xrightarrow{R'MgX} ArCH(R')NHR$$

This method is particularly desirable when the stable and readily available Schiff bases from substituted benzaldehydes are employed. It furnishes a good synthesis for amines of the type ArCH(R')NHR where the two R groups may be widely varied to include those from many Grignard reagents and primary aliphatic amines, e.g., N-methyl-1,2-diphenylethylamine (95%)[470] and 1-ethylamino-1-phenylbutane (90%).[471] The reaction of aliphatic aldimines and Grignard reagents has been found to proceed less readily.[370]

459. Interaction of Grignard Reagents and Halo amines[376]

$$RMgX + NH_2Cl \rightarrow RNH_2 + MgXCl \text{ or } RCl + MgXNH_2$$

460. Reduction of Unsaturated Amines[367,453] (cf. methods 431 and 443)

$$RCH=CHCHO \xrightarrow{2HNR_2} RCH(NR_2)CH=CHNR_2 \xrightarrow[70-93\%]{H_2,Pt} RCH(NR_2)CH_2CH_2NR_2$$

461. Interaction of Sodium Amide and Halogen Compounds[384-387]

$$RX + NaNH_2 \xrightarrow[\text{Ammonia}]{\text{Liquid}} RNH_2 + NaX$$

R = n-hexyl (74%);[384] R = 2-pyridyl (67%).[387]

462. Rearrangement of Hydrazobenzenes[489,490]

$$C_6H_5NHNHC_6H_5 \xrightarrow{H^+} H_2NC_6H_4C_6H_4NH_2$$

463. Interaction of Amines and β-Keto Esters[511]

$$RCOCH_2CO_2C_2H_5 \xrightarrow{R'NH_2} RC(NHR') = CHCO_2C_2H_5$$

464. Condensation of Unsaturated Amines and Aromatic Compounds[496]

$$CH_2 = CHCH_2NH_2 + ArH \xrightarrow{AlCl_3} ArCH(CH_3)CH_2NH_2$$

TABLE 81. AMINES 683

TABLE 81. AMINES

C_n	Compound	Method	Yield (%)	Chapter[ref.]	B.p./mm., n_D^t, (M.p.), Deriv.
			Aliphatic Amines		
C_1	Methylamine	437	72	24[235]	−6.5*
		431	51	24[128]	
		446	78	24[247]	
		447	60 †	24[271]	
C_2	Ethylamine	437	83	24[235]	16.6*, 160HBr*
		446	90	24[245]	
	Dimethylamine	431	95	24[129]	171HCl*
C_3	n-Propylamine	446	90	24[245]	48, 158HCl*
	Isopropylamine	446	70	24[245]	32
		426	89	24[347]	34
	Trimethylamine	431	90	24[127]	3.5*, 275HCl*
C_4	n-Butylamine	426	60	24[350]	75-80, 195HCl*
		435	47	24[84]	76.5/742, 1.4008
		457	63	24[512]	78, 151Pi*
	s-Butylamine	426	54	24[174]	63/745, 1.3939
		426	60	24[350]	59-65
		431	80	24[209]	66
	Isobutylamine	426	52	24[174]	68/745, 1.3969
		446	90	24[245]	67
		447	71†	24[271]	164HCl
		457	90	24[512]	69, 150Pi
	t-Butylamine	429	82	24[371]	44.5, 1.3770
		450	78	24[454]	46, 1.3800
		451	78	24[506]	310HCl
		452	67†	24[430]	46, 198Pi*
		457	70	24[512]	45, 1.3789, 134Bz
	Methylisopropylamine	431	65	24[220]	50, 74HCl
		431	59	24[212]	45-55, 135Pi
	Tetramethylammonium chloride	436	95	24[537]	
C_5	n-Amylamine	426	62	24[346]	100-104
		427	95	24[203]	
		427	68	24[303]	105
		446	88	24[245]	96
		449	75	24[293]	138Pi
		457	65	24[512]	104, 139Pi
	2-Aminopentane	431	66	24[227]	89
	3-Aminopentane	431	60	24[227]	92
	Isoamylamine	446	88	24[245]	78
		457	71	24[512]	96, 138Pi
	t-Amylamine	452	63†	24[430]	78
		457	48	24[512]	78, 183Pi
	Neopentylamine hydrochloride	446	94	24[248]	(273d)

For explanations and symbols see pp. xi-xii.

TABLE 81 *(continued)*

C_n	Compound	Method	Yield (%)	Chapter[ref.]	B.p./mm., n_D^t, (M.p.), Deriv.
				Aliphatic Amines *(continued)*	
C_5	Methyl-*n*-butylamine	429	26[†]	24[369]	91/750, 1.4011
	Ethyl-*n*-propylamine	428	53	24[344]	78, 223HCl
		429	43[†]	24[368]	80/738, 1.3966, 224HCl
	N,N-Diethylmethylamine	431	92	24[212]	185Pi
C_6	*n*-Hexylamine	427	70	24[310]	130
		446	70	24[245]	128
		449	75	24[293]	126Pi
		461	74	24[384]	
	2-Methyl-4-aminopentane	431	55	24[207]	109, 1.4063[25], 139HCl *
	2,2-Dimethyl-3-aminobutane	431	51	24[203]	102, 297HCl
	Ethyl-*n*-butylamine	429	52[†]	24[368]	109/737, 1.4056, 197HCl
	Dimethyl-*n*-butylamine	432	80	24[123]	94
	Triethylamine	428	50	24[344]	89
C_7	*n*-Heptylamine	426	64	24[347]	153
		426	73	24[350]	152-157
		427	95	24[203]	
		431	63	24[208]	58/23, 122Pi *
		446	65	24[246]	156
		449	75	24[293]	119Pi
	2-Aminoheptane	426	80	24[206]	142.5
		431	80	24[206]	142, 1.4150[24], 83HCl
		432	55	24[206]	142.5
	n-Propyl-*n*-butylamine	429	54[†]	24[368]	93/200, 1.4112, 268HCl
	Isopropyl-*n*-butylamine	429	52[†]	24[369]	125/748, 1.4050
	Diethylisopropylamine	436	60	24[126]	108
	n-Butyltrimethylammonium bromide	436	93	24[139]	(198)
C_8	Ethyl-*n*-hexylamine	434	76	24[125]	158/743, 191HCl
	Di-*n*-butylamine	455	75	24[460]	160
C_{12}	Di-*n*-hexylamine	434	100	24[557]	122/15, 270HCl
				Alicyclic Amines	
C_3	Cyclopropylamine	446	50[†]	24[250]	50/750, 149Pi
C_5	Cyclopentylamine	426	80	24[14]	
C_6	Cyclohexylamine	426	60	24[350]	135
		426	90	24[308]	48-52/30, 1.4569[25], 206HCl
		430	94	24[377]	
		431	50	24[207]	
		432	75	24[547]	
		449	82	24[294]	
C_7	2-Methyl-1-aminocyclohexane	446	77[†]	24[251]	150, 1.4575[16], 147Bz

TABLE 81. AMINES   685

TABLE 81 *(continued)*

C_n	Compound	Method	Yield (%)	Chapter[ref.]	B.p./mm., n_D^t, (M.p.), Deriv.
		Alicyclic Amines (continued)			
C_7	3-Methyl-1-aminocyclohexane	446	66[†]	24[251]	150/747, 1.4488[22], 163Bz
	4-Methyl-1-aminocyclohexane	446	90	24[251]	150/743, 1.4535[15], 260HCl
C_8	β-Cyclohexylethylamine	430	79	24[378]	85/25, 1.4656, 256HCl
	trans-2-Ethylcyclohexylamine	426	80	24[348]	151/745, 65/17, 198Pi
	N-Ethylcyclohexylamine	430	91	24[309]	165/745
C_9	1-Cyclohexyl-2-aminopropane	430	77	24[378]	87/21, 1.4615, 192HCl
	β-Methyl-β-cyclohexylethylamine	430	86	24[378]	91/17, 1.4718, 196HCl
	N-Methyl-β-cyclohexylethylamine	430	85	24[378]	78/9, 1.4586, 172HCl
C_{10}	9-Aminodecalin	425	73	24[3]	92/12, 148Bz
C_{12}	Dicyclohexylamine	430	95	24[14]	145/30
		431	70	24[215]	115–120/10, 333HCl
		Aromatic Amines			
C_6	Aniline	425	86	24[5]	184, 195HCl
		447	76	24[271]	115Ac
		449	85	24[294]	
C_7	Benzylamine	426	73	24[346]	74/15
		427	72	24[302]	
		427	69	24[307]	85/24
		431	89	24[204]	80/8
		432	60	24[547]	182/680, 198Pi
		435	53	24[96]	75/14, 105Bz*
		437	84	24[234]	184
		446	85	24[254]	184, 258HCl
		447	94[†]	24[278]	257HCl
		449	75	24[294]	
		451	81	24[375]	84/20, 60Ac
		452	75[†]	24[428]	187, 60Ac
		457	57	24[512]	90/12, 194Pi
	N-Methylaniline	431	50	24[211]	196*
		436	90	24[117]	
		436	73	24[135]	101Ac
	o-Toluidine	425	73	24[4]	199*, 111Ac
	m-Toluidine	425	25[†]	24[528]	201/756, 65Ac
	p-Toluidine	425	91	24[4]	200*, 149Ac
C_8	α-Phenylethylamine	426	97	24[347]	76/13, 158HCl
		431	52	24[208]	81/18

For explanations and symbols see pp. xi–xii.

TABLE 81 *(continued)*

C_n	Compound	Method	Yield (%)	Chapter[ref.]	B.p./mm., n_D^t, (M.p.), Deriv.
		Aromatic Amines *(continued)*			
C_8	α-Phenylethylamine	431	69	24[207]	
	(continued)	432	66	24[399]	186
		446	60	24[255]	73/14, 104Ac
		447	68†	24[275]	70/12, 104Ac
	β-Phenylethylamine	427	87	24[310]	93/15, 219HCl
		427	72	24[308]	107/37, 1.5306, 174Pi
		437	54	24[235]	
		446	60	24[254]	
		449	70	24[294]	
		452	95	24[428]	205
		457	68	24[512]	78/10, 167Pi
	o-Methylbenzylamine	427	69	24[309]	105/20
		427	88	24[302]	134/85, 1.5412
		431	83	24[204]	
	p-Methylbenzylamine	427	88	24[307]	108/54, 234HCl
		432	62	24[547]	200/680, 205Pi
	p-Ethylaniline	425	90	24[7]	
		440	83	24[395]	216, 94Ac*
	3-Amino-1,2-dimethyl-benzene	425	92	24[11]	119/25, 134Ac
	4-Amino-1,2-dimethyl-benzene	425	69	24[12]	
		435	66	24[87]	118/25, (49)
		449	21†	24[297]	(51)
	1,3-Dimethyl-5-amino-benzene	438	75	24[12]	218/760, (10), 1.5581
	N-Ethylaniline	431	63	24[211]	205*, 135Pi
		436	75	24[135]	
	N-Methylbenzylamine	429	72	24[373]	186
	N,N-Dimethylaniline	431	79	24[217]	195
		436	86	24[135]	
		436	68	24[131]	
C_9	1-Phenyl-1-aminopropane	431	65	24[207]	
	2-Phenyl-1-aminopropane	435	51	24[86]	83/10, 145HCl
		446	60	24[257]	92/12, 147HCl
		464	94	24[496]	98/19, 1.5255, 144HCl
	1-Phenyl-2-aminopropane	426	55	24[349]	
		431	85	24[205]	80/10, 146HCl
		435	51	24[86]	82/11, 149HCl
		446	42	24[256]	104/22, 152HCl
		449	73	24[296]	146HCl
	α,α-Dimethylbenzylamine	446	84	24[258]	73/8, 1.5175-85[25], 241HCl
	p-n-Propylaniline	440	67	24[395]	220-225, 96Ac
	p-Isopropylaniline (p-cumidine)	425	58	24[8]	105/20, 102Ac
	N-Methyl-α-phenethyl-amine	432	60	24[401]	179HCl

TABLE 81. AMINES   687

TABLE 81 *(continued)*

C_n	Compound	Method	Yield (%)	Chapter[ref.]	B.p./mm., n_D^t, (M.p.), Deriv.
		Aromatic Amines (continued)			
C_9	N-Ethyl *m*-toluidine	436	66	24[115]	112/20
	Benzyldimethylamine	436	80	24[123]	176-180
	N-Methyl-N-ethylaniline	431	88	24[217]	209, 129Pi
	N,N-dimethyl-*m*-toluidine	436	60	24[132]	206/740
	N,N-Dimethyl-*p*-toluidine	436	53	24[132]	206/740
	Phenyltrimethylammonium sulfate	436	90	24[143]	(126), 124Pi
	5-Aminohydrindene	451	92	24[505]	247, (34)
C_{10}	1-Phenyl-3-aminobutane	431	67	24[205]	80/4, 148HCl
	2-Amino-3-phenylbutane	447	96 †	24[274]	111/14
	o-Amino-*t*-butylbenzene	425	85	24[10]	161Ac
	p-Amino-*t*-butylbenzene	425	73	24[9]	93/3, (16), 170Ac
	2-Amino-*p*-cymene	425	90	24[15]	242/760, 110/10
	3,4-Diethylaniline	425	99	24[13]	117/10, 1.5458[29], 119Ac
	1-Methylamino-1-phenyl-propane	458	75	24[471]	
	1-Methylamino-2-phenyl-propane	436	44	24[86]	100/20, 133HCl
		454	80	24[214]	98/18, 159HCl
		464	47	24[496]	87/10, 1.5112, 146HCl
	2-Methylamino-1-phenyl-propane	454	93	24[214]	80/6, 136HCl
	N-Ethyl-α-phenethylamine	432	70	24[401]	200HCl
	N,N-Dimethylphenethyl-amine	432	83	24[400]	98/22
	Benzylmethylethylamine	436	100	24[122]	80/16, 152HCl
	N,N-Diethylaniline	431	70	24[212]	140Pi
		436	87	24[135]	216
		436	99	24[131]	
	p-Dimethylaminoethyl-benzene	436	27	24[395]	104/16
	1-Naphthylamine	425	96	24[4]	(50), 159Ac*
		449	70 †	24[298]	
	2-Naphthylamine	438	96	24[389]	(112), 132Ac*
	1,2,3,4-Tetrahydro-2-naphthylamine	430	57	24[383]	118/8, 140/20
C_{11}	1-Ethylamino-2-phenyl-propane	431	94	24[214]	127/30, 160HCl
		464	77	24[496]	93/10, 1.5032, 159HCl
	1-Dimethylamino-2-phenylpropane	464	62	24[496]	80/10, 1.4983, 222HCl
	2-Dimethylamino-1-phenylpropane	431	67	24[214]	100/12, 161HCl
	7-Methyl-1-naphthylamine	438	90	24[389]	140/3, (59)
	α-Aminomethylnaphthalene	435	72	24[96]	135/0.3

For explanations and symbols see pp. xi–xii.

TABLE 81 *(continued)*

C_n	Compound	Method	Yield (%)	Chapter[ref.]	B.p./mm., n_D^t, (M.p.), Deriv.
			Aromatic Amines *(continued)*		
C_{11}	N-Methylnaphthylamine	437	73	24^{243}	200–205/30, 262HCl
		451	70	24^{492}	170/12
C_{12}	β-(α-Naphthyl)-ethylamine	447	45[†]	24^{276}	170/12, 245HCl
	α-(β-Naphthyl)-ethylamine	432	84	24^{399}	199HCl
	N-Ethyl-α-naphthylamine	431	88	24^{213}	190/20*
	N-Ethyl-β-naphthylamine	431	64	24^{213}	316*
	N,N-Dimethyl-α-naphthylamine	436	70	24^{133}	272*
	N,N-Dimethyl-β-naphthylamine	436	64	24^{131}	305*
	2-Aminobiphenyl	425	93	24^{18}	182/30, (49)
	3-Aminobiphenyl	425	99	24^{19}	178/18, (31)
	4-Aminobiphenyl	425	93	24^4	211/30, (54)*, 171Ac
	o-Aminocyclohexylbenzene	425	85	24^{17}	134/3, 106/0.5
	3-Aminoacenaphthene	425	85	24^{22}	(81.5), 193Ac
C_{13}	Benzhydrylamine	426	87	24^{347}	171/16, 270HCl
		432	96	24^{405}	
	o-Phenylbenzylamine	427	60	24^{312}	168/15, 179/12, 217HCl
	N-Phenyl benzylamine	429	97	24^{215}	146/1
	(benzylaniline)	436	87	24^{114}	180/12, (36)
	N-Phenyl-p-toluidine	451	40[†]	24^{493}	
	Methyldiphenylamine	431	65	24^{216}	148/13
	2-Aminofluorene	425	82	24^{21}	(127)
	9-Aminofluorene	426	74	24^{351}	(65), 255HCl
		432	75	24^{404}	
		452	87[†]	24^{431}	(62)
C_{14}	β,β-Diphenylethylamine	427	76	24^{311}	134/2, (43.5)
	Dibenzylamine	429	50	24^{375}	150–155/4–5
	m-Tolylbenzylamine	429	94	24^{372}	157/4, 199HCl
	Ethyldiphenylamine	431	80	24^{216}	150/13
	2-Dimethylaminobiphenyl	436	94	24^{130}	145/11
	N,N-Diethyl-α-naphthylamine	431	40	24^{212}	155–165/30, 1.5961, 154Pi
		436	60	24^{131}	
	1-Aminophenanthrene	451	72[†]	24^{504}	(146), 220Ac
		456	60	24^{491}	(147), 204Pi*
	2-Aminophenanthrene	449	88[†]	24^{298}	(84)
		451	86[†]	24^{503}	(86)
		456	68	24^{450}	(86)
	3-Aminophenanthrene	449	80[†]	24^{298}	(86)
		451	70[†]	24^{503}	(87)
	9-Aminophenanthrene	447	81[†]	24^{277}	(137.5)
		449	73[†]	24^{298}	(137)
		451	60[†]	24^{502}	(130)

TABLE 81. AMINES   689

TABLE 81 *(continued)*

C_n	Compound	Method	Yield (%)	Chapter[ref.]	B.p./mm., n_D^t, (M.p.), Deriv.
		Aromatic Amines *(continued)*			
C_{14}	9-Aminoanthracene	425	91	24[20]	(135–140), 274Ac
C_{15}	β,γ-Diphenylpropylamine	427	88	24[311]	171/6
	γ,γ-Diphenylpropylamine	427	81	24[311]	150/2, 218HCl
	N-Methyl-1,2-diphenyl-ethylamine	458	95	24[470]	186HCl
	9-Aminomethylphenan-threne	427	100	24[313]	(108.5), 294HCl
		435	70	24[96]	165/0.15
C_{18}	Triphenylamine	436	85	24[136]	(126)
C_{24}	p-Aminotetraphenyl-methane	1	74	24[552]	(250)
		Heterocyclic Amines			
C_4	2-Aminofuran	447	54†	24[282]	124Bz
C_5	Furfurylamine	431	79	24[204]	146*
	2-Methyl-3-aminofuran	447	54†	24[281]	52/4, 137Bz
	2-Methylaminofuran	427	84	24[321]	50/10
	2-Thenylamine	444	45	24[411]	65/4, 1.5628, 189HCl
	α-Thienylaminomethane	437	84	24[242]	75/11, 194HCl
	2-Aminopyridine	435	70	24[93]	(57)
		439	76	24[508]	120/36
	3-Aminopyridine	425	93	24[23]	(64)
		435	80	24[93]	(64), 133Ac
		435	60	24[532]	109/3, (61)
		446	89	24[542]	(64)
	4-Aminopyridine	435	30	24[532]	(159)
		446	74	24[532]	(159)
	2-Aminopiperidine	430	78	24[380]	68/17, (57), 197Bz
		554	90	39[120]	68/17, (57), 225HCl
C_6	N-Methylfurfurylamine	436	50	24[120]	149/761, 1.4729, 146HCl
	1-(α-Thienyl)-1-aminoethane	432	51	24[242]	84/16, 142HCl
	β-(2-Thienyl)-ethylamine	425	63	24[31]	78/7.0, 202HCl
		427	34	24[314]	74/3, 203HCl
		446	63	24[522]	201/750, 202HCl
	2-Methyl-5-aminopyridine	446	55	24[260]	(96), 123Ac*
		447	93	24[260]	(96), 218HCl
	6-Amino-2-picoline	439	61	24[509]	125/20, (40)
	2-Aminomethylpyridine	427	38	24[315]	93/3, 76/3, 138NBz
	3-Aminomethylpyridine	427	60	24[315]	98/3, 116/3, 191NBz
	4-Aminomethylpyridine	427	60	24[315]	117/5, 112/4, 180Pi*
	2-Aminomethylpiperidine	554	61	39[126]	81/18
C_7	1-Furyl-2-aminopropane	426	90	24[349]	

For explanations and symbols see pp. xi–xii.

TABLE 81 *(continued)*

C_n	Compound	Method	Yield (%)	Chapter$^{ref.}$	B.p./mm., n_D^t, (M.p.), Deriv.
	Heterocyclic Amines (continued)				
C_7	N-Ethylfurfurylamine	429	49	24[138]	75/25, 121HCl
		436	58	24[120]	167/761, 1.4688, 128HCl
	N,N-Dimethylfurfurylamine	• 432	60	24[397]	146
		432	85	24[141]	145, 103Pi
	2-Dimethylaminomethyl-pyrrole	444	77	24[409]	94/19, 137Pi
	α-(Ethylamino)-pyridine	451	81	24[494]	82/4
C_8	1-(α-Furyl)-3-aminobutane	431	50	24[205]	190/760, 102/25
	N-Ethyl-5-methylfurfuryl-amine	444	45	24[410]	76/17, 1.4689[25], 139HCl
	N,N-Dimethyl-5-methyl-furfurylamine	444	65	24[410]	70/25, 1.4620[25], 158HCl
	β-(3-Pyridyl)-isopropyl-amine	432	36	24[406]	88/1, 187Pi
	γ-Piperidinopropylamine	427	69	24[195]	205/730, 1.4750, 210Pi
	3-Aminothianaphthene	425	67	24[34]	168Ac
	5-Aminothianaphthene	425	65	24[32]	(72)
C_9	N,N-Diethylfurfurylamine	432	68	24[141]	172, 85Pi
	δ-Piperidinobutylamine	427	54	24[195]	120/25, 1.4756, 160Pi
	2-Aminoquinoline	435	50	24[94]	(129)
	3-Aminoquinoline	425	97	24[24]	(83), 172Ac
		435	60	24[94]	(84)
		435	73	24[164]	(83), 172Ac
	4-Aminoquinoline	435	70	24[532]	(154)
		446	90	24[24]	(69), (156), 178Ac
		446	90	39[164]	(156), 178Ac
		575	43[†]	39[163]	(153)
	5-Aminoquinoline	425	80	24[25]	181/7, (110), 240HCl
	6-Aminoquinoline	425	85	24[29]	187-200/10-13, (114)
	7-Aminoquinoline	425	95	24[28]	(75), (93)
	8-Aminoquinoline	425	95	24[26]	141/7, (65)
		438	88	24[393]	(65.5)
	1-Aminoisoquinoline	439	70	24[510]	(123)*
	4-Aminoisoquinoline	435	70	24[33]	(108.5), 168Ac
	5-Aminoisoquinoline	425	80	24[33]	(129), 166Ac
		438	65	24[392]	(132)
	6-Aminoisoquinoline	438	85	24[546]	(218)
	cis-trans-Decahydro-quinoline	430	95	24[309]	206
C_{10}	β-3-Thianaphthylethyl-amine	427	32	24[544]	125/1, 177Pi
	1-(β-Diethylaminoethyl)-pyrrole	436	66	24[388]	80/4

TABLE 82. DIAMINES   691

TABLE 81 *(continued)*

C_n	Compound	Method	Yield (%)	Chapter[ref.]	B.p./mm., n_D^t, (M.p.), Deriv.
		Heterocyclic Amines *(continued)*			
C_{10}	N,N-Diethyl-β-pyridyl-methylamine	428	55	24[344]	100/12, 170Pi
	2-Aminolepidine	435	78	24[95]	(133), 232Ac
C_{11}	3-Dimethylaminomethyl-indole	444	100	24[412]	(134), 142Pi
	2-Dimethylaminoquinoline	436	91	24[137]	(71)
C_{12}	1-Aminodibenzofuran	435	24	24[90]	(74), 205Ac
	3-Aminodibenzofuran	425	91	24[551]	(94)*
	4-Aminodibenzofuran	438	45	24[394]	(85)*
		446	55	24[261]	
	2-Aminodibenzothiophene	425	91	24[35]	(133)
		435	62	24[91]	(129), 178Ac
		451	72	24[35]	(131)
	3-Aminodibenzothiophene	461	50	24[385]	(122), 200Ac
	4-Aminodibenzothiophene	435	37†	24[91]	(110), 198Ac
		....	64	24[36]	(110)
C_{13}	2-Aminoacridine	....	60	39[219]	(216)
	9-Aminoacridine	435	89	39[217]	(233)

For explanations and symbols see pp. xi–xii.

TABLE 82. DIAMINES

C_n	Compound	Method	Yield (%)	Chapter[ref.]	B.p./mm., n_D^t, (M.p.), Deriv.
		Aliphatic Diamines			
C_2	Ethylenediamine	447	75†	24[280]	172Ac
		452	60	24[432]	116, 172Ac
C_3	1,2-Diaminopropane	425	52	24[487]	221HCl
	Trimethylenediamine	427	23	24[195]	138/735, 1.4600, 178Pi
		446	54	24[220]	131/760*, 250Pi
		449	65	24[220]	250Pi
		452	90	24[432]	136, 140Bz*
	N-Methylethylenediamine	427	66	24[341]	111, 112Bz*
		451	33†	24[497]	116/757, 220Pi
C_4	1,2-Butylenediamine	441	55	24[452]	140, 1.4490, 187Bz
	Tetramethylenediamine	446	60	24[262]	177Bz
		447	48†	24[280]	
		449	80	24[294]	
		452	74	24[434]	159/760

For explanations and symbols see pp. xi–xii.

TABLE 82 *(continued)*

C_n	Compound	Method	Yield (%)	Chapter[ref.]	B.p./mm., n_D^t, (M.p.), Deriv.
	Aliphatic Diamines (continued)				
C_4	2,3-Diaminobutane	425	40	24[487]	312HCl
	Isobutylenediamine	427	80	24[318]	115/754*, 100Ac
	γ-Methylaminopropylamine	427	70	24[319]	141, 1.4479, 226Pi
	N-Monoethylethyl- enediamine	451	20 †	24[497]	131/759, 195Pi
	β-Dimethylaminoethyl- amine	427	47	24[316]	108
	N,N'-Dimethylethylene- diamine	436	50	24[147]	150-160, 160Pi
C_5	Pentamethylenediamine (cadaverine)	457	68	24[512]	180, 237Pi
	2-Methyl-1,2-diamino- butane	427	61 †	24[322]	143/752, 1.4483, 229Pi
	2-Methyl-1,4-diamino- butane	446	72	24[263]	154Bz
	2,2-Dimethyl-1,3-propane- diamine	425	90	24[1]	78/50, (29), 257HCl*
		425	67	24[37]	153/737, 1.4566, 240Pi
	γ-Ethylaminopropylamine	427	74	24[195]	156/735, 1.4441, 193Pi
	1-Dimethylamino-2- aminopropane	431	40	24[178]	113, 1.4177[25]
C_6	Hexamethylenediamine	452	86 †	24[435]	258HCl
		457	51	24[512]	204, 220Pi
	1-Ethylamino-2- aminobutane	441	20	24[452]	157, 1.4431, 116Bz
	2-Methyl-2-methylamino- 1-aminobutane	427	66 †	24[322]	155/737, 1.4502, 203Pi
	3-Ethylamino-2-methyl-2- aminopropane	441	42	24[452]	141, 1.4300, 108Bz
	β-Diethylaminoethylamine	427	53	24[304]	145/760, 99/13, 207Pi
		427	62	24[317]	144-150, 211Pi
		441	89	24[451]	
		452	57	24[353]	145-149
C_7	1-Diethylamino-2- aminopropane	431	62	24[218]	153, 182Pi
		431	65	24[205]	154/760, 70/20
	γ-Diethylaminopropyl- amine	427	72	24[195]	168/735, 1.4355, 194Pi
		452	60	24[433]	170, 1.4437
	1-Dimethylamino-3- methylaminobutane	436	100	24[148]	56/14, 186Pi
	1,3-bis-Dimethylamino- propane	460	78	24[453]	145, 207Pi
	β-Diethylaminoethyl- methylamine	436	40	24[147]	160

TABLE 82. DIAMINES   693

TABLE 82 (continued)

C_n	Compound	Method	Yield (%)	Chapter[ref.]	B.p./mm., n_D^t, (M.p.), Deriv.
		Aliphatic Diamines (continued)			
C_8	1-Diethylamino-2-amino-butane	425	55	24[39]	80/16
		441	54	24[452]	173, 1.4347
	1-Diethylamino-3-amino-butane	426	60	24[353]	74/12, 1.4428[18]
		431	72	24[205]	70/10, 1.4430[18]
	4-Diethylaminobutylamine	427	97	24[321]	88/18, 1.4462*, 156Pi
		427	50	24[194]	86/16, 1.4420[25]
	1,3-bis-Dimethylamino-butane	436	100	24[148]	56/12
		460	74	24[453]	
	1,4-bis-Dimethylamino-butane	436	92	24[123]	167, 199Pi
	1-Diethylamino-3-methylaminopropane	453	65	24[158]	60/8, 1.4390[19]
C_9	1-Diethylamino-3-aminopentane	426	75	24[538]	86–95/22, 1.4421, 155Pi
	Tetraethylmethylene-diamine	....	76	24[513]	167/757
C_{10}	Decamethylenediamine	427	80	24[323]	146/14, (60)
	1-Diethylamino-4-aminohexane	426	64	24[352]	105–112/20
	β-Diethylaminoethyl-diethylamine	436	50	24[147]	151Pi
		Alicyclic Diamines			
C_4	trans-1,2-Diaminocyclo-butane	447	12†	24[273]	74/50, 1.4837
		449	55†	24[273]	74/50, 1.4837
C_6	1,3-Diaminocyclohexane	430	60	24[279]	265Pi
		447	50†	24[279]	198/760, 265Pi
		450	100	24[279]	198/760, 265Pi
	1,4-Diaminocyclohexane	447	72†	24[278]	
C_8	cis-1,4-Diaminomethyl-cyclohexane	427	33†	24[324]	115/8, 350HCl
	trans-1,4-Diaminomethyl-cyclohexane	427	22†		118/10, (27), 380HCl
	N-Ethyl-1,4-cyclohexane-diamine	430	63	24[198]	87/11, 1.4767[25]
C_{10}	N,N-Diethyl-1,4-cyclohex-anediamine	430	70	24[198]	85/4, 1.4720[25]
		Aromatic Diamines			
C_6	o-Phenylenediamine	425	85	24[41]	(101)
	m-Phenylenediamine	425	95	24[14]	154/10, 70Ac
	sym-Triaminobenzene	425	76	24[42]	(84), (112), 357Bz

For explanations and symbols see pp. xi–xii.

TABLE 82 (*continued*)

C_n	Compound	Method	Yield (%)	Chapter[ref.]	B.p./mm., n_D^t, (M.p.), Deriv.
		Aromatic Diamines (*continued*)			
C_7	o-Aminobenzylamine	425	43	24[38]	85–90/1, (59), 138Ac
	m-Aminobenzylamine	452	28 †	24[38]	134/4, 1.6092, 174Bz
	2,4-Diaminotoluene	425	74	24[43]	(98)
	sym-Triaminotoluene	425	60	24[42]	(122)
C_8	Phenylethylenediamine	427	90	24[318]	159Ac
	m-Xylylendiamine	452	38 †	24[436]	141/14, 135Ac
	N-Phenylaminoethyl-amine	441	89	24[451]	
	p-Aminodimethylaniline	....	75	24[517]	140/12, 130Ac
C_{10}	m-Phenylen-β,β'-diethylamine	427	79	24[325]	161/14, 302HCl
	p-Phenylen-β,β'-diethylamine	427	75	24[325]	116/0.9, (36), 210Ac
	N-(2-Dimethylamino-ethyl)-aniline	436	88	24[149]	127/3, 1.5251[25], 124HCl
C_{12}	3,3'-Diaminobiphenyl	425	95	24[14]	
	4,4'-Diaminobiphenyl (benzidine)	425	82	24[44]	(125)
C_{13}	4,4'-Diaminodiphenyl-methane	....	70	24[516]	(91), 237Ac
C_{14}	p,p'-bis-Aminomethyl-biphenyl	427	80	24[326]	180/0.5, (145), 235Pi
C_{15}	p,p'-bis-Aminomethyl-diphenylmethane	427	80	24[326]	(90), 224Bz

For explanations and symbols see pp. xi–xii.

TABLE 83. OLEFINIC AMINES

C_n	Compound	Method	Yield (%)	Chapter[ref.]	B.p./mm., n_D^t, (M.p.), Deriv.
C_3	Allylamine	450	73	24[456]	57/746
C_4	Methallyl amine	435	70	24[100]	78.8, 1.431
		450	35	24[457]	62, 1.4155, 158Pi
	Allylmethylamine	451	48	24[496]	65, 1.4065
		454	71	24[553]	64
C_5	1-Amino-4-pentene	427	60	24[327]	106/767, 1.428[16], 116Pi
	Allyldimethylamine	436	43	24[151]	64, 1.3981[25], 116Pi
C_6	1-Ethylamino-3-butene	436	42	24[152]	109
	Diallylamine	455	88	24[460]	111

TABLE 85. HALO AMINES 695

TABLE 83 *(continued)*

C_n	Compound	Method	Yield (%)	Chapter[ref.]	B.p./mm., n_D^t, (M.p.), Deriv.
C_7	1-Dimethylamino-4-pentene	29	80	2^{193}	118/750, 1.4202[18]
	Allyldiethylamine	436	84	24^{151}	111, 1.4170[25], 91Pi
C_8	p-Aminostyrene	19	20	2^{166}	79/2.5, 1.6070[25]
C_9	1-Diethylamino-4-pentene	29	85	2^{193}	156/746, 1.4310
	2-(o-Aminophenyl)-propene	19	87	2^{103}	87/2, 1.5676[25]
	N-Allylaniline	451	63	24^{495}	80/2
C_{10}	α-Allylbenzylamine	446	90	24^{264}	75/3.5, 1.5300, 153Pi
	p-Dimethylaminostyrene	19	30	2^{455}	1.6120, (17)
C_{14}	cis-p-Aminostilbene	425	72	24^{48}	150/0.2
	trans-p-Aminostilbene				(151)
	cis-o,o'-Diaminostilbene	30	69	2^{220}	(108), 156Pi
	cis-p,p'-Diaminostilbene	30	89	2^{221}	(121), 172Ac
	trans-p,p'-Diaminostilbene	425	81	24^{46}	(229)
	cis-p,p'-Diaminostilbene }	425	89	24^{45}	(121), 172Ac
	trans-p,p'-Diaminostilbene }				(231)

For explanations and symbols see pp. xi–xii.

TABLE 84. ACETYLENIC AMINES

C_n	Compound	Method	Yield (%)	Chapter[ref.]	B.p./mm., n_D^t, (M.p.), Deriv.
C_6	3-Dimethylamino-1-butyne	443	63	24^{472}	95
C_7	1-Diethylamino-2-propyne	43	83	3^{55}	120, 1.4296[25]
C_8	3-Diethylamino-1-butyne	443	65	24^{472}	126, (10), 179HCl
	1-Diethylamino-2-butyne	44	74	3^{55}	153, 1.4413[25]
C_{13}	3-Diethylamino-1-phenyl-1-propyne	444	80	24^{413}	137/18, 137HCl
C_{14}	p,p'-Diaminotolane	425	60	24^{47}	(235), 281Ac

For explanations and symbols see pp. xi–xii.

TABLE 85. HALO AMINES

C_n	Compound	Method	Yield (%)	Chapter[ref.]	B.p./mm., n_D^t, (M.p.), Deriv.
	Aliphatic and Alicyclic Halo Amines				
C_2	β-Bromoethylamine	51	83	4^{70}	
		52	72	4^{138}	173HBr
		....	80	24^{515}	(174)
	β-Iodoethylamine	51	77	4^{573}	
	N-Tetrachloro-1,2-diaminoethane	69	92	4^{656}	78/10, (4.5)

For explanations and symbols see pp. xi–xii.

TABLE 85 *(continued)*

C_n	Compound	Method	Yield (%)	Chapter[ref.]	B.p./mm., n_D^t, (M.p.), Deriv.

Aliphatic and Alicyclic Halo Amines *(continued)*

C_n	Compound	Method	Yield (%)	Chapter[ref.]	B.p./mm., n_D^t, (M.p.), Deriv.
C_3	1-Amino-2-bromopropane	52	70	4[138]	159HBr
	γ-Bromopropylamine	452	89	24[438]	163HBr
	Isopropyldichloroamine	69	76	4[656]	43/15, 1.4572[23]
C_4	2-Chloroethylethylamine	53	91	4[176]	223HCl
	β,β'-Dichlorodiethylamine	53	59	4[177]	217HCl, 136Bz
	β-Dimethylaminoethyl chloride	53	90	4[696]	203HCl
	β-Dimethylaminoethyl bromide	51	83	4[70]	
	t-Butylchloroamine	69	75	4[657]	
	n-Butyldichloroamine	69	92	4[656]	40/17, 46/30, 1.4553
	N-Chlorodiethylamine	69	94	4[655]	
C_5	1-Dimethylamino-2-chloropropane	53	68	4[171]	186HCl, 103Pi
	1-Dimethylamino-3-chloropropane	53	96	4[584]	145HCl
	2-Dimethylamino-1-chloropropane	53	41	4[171]	104HCl, 167Pi
	3-Bromopropyldimethylamine	54	75	4[376]	51/15, 1.4602
C_6	1-Dimethylamino-3-chlorobutane	53	85	4[175]	39/10, 168HCl
	β-Diethylaminoethyl chloride	53	85†	4[170]	69/50
	β-Diethylaminoethyl bromide	51	80	4[70]	
	β,β',β''-Trichlorotriethylamine	53	66	4[178]	133HCl, 137Pi
	o-Chlorocyclohexylamine	52	80	4[137]	85/15
	o-Bromocyclohexylamine	52	70	4[137]	168HCl
	Cyclohexyldichloroamine	69	95	4[656]	90/17
C_7	1-Methylamino-6-bromohexane	54	100	4[128]	60HBr
	1-Diethylamino-2-chloropropane	53	78	4[172]	107HCl, 126Pi
	1-Diethylamino-3-chloropropane	53	57	4[173]	82/28, 171/169, 64HCl
		436	70	24[541]	86HCl
		436	70	24[153]	70/20
	2-Diethylamino-1-chloropropane	53	73	4[172]	107HCl, 113Pi
	3-Bromopropyldiethylamine	54	80	4[375]	94HBr

TABLE 85. HALO AMINES 697

TABLE 85 (continued)

C_n	Compound	Method	Yield (%)	Chapter[ref.]	B.p./mm., n_D^t, (M.p.), Deriv.
	Aliphatic and Alicyclic Halo Amines (continued)				
C_8	1-Bromo-6-dimethylamino-hexane	54	100	4[377]	
	1-Diethylamino-3-chloro-butane	53	87	4[174]	72/17, 82HCl
		436	68	24[541]	84HCl
C_9	1-Diethylamino-3-chloro-pentane	53	72	4[174]	87/18
	1-Diethylamino-4-chloro-pentane	73	90	4[204]	67/5
C_{10}	1-Bromo-6-diethylamino-hexane	54	98	4[377]	
	1-Diethylamino-4-methyl-4-chloropentane	73	75	4[204]	65/3, 1.4459
	Aromatic Halo Amines				
C_6	o-Chloroaniline	425	97	24[50]	95–100/8, 235HCl
		425	92	24[4]	209*, 86Ac
	o-Bromoaniline	425	82	24[6]	229, (32)*, 99Ac*
	o-Iodoaniline	425	83	24[53]	(61), 110Ac*
	m-Fluoroaniline	425	90	24[558]	187/770
	m-Chloroaniline	425	90	24[50]	95–100/9, 119Bz
	m-Bromoaniline	425	80	24[51]	124/10, (17), 120Bz*
		446	87	24[253]	250, 88Ac
	m-Iodoaniline	425	83	24[53]	146/15, (33)*, 119Ac*
	p-Fluoroaniline	425	95	24[52]	99/33, 152Ac*
		425	91	24[558]	188/762, 185Bz*
	p-Chloroaniline	425	100	24[49]	(71), 173Ac
		425	97	24[50]	100–110/8, 188Bz
	p-Bromoaniline	425	97	24[4]	(66)*, 168Ac
		425	83	24[50]	(60), 202Bz
	p-Iodoaniline	64	84	4[290]	(63)
C_7	o-Chlorobenzylamine	426	81	24[50]	95–100/9, 116Bz
		431	88	24[50]	90–95/8, 116Bz
	p-Chlorobenzylamine	427	64	24[50]	98–102/10, 240HCl
		447	100	24[285]	215/734, 259HCl
	o-Aminobenzyl chloride	51	84	4[69]	
	o-Aminobenzyl bromide	51	91	4[208]	
	4-Amino-3-chlorotoluene	64	60	4[291]	225
C_8	1-Phenyl-1-amino-2-chloroethane	52	76	4[138]	190HCl
	N,N-Dimethyl-o-chloro-aniline	436	90	24[132]	206/740
	N,N-Dimethyl-o-bromo-aniline	436	70	24[155]	101/12

For explanations and symbols see pp. xi–xii.

TABLE 85 (continued)

C_n	Compound	Method	Yield (%)	Chapter[ref.]	B.p./mm., n_D^t, (M.p.), Deriv.
	Aromatic Halo Amines (continued)				
C_8	N,N-Dimethyl-m-chloro-aniline	436	75	24[132]	232/740
	N,N-Dimethyl-m-bromo-aniline	436	54	24[155]	119/8, 135Pi
	N,N-Dimethyl-p-fluoro-aniline	436	45	24[154]	(35)
	N,N-Dimethyl-p-chloro-aniline	56	80	4[336]	(33.5)
		436	70	24[154]	(35.5)
		436	72	24[132]	236/740, (33)
	N,N-Dimethyl-p-iodo-aniline	59	48	4[601]	(81)
C_{10}	N,N-Diethyl-o-chloro-aniline	436	91	24[132]	221/740, 164Pi
	N,N-Diethyl-m-chloro-aniline	436	95	24[132]	250/740
	N,N-Diethyl-p-chloro-aniline	436	95	24[132]	253/740, (46)
C_{12}	3,3′-Dibromobenzidene	462	75	24[489]	(129)

For explanations and symbols see pp. xi–xii.

TABLE 86. HYDROXY AMINES

C_n	Compound	Method	Yield (%)	Chapter[ref.]	B.p./mm., n_D^t, (M.p.), Deriv.
	Aliphatic Hydroxy Amines				
C_3	2-Amino-1-propanol	84	80	5[15]	80/18, 1.4502, 114Pi
		425	74	24[57]	78/15
		434	95	24[446]	73/11
	1-Amino-2-hydroxy-propane	442	25	24[467]	65/4, 158/738
	3-Hydroxypropylamine	452	85	24[556]	186
	2-Amino-1,3-propanediol	84	80	5[15]	116/1, 1.4891, 97HCl
	2-(N-Methylamino)-1-ethanol	84	63	5[15]	56/11, 1.4385, 148Pi
	Dimethylaminomethanol	....	70	24[514]	1.4050
C_4	2-Amino-1-butanol	425	90	24[1]	173*
		434	100	24[446]	80/11
	1-Amino-2-butanol (as oxalate)	425	83	24[529]	(200d), 113Bz
	3-Amino-2-butanol	435	49	24[467]	162/742, 1.4482
	2-Amino-2-methyl-1-propanol	84	80	5[15]	69/10, 1.4486, 205HCl
		425	90	24[1]	

TABLE 86. HYDROXY AMINES 699

TABLE 86 *(continued)*

C_n	Compound	Method	Yield (%)	Chapter[ref.]	B.p./mm., n_{D}^t, (M.p.), Deriv.
		Aliphatic Hydroxy Amines *(continued)*			
C_4	1-Amino-2-methyl-2-propanol	442	30	24[465]	145–155
	β-Ethylaminoethanol	436	35	24[156]	169, 1.4440
		442	55	24[462]	169
	2-Amino-1,3-butanediol	84	80	5[15]	113/2, 1.4833[21]
	2-Amino-2-methyl-1,3-propanediol	425	96	24[1]	
C_5	4-Amino-1-pentanol	426	80	24[354]	119/25, 100Bz
	5-Amino-1-pentanol	431	77	24[228]	81/1, (39)
		452	60	24[556]	271
	3-Amino-2-pentanol	425	92	24[54]	100/10, 1.4419
	1-Amino-4-pentanol	436	32	24[152]	81/1, 1.4551[25]
	2-Methyl-2-amino-1-butanol	425	86	24[54]	98/10, 1.4468
	2-Amino-3-methyl-1-butanol (valinol)	84		5[82]	(119)
	2-Methyl-3-amino-2-butanol	91	66	5[438]	117HCl
	3-Methylamino-2-methyl-2-propanol	436	52	24[164]	143, 1.4338, 138Pi
	2-Isopropylaminoethanol	431	95	24[223]	87/23
		442	76	24[463]	171
	2-Dimethylamino-1-propanol	436	82	24[57]	65/37
	3-Dimethylamino-1-propanol	443	65	24[473]	113/150
	1-Dimethylamino-2-propanol	442	70	24[464]	126/758
	2-Amino-2-ethyl-1,3-propanediol	425	92	24[1]	
C_6	2-Amino-1-hexanol	84	65	5[84]	104/13, 114Pi
	2-Hydroxy-3-aminohexane	97	45	5[292]	95/20, 207Db
	2-Amino-4-methyl-1-pentanol	84	55	5[84]	95/11, (44), 163HCl
		434	90	24[446]	99/11
	4-Methyl-4-amino-2-pentanol	79	34	5[170]	75/15
	5-Methylamino-1-pentanol	431	50†	24[229]	97/3
	2,2-Dimethyl-3-methylamino-1-propanol	79	72	5[675]	70–82/12
		436	57	24[166]	71/14, (46), 173HCl
	1-Isopropylamino-2-propanol	431	97	24[224]	76/22, 1.4322[25], 131Pi
	3-Ethylamino-2-methyl-2-propanol	436	56	24[164]	153, 1.4344, 133Pi
	3-Dimethylamino-1-butanol	79	35	5[185]	78/14, 105BzHCl

For explanations and symbols see pp. xi–xii.

TABLE 86 *(continued)*

C_n	Compound	Method	Yield (%)	Chapter[ref.]	B.p./mm., n_D^t, (M.p.), Deriv.

Aliphatic Hydroxy Amines *(continued)*

C_n	Compound	Method	Yield (%)	Chapter[ref.]	B.p./mm., n_D^t, (M.p.), Deriv.
C_6	4-Dimethylamino-2-butanol	79	85	5[172]	
	3-Dimethylamino-2-methyl-1-propanol	84	50	5[85]	164
	3-Dimethylamino-2-methyl-2-propanol	436	40[†]	24[163]	130/743, 1.4215, 115HCl
	β-Diethylaminoethanol	436	70	24[156]	65/18, 1.4389[25]
		442	81	24[461]	160/741, 1.4389[25]
C_7	2-Amino-2,4-dimethyl-1-pentanol	84	80	5[15]	98/12, 1.4563
	1-Ethylamino-4-pentanol	436	32	24[152]	81/1.0, 1.4551[25], 148HBr
	5-Dimethylamino-1-pentanol	431	59[†]	24[229]	114/23
	4-Dimethylamino-2-methyl-2-butanol	436	34[†]	24[163]	160/743, 1.4295, 141HCl
	2-Diethylamino-1-propanol	84	63	5[83]	66/18, 1.4332
	3-Diethylamino-1-propanol	436	91	24[158]	95/28
	2,2-Dimethyl-3-dimethyl-amino-1-propanol	436	64	24[166]	63/15, 132HCl
	1-Diethylamino-2-propanol	442	88	24[464]	63/22, 1.4265*, 139HCl*
C_8	5-Isopropylamino-1-pentanol	431	71[†]	24[230]	98HCl
	5-Dimethylamino-2-methyl-2-pentanol	436	34[†]	24[163]	99/30, 1.4400, 154HCl
	3-Diethylamino-1-butanol	79	45	5[185]	85/13, 161BzHCl
	4-Diethylamino-1-butanol	84	52	5[86]	92/9, 1.4474
	1-Diethylamino-3-butanol	79	40	5[168]	73/20, 116HCl
		436	60	24[165]	82/18, 1.4372[25], 116HCl
C_9	5-Diethylamino-1-pentanol	95	68	5[709]	131/23, 1.4544
	2-Diethylamino-3-methyl-1-butanol	84	44	5[86]	90/14
	2,2-Dimethyl-3-diethyl-amino-1-propanol	79	86	5[675]	88/12
C_{10}	1-Diethylamino-5-hexanol	80	88	5[192]	108/10, 1.4490[25]

Alicyclic Hydroxy Amines

C_n	Compound	Method	Yield (%)	Chapter[ref.]	B.p./mm., n_D^t, (M.p.), Deriv.
C_5	*trans*-2-Aminocyclo-pentanol	442	40	24[466]	194HCl
C_6	2-Aminocyclohexanol	442	63	24[467]	214, (66)
	cis-2-Aminocyclohexanol	447	68	24[284]	110/15, (70), 185HCl
	trans-2-Aminocyclo-hexanol				108/15, (67), 175HCl
	cis-2-Aminocyclohexanol	435	50	24[99]	(73), 187HCl
	trans-2-Aminocyclo-hexanol	435	72	24[99]	104/7, (66), 175HCl
		442	64	24[549]	111/16, (69), 169Bz

TABLE 86. HYDROXY AMINES 701

TABLE 86 *(continued)*

C_n	Compound	Method	Yield (%)	Chapter[ref.]	B.p./mm., n_D^t, (M.p.), Deriv.

Alicyclic Hydroxy Amines *(continued)*

C_n	Compound	Method	Yield (%)	Chapter[ref.]	B.p./mm., n_D^t, (M.p.), Deriv.
C_6	*cis-trans-*4-Aminocyclo-hexanol	430	98	24[381]	(80), (111)
	1-Amino-1-hydroxymethyl-cyclopentane	84	80	5[15]	69/1, 1.4899, 131HCl
	1-Aminomethyl cyclo-pentanol	427	50	24[543]	140/40, 190HCl
C_7	1-Aminomethylcyclo-hexanol	427	70	24[543]	115/20, 190HCl
	2-Aminomethylcyclo-hexanol	427	68	24[335]	133/17, 1.4910[25], 150HCl
	1-Amino-1-hydroxy-methylcyclohexane	84	80	5[15]	118/27, 1.4970, 159HCl
C_8	2-(N-Cyclohexylamino)-1-ethanol	84	80	5[15]	97/3, 1.4862, 130Pi
C_9	2-Amino-2-cyclohexyl-1-propanol	84	80	5[15]	104/2, (80), 202HCl
	2-Amino-3-cyclohexyl-1-propanol	84	80	5[15]	108/1, 1.4989, 192HCl

Aromatic Hydroxy Amines

C_n	Compound	Method	Yield (%)	Chapter[ref.]	B.p./mm., n_D^t, (M.p.), Deriv.
C_6	*o*-Aminophenol	446	72	24[266]	(171)
	m-Aminophenol	438	50	24[390]	(123), 229HCl
C_7	*o*-Aminobenzyl alcohol	84	78	5[81]	(81)
	m-Aminobenzyl alcohol	425	100	24[61]	(96)
C_8	β-Amino-α-phenylethyl alcohol	427	80	24[333]	(57)
		442	18	24[468]	149-155/16
	β-Amino-β-phenylethyl alcohol	84	93	5[84]	103/2, (111), 208Pi
	β-(4-Aminophenyl)-ethanol	425	88	24[62]	(108)
	m-Aminophenylmethyl-carbinol	425	94	24[60]	(64)
	2-Anilinoethanol	450	75	24[458]	170/19, 1.5749
C_9	2-Amino-1-phenyl-1-propanol	425	87	24[55]	122/4-5
		426	71†	24[356]	(103), 191HCl
	2-Amino-3-phenyl-1-propanol	84	52	5[84]	156HCl
	3-Amino-1-phenyl-1-propanol	79	70	5[166]	(64), 86Bz
	α-Phenyl-β-methyl-aminoethanol	79	90	5[167]	(76)
	3-Anilino-1-propanol	436	68	24[159]	192/30, 1.502
		450	80	24[459]	154/5, 1.568[18]

For explanations and symbols see pp. xi–xii.

TABLE 86 *(continued)*

C_n	Compound	Method	Yield (%)	Chapter[ref.]	B.p./mm., n_D^t, (M.p.), Deriv.
		Aromatic Hydroxy Amines *(continued)*			
C_9	p-Dimethylaminobenzyl alcohol	79	96	5[2]	1.5775[25]
		....	65	5[781]	125/1, 1.5727[14]
C_{10}	1-Amino-2-phenyl-2-butanol	89	73	5[403]	181HCl
	2-Amino-3-phenyl-3-butanol	89	63	5[403]	239HCl
	2-Methylamino-1-phenyl-1-propanol	431	81	24[55]	115–120/5
		79	90	5[167]	(77)
	β-Ethylamino-α-phenylethyl alcohol	442	56	24[468]	140–164/14, (78)
	4-Amino-1-naphthol	433	75	24[554]	
	1-Amino-2-naphthol	433	85	24[554]	
C_{11}	2-Amino-3-phenyl-3-pentanol	89	93	5[403]	222HCl
	1-Phenyl-2-methylamino-1-butanol	79	60	5[169]	202HCl, 168Pi
		79	90	5[167]	(90)
	2-Methylamino-3-phenyl-3-butanol	89	75	5[403]	235HCl
	5-Anilino-1-pentanol	436	45	24[167]	164/1.4
	2-Diethylaminomethylphenol	444	69	24[415]	67/2, 1.5108[25]
C_{12}	Phenyl-γ-dimethylaminopropylcarbinol	89	70	5[402]	107/0.07, (48)
	β-Diethylamino-α-phenylethyl alcohol	436	66	24[468]	145/14, 1.5101[25]
	6-Anilino-1-hexanol	436	74	24[167]	138/0.05, (42)

For explanations and symbols see pp. xi–xii.

TABLE 87. AMINO ETHERS

C_n	Compound	Method	Yield (%)	Chapter[ref.]	B.p./mm., n_D^t, (M.p.), Deriv.
		Aliphatic Amino Ethers			
C_4	γ-Methoxy-n-propylamine	427	50	24[329]	118/733, 1.4182
C_5	γ-Ethoxy-n-propylamine	427	50	24[329]	136/732, 1.4201
	β-Methoxyisobutylamine	428	42	24[330]	121, 1.4204
	γ-Methoxyisobutylamine	427	59	24[330]	128, 1.4192[23]
C_6	β-Ethoxy-n-butyl amine	435	42	24[101]	140, 1.4190
	Diethylaminomethyl methyl ether	445	40	24[513]	116/755
	Di-(γ-aminopropyl) ether	427	77	24[328]	59/1.5, 1.4605, 152Pi
C_7	2-Methoxy-3-aminohexane	432	34	24[407]	98/100

TABLE 87. AMINO ETHERS 703

TABLE 87 *(continued)*

C_n	Compound	Method	Yield (%)	Chapter[ref.]	B.p./mm., n_D^t, (M.p.), Deriv.
		Aliphatic Amino Ethers *(continued)*			
C_7	β-Ethoxy-*n*-amyl amine	435	44	24[101]	56/15, 1.4220
	Diethylaminomethyl ethyl ether	445	69	24[513]	134/756
C_8	β-Ethoxy-*n*-hexyl amine	435	60	24[101]	69/13, 1.4271
	1-Methylamino-6-methoxy-hexane	436	79	24[152]	84/15
C_9	1-Ethylamino-6-methoxy-hexane	436	73	24[173]	90/2, 1.4269[27]
	1-Methoxy-4-ethylamino-hexane	436	60	24[152]	89/16
	1-Dimethylamino-6-methoxyhexane	436	78	24[173]	78/11
C_{10}	1-Diethylamino-5-methoxy-pentane	436	91	24[152]	77/18, 1.2490
C_{12}	β,β′,β″-Triethoxytri-ethylamine	115	66	6[61]	137/12, 195HCl
		Aromatic Amino Ethers			
C_7	*m*-Aminoanisole (*m*-anisidine)	425	80	24[63]	125/13
C_8	β-Phenoxyethylamine	428	80	24[344]	104/12, 168Pi
		435	65	24[96]	115/12
	p-Aminophenetole	425	78	24[6]	254*, 138Ac*
	3,4-Dimethoxyaniline (4-aminoveratrole)	446	82	24[265]	174/24, (88)
C_9	γ-Phenoxypropyl amine	435	71	24[96]	126/15, (13)
	2-Phenoxyisopropylamine	426	65	24[355]	120/13, 1.5237, 148HCl
	N-Ethyl-*p*-anisidine	431	51	24[213]	135–140/20, 1.5444
	p-Methoxydimethylamino-benzene	436	55	24[132]	234/740, (38.5)
C_{10}	δ-Phenoxy-*n*-butylamine	427	87	24[331]	148/17
	3-Phenoxypropylmethyl-amine	436	61	24[172]	133–138/23, 1.5255, 151HCl
	β-Ethoxy-β-phenylethyl amine	435	62	24[101]	109/12, 1.5102
C_{11}	3-Phenoxypropylethylamine	436	66	24[172]	148/26, 1.5127, 155HCl
	3-Phenoxypropyldimethyl-amine	436	82	24[171]	132/20
	p-Methoxydiethylamino-benzene	436	74	24[132]	247/740
C_{12}	2-Aminodiphenyl ether	425	94	24[65]	173/14, (47), 81Ac

For explanations and symbols see pp. xi–xii.

TABLE 87 *(continued)*

C_n	Compound	Method	Yield (%)	Chapter[ref.]	B.p./mm., n_D^t, (M.p.), Deriv.
		Aromatic Amino Ethers *(continued)*			
C_{12}	3-Aminodiphenyl ether	115	57	6[14]	191/14, (37)
		425	84	24[64]	148/1, 141HCl
	4-Aminodiphenyl ether	115	65	6[14]	(83.5)
		425	100	24[66]	189/14, (83.5)
C_{13}	3-Phenoxypropyldiethyl- amine	436	94	24[170]	150/20, 1.4987, 102HCl
C_{14}	1-Phenoxy-6-ethylamino- hexane	436	90	24[174]	148/3, 1.5010, 135HCl

For explanations and symbols see pp. xi–xii.

TABLE 88. AMINO ALDEHYDES

C_n	Compound	Method	Yield (%)	Chapter[ref.]	B.p./mm., n_D^t, (M.p.), Deriv.
C_6	α-Dimethylaminoisobutyr- aldehyde	436	32	24[175]	129
C_7	α,α-Dimethyl-β-dimethyl- aminopropionaldehyde	444	80	24[416]	144, 153HCl
	o-Aminobenzaldehyde	425	75	24[67]	(40)*
	m-Aminobenzaldehyde	149	52	9[127]	162Ph
	p-Aminobenzaldehyde	155	52	9[156]	
		425	50	24[560]	(70)
C_9	m-Dimethylaminobenz- aldehyde	425	74†	24[68]	112/7, 229Se
		431	27	24[530]	114/3, 76-Ox*
	p-Dimethylaminobenz- aldehyde	142	80	9[103]	166/15, (73)
		144	45	9[99]	180/20, (73), 148Ph
		150	59	9[187]	(73), 144-Ox*
C_{10}	p-Formylphenyl-tri- methylammonium iodide	148	68	9[261]	(152d)
C_{11}	m-Diethylaminobenz- aldehyde	436	48†	24[177]	138/7, 165Se
	p-Diethylaminobenz- aldehyde	144	45	9[99]	(41), 121Ph
		150	50	9[188]	(41), 93-Ox*

For explanations and symbols see pp. xi–xii.

TABLE 89. AMINO KETONES   705

TABLE 89. AMINO KETONES

C_n	Compound	Method	Yield (%)	Chapter[ref.]	B.p./mm., n_D^t, (M.p.), Deriv.
		Aliphatic and Alicyclic Amino Ketones			
C_3	Aminoacetone	426	96	24[358]	75HCl
	Diaminoacetone	426	83	24[359]	
C_5	Dimethylaminoacetone	436	74	24[178]	36/25, 1.4128, 137Se*
C_6	1-Dimethylamino-3-butanone	444	45	24[417]	70/40, 1.4213[25]
	Diacetonamine (as acid oxalate)	443	70	24[474]	(127)
C_7	Diethylaminoacetone	436	72	24[179]	70/32, 1.4249, 143Se
C_8	1-Diethylamino-3-butanone	444	59	24[417]	70/11, 1.4333[24]
	Diacetonethylamine	443	42	24[476]	191
C_9	1-Dimethylamino-3-methyl-5-hexanone	184	46	10[308]	83/11
	1-Diethylamino-2-pentanone	436	79	24[538]	91/24, 104Se
	1-Diethylamino-3-pentanone	436	55	24[180]	84/13, 1.4368[15]
		443	37	24[538]	96/36, 102Se
	2-Dimethylaminomethyl-cyclohexanone	444	71	24[419]	97/11.5, 146HCl
C_{10}	5-Diethylamino-2-hexanone	184	42	10[309]	95/16, 1.4337[25]
	1-Diethylamino-4-hexanone	184	44†	10[306]	108/20
	1-Diethylamino-5-hexanone	184	60†	10[307]	98/11, 1.4380[25]
	2-Diethylaminomethyl-cyclopentanone	444	85	24[418]	103/13
		Aromatic Amino Ketones			
C_8	ω-Aminoacetophenone hydrochloride	437	75	24[238]	(187)
	o-Aminoacetophenone	425	78	24[69]	113/6, 75Ac
	m-Aminoacetophenone	425	71	24[70]	(99), 128Ac
	p-Acetylaniline	178	19	10[26]	168/6, (106), 166Ac
	N,N-Dimethyl-p-bromoaniline	431	88	24[221]	145/22, (53)
C_9	α-Aminopropiophenone	426	88	24[357]	114HCl
	β-Aminopropiophenone	452	80	24[440]	127HCl
	o-Aminopropiophenone	425	76	24[81]	146/17, 74Ac
	m-Aminopropiophenone	425	96	24[71]	169/15, (42), 93Ac
C_{10}	2-Phenylamino-3-butanone	436	80	24[182]	121/4, (52)

For explanations and symbols see pp. xi-xii.

TABLE 89 *(continued)*

C_n	Compound	Method	Yield (%)	Chapter ref.	B.p./mm., n_D^t, (M.p.), Deriv.
		Aromatic Amino Ketones (continued)			
C₁₀	α-Methylamino-propiophenone	436	57	24[185]	177HCl
	o-Dimethylamino-acetophenone	436	56	24[186]	94/1.5, 184Pi
C₁₁	3-Phenylamino-2-pentanone	436	72	24[181]	120/1
	α-Methylaminobutyr-ophenone	436	70	24[185]	194HCl
	1-Phenyl-3-dimethyl-amino-2-propanone	187	53	10[676]	141/26, 127Pi
	β-Dimethylaminopro-piophenone	444	72	24[420]	156HCl
C₁₂	1-Dimethylamino-4-phenyl-2-butanone	436	43	24[184]	107/3.5, 1.5070
	β-Dimethylamino-α-methylpropiophenone	444	74	24[421]	82/1, 1.5162²⁵, 154HCl
C₁₃	2-Aminobenzophenone	446	92	24[259]	(107)
	4,4′-Diaminobenzophenone	183	70 †	10[248]	(245), 241Ph
	1-Aminofluorenone	446	56	24[267]	(118.5), 138Ac
	4-Aminofluorenone	446	74	24[267]	(139)
C₁₅	1-Phenyl-1-phenylamino-propanone	436	74	24[183]	(91.5)
C₁₆	p-Dimethylaminobenzil	179	90	10[199]	(116)

For explanations and symbols see pp. xi–xii.

TABLE 90. AMINO ACIDS

C_n	Compound	Method	Yield (%)	Chapter ref.	B.p./mm., n_D^t, (M.p.), Deriv.
C₂	Aminoacetic acid	247	92	13[519]	(263), 67Am*
	(glycine)	247	87	13[518]	(246), 62An*
		435	77	24[104]	(236d)
		447	54 †	24[278]	
		452	85 †	24[443]	
C₃	α-Aminopropionic acid	247	72 †	13[519]	(295), 62Am*
	(alanine)	247	60	13[520]	(295)
		253	44 †	13[526]	163Bz
		435	70	24[105]	(295d)
		451	71	24[500]	
	β-Aminopropionic acid	247	90	13[523]	(198), 123HCl*
	(β-alanine)	247	86	13[521]	

TABLE 90. AMINO ACIDS 707

TABLE 90 *(continued)*

C_n	Compound	Method	Yield (%)	Chapter[ref.]	B.p./mm., n_D^t, (M.p.), Deriv.
C_3	β-Aminopropionic acid	247	90	13[522]	(198)
	(β-alanine) *(continued)*	247	75[†]	13[524]	(200)
		247	69[†]	13[525]	(197)
		248	70	13[201]	
		249	72	13[527]	(195)
		427	75	24[336]	(195)
		437	85	24[239]	(200d)
		446	45	24[268]	(198d)
	α-Amino-β-hydroxypro-	97	40[†]	5[542]	
	pionic acid (serine)	247	51[†]	13[528]	(244), 150Bz
C_4	α-Amino-n-butyric acid	247	61[†]	13[519]	(304), 75Am*
		253	50[†]	13[529]	140Bz
		278	82	13[548]	142Bz
		431	58	24[233]	
		435	60	24[102]	
		447	21[†]	24[290]	182HCl
	γ-Aminobutyric acid	452	62	24[441]	
	α-Aminoisobutyric acid	247	70	13[530]	
		247	33	13[531]	
		247	73[†]	13[519]	
		253	77[†]	13[529]	198Bz
		280	76	13[530]	127Am*
	α-Methyl-β-alanine	427	73	24[339]	(182)
	N-Methylalanine	451	81	24[499]	(317d), 129Bz
	N-Ethylglycine	451	70	24[499]	(182d)
	N,N-Dimethylglycine	431	100	24[232]	(183)
	α-Aminosuccinic (*dl*-	278	43	13[643]	162Bz
	aspartic) acid	451	95	24[498]	(280d)
	α,γ-Diaminobutyric acid	449	41	24[300]	(215d), 181Pi
	meso-α,β-Diamino-	434	90	24[448]	(306d)
	succinic acid				
	α-Amino-β-hydroxy-	97	90	5[543]	(235)
	butyric acid				
C_5	α-Aminovaleric acid	247	68[†]	13[519]	(291), 188HCl*
	(norvaline)	278	86	13[557]	117Ac
		447	43	24[289]	188HCl
		447	31	24[287]	152Bz
	γ-Aminovaleric acid	425	99	24[531]	(197)
	δ-Aminovaleric acid	248	71	13[533]	(158)*, 90Bz
		248	80	13[534]	94HCl
	α-Aminoisovaleric acid	278	85	13[644]	
	(*dl*-valine)	435	48	24[106]	(282d)
		447	33[†]	24[289]	
		447	60	24[288]	
	γ-Amino-β-methylbutyric	452	40	24[442]	(174)
	acid				

For explanations and symbols see pp. xi–xii.

TABLE 90 (*continued*)

C_n	Compound	Method	Yield (%)	Chapter[ref.]	B.p./mm., n_D^t, (M.p.), Deriv.
C_5	*dl*-α-Methylaminobutyric acid	431	62	24[233]	
	γ-N-Methylaminobutyric acid	248	90	13[598]	121HCl
	N-Methyl-α-aminoisobutyric acid	247	43†	13[537]	
	N,N-Dimethylalanine monohydrate	431	100	24[232]	(182), 148HCl
	α-Aminoglutaric (*dl*-glutamic) acid	247	75	13[182]	
		278	64†	13[557]	(199)*, 193HCl*
		278	75	13[535]	
		....	....	13[536]	(213), 202HCl*
	α-Amino-α-methyl-succinic acid	247	51†	13[519]	(230)
	α,δ-Diamino-*n*-valeric acid (*dl*-ornithine)	449	75	24[300]	200Pi, 187Bz
	Methyliminodiacetic acid	436	71	24[187]	(215)
	γ-Methylmercapto-α-amino-butyric acid (*dl*-methionine)	278	85	13[642]	(280), 145Bz
C_6	*dl*-α-Amino-*n*-caproic acid (norleucine)	435	67	24[108]	
	γ-Amino-*n*-caproic acid	426	47	24[366]	(181), 121HCl
	ε-Aminocaproic acid	248	100	13[540]	(202), 105HBr*
		248	92	13[541]	(203)
	dl-α-Amino-β-methyl-valeric acid	247	74†	13[519]	(318)
		435	49	24[109]	(280d)
	α-Aminoisocaproic acid (leucine)	278	64	13[557]	(295)*, 161Ac
		278	87	13[542]	(283), 141Bz
		435	45	24[107]	(292d)
		447	51	24[287]	(293)
		447	68	24[289]	(282)
	α-Amino-α-ethylbutyric acid	247	43†	13[543]	
	α-Dimethylaminoiso-butyric acid	436	80	24[123]	264HCl
	α-Aminoadipic acid	253	48†	13[608]	(189)
		435	86	24[534]	(202)
		452	84	24[534]	(202)
	α,δ-Diaminoadipic acid	452	91	24[429]	(300)
	α,ε-Diaminocaproic acid (*dl*-lysine)	280	78	13[649]	253HCl
		435	69	24[110]	189HCl
		449	74	24[300]	189HCl
	dl-lysine dihydrochloride	435	62	24[533]	188HCl
	l-Cystine	....	....	13[545]	(261)*
		....	....	13[546]	

TABLE 90. AMINO ACIDS 709

TABLE 90 *(continued)*

C_n	Compound	Method	Yield (%)	Chapter[ref.]	B.p./mm., n_D^t, (M.p.), Deriv.
C_6	Histidine	278	45	13[542]	(272)
	l-Histidine hydrochloride	....	....	13[544]	(252)
	d-Arginine hydrochloride	....	90	13[547]	(220)
C_7	α-Aminoheptanoic acid	278	55	13[548]	(281), 135Bz
	7-Aminoheptanoic acid	427	30	24[337]	(187)
	β,β-Diethyl-β-amino-propionic acid	443	30	24[486]	(184)
	N,N-Dimethyl-*dl*-valine	431	100	24[232]	(152), 164HCl
	α-Methyl-γ-dimethyl-aminobutyric acid	249	90	13[549]	(76)
	β-Dimethylaminopivalic acid	253	74	13[436]	(99)
	β-2-Thienylalanine	426	68	24[314]	(275)
C_8	α-Aminoöctanoic acid	247	47†	13[550]	
		278	82	13[548]	(270), 128Bz
	N,N-Dimethyl-*dl*-leucine	431	100	24[232]	(188)
	α-Aminophenylacetic acid	247	37†	13[551]	176Bz*
	o-Aminophenylacetic acid	425	85	24[74]	(119)
	m-Aminophenylacetic acid	248	61	13[147]	(146), 166Am*
	p-Aminophenylacetic acid	248	51	13[147]	(197), 162Am*
		425	84	24[73]	(200)
	p-Aminomethyl)-benzoic acid	427	80	24[338]	(342), 288HCl
		437	64†	24[240]	
C_9	α-Aminononanoic acid	278	55	13[548]	(273), 128Bz
		280	92	13[552]	
	α-Amino-α-phenyl-propionic acid	247	40†	13[553]	(267)
	α-Amino-β-phenyl-propionic acid	278	83	13[557]	146Ac
		278	67	13[542]	(257), 184Bz
		279	67	13[556]	(288)
	dl-α-Amino-β-phenyl-propionic acid	431	62	24[233]	
		435	62†	24[111]	(273d)
		447	50	24[288]	(265)
		447	44†	24[278]	235HCl
	β-Amino-α-phenyl-propionic acid	446	66	24[269]	(223)
	β-Amino-β-phenyl-propionic acid	264	50	13[554]	
		264	70	13[555]	(222)
		443	34	24[485]	(221d)
	p-(β-Aminoethyl)-benzoic acid	260	48†	13[558]	175Ac
	m-Dimethylaminobenzoic acid	431	100	24[232]	(150)
	p-Dimethylaminobenzoic acid	431	80	24[232]	(240)
		263	50	13[619]	(243)*

For explanations and symbols see pp. xi–xii.

TABLE 90 *(continued)*

C_n	Compound	Method	Yield (%)	Chapter[ref.]	B.p./mm., n_D^t, (M.p.), Deriv.
C$_9$	β-Anilinopropionic acid	249	65	13[265]	(60)
C$_{10}$	dl-γ-Phenyl-α-amino-butyric acid	431	62	24[233]	
C$_{11}$	Tryptophane	278	45[†]	13[560]	(282), 206Ac
		278	88	13[561]	193Bz

For explanations and symbols see pp. xi–xii.

TABLE 91. AMINO ESTERS

C_n	Compound	Method	Yield (%)	Chapter[ref.]	B.p./mm., n_D^t, (M.p.), Deriv.
		Aliphatic Amino Esters			
C$_4$	Methyl β-aminopropionate	292	67	14[301]	51/12
	Ethyl aminoacetate	293	90	14[171]	143HCl
C$_5$	Methyl α-aminoisobutyrate	285	64	14[73]	134, 183HCl
	Ethyl α-aminopropionate	285	95	14[7]	
	Ethyl β-aminopropionate	427	74	24[340]	56/10
		434	100	24[447]	67HCl
	Methyl β-methylamino-propionate	443	40	24[447]	50/11
C$_6$	Ethyl β-amino-n-butyrate	426	21[†]	24[367]	69/17, 148Pi
		443	55	24[482]	62/10, 74Am
	Ethyl β-methylamino-propionate	443	49	24[478]	68/18, 1.4218[22]
C$_7$	Ethyl β-amino-n-valerate	426	23[†]	24[367]	84/17
	Ethyl α-methylamino-butyrate	436	63	24[190]	65/20, 1.4174, 104Pi
	Ethyl β-methylamino-n-butyrate	443	89	24[482]	66/10
	Ethyl aminomalonate (as acetyl derivative)	426	44[†]	24[364]	(96)
C$_8$	Ethyl α-amino-n-caproate	426	86	24[361]	88/11
	Ethyl β-amino-n-caproate	426	48	24[367]	104/25
	Isobutyl α-aminoiso-butyrate	285	66	14[72]	61/4, 1.4210, 103HCl
	Ethyl β-ethylamino-n-butyrate	431	68	24[367]	75/12
	Methyl β-diethylamino-propionate	443	100	24[477]	66.5/8
	Ethyl α-aminosuccinate (dl-aspartic ester)	426	70	24[365]	98/1

TABLE 92. AMINO CYANIDES   711

TABLE 91 *(continued)*

C_n	Compound	Method	Yield (%)	Chapter[ref.]	B.p./mm., n_D^t, (M.p.), Deriv.
		Aliphatic Amino Esters *(continued)*			
C_9	Ethyl α-methyl-γ-dimethylaminobutyrate	285	63 [‡]	14[290]	83/16
	Methyl γ-diethylaminobutyrate	436	74	24[189]	63/3, 102HCl
	Ethyl α-diethylaminopropionate	436	84	24[188]	75/13
	Diethyl dimethylaminomalonate	436	74	24[521]	117/15, 1.4320[19]
C_{10}	Ethyl γ-diethylaminobutyrate	285	70 [‡]	14[291]	105/17, 1.4342
		Aromatic Amino Esters			
C_8	Methyl o-aminobenzoate	285	85	14[1]	139/19
	Methyl m-aminobenzoate	321	48	14[428]	(37)
		425	95	24[76]	153/11, (37), 137Ac
	Methyl p-aminobenzoate	285	53	14[1]	
C_9	Ethyl p-aminobenzoate	425	100	24[75]	(90)
C_{10}	Ethyl α-aminophenylacetate	285	65	14[74]	115/5, 1.500[25], 200HCl
	Ethyl m-aminophenylacetate	425	87	24[77]	140/4, 1.5435[21], 131HCl
	Ethyl p-(aminomethyl)benzoate	437	40	24[240]	148/8, 237HCl
	Methyl β-anilinopropionate	443	69	24[479]	160/14, (38)
	Methyl o-dimethylaminobenzoate	436	60	24[192]	137–142/17
C_{11}	Ethyl α-amino-β-phenylpropionate	426	53	24[361]	142/10
	Ethyl β-amino-β-phenylpropionate	443	35	24[483]	146/11

For explanations and symbols see pp. xi–xii.

TABLE 92. AMINO CYANIDES

C_n	Compound	Method	Yield (%)	Chapter[ref.]	B.p./mm., n_D^t, (M.p.), Deriv.
		Aliphatic and Alicyclic Amino Cyanides			
C_2	Aminoacetonitrile hydrochloride	391	95	20[328]	(166)
	Aminoacetonitrile hydrogen sulfate	....	81	24[525]	

For explanations and symbols see pp. xi–xii.

TABLE 92 *(continued)*

C_n	Compound	Method	Yield (%)	Chapter[ref.]	B.p./mm., n_D^t, (M.p.), Deriv.
		Aliphatic and Alicyclic Amino Cyanides (continued)			
C_3	β-Aminopropionitrile	388	33	20[247]	89/20, 1.3496
	Methylaminoacetonitrile	391	93	20[390]	65/20
	Methyleneaminoaceto-nitrile	391	71	20[312]	(129)
C_4	3-Amino-*n*-propyl cyanide	452	38†	24[445]	97/20, 140HCl
	α-Aminoisobutyronitrile	391	77	20[317]	48/11
		391	80	20[327]	68/24, 1.4198
	β-Methylaminopropio-nitrile	388	78	20[248]	74/16, 1.4342[15]
	Ethylaminoacetonitrile	391	70	20[324]	83/29
	Dimethylaminoacetonitrile	391	83	20[313]	134–137, 1.4095[25]
	Iminodiacetonitrile	392	100	20[341]	(75)
C_5	α-Methylaminoisobutyro-nitrile	391	57	20[388]	54/18, 133/747, 1.4176
	β-Ethylaminopropionitrile	388	90	20[250]	95/30, 1.4322
	Isopropylaminoaceto-nitrile	391	89	20[389]	169HCl
		391	90	20[390]	85/20
C_6	5-Amino-*n*-amyl cyanide	452	68†	24[445]	118/14, 98Bz
	α-Aminodiethylaceto-nitrile	391	40	20[317]	71/11
	α-Methylamino-*n*-valeronitrile	391	85	20[390]	85/25
		392	77	20[391]	74/14, 167, 1.4362[14], 103Pi
	α-Methylaminoiso-valeronitrile	391	80	20[390]	70/20
	α-Methylamino-α-methyl-*n*-butyronitrile	391	83	20[388]	68/17, 1.4282[21], 83Bz
	α-Ethylaminoisobutyro-nitrile	391	94	20[321]	144/761
	β-*n*-Propylaminopropio-nitrile	388	92	20[249]	121/30, 1.4362
	β-Isopropylaminopropio-nitrile	388	95	20[251]	87/17, 1.4290[25]
	α-Dimethylaminobutyro-nitrile	391	78	20[319]	68/23
	4-Dimethylaminobutyro-nitrile	387	64	20[215]	44–47/1.5
	α-Dimethylaminoisobutyro-nitrile	391	69	20[319]	57/25
		391	88	20[327]	50/20, 1.4215
	Diethylaminoacetonitrile	391	90	20[322]	63/14, 1.4230[25]
C_7	α-Aminomethylbutylaceto-nitrile	391	51	20[317]	88/10
	α-Aminomethylisobutylaceto-nitrile	391	53	20[317]	76/10

TABLE 92. AMINO CYANIDES 713

TABLE 92 *(continued)*

C_n	Compound	Method	Yield (%)	Chapter[ref.]	B.p./mm., n_D^t, (M.p.), Deriv.
		Aliphatic and Alicyclic Amino Cyanides *(continued)*			
C_7	α-Methylamino-α-ethyl-butyronitrile	391	73	20[321]	167/765
	α-Dimethylamino-α-methyl-butyronitrile	391	70	20[319]	63/12
	α-Methylethylaminoiso-butyronitrile	391	53	20[319]	58/14
	α-Diethylaminopropio-nitrile	391	65	20[323]	49/7, 68/17
		391	68	20[319]	55/11
	β-Diethylaminopropio-nitrile	388	97	20[250]	120/70, 1.4353
		436	56	24[194]	84/13, 1.4343[25]
	1-Amino-1-cyanocyclo-hexane hydrochloride		77	20[315]	(204)
C_8	α-Ethylamino-α-isobutyl-acetonitrile	391	84	20[324]	84/12
	α-Dimethylamino-α-methyl-*n*-valeronitrile	391	49	20[319]	75/10
	α-Dimethylamino-α-methyl-isovaleronitrile	391	49	20[319]	63/7
	α-Dimethylamino-α-ethyl-butyronitrile	391	75	20[319]	69–73/10
	γ-Diethylaminobutyro-nitrile	378	84	20[113]	93/14
		387	83	20[215]	89/9
		436	97	24[193]	103/21, 1.4351, 70Pi
	α-Diethylaminoisobutyro-nitrile	391	59	20[327]	68/14, 1.4312
		391	39	20[319]	74/14
C_9	α-Diethylamino-*n*-valeronitrile	391	44	20[319]	95/15
	α-Diethylaminoiso-valeronitrile	391	39	20[319]	69/4
	β-Cyclohexylamino-propionitrile	388	92	20[249]	124/4, 1.4764
C_{10}	ε-Diethylaminocapronitrile	436	90	24[196]	102/4, 62Pi
	α-Diethylamino-α-iso-butylacetonitrile	391	92	20[324]	89/11
		Aromatic Amino Cyanides			
C_7	*m*-Aminobenzonitrile	425	63	24[79]	(53), 131Ac
C_8	*o*-Aminobenzyl cyanide	425	88	24[520]	(72)
	p-Aminobenzyl cyanide	425	79	24[78]	147/1
	Anilinoacetonitrile	391	35	20[324]	(47)
C_9	Methylphenylaminoaceto-nitrile	391	76	20[319]	141/9

For explanations and symbols see pp. xi–xii.

TABLE 92 *(continued)*

C_n	Compound	Method	Yield (%)	Chapter[ref.]	B.p./mm., n_D^t, (M.p.), Deriv.
		Aromatic Amino Cyanides *(continued)*			
C_{10}	β-Benzylaminopropio-nitrile	388	73	20[252]	185/23
	α-Dimethylaminophenyl-acetonitrile	391	29	20[319]	90/6
	α-Anilinoisobutyronitrile	391	93	20[327]	(94)
C_{12}	α-Diethylaminophenyl-acetonitrile	391	83	20[323]	112/7, 131/11
		391	56	20[319]	124/9
C_{14}	α-Aminodiphenylaceto-nitrile	392	77	20[339]	(102)
	γ-Diethylamino-α-phenyl-butyronitrile	386	74	20[190]	122/1
	9-Amino-9-cyanofluorene	392	70	20[340]	(96)

For explanations and symbols see pp. xi–xii.

REFERENCES FOR CHAPTER 24

[1] Senkus, *Ind. Eng. Chem.*, **40**, 506 (1948); cf. ref. 54.

[2] Johnson and Degering, *J. Am. Chem. Soc.*, **61**, 3194 (1939); Hass and Riley, *Chem. Revs.*, **32**, 389 (1943).

[3] Clemo and Ormston, *J. Chem. Soc.*, 1778 (1932).

[4] Hazlet and Dornfeld, *J. Am. Chem. Soc.*, **66**, 1781 (1944); cf. refs. 6 and 18.

[5] Gattermann and Wieland, *Laboratory Methods of Organic Chemistry,* The Macmillan Co., New York, 1938, p. 165; cf. ref. 4.

[6] West, *J. Chem. Soc.*, 127, 494 (1925).

[7] Cline and Reid, *J. Am. Chem. Soc.*, **49**, 3150 (1927).

[8] Haworth and Barker, *J. Chem. Soc.*, 1302 (1939); Stevens and Beutel, *J. Am. Chem. Soc.*, **63**, 311 (1941).

[9] Marvel et al., *J. Am. Chem. Soc.*, **66**, 916 (1944); ref. 10.

[10] Craig, *J. Am. Chem. Soc.*, **57**, 195 (1935).

[11] Fieser and Cason, *J. Am. Chem. Soc.*, **61**, 1744 (1939); Emerson and Smith, *ibid.,* **62**, 141 (1940).

[12] Birch et al., *J. Am. Chem. Soc.*, **71**, 1362 (1949).

[13] Lambooy, *J. Am. Chem. Soc.*, **71**, 3756 (1949).

[14] Adkins, *Reactions of Hydrogen,* University of Wisconsin Press, Madison, 1937.

[15] Allen and Van Allan, *Org. Syntheses,* **22**, 9 (1942).

[16] Adams, Cohen, and Rees, *J. Am. Chem. Soc.*, **49**, 1093 (1927).

[17] McGuine and Dull, *J. Am. Chem. Soc.*, **69**, 1469 (1947).

[18] Jenkins, McCullough, and Booth, *Ind. Eng. Chem.*, **22**, 31 (1930).

[19] Campaigne and Reid, *J. Am. Chem. Soc.*, **68**, 1663 (1946).

[20] Bartlett and Cohen, *J. Am. Chem. Soc.*, **62**, 1187 (1940).

[21] Kuhn, *Org. Syntheses,* Coll. Vol. II, 447 (1943); Sampey and Reid, *J. Am. Chem. Soc.*, **69**, 712 (1947).

[22] Morgan and Harrison, *J. Soc. Chem. Ind. (London),* **60,** 120T (1941); Friedman et al., *J. Am. Chem. Soc.*, **71**, 3012 (1949).

[23] Binz and v. Schickh, *Ber.*, **68**, 320 (1935).

[24] Renshaw and Friedman, *J. Am. Chem. Soc.*, **61**, 3320 (1939).

[25] Drake et al., *J. Am. Chem. Soc.*, **68**, 1605 (1946); refs. 26 and 27.

[26] Fieser and Hershberg, *J. Am. Chem. Soc.*, **62**, 1640 (1940); cf. ref. 27.

[27] Winterbottom, *J. Am. Chem. Soc.*, **62,** 160 (1940).

[28] Linsker and Evans, *J. Am. Chem. Soc.*, **68,** 149 (1946); also ref. 27.

[29] Linsker and Evans, *J. Am. Chem. Soc.*, **68,** 874 (1946).

[30] Albert and Ritchie, *J. Soc. Chem. Ind. (London),* 60, 120T (1941).

[31] Gilsdorf and Nord, *J. Org. Chem.*, **15**, 807 (1950).

[32] Fieser and Kennelly, *J. Am. Chem. Soc.*, **57**, 1614 (1935).

[33] Craig and Cass, *J. Am. Chem. Soc.*, **64**, 783 (1942).

[34] Fries and Hemmecke, *Ann.*, **470**, 7 (1929).

[35] Gilman and Nobis, *J. Am. Chem. Soc.*, **71**, 274 (1949); cf. ref. 36.

[36] Gilman and Avakian, *J. Am. Chem. Soc.*, **68**, 1514 (1946).

[37] Rockett and Whitmore, *J. Am. Chem. Soc.*, **71**, 3249 (1949).

[38] Kornblum and Iffland, *J. Am. Chem. Soc.*, **71**, 2137 (1949).

[39] Cerf, *Bull. soc. chim. France,* (5) 4, 1460 (1937).

[40] Senkus, *J. Am. Chem. Soc.*, **68**, 10 (1946); Johnson, *ibid.,* 12, 14 (1946).

[41] Martin, *Org. Syntheses,* Coll. Vol. II, 501 (1943).

[42] Gill, MacGillivray, and Munro, *J. Chem. Soc.*, 1753 (1949).

[43] Mahood and Schaffner, *Org. Syntheses,* Coll. Vol. II, 160 (1943).
[44] Morgan and Walls, *J. Soc. Chem. Ind., (London),* 50, 94T (1931).
[45] Ruggli and Lang, *Helv. Chim. Acta,* 19, 996 (1936).
[46] Huang-Minlon, *J. Am. Chem. Soc.,* 70, 2802 (1948); cf. ref. 326.
[47] Ruggli and Lang, *Helv. Chim. Acta,* 21, 38 (1938).
[48] Weygand and Gabler, *Ber.,* 71, 2474 (1938).
[49] Kiewiet and Stephen, *J. Chem. Soc.,* 82 (1931).
[50] Winans, *J. Am. Chem. Soc.,* 61, 3564 (1939).
[51] Mathieson and Newbery, *J. Chem. Soc.,* 1136 (1949); Natelson and Gottfried, *J. Am. Chem. Soc.,* 61, 1001 (1939).
[52] Bradlow and Vanderwerf, *J. Am. Chem. Soc.,* 70, 654 (1948); Dunker and Starkey, *ibid.,* 61, 3005 (1939); Schiemann and Pillarsky, *Ber.,* 62, 3041 (1929).
[53] Steck, Hallock, and Holland, *J. Am. Chem. Soc.,* 68, 1243 (1946); von Baeyer, *Ber.,* 38, 2761 (1905).
[54] Johnson and Degering, *J. Org. Chem.,* 8, 7 (1943); Vanderbilt and Hass, *Ind. Eng. Chem.,* 32, 34 (1940).
[55] Hoover and Hass, *J. Org. Chem.,* 12, 506 (1947).
[56] Gakenheimer and Hartung, *J. Org. Chem.,* 9, 85 (1944).
[57] Attenburrow et al., *J. Chem. Soc.,* 514 (1949).
[58] Galatis, *J. prakt. Chem.,* 151, 334 (1938); Hewitt and King, *J. Chem. Soc.,* 822 (1926).
[59] Rupe and Brentano, *Helv. Chim. Acta,* 19, 594 (1936).
[60] Marvel and Overberger, *J. Am. Chem. Soc.,* 68, 185 (1946).
[61] Phillips and Maggiolo, *J. Org. Chem.,* 15, 659 (1950).
[62] Woodburn and Stuntz, *J. Am. Chem. Soc.,* 72, 1361 (1950).
[63] Lempert and Robinson, *J. Chem. Soc.,* 1420 (1934); cf. ref. 6.
[64] Clinton and Suter, *J. Am. Chem. Soc.,* 69, 704 (1947).
[65] Tarbell et al., *J. Am. Chem. Soc.,* 70, 1384 (1948); cf. ref. 66.
[66] Suter, *J. Am. Chem. Soc.,* 51, 2581 (1929).
[67] Smith and Opie, *Org. Syntheses,* 28, 11 (1948).
[68] Cocker, Harris, and Loach, *J. Chem. Soc.,* 751 (1938).
[69] Leonard and Boyd, *J. Org. Chem.,* 11, 405 (1946).
[70] Marvel, Allen, and Overberger, *J. Am. Chem. Soc.,* 68, 1088 (1946); King, McWhirter, and Barton, *ibid.,* 67, 2091 (1945); also ref. 69.
[71] Keneford and Simpson, *J. Chem. Soc.,* 356 (1948).
[72] Simpson et al., *J. Chem. Soc.,* 646 (1945).
[73] Robertson, *Org. Syntheses,* Coll. Vol. I, 52 (1941).
[74] Hahn and Tulus, *Ber.,* 74, 515 (1941).
[75] Adams and Cohen, *Org. Syntheses,* Coll. Vol. I, 240 (1941).
[76] Ungnade and Henick, *J. Am. Chem. Soc.,* 64, 1737 (1942).
[77] Cronyn, *J. Org. Chem.,* 14, 1013 (1949).
[78] Wawzonek, *J. Am. Chem. Soc.,* 68, 1157 (1946).
[79] Blanksma and Petri, *Rec. trav. chim.,* 66, 353 (1947).
[80] Gattermann and Wieland, *Laboratory Methods of Organic Chemistry,* The Macmillan Co., New York, 1938, p. 171.
[81] Hodgson and Ward, *J. Chem. Soc.,* 663, 794 (1945).
[82] Hodgson and Birtwell, *J. Chem. Soc.,* 318 (1943); Brady et al., *ibid.,* 2264 (1929).
[83] Fieser and Martin, *J. Am. Chem. Soc.,* 57, 1838 (1935).
[84] Whitmore and Langlois, *J. Am. Chem. Soc.,* 54, 3441 (1932).

[85]Westphal and Jerchel, *Ber.*, **73**, 1002 (1940); v. Braun and Klar, *ibid.*, **73**, 1417 (1940).

[86]Patrick, McBee, and Hass, *J. Am. Chem. Soc.*, **68**, 1009 (1946).

[87]Wisansky and Ansbacher, *Org. Syntheses*, **28**, 46 (1948).

[88]Groggins and Stirton, *Ind. Eng. Chem.*, **28**, 1051 (1936); **29**, 1353 (1937).

[89]Pinck and Hilbert, *J. Am. Chem. Soc.*, **68**, 377 (1946).

[90]Gilman and Van Ess, *J. Am. Chem. Soc.*, **61**, 1369 (1939).

[91]Gilman and Jacoby, *J. Org. Chem.*, **3**, 108 (1938).

[92]Albert et al., *Org. Syntheses*, **22**, 5 (1942); *J. Soc. Chem. Ind. (London)*, **64**, 170 (1945).

[93]Hertog and Wibaut, *Rec. trav. chim.*, **55**, 122 (1936); Maier-Bode, *Ber.*, **69**, 1534 (1936).

[94]Jansen and Wibaut, *Rec. trav. chim.*, **56**, 709 (1937).

[95]Kaye, *J. Am. Chem. Soc.*, **71**, 2322 (1949).

[96]v. Braun, *Ber.*, **70**, 979 (1937).

[97]Amundsen and Krantz, *J. Am. Chem. Soc.*, **63**, 305 (1941); *Org. Syntheses*, **23**, 23 (1943).

[98]Fargher, *J. Chem. Soc.*, 117, 1351 (1920); Groggins and Stirton, *Ind. Eng. Chem.*, **29**, 1355 (1937).

[99]Osterberg and Kendall, *J. Am. Chem. Soc.*, **42**, 2616 (1920); Johnson and Schubert, *ibid.*, **72**, 2189 (1950); Wilson and Read, *J. Chem. Soc.*, 1272 (1935).

[100]Tamele et al., *Ind. Eng. Chem.*, **33**, 115 (1941).

[101]Wernert and Brode, *J. Am. Chem. Soc.*, **54**, 4365 (1932).

[102]Cheronis et al., *J. Org. Chem.*, **6**, 349, 467 (1941).

[103]Block, *Chem. Revs.*, **38**, 501 (1946).

[104]Orten and Hill, *Org. Syntheses*, Coll. Vol. I, 300 (1941); Tobie and Ayres, *J. Am. Chem. Soc.*, **64**, 725 (1942).

[105]Tobie and Ayres, *Org. Syntheses*, Coll. Vol. I, 23 (1941).

[106]Marvel, *Org. Syntheses*, **20**, 106 (1940).

[107]Marvel, *Org. Syntheses*, **21**, 74 (1941).

[108]Marvel and du Vigneaud, *Org. Syntheses*, Coll. Vol. I, 48 (1941).

[109]Marvel, *Org. Syntheses*, **21**, 60 (1941).

[110]Eck and Marvel, *Org. Syntheses*, Coll. Vol. II, 374 (1943).

[111]Marvel, *Org. Syntheses*, **21**, 101 (1941).

[112]Elks, Hems, and Ryman, *J. Chem. Soc.*, 1386 (1948).

[113]Wells and Allen, *Org. Syntheses*, Coll. Vol. II, 221 (1943).

[114]Willson and Wheeler, *Org. Syntheses*, Coll. Vol. I, 102 (1941).

[115]Buck and Ferry, *Org. Syntheses*, Coll. Vol. II, 290 (1943).

[116]Lazier and Adkins, *J. Am. Chem. Soc.*, **46**, 741 (1924).

[117]Hughes, Veatch, and Elersich, *Ind. Eng. Chem.*, **42**, 787 (1950).

[118]Speer and Hill, *J. Org. Chem.*, **2**, 139 (1937).

[119]Hickinbottom, *J. Chem. Soc.*, 992 (1930).

[120]Zanetti and Bashour, *J. Am. Chem. Soc.*, **61**, 3133 (1939), cf. ref. 138.

[121]Blicke, Monroe, and Zienty, *J. Am. Chem. Soc.*, **61**, 91, 93, 771, 775 (1939).

[122]Buck and Baltzly, *J. Am. Chem. Soc.*, **63**, 1964 (1941).

[123]Clarke, Gillespie, and Weisshaus, *J. Am. Chem. Soc.*, **55**, 4571 (1933).

[124]Borrows et al., *J. Chem. Soc.*, 197 (1947).

[125]King and Work, *J. Chem. Soc.*, 401 (1942).

[126]Caspe, *J. Am. Chem. Soc.*, **54**, 4457 (1932).

[127]Adams, Brown, and Marvel, *Org. Syntheses*, Coll. Vol. I, 528, 531 (1941).

[128]Marvel and Jenkins, *Org. Syntheses*, Coll. Vol. I, 347 (1941).

[129] Werner, J. Chem. Soc., 111, 850 (1917).
[130] Evans and Williams, J. Chem. Soc., 1199 (1939).
[131] Billman, Radike, and Mundy, J. Am. Chem. Soc., 64, 2977 (1942).
[132] Thomas, Billman, and Davis, J. Am. Chem. Soc., 68, 895 (1946).
[133] Gokhlé and Mason, J. Chem. Soc., 1757 (1930); cf. ref. 134.
[134] Germuth, J. Am. Chem. Soc., 51, 1555 (1929).
[135] Knoevenagel, J. prakt. Chem., 89, 30 (1913).
[136] Hager, Org. Syntheses, Coll. Vol. I, 544 (1941).
[137] Gilman et al., J. Am. Chem. Soc., 67, 2106 (1945).
[138] Lutz et al., J. Org. Chem., 12, 760 (1947).
[139] Hurd and Drake, J. Am. Chem. Soc., 61, 1943 (1939).
[140] Shelton et al., J. Am. Chem. Soc., 68, 753, 755, 757 (1946).
[141] Weilmuenster and Jordan, J. Am. Chem. Soc., 67, 415 (1945).
[142] Reck, Harwood, and Ralston, J. Org. Chem., 12, 517 (1947).
[143] Groenewoud and Robinson, J. Chem. Soc., 1692 (1934).
[144] Linsker and Evans, J. Am. Chem. Soc., 67, 1581 (1945).
[145] Linsker and Evans, J. Am. Chem. Soc., 68, 1432 (1946).
[146] Donia et al., J. Org. Chem., 14, 946 (1949).
[147] Kermack and Wight, J. Chem. Soc., 1425 (1935).
[148] Mannich and Margotte, Ber., 68, 273 (1935).
[149] Stahmann and Cope, J. Am. Chem. Soc., 68, 2494 (1946).
[150] Linsker and Evans, J. Org. Chem., 10, 283 (1945).
[151] Cope and Towle, J. Am. Chem. Soc., 71, 3423 (1949).
[152] Elderfield et al., J. Am. Chem. Soc., 68, 1579 (1946).
[153] Breslow et al., J. Am. Chem. Soc., 67, 1472 (1945).
[154] Davies and Cox, J. Chem. Soc., 614 (1937); cf. ref. 130.
[155] Gilman and Banner, J. Am. Chem. Soc., 62, 344 (1940).
[156] Hartman, Org. Syntheses, Coll. Vol. II, 183 (1943).
[157] Pierce, Salsbury, and Fredericksen, J. Am. Chem. Soc., 64, 1691 (1942).
[158] Munch, Thannhauser, and Cottle, J. Am. Chem. Soc., 68, 1297 (1946).
[159] Rindfusz and Harnack, J. Am. Chem. Soc., 42, 1723 (1920).
[160] Hancock et al., J. Am. Chem. Soc., 66, 1747 (1944).
[161] Bachman and Mayhew, J. Org. Chem., 10, 243 (1945).
[162] Kremer and Waldman, J. Am. Chem. Soc., 64, 1089 (1942); Pierce et al., ibid., 64, 2884 (1942).
[163] Campbell and Campbell, J. Am. Chem. Soc., 60, 1372 (1938).
[164] Goldberg, Ringk, and Spoerri, J. Am. Chem. Soc., 61, 3562 (1939).
[165] Elderfield et al., J. Am. Chem. Soc., 68, 1516 (1946).
[166] Fourneau, Benoit, and Firmenich, Bull. soc. chim. France, (4) 47, 880 (1930).
[167] Kon and Roberts, J. Chem. Soc., 980 (1950).
[168] Elderfield et al., J. Am. Chem. Soc., 69, 1258 (1947); Campbell et al., ibid., 68, 1556 (1946); cf. ref. 174.
[169] Moffett, J. Org. Chem., 14, 862 (1949).
[170] Marvel, Zartman, and Bluthardt, J. Am. Chem. Soc., 49, 2300 (1927).
[171] Gibbs, Littmann, and Marvel, J. Am. Chem. Soc., 55, 753 (1933).
[172] Cowan and Marvel, J. Am. Chem. Soc., 58, 2277 (1936).
[173] Drake et al., J. Am. Chem. Soc., 68, 1536 (1946).
[174] Campbell et al., J. Am. Chem. Soc., 68, 1556 (1946).
[175] Alexander, J. Am. Chem. Soc., 70, 2592 (1948).
[176] Johnson et al., J. Am. Chem. Soc., 69, 2364 (1947).
[177] Cocker and Harris, J. Chem. Soc., 1092 (1939).

[178] Zaugg and Horrom, *J. Am. Chem. Soc.*, **72**, 3004 (1950).

[179] Magee and Henze, *J. Am. Chem. Soc.*, **60**, 2148 (1938); cf. ref. 218.

[180] Adamson et al., *J. Chem. Soc.*, 1578 (1937).

[181] Janetzky and Verkade, *Rec. trav. chim.*, **65**, 909 (1946).

[182] Janetzky and Verkade, *Rec. trav. chim.*, **65**, 697 (1946).

[183] Verkade and Janetzky, *Rec. trav. chim.*, **62**, 780 (1943).

[184] Henze and Holder, *J. Am. Chem. Soc.*, **63**, 1943 (1941).

[185] Hyde, Browning, and Adams, *J. Am. Chem. Soc.*, **50**, 2287 (1928); Fourneau and Barrelet, *Bull. soc. chim. France*, **47**, 72 (1930).

[186] Bogert and Nabenhauer, *J. Am. Chem. Soc.*, **46**, 1702 (1924).

[187] Berchet, *Org. Syntheses*, Coll. Vol. II, 397 (1943).

[188] Biilmann and Berg, *Bull. soc. chim. France*, (5) 1, 1657 (1934).

[189] Blicke, Wright, and Zienty, *J. Am. Chem. Soc.*, **63**, 2488 (1941).

[190] Leonard and Ruyle, *J. Am. Chem. Soc.*, **71**, 3094 (1949).

[191] Magidson et al., *Arch. Pharm.*, **272**, 77 (1934).

[192] Mills and Dazeley, *J. Chem. Soc.*, 460 (1939).

[193] Clark and Mosher, *J. Am. Chem. Soc.*, **72**, 1026 (1950); ref. 195.

[194] Utermohlen and Hamilton, *J. Am. Chem. Soc.*, **63**, 156 (1941).

[195] Whitmore et al., *J. Am. Chem. Soc.*, **66**, 725 (1944).

[196] Breslow and Hauser, *J. Am. Chem. Soc.*, **67**, 686 (1945).

[197] Campbell, *J. Am. Chem. Soc.*, **71**, 740 (1949).

[198] Behr et al., *J. Am. Chem. Soc.*, **68**, 1296 (1946).

[199] Burckhalter et al., *J. Am. Chem. Soc.*, **70**, 1363 (1948).

[200] Johnson, Hill, and Donleavy, *Ind. Eng. Chem.*, **12**, 636 (1920); ibid., **13**, 504 (1921).

[201] Swann in *Technique of Organic Chemistry*, Vol. II, Interscience Publishers, New York, pp. 143–208.

[202] Emerson in *Organic Reactions*, Vol. 4, John Wiley & Sons, New York, 1948, p. 174.

[203] Schwoegler and Adkins, *J. Am. Chem. Soc.*, **61**, 3499 (1939).

[204] Winans, *J. Am. Chem. Soc.*, **61**, 3566 (1939).

[205] Haskelberg, *J. Am. Chem. Soc.*, **70**, 2811 (1948).

[206] Rohrmann and Schonle, *J. Am. Chem. Soc.*, **66**, 1516 (1944).

[207] Alexander and Misegades, *J. Am. Chem. Soc.*, **70**, 1315 (1948); cf. ref. 203.

[208] Robinson and Snyder, *Org. Syntheses*, **23**, 68 (1943).

[209] Fleury-Larsonneau, *Bull. soc. chim. France*, (5) 6, 1576 (1939).

[210] Emerson and Walters, *J. Am. Chem. Soc.*, **60**, 2023 (1938).

[211] Emerson and Mohrman, *J. Am. Chem. Soc.*, **62**, 69 (1940); cf. ref. 210.

[212] Emerson and Uraneck, *J. Am. Chem. Soc.*, **63**, 749 (1941).

[213] Emerson and Robb, *J. Am. Chem. Soc.*, **61**, 3145 (1939).

[214] Woodruff, Lambooy, and Burt, *J. Am. Chem. Soc.*, **62**, 922 (1940).

[215] Winans and Adkins, *J. Am. Chem. Soc.*, **54**, 306 (1932).

[216] Skita, Keil, and Havemann, *Ber.*, **63**, 39 (1930); ibid., **66**, 1400 (1933).

[217] Wagner, *J. Am. Chem. Soc.*, **55**, 724 (1933).

[218] Breslow et al., *J. Am. Chem. Soc.*, **68**, 100 (1946).

[219] Pearson, Jones, and Cope, *J. Am. Chem. Soc.*, **68**, 1225 (1946).

[220] Crum and Robinson, *J. Chem. Soc.*, 561 (1943).

[221] Emerson, Dorf, and Deutschman, *J. Am. Chem. Soc.*, **62**, 2159 (1940).

[222] Cope and Hancock, *J. Am. Chem. Soc.*, **64**, 1503 (1942).

[223] Hancock and Cope, *Org. Syntheses*, **26**, 38 (1946).

[224] Cope and Hancock, *J. Am. Chem. Soc.*, **66**, 1453 (1944).

[225] Hancock and Cope, *J. Am. Chem. Soc.*, **66**, 1738 (1944).

[226] Engelhardt, Crossley, and Sprague, *J. Am. Chem. Soc.*, **72**, 2718 (1950).

[227] Drake et al., *J. Am. Chem. Soc.*, **71**, 455 (1949).

[228] Woods and Sanders, *J. Am. Chem. Soc.*, **68**, 2111 (1946); cf. ref. 229.

[229] Scriabine, *Bull. soc. chim. France*, (5) **14**, 455 (1947).

[230] Drake et al., *J. Am. Chem. Soc.*, **68**, 1529 (1946).

[231] Skita, Keil, and Baesler, *Ber.*, **66**, 858 (1933).

[232] Bowman and Stroud, *J. Chem. Soc.*, 1342 (1950).

[233] Knoop and Oesterlin, *Z. physiol. Chem.*, **148**, 294 (1925); **170**, 186 (1927).

[234] Heidelberger, *An Advanced Laboratory Manual for Organic Chemistry*, Chemical Catalog Co., New York, 1923, p. 24; Delépine, *Bull. soc. chim. France*, (3) **17**, 293 (1897); cf. ref. 235.

[235] Galat and Elion, *J. Am. Chem. Soc.*, **61**, 3585 (1939).

[236] Delépine, *Bull. soc. chim. France*, (4) **31**, 108 (1922).

[237] Graymore, *J. Chem. Soc.*, 1116 (1947).

[238] Mannich and Hahn, *Ber.*, **44**, 1542 (1911).

[239] Wendler, *J. Am. Chem. Soc.*, **71**, 375 (1949).

[240] Blicke and Lilienfeld, *J. Am. Chem. Soc.*, **65**, 2281 (1943).

[241] Baniel et al., *J. Org. Chem.*, **13**, 791 (1948).

[242] Blicke and Burckhalter, *J. Am. Chem. Soc.*, **64**, 477 (1942).

[243] Blicke and Maxwell, *J. Am. Chem. Soc.*, **61**, 1780 (1939).

[244] Wallis and Lane in *Organic Reactions*, Vol. 3, John Wiley & Sons, New York, 1946, p. 267.

[245] Hofmann, *Ber.*, **15**, 762 (1882).

[246] Hoogewerff and van Dorp, *Rec. trav. chim.*, **6**, 386 (1887).

[247] Whitmore and Thorpe, *J. Am. Chem. Soc.*, **63**, 1118 (1941).

[248] Whitmore and Homeyer, *J. Am. Chem. Soc.*, **54**, 3435 (1932).

[249] Jeffreys, *Am. Chem. J.*, **22**, 14 (1899).

[250] Schlatter, *J. Am. Chem. Soc.*, **63**, 1733 (1941).

[251] Gutt, *Ber.*, **40**, 2061 (1907).

[252] Hauser and Renfrow, *J. Am. Chem. Soc.*, **59**, 121 (1937).

[253] Beckmann and Correns, *Ber.*, **55**, 848 (1922).

[254] Hoogewerff and van Dorp, *Rec. trav. chim.*, **5**, 252 (1886).

[255] Arcus and Kenyon, *J. Chem. Soc.*, 916 (1939).

[256] Woodruff and Conger, *J. Am. Chem. Soc.*, **60**, 465 (1938).

[257] Woodruff and Pierson, *J. Am. Chem. Soc.*, **60**, 1075 (1938).

[258] Cope, Foster, and Towle, *J. Am. Chem. Soc.*, **71**, 3932 (1949).

[259] Hewett et al., *J. Chem. Soc.*, 292 (1948).

[260] Graf, *J. prakt. Chem.*, **133**, 19 (1932).

[261] Gilman and Swiss, *J. Am. Chem. Soc.*, **66**, 1884 (1944); cf. ref. 90.

[262] v. Braun and Lemke, *Ber.*, **55**, 3526 (1922).

[263] v. Braun and Jostes, *Ber.*, **59**, 1091 (1926).

[264] Horowitz and Geissman, *J. Am. Chem. Soc.*, **72**, 1518 (1950).

[265] Buck and Ide, *Org. Syntheses*, Coll. Vol. II, 44 (1943).

[266] Graebe and Rostovzeff, *Ber.*, **35**, 2747 (1902).

[267] Huntress, Pfister, and Pfister, *J. Am. Chem. Soc.*, **64**, 2845 (1942).

[268] Clarke and Behr, *Org. Syntheses*, Coll. Vol. II, 19 (1943).

[269] Natarajan and Swaminathan, *J. Am. Chem. Soc.*, **69**, 2560 (1947).

[270] Smith in *Organic Reactions*, Vol. 3, John Wiley & Sons, New York, 1946, p. 337.

[271] Naegeli, Grüntuch, and Lendorff, *Helv. Chim. Acta*, **12**, 227 (1929).

[272] Manske, *J. Am. Chem. Soc.*, **51**, 1202 (1929).

[273] Buchman et al., *J. Am. Chem. Soc.*, **64**, 2696 (1942).

[274] McCoubrey and Mathieson, *J. Chem. Soc.*, 696 (1949).

[275] Kenyon and Young, *J. Chem. Soc.*, 263 (1941).

[276] Mayer and Sieglitz, *Ber.*, **55**, 1847 (1922).

[277] Goldberg, Ordas, and Carsch, *J. Am. Chem. Soc.*, **69**, 260 (1947).

[278] Smith, ref. 270, p. 381.

[279] Skita and Rössler, *Ber.*, **72**, 461 (1939).

[280] Naegeli and Lendorff, *Helv. Chim. Acta*, **15**, 49 (1932).

[281] Stevenson and Johnson, *J. Am. Chem. Soc.*, **59**, 2525 (1937).

[282] Singleton and Edwards, *J. Am. Chem. Soc.*, **60**, 540 (1938).

[283] Mayer and Krieger, *Ber.*, **55**, 1659 (1922).

[284] Mousseron and Jacquier, *Bull. soc. chim. France*, (5) **17**, 238 (1950).

[285] Curtius, *J. prakt. Chem.*, **89**, 508 (1914).

[286] Curtius, *J. prakt. Chem.*, **58**, 190 (1898); Naegeli and Tyabji, *Helv. Chim. Acta*, **16**, 349 (1933).

[287] Darapsky, *J. prakt. Chem.*, **146**, 250 (1936).

[288] Gagnon, Gaudry, and King, *J. Chem. Soc.*, 13 (1944).

[289] Curtius, *J. prakt. Chem.*, **125**, 211 (1930).

[290] Curtius and Sieber, *Ber.*, **55**, 1543 (1922).

[291] Yale, *Chem. Revs.*, **33**, 209 (1943).

[292] Wolff in *Organic Reactions*, Vol. 3, John Wiley & Sons, New York, 1946, p. 307.

[293] Adamson and Kenner, *J. Chem. Soc.*, 842 (1934).

[294] Oesterlin, *Z. angew. Chem.*, **45**, 536 (1932).

[295] Briggs and Lyttleton, *J. Chem. Soc.*, 421 (1943).

[296] v. Braun and Friehmelt, *Ber.*, **66**, 684 (1933).

[297] Benson, Hartzel, and Savell, *J. Am. Chem. Soc.*, **71**, 1111 (1949).

[298] Dice and Smith, *J. Org. Chem.*, **14**, 179 (1949).

[299] Fuson, Maynert, and Shenk, *J. Am. Chem. Soc.*, **67**, 1939 (1945).

[300] Adamson, *J. Chem. Soc.*, 1564 (1939).

[301] Schmidt, *Ber.*, **57**, 704 (1924).

[302] Nystrom and Brown, *J. Am. Chem. Soc.*, **70**, 3738 (1948).

[303] Adams and Marvel, *J. Am. Chem. Soc.*, **42**, 314 (1920); Suter and Moffett, *ibid.*, **56**, 487 (1934).

[304] Bloom, Breslow, and Hauser, *J. Am. Chem. Soc.*, **67**, 539 (1945).

[305] Walter and McElvain, *J. Am. Chem. Soc.*, **56**, 1614 (1934).

[306] Suida and Drahowzal, *Ber.*, **75**, 995 (1942).

[307] Carothers and Adams, *J. Am. Chem. Soc.*, **47**, 3051 (1925).

[308] Adkins and Billica, *J. Am. Chem. Soc.*, **70**, 695 (1948).

[309] Adkins and Cramer, *J. Am. Chem. Soc.*, **52**, 4349 (1930).

[310] Robinson and Snyder, *Org. Syntheses*, **23**, 71 (1943), footnote 5.

[311] Freeman, Ringk, and Spoerri, *J. Am. Chem. Soc.*, **69**, 858 (1947).

[312] Geissman and Tess, *J. Am. Chem. Soc.*, **62**, 514 (1940); St. Goldschmidt and Veer, *Rec. trav. chim.*, **67**, 489 (1948).

[313] van de Kamp, Burger, and Mosettig, *J. Am. Chem. Soc.*, **60**, 1321 (1938).

[314] Crowe and Nord, *J. Org. Chem.*, **15**, 81 (1950).

[315] Kolloff and Hunter, *J. Am. Chem. Soc.*, **63**, 490 (1941); cf. Prijs, Lutz, and Erlenmeyer, *Helv. Chim. Acta*, **31**, 571 (1948).

[316] Turner, *J. Am. Chem. Soc.*, **68**, 1607 (1946).

[317] King and Acheson, *J. Chem. Soc.*, 683 (1946).

[318] Reihlen et al., *Ann.*, **493**, 20 (1932).

[319]Tarbell et al., *J. Am. Chem. Soc.*, **68**, 1217 (1946).

[320]Corse, Bryant, and Shonle, *J. Am. Chem. Soc.*, **68**, 1905 (1946).

[321]Huber, *J. Am. Chem. Soc.*, **66**, 876 (1944).

[322]Hawkins and Briggs, *J. Am. Chem. Soc.*, **71**, 2530 (1949).

[323]Biggs and Bishop, *Org. Syntheses*, **27**, 18 (1947).

[324]Malachowski et al., *Ber.*, **71**, 759 (1938).

[325]Ruggli and Prijs, *Helv. Chim. Acta*, **28**, 674 (1945).

[326]Albert, Mills, and Royer, *J. Chem. Soc.*, 1452 (1947).

[327]Paul and Cottin, *Bull. soc. chim. France*, (5) **4**, 933 (1937).

[328]Wiley, *J. Am. Chem. Soc.*, **68**, 1867 (1946).

[329]Utermohlen, *J. Am. Chem. Soc.*, **67**, 1505 (1945).

[330]Tarbell and Noble, *J. Am. Chem. Soc.*, **72**, 2657 (1950).

[331]Marvel and Tanenbaum, *J. Am. Chem. Soc.*, **44**, 2649 (1922).

[332]Buck, *J. Am. Chem. Soc.*, **55**, 2593, 3388 (1933).

[333]Kindler and Peschke, *Arch. Pharm.*, **269**, 581 (1931).

[334]Wiley and Adkins, *J. Am. Chem. Soc.*, **60**, 914 (1938).

[335]Mousseron, Jullien, and Winternitz, *Bull. soc. chim. France*, (5) **15**, 884 (1948).

[336]Ruggli and Businger, *Helv. Chim. Acta*, **25**, 35 (1942).

[337]Schultz, *J. Am. Chem. Soc.*, **69**, 1056 (1947).

[338]Albert and Magrath, *J. Chem. Soc.*, 678 (1944); Havinga and Veldstra, *Rec. trav. chim.*, **66**, 271 (1947).

[339]Pollack, *J. Am. Chem. Soc.*, **65**, 1335 (1943).

[340]Weygand, *Ber.*, **74**, 256 (1941).

[341]Winans and Adkins, *J. Am. Chem. Soc.*, **55**, 4167 (1933).

[342]Biggs and Bishop, *Ind. Eng. Chem.*, **38**, 1084 (1946); Kindler and Hess, *Arch. Pharm.*, **271**, 439 (1933).

[343]Wojcik and Adkins, *J. Am. Chem. Soc.*, **56**, 2419 (1934).

[344]Uffer and Schlittler, *Helv. Chim. Acta*, **31**, 1397 (1948).

[345]Gavrilov, Koperina, and Klyuchareva, *Bull. soc. chim. France*, (5) **12**, 773 (1945).

[346]Winans and Adkins, *J. Am. Chem. Soc.*, **55**, 2051 (1933).

[347]Paul, *Bull. soc. chim. France*, (5) **4**, 1121 (1937).

[348]King, Barltrop, and Walley, *J. Chem. Soc.*, 277 (1945).

[349]Hass, Susie, and Heider, *J. Org. Chem.*, **15**, 8 (1950).

[350]Lycan, Puntambeker, and Marvel, *Org. Syntheses*, Coll. Vol. II, 318 (1943).

[351]Pinck and Hilbert, *J. Am. Chem. Soc.*, **54**, 710 (1932).

[352]Breslow et al., *J. Am. Chem. Soc.*, **66**, 1921 (1944).

[353]Magidson and Grigorowsky, *Ber.*, **69**, 396 (1936).

[354]Carmack et al., *J. Am. Chem. Soc.*, **68**, 1220 (1946).

[355]Hurd and Perletz, *J. Am. Chem. Soc.*, **68**, 38 (1946).

[356]Hartung and Munch, *J. Am. Chem. Soc.*, **51**, 2262 (1929).

[357]Mills and Grigor, *J. Chem. Soc.*, 1568 (1934).

[358]Fischer, Sturm, and Friedrich, *Ann.*, **461**, 257 (1928).

[359]Koessler and Hanke, *J. Am. Chem. Soc.*, **40**, 1716 (1918).

[360]Barry and Hartung, *J. Org. Chem.*, **12**, 460 (1947).

[361]Shivers and Hauser, *J. Am. Chem. Soc.*, **69**, 1264 (1947).

[362]Hamlin and Hartung, *J. Biol. Chem.*, **145**, 349 (1942).

[363]Snyder and Smith, *J. Am. Chem. Soc.*, **66**, 350 (1944).

[364]Gränacher, *Helv. Chim. Acta*, **6**, 458 (1923).

[365]Cocker, *J. Chem. Soc.*, 1489 (1940).

[366]Müller and Feld, *Monatsh.*, **58**, 22 (1931).

[367]Decombe, *Ann. chim.*, (10) **18**, 126 (1932).

[368]Campbell, Sommers, and Campbell, *J. Am. Chem. Soc.*, **66**, 82 (1944).

[369]Henze and Humphreys, *J. Am. Chem. Soc.*, **64**, 2878 (1942); cf. ref. 368.

[370]Tiollais, *Bull. soc. chim. France*, (5) **14**, 959 (1947).

[371]Campbell, Sommers, and Campbell, *Org. Syntheses*, **27**, 12 (1947).

[372]Allen and Van Allan, *Org. Syntheses*, **21**, 108 (1941).

[373]Cromwell, Babson, and Harris, *J. Am. Chem. Soc.*, **65**, 312 (1943).

[374]Cromwell and Heksema, *J. Am. Chem. Soc.*, **67**, 1658 (1945).

[375]Phillips, *J. Soc. Chem. Ind. (London)*, **66**, 325 (1947).

[376]Coleman and Blomquist, *J. Am. Chem. Soc.*, **63**, 1692 (1941).

[377]Winans, *Ind. Eng. Chem.*, **32**, 1215 (1940).

[378]Zenitz, Macks, and Moore, *J. Am. Chem. Soc.*, **69**, 1117 (1947); cf. ref. 379.

[379]Kindler, Hedemann, and Schärfe, *Ann.*, **560**, 215 (1948); Métayer, *Ann. chim.*, (12) **4**, 226 (1949).

[380]Nienberg, *Ber.*, **70**, 635 (1937).

[381]Ferber and Brückner, *Ber.*, **72**, 995 (1939).

[382]Ferber and Bendix, *Ber.*, **72**, 839 (1939).

[383]Waser and Möllering, *Org. Syntheses*, Coll. Vol. I, 499 (1941); cf. ref. 309.

[384]Shreve et al., *Ind. Eng. Chem.*, **29**, 1361 (1937); **33**, 218 (1941).

[385]Gilman and Nobis, *J. Am. Chem. Soc.*, **67**, 1479 (1945).

[386]Horning and Bergstrom, *J. Am. Chem. Soc.*, **67**, 2110 (1945).

[387]Hauser and Weiss, *J. Org. Chem.*, **14**, 310 (1949).

[388]Eisleb, *Ber.*, **74**, 1433 (1941).

[389]Drake in *Organic Reactions*, Vol. 1, John Wiley & Sons, New York, 1942, p. 105.

[390]Ikuta, *Am. Chem. J.*, **15**, 39 (1893).

[391]Hartung, Minnick, and Koehler, *J. Am. Chem. Soc.*, **63**, 507 (1941).

[392]Robinson, *J. Am. Chem. Soc.*, **69**, 1942 (1947).

[393]Woroshtzow and Kogan, *Ber.*, **65**, 142 (1932).

[394]Gilman and Swiss, *J. Am. Chem. Soc.*, **66**, 1884 (1944).

[395]Davies and Hulbert, *J. Soc. Chem. Ind. (London)*, **57**, 349T (1938).

[396]Hickinbottom, *J. Chem. Soc.*, 1119 (1937).

[397]Moore in *Organic Reactions*, Vol. 5, John Wiley & Sons, New York, 1949, p. 301.

[398]Stevens and Richmond, *J. Am. Chem. Soc.*, **63**, 3132 (1941); cf. ref. 397.

[399]Ingersoll, *Org. Syntheses*, Coll. Vol. II, 503 (1943); Ingersoll et al., *J. Am. Chem. Soc.*, **58**, 1808 (1936).

[400]Icke, Wisegarver, and Alles, *Org. Syntheses*, **25**, 89 (1945).

[401]Novelli, *J. Am. Chem. Soc.*, **61**, 520 (1939).

[402]Bunnett and Marks, *J. Am. Chem. Soc.*, **71**, 1587 (1949).

[403]Staple and Wagner, *J. Org. Chem.*, **14**, 559 (1949).

[404]Schiedt, *J. prakt. Chem.*, (2) **157**, 203 (1941).

[405]Webers and Bruce, *J. Am. Chem. Soc.*, **70**, 1422 (1948).

[406]Burger and Walters, *J. Am. Chem. Soc.*, **72**, 1988 (1950).

[407]Niemann, Benson, and Mead, *J. Org. Chem.*, **8**, 401 (1943).

[408]Wright et al., *J. Am. Chem. Soc.*, **72**, 3536 (1950); Biel, *ibid.*, **71**, 1306 (1949).

[409]Herz, Dittmer, and Cristol, *J. Am. Chem. Soc.*, **69**, 1698 (1947); Bachman and Heisey, *ibid.*, **68**, 2496 (1946).

[410]Holdren and Hixon, *J. Am. Chem. Soc.*, **68**, 1198 (1946).

[411] Hartough et al., *J. Am. Chem. Soc.*, **70**, 4013, 4018 (1948).

[412] Kühn and Stein, *Ber.*, **70**, 567 (1937).

[413] Mannich and Chang, *Ber.*, **66**, 418 (1933).

[414] Jones, Marszak, and Bader, *J. Chem. Soc.*, 1578 (1947).

[415] Grillot and Gormley, *J. Am. Chem. Soc.*, **67**, 1968 (1945).

[416] Mannich, Lesser, and Silten, *Ber.*, **65**, 378 (1932).

[417] Wilds and Shunk, *J. Am. Chem. Soc.*, **65**, 469 (1943); Spaeth, Geissman, and Jacobs, *J. Org. Chem.*, **11**, 399 (1946).

[418] Skoda, *Bull. soc. chim. France*, (5) **13**, 328 (1946).

[419] Howton, *J. Org. Chem.*, **12**, 379 (1947); cf. Mannich, *Ber.*, **75**, 49 (1942).

[420] Maxwell, *Org. Syntheses*, **23**, 30 (1943).

[421] Ruddy and Buckley, *J. Am. Chem. Soc.*, **72**, 718 (1950); Burckhalter and Fuson, *ibid.*, **70**, 4184 (1948).

[422] Fry, *J. Org. Chem.*, **10**, 259 (1945); Winstein et al., *ibid.*, **11**, 215 (1946).

[423] Plati et al., *J. Org. Chem.*, **14**, 543, 873 (1949).

[424] Mannich and Ganz, *Ber.*, **55**, 3486 (1922).

[425] Butler and MacMillan, *J. Am. Chem. Soc.*, **72**, 2978 (1950).

[426] Blomquist and Shelley, *J. Am. Chem. Soc.*, **70**, 147 (1948).

[427] Blicke in *Organic Reactions*, Vol. 1, John Wiley & Sons, New York, 1942, p. 303.

[428] Ing and Manske, *J. Chem. Soc.*, 2348 (1926); cf. *Org. Syntheses*, Coll. Vol. II, 83 (1943).

[429] Sheehan and Bolhofer, *J. Am. Chem. Soc.*, **72**, 2786 (1950).

[430] Smith and Emerson, *Org. Syntheses*, **29**, 18 (1949).

[431] Loevenich, Becker, and Schröder, *J. prakt. Chem.*, **127**, 254 (1930).

[432] Putochin, *Ber.*, **59**, 625 (1926); *C. A.* **24**, 3756 (1930); cf. ref. 428; also Bailar, *J. Am. Chem. Soc.*, **56**, 955 (1934).

[433] Amundsen and Sanderson, *Org. Syntheses*, **24**, 44 (1944); Shriner and Hickey, *J. Am. Chem. Soc.*, **61**, 888 (1939).

[434] Chambret and Joly, *Bull. soc. chim. France*, (5) **14**, 1023 (1947).

[435] Müller and Feld, *Monatsh.*, **58**, 15 (1931).

[436] Ruggli, Leupin, and Dahn, *Helv. Chim. Acta*, **30**, 1845 (1947).

[437] Sakellarios, *Helv. Chim. Acta*, **29**, 1675 (1946).

[438] Hamer and Rathbone, *J. Chem. Soc.*, 246 (1943).

[439] Weizmann and Malkowa, *Bull. soc. chim. France*, (4) **47**, 356 (1930).

[440] Davies and Powell, *J. Am. Chem. Soc.*, **67**, 1466 (1945).

[441] DeWitt, *Org. Syntheses*, Coll. Vol. II, 25 (1943).

[442] Cloke et al., *J. Am. Chem. Soc.*, **67**, 1587 (1945).

[443] Billman and Parker, *J. Am. Chem. Soc.*, **65**, 761 (1943).

[444] Birkofer, *Ber.*, **75**, 429 (1942).

[445] Goldberg and Kelly, *J. Chem. Soc.*, 1369 (1947).

[446] Stoll, Peyer, and Hofmann, *Helv. Chim. Acta*, **26**, 929 (1943).

[447] Mattocks and Hartung, *J. Am. Chem. Soc.*, **68**, 2108 (1946).

[448] Wenner, *J. Org. Chem.*, **13**, 26 (1948).

[449] Horning, Horning, and Platt, *J. Am. Chem. Soc.*, **70**, 288 (1948).

[450] Riegel, Gold, and Kubico, *J. Am. Chem. Soc.*, **64**, 2221 (1942).

[451] Coleman and Callen, *J. Am. Chem. Soc.*, **68**, 2006 (1946).

[452] Clapp, *J. Am. Chem. Soc.*, **70**, 184 (1948); cf. ref. 451.

[453] Mannich, Handke, and Roth, *Ber.*, **69**, 2112 (1936).

[454] Pearson, Baxter, and Carter, *Org. Syntheses*, **29**, 21 (1949); cf. ref. 455.

[455] Schmidt et al., *Ann.*, **568**, 192 (1950).

[456]Leffler, *Org. Syntheses,* Coll. Vol. II, 24 (1943).

[457]Krueger and Schwarcz, *J. Am. Chem. Soc.,* **63**, 2512 (1941).

[458]Adams and Segur, *J. Am. Chem. Soc.,* **45**, 785 (1923).

[459]Pierce and Adams, *J. Am. Chem. Soc.,* **45**, 790 (1923).

[460]Vliet, *Org. Syntheses,* Coll. Vol. I, 201, 203 (1943).

[461]Headlee, Collett, and Lazzell, *J. Am. Chem. Soc.,* **55**, 1066 (1933); Horne and Shriner, *ibid.,* **54**, 2925 (1932).

[462]Lasselle and Sundet, *J. Am. Chem. Soc.,* **63**, 2374 (1941).

[463]Biel, *J. Am. Chem. Soc.,* **71**, 1306 (1949).

[464]Goldfarb, *J. Am. Chem. Soc.,* **63**, 2280 (1941).

[465]Cairns and Fletcher, *J. Am. Chem. Soc.,* **63**, 1034 (1941).

[466]McCasland and Smith, *J. Am. Chem. Soc.,* **72**, 2190 (1950).

[467]Leffler and Adams, *J. Am. Chem. Soc.,* **59**, 2252 (1937).

[468]Emerson, *J. Am. Chem. Soc.,* **67**, 516 (1945).

[469]Lutz, Freek, and Murphey, *J. Am. Chem. Soc.,* **70**, 2015 (1948).

[470]Moffett and Hoehn, *J. Am. Chem. Soc.,* **69**, 1792 (1947).

[471]Campbell et al., *J. Am. Chem. Soc.,* **70**, 3868 (1948).

[472]Gardner et al., *J. Chem. Soc.,* 780 (1949).

[473]Kyrides et al., *J. Am. Chem. Soc.,* **72**, 745 (1950); Gawron and Spoerri, *ibid.,* **67**, 514 (1945); Hromatka, *Ber.,* **75**, 131 (1942).

[474]Haeseler, *Org. Syntheses,* Coll. Vol. I, 196 (1941).

[475]Cromwell, *Chem. Revs.,* **38**, 83 (1946).

[476]Kohn, *Monatsh.,* **25**, 841 (1904).

[477]Morsch, *Monatsh.,* **63**, 220 (1934).

[478]Holley and Holley, *J. Am. Chem. Soc.,* **71**, 2124 (1949).

[479]Johnson, Woroch, and Buell, *J. Am. Chem. Soc.,* **71**, 1901 (1949); Southwick and Seivard, *ibid.,* 71, 2532 (1949).

[480]Stork and McElvain, *J. Am. Chem. Soc.,* **69**, 971 (1947).

[481]Mozingo and McCracken, *Org. Syntheses,* **20**, 35 (1940); Fuson, Parham, and Reed, *J. Am. Chem. Soc.,* **68**, 1239 (1946); McElvain and Rorig, *ibid.,* **70**, 1820, 1826 (1948).

[482]Morsch, *Monatsh.,* **60**, 50 (1932).

[483]Morsch, *Monatsh.,* **61**, 299 (1932).

[484]McElvain and Stork, *J. Am. Chem. Soc.,* **68**, 1049 (1946).

[485]Steiger, *Org. Syntheses,* **22**, 26 (1942).

[486]Philippi, Hendgen, and Hernler, *Monatsh.,* **69**, 282 (1936).

[487]Heath and Rose, *J. Chem. Soc.,* 1471, 1486 (1947).

[488]Worrall, *J. Am. Chem. Soc.,* **49**, 1598 (1927).

[489]Snyder, Weaver, and Marshall, *J. Am. Chem. Soc.,* **71**, 289 (1949).

[490]Robinson, *J. Chem. Soc.,* 220 (1941).

[491]Bachmann, *J. Am. Chem. Soc.,* **59**, 420 (1937).

[492]Pschorr and Karo, *Ber.,* **39**, 3140 (1906).

[493]Weston and Adkins, *J. Am. Chem. Soc.,* **50**, 859 (1928).

[494]Blicke and Tsao, *J. Am. Chem. Soc.,* **68**, 905 (1946).

[495]Fones, *J. Org. Chem.,* **14**, 1099 (1949).

[496]Weston, Ruddy, and Suter, *J. Am. Chem. Soc.,* **65**, 674 (1943).

[497]Aspinall, *J. Am. Chem. Soc.,* **63**, 852 (1941).

[498]Klosterman and Painter, *J. Am. Chem. Soc.,* **69**, 1674 (1947).

[499]Cocker, *J. Chem. Soc.,* 1693 (1937); 1290 (1940).

[500]Billman and Parker, *J. Am. Chem. Soc.,* **65**, 2455 (1943).

[501]Verkade and Witjens, *Rec. trav. chim.,* **62**, 201 (1943).

[502]Krueger and Mosettig, *J. Org. Chem.*, **5**, 313 (1940).
[503]Mosettig and Krueger, *J. Org. Chem.*, **3**, 317 (1938).
[504]Bachmann and Boatner, *J. Am. Chem. Soc.*, **58**, 2097 (1936).
[505]Baker, *J. Chem. Soc.*, 476 (1937).
[506]Ritter and Kalish, *J. Am. Chem. Soc.*, **70**, 4048 (1948).
[507]Price and Voong, *Org. Syntheses*, **28**, 80 (1948).
[508]Leffler in *Organic Reactions*, Vol. 1, John Wiley & Sons, New York, 1942, p. 91; cf. Deasy, *J. Org. Chem.*, **10**, 141 (1945).
[509]Parker and Shive, *J. Am. Chem. Soc.*, **69**, 63 (1947).
[510]Bergstrom, Sturz, and Tracy, *J. Org. Chem.*, **11**, 239 (1946).
[511]Glickman and Cope, *J. Am. Chem. Soc.*, **67**, 1017 (1945); Coffey, Thomson, and Wilson, *J. Chem. Soc.*, 856 (1936); Décombe, *Ann. chim.*, (10) **18**, 103 (1932).
[512]Brown and Jones, *J. Chem. Soc.*, 781 (1946).
[513]Stewart and Bradley, *J. Am. Chem. Soc.*, **54**, 4172 (1932).
[514]Alexander and Underhill, *J. Am. Chem. Soc.*, **71**, 4014 (1949).
[515]Masters and Bogert, *J. Am. Chem. Soc.*, **64**, 2710 (1942).
[516]Rivier and Farine, *Helv. Chim. Acta*, **12**, 866 (1929); Scanlan, *J. Am. Chem. Soc.*, **57**, 887 (1935).
[517]Gattermann and Wieland, *Laboratory Methods of Organic Chemistry*, The Macmillan Co., New York, 1938, p. 317.
[518]Lambert, Scaife, and Wilder-Smith, *J. Chem. Soc.*, 1474 (1947).
[519]Buckley, Heath, and Rose, *J. Chem. Soc.*, 1500 (1947).
[520]Rousseau and Lindwall, *J. Am. Chem. Soc.*, **72**, 3047 (1950).
[521]Jones and Wilson, *J. Chem. Soc.*, 550 (1949).
[522]Barger and Easson, *J. Chem. Soc.*, 2100 (1938).
[523]Hiers and Adams, *J. Am. Chem. Soc.*, **49**, 1099 (1927); *Ber.*, **59**, 162 (1926).
[524]Allen and Bell, *Org. Syntheses*, **22**, 19 (1942).
[525]Anslow and King, *Org. Syntheses*, Coll. Vol. I, 298 (1941).
[526]Neunhoeffer and Liebich, *Ber.*, **71**, 2247 (1938); Bell, Kenyon, and Robinson, *J. Chem. Soc.*, 1243 (1926).
[527]Kamm, *Org. Syntheses*, Coll. Vol. I, 445 (1941).
[528]Salzberg, *J. Am. Chem. Soc.*, **72**, 4307 (1950).
[529]Ettlinger, *J. Am. Chem. Soc.*, **72**, 4795 (1950).
[530]Ingram, *J. Chem. Soc.*, 2247 (1950).
[531]Theilacker and Wendtland, *Ann.*, **570**, 50 (1950).
[532]Hauser and Reynolds, *J. Org. Chem.*, **15**, 1224 (1950).
[533]Degering and Boatright, *J. Am. Chem. Soc.*, **72**, 5137 (1950).
[534]Waalkes et al., *J. Am. Chem. Soc.*, **72**, 5760 (1950).
[535]Groggins, *Unit Processes in Organic Synthesis*, McGraw-Hill Book Co., New York, 1947, pp. 73–128.
[536]Ref. 535, pp. 338–423.
[537]Baret and Léveque, *Bull. soc. chim. France*, (5) **16**, 832 (1949).
[538]Elderfield and Ressler, *J. Am. Chem. Soc.*, **72**, 4067 (1950).
[539]May and Mosettig, *J. Am. Chem. Soc.*, **70**, 1077 (1948).
[540]Julian et al., *J. Am. Chem. Soc.*, **67**, 1203 (1945).
[541]Hass and Huffman, *J. Am. Chem. Soc.*, **63**, 1233 (1941).
[542]Allen and Wolf, *Org. Syntheses*, **30**, 3 (1950).
[543]Tchoubar, *Bull. soc. chim. France*, (5) **16**, 160 (1949).
[544]Herz, *J. Am. Chem. Soc.*, **72**, 4999 (1950).
[545]Burger and Bennet, *J. Am. Chem. Soc.*, **72**, 5414 (1950).
[546]Manske and Kulka, *J. Am. Chem. Soc.*, **72**, 4997 (1950).

[547]Lewis, *J. Chem. Soc.*, 2249 (1950).

[548]Snyder and Hamlin, *J. Am. Chem. Soc.*, **72**, 5082 (1950).

[549]Winstein and Boschan, *J. Am. Chem. Soc.*, **72**, 4675 (1950); cf. ref. 467.

[550]Roeder and Day, *J. Org. Chem.*, **6**, 28 (1941).

[551]Gilman and Avakian, *J. Am. Chem. Soc.*, **68**, 580 (1946).

[552]Witten and Reid, *Org. Syntheses*, **30**, 5 (1950).

[553]Morrison and Rinderknecht, *J. Chem. Soc.*, 1478 (1950).

[554]Fieser, *Org. Syntheses*, Coll. Vol. II, 35, 39 (1943).

[555]Stevenson, *Ind. Eng. Chem.*, **42**, 1664 (1950).

[556]Kremer, *J. Am. Chem. Soc.*, **61**, 1321 (1939).

[557]King and Work, *J. Chem. Soc.*, 1307 (1940).

[558]Wilkinson and Finar, *J. Chem. Soc.*, 759 (1947).

[559]Brown in *Organic Reactions*, Vol. 6, John Wiley & Sons, New York, 1951, p. 469.

[560]Campaigne, Budde, and Schaefer, *Org. Syntheses*, **31**, 6 (1951).

[561]Schultz, *Org. Syntheses*, **31**, 45 (1951).

25

Imines

465. Condensation of Carbonyl Compounds with Amines

$$RCHO + R'NH_2 \rightarrow RCH=NR' + H_2O$$

Both aliphatic and aromatic aldehydes condense with primary amines, aliphatic and aromatic, to form N-substituted imines. The purely aliphatic imines (C_5 to C_{10}) can be obtained in 50–80% yield; however, these compounds are unstable and should be used immediately after distillation.[1] Side reactions which may occur during their formation have been studied.[2] On the other hand, Schiff bases from substituted benzaldehydes and amines, aliphatic and aromatic, are more stable and have been prepared in large numbers.[3-6] The benzaldehyde entity may carry a halo, hydroxyl, methoxyl, dialkylamino, or nitro group.[5] Usually, an immediate reaction occurs upon mixing the two reactants either without a solvent or in dilute alcohol, as illustrated by the synthesis of benzalaniline, $C_6H_5CH=NC_6H_5$ (87%).[3]

The formation of Schiff bases by the reaction of ketones with amines is more difficult. Acetophenone and other aryl alkyl ketones which are slow to react under the usual conditions will combine with aromatic amines at 160–180° in the presence of a zinc chloride-aniline salt.[21] In another procedure, 2-acetylthiophene and aniline are condensed in boiling toluene with the aid of a water separator.[26]

Ketones like acetophenone have been heated with ammonia in the presence of a dehydrating agent, but the formation of the ketimines is poor.[7] A successful conversion of 9-fluorenone to its ketimine has been described in which anhydrous ammonia is passed through the molten ketone at 165° (66%).[8]

Invariably, the combination of ammonia and aldehydes forms other products; these reactions have been reviewed.[9] Monochloramine (NH_2Cl) reacts readily with substituted benzaldehydes to form aldchlorimines ($ArCH=NCl$).[10]

466. Cyclization of β-Amino Alcohols

$$
\begin{array}{c}
H_2COH \\
| \\
H_2CNH_2
\end{array}
\xrightarrow[\text{Heat}]{H_2SO_4}
\begin{array}{c}
H_2COSO_2O^- \\
| \\
H_2CNH_3{}^+
\end{array}
\xrightarrow{NaOH}
\begin{array}{c}
H_2C \\
\diagdown \\
\diagup\quad NH \\
H_2C
\end{array}
$$

Ethylenimine is conveniently prepared from ethanolamine by heating the inner salt of the sulfate ester with aqueous alkali (37%).[11] The method has been applied to other β-amino alcohols to form the C-alkyl homologs of ethylenimine in which one to three of the four hydrogens may be substituted.[12] The general procedure is illustrated by the synthesis of 2,2-dimethylethylenimine (51%).[13] The N-alkyl analogs can be made by treating the N-alkylethanolamine hydrochlorides with chlorosulfonic acid followed by the action of base on the intermediate sulfuric acid esters, as in the preparation of N-ethylethylenimine (70%).[14]

Aryl-substituted amino alcohols fail to undergo this reaction but instead are dehydrated to vinylamines.

The reactions of ethylenimine have been studied extensively.[25]

467. Action of Grignard Reagents on Oximes

$$
\begin{array}{c}
ArC-CH_3 \\
\| \\
NOH
\end{array}
\xrightarrow{2RMgX}
\begin{array}{c}
R \\
| \\
Ar-C-CH_2 \\
\diagdown\diagup \\
NMgBr
\end{array}
\xrightarrow{H_2O}
\begin{array}{c}
R \\
| \\
Ar-C-CH_2 \\
\diagdown\diagup \\
NH
\end{array}
$$

Certain substituted ethylenimines are obtained by the action of aliphatic or aromatic Grignard reagents on aryl alkyl ketoximes with subsequent non-acidic decomposition of the intermediate complex (20–60%).[15,16]

468. Action of Grignard Reagents on Nitriles

$$
ArCN \xrightarrow{RMgX} ArRC=NMgX \xrightarrow{NH_3} ArRC=NH
$$

The interaction of Grignard reagents and nitriles produces ketimines which may be hydrolyzed to ketones without isolation (method 187). Many of the alkyl aryl ketimines have been isolated for further study. For this purpose, the intermediate addition compound is decomposed by treatment with anhydrous hydrogen chloride or, preferably, with anhydrous ammonia.[17-19] The yields range from 50% to 86%. Often, the ketimines are non-hydrolyzable or hydrolyzed with difficulty, allowing them to be easily isolated;[18] others must be isolated and stored under anhydrous conditions.[19,20]

469. β-Iminonitriles by Condensation of Nitriles [22]

$$2CH_3CN \xrightarrow[H_2O]{NaNH_2;} CH_3C(=NH)CH_2CN$$

470. Ethylene Imino Ketones by the Action of Amines on α,β-Dibromo Ketones [23]

$$\underset{\substack{| \quad | \\ Br \quad Br}}{ArCH-CH-COAr} \xrightarrow{RNH_2} \underset{NR}{ArCH-CHCOAr}$$

TABLE 93. IMINES 731

TABLE 93. IMINES

C_n	Compound	Method	Yield %	Chapter[ref.]	B.p./mm., n_D^t, (M.p.), Deriv.
C_2	Ethylenimine	466	37	25[11]	58, 1.4123[25]
C_3	1,2-Propylenimine	466	65	25[12]	64, 1.4095[25]
	Ethylidenemethylamine	465	55	25[1]	28/754, 1.4010[14]
C_4	1,2-Butylenimine	466	46	25[12]	89, 1.4165[25]
	trans-2,3-Butylenimine	466	47	25[12]	76, 1.4070[25]
	2,2-Dimethylethylenimine	466	51	25[13]	72, 1.4050[25]
	N-Ethylethylenimine	466	70	25[14]	222HCl
	Propylidenemethylamine	465	77	25[1]	53/758, 1.4033[13]
	Ethylidene-ethylamine	465	77	25[1]	48/774, 1.3953[13]
C_5	Propylidene-ethylamine	465	81	25[1]	74/764, 1.4053[14]
	Butylidenemethylamine	465	76	25[1]	81/764, 1.4095[13]
C_6	Butylidene-ethylamine	465	84	25[1]	102/763, 1.4105[21]
C_8	N-Benzylidenemethylamine	465	70	25[4]	185, 69/20, 1.5519
C_9	N-Benzylidene-ethylamine	465	90	25[24]	99/28, 1.5397
C_{10}	2-Phenyl-2-ethylethylenimine	467	60	25[16]	86/7, 1.5318, 191HCl
C_{12}	N-Phenyl 2-thienyl methyl ketimine	465	46	25[6]	155/5, (70)
C_{13}	Diphenylmethane imine hydrochloride	....	66	25[20]	
	Fluorenyllidenimine	465	66	25[8]	(124)
	N-Benzylideneaniline (benzalaniline)	465	87	25[3]	(52)
C_{14}	Acetophenonanil	465	42	25[21]	167/12, (99)
C_{15}	2,2-Diphenyl-3-methylethylenimine	467	70	25[15]	132/1, (75), 140HCl

For explanations and symbols see pp. xi–xii.

REFERENCES FOR CHAPTER 25

[1] Tiollais, *Bull. soc. chim. France,* (5) **14,** 708 (1947); Campbell, Sommers, and Campbell, *J. Am. Chem. Soc.,* **66,** 82 (1944).

[2] Emerson, Hess, and Uhle, *J. Am. Chem. Soc.,* **63,** 872 (1941); Paquin, *Chem. Ber.,* **82,** 316 (1949).

[3] Bigelow and Eatough, *Org. Syntheses,* Coll. Vol. I, 80 (1941).

[4] Cromwell, Babson, and Harris, *J. Am. Chem. Soc.,* **65,** 312 (1943); ref. 6.

[5] Cromwell and Hoeksema, *J. Am. Chem. Soc.,* **67,** 1658 (1945); Moffett and Hoehn, *ibid.,* **69,** 1792 (1947); Lutz et al., *J. Org. Chem.,* **12,** 760 (1947); Jensen and Bang, *Ann.,* **548,** 106 (1941).

[6] Campbell et al., *J. Am. Chem. Soc.,* **70,** 3868 (1948).

[7] Strain, *J. Am. Chem. Soc.,* **52,** 820 (1930).

[8] Harris, Harriman, and Wheeler, *J. Am. Chem. Soc.,* **68,** 846 (1946).

[9] Sprung, *Chem. Revs.,* **26,** 297 (1940).

[10] Hauser, Gillaspie, and LeMaistre, *J. Am. Chem. Soc.,* **57,** 567 (1935).

[11] Allen, Spangler, and Webster, *Org. Syntheses,* **30,** 38 (1950); Leighton, Perkins, and Renquist, *J. Am. Chem. Soc.,* **69,** 1540 (1947); cf. ref. 12.

[12] Jones et al., *J. Org. Chem.,* **9,** 125, 484 (1944).

[13] Campbell, Sommers, and Campbell, *Org. Syntheses,* **27,** 12 (1947).

[14] Elderfield and Hageman, *J. Org. Chem.,* **14,** 622 (1949).

[15] Campbell et al., *J. Org. Chem.,* **8,** 103 (1943).

[16] Campbell et al., *J. Org. Chem.,* **9,** 184 (1944).

[17] Moureu and Mignonac, *Ann. chim.,* (9) **14,** 322 (1920).

[18] Pickard and Vaughan, *J. Am. Chem. Soc.,* **72,** 876, 5017 (1950).

[19] Cloke, *J. Am. Chem. Soc.,* **62,** 117 (1940).

[20] Lachman, *Org. Syntheses,* Coll. Vol. II, 234 (1941).

[21] Reddelien, *Ann.,* **388,** 165 (1912); *Ber.,* **43,** 2476 (1910).

[22] Adkins and Whitman, *J. Am. Chem. Soc.,* **64,** 150 (1942); Darnow, Kühlcke, and Baxmann, *Chem. Ber.,* **82,** 254 (1949).

[23] Cromwell and Caughlan, *J. Am. Chem. Soc.,* **67,** 2235 (1945); 69, 258 (1947).

[24] Campbell et al., *J. Am. Chem. Soc.,* **70,** 3868 (1948).

[25] Bestian, *Ann.,* **566,** 210 (1950).

[26] Hartough, *J. Am. Chem. Soc.,* **70,** 1282 (1948).

26

Hydrazines

CONTENTS

These compounds are prepared in part by methods similar to those for amines; in addition, specific methods are employed including the reduction of diazonium compounds, reduction of azo compounds, and reduction of nitrosamines leading to *sym*- or *unsym*-substituted hydrazines.

471. Alkylation of Hydrazines

$$RX + NH_2NH_2 \rightarrow RNHNH_2$$

High-molecular-weight monoalkylhydrazines (C_6 and above) can be made from anhydrous hydrazine[33] and alkyl halides in a manner similar to the alkylation of amines.[2] On the other hand, alkylation with the lower halides leads chiefly to di-, tri-, and tetra-substituted hydrazines.[2] Ethylhydrazine has been obtained by alkylation of hydrazine with ethyl sulfate (32%).[3] Methylhydrazine is synthesized by a special variation of this method (54%).[9]

If activated by nitro groups, aryl halogens are easily replaced by the hydrazino group, as illustrated by the synthesis of 2,4-dinitrophenylhydrazine (85%).[4] Other nitrophenylhydrazines may be obtained by the action of hydrazine or methylhydrazine.[5]

Alkali metal phenylhydrazines, $ArN(Na)NH_2$, which are prepared by the direct reaction of primary hydrazines with alkali amide in liquid ammonia are readily alkylated by alkyl halides to furnish N,N-alkyl-arylhydrazines, Ar(R)NNH$_2$ (73–94%).[7]

sym-Hydrazines, RNHNHR, are prepared by the alkylation of dibenzoyl-hydrazine (C$_6$H$_5$CONHNHCOC$_6$H$_5$) followed by hydrolytic treatment, as shown by the synthesis of sym-dimethylhydrazine (73% over-all).[8] This procedure may be applied to dibenzoylalkylhydrazines which upon alkylation and hydrolysis yield sym-hydrazines substituted with different groups, e.g., sym-methylisopropylhydrazine.[10]

The interaction of hydrazine hydrate and ethyl chlorocarbonate in methanol solution yields methyl hydrazinecarboxylate, H$_2$NNHCO$_2$CH$_3$ (49%).[11]

472. Interaction of Amines and Hydroxylamine-O-Sulfonic Acid

$$RNH_2 + NH_2O \cdot SO_2OH \xrightarrow{Heat} RNHNH_2$$

Monoalkylhydrazines (C$_2$ to C$_5$) are readily prepared by heating amines with hydroxylamine-O-sulfonic acid in the presence of alkali (31–60%).[1] The products are isolated as the oxalate salts.

473. Reduction of Diazonium Compounds

$$ArN_2^+Cl^- \xrightarrow{Na_2SO_3} ArNHNH_2 \cdot HCl$$

The reduction of diazonium salts by sodium sulfite forms monosubstituted arylhydrazines. An improved procedure for the synthesis of phenylhydrazine in 84% yield is typical.[12] Arylhydrazine salts substituted in the nucleus with halo,[14] ether,[15] carboxyl,[16,19] or nitro[17,18] groups have been prepared. The free bases are liberated from the salts by the action of aqueous sodium hydroxide or sodium acetate.

474. Reduction of Nitrosoamines

$$R_2NH \xrightarrow{(HONO)} R_2NNO \xrightarrow[CH_3COOH]{Zn} R_2NNH_2$$

unsym-Disubstituted hydrazines, R$_2$NNH$_2$, are prepared by the zinc-acetic acid reduction of either aliphatic or aromatic nitrosoamines. In this manner, unsym-dimethylhydrazine is synthesized in 73% yield from nitrosodimethylamine.[20] Similarly, α-methyl-α-phenylhydrazine is prepared (56%).[21] Preparations of the nitrosoamines from the corresponding secondary amines are also described.

Ethylhydrazine is made from nitrosodiethylurea, C$_2$H$_5$N(NO)CONHC$_2$H$_5$, by the usual steps of reduction and hydrolysis.[22]

475. Reduction of Azo Compounds

$$ArNO_2 \xrightarrow{(H)} ArN=NAr \xrightarrow{(H)} ArNHNHAr$$

Aromatic *sym*-disubstituted hydrazines are obtained by reduction of azo compounds, which in turn are intermediates in properly controlled reductions of nitro compounds. The over-all reduction can be accomplished with zinc dust and alkali or electrolytically. For example, hydrazobenzene, the simplest member, is made by both procedures.[23,24] Chemical reduction is carried out on *o*-nitrobromobenzene to form 2,2'-dibromohydrazobenzene (57%), the halo groups remaining intact.[25] Many examples of the electrolytic procedure have been cited; the yields vary from 50% to 95%.[26] To a limited extent, a magnesium-magnesium iodide system has been employed as a reducing agent for the azobenzenes.[27]

476. Action of Grignard Reagents on Diazomethane[29]

$$CH_3(CH_2)_2CH_2MgX \xrightarrow[H_2O]{CH_2N_2;} CH_3(CH_2)_2CH_2NHNHCH_3 \quad (53\%)$$

477. Reductive Hydrazination of Carbonyl Compounds[30]

$$2R_2CO + H_2NNH_2 \xrightarrow[\text{Catalyst}]{H_2} R_2CHNHNHCHR_2$$

R = isopropyl (80%)

478. Addition of Grignard Reagents to Dialkyl-alkylidenhydrazones[31,32]

$$R_2NNH_2 \xrightarrow{H_2CO} R_2NN=CH_2 \xrightarrow[H_2O]{CH_3MgX;} R_2NNHCH_2CH_3$$

R = ethyl (22% over-all)

TABLE 94. HYDRAZINES

C_n	Compound	Method	Yield (%)	Chapter[ref.]	B.p./mm., n_D^t, (M.p.), Deriv.
C_1	Methylhydrazine (as sulfate)	471	54	26[9]	(142)
C_2	Ethylhydrazine	471	32	26[3]	99.5/709, 110HCl
	Ethylhydrazine (as oxalate)	472	42	26[1]	(171)
	sym-Dimethylhydrazine (as hydrochloride)	471	78	26[8]	(167)
	unsym-Dimethylhydrazine	474	73	26[20]	65/765, 82HCl
	Methyl hydrazino-carboxylate	471	49	26[11]	108/12, (63), 160HCl
C_3	n-Propylhydrazine (as oxalate)	472	52	26[1]	(175)
	Isopropylhydrazine	477	90	26[30]	107/750, 114HCl
	Isopropylhydrazine (as oxalate)	472	44	26[1]	(172)
C_4	n-Butylhydrazine (as oxalate)	472	45	26[1]	(165)
	sym-Methylisopropyl-hydrazine	471	50	26[10]	79/37
	N,N-Dimethyl-N'-ethylhydrazine	478	65	26[31]	77/720, 93Pi
C_5	n-Amylhydrazine (as oxalate)	472	31	26[1]	(164)
	sym-Methyl-n-butyl-hydrazine	476	53	26[29]	115HCl
C_6	n-Hexylhydrazine	471	26	26[2]	81/14
	sym-Diisopropyl-hydrazine	477	100	26[30]	124/750, 1.4125[24]
	Triethylhydrazine	478	22[†]	26[32]	39/37
	Phenylhydrazine	473	84	26[12]	138/18, (23)
	p-Fluorophenylhydrazine	473	74	26[14]	129/21, (39)
	o-Nitrophenylhydrazine	473	64	26[18]	(90)*, 140Ac*
	p-Nitrophenylhydrazine	473	66	26[17]	(157), 120Pi*
	2,4-Dinitrophenylhydrazine	471	85	26[4]	(192)
C_7	a-Methyl-a-phenyl-hydrazine	474	56	26[21]	109/13
	o-Carboxyphenylhydrazine	473	84	26[16]	(247), 190HCl
	p-Carboxyphenylhydrazine	473	76	26[19]	253HCl
C_8	N,N-Ethylphenylhydrazine	471	88	26[7]	120–7/25, 147HCl
C_{12}	2-Phenoxyphenylhydrazine	473	45	26[15]	(154)
	Hydrazobenzene	475	85	26[23]	(124)
	2,2'-Dibromohydrazo-benzene	475	57	26[25]	(98)

TABLE 94. HYDRAZINES 737

TABLE 94 (*continued*)

C_n	Compound	Method	Yield (%)	Chapter[ref.]	B.p./mm., n_D^t, (M.p.), Deriv.
C_{13}	4,4'-Dihydrazinodiphenyl-methane	473	35	26[13]	(141)
C_{24}	Tetraphenylhydrazine	....	70	26[28]	(144)

For explanations and symbols see pp. xi–xii.

REFERENCES FOR CHAPTER 26

[1]Gever and Hayes, *J. Org. Chem.*, **14**, 813 (1949).

[2]Westphal, *Ber.*, **74**, 759 (1941).

[3]Brown and Kearley, *J. Am. Chem. Soc.*, **72**, 2762 (1950).

[4]Allen, *Org. Syntheses*, Coll. Vol. II, 228 (1943).

[5]Vis, *Rec. trav. chim.*, **58**, 387 (1939).

[6]Koenigs and Loesch, *J. prakt. Chem.*, **143**, 59 (1935).

[7]Audrieth, Weisiger, and Carter, *J. Org. Chem.*, **6**, 417 (1941).

[8]Hatt, *Org. Syntheses*, Coll. Vol. II, 208 (1943).

[9]Hatt, *Org. Syntheses*, Coll. Vol. II, 395 (1943).

[10]Ramsperger, *J. Am. Chem. Soc.*, **51**, 918 (1929).

[11]Diels and Fritzsche, *Ber.*, **44**, 3022 (1911).

[12]Coleman, *Org. Syntheses*, Coll. Vol. I, 442 (1941).

[13]Parkes and Morley, *J. Chem. Soc.*, 315 (1936).

[14]Schiemann and Winkelmüller, *Ber.*, **66**, 729 (1933).

[15]Tarbell et al., *J. Am. Chem. Soc.*, **70**, 1381 (1948).

[16]Pfannstiel and Janecke, *Ber.*, **75**, 1096 (1942).

[17]Davies, *J. Chem. Soc.*, 715 (1922).

[18]Brady and Reynolds, *J. Chem. Soc.*, 196 (1928).

[19]Veibel and Hauge, *Bull. soc. chim. France*, (5) 5, 1506 (1938).

[20]Hatt, *Org. Syntheses*, Coll. Vol. II, 211 (1943).

[21]Hartman and Roll, *Org. Syntheses*, Coll. Vol. II, 418 (1943).

[22]Weygand, *Organic Preparations*, Interscience Publishers, New York, 1945, p. 241.

[23]Gattermann and Wieland, *Laboratory Methods of Organic Chemistry*, The Macmillan Co., New York, 1938, p. 183; cf. ref. 24.

[24]McKee and Gerapostolou, *Trans. Electrochem. Soc.*, **68**, 329 (1935).

[25]Snyder, Weaver, and Marshall, *J. Am. Chem. Soc.*, **71**, 289 (1949).

[26]Swann, *Trans. Electrochem. Soc.*, **69**, 307 (1936); **77**, 479 (1940); Swann in *Technique of Organic Chemistry*, Vol. II, Interscience Publishers, New York, 1948, p. 143.

[27]Bachmann, *J. Am. Chem. Soc.*, **53**, 1524 (1931).

[28]See ref. 23, p. 355.

[29]Coleman et al., *J. Org. Chem.*, **3**, 99 (1938).

[30]Lochte, Noyes, and Bailey, *J. Am. Chem. Soc.*, **44**, 2556 (1922).

[31]Klages et al., *Ann.*, **547**, 1, 28 (1941).

[32]Westphal and Eucken, *Ber.*, **76**, 1137 (1943).

[33]Smith and Howard, *Org. Syntheses*, **24**, 53 (1944); cf. Barber and Wragg, *J. Chem. Soc.*, 1458 (1948).

27

Oximes and Nitroso Compounds

479. Oximination of Carbonyl Compounds

$$R_2CO + H_2NOH \cdot HCl + NaOH \rightarrow R_2C=NOH + H_2O + NaCl$$

Oximes are commonly prepared by the interaction of ketones with hydroxylamine hydrochloride (or sulfate) in the presence of an inorganic base. The reaction is reversible, but the state of equilibrium highly favors the desired products. Preparations of large quantities for synthetic work are illustrated for methyl ethyl ketoxime,[1] cyclohexanone oxime,[2,3] heptaldoxime,[3] and benzophenone oxime,[4] the procedures varying somewhat with the nature of the carbonyl compound. In some instances, a readily available and cheap reagent like sodium hydroxylamine disulfonate, $HON(SO_3Na)_2$, is first prepared from sodium nitrite and sodium bisulfite and, without isolation, treated with the carbonyl compound,[2,6,7,15] Hydroxylamine-O-sulfonic acid, H_2NOSO_3H, is still another reagent and, like sodium hydroxylamine disulfonate, is used in the absence of a base. The preparation of hydroxylamine hydrochloride is described.[6]

The oximes of ketones with large hydrocarbon radicals like the acetylphenanthrenes are readily prepared by the action of hydroxylamine hydrochloride in the presence of pyridine.[12] Special studies have been made for the synthesis of 1,2-cyclohexanedione dioxime[14] as well as the next higher homolog.[13] Dimethylglyoxime, $CH_3C(=NOH)C(=NOH)CH_3$, is prepared by the action of sodium hydroxylamine monosulfonate on biacetyl monoxime.[15]

480. Nitrosation of Active Methylene Compounds

$$RCOCH_2R + R'ONO \xrightarrow{HCl} RCOC(=NOH)R + R'OH$$

Compounds having active methylene groups react with nitrous acid to form oximino derivatives. The attack on the α-methylene group of ketones is illustrated by the action of ethyl nitrite on methyl ethyl ketone, and by the action of methyl nitrite on propiophenone, to form biacetyl monoxime (60%)[15] and isonitrosopropiophenone (68%),[16] respectively. Methyl and ethyl nitrites are passed in gaseous form into the ketones in the presence of hydrochloric acid. In other preparations, n-butyl, amyl, or octyl nitrite in liquid form is employed.[14,17,18]

Similarly, the α-methylene group of acetoacetic ester is oximinated by the action of sodium nitrite in glacial acetic acid (63%).[19] Nitrosation of alkylated malonic, [20,21] acetoacetic,[21] and benzoylacetic[22] esters with subsequent cleavage affords an excellent synthesis for α-oximino esters, $RC(=NOH)CO_2C_2H_5$. A survey of several possible procedures for this conversion has been made.[21] If a β-keto $acid$ is nitrosated, then the carboxyl group is lost and an α-oximino ketone is formed, viz.,

$$CH_3COCHRCO_2H \xrightarrow{(HONO)} CH_3COC(=NOH)R + CO_2$$

The conversion of o- and p-nitroethylbenzenes with t-butyl nitrite and sodium t-butoxide into the corresponding nitroacetophenone oximes is accomplished in 67–74% yields.[25]

481. Partial Reduction of Nitro Compounds

Various procedures have been developed for the production of oximes from nitroparaffins. Direct reduction with zinc dust and acetic acid has been proposed, but the yields are poor because of the simultaneous formation of amines.[26] A synthesis for cyclohexanone oxime has been demonstrated which involves the formation and selective hydrogenation of 1-chloro-1-nitrocyclohexane. The halogenated intermediate is prepared in quantitative yield by chlorination of the sodium salt of aci-nitrocyclohexane, and subsequent hydrogenation is performed in an 80% yield over palladium-on-charcoal.[27]

Still another scheme is concerned with the zinc-acetic acid reduction of an aliphatic nitro olefin, which is readily prepared by the condensation of an aldehyde with the nitroparaffin (method 37).[28]

$$RCH_2NO_2 \xrightarrow{R'CHO} R'CH=C(R)NO_2 \xrightarrow[CH_3COOH]{Zn} R'CH_2C(=NOH)R$$

α-Nitrostilbene, $C_6H_5CH=C(NO_2)C_6H_5$, is selectively hydrogenated over a palladium catalyst to desoxybenzoin oxime in an almost quantitative yield.[29]

482. Hydroxylamination of Dihydropyridines[30]

(90% over-all)

483. Nitrosation of Secondary Amines

$$R_2NH \cdot HCl \xrightarrow{\text{(HONO)}} R_2NNO$$

Aliphatic and aromatic amines react with nitrous acid to form N-nitroso derivatives. For example, dimethylamine hydrochloride on treatment with sodium nitrite and hydrochloric acid is converted to nitrosodimethyl-amine in 90% yield.[39] In like manner, N-nitrosomethylaniline is synthe-sized from N-methylaniline in 93% yield.[40] The ready formation of these derivatives and the easy reconversion to the amine by reduction affords an advantageous procedure for separating secondary amines from primary and tertiary amines, as shown in the synthesis of N-ethyl-*m*-toluidine and other N-alkyl derivatives by the alkylation of *m*-toluidine.[41]

Certain N-nitroso derivatives are important intermediates in the synthe-sis of diazomethane and homologs. One synthesis involves the nitro-sation of a β-alkylaminoisobutyl methyl ketone; the corresponding N-nitrosoamine is readily decomposed to the diazoalkane and mesityl oxide by treatment with sodium isopropoxide.[42]

$$(CH_3)_2CCH_2COCH_3 \xrightarrow{\text{(HONO)}} (CH_3)_2CCH_2COCH_3 \xrightarrow{\text{NaOR}} CH_2N_2 +$$
$$\quad\quad | \qquad\qquad\qquad\qquad\qquad | $$
$$\quad CH_3NH \qquad\qquad\qquad\qquad CH_3NNO$$

$$(CH_3)_2C=CHCOCH_3 + H_2O$$

Other intermediates for the synthesis of diazomethane are nitrosomethyl-urea, $CH_3N(NO)CONH_2$,[43] and nitrosomethylurethane, $CH_3N(NO)CO_2C_2H_5$.[44]

Certain α-anilino acids like phenylglycine and α-anilinopropionic acid have been converted to their N-nitroso derivatives.[45]

484. Nitrosation of an Aromatic Nucleus

$$C_6H_5N(CH_3)_2 \xrightarrow{\text{(HONO)}} p\text{-}ONC_6H_4N(CH_3)_2$$

Aromatic tertiary amines and phenolic compounds undergo nuclear nitrosation, as illustrated by the synthesis of p-nitrosodimethylaniline (89%),[31] p-nitrosophenol (80%),[33] and 1-nitroso-2-naphthol (99%).[32] In the reaction of α-naphthol, an isomeric mixture of the nitrosonaphthols is obtained.[34] The nitrosation of phenols with nitrous acid usually produces p-nitroso compounds; however, o-nitrosophenols can be prepared by nitrosating phenols in the presence of cupric sulfate.[35]

N-Nitroso derivatives of secondary amines are transformed into p-nitroso derivatives by the action of hydrogen chloride in alcohol and ether solution (Fischer-Hepp). The conversion is believed to occur through the liberation of nitrosyl chloride followed by p-nitrosation, viz.,[38]

$$C_6H_5N(NO)CH_3 \xrightarrow{\text{HCl}} C_6H_5NHCH_3 \xrightarrow{\text{NOCl}} p\text{-}ONC_6H_4NHCH_3$$

485. Oxidation of Hydroxylamines and Amines

$$ArNO_2 \xrightarrow[\text{NH}_4\text{Cl}]{\text{Zn}} ArNHOH \xrightarrow{\text{(O)}} ArNO \xleftarrow{\text{(O)}} ArNH_2$$

Nitrosobenzene is readily synthesized by the chromic acid oxidation of β-phenylhydroxylamine, which in turn is prepared by the reduction of nitrobenzene by the action of zinc dust and ammonium chloride (53%).[46] The hydroxylamines need not be isolated. In other preparations, ferric chloride is employed as oxidant.[47,48]

Primary aromatic amines react with Caro's acid to form nitroso derivatives, as in the preparation of 5-nitro-2-nitrosotoluene from 2-amino-5-nitrotoluene (71%).[49]

TABLE 95. OXIMES (ISONITROSO COMPOUNDS)   743

TABLE 95. OXIMES (ISONITROSO COMPOUNDS)

C_n	Compound	Method	Yield (%)	Chapter[ref.]	B.p./mm., n_D^t, (M.p.)
C_2	Acetaldoxime	479	80	27^{24}	114
C_3	Acetoxime	479	76	27^6	136, (61)
	Methylglyoxime	479	62	27^{23}	(154)
	α-Oximinopropionic acid	480	90	27^{21}	(181d)
C_4	Methyl ethyl ketoxime	479	85	27^1	150–155
	Biacetyl monoxime	480	60	27^{15}	(76.5)
	Dimethylglyoxime	479	60	27^{15}	(240)
	α-Oximinobutyric acid	480	65	27^{21}	(154d)
C_5	Glutardialdoxime	482	90 †	27^{30}	(175)
	Cyclopentanone oxime	479	93	27^5	97/24, (54)
C_6	Cyclohexanone oxime	479	93	27^3	105/12, (88)
		479	65	27^2	95–100/5, (80)
		481	80	27^{27}	(88)
	2-Isonitrosocyclohexanone	480	82	27^{14}	
	1,2-Cyclohexanedione dioxime	479	70	27^{14}	(188)
	α-Oximinocaproic acid	480	70	27^{21}	(135d)
	Ethyl α-oximinoacetoacetate	480	63	27^{19}	(58)
C_7	Heptaldoxime	479	93	27^3	107/6, (55)
	3-Heptanone oxime	481	60	27^{28}	56/1, 1.4522^{25}
	1,2-Cycloheptanedione dioxime	479	46	27^{13}	(180)
	Ethyl α-oximinovalerate	480	75	27^{22}	124/5, (48)
C_8	Acetophenone oxime	479	90	27^9	(59)
	p-Chloroacetophenone oxime	479	94	27^{10}	(98)
	o-Nitroacetophenone oxime	480	74	27^{25}	(117)
	p-Nitroacetophenone oxime	480	67	27^{25}	(174)
	Ethyl α-oximinocaproate	480	80	27^{20}	(55)
C_9	Isonitrosopropiophenone	480	68	27^{16}	(113)
	p-Methylacetophenone oxime	479	95	27^{10}	(87)
	α-Oximino-β-phenylpropionic acid	480	95	27^{21}	(169)
C_{12}	Methyl α-naphthyl ketoxime	479	98	27^{10}	(137)
C_{13}	Benzophenone oxime	479	99	27^4	(142)
		479	98	27^{11}	(144)*
C_{14}	p-Phenylacetophenone oxime	479	90	27^9	(186)
	Desoxybenzoin oxime	481	100	27^{29}	(94)
C_{16}	3-Acetylphenanthrene oxime	479	100	27^{12}	(72)

*For explanations and symbols see pp. xi–xii.

TABLE 96. NITROSO COMPOUNDS

C_n	Compound	Method	Yield (%)	Chapter[ref.]	B.p./mm., n_D^t, (M.p.)
		C-Nitroso Compounds			
C_6	Nitrosobenzene	485	53	27[46]	(67)
	p-Dinitrosobenzene	484	40[†]	27[37]	(180)
	o-Chloronitrosobenzene	485	40	27[47]	(56)
	o-Bromonitrosobenzene	485	35	27[47]	(97)
	p-Nitrosophenol	484	80	27[33]	(125d)
C_7	o-Nitrosotoluene	485	20	27[47]	(72.5)
C_8	p-Nitrosodimethylaniline	484	89	27[31]	
C_{10}	p-Nitrosodiethylaniline	484	95	27[31]	
		N-Nitroso Compounds			
C_2	Nitrosodimethylamine	483	90	27[39]	150/755
	Nitrosomethylurea	483	72	27[43]	
C_4	Nitrosomethylurethane	483	76	27[44]	61/10
C_7	N-Nitroso-β-methylamino-isobutyl methyl ketone	483	80[†]	27[42]	101/1.5
	N-Nitrosomethylaniline	483	93	27[40]	137/13
C_8	N-Nitrosophenylglycine	483	90	27[45]	(·103d)

For explanations and symbols see pp. xi–xii.

REFERENCES FOR CHAPTER 27

[1] Marvel and Noyes, *J. Am. Chem. Soc.*, **42**, 2276 (1920).
[2] Eck and Marvel, *Org. Syntheses*, Coll. Vol. II, 76 (1943).
[3] Bousquet, *Org. Syntheses*, Coll. Vol. II, 313 (1943).
[4] Lachman, *Org. Syntheses*, Coll. Vol. II, 70 (1943).
[5] Fox, Dunn, and Stoddard, *J. Org. Chem.*, **6**, 410 (1941).
[6] Semon, *Org. Syntheses*, Coll. Vol. I, 318 (1941).
[7] Semon and Damerell, *J. Am. Chem. Soc.*, **46**, 1290 (1924).
[8] Sanford et al., *J. Am. Chem. Soc.*, **67**, 1941 (1945).
[9] Campbell, Campbell, and Chaput, *J. Org. Chem.*, **8**, 99 (1943).
[10] Campbell and McKenna, *J. Org. Chem.*, **4**, 198 (1939).
[11] Lachman, *J. Am. Chem. Soc.*, **47**, 262 (1925).
[12] Bachmann and Boatner, *J. Am. Chem. Soc.*, **58**, 2097 (1936).
[13] Haar, Voter, and Banks, *J. Org. Chem.*, **14**, 836 (1949).
[14] Banks and Diehl, *J. Org. Chem.*, **10**, 199 (1945).
[15] Semon and Damerell, *Org. Syntheses*, Coll. Vol. II, 204 (1943).
[16] Hartung and Crossley, *Org. Syntheses*, Coll. Vol. II, 363 (1943); cf. ref. 17.
[17] Hartung and Munch, *J. Am. Chem. Soc.*, **51**, 2262 (1929).
[18] Noyes, *Org. Syntheses*, Coll. Vol. II, 108 (1943).
[19] Adkins and Reeve, *J. Am. Chem. Soc.*, **60**, 1328 (1938).
[20] Shivers and Hauser, *J. Am. Chem. Soc.*, **69**, 1264 (1947).
[21] Barry and Hartung, *J. Org. Chem.*, **12**, 460 (1947); cf. Weaver and Hartung, *ibid.*, **15**, 741 (1950).
[22] Hauser and Reynolds, *J. Am. Chem. Soc.*, **70**, 4250 (1948).
[23] Cox et al., *J. Chem. Soc.*, 129 (1936).
[24] Wieland, *Ber.*, **40**, 1677 (1907), footnote 1.
[25] Food-Moore and Rydon, *J. Chem. Soc.*, 679 (1946).
[26] Johnson and Degering, *J. Am. Chem. Soc.*, **61**, 3194 (1939).
[27] Robertson, *J. Org. Chem.*, **13**, 395 (1948).
[28] Nightingale and Janes, *J. Am. Chem. Soc.*, **66**, 352 (1944).
[29] Reichert and Hoffmann, *Arch. Pharm.*, **274**, 161 (1936).
[30] Shaw, *J. Chem. Soc.*, 300 (1937).
[31] Bennett and Bell, *Org. Syntheses*, Coll. Vol. II, 223 (1943); cf. Hodgson and Nicholson, *J. Chem. Soc.*, 470 (1941).
[32] Marvel and Porter, *Org. Syntheses*, Coll. Vol. I, 411 (1941).
[33] Bridge, *Ann.*, **277**, 85 (1893).
[34] Ilinski and Henriques, *Ber.*, **18**, 706 (1885).
[35] Cronheim, *J. Org. Chem.*, **1**, 7 (1947).
[36] Hodgson et al., *J. Chem. Soc.*, 1405 (1939); 221 (1943).
[37] Ruggli and Bartusch, *Helv. Chim. Acta*, **27**, 1371 (1944).
[38] Neber and Rauscher, *Ann.*, **550**, 182 (1942).
[39] Hatt, *Org. Syntheses*, Coll. Vol. II, 211 (1943).
[40] Hartman and Roll, *Org. Syntheses*, Coll. Vol. II, 460 (1943).
[41] Buck and Ferry, *Org. Syntheses*, Coll. Vol. II, 290 (1943).
[42] Redemann et al., *Org. Syntheses*, **25**, 28 (1945); Adamson and Kenner, *J. Chem. Soc.*, 1551 (1937).
[43] Arndt, *Org. Syntheses*, Coll. Vol. II, 461 (1943).
[44] Hartman and Phillips, *Org. Syntheses*, Coll. Vol. II, 464 (1943).
[45] Earl and Mackney, *J. Chem. Soc.*, 899 (1935).
[46] Coleman, McCloskey, and Stuart, *Org. Syntheses*, **25**, 80 (1945).
[47] Lutz and Lytton, *J. Org. Chem.*, **2**, 73 (1937); ref. 48.
[48] Barrow and Thorneycroft, *J. Chem. Soc.*, 773 (1939).
[49] Langley, *Org. Syntheses*, **22**, 44 (1942).

28

Nitro Compounds

CONTENTS

486. Direct Nitration

$$RH + HNO_3 \longrightarrow RNO_2 + H_2O$$

Paraffins and cycloparaffins undergo nitration at high temperatures (400°) upon short contact with nitric acid vapor. In general, a mixture of mononitroparaffins is obtained which includes compounds corresponding to the replacement of any hydrogen or alkyl group present in the original paraffin. For example, nitration of n-butane in the vapor phase produces nitromethane, nitroethane, 1-nitropropane, 1-nitrobutane, and 2-nitrobutane. Pyrolysis and oxidation products also occur. Vapor-phase nitration of paraffins under these conditions does not produce dinitroparaffins; also a nitroparaffin as reactant is oxidized and pyrolyzed rather than further nitrated. However, at a lower temperature and a high pressure,

2-nitropropane has been successfully converted to 2,2-dinitropropane (50%).[23] Commercial products from the nitration of propane include nitromethane, nitroethane, 1-nitropropane, and 2-nitropropane. These reactions are not conveniently adapted to laboratory work. Extensive reviews have been presented.

Aromatic compounds are usually nitrated in liquid phase by treatment with a mixture of concentrated nitric acid and concentrated sulfuric acid. Sulfuric acid serves as a dehydrating agent which prevents dilution of the nitric acid by the liberated water. Acetic anhydride in acetic acid[12] and boron trifluoride[26] also serve this purpose.

Mononitration of benzene is carried out at about 60° and dinitration (*meta* isomer) at about 95°; further nitration is difficult.[2, 27] In a similar manner, toluene gives rise to *o*- and *p*-nitrotoluenes (90%) and a small quantity of the *meta* isomer,[3] isopropylbenzene (cumene) goes predominantly to *p*-nitrocumene (89%),[4] and *t*-butylbenzene to *p*-nitro-*t*-butylbenzene (74%).[6] For the nitration of an easily oxidizable substance like *p*-cymene, a good emulsion and careful temperature control are important.[11]

Polymethylbenzenes undergo nitration more readily as illustrated by the conversion of *sym*-trimethylbenzene (mesitylene) to nitromesitylene (76%).[12] Durene (*sym*-tetramethylbenzene) gives dinitrodurene (94%); no mononitrodurene is ever obtained.[24] In the nitration of other polysubstituted benzenes, certain anomalous reactions occur.[13] Thus nitration of *p*-cymene (*p*-isopropyltoluene) and *p*-diisopropylbenzene gives in part *p*-nitrotoluene (8%) and *p*-nitroisopropylbenzene (50%), respectively, each resulting from the replacement of an isopropyl group by the nitro group. In other instances, several alkyl groups in polymethylbenzenes[14] and polyethylbenzenes[15] are replaced. The nitration of pentamethylbenzene gives dinitroprehnitene (70%).[14]

Nitration of polycyclic aromatic compounds has also been well studied, e.g., 1-nitronaphthalene (92%),[17, 27] 4-nitrobiphenyl (49%),[16] and 2-nitrofluorene (79%).[18] One unusual aspect is the nitration of acenaphthene to 2-nitroacenaphthene (41%) by the action of benzoyl nitrate, whereas the customary nitration procedure yields mainly 4-nitroacenaphthene.[20]

Benzoyl and acetyl nitrates direct the nitro group to the *ortho* position of substituted benzenes; however, detailed procedures are lacking.[104] Acetyl nitrate is presumed to be present in solutions of nitric acid in acetic anhydride. Another reagent is the combination of nitrogen tetroxide and sulfuric acid.[21] A review of these and other nitration processes to 1950 has been made;[22] in addition, the general mechanisms of aromatic nitrations have been extensively studied.[100]

Certain nitro-substituted heterocyclic compounds are formed by direct nitration,[28-35] e.g., 2-nitrothiophene (85%),[28] 7-methyl-8-nitroquinoline (67%),[33] and 3-nitrodibenzofuran (76%).[35]

Examples of nitration of nuclear and side-chain *halogenated compounds* are found in the preparation of *p*-nitrofluorobenzene (80%)[36] and the isomeric *o*- and *p*-nitrophenylethyl bromides[37] in 30% and 50% yields, respectively.

Phenol is liable to undergo extensive oxidation during nitration so that carefully controlled conditions are required; it forms 40% *o*- and 13% *p-nitrophenol*.[38] A solvent like chloroform or acetic acid is recommended. The nitration of *p*-cresol is carried out in benzene and acetic acid solution at 0°, the product being 3-nitro-4-hydroxytoluene (77%).[39] The nitration of *m*-cresol is discussed under method 491. Benzene is oxidized and nitrated (oxynitration) to 2,4-dinitrophenol (72%) or to picric acid (2,4,6-trinitrophenol) by the action of mercuric nitrate in nitric acid.[40] Aromatic alcohols like β-phenylethanol are nitrated as the esters to avoid oxidation products.[41]

The nitration of aromatic ethers leads to a mixture of *nitro ethers* and nitrophenols in proportions which depend upon experimental conditions.[42] Benzoyl nitrate favors almost exclusively the formation of *o*-nitrophenetole; however, detailed directions are lacking.[43] Treatment of diphenyl ether with nitric acid in acetic anhydride-acetic acid gives a separable mixture of the *ortho* and *para* isomers (86% total).[45]

The nitration of acetophenone has been extensively studied.[16] It is carried out at a low temperature (5° to −20°) by the action of nitric and sulfuric acids and gives *m-nitroacetophenone* (55–83%) and smaller amounts of *o*-nitroacetophenone. Under similar conditions, benzaldehyde is converted to *m-nitrobenzaldehyde* (84%).[47] If nitration is performed on benzaldehyde diacetate, $C_6H_5CH(OCOCH_3)_2$, with subsequent hydrolysis, *p*-nitrobenzaldehyde (73%) is obtained; furthermore, a slight modification of this procedure causes the formation of mainly the *ortho* isomer (43%).[48]

Aromatic *amines* are often acetylated before nitration. Examples include the nitration of *p*-acetotoluide[59] and 2-acetylaminonaphthalene,[60] the products being 3-nitro-*p*-acetotoluide (90%) and 1-nitro-2-acetylaminonaphthalene (49%), respectively. The *p*-tolylsulfonyl derivative is readily formed and hydrolyzed after nitration.[61] On the other hand, if unacetylated and in the presence of a large excess of sulfuric acid, *p*-toluidine gives mainly 2-nitro-*p*-toluidine (71%),[63] the arylammonium ion being *meta*-directing.

Similarly, m-nitrodimethylaniline is synthesized by nitration of the amine in concentrated sulfuric acid (63%).[62]

487. Replacement of the Diazonium Group

$$ArN_2^+X^- \xrightarrow[\text{Catalyst}]{NaNO_2} ArNO_2 + N_2$$

Aromatic diazonium salts on treatment with sodium nitrite decompose to form nitro compounds. This method represents a good procedure for obtaining o- and p-dinitrobenzenes, in 70% and 76% yield, respectively, from the corresponding diazonium sulfates.[64] Improved yields in the preparation of dinitronaphthalenes are obtained when the decomposition of the diazonium sulfates is catalyzed by a cupro-cupri sulfite prepared by the interaction of copper sulfate and sodium nitrite. The procedure is illustrated by the synthesis of 1,4-dinitronaphthalene (60%).[65] Occasionally, diazonium fluoborates are first formed,[66] and these compounds are treated with sodium nitrite in the presence of copper powder, viz.,

$$ArN_2^+BF_4 + NaNO_2 \xrightarrow{Cu} ArNO_2 + N_2 + NaBF_4$$

In this manner, p-dinitrobenzene is obtained in 82% yield from p-nitroaniline.[67] Similar treatment of diazonium cobaltinitrites has led to nitro compounds.[68, 69]

488. Interaction of Silver Nitrite and Alkyl Halides

$$RX + AgNO_2 \rightarrow RNO_2 + AgX$$

The interaction of alkyl halides with silver nitrite produces a mixture of the alkyl nitrite and the isomeric nitro compound;[70, 73] in addition, alkyl nitrates may be formed.[71] Straight-chain primary halides, preferably the bromides, give better yields than branched-chain primary, secondary, and tertiary halides. For the most part, the yields are low. In a similar manner, polynitroparaffins are obtained from polyhalides.[74]

In the laboratory preparation of nitroethane, the substitution of ethyl sulfate for ethyl iodide and sodium nitrite for silver nitrite leads to a more economical and convenient process (46%).[72]

Salts of α-halocarboxylic acids react similarly with sodium nitrite to yield salts of α-nitro acids (method 490).

489. Alkylation of Nitro Compounds

$$RX + RCH = NONa \rightarrow R_2CHNO_2 \text{ and } RCH = NOR$$
$$\qquad\qquad\quad \downarrow \qquad\qquad\qquad\qquad\qquad \downarrow$$
$$\qquad\qquad\quad O \qquad\qquad\qquad\qquad\qquad\; O$$

A few nitro compounds have been obtained in good yields by the inter-action of reactive halogen compounds with *aci*-nitro alkanes. The reaction is usually complicated in that both C- and O-alkylation occurs. If the stability of the *aci* form of the nitro compound is high, then the tendency is toward alkylation on carbon rather than on oxygen. An example is the condensation of *p*-nitrobenzyl chloride with the sodium salt of nitro-ethane to give an 83% yield of 1-*p*-nitrobenzylnitroethane, p-$O_2NC_6H_4CH_2CH(NO_2)CH_3$.[77]

Certain tertiary dinitroparaffins are produced by treating secondary nitroparaffins with one mole of alkali and one-half mole of halogen.

$$R_2C = NO_2Na \xrightarrow{Br_2} R_2CBrNO_2 \xrightarrow{R_2C=NO_2Na} R_2C - CR_2$$
$$\underset{NO_2 \quad NO_2}{\vert \quad\quad \vert}$$

The yield for the conversion of 2-nitropropane to 2,3-dimethyl-2,3-dinitro-butane $(R = CH_3)$ is 80%.[78]

490. Decarboxylation of Nitro Acids

$$ClCH_2CO_2H + NaNO_2 \rightarrow NO_2CH_2CO_2H \rightarrow CH_3NO_2 + CO_2$$

A number of α-nitro carboxylic acids are easily dicarboxylated to fur-nish nitro compounds. The synthesis of nitromethane in this manner is a classical example (38%).[79] Nitroethane and higher homologs have been similarly prepared from the α-bromo acids and sodium nitrite.[80] Another example is found in the synthesis of phenylnitromethane. Treatment of benzyl cyanide with methyl nitrate in the presence of sodium ethoxide gives the sodium salt of the *aci*-nitro compound, which is then hydrolyzed and decarboxylated.[81]

$$C_6H_5CH_2CN \xrightarrow[NaOC_2H_5]{CH_3ONO_2} C_6H_5C(CN) = NO_2Na \xrightarrow{NaOH} C_6H_5C(COONa) = NO_2Na$$

$$\xrightarrow{HCl} C_6H_5CH_2NO_2$$

Other than in the preparation of nitromethane and phenylnitromethane, the method has had limited application.

Other decarboxylations are noteworthy. Thermal decomposition of 2,4,6-trinitrobenzoic acid furnishes 1,3,5-trinitrobenzene in 46% yield.[82] In an adaptation of a procedure for the decarboxylation of halogenated furoic acids with boiling quinoline and powdered copper, 2- and 3-nitro-benzofuran are prepared from nitro acids[83] and 5-nitrothionaphthene is formed from the corresponding 2-carboxylic acid.[97]

491. **Oxidation of Aromatic Amines and Nitroso Compounds**

The oxidation of amines to nitro compounds has preparative value when the amines are more readily available than the corresponding nitro compounds, as in the case of the aminopyridines and aminoquinolines (cf. method 439). Oxidation is accomplished with hydrogen peroxide, as shown in the formation of 2-nitropyridine (75%).[84]

The direct nitration of m-cresol is unsatisfactory for obtaining 4-nitro-3-methylphenol (29%). A better procedure is to form the nitroso compound and oxidize it to the nitro compound (66% over-all).[85]

$$\text{HO}\!\!\bigcirc\!\!\text{CH}_3 \xrightarrow[\text{H}_2\text{SO}_4]{\text{NaNO}_2} \text{HO}\!\!\bigcirc\!\!\overset{\text{CH}_3}{\text{NO}} \xrightarrow[\text{HNO}_3]{\text{Dil.}} \text{HO}\!\!\bigcirc\!\!\overset{\text{CH}_3}{\text{NO}_2}$$

In a similar manner, p-nitrophenol is prepared from p-nitrosophenol (60%);[86] also, several o-dinitro compounds including o-dinitrobenzene and 1,2-dimethyl-4,5-dinitrobenzene are obtained from the corresponding nitronitroso compounds.[87]

492. **Addition of Nitroparaffins to α-Nitro Olefins**

$$\text{RR}'\text{CHNO}_2 + \text{R}''\text{CH}\!=\!\text{C(R}''')\text{NO}_2 \xrightarrow{\text{NaOC}_2\text{H}_5} \text{RR}'\text{C(NO}_2)\text{CHR}''\text{CH(R}''')\text{NO}_2$$

In a variation of the Michael condensation, nitroparaffins having active α-methylene groups add to reactive olefinic compounds including α,β-unsaturated esters (method 301), α,β-unsaturated cyanides (method 388), and α-nitro olefins.[88] Interaction of primary or secondary aliphatic nitro compounds with the unsaturated nitro compounds in the presence of sodium ethoxide in alcohol yields 1,3-dinitroparaffins. The reaction is general, but the yields vary, depending on the degree of polymerization that the nitro olefin undergoes and the amount of addition of alcohol to it as well as on the reactivity of the product toward further condensation. The principal product from the reaction of 2-nitro-2-butene $(\text{R}''\!=\!\text{R}'''\!=\!\text{CH}_3)$ and 2-nitropropane is 2,4-dinitro-2,3-dimethylpentane $(\text{R}\!=\!\text{R}'\!=\!\text{R}''\!=\!\text{R}'''\!=\!\text{CH}_3)$ in 47% yield.

493. **Addition of Nitryl Chloride to Unsaturated Halides**[89]

$$\text{H}_2\text{C}\!=\!\text{CHBr} + \text{NO}_2\text{Cl} \rightarrow \text{O}_2\text{NCH}_2\text{CHBrCl} \quad (85\%)$$

TABLE 97. NITRO COMPOUNDS

C_n	Compound	Method	Yield (%)	Chapter[ref.]	B.p./mm., n_D^t, (M.p.)
		Aliphatic and Aromatic Nitro Compounds			
C_1	Nitromethane	490	38	28[79]	101
C_2	Nitroethane	488	46	28[72]	115
		490	50	28[80]	
C_4	1-Nitrobutane	488	37	28[73]	152/780, 1.4103
C_5	1-Nitropentane	488	39	28[73]	66/16, 1.4175
C_6	Nitrobenzene	486	85	28[2]	207
C_7	Phenylnitromethane	490	55	28[81]	92/3
	m-Nitrotoluene	14	72	28[95]	114/15, (16)
C_8	1-Nitro-2-phenylethane	488	60	28[75]	133/14
	o-Nitroethylbenzene ⎱	486	51	28[3]	135/37
	p-Nitroethylbenzene ⎰		42	28[3]	154/37
	3-Nitro-1,2-dimethylbenzene	486	86	28[8]	130/18
	4-Nitro-1,2-dimethylbenzene	486	30	28[7]	130/12, (28.5)
	2-Nitro-1,4-dimethylbenzene	486	89	28[9]	65/0.35
C_9	p-Nitrocumene (p-Nitroisopropylbenzene)	486	89	28[4]	132/15
	Nitromesitylene	486	76	28[12]	243-250, (44)
C_{10}	p-Nitro-s-butylbenzene	486	57	28[5]	130/9
	p-Nitro-t-butylbenzene	486	74	28[6]	158/30, (28)
	2-Nitro-4-isopropyltoluene	486	82	28[11]	126/10, 1.5287
	4-Nitro-1,2-diethylbenzene	486	41	28[10]	141/10, 1.5440[25]
	1-Nitronaphthalene	486	92	28[17]	(56.6)
	2-Nitronaphthalene	487	40	28[65]	(79)*
C_{12}	2-Nitrobiphenyl	12	60	28[92]	(36)
	2-Nitrobiphenyl ⎱	486	27	28[16]	166/4, (37)
	4-Nitrobiphenyl ⎰		49		(114)
	3-Nitrobiphenyl	12	60	28[91]	(59)
		14	40	28[94]	(62)
	4-Nitrobiphenyl	12	60	28[92]	(113)
	2-Nitroacenaphthene	486	41	28[20]	(151)
C_{13}	2-Nitrofluorene	486	79	28[18]	(157)
C_{14}	9-Nitroanthracene	486	56	28[19]	(146)
		486	70	28[103]	(146)
		Heterocyclic Nitro Compounds			
C_4	2-Nitrothiophene	486	85	28[28]	(45)
C_5	2-Nitropyridine	491	75	28[84]	256, (71)
C_8	3-Nitrothionaphthene	486	48	28[29]	(81)
	5-Nitrothionaphthene	490	69	28[97]	(150)
		559	69	39[62]	(150)
	3-Nitro-2,4,6-trimethylpyridine	486	90	28[31]	229/733

TABLE 98. DINITRO COMPOUNDS   753

TABLE 97 (continued)

C_n	Compound	Method	Yield (%)	Chapter[ref]	B.p./mm., n_D^t, (M.p.)
	Heterocyclic Nitro Compounds (continued)				
C_9	3-Nitroquinoline	575	48	39[162]	(126)
	5-Nitroquinoline	559	16	39[146]	(70)
	6-Nitroquinoline	575	72	39[130]	(151)
	7-Nitroquinoline	575	14	39[130]	(130)
	5-Nitroquinoline ⎱	486	35	28[32]	(71)
	8-Nitroquinoline ⎰		43		(89)
C_{10}	7-Methyl-8-nitroquinoline	486	67	28[33]	(187)
C_{12}	3-Nitrodibenzofuran	486	76	28[35]	(182)
	2-Nitrodibenzothiophene	486	28	28[30]	(187)
	3-Nitrocarbazole	557	85	39[158]	(206)
C_{13}	2-Nitroacridine	486	60	28[34]	(215)

For explanations and symbols see pp. xi–xii.

TABLE 98. DINITRO COMPOUNDS

C_n	Compound	Method	Yield (%)	Chapter[ref]	B.p./mm., n_D^t, (M.p.)
C_1	Tetranitromethane	....	65	28[98]	40/26, 1.4384
C_3	1,3-Dinitropropane (purified)	488	7	28[74]	103/1, 1.4638[25]
C_6	2,4-Dinitro-3-methylpentane	492	28	28[88]	95/0.5
	2,3-Dimethyl-2,3-dinitrobutane	489	80	28[78]	(209)
	o-Dinitrobenzene	487	70	28[64]	(117)
		491	60	28[87]	
	m-Dinitrobenzene	486	88	28[2]	(90)
	p-Dinitrobenzene	487	76	28[64]	(173)
		487	82	28[67]	(173)
	1,3,5-Trinitrobenzene	14	65	28[96]	(123)
		490	46	28[82]	(122)
C_7	2,4-Dinitro-2,3-dimethylpentane	492	47	28[88]	92/0.5
C_{10}	Dinitrodurene	486	94	28[24]	(208)
	Dinitroprehnitene	486	70	28[14]	(177)
	1,3-Dinitronaphthalene	7	74	28[101]	(146)
	1,4-Dinitronaphthalene	487	60	28[65]	(134)
C_{12}	2,2′-Dinitrobiphenyl	11	61	28[90]	(124)
C_{14}	4,4′-Dinitrodiphenylethane	486	95	28[25]	(180)

For explanations and symbols see pp. xi–xii.

TABLE 99. NITRO OLEFINS

C_n	Compound	Method	Yield (%)	Chapter[ref.]	B.p./mm., n_D^t, (M.p.)
C_2	Nitroethylene	24	67	2^{443}	39/80
C_3	1-Nitro-1-propene	24	67	2^{443}	54/28
	2-Nitro-1-propene	24	56	2^{443}	58/90
		24	84	2^{240}	49/60, 1.4292^{23}
		26	50	2^{284}	
C_4	2-Nitro-1-butene	26	73	2^{284}	61/50, 1.4356
	2-Nitro-2-butene	24	85	2^{468}	56/15, 1.4600^{22}
C_5	2-Nitro-1-pentene	26	75	2^{284}	68/50, 1.4403
C_6	2-Nitro-1-hexene	26	70	2^{284}	82/50, 1.4462
	2-Nitro-2-hexene	24	90	2^{241}	53/1, 1.4513^{25}
	3-Nitro-3-hexene	24	90	2^{241}	53/1, 1.4521^{25}
	2-Nitro-4-methyl-2-pentene	24	90	2^{241}	57/1, 1.4520^{25}
	ω-Nitro-2-vinylthiophene	37	78	2^{352}	(80)
C_7	1-Nitro-1-heptene	24	90	2^{241}	57/1, 1.4524^{25}
	2-Nitro-1-heptene	26	70	2^{284}	94/30, 1.4482
	3-Nitro-5-methyl-3-hexene	24	90	2^{241}	53/1, 1.4528^{25}
	1-Cyclohexenylnitromethane	19	75	2^{444}	107/17, 1.4856
		20	85	2^{519}	100/9
	1-(2-Thienyl)-2-nitropropene	37	44	2^{352}	(69)
C_8	2-Nitro-4-ethyl-2-hexene	24	90	2^{241}	84/1, 1.4602^{25}
	β-Nitrostyrene	37	83	2^{489}	(58)
	m-Nitrostyrene	27	60	2^{258}	96/3.5, 1.5830
	p-Nitrostyrene	20	70	2^{455}	(21)
	2,4,6-Trinitrostyrene	26	49	2^{479}	(65)
	ω,3-Dinitrostyrene	37	76	2^{403}	(125)
C_9	3-Nitro-5-ethyl-3-heptene	24	90	2^{241}	65/1, 1.4598^{25}
		14	45	28^{93}	(73)
		28	32	2^{273}	(72)
	m-Nitrostilbene	28	33	2^{477}	(112)
	cis-p-Nitrostilbene	27	64	2^{259}	(65)
	p-Nitrostilbene	28	48	2^{273}	(155)

For explanations and symbols see pp. xi–xii.

TABLE 100. NITRO HALIDES

C_n	Compound	Method	Yield (%)	Chapter[ref.]	B.p./mm., n_D^t, (M.p.)
C_2	1-Chloro-1-bromo-2-nitroethane	493	85	28^{89}	77/15
C_3	1-Chloro-2-nitropropane	52	47	4^{580}	82/28
	2-Bromo-2-nitropropane	64	89	4^{297}	151.8/745
C_4	1-Chloro-4-nitrobutane	64	35	4^{591}	105/10
C_6	o-Chloronitrobenzene	487	81	28^{68}	(33)*

TABLE 101. NITRO ALCOHOLS AND PHENOLS   755

TABLE 100 *(continued)*

C_n	Compound	Method	Yield (%)	Chapter[ref.]	B.p./mm., n_D^t, (M.p.)
C_6	o-Bromonitrobenzene	56	83	4^{316}	(42)*
	m-Fluoronitrobenzene	56	54	4^{303}	54/2
	m-Chloronitrobenzene	56	71	4^{337}	117/12, (45)
		487	89	28^{68}	(46)*
	m-Bromonitrobenzene	56	87	4^{316}	(56)*
		64	75	4^{295}	(52)
	p-Fluoronitrobenzene	486	80	28^{36}	109/36
	p-Chloronitrobenzene	56	33	4^{316}	(83)*
		487	70	28^{68}	
	p-Bromonitrobenzene	56	79	4^{316}	(127)*
	1,2,3-Triiodo-5-nitrobenzene	56	70	4^{595}	(162)
C_7	o-Nitrobenzyl bromide	64	51	4^{181}	(46)
	m-Nitrobenzyl chloride	51	57	4^{31}	(47)
	m-Nitrobenzyl bromide	52	85	4^{181}	(58)
	p-Nitrobenzyl chloride	51	67	4^{31}	(71)
	p-Nitrobenzyl bromide	64	59	4^{296}	(99)
	p-Nitrobenzyl iodide	55	100	4^{378}	(124)
C_8	o-Nitrophenylethyl bromide ⎫	486	30	28^{37}	120/0.5, (38)
	p-Nitrophenylethyl bromide ⎭		54		(70)

For explanations and symbols see pp. xi–xii.

TABLE 101. NITRO ALCOHOLS AND NITRO PHENOLS

C_n	Compound	Method	Yield (%)	Chapter[ref.]	B.p./mm., n_D^t, (M.p.), Deriv.
C_2	2,2,2-Trinitroethanol	102	75	5^{747}	103/14, (30)
C_3	2-Nitro-1-propanol	102	65	5^{748}	100/12
C_4	3-Nitro-2-butanol	102	92	5^{743}	90/11, 1.4425^{22}, 123Nu
	Nitro-t-butyl alcohol	102	30	5^{751}	77/10
C_5	1-Nitro-2-pentanol	102	71	5^{750}	88/3, 1.4439^{25}, 100Nu
	1-Nitro-3-methyl-2-butanol	102	68	5^{750}	84/4, 1.4455^{25}, 98Nu
	2-Ethyl-2-nitro-1,3-propanediol	102	99	5^{745}	(56)
C_6	2-Nitro-3-hexanol	102	73	5^{746}	84/3, 1.4455^{25}, 137Nu
	3-Nitro-4-hexanol	102	81	5^{746}	85/2, 1.4441^{25}, 114Nu
	1-Nitro-4-methyl-2-pentanol	102	65	5^{750}	99/2, 1.4433
	o-Nitrophenol ⎫	486	40	28^{38}	(45)
	p-Nitrophenol ⎭		13		(114)
	m-Nitrophenol	93	86	5^{490}	163/12, (96)
	p-Nitrophenol	491	60	28^{86}	(114)
	2-Nitrohydroquinone	110	30	5^{791}	(133)
	2,4-Dinitrophenol	486	72	28^{40}	(113)

For explanations and symbols see pp. xi–xii.

TABLE 101 *(continued)*

C_n	Compound	Method	Yield (%)	Chapter[ref.]	B.p./mm., n_D^t, (M.p.), Deriv.
C_7	4-Nitro-3,5-heptanediol	102	50	5[753]	(97)
	1-Nitromethyl-1-cyclo-hexanol	102	75	5[752]	118/9
	o-Nitrobenzyl alcohol	80	90	5[195]	(74)
		81	91	5[511]	(74)
		96	50	5[558]	
	m-Nitrobenzyl alcohol	79	82	5[2]	(31)
		80	86	5[191]	169/6, 1.5731[28]
	p-Nitrobenzyl alcohol	80	92	5[251]	
		95	71	5[524]	(93)
	2-Nitro-4-methylphenol	93	69	5[501]	(36)
		486	77	28[39]	(33)
C_8	1-Nitro-2-octanol	102	88	5[744]	120/2
	5-Nitro-4-octanol	102	89	5[745]	124/10, 1.4463
	1-Phenyl-2-nitroethanol	102	78	5[742]	
	m-Nitrophenylmethylcarbinol	80	76	5[177]	(63)
	β-(4-Nitrophenyl)-ethanol	486	50	28[41]	(62)
C_9	2-Nitro-1-phenyl-1-propanol	102	62	5[749]	125/3

For explanations and symbols see pp. xi–xii.

TABLE 102. NITRO ETHERS

C_n	Compound	Method	Yield (%)	Chapter[ref.]	B.p./mm., n_D^t, (M.p.)
C_3	Methyl 2-nitroethyl ether	121	60	6[165]	38/1, 67/12, 1.417
C_7	o-Nitroanisole	487	63 †	28[69]	277*, (10)*
	p-Nitroanisole	487	68	28[69]	274*, (54)*
C_8	2-Nitro-5-methoxytoluene	486	60	28[44]	(55)
		491	66 †	28[85]	(55)
	o-Nitroethoxybenzene	116	80	6[104]	148/15
C_{12}	o-Nitrodiphenyl ether	115	84	6[24]	185/8
	p-Nitrodiphenyl ether	115	82	6[24]	190/8, (58)
		486	36	28[45]	(57)

For explanations and symbols see pp. xi–xii.

TABLE 104. NITRO ACIDS 757

TABLE 103. NITRO ALDEHYDES AND KETONES

C_n	Compound	Method	Yield (%)	Chapter[ref.]	B.p./mm., n_D^t, (M.p.), Deriv.
C_7	5-Nitro-4,4-dimethyl-2-pentanone	301	63	14^{416}	110/11, 1.4422^{25}
	o-Nitrobenzaldehyde	147	36	9^{244}	(38)
		155	18 †	9^{150}	(45)
		158	85	9^{14}	(45)
		486	43	28^{48}	(43)
	m-Nitrobenzaldehyde	147	45	9^{244}	(52)
		149	42	9^{123}	
		486	84	28^{47}	119–123/4, (58)
	p-Nitrobenzaldehyde	147	59	9^{244}	(105)
		155	51 †	9^{149}	(106)
		155	56	9^{91}	(106), 159Ph
		158	80	9^{14}	(107)
		162	91	9^{65}	(106), 156Ph
		486	73	28^{48}	(106), 132-Ox
	2,4-Dinitrobenzaldehyde	150	32	9^{186}	(71)
C_8	Nitroterephthaldehyde	486	52	28^{49}	(97), 176-Ox
	α-Nitroacetophenone	179	80	10^{219}	(105)
	o-Nitroacetophenone	179	23 †	10^{220}	135/4
		185	83	10^{314}	159/16, 1.551
	m-Nitroacetophenone	486	55	28^{46}	(78)
	p-Nitroacetophenone	179	21 †	10^{220}	(80)
		185	74	10^{315}	(80), 132Ph*
		228	47	10^{538}	(80)
C_9	m-Nitropropiophenone	486	75	28^{53}	(102)
C_{11}	o-Nitrophenyl 2-thienyl ketone	178	60	10^{155}	(98)
C_{13}	2,4,7-Trinitrofluorenone	486	78	28^{54}	(176)
C_{14}	o,o'-Dinitrobenzil	230	60	10^{592}	(206)

For explanations and symbols see pp. xi–xii.

TABLE 104. NITRO ACIDS

C_n	Compound	Method	Yield (%)	Chapter[ref.]	B.p./mm., n_D^t, (M.p.), Deriv.
C_5	4-Nitropentanoic acid	249	92	13^{301}	118/0.6, (34)
C_7	o-Nitrobenzoic acid	255	98	13^{565}	(147), 155An*
		257	80	13^{562}	(148), 174Am*
		261	91	13^{563}	(146)
	m-Nitrobenzoic acid	249	96	13^{564}	(140), 142Am*
		253	90	13^{565}	(141)
	p-Nitrobenzoic acid	257	62	13^{259}	(242)
		257	86	13^{566}	(238), 204An*

For explanations and symbols see pp. xi–xii.

TABLE 104 *(continued)*

C_n	Compound	Method	Yield (%)	Chapter[ref.] B.p./mm., n_D^t, (M.p.), Deriv.		
C_7	2,4-Dinitrobenzoic acid	247	95	13^{567}	(180), 203Am*	
	3,5-Dinitrobenzoic acid	486	60	28^{55}	(207)	
	2,4,6-Trinitrobenzoic acid	257	90	13^{494}	(228)*	
C_8	o-Nitrophenylacetic acid	259	.....	13^{568}	(139), 161Am*	
	m-Nitrophenylacetic acid	247	62†	13^{569}	(120)	
		248	22†	13^{147}	(119), 110Am*	
	p-Nitrophenylacetic acid	247	95	13^{570}	(152), 198Am*	
		247	97	13^{570}	(153)	
	3-Nitrophthalic acid	250	26	13^{388}	(217)	
		486	31	28^{52}	(218)	
	4-Nitrophthalic acid	248	99	13^{340}	(164)	

For explanations and symbols see pp. xi–xii.

TABLE 105. NITRO ESTERS

C_n	Compound	Method	Yield (%)	Chapter[ref.] B.p./mm., n_D^t, (M.p.)	
C_3	Methyl nitroacetate	285	60	14^{398}	94/15, 1.4245
C_4	Ethyl nitroacetate	285	60	14^{398}	106/25, 1.4252
		486	30	28^{102}	91/12
C_5	Methyl γ-nitrobutyrate	301	35	14^{415}	68/0.3, 1.4375
	2-Nitrobutyl formate	287	88	14^{125}	76/5, 1.4345[26]
	2-Nitroisobutyl formate	287	61	14^{125}	87/10, 1.4327[26]
	2-Nitroethyl propionate	285	90	14^{76}	107/10, 1.4336
	Dimethyl nitromalonate	486	59	28^{102}	124/16, 100/1
C_7	Ethyl 3-methyl-4-nitrobutanoate	301	55	14^{415}	85/1, 1.4350
	Diethyl nitromalonate	486	92	28^{56}	83/0.3, 1.4274[21]
C_8	Methyl m-nitrobenzoate	321	52	14^{428}	(78)
		486	85	28^{50}	(78)
	Methyl p-nitrobenzoate	285	100	14^1	(93)
		294	100	14^{185}	(96)
	Methyl 2,4-dinitrobenzoate	285	91	14^{19}	(83)
	o-Nitrophenyl acetate	287	93	14^{133}	(38)
		287	90	14^{119}	(41)
	p-Nitrophenyl acetate	286	96	14^{88}	(82)
		287	94	14^{119}	(83)
C_9	Methyl p-nitrophenylacetate	285	84	14^{75}	(54)
	Ethyl p-nitrobenzoate	294	100	14^{185}	(57)
	p-Nitrobenzyl acetate	290	82	14^{197}	(78)
C_{10}	Ethyl o-nitrophenylacetate	486	25	28^{51}	(67)
	Ethyl p-nitrophenylacetate	293	97	14^{177}	(66)

For explanations and symbols see pp. xi–xii.

TABLE 107. NITRO AMINES 759

TABLE 106. NITRO CYANIDES

C_n	Compound	Method	Yield (%)	Chapter[ref.]	B.p./mm., n_D^t, (M.p.)
C_4	2-Nitro-n-propyl cyanide	389	15	20[307]	82/0.5
	2-Nitroisopropyl cyanide	389	25	20[307]	70/0.5
C_5	4-Nitro-n-butyl cyanide	388	30	20[383]	84/0.25
	2-Nitro-1-methyl-n-propyl cyanide	389	50	20[307]	61-65/0.2
	Nitro-t-butyl cyanide	389	75	20[307]	67/0.2, (42)
C_6	3-Nitro-3-methyl-n-butyl cyanide	388	80	20[383]	70/0.09
C_7	3-Nitro-1,2-dimethyl-n-butyl cyanide	388	80	20[383]	87/0.24
	o-Nitrobenzonitrile	384	95	20[127]	(115)
	m-Nitrobenzonitrile	384	90	20[122]	(117)
		396	83	20[336]	
		486	82	28[57]	(116)
	p-Nitrobenzonitrile	384	90	20[156]	(148)
	2,4-Dinitrobenzonitrile	380	85	20[234]	(104)
	3,5-Dinitrobenzonitrile	384	55	20[155]	(127)
C_8	o-Nitrobenzyl cyanide	385	66	20[379]	(84)
	m-Nitrobenzyl cyanide	378	85	20[365]	180/1.5
	p-Nitrobenzyl cyanide	380	75	20[384]	(146)
		486	54	28[58]	(117)

For explanations and symbols see pp. xi–xii.

TABLE 107. NITRO AMINES

C_n	Compound	Method	Yield (%)	Chapter[ref.]	B.p./mm., n_D^t, (M.p.), Deriv.
C_3	2-Amino-1-nitropropane	443	55	24[487]	55/10, 114HCl
C_4	2-Nitro-3-aminobutane	443	60	24[487]	78/20, 1.4720[18], 115HCl
	1-Nitro-2-amino-2-methylpropane	443	40	24[487]	65/11, 182HCl
C_5	N-(2-Nitroisobutyl)-methylamine	444	48	24[40]	62/6, 1.4368
C_6	N-(2-Nitrobutyl)-dimethylamine	444	70	24[548]	94/15, 1.4338
	N-(2-Nitroisobutyl)-dimethylamine	444	74	24[40]	66/10, 1.4330
	o-Nitroaniline	15	56	28[99]	(70)
		451	97	24[501]	(72), 93Ac
		449	83	24[294]	
	m-Nitroaniline	425	80	24[80]	(114)
	2,4-Dinitroaniline	435	76	24[113]	(177)
	2,6-Dinitroaniline	435	36†	24[561]	(140)
C_7	N-(2-Nitropropyl)-diethylamine	444	83	24[426]	1.4420

For explanations and symbols see pp. xi–xii.

TABLE 107 *(continued)*

C_n	Compound	Method	Yield (%)	Chapter[ref.]	B.p./mm., n_D^t, (M.p.), Deriv.
C_7	N-(2-Nitro-2-methylbutyl)-dimethylamine	444	76	24[40]	64/3, 1.4410
	o-Nitrobenzylamine	452	90	24[428]	248HCl
	m-Nitrobenzylamine	452	90	24[428]	220HCl
	p-Nitrobenzylamine	437	61	24[235]	
		447	91†	24[285]	222HCl
		452	80	24[428]	250HCl
	3-Nitro-p-toluidine	486	90	28[59]	(117), 95Ac
	2-Nitro-p-toluidine	486	71	28[63]	(77)
	o-Nitromethylaniline	451	89	24[550]	(34), 71Ac
C_8	1-Diethylamino-2-nitrobutane	444	100	24[39]	103/14
		444	79	24[126]	79/2, 1.4405
	2-Nitro-3-diethylaminobutane	443	65	24[487]	90–95/11, 267Pi
	1-Diethylamino-2-methyl-2-nitropropane	444	74	24[425]	64/2, 1.4393[25]
	N,N-Dimethyl-o-nitroaniline	436	85	24[197]	149/20, 1.6080[25]
	N,N-Dimethyl-m-nitroaniline	486	63	28[62]	(60)
	N,N-Dimethyl-p-nitroaniline	436	97	24[197]	(164)
C_{10}	N-(2-Nitroisobutyl)-aniline	444	93	24[40]	(64)
	N,N-Diethyl-p-nitroaniline	436	94	24[198]	(76)
C_{11}	N,N-Diethyl-3-nitrobenzylamine	436	60	24[199]	148/6, 161Pi
	N,N-Diethyl-4-nitrobenzylamine	436	45	24[199]	162HCl
C_{14}	α-Nitro-β-anilino-β-phenylethane	443	79	24[488]	(87), 127HCl

For explanations and symbols see pp. xi–xii.

REFERENCES FOR CHAPTER 28

[1] Hass and Riley, *Chem. Revs.*, 32, 373 (1943); Hass, *Ind. Eng. Chem.*, 35, 1146 (1943); Levy and Rose, *Quarterly Reviews*, 1, 358 (1948).

[2] Gattermann and Wieland, *Laboratory Methods of Organic Chemistry*, The Macmillan Co., New York, 1938, p. 161.

[3] Cline and Reid, *J. Am. Chem. Soc.*, 49, 3150 (1927); Birch et al., *ibid.*, 71, 1367 (1949); Jones and Russell, *J. Chem. Soc.*, 921 (1947).

[4] Haworth and Barker, *J. Chem. Soc.*, 1302 (1939); Sterling and Bogert, *J. Org. Chem.*, 4, 25 (1939).

[5] Glattfeld and Wertheim, *J. Am. Chem. Soc.*, 43, 2682 (1921).

[6] Craig, *J. Am. Chem. Soc.*, 57, 195 (1935).

[7] Birch et al., *J. Am. Chem. Soc.*, 71, 1364 (1949); ref. 8.

[8] Emerson and Smith, *J. Am. Chem. Soc.*, 62, 141 (1940); ref. 7.

[9] Snyder and Pilgrim, *J. Am. Chem. Soc.*, 70, 3787 (1948); Kobe and Levin, *Ind. Eng. Chem.*, 42, 352 (1950).

[10] Lambooy, *J. Am. Chem. Soc.*, 71, 3756 (1949).

[11] Kobe and Doumani, *Org. Syntheses*, 21, 96 (1941).

[12] Powell and Johnson, *Org. Syntheses*, Coll. Vol. II, 449 (1943).

[13] Nightingale, *Chem. Revs.*, 40, 117 (1947).

[14] Smith and Harris, *J. Am. Chem. Soc.*, 57, 1289 (1935).

[15] Smith and Guss, *J. Am. Chem. Soc.*, 62, 2635 (1940).

[16] Morgan and Walls, *J. Soc. Chem. Ind. (London)*, 49, 15T (1930); Jenkins, McCullough, and Booth, *Ind. Eng. Chem.*, 22, 31 (1930).

[17] Berkebile and Fries, *J. Chem. Education*, 25, 617 (1948).

[18] Kuhn, *Org. Syntheses*, Coll. Vol. II, 447 (1943); cf. Schulman, *J. Org. Chem.*, 14, 385 (1949).

[19] Bartlett and Cohen, *J. Am. Chem. Soc.*, 62, 1187 (1940).

[20] Morgan and Harrison, *J. Soc. Chem. Ind. (London)*, 49, 413T (1930).

[21] Pinck, *J. Am. Chem. Soc.*, 49, 2536 (1927).

[22] Crater, *Ind. Eng. Chem.*, 40, 1627 (1948); 42, 1716 (1950).

[23] Denton et al., *Ind. Eng. Chem.*, 40, 381 (1948).

[24] Smith, *Org. Syntheses*, Coll. Vol. II, 254 (1943).

[25] Rinkenbach and Aaronson, *J. Am. Chem. Soc.*, 52, 5040 (1930).

[26] Thomas, Anzilotti, and Hennion, *Ind. Eng. Chem.*, 32, 408 (1940).

[27] McCormack, *Ind. Eng. Chem.*, 29, 1333 (1937).

[28] Babasinian, *Org. Syntheses*, Coll. Vol. II, 466 (1943).

[29] Fries and Hemmecke, *Ann.*, 470, 6 (1929).

[30] Gilman and Nobis, *J. Am. Chem. Soc.*, 71, 274 (1949).

[31] Plazek, *Ber.*, 72, 577 (1939).

[32] Fieser and Hershberg, *J. Am. Chem. Soc.*, 62, 1643 (1940).

[33] Capps, *J. Am. Chem. Soc.*, 69, 179 (1947).

[34] Lehmstedt, *Ber.*, 71, 808 (1938).

[35] Gilman, Bywater, and Parker, *J. Am. Chem. Soc.*, 57, 885 (1935).

[36] Bradlow and Vanderwerf, *J. Am. Chem. Soc.*, 70, 654 (1948).

[37] Foreman and McElvain, *J. Am. Chem. Soc.*, 62, 1436 (1940).

[38] Ref. 2, p. 246; also Fishman, *J. Am. Chem. Soc.*, 42, 2291 (1920); Baroni and Kleinau, *Monatsh.*, 68, 251 (1936).

[39] Adams and Kornblum, *J. Am. Chem. Soc.*, 63, 196 (1941).

[40] Bachmann et al., *J. Org. Chem.*, 13, 390 (1948); Wright et al., *Ind. Eng. Chem.*, 40, 1281 (1948).

[41] Woodburn and Stuntz, *J. Am. Chem. Soc.*, 72, 1361 (1950).

[42] Schramm and Westheimer, *J. Am. Chem. Soc.*, 70, 1782 (1948).

[43] Francis, *J. Chem. Soc.*, 89, 1 (1906).

[44] Cook et al., *J. Chem. Soc.*, 1076 (1949).

[45] Suter, *J. Am. Chem. Soc.*, 51, 2581 (1929).

[46] Corson and Hazen, *Org. Syntheses*, Coll. Vol. II, 434 (1943); Leonard and Boyd, *J. Org. Chem.*, 11, 409 (1946); Morgan and Watson, *J. Soc. Chem. Ind. (London)*, 55, 29T (1936).

[47] Icke et al., *Org. Syntheses*, 29, 72 (1949).

[48] Davey and Gwilt, *J. Chem. Soc.*, 204 (1950).

[49] Ruggli and Preiswerk, *Helv. Chim. Acta*, 22, 484 (1939).

[50] Kamm and Segur, *Org. Syntheses*, Coll. Vol. I, 372 (1941); cf. ref. 26.

[51] Dippy and Page, *J. Soc. Chem. Ind. (London)*, 55, 190T (1936).

[52] Culhane and Woodward, *Org. Syntheses*, Coll. Vol. I, 408 (1941); cf. ref. 26.

[53] Keneford and Simpson, *J. Chem. Soc.*, 356 (1948).

[54] Woolfolk and Orchin, *Org. Syntheses*, 28, 91 (1948).

[55] Brewster, Williams, and Phillips, *Org. Syntheses*, 22, 48 (1942).

[56] Weisblat and Lyttle, *J. Am. Chem. Soc.*, 71, 3079 (1949).

[57] Blanksma and Petri, *Rec. trav. chim.*, 66, 355 (1947).

[58] Robertson, *Org. Syntheses*, Coll. Vol. I, 396 (1941).

[59] McGookin and Swift, *J. Soc. Chem. Ind. (London)*, 58, 152 (1939).

[60] Hartman and Smith, *Org. Syntheses*, Coll. Vol. II, 438 (1943).

[61] King and Beer, *J. Chem. Soc.*, 791 (1945).

[62] Fitch, *Org. Syntheses*, 27, 62 (1947).

[63] Nölting and Collin, *Ber.*, 17, 261 (1884).

[64] Hodgson, Heyworth, and Ward, *J. Chem. Soc.*, 1512 (1948).

[65] Hodgson, Mahadevan, and Ward, *Org. Syntheses*, 28, 52 (1948); *J. Chem. Soc.*, 1392 (1947).

[66] Roe in *Organic Reactions*, Vol. 5, John Wiley & Sons, New York, 1949, p. 193.

[67] Starkey, *Org. Syntheses*, Coll. Vol. II, 225 (1943).

[68] Hodgson and Heyworth, *J. Chem. Soc.*, 1624 (1949); cf. ref. 65.

[69] Hodgson and Marsden, *J. Chem. Soc.*, 22 (1944); Hodgson and Ward, *ibid.*, 127 (1947).

[70] Reynolds and Adkins, *J. Am. Chem. Soc.*, 51, 279 (1929).

[71] Kornblum et al., *J. Am. Chem. Soc.*, 69, 307 (1947).

[72] McCombie, Saunders, and Wild, *J. Chem. Soc.*, 24 (1944).

[73] Vogel, *J. Chem. Soc.*, 1847 (1948).

[74] Kispersky, Hass, and Holcomb, *J. Am. Chem. Soc.*, 71, 516 (1949).

[75] Borsche and Sinn, *Ann.*, 553, 265 (1942).

[76] Thurston and Shriner, *J. Org. Chem.*, 2, 183 (1937).

[77] Hoover and Hass, *J. Org. Chem.*, 12, 501 (1947).

[78] Seigle and Hass, *J. Org. Chem.*, 5, 100 (1940); Hudgin, M.S. Thesis, Purdue University, 1940.

[79] Whitmore and Whitmore, *Org. Syntheses*, Coll. Vol. I, 401 (1941).

[80] Auger, *Bull. soc. chim. France*, 23, 333 (1900).

[81] Black and Babers, *Org. Syntheses*, Coll. Vol. II, 512 (1943).

[82] Clarke and Hartman, *Org. Syntheses*, Coll. Vol. I, 541 (1941).

[83] Gilman, Van Ess, and Hayes, *J. Am. Chem. Soc.*, 61, 643 (1939).

[84] Kirpal and Böhm, *Ber.*, 65, 680 (1932).

[85] Koelsch, *J. Am. Chem. Soc.*, 66, 2019 (1944).

[86] Robertson, *J. Chem. Soc.*, 81, 1477 (1902).

[87] Kuhn and Klaveren, *Ber.*, 71, 779 (1938).

[88] Lambert and Piggott, *J. Chem. Soc.*, 1489 (1947).

[89] Steinkopf and Kühnel, *Ber.*, **75**, 1323 (1942).

[90] Fuson and Cleveland, *Org. Syntheses*, **20**, 45 (1940).

[91] Bachmann and Hoffman in *Organic Reactions*, Vol. 2, John Wiley & Sons, New York, 1944, p. 249.

[92] France, Heilbron, and Hey, *J. Chem. Soc.*, 369 (1940); cf. ref. 91.

[93] Ruggli and Schmid, *Helv. Chim. Acta*, **18**, 1232 (1935).

[94] Campbell, Anderson, and Gilmore, *J. Chem. Soc.*, 449 (1940).

[95] Clarke and Taylor, *Org. Syntheses*, Coll. Vol. I, 415 (1941); ref. 96, p. 294.

[96] Kornblum in *Organic Reactions*, Vol. 2, John Wiley & Sons, New York, 1944, p. 296.

[97] Fieser and Kennelly, *J. Am. Chem. Soc.*, **57**, 1614 (1935).

[98] Liang, *Org. Syntheses*, **21**, 105 (1941); Nicholson, *J. Chem. Soc.*, 1553 (1949).

[99] Ehrenfeld and Puterbaugh, *Org. Syntheses*, Coll. Vol. I, 388 (1941).

[100] Hughes, Ingold, Gillespie, et al., *J. Chem. Soc.*, 2400–2558 (1950); Hughes, Ingold et al., *ibid.*, 2628–2677 (1950).

[101] Smith, *J. Am. Chem. Soc.*, **71**, 2855 (1949).

[102] Arndt and Rose, *J. Chem. Soc.*, 6 (1935).

[103] Braun and Cook, *Org. Syntheses*, **31**, 77 (1951).

[104] Pictet and Khotinsky, *Ber.*, **40**, 1163 (1907).

29

Azo and Azoxy Compounds

CONTENTS

494. Coupling of Aromatic Diazonium Compounds with Phenols and Amines

$$ArN_2^+Cl^- + C_6H_5OH \rightarrow p\text{-}HOC_6H_4N=NAr$$

Aromatic diazonium compounds react with phenols and anilines in aqueous solution to produce azo compounds, the azo group occupying the *ortho* or preferably the *para* position. It has been shown that the active components are the diazonium cation and the phenoxide ion or free amine.[1] Hence free mineral acid should be absent. On the other hand, strong basic solutions should be avoided in order to prevent the formation of the stable, inactive *anti*-diazotate;[2] for these reasons the acidity of the diazonium solution is carefully regulated. The stability of the diazonium compound is influenced by several factors including nuclear substituents.[3] Also, the coupling capacity of phenols and amines is affected by substituents.[4] Sometimes certain groups are eliminated during the coupling reaction.[16]

Primary and secondary amines react with diazonium salts to form initially the N-azo derivatives, e.g., diazoaminobenzene, $C_6H_5NHN=NC_6H_5$, from aniline and benzenediazonium chloride.[5] In the presence of acids, these compounds isomerize to the corresponding *p*-aminoazo derivatives; for example, the above compound goes to *p*-aminoazobenzene, $p\text{-}NH_2C_6H_4N=NC_6H_5$. If the *para* position is not free, isomerization to the *ortho* position occurs.[15] The isomerization may proceed by a fission of the diazoamino compound to the progenitors, which then undergo coupling. Aminonaphthalenes couple with diazonium compounds to form the amino azo compounds directly.

In some instances, diazo compounds and primary aromatic amines undergo an exchange reaction. Thus p-nitrobenzenediazonium chloride and aniline hydrochloride in a weakly acidic solution are converted to p-nitroaniline and benzenediazonium chloride.[17]

The coupling reaction is important in the industrial preparation of azo dyes as well as in the analytical determination of diazonium compounds. The reaction has been reviewed,[4] and experimental procedures have been given.[6-8]

495. Condensation of Nitroso Compounds with Amines

$$ArNO + Ar'NH_2 \longrightarrow ArN = NAr$$

Condensation of aromatic nitroso compounds with primary amines is a satisfactory procedure for obtaining azo compounds. An example is the combination of nitrosobenzene and aniline in acetic acid, which results in a quantitative yield of azobenzene.[9] Similarly, a series of methyl-substituted azobenzenes have been prepared, although the yields are poor in the case of the *ortho*-substituted compounds.[10] As an illustration of the versatility of the reaction, nitrosobenzene can be condensed with o-methoxyaniline (o-anisidine),[11] p-aminobenzoic acid,[12] o-phenylene-diamine monobenzoate,[13] and m-nitroaniline[14] to form the corresponding substituted azobenzenes.

496. Reduction of Nitro Compounds

$$2ArNO_2 \xrightarrow{(H)} ArN = NAr \xrightarrow{(H)} ArN = NAr$$
$$\downarrow$$
$$O$$

Aromatic azo and azoxy compounds may be prepared by chemical or electrolytic reduction of nitro compounds, the degree of reduction depending upon the experimental conditions.

Several chemical reducing agents are available for obtaining the azo compounds. An example is the synthesis of azobenzene by the action of zinc dust and alkali on nitrobenzene (86%).[18] Lithium aluminum hydride in ether gives satisfactory results in the conversion of nitrobenzene and nitromesitylene to the azo compounds.[21] Reduction by the action of hydrazine in alcohol solution over a palladium catalyst has been a successful procedure for converting the halonitrobenzenes to the azo compounds.[20]

Other agents are employed for obtaining azoxy compounds. The earliest procedure involved the reducing action of sodium methoxide, *viz.*,[33]

$$4C_6H_5NO_2 + 3CH_3ONa \longrightarrow 2C_6H_5N=N(O)C_6H_5 + 3HCOONa + 3H_2O$$

When sodium arsenite is the reducing agent, nitrobenzene is changed to azoxybenzene in an 85% yield.[32]

Another convenient procedure utilizes dextrose as the reductant, furnishing azoxybenzene in an 82% yield.[32] This same reductant converts p-nitrobenzoic acid to its azoxy derivative or its azo derivative, depending upon slight changes in the experimental conditions.[34] Also, by slight changes in the procedure, m-nitrophenol may be converted by the action of zinc dust and alkali to the corresponding azo or azoxy compound.[23] A combination of magnesium and methanol has been applied to the nitrotoluenes and halonitrobenzenes to yield the alkyl- and halo-substituted azoxy compounds in good yields.[22]

Directions have been given for the electrolytic reduction of nitrobenzene to azobenzene.[19] Azoxy compounds are also formed by this technique.[36]

497. Oxidation of Hydrazines

$$RNHNHR \xrightarrow{(O)} RN=NR$$

Aromatic hydrazines like hydrazobenzene are readily oxidized to azobenzenes with air in the presence of alkali or by the action of sodium hypobromite.[24] Aliphatic azo compounds are also prepared from the corresponding hydrazo compounds. Thus azomethane, $CH_3N=NCH_3$, is prepared by the oxidation of sym-dimethylhydrazine with cupric chloride (70%).[28] The oxidation of ω,ω'-hydrazotoluene, $C_6H_5CH_2NHNHCH_2C_6H_5$, to the azo compound is accomplished with mercuric oxide in boiling ether (76%).[25]

Aliphatic hydrazines of the type $R_2C(CN)NHNHC(CN)R_2$ are prepared by the interaction of ketone cyanohydrins and hydrazine. These compounds can be oxidized to azonitriles with hypobromous acid in methanol.[26] In a similar manner, ethyl azodicarboxylate, $C_2H_5O_2CN=NCO_2C_2H_5$, is synthesized by the action of hypochlorous acid on ethyl hydrazodicarboxylate (83%).[27]

498. Oxidation of Azo Compounds [10, 37]

$$C_6H_5N=NC_6H_5 \xrightarrow[CH_3COOH]{H_2O_2} C_6H_5N=N(O)C_6H_5$$

499. Isomerization of Diazoamino Compounds [15] (cf. method 494)

$$C_6H_5N=N-NHC_6H_5 \xrightarrow{H^+} p\text{-}H_2NC_6H_4N=NC_6H_5$$

TABLE 108. AZO AND AZOXY COMPOUNDS 767

TABLE 108. AZO AND AZOXY COMPOUNDS

C_n	Compound	Method	Yield (%)	Chapter ref.	B.p./mm., n_D^t, (M.p.)
C_2	Azomethane	497	70	29 28	
C_6	Ethyl azodicarboxylate	497	83	29 27	111/15
C_{10}	2,2′-Azomethylethylacetonitrile	497	70	29 26	(57)
	Dimethyl 2,2′-azoisobutyrate	497	90	29 25	(32)
C_{12}	Azobenzene	495	100	29 9	(68)
		496	86	29 18	(67.5)
		497	100	29 24	(68)
	p,p′-Dibromoazobenzene	496	80	29 20	(204)
	m,m′-Dihydroxyazobenzene	496	63	29 23	(205)
	o-Aminoazobenzene	495	54	29 13	
	m-Aminoazobenzene	425	69	29 14	(67)
	p-Aminoazobenzene	425	81	29 31	(124)
	p,p′-Diaminoazobenzene	425	40	29 30	(246)
	m-Nitroazobenzene	495	70	29 14	(96)
	Azoxybenzene	496	85	29 32	(36.5)
	p,p′-Dichloroazoxybenzene	496	81	29 22	(158)
	p,p′-Dibromoazoxybenzene	496	84	29 22	(176)
	m,m′-Dihydroxyazoxybenzene	496	65	29 23	(183)
C_{13}	2-Methoxyazobenzene	495	45	29 11	197/14, (41)
	2-Methylazobenzene	498	49	29 10	186/25
	p-Phenylazobenzoic acid	495	61	29 12	(249)
C_{14}	ω,ω′-Azotoluene	497	76	29 25	(29)
	o-Aminoazo-p-toluene	494	70	29 15	(118)
	p,p′-Dimethylazoxybenzene	496	61	29 22	(70)
	p-Azoxybenzoic acid	496	95	29 34	
C_{15}	Methyl red	494	66	29 7	(182)
C_{20}	1,1′-Azonaphthalene	14	30	29 29	(189)
C_{26}	2,2′-Azoxyfluorene	496	60	29 35	(279)

For explanations and symbols see pp. xi–xii.

REFERENCES FOR CHAPTER 29

[1] Wistar and Bartlett, *J. Am. Chem. Soc.*, 63, 413 (1941); Hauser and Breslow, *ibid.*, 63, 418 (1941).

[2] Saunders, *The Aromatic Diazo Compounds*, Longmans, Green & Co., New York, 1949, p. 383.

[3] Ref. 2, p. 61.

[4] Ref. 2, p. 194.

[5] Hartman and Dickey, *Org. Syntheses*, Coll. Vol. II, 163 (1943).

[6] Conant, Lutz, and Corson, *Org. Syntheses*, Coll. Vol. I, 49 (1941).

[7] Clarke and Kirner, *Org. Syntheses*, Coll. Vol. I, 374 (1941).

[8] Fieser, *Org. Syntheses*, Coll. Vol. II, 35 (1943).

[9] Mills, *J. Chem. Soc.*, 67, 928 (1895).

[10] Parsons and Bailar, *J. Am. Chem. Soc.*, 58, 268 (1936).

[11] Bamberger, *Ber.*, 33, 3188 (1900).

[12] Anspon, *Org. Syntheses*, 25, 86 (1945).

[13] Ruggli and Rogner, *Helv. Chim. Acta*, 25, 1533 (1942).

[14] Ruggli and Wüst, *Helv. Chim. Acta*, 28, 781 (1945).

[15] Ruggli and Courtin, *Helv. Chim. Acta*, 15, 90 (1932).

[16] Ref. 2, p. 221.

[17] Ref. 2, p. 223.

[18] Bigelow and Robinson, *Org. Syntheses*, 22, 28 (1942); cf. 19.

[19] Weygand, *Organic Preparations*, Interscience Publishers, New York, 1945, p. 249.

[20] Busch and Schulz, *Ber.*, 62, 1458 (1929).

[21] Nystrom and Brown, *J. Am. Chem. Soc.*, 70, 3738 (1948).

[22] Zechmeister and Rom, *Ann.*, 468, 128 (1929).

[23] Ruggli and Hinovker, *Helv. Chim. Acta*, 17, 410 (1934).

[24] Gattermann and Wieland, *Laboratory Methods of Organic Chemistry*, The Macmillan Co., New York, 1938, p. 184.

[25] Bickel and Waters, *Rec. trav. chim.*, 69, 312 (1950).

[26] Dox, *J. Am. Chem. Soc.*, 47, 1473 (1925).

[27] Rabjohn, *Org. Syntheses*, 28, 58 (1948).

[28] Jahn, *J. Am. Chem. Soc.*, 59, 1761 (1937).

[29] Cumming and Howie, *J. Chem. Soc.*, 134 (1933).

[30] Ashley et al., *J. Chem. Soc.*, 112 (1942).

[31] Ruggli and Iselin, *Helv. Chim. Acta*, 30, 733 (1947).

[32] Bigelow and Palmer, *Org. Syntheses*, Coll. Vol. II, 57 (1943).

[33] Fry and Cameron, *J. Am. Chem. Soc.*, 49, 864 (1927); Suter and Dains, *ibid.*, 50, 2733 (1928).

[34] Bacharach and Weinstein, *Rec. trav. chim.*, 54, 932 (1935).

[35] Cislack, Eastman, and Senior, *J. Am. Chem. Soc.*, 49, 2318 (1927).

[36] Swann in *Technique of Organic Chemistry*, Vol. II, Interscience Publishers, New York, 1948, pp. 177–179.

[37] Swern, *Chem. Revs.*, 45, 38 (1949).

30

Diazo and Diazonium Compounds

The chemistry of aliphatic diazo compounds of the general formula $RCHN_2$, among which are the important diazo ketones $RCOCHN_2$ and diazo esters N_2CRCO_2R, has been reviewed.[52-54] In addition, the formation of aromatic diazonium salts, $ArN_2^+Cl^-$, has been extensively studied and fully described in several monographs.[1] For this reason, only the most pertinent points are included here along with key references.

500. Decomposition of N-Nitroso Compounds

$$(1) \quad RCH_2N(NO)CO_2C_2H_5 + 2KOH \rightarrow RCHN_2 + K_2CO_3 + C_2H_5OH + H_2O$$

$$(2) \quad RCH_2N(NO)CONH_2 + KOH \rightarrow RCHN_2 + KCNO + 2H_2O$$

$$(3) \quad RCH_2N(NO)CCH_2COCH_3 \xrightarrow{NaOR} RCHN_2 + (CH_3)_2C=CHCOCH_3 + H_2O$$
$$\quad\quad\quad\quad\quad | $$
$$\quad\quad\quad\quad (CH_3)_2$$

Low-molecular-weight diazoalkanes are prepared by three general methods, all of which involve the basic decomposition of an N-nitroso compound. The first is concerned with the alkaline degradation of an N-nitroso-N-alkylurethane (equation 1). Thus, the synthesis of diazoethane and 1-diazopropane is accomplished in 75% and 57% yields, respectively, by the rapid addition of the corresponding nitrosourethane to a solution of potassium hydroxide in n-propyl alcohol.[34] The procedure has been extended to the formation of a more complex product, diazo-

β,β,β-triphenylethane (100%).[38] Diazomethane is also prepared in this way from the commercially available nitrosomethylurethane;[35] however, other procedures are preferred.

A closely related method consists in treating an N-nitroso-N-alkylurea with strong aqueous potassium hydroxide (equation 2). Although this procedure has been adapted to the formation of several diazoalkanes,[42] it is particularly suited for forming diazomethane.[36]

Treatment of methyl N-nitroso-β-alkylaminoisobutyl ketones with sodium isopropoxide or sodium cyclohexoxide furnishes a third method (equation 3). The preparation of the starting materials involves simply the addition of an amine to mesityl oxide with subsequent nitrosation.[39, 41] In this case the starting material (equation 3, R = H) for diazomethane is more stable than nitrosomethylurea and does not have an irritating action like methylnitrosourethane.[39]

The diazoalkanes are not isolated but are collected in ether for immediate consumption. The quantity and yield from the N-nitroso compound are determined by treating an aliquot with excess benzoic acid and titrating the unreacted acid with standard alkali.[36] The diazoalkanes should be handled with care.[39]

501. Diazotization of Aliphatic Amino Compounds

$$CH_2(\overset{+}{N}H_3\overset{-}{Cl})CO_2C_2H_5 + NaNO_2 \rightarrow N_2CHCO_2C_2H_5 + NaCl + 2H_2O$$

Primary amino groups *alpha* to a carbethoxyl, cyano, ketone, sulfonic acid,[43] or trifluoromethyl group[44] react with nitrous acid to form stable diazo groups. An example is the conversion of glycine ethyl ester hydrochloride to ethyl diazoacetate (85%).[45] The reaction has been applied to higher amino esters.[46] It may be recalled that aliphatic primary amines in general react with nitrous acid to give nitrogen, alcohols, and olefins. However, the above groups adjacent to the amino group have special effects; even the closely related α-amino acids are converted to hydroxy acids by this treatment.

502. Oxidation of Hydrazones

$$R_2C = NNH_2 + HgO \rightarrow R_2CN_2 + H_2O + Hg$$

Certain aromatic diazohydrocarbons are conveniently prepared by the oxidation of hydrazones. Thus benzophenone hydrazone ($R = C_6H_5$) reacts with mercuric oxide in petroleum ether at room temperature during 6 hours to furnish diphenyldiazomethane in 89% to 96% yield.[47] Hydrazones of substituted benzophenones have been similarly treated.[48] Phenylbenzoyldiazomethane is synthesized by this same procedure (94%).[50] A few simpler diazo compounds like dimethyldiazomethane (R = CH$_3$), phenyl-diazomethane, C$_6$H$_5$CHN$_2$, and phenylmethyldiazomethane, C$_6$H$_5$(CH$_3$)CN$_2$, have been made, although no indication of yields is given.[49]

503. Interaction of Acyl Halides and Diazoalkanes

$$2CH_2N_2 + RCOX \longrightarrow RCOCHN_2 + CH_3X + N_2$$

The preparation of diazo ketones by the interaction of acyl chlorides and diazoalkanes has become a well-established reaction, for these compounds represent important starting materials for the synthesis of many ketone and acid derivatives. Excellent surveys of the reaction and its uses have been made.[52-54]

Diazomethane is the most common reagent for this reaction although other diazohydrocarbons have been successfully employed.[34] In the standard procedure, the acyl chloride is added slowly to an ethereal solution of excess diazomethane (2.5 to 3 moles) at 0° and the mixture is allowed to stand for varying periods of time. The yields are practically quantitative. The initial reaction is the formation of the diazo ketone with the liberation of hydrogen halide, which then reacts with a second molecule of diazomethane to form methyl halide and nitrogen. If the hydrogen halide is not consumed by excess diazomethane, it will react with the diazo ketone to yield an ω-halogenated ketone. In some instances, an organic base like trimethylamine is present at the start of the reaction for the purpose of removing the liberated acid, thus curtailing the consumption of the expensive diazomethane.[55] Quite often the diazo ketones are used without purification, but many have been crystallized. A few compounds have been distilled at reduced pressure without violent decomposition.[56]

The method has been adapted to the formation of *bis*-diazoacetylalkanes from dibasic acid chlorides.[57] Diazo ketones have been obtained from acyl chlorides containing a β,γ-double bond, an ester group, and certain heterocyclic and aryl nuclei having alkyl, methoxyl, and nitro substituents. On the other hand, functional groups such as phenolic hydroxyl, arylamino, aldehyde, active methylene, and α,β-unsaturated linkages may interfere. The method is ideal for application to complex molecules.

Experimental conditions and procedures have been presented.[52, 53] It should be recalled that diazomethane is toxic and explosive in the gaseous state.

The applications of diazo ketones for the synthesis of other homologous series are summarized elsewhere, i.e., halo ketones (method 57), hydroxy ketones (method 114), alkoxy ketones (method 124), keto esters (method 311), higher acids (method 271), higher esters (method 295), and amides (method 360).

504. Diazotization of Aromatic Amines

$$ArNH_2 + HX + HNO_2 \rightarrow ArN_2^+ X^- + 2H_2O$$

Salts of primary aromatic amines react with nitrous acid to produce diazonium salts.[1] The reaction is usually performed by adding a cold solution of sodium nitrite to a cold solution of the arylamine in aqueous mineral acid. The end point of the reaction is conveniently determined by the detection of excess nitrous acid with potassium iodide-starch paper. Sulfamic acid has long been used both in industry and in the laboratory to remove excess nitrous acid. It has been found to react with the more active diazo compounds.[2] In most cases, high temperatures are avoided to prevent the formation of phenols and the decomposition of the unstable nitrous acid. An excess of mineral acid is necessary to prevent coupling between the diazonium salt and unreacted amine (cf. method 494). If the amine salt is somewhat insoluble, a fine crystalline form, which is produced by rapid crystallization from a warm aqueous solution, may be employed.[17]

Amines having sulfonic acid or carboxyl groups may be mixed with sodium nitrite in basic solution and the mixture then added to excess mineral acid, or the amine may be ground with concentrated acid and the mixture then treated with aqueous sodium nitrite.[25]

Many diazonium salts are unstable and must be handled with care, preferably in solution rather than in the dry state. Procedures have been perfected for making stabilized diazonium salts, which can be isolated and dried.[3] If a solid non-stabilized diazonium salt is desired, an alcoholic solution of the amine salt is treated with an alkyl nitrite, and the product is crystallized or precipitated with ether. Glacial acetic acid and dioxane may also be employed as solvents.[7]

In the event that the amine is only slightly soluble in the aqueous mineral acid, as is true of weakly basic amines having negative substituents, special techniques are employed to bring about the reaction. A successful procedure involves the treatment of the weakly basic amine in concentrated acid, sulfuric, phosphoric, or glacial acetic, with nitrosylsulfuric acid.[4, 28] In this manner, the more intractable amines having two or more *meta*-directing or halogen substituents are subjected to diazotization, e.g., 2,4,6-trinitroaniline (picramide)[4] and 2,6-diiodo-4-nitroaniline.[5] Pyridine has been used as a solvent in diazotizations with nitrosylsulfuric acid.[6]

The common procedure for diazotization by means of nitrous acid in aqueous solutions is illustrated by the synthesis of benzenediazonium chloride,[8] *o*-, *m*-, and *p*-methylbenzenediazonium sulfates,[9, 11] and β-naphthalenediazonium chloride.[10]

The tetrazotization of *m*-phenylenediamine has been described;[12] also, under special conditions (nitrosylsulfuric acid in glacial acetic acid) a similar conversion of the *ortho* isomer has been accomplished.[13] This procedure has been adapted to the tetrazotization of certain naphthalene diamines.[14] The simultaneous diazotization of two amino groups in the biphenyl series is illustrated by the synthesis of 4,4'-biphenylene-*bis*-diazonium chloride [15] and its 3,3'-dimethyl analog.[16]

Syntheses are also recorded that illustrate diazotization in the presence of a single substituent like a halo,[17, 18] phenolic hydroxyl,[51] alkoxyl,[20] aldo,[21, 22] carbethoxyl,[23] carboxyl,[24, 25] or nitro group.[26–31]

Certain nuclear substituents *ortho* to a newly formed diazonium group may interact to form a cyclic structure with or without retention of the nitrogen atoms.[32] Such is the case in the diazotization of o-phenylene-diamine in aqueous solution, the product being 1,2,3-benzotriazole (81%).[30] If the *ortho* substituent is an activated methyl group, an indazole is formed.[31] Hydroxyl groups *ortho* or *para* to the diazonium group may interact to form internal condensation products called diazo oxides.[33] These compounds may also form in the reaction of halo- and nitro-substituted aminophenols.

Further discussion of the formation of diazonium salts and their reactions is found under the many methods involving the replacement and modification of the diazonium group (methods 12, 14, 56, 93, 380, 401, 473, 487, 494, 506, and 521).

TABLE 109. DIAZO AND DIAZONIUM COMPOUNDS

C_n	Compound	Method	Yield (%)	Chapter[ref.]	B.p./mm., n_D^t, (M.p.)
	Diazo Compounds				
C_1	Diazomethane	500	84	30[39]	-24/760
		500	70	30[36]	
C_2	Diazoethane	500	50	30[41]	-17/89.5
		500	75	30[34]	
	Trifluorodiazoethane	501	67	30[44]	13/752
C_3	1-Diazopropane	500	47	30[41]	-8/41.5
		500	57	30[34]	
	Vinyldiazomethane	500	23	30[37]	
C_4	1-Diazobutane	500	45	30[41]	-3.5/26
		500	....	30[34]	
	Ethyl diazoacetate	501	85	30[45]	
C_6	Isovaleryldiazomethane	503	85	30[56]	62/4
C_8	Diazoacetophenone	503	100	30[55]	(48)
	1,4-bis-Diazoacetyl-n-butane	503	73	30[57]	(71)
C_9	1-p-Chlorobenzoyl-1-diazo-ethane	503	71	30[34]	(57)
	Benzyl diazomethyl ketone	503	85	30[35]	(50)*
	p-Methoxybenzoyldiazo-methane	503	70	30[53]	(91)
C_{12}	α-Naphthoyldiazomethane	503	92	30[53]	(55)
C_{13}	Diphenyldiazomethane	502	96	30[47]	(30)
	1-(2'-Naphthoyl)-1-diazoethane	503	78	30[34]	(110d)
C_{14}	Phenylbenzoyldiazomethane	502	94	30[50]	(79)
C_{20}	Diazo-β,β,β-triphenylethane	500	100	30[38]	
	Diazonium Compounds				
C_6	Benzenediazonium chloride	504		30[8]	
	o-Benzenetetrazonium chloride	504		30[13]	
	m-Benzenetetrazonium chloride	504		30[12]	
	o-Chlorobenzenediazonium bromide	504		30[18]	
	p-Bromobenzenediazonium chloride	504		30[17]	
	p-Hydroxybenzenediazonium sulfate	504		30[51]	
	m-Nitrobenzenediazonium chloride (sulfate)	504		30[26]	
	p-Nitrobenzenediazonium fluoborate	504		30[27]	
C_7	o-Methylbenzenediazonium bromide (sulfate)	504		30[9]	
	m-Methylbenzenediazonium chloride	504		30[11]	

TABLE 109. DIAZO AND DIAZONIUM COMPOUNDS 775

TABLE 109 (*continued*)

C_n	Compound	Method	Yield (%)	Chapter[ref.]	B.p./mm., n_D^t, (M.p.)
		Diazonium Compounds (*continued*)			
C_7	p-Methylbenzenediazonium bromide (sulfate)	504		30[9]	
	2-Bromo-4-methylbenzene-diazonium sulfate	504		30[19]	
	m-Benzaldehydediazonium sulfate	504		30[21]	
	p-Benzaldehydediazonium sulfate	504		30[22]	
	o-Carboxybenzenediazonium chloride	504		30[24]	
	2-Nitro-4-methylbenzenedia-zonium sulfate	504		30[29]	
C_9	p-Carbethoxybenzenedia-zonium chloride	504		30[23]	
C_{10}	β-Naphthalenediazonium chloride	504		30[10]	
	4-Nitronaphthalenediazonium sulfate	504		30[28]	
C_{12}	4,4'-Biphenylene-*bis*-diazonium chloride	504		30[15]	

For explanations and symbols see pp. xi–xii.

REFERENCES FOR CHAPTER 30

[1] Saunders, *The Aromatic Diazo-Compounds and Their Technical Applications*, Longmans, Green & Co., New York, 1949, pp. 1-60; Groggins, *Unit Processes in Organic Synthesis*, McGraw-Hill Book Co., New York, 1947, pp. 129-167.

[2] Grimmel and Morgan, *J. Am. Chem. Soc.*, 70, 1750 (1948).

[3] Saunders, ref. 1, pp. 61-104; Hodgson and Marsden, *J. Chem. Soc.*, 207 (1940); cf. Kornblum in *Organic Reactions*, Vol. 2, John Wiley & Sons, New York, 1946, p. 285.

[4] Hodgson and Walker, *J. Chem. Soc.*, 1620 (1933); Misslin, *Helv. Chim. Acta*, 3, 626 (1920); Schoutissen, *J. Am. Chem. Soc.*, 55, 4531 (1933).

[5] Niemann and Redemann, *J. Am. Chem. Soc.*, 63, 1550 (1941).

[6] DeMilt and Van Zandt, *J. Am. Chem. Soc.*, 58, 2044 (1936); Bachmann and Boatner, *ibid.*, 58, 2194 (1936); cf. Lothrop, *ibid.*, 60, 725 (1938).

[7] Schoutissen, *Rec. trav. chim.*, 40, 764 (1921); Pray, *J. Phys. Chem.*, 30, 1477 (1926); Smith and Waring, *J. Am. Chem. Soc.*, 64, 469 (1942).

[8] Conant, Lutz, and Corson, *Org. Syntheses*, Coll. Vol. I, 49 (1941); Coleman, *ibid.*, Coll. Vol. I, 442 (1941).

[9] Marvel and McElvain, *Org. Syntheses*, Coll. Vol. I, 170 (1941); Bigelow, *ibid.*, Coll. Vol. I, 135, 136 (1941); Clarke and Read, *ibid.*, Coll. Vol. I, 514 (1941).

[10] Nesmajanow, *Org. Syntheses*, Coll. Vol. II, 432 (1943).

[11] Tarbell and Fukushima, *Org. Syntheses*, 27, 81 (1947).

[12] Schoutissen, *Rec. trav. chim.*, 54, 381 (1935); Heertjes, Kolb, and Waterman, *J. Soc. Chem. Ind. (London)*, 56, 173T (1937).

[13] Hodgson and Walker, *J. Chem. Soc.*, 530 (1935).

[14] Hodgson and Whitehurst, *J. Chem. Soc.*, 80 (1947).

[15] Schiemann and Winkelmüller, *Org. Syntheses*, Coll. II, 188 (1943).

[16] Hartwell and Fieser, *Org. Syntheses*, 16, 12 (1936).

[17] Gomberg and Bachmann, *Org. Syntheses*, Coll. Vol. I, 113 (1941).

[18] Hartwell, *Org. Syntheses*, 24, 22 (1944).

[19] Bigelow, Johnson, and Sandborn, *Org. Syntheses*, Coll. Vol. I, 133 (1941); Ungnade and Orwoll, *ibid.*, 23, 11 (1943).

[20] Kornblum, *Org. Syntheses*, 21, 30 (1941).

[21] Woodward, *Org. Syntheses*, 25, 56 (1945); Icke et al., *ibid.*, 29, 63 (1949).

[22] Schoutissen, *Rec. trav. chim.*, 54, 97 (1935).

[23] Schiemann and Winkelmüller, *Org. Syntheses*, Coll. Vol. II, 299 (1943).

[24] Clarke and Kirner, *Org. Syntheses*, Coll. Vol. I, 374 (1941); Stephenson, *ibid.*, 29, 54 (1949); cf. ref. 25; Allen and MacKay, *ibid.*, Col. Vol. II, 580 (1943).

[25] Atkinson and Lawler, *Org. Syntheses*, Coll. Vol. I, 222 (1941).

[26] Hartman and Brethen, *Org. Syntheses*, Coll. Vol. I, 162 (1941); Manske, *ibid.*, Coll. Vol. I, 404 (1941).

[27] Starkey, *Org. Syntheses*, Coll. Vol. II, 225 (1943).

[28] Hodgson, Mahadevan, and Ward, *Org. Syntheses*, 28, 52 (1948).

[29] Clarke and Taylor, *Org. Syntheses*, Coll. Vol. I, 415 (1941).

[30] Damschroder and Peterson, *Org. Syntheses*, 20, 16 (1940).

[31] Porter and Peterson, *Org. Syntheses*, 20, 73 (1940).

[32] Saunders, ref. 1, pp. 241-267.

[33] Saunders, ref. 1, pp. 28-35.

[34] Wilds and Meader, *J. Org. Chem.*, 13, 763 (1948).

[35] McPhee and Klingsberg, *Org. Syntheses*, 26, 13 (1946).

[36] Arndt, *Org. Syntheses*, Coll. Vol. II, 165 (1943); cf. ref. 35.

[37] Hurd and Lui, *J. Am. Chem. Soc.*, **57**, 2656 (1935).
[38] Hellerman and Garner, *J. Am. Chem. Soc.*, **57**, 139 (1935).
[39] Redemann et al., *Org. Syntheses*, **25**, 28 (1945); cf. refs. 40 and 41.
[40] Berenbom and Fones, *J. Am. Chem. Soc.*, **71**, 1629 (1949).
[41] Adamson and Kenner, *J. Chem. Soc.*, 1551 (1937); 286 (1935).
[42] Werner, *J. Chem. Soc.*, 115, 1093 (1919).
[43] Angeli, *Ber.*, **37**, 2080 (1904).
[44] Gilman and Jones, *J. Am. Chem. Soc.*, **65**, 1458 (1943).
[45] Womack and Nelson, *Org. Syntheses*, **24**, 56 (1944); Smith and McKenzie, *J. Org. Chem.*, **15**, 74 (1950).
[46] Marvel and Noyes, *J. Am. Chem. Soc.*, **42**, 2259 (1920).
[47] Smith and Howard, *Org. Syntheses*, **24**, 53 (1944).
[48] Staudinger et al., *Ber.*, **49**, 1897, 1923, 1928, 1951, 1969, 1973 (1916).
[49] Staudinger and Gaule, *Ber.*, **49**, 1897 (1916); Guha and Sankaran, *ibid.*, **70**, 1689 (1937).
[50] Nenitzescu and Solomonica, *Org. Syntheses*, Coll. Vol. II, 496 (1943).
[51] Dains and Eberly, *Org. Syntheses*, Coll. Vol. II, 355 (1943).
[52] Eistert in *Newer Methods of Preparative Organic Chemistry*, Interscience Publishers, New York, 1948, pp. 513–570.
[53] Bachmann and Struve in *Organic Reactions*, Vol. 1, John Wiley & Sons, New York, 1942, p. 38.
[54] Smith, *Chem. Revs.*, **23**, 193 (1938).
[55] Newman and Beal, *J. Am. Chem. Soc.*, **71**, 1506 (1949); ref. 40.
[56] Birkofer, *Ber.*, **80**, 88 (1947).
[57] Walker, *J. Chem. Soc.*, 1304 (1940).

31

Mercaptans

CONTENTS

505. Alkylation of Metallic Hydrosulfides

$$RX + NaSH \longrightarrow RSH + NaX$$

The direct introduction of the mercapto group into the organic molecule is accomplished by the alkylation of hydrogen sulfide[15] or an alcoholic solution of sodium or potassium hydrosulfide. The hydrosulfide solution is prepared by saturating alcoholic potassium hydroxide,[16] molten sodium sulfide nonahydrate,[23] or a solution of sodium in absolute alcohol[14] with hydrogen sulfide. Alkyl sulfates and primary or secondary alkyl halides serve as alkylating agents. Dithiols are obtained from polymethylene halides in 70–85% yields.[14] Chlorohydrins,[18] β-chloro ethers,[19] α-chloro ketones,[20] and diethylaminoalkyl chlorides[23] have also been converted to mercaptans by this method. Potassium hydrosulfide in propylene glycol at 175° converts 2-bromopyridine to 2-mercaptopyridine in 87% yield.[17] The nitro group of p-nitrochlorobenzene is reduced in the preparation of p-aminothiophenol (69%).[22] The active halide, p-cyanobenzyl chloride, gives only a 10% yield of mercaptan; the main product is the sulfide formed by further alkylation of the mercaptan.[21] Alkyl sulfides are often by-products of the reaction (cf. method 515). Their formation is minimized by an excess of hydrogen sulfide.

506. Hydrolysis of S-Alkylthiouronium Salts

$$CS(NH_2)_2 \xrightarrow{RX} RSC(NH_2)=NH_2^+X^- \xrightarrow{NaOH} RSH + (NH_2CN)_x$$

The carbon-sulfur linkage is readily established by alkylation of thiourea by means of halides,[1, 3] sulfates,[13] or alcohol-hydrogen halide mixtures.[2] Many types of groups have been introduced, including primary,[1, 2] secondary,[1, 2, 5] tertiary,[1, 6] allyl,[1, 7] benzyl,[1, 2] and furfuryl.[12] A few aryl groups have been introduced by means of active aromatic[8] and heterocyclic[11] halides or by treating the thiourea with a diazonium salt.[4] Mercaptans are formed by alkaline hydrolysis of the resulting isothiouronium salts. Over-all yields vary from 40% to 90%. Polymethylene halides give dithiols,[2, 14, 51] and halo alcohols and halo acids lead to *mercapto alcohols*[10] and *mercapto acids,*[9] respectively. A convenient procedure for the disposal of mercaptan vapors in the laboratory has been described.[50]

507. Hydrolysis of Xanthates

$$ArN_2^+X^- \xrightarrow{C_2H_5OCSSK} C_2H_5OCSSAr \xrightarrow[H^+]{KOH;} ArSH + COS + C_2H_5OH$$

The replacement of an amino group by a mercapto group on an aromatic nucleus is effected by treating the diazotized amine with potassium ethyl xanthate and hydrolyzing the resulting aryl ethyl xanthate (Leuckart). Yields of 40–80% are reported for thiophenols containing methyl,[25] halo,[26, 54] and methoxyl[57] groups. Potassium ethyl xanthate is readily prepared from alcoholic potassium hydroxide and carbon disulfide.[52]

508. Hydrolysis of Thiol Esters

$$RCOSR' \xrightarrow[H^+ \text{ or } OH^-]{H_2O} RCO_2H + R'SH$$

The hydrolysis of thiol esters is achieved in either acidic or basic media. Alcoholic solutions of hydrogen chloride or potassium hydroxide are the most common reagents. Dithiols,[42] hydroxy mercaptans,[33] and mercapto ethers,[42] ketones,[48] and acids[41] have been prepared by this method. The corresponding thiol esters are obtained by the addition of thioacetic acid to oxides[33] and olefinic acids[41] or by the action of its potassium salt on halo ketones[48] or sulfonic esters.[42]

509. Reduction of Sulfonyl Halides

$$RSO_2Cl \xrightarrow{(H)} RSH$$

Arylsulfonyl chlorides are reduced by zinc dust and sulfuric acid at 0° to give high yields of thiophenols.[35, 37, 56] Tin and hydrochloric acid[7] and a mixture of phosphorus, potassium iodide, and phosphoric acid[38] have also been used. Preliminary experiments with lithium aluminum hydride on both alkyl- and aryl-sulfonyl chlorides gave 45-50% yields of mercaptans.[36] Halogen atoms on the benzene ring are stable during the reduction.[7]

510. Reduction of Disulfides

$$RSSR \xrightarrow{(H)} 2RSH$$

This reaction has found little application to mercaptan syntheses since the mercaptans are usually as readily available (by other methods) as the disulfides. The S-S linkage is reduced by zinc in acetic[29, 32, 53] or sulfuric[30] acid, lithium aluminum hydride,[34] or metallic sodium.[31] γ-Hydroxypropyl disulfide is reduced electrolytically in 70% yield.[33] Reduction by sodium disulfide does not reduce the nitro group in the preparation of p-nitrothiophenol (65%),[8] whereas zinc and acetic acid converts o-nitrophenyl disulfide to o-aminothiophenol (90%).[32] Disulfides made by the action of ammonium hydrogen sulfide on aldehydes are sources for difficultly available aromatic and heterocyclic mercaptans. The disulfides are reduced by aluminum amalgam and water.[49]

511. Action of Sulfur on Organometallic Reagents

$$ArLi \xrightarrow{S} ArSLi \xrightarrow[H^+]{H_2O} ArSH$$

Phenyllithium and p-dimethylaminophenyllithium react with sulfur with the liberation of heat. Hydrolysis of the products by dilute hydrochloric acid gives thiophenol (62%) and p-dimethylaminothiophenol (50%), respectively.[9] The Grignard reagent has been employed in a similar manner.[40, 55]

512. Addition of Hydrogen Sulfide to Olefinic Compounds

$$(CH_3)_2C=CH_2 + H_2S \longrightarrow (CH_3)_3CSH$$

Small yields (4-36%) of mercaptans have been obtained by the addition of hydrogen sulfide under pressure to simple olefins.[27] The addition follows Markownikoff's rule. Hydrogen sulfide has been added to conjugated olefinic ketones, acids, and nitro compounds.[28]

513. Action of Hydrogen Sulfide on Alcohols [24]

$$ROH + H_2S \xrightarrow[380°]{ThO_2} RSH + H_2O$$

514. Addition of Amines to Olefin Sulfides [45, 46]

$$R_2C\!\!-\!\!CR_2 + R'_2NH \rightarrow R'_2NCR_2CR_2SH$$
$$\diagdown\!\!\diagup$$
$$S$$

TABLE 110. MERCAPTANS

C_n	Compound	Method	Yield (%)	Chapter[ref.]	B.p./mm., n_D^t, (M.p.)
		Aliphatic Mercaptans			
C_1	Methyl mercaptan	506	90	31[13]	7.6*
C_2	Ethyl mercaptan	506	75	31[3]	35
C_3	n-Propyl mercaptan	505	49	31[16]	67/763, 1.4351[25]
	Isopropyl mercaptan	505	36	31[16]	53/753, 1.4223[25]
	Allyl mercaptan	506	41	31[7]	68
C_4	n-Butyl mercaptan	505	54	31[16]	99/768, 1.4401[25]
	n-Butyl mercaptan	506	91	31[2]	98
	s-Butyl mercaptan	506	64	31[2]	
	Isobutyl mercaptan	506	56	31[2]	88
	Isobutenyl mercaptan	506	68	31[7]	93/750
C_5	n-Amyl mercaptan	505	69	31[16]	126/760, 1.4440[25]
	3-Pentanethiol	506	48	31[5]	
	t-Amyl mercaptan	506	65	31[6]	97
C_6	n-Hexyl mercaptan	505	67	31[16]	86/90, 1.4473[25]
		506	71	31[2]	153/762
		Aromatic and Heterocyclic Mercaptans			
C_5	α-Furfuryl mercaptan	506	33	31[12]	84/65, 1.5329
		510	73	31[29]	155
	2-Mercaptomethyltetrahydro-furan	508	55	31[42]	113/145, 1.4910
	2-Mercaptopyridine	505	87	31[17]	(128)
		506	47	31[11]	(125)
C_6	Thiophenol	509	91	31[35]	71/15
		511	62	31[39]	68/20, 1.5885
C_7	Benzyl mercaptan	506	72	31[2]	195
	m-Thiocresol	507	75	31[25]	107/50, 1.570[25]
	p-Methylthiophenol (p-thio-cresol)	509	82	31[38]	90/13, (43)
		510	75	31[34]	(43)
C_8	β-Phenylethyl mercaptan	506	70	31[2]	
	o-Ethylthiophenol	509	68	31[37]	208/730
C_9	o-n-Propylthiophenol	509	76	31[37]	220/730
	o-Isopropylthiophenol	509	70	31[37]	226/730
	p-Isopropylthiophenol	509	64	31[56]	104/14, 1.5542
C_{13}	Triphenylmethyl mercaptan	505	80	31[15]	(107)
		Dithiols			
C_2	Ethylene mercaptan (1,2-ethanedithiol)	506	62	31[51]	63/46
C_3	Trimethylene mercaptan	508	57	31[42]	110/120, 1.5380[21]
C_4	Tetramethylene mercaptan	506	85	31[14]	128/100, 1.5265[25]

TABLE 110. MERCAPTANS 783

TABLE 110 (*continued*)

C_n	Compound	Method	Yield (%)	Chapter[ref.]	B.p./mm., n_D^t, (M.p.)
		Dithiols (*continued*)			
C_5	Pentamethylene mercaptan	506	83	31[14]	147/100, 1.5194[25]
C_6	Hexamethylene mercaptan	506	63	31[2]	
C_7	Heptamethylene mercaptan	505	88	31[14]	178/100, 1.4950[25]
		Halo Mercaptans			
C_3	β-Chloropropyl mercaptan	51	69	31[33]	125/764, 1.4852
	γ-Bromopropyl mercaptan	52	53	31[18]	56/12
C_6	o-Bromothiophenol	507	80	31[26]	97/11
		507	55	31[54]	118/18, 1.6321[24]
	o-Iodothiophenol	507	40	31[26]	120/11
	m-Bromothiophenol	507	50	31[54]	120/21, 1.6310[25]
	p-Fluorothiophenol	511	26	31[40]	(162)
	p-Chlorothiophenol	509	50	31[7]	(53)
	p-Bromothiophenol	509	60	31[7]	(75)
		509	87	31[54]	(75)
C_7	m-Trifluoromethylthiophenol	511	84	31[55]	85/40
		Mercapto Alcohols, Ethers, and Ketones			
C_3	2-Methoxyethyl mercaptan	508	55	31[42]	112, 1.4488[23]
	β-Hydroxypropyl mercaptan	508	85	31[33]	51/12, 1.4862
	γ-Hydroxypropyl mercaptan	505	65	31[18]	82/10
		506	43	31[10]	75–80/7
		510	70	31[33]	80/1.2, 1.4952
	Mercaptoacetone	505	68	31[20]	(110)
C_4	β-Ethoxyethyl mercaptan	505	74	31[19]	126
C_5	β-Ethoxypropyl mercaptan	505	36	31[19]	134
C_6	β-Ethoxybutyl mercaptan	505	61	31[19]	157
C_7	p-Methoxythiophenol	507	79	31[57]	89/5, 1.5801[25]
C_8	2-Phenoxyethyl mercaptan	508	90	31[42]	134/29, 1.5597[23]
C_9	α-Mercapto-α-phenylacetone	508	80	31[48]	(110)
		Mercapto Acids and Esters			
C_3	β-Mercaptopropionic acid	506	72	31[9]	106/4, (17.5), 1.4910
C_4	Ethyl mercaptoacetate (ethyl thioglycolate)	285	89	31[44]	63/20
C_5	β-Mercaptovaleric acid	508	80	31[41]	109/4, 1.4784
	γ-Mercaptovaleric acid	508	85	31[41]	91/0.05, 1.4802
	δ-Mercaptovaleric acid	508	83	31[41]	111/0.8, (25), 1.4882
	Ethyl β-mercaptopropionate	285	79	31[43]	78/20
C_7	o-Carboxythiophenol (thio-salicylic acid)	510	84 †	31[53]	(164)
	m-Mercaptobenzoic acid	509	84	31[38]	(148)

For explanations and symbols see pp. xi–xii.

TABLE 110 (*continued*)

C_n	Compound	Method	Yield (%)	Chapter[ref.]	B.p./mm., n_D^t, (M.p.)
		Mercapto Amines and Nitro Compounds			
C_2	β-Aminoethyl mercaptan	....	97	31[47]	(98)
C_6	β-Diethylaminoethyl mer-	505	57	31[23]	64/21, 1.4680
	captan	514	48	31[45]	65/20
	o-Aminothiophenol	510	90	31[32]	(26)*
	p-Aminothiophenol	505	69	31[22]	145/17, (45)
	p-Nitrothiophenol	510	65	31[8]	(75)
C_8	β-Phenylaminoethyl mercaptan	514	52	31[46]	96/2.5, 1.6040
	p-Dimethylaminothiophenol	511	50	31[39]	122/2

For explanations and symbols see pp. xi-xii.

REFERENCES FOR CHAPTER 31

[1] Urquhart, Gates, and Connor, *Org. Syntheses*, **21**, 36 (1941); Vogel, *J. Chem. Soc.*, 1822 (1948); Backer and Dijkstra, *Rec. trav. chim.*, **51**, 290 (1932).

[2] Frank and Smith, *J. Am. Chem. Soc.*, **68**, 2103 (1946).

[3] Hackmann and Berkenbosch, *Rec. trav. chim.*, **68**, 752 (1949); cf. ref. 13.

[4] Busch and Schulz, *J. prakt. Chem.*, **150**, 173, 180 (1938).

[5] King and McMillan, *J. Am. Chem. Soc.*, **68**, 1369 (1946).

[6] Backer, *Rec. trav. chim.*, **54**, 216 (1935).

[7] Backer and Kramer, *Rec. trav. chim.*, **53**, 1102 (1934).

[8] Price and Stacy, *J. Am. Chem. Soc.*, **68**, 498 (1946).

[9] Baker et al., *J. Org. Chem.*, **12**, 171 (1947); Cheney and Piening, *J. Am. Chem. Soc.*, **67**, 733 (1945).

[10] Clinton et al., *J. Am. Chem. Soc.*, **67**, 594 (1945).

[11] Phillips and Shapiro, *J. Chem. Soc.*, 584 (1942).

[12] Kirner and Richter, *J. Am. Chem. Soc.*, **51**, 3134 (1929).

[13] Arndt, *Ber.*, **54**, 2236 (1921).

[14] Hall and Reid, *J. Am. Chem. Soc.*, **65**, 1466 (1943).

[15] Kharasch and Williams, *J. Am. Chem. Soc.*, **72**, 1843 (1950).

[16] Ellis and Reid, *J. Am. Chem. Soc.*, **54**, 1674 (1932); Hoffman and Reid, *ibid.*, **45**, 1831 (1923); Collin et al., *J. Soc. Chem. Ind. (London)*, **52**, 272T (1933).

[17] Thirtle, *J. Am. Chem. Soc.*, **68**, 342 (1946).

[18] Karjala and McElvain, *J. Am. Chem. Soc.*, **55**, 2969 (1933).

[19] Swallen and Boord, *J. Am. Chem. Soc.*, **52**, 655 (1930).

[20] Hromatka and Engel, *Monatsh.*, **78**, 32 (1948).

[21] Barkenbus, Friedman, and Flege, *J. Am. Chem. Soc.*, **49**, 2552 (1927).

[22] Gilman and Gainer, *J. Am. Chem. Soc.*, **71**, 1749 (1949).

[23] Gilman et al., *J. Am. Chem. Soc.*, **67**, 1846 (1945).

[24] Kramer and Reid, *J. Am. Chem. Soc.*, **43**, 887 (1921); Binz and Pence, *ibid.*, **61**, 3136 (1939).

[25] Tarbell and Fukushima, *Org. Syntheses*, **27**, 81 (1947).

[26] Schwarzenbach and Egli, *Helv. Chim. Acta*, **17**, 1177 (1934).

[27] Ipatieff and Friedman, *J. Am. Chem. Soc.*, **61**, 71 (1939); Jones and Reid, *ibid.*, **60**, 2452 (1938).

[28] Földi and Kollonitsch, *J. Chem. Soc.*, 1683 (1948); Heath and Lambert, *ibid.*, 1477 (1947).

[29] Gilman and Hewlett, *J. Am. Chem. Soc.*, **52**, 2142 (1930).

[30] Noller and Gordon, *J. Am. Chem. Soc.*, **55**, 1090 (1933).

[31] Stutz and Shriner, *J. Am. Chem. Soc.*, **55**, 1244 (1933).

[32] Bogert and Snell, *J. Am. Chem. Soc.*, **46**, 1309 (1924).

[33] Sjöberg, *Ber.*, **75**, 13 (1942).

[34] Strating and Backer, *Rec. trav. chim.*, **69**, 644 (1950).

[35] Adams and Marvel, *Org. Syntheses*, Coll. Vol. I, 504 (1941).

[36] Marvel and Caesar, *J. Am. Chem. Soc.*, **72**, 1033 (1950).

[37] Hansch and Blondon, *J. Am. Chem. Soc.*, **70**, 1561 (1948).

[38] Miescher and Billeter, *Helv. Chim. Acta*, **22**, 609, 610 (1939); cf. ref. 7.

[39] Gilman and Fullhart, *J. Am. Chem. Soc.*, **71**, 1480 (1949).

[40] Seyhan, *Ber.*, **72B**, 594 (1939).

[41] Schjanberg, *Ber.*, **74**, 1751 (1941).

[42] Chapman and Owen, *J. Chem. Soc.*, 579 (1950).

[43] Karrer and Schmid, *Helv. Chim. Acta*, **27**, 125 (1944).

[44] Baker et al., *J. Org. Chem.*, 12, 144 (1947).
[45] Gilman and Woods, *J. Am. Chem. Soc.*, 67, 1844 (1945).
[46] Snyder, Stewart, and Ziegler, *J. Am. Chem. Soc.*, 69, 2672 (1947).
[47] Barnett, *J. Chem. Soc.*, 6 (1944); Bogert et al., *J. Am. Chem. Soc.*, 62, 1177 (1940); 63, 2363 (1941); Bestian, *Ann.*, 566, 240 (1950).
[48] von Wacek, Kratzl, and Bezard, *Ber.*, 75, 1353 (1942).
[49] Kipnis, Levy, and Ornfelt, *J. Am. Chem. Soc.*, 71, 2270 (1949).
[50] Hill and Wolfrom, *J. Am. Chem. Soc.*, 69, 1539 (1947).
[51] Speziale, *Org. Syntheses*, 30, 35 (1950).
[52] Price and Stacy, *Org. Syntheses*, 28, 82 (1948), note 1.
[53] Allen and MacKay, *Org. Syntheses*, Coll. Vol. II, 580 (1943).
[54] Wilson and Tarbell, *J. Am. Chem. Soc.*, 72, 5203 (1950).
[55] Soper et al., *J. Am. Chem. Soc.*, 70, 2849 (1948).
[56] Gilman and Broadbent, *J. Am. Chem. Soc.*, 69, 2054 (1947).
[57] Suter and Hansen, *J. Am. Chem. Soc.*, 54, 4102 (1932).

32

Sulfides

CONTENTS

515. Alkylation of Mercaptans

$$\text{RSH} \xrightarrow{\text{NaOH}} \text{RSNa} \xrightarrow[\text{R}'_2\text{SO}_4]{\text{R}'\text{X or}} \text{RSR}'$$

This reaction is analogous to similar methods for the preparation of ethers (methods 115 and 116). Both simple and mixed sulfides may be made from aliphatic mercaptans or thiophenols. The sodium mercaptides are formed from the mercaptans and aqueous or alcoholic solutions of sodium hydroxide or alcoholic sodium ethoxide. Alkylation is effected by halides,[2-4, 9] alkyl sulfates,[5, 6] or esters of sulfonic acids.[11] The over-all yields of sulfides are usually above 70%. t-Butyl mercaptan is alkylated directly by t-butyl alcohol in strong sulfuric acid to give t-butyl sulfide in 87% yield.[9]

A variety of *other functional groups* may be present in either the halide or the mercaptan. Olefinic sulfides are obtained by the action of allyl halides on benzyl or phenyl mercaptides.[13, 15] Ethylene, trimethylene, and 1-pentene chlorohydrins give hydroxyalkyl sulfides, from which chloroalkyl sulfides are obtained by the Darzens procedure (method 53).[16-18] Phenacyl chloride gives keto sulfides of the type $C_6H_5COCH_2SR$.[22] Alkylmercapto acids are prepared from either halo acids or mercapto acids.[31, 33] In addition, halo,[30] alkoxyl,[21] carboxyl,[32] cyano,[23, 24] and nitro[28, 30] groups on aromatic nuclei have been present during the alkylation.

516. Action of Halides on Metallic Sulfides

$$2RX + Na_2S \longrightarrow RSR + 2NaX$$

Symmetrical sulfides are obtained in 70–90% yields by refluxing aqueous alcoholic solutions of halides with sodium sulfide.[2, 7] The nonahydrate of sodium sulfide is a satisfactory reagent for the reaction.[1, 12] Tetramethylene[12] and pentamethylene[27] halides give cyclic sulfides, e.g., tetramethylene sulfide (tetrahydrothiophene) (64%). Halides containing several other important functional groups have been employed. Typical examples include methallyl chloride,[14] and halides with hydroxyl,[19] ethoxyl,[20] carboxyl,[26] and diethylamino[25] groups in the *beta* position. A "dry" synthesis of phenyl sulfide from calcium oxide, sulfur, and chlorobenzene at 300° has been reported.[8]

517. Addition of Mercaptans to Olefinic Compounds

$$RCH{=}CH_2 + R'SH \left\{ \begin{array}{l} \xrightarrow{\text{H}_2\text{SO}_4} RCH(SR')CH_3 \\ \xrightarrow{\text{Peroxides}} RCH_2CH_2SR' \end{array} \right.$$

Mercaptans add to olefins according to Markownikoff's rule in the presence of sulfur[35] or sulfuric acid.[36] The mode of addition is reversed by peroxides.[35, 38] The yields of sulfides are generally in the range of 60–90%. Somewhat lower yields (50–60%) are obtained by the addition of mercaptans to vinyl chloride[38] and allyl alcohol.[37, 39, 42] Conjugated olefinic aldehydes,[40, 41] ketones,[9, 42] esters,[42, 44, 45, 69] and cyanides[42–45] add mercaptans and thiophenols in excellent yield. In certain cases the unsaturated compound may be converted directly to a symmetrical sulfide by addition of hydrogen sulfide[45] (cf. method 388).

$$CH_2{=}CHCN \xrightarrow{\text{H}_2\text{S}} HSCH_2CH_2CN \xrightarrow{CH_2=CHCN} S(CH_2CH_2CN)_2$$

These additions to the conjugated system are catalyzed by bases such as sodium hydroxide, sodium methoxide, tertiary amines, piperidine, and quaternary ammonium hydroxides. Cupric acetate catalyst is used in the conversion of acrolein to β-methylmercaptopropionaldehyde, $CH_3SCH_2CH_2CHO$ (84%).[40] The addition of mercaptans is analogous to the addition of alcohols to these systems (method 121). However, the thiol group is more active than the hydroxyl group, as is shown by the formation of β-(2-hydroxyethylmercapto)-propionitrile, $HOCH_2CH_2SCH_2CH_2CN$, from acrylonitrile and 2-mercaptoethanol, $HOCH_2CH_2SH$.[44]

518. Haloalkylation of Mercaptans

$$RSH + R'CHO + HX \rightarrow RSCHXR'$$

α-Halo sulfides are available from mercaptans by direct haloalkylation. Chloromethylation and bromomethylation of the simpler mercaptans is effected by shaking at $-15°$ with paraformaldehyde and hydrogen halide. The yields of halomethyl derivatives are 43-93%.[55-57] Somewhat lower yields (30-47%) are obtained when acetaldehyde is substituted for paraformaldehyde.[55]

519. Cleavage of Ethylene Oxide and Analogs

Ethylene oxide reacts with hydrogen sulfide at 45-60° to produce β-hydroxyethyl sulfide in 90% yield.[61] The reaction can be stopped at the mercaptan stage with excess hydrogen sulfide. Analogous reactions of ethylenimine[60] and ethylene sulfide[62] produce both the sulfides and substituted mercaptans. Cleavage of the ethylene oxide ring by mercaptans gives β-hydroxyethyl alkyl sulfides in 70-90% yields.[61]

520. Conversion of Oxides to Cyclic Sulfides

Thiourea or potassium or ammonium thiocyanates react with alkene oxides at room temperature in aqueous solution to give cyclic sulfides in 50—73% yields.[63, 64]

521. Decomposition of Diazosulfides[53]

$$ArN_2^+X^- \xrightarrow{RSNa} ArN = NSR \rightarrow ArSR$$

522. Action of Organometallic Compounds on Disulfides[58]

$$ArSSAr + C_6H_5Li \rightarrow ArSC_6H_5 + ArSLi$$

523. Action of Mercaptides on Lactones [59]

$$CH_2CH_2CH_2CO \xrightarrow[170^\circ]{CH_3SNa} CH_3SCH_2CH_2CH_2CO_2Na$$

(with the lactone oxygen bridging $CH_2CH_2CH_2CO$ and O)

524. Action of Sodium Sulfide on Dithiocyanates [65]

$$(CH_3)_2C(SCN)C(SCN)(CH_3)_2 \xrightarrow{Na_2S \cdot 9H_2O} (CH_3)_2C \overset{}{\underset{S}{\diagdown \diagup}} C(CH_3)_2 \quad (90\%)$$

TABLE 111. SULFIDES 791

TABLE 111. SULFIDES

C_n	Compound	Method	Yield (%)	Chapter[ref.]	B.p./mm., n_D^t, (M.p.)
	Aliphatic Sulfides				
C_2	Methyl sulfide	516	50	32^{12}	38
C_4	Ethyl sulfide	516	78	32^{12}	91
	Vinyl sulfide	20	25 †	32^{48}	84/759
C_5	Ethyl n-propyl sulfide	517	64	32^{36}	116/750, 1.4471
	bis-Ethylthiomethane	515	90	32^{55}	181/760
C_6	n-Butyl ethyl sulfide	515	78	32^{11}	144
	n-Propyl sulfide	516	85	32^7	142
C_8	t-Butyl sulfide	515	87	32^9	149
	Methallyl sulfide	516	75	32^{14}	173, 1.4862
	Cyclic Sulfides				
C_3	Propylene sulfide	520	70	32^{70}	75
C_4	Isobutylene sulfide	520	73	32^{64}	85, 1.4641
	Tetramethylene sulfide (cf. tetrahydrothiophene)	516	64	32^{12}	120, 1.5037 [21]
C_5	Pentamethylene sulfide	516	34	32^{27}	140/756, 1.5055
C_6	Tetramethylethylene sulfide	524	90	32^{65}	127, (77)
	Cyclohexene sulfide	520	60	32^{64}	85/46, 1.5292
	Aromatic and Heterocyclic Sulfides				
C_7	Phenyl methyl sulfide	515	76	32^5	192/761
	2-Thenyl ethyl sulfide	515	76	32^4	68/3
	α-Furfuryl ethyl sulfide	515	80	32^3	91/28, 1.5140
C_8	Phenyl ethyl sulfide	515	65	32^{11}	204
		515	92	32^5	69/6
	Methyl m-tolyl sulfide	515	90	32^6	110/31, 1.5736 [24]
C_9	Phenyl n-propyl sulfide	515	60	32^{36}	219/750, 1.5571
	Phenyl isopropyl sulfide	515	60	32^{36}	207/750, 1.5468
	Allyl phenyl sulfide	515	100	32^{15}	105/25, 1.4772
C_{10}	Phenethyl ethyl sulfide	515	81	32^9	96/4
	Phenyl t-butyl sulfide	517	70	32^{36}	73/5, 1.5335
	Allyl benzyl sulfide	515	83	32^{13}	118/13
C_{12}	Phenyl sulfide	....	83	32^{46}	163/18
C_{13}	Benzyl phenyl sulfide	515	60	32^2	(41)
C_{14}	Benzyl sulfide	516	83	32^2	(49)
C_{22}	α-Naphthylmethyl sulfide	516	90	32^1	(119)
	β-Naphthylmethyl sulfide	516	84	32^1	(127)
	Halo Sulfides				
C_2	Methyl chloromethyl sulfide	518	60	32^{57}	106/760
	Methyl bromomethyl sulfide	518	56	32^{55}	134/760

For explanations and symbols see pp. xi-xii.

TABLE 111 (continued)

C_n	Compound	Method	Yield (%)	Chapter[ref.]	B.p./mm., n_D^t, (M.p.)
		Halo Sulfides (continued)			
C_3	Methyl α-chloroethyl sulfide	518	30	32[55]	53/100
	β-Chloroethyl methyl sulfide	53	80	32[16]	44/20, 1.4902[30]
		53	85	32[34]	56/30
	Ethyl chloromethyl sulfide	518	60	32[57]	128/760
	Ethyl bromomethyl sulfide	518	44	32[55]	67/45
C_4	n-Propyl chloromethyl sulfide	518	93	32[57]	150/760
	γ-Chloropropyl methyl sulfide	53	75	32[16]	71/29, 1.4833[30]
	Ethyl α-chloroethyl sulfide	518	47	32[55]	39/24
	Ethyl β-chloroethyl sulfide	53	94	32[51]	70/51
C_5	t-Butyl chloromethyl sulfide	518	24	32[57]	58/12
C_6	1-Methylthiol-2-chloropentane	53	70	32[18]	85/20, 1.4860
C_7	Phenyl chloromethyl sulfide	518	50	32[55]	98/12
C_8	Benzyl chloromethyl sulfide	518	75	32[55]	138/25
	β-Chloroethyl phenyl sulfide	53	85	32[17]	101/4, 1.5838
C_9	γ-Chloropropyl phenyl sulfide	53	85	32[17]	117/4, 1.5752
C_{14}	p,p'-Dichlorobenzyl sulfide	516	86	32[1]	(41)
		Hydroxy and Alkoxy Sulfides			
C_3	β-Hydroxyethyl methyl sulfide	515	82	32[16]	69/20, 1.4867[30]
C_4	γ-Hydroxypropyl methyl sulfide	515	76	32[16]	94/17, 1.4832[30]
	Ethyl β-hydroxyethyl sulfide	519	70	32[61]	181
	β-Hydroxyethyl sulfide (thiodiglycol)	516	86	32[19]	165/20
		519	90	32[61]	146/7
C_5	Ethyl 2-hydroxypropyl sulfide	80	56	32[37]	77/15, 1.4734
	Ethyl 2-hydroxyisopropyl sulfide	517	59	32[37]	80–90/17, 1.4777
	Ethyl ethoxymethyl sulfide	115	50	32[56]	135/755
C_6	1-Methylthiol-2-pentanol	515	45	32[18]	90/18, 1.4792
C_7	p-Hydroxyphenyl methyl sulfide	97	55	32[21]	(84)
C_8	β-Hydroxyethyl phenyl sulfide	515	80	32[17]	141/11, 1.5870[22]
		519	78	32[61]	120/4
	β-Ethoxyethyl sulfide	516	51	32[20]	229
	p-Methoxyphenyl methyl sulfide	515	90	32[21]	100/4, (23)
C_9	γ-Hydroxypropyl phenyl sulfide	515	100	32[17]	135/2, 1.5813

TABLE 111. SULFIDES   793

TABLE 111 (continued)

C_n	Compound	Method	Yield (%)	Chapter[ref.]	B.p./mm., n_D^t, (M.p.)
		Aldo and Keto Sulfides			
C_4	β-Methylmercaptopropion-aldehyde	517	84	32[40]	53/11, 1.4850
C_6	β-Ethylmercaptobutyralde-hyde	517	60	32[41]	93/24, 1.4720
	β-Ethylmercaptoethyl methyl ketone	517	61	32[9]	79/10
C_9	Methyl phenacyl sulfide	515	88	32[22]	104/2, 1.5836
	p-Methylmercaptoaceto-phenone	178	70	32[49]	(80)
C_{10}	Ethyl phenacyl sulfide	515	87	32[22]	106/2, 1.5700
C_{11}	β-Ethylmercaptopropiophe-none	517	53	32[9]	(47)
		Carboxy and Carbalkoxy Sulfides			
C_4	Ethylmercaptoacetic acid	247	80	32[56]	118/11
	2-Methylmercaptopropionic acid	515	27	32[31]	106/8, 1.4815[25]
	3-Methylmercaptopropionic acid	515	88	32[31]	119–123/12, 1.4884[25]
C_5	γ-Methylmercaptobutyric acid	523	50	32[59]	128/5
	Methyl β-methylmercapto-propionate	517	84	32[42]	78/4, 1.4600[32]
		517	86	32[44]	81/15, 1.4646
C_8	Methyl β-thiodipropionate	517	81	32[69]	139/6, 1.4713[25]
	Diethyl thiodiglycolate	516	57	32[67]	115/5, 1.4619[26]
	3-Methylmercaptobenzoic acid	515	73	32[32]	(127)
C_{10}	Methyl β-phenylmercapto-propionate	517	96	32[44]	154/12, 1.5510
	Ethyl phenylmercaptoacetate	....	60	32[54]	148/12
		Cyano Sulfides			
C_4	β-Methylmercaptopropio-nitrile	517	91	32[44]	97/15, 1.4840
	Ethylmercaptoacetonitrile	378	45	32[56]	73/13
C_5	β-Ethylmercaptopropio-nitrile	517	83	32[44]	109/21, 1.4790
C_6	2-Cyanoethyl sulfide	517	93	32[45]	193/7
C_8	p-Methylmercaptobenzo-nitrile	380	52	32[50]	272/760, (64)

For explanations and symbols see pp. xi-xii.

TABLE 111 (continued)

C_n	Compound	Method	Yield (%)	Chapter[ref.]	B.p./mm., n_D^t, (M.p.)
		Cyano Sulfides (continued)			
C_9	Phenylmercaptopropio-nitrile	517	97	32[44]	154/8, 1.5735
	p-Cyanobenzyl methyl sulfide	515	85	32[24]	178/25
C_{10}	β-Methyl-β-phenylmercapto-propionitrile	517	89	32[43]	114/0.9, 1.5581
C_{16}	p-Cyanobenzyl sulfide	515	68	32[23]	(115)
		Amino and Nitro Sulfides			
C_3	Methyl 2-nitroethyl sulfide	517	80	32[68]	105/20
C_4	β-Aminoethyl sulfide	519	50	32[60]	131/22
C_8	Ethyl m-aminophenyl sulfide	425	80	32[52]	103/3
	Ethyl m-nitrophenyl sulfide	515	50 †	32[52]	117/3
C_{12}	β-Diethylaminoethyl sulfide	516	36	32[25]	
	2-Aminodiphenyl sulfide	515	46	32[28]	154–160/3, (33)
	4-Aminodiphenyl sulfide	425	89	32[30]	(95)
	2-Nitrodiphenyl sulfide	515	87	32[28]	(80)
	4-Nitrodiphenyl sulfide	515	86	32[30]	(55)
	p-Aminophenyl sulfide	425	82	32[47]	(111)
	p-Nitrophenyl sulfide	515	82	32[29]	(161)
		Other Sulfides			
C_3	Methylmercaptoacetyl chloride	335	45	32[31]	50/14, 1.4967[25]
C_4	Diacetyl sulfide	....	90	32[66]	63/20, 1.4810[21]
	2-Methylmercaptopropionyl chloride	335	52	32[31]	78/45, 1.4873[25]
	3-Methylmercaptopropionyl chloride	335	37	32[31]	97/45, 1.4941[25]
	Ethylmercaptoacetyl chloride	335	75	32[31]	63/14, 1.4888[25]
C_8	Phenylmercaptoacetyl chloride	335	93	32[31]	118/6, 1.5806[25]
C_{14}	Dibenzoyl sulfide	341	85	18[2]	(48)

For explanations and symbols see pp. xi–xii.

REFERENCES FOR CHAPTER 32

[1] Overberger, Ligthelm, and Swire, *J. Am. Chem. Soc.*, **72**, 2858 (1950).

[2] Shriner, Struck, and Jorison, *J. Am. Chem. Soc.*, **52**, 2066 (1930).

[3] Kirner and Richter, *J. Am. Chem. Soc.*, **51**, 3135 (1929).

[4] Kipnis and Ornfelt, *J. Am. Chem. Soc.*, **71**, 3571 (1949).

[5] Vogel, *J. Chem. Soc.*, 1822 (1948).

[6] Tarbell and Fukushima, *J. Am. Chem. Soc.*, **68**, 1458 (1946).

[7] Bost and Conn, *Org. Syntheses*, Coll. Vol. II, 547 (1943).

[8] Macallum, *J. Org. Chem.*, **13**, 154 (1948).

[9] Fehnel and Carmack, *J. Am. Chem. Soc.*, **71**, 92 (1949).

[10] Wood, *J. Am. Chem. Soc.*, **47**, 2062 (1925).

[11] Gilman and Beaber, *J. Am. Chem. Soc.*, **47**, 1449 (1925).

[12] Tarbell and Weaver, *J. Am. Chem. Soc.*, **63**, 2940 (1941).

[13] Backer and Jong, *Rec. trav. chim.*, **67**, 889 (1948).

[14] Tamele, Ott, Marple, and Hearne, *Ind. Eng. Chem.*, **33**, 116, 120 (1941).

[15] Hurd and Greengard, *J. Am. Chem. Soc.*, **52**, 3357 (1930).

[16] Windus and Shildneck, *Org. Syntheses*, Coll. Vol. II, 345 (1943); Kirner, *J. Am. Chem. Soc.*, **50**, 2451, 2452 (1928).

[17] Ford-Moore, Peters, and Wakelin, *J. Chem. Soc.*, 1755 (1949); Kirner and Richter, *J. Am. Chem. Soc.*, **51**, 3413 (1929).

[18] Glavis, Ryden, and Marvel, *J. Am. Chem. Soc.*, **59**, 709 (1937).

[19] Faber and Miller, *Org. Syntheses*, Coll. Vol. II, 576 (1943).

[20] Swallen and Boord, *J. Am. Chem. Soc.*, **52**, 657 (1930).

[21] Suter and Hansen, *J. Am. Chem. Soc.*, **54**, 4102 (1932).

[22] Prelog et al., *Helv. Chim. Acta*, **27**, 1214 (1944); Long, *J. Am. Chem. Soc.*, **68**, 2159 (1946).

[23] Barkenbus, Friedman, and Flege, *J. Am. Chem. Soc.*, **49**, 2551 (1927).

[24] Forrest, Fuller, and Walker, *J. Chem. Soc.*, 1503 (1948).

[25] Cook and Kreke, *J. Am. Chem. Soc.*, **61**, 2971 (1939).

[26] Bennett and Scorah, *J. Chem. Soc.*, 196 (1927).

[27] Naylor, *J. Chem. Soc.*, 1107 (1947).

[28] Tarbell et al., *J. Am. Chem. Soc.*, **70**, 1384 (1948); cf. ref. 30.

[29] Price and Stacy, *Org. Syntheses*, **28**, 82 (1948); *J. Am. Chem. Soc.*, **68**, 498 (1946).

[30] Gilman and Broadbent, *J. Am. Chem. Soc.*, **69**, 2055 (1947).

[31] Mooradian et al., *J. Am. Chem. Soc.*, **71**, 3372 (1949).

[32] Brand, Gabel, and Rosenkranz, *Ber.*, **70**, 305 (1937).

[33] Larsson and Jönsson, *Ber.*, **67**, 757 (1934); Karrer and Schmid, *Helv. Chim. Acta*, **27**, 121 (1944).

[34] Kirner and Windus, *Org. Syntheses*, Coll. Vol. II, 136 (1943).

[35] Jones and Reid, *J. Am. Chem. Soc.*, **60**, 2452 (1938).

[36] Ipatieff, Pines, and Friedman, *J. Am. Chem. Soc.*, **60**, 2731 (1938); Ipatieff and Friedman, *ibid.*, **61**, 71 (1939).

[37] Fuson, Price, and Burness, *J. Org. Chem.*, **11**, 475 (1946).

[38] Fuson and Ziegler, *J. Org. Chem.*, **11**, 510 (1946).

[39] Fuson and Koehneke, *J. Org. Chem.*, **14**, 707 (1949).

[40] Pierson, Giella, and Tishler, *J. Am. Chem. Soc.*, **70**, 1450 (1948).

[41] Hall and Howe, *J. Chem. Soc.*, 2723 (1949).

[42] Szabo and Stiller, *J. Am. Chem. Soc.*, **70**, 3667 (1948).

[43] Ross, *J. Am. Chem. Soc.*, **71**, 3458 (1949).

44 Hurd and Gershbein, *J. Am. Chem. Soc.*, **69**, 2328 (1947).
45 Gershbein and Hurd, *J. Am. Chem. Soc.*, **69**, 241 (1947).
46 Hartman, Smith, and Dickey, *Org. Syntheses*, Coll. Vol. II, 242 (1943).
47 Price, Leonard, and Stacy, *J. Am. Chem. Soc.*, **69**, 856 (1947).
48 Ruigh and Erickson, *J. Am. Chem. Soc.*, **61**, 916 (1939).
49 King, McWhirter, and Rowland, *J. Am. Chem. Soc.*, **70**, 241 (1948).
50 Buu-Hoi and Lecocq, *Bull. soc. chim. France*, (5) **13**, 142, 476 (1946).
51 Mohler and Sorge, *Helv. Chim. Acta*, **23**, 1210 (1940).
52 Donleavy and English, *J. Am. Chem. Soc.*, **62**, 2965 (1940).
53 Miller, Crossley, and Moore, *J. Am. Chem. Soc.*, **64**, 2322 (1942).
54 Müller and Freytag, *J. prakt. Chem.*, **146**, 56 (1936).
55 Böhme, Fischer, and Frank, *Ann.*, **563**, 62 (1949).
56 Böhme, *Ber.*, **69**, 1610 (1936).
57 Walter, Goodson, and Fosbinder, *J. Am. Chem. Soc.*, **67**, 655 (1945).
58 Schönberg et al., *Ber.*, **66**, 237 (1933).
59 Plieninger, *Chem. Ber.*, **83**, 267 (1950).
60 Nathan and Bogert, *J. Am. Chem. Soc.*, **63**, 2363 (1941).
61 Woodward, *J. Chem. Soc.*, 1892 (1948); Nenitzescu and Scarlatescu, *Ber.*, **68**, 587 (1935); Gilman and Fullhart, *J. Am. Chem. Soc.*, **71**, 1478 (1949).
62 Meade and Woodward, *J. Chem. Soc.*, 1894 (1948).
63 Culvenor, Davies, and Pausacker, *J. Chem. Soc.*, 1050 (1946).
64 Snyder, Stewart, and Ziegler, *J. Am. Chem. Soc.*, **69**, 2674 (1947).
65 Youtz and Perkins, *J. Am. Chem. Soc.*, **51**, 3510 (1929).
66 Bonner, *J. Am. Chem. Soc.*, **72**, 4270 (1950).
67 Overberger, Mallon, and Fine, *J. Am. Chem. Soc.*, **72**, 4959 (1950).
68 Heath and Lambert, *J. Chem. Soc.*, 1477 (1947).
69 Fehnel and Carmack, *Org. Syntheses*, **30**, 65 (1950).
70 Davies and Savige, *J. Chem. Soc.*, 320 (1950).

33

Disulfides

CONTENTS

525. Oxidation of Mercaptans and Related Compounds

$$2RSH + H_2O_2 \longrightarrow RSSR + 2H_2O$$

Sulfhydryl compounds are oxidized with ease to disulfides. It is necessary to employ mild oxidizing agents that do not attack the product. Oxidation of an alkaline solution of n-amyl mercaptan by iodine is described for n-amyl disulfide (68%).[11] A mixed disulfide, ethyl t-butyl disulfide, is obtained in 63% yield by treatment of an equimolecular mixture of ethyl and t-butyl mercaptans with iodine in ethanol.[1] Hydrogen peroxide is probably the best reagent for the oxidation.[3-5] Halo and amino groups in the molecule are unaffected. Benzoyl disulfide, $C_6H_5COSSCOC_6H_5$, is conveniently prepared by the iodine oxidation of the potassium salt of thiobenzoic acid, C_6H_5COSK.[6]

526. Decomposition of Alkyl Thiosulfates

$$2RSSO_3Na \longrightarrow RSSR + SO_2 + Na_2SO_4$$

Sodium thiosulfate reacts with alkyl halides to form salts of the type $RSSO_3Na$ (Bunte salts). Alkyl disulfides may be obtained from these salts by pyrolysis[9] or reaction with iodine or hydrogen peroxide.[7] The yields range from 47% to 69%. Cyano and carboxyl groups do not interfere.[8] Benzoylation of sodium thiosulfate produces benzoyl disulfide in 58% yield.[10]

527. Alkylation of Sodium Disulfide

$$2RX + Na_2S_2 \rightarrow RSSR + 2NaX$$

Alkylation of an ethanolic solution of sodium sulfide containing an equivalent amount of dissolved sulfur produces disulfides in 60–80% yields from alkyl[11] or o- and p-nitrophenyl halides.[14] Cyclic disulfides are prepared by alkylation with 1,3-dihalides.[12] Hydroxyl[13] and nitro[15] groups do not interfere. Alkylation of a solution of sodium sulfide containing 2–5 equivalents of sulfur produces polysulfides.

528. Reduction of Sulfonyl Halides [16–19]

$$2RSO_2Cl \xrightarrow{HI} RSSR$$

TABLE 112. DISULFIDES 799

TABLE 112. DISULFIDES

C_n	Compound	Method	Yield (%)	Chapter[ref.]	B.p./mm., n_D^t, (M.p.)
C_2	Methyl disulfide	528	26	33[19]	108/748
C_3	Trimethylene disulfide	526	60	33[20]	
C_4	Ethyl disulfide	528	54	33[19]	152/736
	2-Chloroethyl disulfide	525	94	33[5]	98/0.4, 1.5656
	β-Aminoethyl disulfide dihydrochloride	525	80	33[4]	(217)
	Dithiodiacetic acid	526	50	33[8]	(106)
C_6	Ethyl t-butyl disulfide	525	63	33[1]	60/11
	Allyl disulfide	525	70	33[1]	59/5
	γ-Hydroxypropyl disulfide	527	60	33[13]	160/0.8
	α,α-Dithiodipropionic acid	526	57	33[8]	
	β,β-Dithiodipropionic acid	526	80	33[8]	(154)
C_8	n-Butyl disulfide	526	47	33[9]	123/30, 1.4926
		528	52	33[19]	229/735
	γ,γ-Dithiodibutyronitrile	526	70	33[8]	1.606
C_{10}	n-Amyl disulfide	525	68	33[11]	102/2, 1.4868[25]
		527	80	33[11]	91/1, 1.4875[25]
C_{12}	o-Aminophenyl disulfide	525	65	33[2]	(93)
	p-Aminophenyl disulfide	525	64	33[3]	(76)
	o-Nitrophenyl disulfide	527	66	33[14]	(195)
	m-Nitrophenyl disulfide	528	80	33[16]	(82)
	p-Nitrophenyl disulfide	527	68	33[15]	(180)
C_{14}	m-Carboxyphenyl disulfide	528	85	33[17]	(246)
	p-Cyanophenyl disulfide	528	66	33[18]	(173)
	Benzoyl disulfide	525	73	33[6]	(130)
		526	58	33[10]	(135)

For explanations and symbols see pp. xi–xii.

REFERENCES FOR CHAPTER 33

[1] Small, Bailey, and Cavallito, *J. Am. Chem. Soc.*, 69, 1711 (1947).
[2] Bogert and Snell, *J. Am. Chem. Soc.*, 46, 1309 (1924).
[3] Price and Stacy, *Org. Syntheses*, 28, 14 (1948).
[4] Barnett, *J. Chem. Soc.*, 7 (1944); Nathan and Bogert, *J. Am. Chem. Soc.*, 63, 2363 (1941).
[5] Fuson et al., *J. Org. Chem.*, 11, 491 (1946).
[6] Frank and Blegen, *Org. Syntheses*, 28, 16 (1948).
[7] Westlake and Dougherty, *J. Am. Chem. Soc.*, 64, 149 (1942).
[8] Stoner and Dougherty, *J. Am. Chem. Soc.*, 63, 987 (1941).
[9] Stutz and Shriner, *J. Am. Chem. Soc.*, 55, 1243 (1933); cf. ref. 7.
[10] Westlake and Dougherty, *J. Am. Chem. Soc.*, 67, 1861 (1945).
[11] Miller, Crossley, and Moore, *J. Am. Chem. Soc.*, 64, 2323 (1942).
[12] Backer and Evenhuis, *Rec. trav. chim.*, 56, 129 (1937).
[13] Sjöberg, *Ber.*, 75, 26 (1942).
[14] Elgersma, *Rec. trav. chim.*, 48, 752 (1929); Bogert and Stull, *Org. Syntheses*, Coll. Vol. I, 220 (1941).
[15] Schreiber and Shriner, *J. Am. Chem. Soc.*, 56, 115 (1934); cf. ref. 14.
[16] Foss et al., *J. Am. Chem. Soc.*, 60, 2729 (1938).
[17] Brand, Gabel, and Rosenkranz, *Ber.*, 70, 304 (1937).
[18] Bauer and Cymerman, *J. Chem. Soc.*, 3434 (1949).
[19] Hunter and Sorenson, *J. Am. Chem. Soc.*, 54, 3364 (1932).
[20] Affleck and Dougherty, *J. Org. Chem.*, 15, 865 (1950).

34

Sulfoxides and Sulfones

529. Oxidation of Sulfides

$$RSR' \xrightarrow{(O)} RSOR' \xrightarrow{(O)} RSO_2R'$$

The best general reagent for this oxidation is 30% hydrogen peroxide.[1-8] Sulfoxides are isolated in 60–90% yields when a limited quantity of reagent is used in acetone or acetic acid solution at room temperature. With more peroxide and sometimes higher temperatures the yields of sulfones are equally high. In acetic acid solution, the active oxidizing agent is peracetic acid.[10] This reagent is improved by substituting a part of the acetic acid by acetic anhydride.[10, 15] Other oxidizing agents that sometimes give good results include chromic anhydride,[3, 7] perbenzoic acid,[4] and potassium permanganate.[2, 18] Symmetrical sulfoxides and sulfones form a continuous series of mixed crystals.[2]

Hydrogen peroxide attacks the sulfur atom in preference to the double bond in allyl phenyl sulfide and allyl benzyl sulfide to give allyl phenyl sulfoxide (64%)[5] and allyl benzyl sulfone (85%),[9] respectively. *Olefinic sulfones* may also be obtained by dehydrohalogenation of β-haloalkyl *sulfones* prepared by this method.[6, 12, 20] Oxidation of sulfides has been utilized in the preparation of sulfones containing other common functional groups such as the *amide*,[14, 15] *nitro*,[13, 14, 16, 19] *amino*,[18] and *ester*[17] groups.

530. Sulfones by the Alkylation of Sulfinates

$$RSO_2Na \xrightarrow[R'_2SO_4]{R'X \text{ or}} RSO_2R'$$

Salts of sulfinic acids are converted to sulfones by the action of primary,[22, 23] secondary,[23] and benzyl halides,[3] alkyl sulfates,[23] and aryl halides in which the halogen atoms are activated by nitro groups in the *ortho* or *para* positions.[24, 25] The reaction fails with *t*-amyl halide.[21] The yields vary widely, depending upon the nature of the reactants. From salts of benzenesulfinic acid and simple alkylating agents, sulfones are produced in 50–90% yields. Satisfactory results have been obtained when the aryl sulfinic acid contains nitro, cyano, and acetamido groups. Keto sulfones are made in 48–62% yields by alkylation with α-halo ketones.[20]

531. Sulfonation of Aromatic Hydrocarbons

$$ArH + H_2SO_4 \longrightarrow ArSO_3H + H_2O$$

$$ArSO_3H + Ar'H \longrightarrow ArSO_2Ar' + H_2O$$

Sulfones are often produced as by-products in the sulfonation of aromatic hydrocarbons (method 540). Aromatic hydrocarbons react with sulfonic acids less readily than with sulfuric acid. The success of the reaction depends upon the removal of the water as it is formed. An automatic water separator is used in the conversion of a refluxing mixture of benzene and sulfuric acid to diphenyl sulfone (80%).[31] A similar technique has been employed in the preparation of unsymmetrical sulfones. The vapor of an aromatic hydrocarbon is passed through the sulfonic acid at 150–200°, and water is removed by the excess hydrocarbon vapor.[30, 32] Chlorobenzene has been substituted for the aromatic hydrocarbon in this reaction. Intermolecular migration of the sulfonic acid group occurs in some cases.

532. Diaryl Sulfoxides and Sulfones by the Friedel-Crafts Reaction

$$2ArH + SOCl_2 \xrightarrow{AlCl_3} ArSOAr + 2HCl \quad \text{when } Ar = C_6H_5 \quad (51\%)^{[1, 3, 26]}$$

$$ArH + Ar'SO_2Cl \xrightarrow{AlCl_3} ArSO_2Ar' + HCl \quad (47–79\%)^{[27, 28]}$$

533. Addition of Sulfur Dioxide to Dienes

$$RCH = CRC(R) = CHR \xrightarrow{SO_2} \begin{array}{c} RC = CR \\ | \quad\quad | \\ RHC \quad CHR \\ \diagdown \diagup \\ SO_2 \end{array} \quad (50–85\%)^{[29]}$$

534. Action of Grignard Compounds on Sulfonyl Halides and Sulfonates [33-35]

$$ \left. \begin{array}{l} ArSO_2Cl \\ ArSO_3Ar' \end{array} \right\} \xrightarrow{\ Ar''MgX\ } ArSO_2Ar'' $$

TABLE 113. SULFOXIDES AND SULFONES

C_n	Compound	Method	Yield (%)	Chapter[ref.]	B.p./mm., n_D^t, (M.p.)
		Sulfoxides			
C_2	Dimethyl sulfoxide	529	50	34[1]	86/25
C_4	Diethyl sulfoxide	529	70	34[1]	84/12
	Tetramethylene sulfoxide	529	90	34[1]	106/12, 1.5198[23]
	bis-β-Aminoethyl sulfoxide	529	97	34[18]	
C_9	Ethyl benzyl sulfoxide	529	60	34[4]	(49)
	Allyl phenyl sulfoxide	529	64	34[5]	104/0.36, 1.5765[25]
C_{12}	Diphenyl sulfoxide	532	51	34[26]	(71)
C_{13}	Benzyl phenyl sulfoxide	529	69	34[3]	(123)
C_{14}	Dibenzyl sulfoxide	529	75	34[3]	(133)
		Sulfones			
C_3	Methyl vinyl sulfone	20	62	34[6]	116/19
	Chloromethyl ethyl sulfone	529	80	34[4]	128/14, (33)
C_4	Tetramethylene sulfone	529	97	34[1]	(11)
	Vinyl ethyl sulfone	20	79	34[20]	106/8
	Divinyl sulfone	20	85	34[12]	99/7
C_5	Allyl vinyl sulfone	20	63	34[5]	119/10, 1.4815[25]
	Ethoxymethyl ethyl sulfone	529	95	34[4]	122/13
C_7	Phenyl methyl sulfone	530	75	34[23]	(88)
	n-Butylsulfonylacetone	530	62	34[20]	137/4
	Methyl p-aminophenyl sulfone	530	49 †	34[22]	(134)
	Methyl p-nitrophenyl sulfone	529	84	34[19]	(143)
C_8	Phenyl ethyl sulfone	530	80	34[23]	(42)
	Phenyl vinyl sulfone	20	79	34[12]	(69)
	Phenyl 2-chloroethyl sulfone	529	79	34[12]	(55)
C_9	Ethyl benzyl sulfone	529	80	34[4]	(84)
	Phenyl n-propyl sulfone	530	80	34[23]	(46)
	Phenyl isopropyl sulfone	530	80	34[23]	145–150/1
	Allyl phenyl sulfone	530	53	34[5]	112/0.5, 1.5460[25]
	Ethyl p-cyanophenyl sulfone	530	94	34[22]	(95)
C_{10}	Phenyl n-butyl sulfone	530	80	34[23]	165–170/1
	s-Butyl phenyl sulfone	529	78	34[5]	114/0.2, 1.5271[25]
	Allyl benzyl sulfone	529	85	34[9]	(64)
	Crotyl phenyl sulfone	529	43	34[5]	108/0.1, 1.5421[25]
C_{12}	Diphenyl sulfone	531	80	34[31]	(128)
		532	82	34[27]	(124)
		534	35	34[33]	
	p,p'-Dichlorodiphenyl sulfone	531	42	34[30]	(149)
	p-Aminophenyl phenyl sulfone	425	68	34[16]	(175)
	p-Nitrophenyl phenyl sulfone	529	98	34[16]	(143)

TABLE 113. SULFOXIDES AND SULFONES 805

TABLE 113 (*continued*)

C_n	Compound	Method	Yield (%)	Chapter[ref.]	B.p./mm., n_D^t, (M.p.)
		Sulfones (*continued*)			
C_{12}	*p,p'*-Diaminodiphenyl sulfone	425	77	34[25]	(176)
		435	78	34[30]	(177)
C_{13}	Phenyl benzyl sulfone	530	52	34[3]	(146)
	Phenyl *p*-tolyl sulfone	534	33	34[33]	
		534	44	34[34]	
C_{14}	Dibenzyl sulfone	529	98	34[11]	(153)
	Di-*p*-tolyl sulfone	531	80	34[32]	(158)
		534	45	34[34]	
C_{18}	Dimesityl sulfone	532	75	34[28]	(204)

For explanations and symbols see pp. xi–xii.

REFERENCES FOR CHAPTER 34

[1] Tarbell and Weaver, *J. Am. Chem. Soc.*, **63**, 2941 (1941).

[2] Rheinboldt and Giesbrecht, *J. Am. Chem. Soc.*, **68**, 973 (1946).

[3] Shriner, Struck, and Jorison, *J. Am. Chem. Soc.*, **52**, 2060 (1930).

[4] Böhme, *Ber.*, **69**, 1610 (1936).

[5] Cope, Morrison, and Field, *J. Am. Chem. Soc.*, **72**, 59 (1950).

[6] Buckley, Charlish, and Rose, *J. Chem. Soc.*, 1515 (1947).

[7] Overberger, Ligthelm, and Swire, *J. Am. Chem. Soc.*, **72**, 2858 (1950).

[8] Klenk, Suter, and Archer, *J. Am. Chem. Soc.*, **70**, 3848 (1948).

[9] Backer and de Jong, *Rec. trav. chim.*, **67**, 890 (1948).

[10] Swern, *Chem. Revs.*, **45**, 33, 35 (1949).

[11] Arbusow, *J. prakt. Chem.*, **131**, 368 (1931); cf. ref. 3.

[12] Ford-Moore, Peters, and Wakelin, *J. Chem. Soc.*, 1756 (1949).

[13] Heath and Lambert, *J. Chem. Soc.*, 1479 (1947).

[14] Raiziss et al., *J. Am. Chem. Soc.*, **61**, 2764 (1939).

[15] Pomerantz and Connor, *J. Am. Chem. Soc.*, **61**, 3388 (1939).

[16] Gilman and Broadbent, *J. Am. Chem. Soc.*, **69**, 2056 (1947).

[17] Hurd and Gershbein, *J. Am. Chem. Soc.*, **69**, 2334 (1947).

[18] Barnett, *J. Chem. Soc.*, 5 (1944).

[19] Waldron and Reid, *J. Am. Chem. Soc.*, **45**, 2405 (1923).

[20] Fehnel and Carmack, *J. Am. Chem. Soc.*, **71**, 237 (1949).

[21] Ipatieff, Pines, and Friedman, *J. Am. Chem. Soc.*, **60**, 2731 (1938).

[22] Fuller, Tonkin, and Walker, *J. Chem. Soc.*, 636 (1945).

[23] Baldwin and Robinson, *J. Chem. Soc.*, 1447 (1932).

[24] Shriner and Greenlee, *J. Org. Chem.*, **4**, 247 (1939).

[25] Ferry, Buck, and Baltzly, *Org. Syntheses*, **22**, 30 (1942).

[26] Schönberg, *Ber.*, **56**, 2275 (1923); cf. refs. 1 and 3.

[27] Buehler and Masters, *J. Org. Chem.*, **4**, 262 (1939); Beckurts and Otto, *Ber.*, **11**, 2066 (1878).

[28] Maclean and Adams, *J. Am. Chem. Soc.*, **55**, 4685 (1933).

[29] Backer and Strating, *Rec. trav. chim.*, **53**, 525 (1934); Backer, Strating, and Kool, *ibid.*, **58**, 778 (1939); Grummitt, Ardis, and Fick, *J. Am. Chem. Soc.*, **72**, 5167 (1950).

[30] Heymann and Fieser, *J. Am. Chem. Soc.*, **67**, 1982 (1945).

[31] Fouque and Lacroix, *Bull. soc. chim. France*, (4) **33**, 180 (1923).

[32] Meyer, *Ann.*, **433**, 336 (1923).

[33] Gilman and Fothergill, *J. Am. Chem. Soc.*, **51**, 3506 (1929).

[34] Gilman, Beaber, and Meyers, *J. Am. Chem. Soc.*, **47**, 2050 (1925).

[35] Hepworth and Clapham, *J. Chem. Soc.*, 1192 (1921).

35

Sulfinic Acids

CONTENTS

535. Reduction of Sulfonyl Halides

$$2RSO_2Cl \xrightarrow{Zn} (RSO_2)_2Zn \xrightarrow{Na_2CO_3} 2RSO_2Na$$

Zinc salts of sulfinic acids are formed by reduction of sulfonyl chlorides by zinc and hot water. The zinc salts may be converted to sodium salts by the action of sodium carbonate. Over-all yields of the sodium salts of p-toluenesulfinic acid[3] and 2-dibenzofuransulfinic acid[4] are 64-67%. Equally good results have been obtained by reduction of sulfonyl halides with aqueous sodium sulfite.[1,2,9] Complete reduction to sulfhydryl compounds occurs with certain reducing agents (method 509).

536. Action of Sulfur Dioxide on Diazonium Salts

$$ArN_2^+SO_4H^- + 2SO_2 + 2H_2O \xrightarrow{Cu} ArSO_2H + N_2 + 2H_2SO_4$$

The replacement of the amino group by the sulfinic acid group on an aromatic nucleus is effected by treating the corresponding diazonium sulfate with sulfur dioxide in the presence of copper catalyst (Gattermann).[10] Copper bronze, powder, and paste have been used; the last is obtained by decomposing copper sulfate with zinc dust.[7] The sulfinic acids may be isolated as the ferric[8] or sodium[5] salts. The yields are often excellent (74-92%). Surprising exceptions are the lower yields sometimes obtained for *meta*- and *para*-substituted acids compared with the corresponding *ortho* isomers.[5,10]

537. Action of Organometallic Compounds on Sulfur Dioxide

$$2RMgX \xrightarrow{2SO_2} (RSO_2)_2Mg \xrightarrow{H^+} 2RSO_2H$$

Magnesium salts of aliphatic sulfinic acids are conveniently prepared in high yield by passing sulfur dioxide into a rapidly stirred, cooled, Grignard reagent.[11-13] Excess sulfur dioxide should be avoided.[12] The magnesium salts are readily converted to the corresponding sodium salts by treatment with sodium carbonate or sodium hydroxide,[13] or to the free sulfinic acids by the action of dilute mineral acid.[12, 13] 1-Dodecanesulfinic acid is more stable than lower-molecular-weight aliphatic sulfinic acids.[12]

538. Reaction of Aromatic Compounds with Sulfur Dioxide (Friedel-Crafts)

$$ArH + SO_2 \xrightarrow{AlCl_3} ArSO_2H \quad (75-94\%)^{6, 14}$$

539. Cleavage of Ethylene Disulfones

$$RSO_2CH_2CH_2SO_2R + 2KCN \longrightarrow 2RSO_2K + NCCH_2CH_2CN \quad (72-80\%)^{12, 15}$$

TABLE 114. SULFINIC ACIDS   809

TABLE 114. SULFINIC ACIDS

C_n	Compound	Method	Yield (%)	Chapter[ref.]	(M.p.)
C_4	1-Butanesulfinic acid (Mg salt)	537	69	35[13]	
	1-Butanesulfinic acid (Na salt)	539	72	35[15]	
C_6	Benzenesulfinic acid	536	86	35[10]	
		536	100	35[8]	
		538	80	35[14]	(83)
	p-Fluorobenzenesulfinic acid (Na salt)	538	75	35[6]	
	p-Chlorobenzenesulfinic acid	535	81	35[1]	(99)
		538	38	35[14]	(99)
	p-Bromobenzenesulfinic acid	538	56	35[14]	(114)
C_7	o-Toluenesulfinic acid	536	90	35[10]	
		536	80	35[10]	(86) *
		538	94	35[14]	(84)
	p-Toluenesulfinic acid (Na salt)	535	64	35[3]	
	o-Methoxybenzenesulfinic acid	536	90	35[10]	(99)
	p-Methoxybenzenesulfinic acid	536	50	35[10]	(98)
C_8	1-Octanesulfinic acid (Mg salt)	537	42	35[13]	
	p-Acetaminobenzenesulfinic acid	535	47 †	35[2]	(155)
C_{10}	α-Naphthalenesulfinic acid	536	74	35[10]	(85)
		538	62	35[14]	(85)
C_{12}	1-Dodecanesulfinic acid	537	77	35[12]	(30)
	2-Dibenzofuransulfinic acid (Na salt)	535	67	35[4]	

For explanations and symbols see pp. xi–xii.

REFERENCES FOR CHAPTER 35

[1] Kulka, *J. Am. Chem. Soc.*, 72, 1216 (1950).

[2] Smiles and Bere, *Org. Syntheses*, Coll. Vol. I, 7 (1941).

[3] Whitmore and Hamilton, *Org. Syntheses*, Coll. Vol. I, 492 (1941).

[4] Gilman, Smith, and Oatfield, *J. Am. Chem. Soc.*, 56, 1413 (1934).

[5] Todd and Shriner, *J. Am. Chem. Soc.*, 56, 1383 (1934).

[6] Hann, *J. Am. Chem. Soc.*, 57, 2166 (1935).

[7] Silvester and Wynne, *J. Chem. Soc.*, 693 (1936).

[8] Thomas, *J. Chem. Soc.*, 342 (1909).

[9] Krishna and Singh, *J. Am. Chem. Soc.*, 50, 794 (1928).

[10] Gattermann, *Ber.*, 32, 1136 (1899).

[11] Houlton and Tartar, *J. Am. Chem. Soc.*, 60, 544 (1938).

[12] Marvel and Johnson, *J. Org. Chem.*, 13, 822 (1948).

[13] Allen, *J. Org. Chem.*, 7, 23 (1942).

[14] Knoevenagel and Kenner, *Ber.*, 41, 3315 (1908).

[15] Ziegler and Connor, *J. Am. Chem. Soc.*, 62, 2596 (1940).

36

Sulfonic Acids

CONTENTS

540. Direct Sulfonation

$$ArH + H_2SO_4 \rightleftharpoons ArSO_3H + H_2O$$

Sulfonation of aromatic hydrocarbons is usually accomplished by treating with sulfuric acid, preferably containing 5-20% sulfur trioxide to remove the water formed in the reaction. Other sulfonating agents are generally less satisfactory. Sulfur trioxide[14, 30] gives sulfones as by-products, and chlorosulfonic acid frequently produces sulfonyl chlorides rather than sulfonic acids (method 550). Sulfonation by these and ten additional reagents has been extensively reviewed.[10-14] The sulfonation reaction is reversible (method 15). Catalysts such as boron trifluoride,[3] mercury,[1, 19] and vanadium salts[20] are used for compounds that sulfonate with difficulty. For example, benzene is readily sulfonated at room temperature to the monosulfonic acid[8, 18] and at 70-90° to m-benzenedisulfonic acid (90%).[17] Finally, at 275° with 15% oleum and a mercury catalyst, sodium m-benzenedisulfonate is converted to 1,3,5-benzenetrisulfonic acid (73%).[1] Intra- and inter-molecular migration of alkyl and halo groups may occur in the sulfonation of polymethylated or halogenated benzenes (Jacobsen reaction, method 16).[6, 9]

Sulfonation of naphthalene at 40° gives chiefly the α-sulfonic acid; above 160° the *beta* isomer is formed.[7, 8] The mono-, di-, and polysulfonation of naphthalene and alkylnaphthalenes has been extensively studied.[2] From phenanthrene and concentrated sulfuric acid at 120°, low yields of the 2- and 3-sulfonated derivatives are obtained. The product is separated by crystallization of the sodium, barium, and potassium salts.[5] Substitution in the 1-position of anthracene is highly favored by sulfur trioxide in pyridine.[35]

Most heterocyclic nuclei undergo the sulfonation reaction. Sulfonation of pyridine is difficult. The yield of 3-pyridinesulfonic acid by sulfonation at 390° with oleum is only 13%. The yield is greatly improved by the use of vanadium or mercury salts as catalysts. A critical study of the factors influencing the yield has been made, and a maximum yield of 71% is reported.[20] Fuming sulfuric acid converts quinoline to practically pure 8-quinolinesulfonic acid (54%).[21] The action of concentrated sulfuric acid on dibenzofuran gives 2-dibenzofuransulfonic acid (75%).[22]

Although aliphatic and alicyclic hydrocarbons react with most sulfonating agents, the reactions are not suitable for the preparation of the pure sulfonic acids.[4, 11] Certain olefins react with sulfur dioxide-dioxane complex to give *olefinic sulfonic acids*.[23] In this way, cyclohexene is converted to 1-cyclohexene-3-sulfonic acid,[25] whereas with concentrated sulfuric acid in a mixture of acetic acid and acetic anhydride the main product is 2-hydroxycyclohexanesulfonic acid.[26] 1-Propene-1-sulfonic acid is obtained in low yield by the action of oleum on *n*- or isopropyl alcohol.[24]

Aliphatic carboxylic acids may be sulfonated directly to *sulfocarboxylic acids* in which the sulfonic acid group is on the α-carbon atom. Better results are sometimes obtained by sulfonation of the corresponding alkylmalonic acid followed by decarboxylation.[42] Sulfonation of propionic anhydride with pyrosulfuric acid gives α-sulfopropionic acid (75%).[43] Several simple olefinic acids containing a sulfonic acid group in the α-position have been made by direct sulfonation of α,β-olefinic acids or β-halo acids.[40] In the latter case, dehydrohalogenation accompanies sulfonation.

Several *other functional groups* may be present on the aromatic nucleus during the sulfonation reaction,[11] including halo,[10, 28, 29] hydroxyl,[19] phenoxyl,[27] carboxyl,[19] and amino[31-34] groups. Sulfonations of aniline and of dimethylaniline take place by different mechanisms.[32]

541. Oxidation of Thiols and Related Compounds

$$RSH \xrightarrow{\text{(O)}} RSO_3H$$

The end product of the oxidation of mercaptans, sulfides, disulfides, sulfoxides, sulfones, etc., is a sulfonic acid. From a preparative standpoint the mercaptan is the most important of the source materials. Oxidations by potassium permanganate,[56] chromic anhydride,[56] bromine water,[57] hydrogen peroxide,[60] and nitric acid[58] are reported. Best results are obtained by the action of nitric acid on lead mercaptides. The lead sulfonates are obtained in 59-83% yields and are converted to the free sulfonic acids by treatment with dry hydrogen chloride in isopropyl alcohol.[55] Tetradecamethylene disulfonic acid, $HO_3S(CH_2)_{14}SO_3H$, is made in 54% yield by the oxidation of a xanthate ester by bromine water (cf. method 507).[59]

542. Alkylation of Alkali Sulfites (Strecker)

$$RX + Na_2SO_3 \longrightarrow RSO_3Na$$

Many halogen compounds react with sodium, potassium, or ammonium sulfites to give high yields of sulfonic acid salts. High- and low-molecular-weight aliphatic halides have been converted in 70-89% yields.[46, 49] Branched-chain sulfonic acids have been obtained from several simple halides such as isopropyl and t-butyl bromides. The over-all yield from the latter compound is only 23%.[47] Other halides studied include cyclopentyl chloride,[52] benzyl chloride,[52] and various phenyl-substituted alkyl halides.[51] The reaction is carried out by refluxing the halide with a concentrated aqueous solution of the sulfite. A temperature of 200° in an autoclave has been employed for several higher-molecular-weight halides.[46] Polymethylene bromides, $Br(CH_2)_nBr$, lead to α,ω-disulfonic acids in 30-56% yields.[44, 45, 50] When one mole of sodium sulfite is treated with 3.3 moles of ethylene bromide, sodium 2-bromoethanesulfonate is obtained in 80% yield.[73] Sulfonic acids containing keto,[48] carboxyl,[38, 41] and amino[53, 54] groups in various positions on the aliphatic chain have been prepared by this method.

543. Addition of Bisulfites to Unsaturated Compounds

$$RCH = CH_2 + NaHSO_3 \longrightarrow RCH_2CH_2SO_3Na$$

Aqueous solutions of bisulfites react with olefins in the presence of oxygen or certain oxidizing agents. Addition of the bisulfite takes place by a free-radical mechanism contrary to Markownikoff's rule. The yields of sulfonates are usually low (12-62%). Styrene gives mainly 2-hydroxy-2-phenylethanesulfonic acid.[39] Bisulfite has also been added to the double bonds in allyl and cinnamyl alcohols.[39] β-Sulfocarboxylic acids are prepared in this way from α,β-olefinic acids.[38] β,β-Disulfopropionic acid is made in 80% yield by the addition of two molecules of bisulfite to

the triple bond of propiolic acid.[41] 2-Nitro olefins add sodium bisulfite
or sulfurous acid to give 55–99% yields of 2-nitroalkanesulfonic acids.[66]

$$H_2C = CHCH_2NO_2 \xrightarrow{\text{NaHSO}_3} CH_3CH(SO_3Na)CH_2NO_2$$

544. Action of Bisulfites on Aromatic Compounds

These and similar additions of bisulfites to tautomeric systems within
the aromatic nucleus have been extensively reviewed.[65]

545. Sulfomethylation

546. Addition of Bisulfites to Carbonyl Compounds[70]

$$RCHO + NaHSO_3 \rightarrow RCHOHSO_3Na$$

547. Addition of Bisulfites to Alkene Oxides

$$\underset{O}{CH_2CH_2} + NaHSO_3 \rightarrow HOCH_2CH_2SO_3Na \quad (60\%)^{71}$$

TABLE 115. SULFONIC ACIDS 815

TABLE 115. SULFONIC ACIDS

C_n	Compound	Method	Yield (%)	Chapter[ref.]	B.p./mm., n_D^t, (M.p.)
		Monosulfonic Acids			
C_1	Methanesulfonic acid (Ba salt)	542	82	36[49]	
C_2	Ethanesulfonic acid (Ba salt)	542	83	36[49]	
C_3	2-Propanesulfonic acid	542	37 †	36[47]	159/1.4, 1.4332
C_4	1-Butanesulfonic acid (Pb salt)	541	96	36[55]	147/0.5
	2-Methylpropane-1-sulfonic acid	542	43 †	36[47]	171/1.2, 1.4364
		543	62	36[39]	
	2-Methylpropane-2-sulfonic acid	542	23 †	36[47]	173/1.5, 1.4315
C_5	3-Pentanesulfonic acid (Ba salt)	541	62	36[72]	
	Cyclopentanesulfonic acid (Na salt)	542	90	36[52]	
	3-Methylbutane-1-sulfonic acid	542	87 †	36[47]	177/1.5, 1.4400
	3-Pyridinesulfonic acid	540	71	36[20]	(356)
C_6	Benzenesulfonic acid	540	56	36[14]	(53) *
C_7	Benzylsulfonic acid (Na salt)	542	98	36[52]	
	p-Toluenesulfonic acid (Na salt)	540	63	36[74]	
C_8	α-Phenylethanesulfonic acid (Na salt)	542	45	36[51]	
	β-Phenylethanesulfonic acid (Na salt)	542	90	36[51]	
C_9	α-Phenylpropanesulfonic acid (Na salt)	542	32	36[51]	
	p-Isopropylbenzenesulfonic acid (Na salt)	540	65	36[15]	
	Mesitylenesulfonic acid	540	90	36[10]	(78)
	8-Quinolinesulfonic acid	540	54	36[21]	
C_{10}	p-n-Butylbenzenesulfonic acid (Na salt)	540	23	36[16]	
	Prehnitenesulfonic acid	540	70	36[6]	(104)
	Durenesulfonic acid	540	70	36[6]	(113)
	Isodurenesulfonic acid	540	70	36[6]	(79)
	β-Naphthalenesulfonic acid	540	70	36[7]	
C_{12}	2-Dibenzofuransulfonic acid	540	75	36[22]	(147)
C_{14}	2-Phenanthrenesulfonic acid (Ba salt)	540	21	36[5]	
	3-Phenanthrenesulfonic acid (K salt)	540	26	36[5]	

For explanations and symbols see pp. xi–xii.

TABLE 115 (*continued*)

C_n	Compound	Method	Yield (%)	Chapter[ref.]	B.p./mm., n_D^t, (M.p.)
		Disulfonic Acids			
C_2	1,2-Ethanedisulfonic acid	542	46	36[45]	(174)
C_3	1,3-Propanedisulfonic acid	542	56	36[45]	157/1.4, (124)
C_4	1,4-Butanedisulfonic acid (Na salt)	542	93	36[50]	
C_5	1,5-Pentanedisulfonic acid	542	80	36[44]	198/1.7
C_6	1,6-Hexanedisulfonic acid	542	68	36[44]	(78)
	1,3-Benzenedisulfonic acid (Na salt)	540	90	36[17]	
	1,3,5-Benzenetrisulfonic acid (Na salt)	540	73	36[1]	
C_{14}	1,14-Tetradecanedisulfonic acid (Na salt)	541	54	36[59]	
		Sulfo Carboxylic Acids			
C_2	Disulfoacetic acid	253	61	36[62]	(86)
C_3	α-Sulfopropionic acid	540	75	36[43]	
	β,β-Disulfopropionic acid	543	80	36[41]	(93)
	α-Sulfoacrylic acid (Ba salt)	540	70	36[40]	
C_4	α-Sulfocrotonic acid (Ba salt)	20	57	36[40]	
C_5	α-Sulfo-n-valeric acid	264	73	36[42]	(66)
	α-Sulfoisovaleric acid	264	80	36[38]	(68)
	β-Sulfoisovaleric acid (Ba salt)	543	67	36[38]	
	α-Sulfomethylethylacetic acid	540	34	36[38]	(83)
	α-Ethyl-β-sulfopropionic acid (Ba salt)	543	70	36[38]	
	α-Sulfo-β,β-dimethylacrylic acid	540	72	36[40]	
		Amino Sulfonic Acids			
C_2	2-Aminoethanesulfonic acid (taurine)	425 / 542	65 / 73	36[66] / 36[53]	(317)
C_3	2-Aminopropane-1-sulfonic acid	425	60	36[66]	
	3-Aminopropanesulfonic acid	542	60	36[54]	(292)
	1-Aminopropane-2-sulfonic acid	425	79	36[66]	(295)
C_4	4-Aminobutanesulfonic acid	542	24	36[54]	(263)
C_5	5-Aminopentanesulfonic acid	542	60 †	36[54]	(312)
C_6	o-Aminobenzenesulfonic acid (orthanilic acid)	425	57	36[61]	(325)
	p-Aminobenzenesulfonic acid (Na salt)	544	35	36[63]	

TABLE 115. SULFONIC ACIDS   817

TABLE 115 (*continued*)

C$_n$	Compound	Method	Yield (%)	Chapter[ref.]	B.p./mm., n_D^t, (M.p.)
\multicolumn{6}{c}{Amino Sulfonic Acids (*continued*)}					
C$_6$	*p*-Aminobenzenesulfonic (sulfanilic) acid	540	95	36[31]	
C$_7$	*p*-Methylaminobenzenesulfonic acid	540	39	36[34]	(245)
C$_8$	*p*-Dimethylaminobenzenesulfonic acid	540	7	36[33]	
C$_9$	3-Phenylaminopropanesulfonic acid	542	35	36[54]	(265)
C$_{14}$	1-Anthracenesulfonic acid (Na salt)	540	40	36[35]	
\multicolumn{6}{c}{Other Sulfonic Acids}					
C$_2$	Ethylenesulfonic acid (NH$_4$ salt)	....	55	36[68]	
	2-Bromoethanesulfonic acid (Na salt)	542	72	36[73]	
	β-Hydroxyethanesulfonic acid (Na salt)	547	60	36[71]	
	2-Nitroethanesulfonic acid (Na salt)	543	75	36[66]	
C$_3$	1-Propene-1-sulfonic acid	540	18	36[24]	135/0.5
	2-Chloropropane-2-sulfonic acid (Na salt)	53	18	36[24]	
	1-Nitropropane-2-sulfonic acid (Na salt)	543	78	36[66]	
	2-Nitropropane-1-sulfonic acid (Na salt)	543	88	36[66]	
C$_4$	1-Nitro-2-methylpropane-2-sulfonic acid (Na salt)	543	95	36[66]	
	β,β-Disulfodiethyl ether (Ba salt)	541	70	36[60]	
	2-Methyl-2-propene-1-sulfonic acid	540	....	36[23]	
C$_6$	*m*-Hydroxybenzenesulfonic acid (Na salt)	544	26	36[64]	
	2,5-Dichlorobenzenesulfonic acid	540	90	36[29]	
	p-Bromobenzenesulfonic acid (Na salt)	540	37	36[28]	
	m-Hydroxybenzenesulfonic acid	92	78	5[567]	
C$_8$	Acetophenone-ω-sulfonic acid	542	14 †	36[48]	(75)

For explanations and symbols see pp. xi–xii.

TABLE 115 (*continued*)

C_n	Compound	Method	Yield (%)	Chapter[ref.]	B.p./mm., n_D^t, (M.p.)
	Other Sulfonic Acids (continued)				
C_{10}	4-Bromonaphthalene-2-sulfonic acid (Na salt)	56	71	36[69]	
C_{12}	*p*-Phenoxybenzenesulfonic acid (Na salt)	540	93	36[27]	
	Azobenzene-4-sulfonic acid	540	90	36[36]	(129)
C_{14}	1-Anthraquinonesulfonic acid (K salt)	540	86	36[37]	
	Stilbene-4-sulfonic acid	28	42	2[273]	

For explanations and symbols see pp. xi–xii.

REFERENCES FOR CHAPTER 36

[1] Suter and Harrington, *J. Am. Chem. Soc.,* **59,** 2577 (1937).

[2] Othmer, Jacobs, and Buschmann, *Ind. Eng. Chem.,* **35,** 326 (1943); Shreve and Lux, *ibid.,* **35,** 306 (1943); Fieser and Bowen, *J. Am. Chem. Soc.,* **62,** 2105 (1940); Fierz-David and Richter, *Helv. Chim. Acta,* **28,** 257 (1945); Lantz, *Bull. soc. chim. France,* (5) **12,** 245 (1945); Royer, *Ann. chim.,* (12) **1,** 407 (1946).

[3] Thomas, Anzilotti, and Hennion, *Ind. Eng. Chem.,* **32,** 408 (1940).

[4] Burkhardt, *J. Chem. Soc.,* 2387 (1930).

[5] Fieser, *Org. Syntheses,* Coll. Vol. II, 482 (1943).

[6] Smith and Cass, *J. Am. Chem. Soc.,* **54,** 1612 (1932); cf. ref. 9.

[7] Colver and Noyes, *J. Am. Chem. Soc.,* **43,** 900 (1921); cf. refs. 2 and 8.

[8] Gattermann and Wieland, *Laboratory Methods of Organic Chemistry,* The Macmillan Co., New York, 1938, pp. 191–194.

[9] Smith and Lux, *J. Am. Chem. Soc.,* **51,** 2997 (1929).

[10] Suter and Weston in *Organic Reactions,* Vol. 3, John Wiley & Sons, New York, 1946, pp. 141, 162.

[11] Suter, *Organic Chemistry of Sulfur,* John Wiley & Sons, New York, 1944, pp. 94, 195.

[12] Groggins and Simpson in Groggins' *Unit Processes in Organic Synthesis,* 3rd ed., McGraw-Hill Book Co., New York, 1947, p. 260.

[13] Lisk, *Ind. Eng. Chem.,* **40,** 1671 (1948); **41,** 1923 (1949); **42,** 1746 (1950); Simpson and Olsen, *ibid.,* **29,** 1350 (1937).

[14] Leiserson, Bost, and LeBaron, *Ind. Eng. Chem.,* **40,** 508 (1948).

[15] Frank, Berry, and Shotwell, *J. Am. Chem. Soc.,* **71,** 3891 (1949).

[16] Paquette, Lingafelter, and Tartar, *J. Am. Chem. Soc.,* **65,** 686 (1943).

[17] Fierz-David and Stamm, *Helv. Chim. Acta,* **25,** 368 (1942).

[18] Tanasescu and Macarovici, *Bull. soc. chim. France,* (5) **5,** 1126 (1938).

[19] Lauer, *J. prakt. Chem.,* **138,** 81 (1933).

[20] McElvain and Goese, *J. Am. Chem. Soc.,* **65,** 2233 (1943); Webb and Corwin, *ibid.,* **66,** 1456 (1944); Machek, *Monatsh.,* **72,** 84 (1938); Van Gastel and Wibaut, *Rec. trav. chim.,* **53,** 1032 (1934); Craig, *J. Am. Chem. Soc.,* **55,** 2855 (1933).

[21] McCasland, *J. Org. Chem.,* **11,** 277 (1946).

[22] Wendland, Smith, and Muraca, *J. Am. Chem. Soc.,* **71,** 1593 (1949).

[23] Suter et al., *J. Am. Chem. Soc.,* **60,** 538 (1938); **63,** 978, 1594 (1941); **66,** 1105 (1944); **67,** 827 (1945).

[24] Lambert and Rose, *J. Chem. Soc.,* 46 (1949).

[25] Sperling, *J. Chem. Soc.,* 1925 (1949).

[26] Friese, *Ber.,* **64,** 2106 (1931).

[27] Suter, *J. Am. Chem. Soc.,* **53,** 1114 (1931).

[28] Demeny, *Rec. trav. chim.,* **50,** 53 (1931).

[29] Crowell and Raiford, *J. Am. Chem. Soc.,* **42,** 145 (1920).

[30] Lauer and Oda, *J. prakt. Chem.,* **143,** 139 (1935).

[31] Jacobs, Othmer, and Hokanson, *Ind. Eng. Chem.,* **35,** 321 (1943).

[32] Alexander, *J. Am. Chem. Soc.,* **68,** 969 (1946); **69,** 1599 (1947); **70,** 1274 (1948).

[33] Davidson and Reade, *J. Chem. Soc.,* 1702 (1939).

[34] Uppal and Venkataraman, *J. Soc. Chem. Ind. (London),* **57,** 411 (1938).

[35] Battegay and Brandt, *Bull. soc. chim. France,* (4) **33,** 1667 (1923).

[36] Ruggli and Stäuble, *Helv. Chim. Acta,* **24,** 1084 (1941).

[37] Scott and Allen, *Org. Syntheses,* Coll. Vol. II, 539 (1943).

[38] Backer and van der Veen, *Rec. trav. chim.*, **55**, 887 (1936).
[39] Kharasch et al., *J. Am. Chem. Soc.*, **61**, 3092 (1939); *J. Org. Chem.*, **3**, 175 (1938).
[40] Backer and Mulder, *Rec. trav. chim.*, **62**, 46, 53 (1943).
[41] Backer and Beute, *Rec. trav. chim.*, **54**, 601, 621 (1935).
[42] Backer and Toxopeus, *Rec. trav. chim.*, **45**, 890 (1926).
[43] Backer and Dubsky, *Rec. trav. chim.*, **39**, 694 (1920).
[44] Stone, *J. Am. Chem. Soc.*, **58**, 488 (1936); Zuffanti and Hendrickson, *ibid.*, **63**, 2999 (1941).
[45] McElvain, Jelinek, and Rorig, *J. Am. Chem. Soc.*, **67**, 1578 (1945); cf. ref. 44.
[46] Reed and Tarter, *J. Am. Chem. Soc.*, **57**, 571 (1935).
[47] Zuffanti, *J. Am. Chem. Soc.*, **62**, 1044 (1940).
[48] Parkes and Tinsley, *J. Chem. Soc.*, 1861 (1934).
[49] Latimer and Bost, *J. Org. Chem.* **5**, 24 (1940).
[50] Helferich and Grünert, *Ber.*, **74**, 1531 (1941); cf. ref. 44.
[51] Evans, Mabbott, and Turner, *J. Chem. Soc.*, 1159 (1927).
[52] Turkiewicz and Pilat, *Ber.*, **71**, 285 (1938).
[53] Cortese, *J. Am. Chem. Soc.*, **58**, 191 (1936); Marvel and Bailey, *Org. Syntheses*, Coll. Vol. II, 563 (1943); Cortese, *ibid.*, Coll. Vol. II, 564 (1943).
[54] Rumpf, *Bull. soc. chim. France*, (5) **5**, 871 (1938).
[55] Noller and Gordon, *J. Am. Chem. Soc.*, **56**, 1090 (1933); Vivian and Reid, *ibid.*, **57**, 2559 (1935).
[56] Collin et al., *J. Soc. Chem. Ind. (London)*, **52**, 272T (1933).
[57] Clarke, *Org. Syntheses*, **20**, 23 (1940); Young, *J. Am. Chem. Soc.*, **59**, 811 (1937).
[58] Murray, *J. Chem. Soc.*, 739 (1933).
[59] Stone, *J. Am. Chem. Soc.*, **62**, 571 (1940).
[60] Backer, *Rec. trav. chim.*, **54**, 205 (1935).
[61] Wertheim, *Org. Syntheses*, Coll. Vol. II, 471 (1943).
[62] Backer and Benninga, *Rec. trav. chim.*, **55**, 370 (1936).
[63] Hunter and Sprung, *J. Am. Chem. Soc.*, **53**, 1432 (1931); Lauer, Sprung, and Langkammerer, *ibid.*, **58**, 225 (1936).
[64] Lauer and Langkammerer, *J. Am. Chem. Soc.*, **56**, 1628 (1934).
[65] Ref. 11, pp. 353–365.
[66] Heath and Piggott, *J. Chem. Soc.*, 1481 (1947).
[67] Suter, Bair, and Bordwell, *J. Org. Chem.*, **10**, 470 (1945).
[68] Whitmore and Landau, *J. Am. Chem. Soc.*, **68**, 1797 (1946).
[69] Mercanton and Goldstein, *Helv. Chim. Acta*, **28**, 534 (1945).
[70] Ref. 11, pp. 126–130
[71] Lauer and Hill, *J. Am. Chem. Soc.*, **58**, 1873 (1936).
[72] Miron and Richter, *J. Am. Chem. Soc.*, **71**, 453 (1949).
[73] Marvel and Sparberg, *Org. Syntheses*, Coll. Vol. II, 558 (1943).
[74] Ray and Soffer, *J. Org. Chem.*, **15**, 1039 (1950).

37

Derivatives of Sulfonic Acids

CONTENTS

548. Action of Inorganic Acid Halides on Sulfonic Acids

$$RSO_3H \xrightarrow{\text{SOCl}_2,\ \text{PCl}_5,\ \text{etc.}} RSO_2Cl$$

Sulfonic acids are converted to the corresponding acid halides in much the same way as carboxylic acids. Thionyl chloride is the best reagent for the preparation of methanesulfonyl chloride (83%).[4] By heating with a large excess of thionyl chloride, however, p-toluenesulfonic acid is converted into its anhydride (87%).[21] Benzenesulfonyl chloride is made in 80% yield by the action of either phosphorus pentachloride or phosphorus oxychloride at 180° on sodium benzenesulfonate.[5] Chlorosulfonic and fluorosulfonic acids are used in the conversion of sodium p-chlorobenzenesulfonate to the corresponding sulfonyl halides (85–89%).[19]

$$ArSO_3Na + FSO_3H \longrightarrow ArSO_3F + NaHSO_3$$

Nitro,[20] halo,[13, 19] and azo[14] groups on the aromatic nucleus are stable during these conversions.

549. Sulfonyl Halides by Halogenation of Mercaptans and Related Compounds

$$RSH + 3X_2 + 2H_2O \longrightarrow RSO_2X + 5HX$$

A variety of sulfur compounds are converted directly to sulfonyl halides by the action of bromine or chlorine water. The list includes mercaptans,[24] sulfides,[1] disulfides,[1, 2, 16, 24] thiol esters,[24] thiocyanates,[17] alkyl xanthates,[24] and S-alkylthiouronium salts.[7] Chlorination of the thiouronium salts sometimes leads to highly explosive products.[25] Most of the reactions occur at low temperatures and give excellent yields of sulfonyl chlorides. The corresponding bromides are formed in somewhat lower yields (36–67%).[7] Under anhydrous conditions halogenation of disulfides gives sulfenyl halides,[3] viz., RSSR + X_2 → 2RSX.

550. Direct Halosulfonation of Aromatic Compounds

$$ArH + 2XSO_3H \longrightarrow ArSO_2X + HX + H_2SO_4$$

The replacement of a hydrogen atom on an aromatic nucleus by the sulfonyl halide grouping in a one-step process is accomplished by treating the aromatic compound with chloro- or fluoro-sulfonic acid. Two equivalents of the halosulfonic acid are required, and frequently three equivalents are used. The aromatic sulfonic acid is presumably an intermediate in the process and is converted to the sulfonyl halide by the second equivalent of halosulfonic acid (cf. method 540). Reaction usually occurs at $-5°$ to $30°$ in chloroform or carbon tetrachloride solution. Higher temperatures ($100–125°$) are employed when carboxyl or nitro groups are on the nucleus. Benzenesulfonyl fluoride is obtained in 62% yield by the action of excess fluorosulfonic acid at $20°$ on benzene in an iron vessel.[9]

Alkyl groups are sometimes displaced from the aromatic nucleus during the reaction.[10] Various functional groups may be present in the aromatic compound during the halosulfonation reaction. These groups include methoxyl,[12] alkyl,[10, 23] halo,[18] carboxyl,[11] acetamino,[6] and nitro.[15] The yields range from 55% to 100%. Acetophenone gives a disulfonyl chloride in which the sulfonyl groups are in the *ortho* position and on the methyl group.[8]

Simple aliphatic chlorides are chlorosulfonated by a mixture of chlorine and sulfur dioxide in the presence of light. For example, n-propyl chloride gives 3-chloropropanesulfonyl chloride (23%).[22]

551. Action of Sulfonyl Halides on Ammonia or Amines

$$RSO_2X + NH_3 \longrightarrow RSO_2NH_2 + (HX)$$

The action of ammonia[18, 26] or amines[30] on sulfonyl halides gives sulfonamides and N-substituted sulfonamides. The sulfonyl halide is sometimes heated with dry, powdered ammonium carbonate.[18] Aniline and its derivatives react smoothly at 100–120° in acetic acid solution to which are periodically added portions of sodium acetate. The yields of sulfonamides, $ArSO_2NHAr'$, vary from 50% to 91%.[28] Many sulfonamides have been prepared on a small scale by this method, but the yields are not always stated.[18, 41] Sulfanilamide, $NH_2C_6H_4SO_2NH_2$, is prepared from aniline by first protecting the amino group by conversion to formanilide or carbanilide followed by direct halosulfonation and reaction with ammonia. The over-all yields are 62–65%.[29]

552. Action of Sulfonyl Halides on Hydroxy Compounds

$$RSO_2X + R'OH \xrightarrow{Base} RSO_3R' + (HX)$$

Esters of aliphatic and aromatic sulfonic acids are conveniently prepared in high yields from alcohols and sulfonyl halides. A basic medium is required. By substituting sodium butoxide for sodium hydroxide in butanol, the yield of n-butyl p-toluenesulfonate is increased from 54% to 98%.[31] Ethyl benzenesulfonate and nuclear-substituted derivatives carrying bromo, methoxyl, and nitro groups are prepared from the corresponding sulfonyl chlorides by treatment with sodium ethoxide in absolute ethanol; the yields are 74–81%.[12] Pyridine is by far the most popular basic medium for this reaction. Alcohols (C_4–C_{12}) react at 0–10° in 80–90% yields,[32–34, 36] and various phenols can be converted to aryl sulfonates in this base.[32, 40]

A related reaction is the formation of alkyl chlorosulfonates from alcohols and sulfuryl chloride.[39]

$$ROH + SO_2Cl_2 \rightarrow ClSO_3R + HCl$$

553. Sulfonic Esters by Rearrangement of Alkyl Sulfites

$$(RO)_2SO \xrightarrow{R'_3N} RSO_3R \quad (56\%)[35]$$

TABLE 116. DERIVATIVES OF SULFONIC ACIDS

C_n	Compound	Method	Yield (%)	Chapter[ref.]	B.p./mm., n_D^t, (M.p.)
		Sulfonyl Halides			
C_1	Methanesulfonyl chloride	548	83	37[4]	65/20, 1.451[23]
		549	75	37[17]	55/11
		549	76	37[7]	62/21, 1.4490[25]
C_2	Ethanesulfonyl chloride	549	79	37[17]	72/20
		549	82	37[7]	77/26, 1.4506[25]
		549	90	37[1]	174, 1.4518
C_3	2-Propanesulfonyl chloride	549	40	37[7]	75/19, 1.4525[25]
	3-Chloropropanesulfonyl chloride	550	23	37[22]	118/15, 1.4900[23]
C_4	2-Butanesulfonyl chloride	549	50	37[7]	87/18
	2-Methyl-1-propanesulfonyl chloride	549	53	37[7]	74/11, 1.4520[25]
C_5	1-Pentanesulfonyl chloride	549	78	37[24]	78/3, 1.4547[25]
C_6	Benzenesulfonyl fluoride	550	62	37[9]	91/14, 1.4932[18]
	Benzenesulfonyl chloride	548	87	37[5]	147/45
	p-Chlorobenzenesulfonyl fluoride	550	74	37[19]	(49)
	p-Chlorobenzenesulfonyl chloride	548	85	37[13]	(53)
		548	89	37[19]	140/12, (53)
	o-Nitrobenzenesulfonyl chloride	549	80	37[2]	(69)
	m-Nitrobenzenesulfonyl chloride	550	55	37[15]	(62)
	p-Nitrobenzenesulfonyl chloride	549	46 †	37[16]	144/1.5, (80)
		548	90	37[20]	(77)
	2,4-Dinitrobenzenesulfonyl chloride	548	72	37[2]	(101)
C_7	1-Heptanesulfonyl chloride	549	50	37[7]	125/9, 1.4564[25]
	α-Toluenesulfonyl chloride	549	92	37[7]	(92)
	p-Toluenesulfonyl chloride	548	90	37[42]	(69)
	p-Methoxybenzenesulfonyl chloride	550	66	37[12]	104/0.25, (42)
	m-Carboxybenzenesulfonyl chloride	550	100	37[11]	
C_8	β-Phenylethanesulfonyl chloride	549	95	37[7]	122/3, (33)
	p-Acetaminobenzenesulfonyl chloride	550	61	37[6]	(149)
C_9	Mesitylenedisulfonyl chloride	550	70	37[23]	(124)
C_{12}	p-Azobenzenesulfonyl chloride	548	85	37[14]	(125)

TABLE 116. DERIVATIVES OF SULFONIC ACIDS   825

TABLE 116 (*continued*)

C_n	Compound	Method	Yield (%)	Chapter[ref.]	B.p./mm., n_D^t, (M.p.)
		Esters of Sulfonic Acids			
C_2	Methyl methanesulfonate	553	56	37[35]	101/25, 1.4140
C_4	n-Butyl chlorosulfonate	552	77	37[39]	79/14, 1.429[13]
	β-Methoxyethyl methanesulfonate	552	72	37[33]	80/0.4, 1.4314
C_5	n-Butyl methanesulfonate	552	80	37[36]	106/6, 1.4319
C_8	Methyl p-toluenesulfonate	552	90	37[31]	161/10, (28)
	Ethyl benzenesulfonate	552	75	37[12]	97/0.3, 1.5092
	Ethyl p-bromobenzenesulfonate	552	74	37[12]	112/0.15, (39)
	Ethyl p-nitrobenzenesulfonate	552	70	37[12]	(92)
C_9	Ethyl p-toluenesulfonate	552	62	37[32]	(32)
	Ethyl p-methoxybenzenesulfonate	552	83	37[12]	138/0.3, 1.5230
	β-Chloroethyl p-toluenesulfonate	552	69	37[38]	210/21
C_{10}	n-Propyl p-toluenesulfonate	552	82	37[33]	134/0.4, 1.5069
	γ-Chloropropyl p-toluenesulfonate	552	55	37[37]	190/5, 1.5225[21]
	β-Methoxyethyl p-toluenesulfonate	552	82	37[32]	141/0.2, 1.5085[25]
C_{11}	n-Butyl p-toluenesulfonate	552	98	37[31]	171/10
C_{12}	o-Bromophenyl benzenesulfonate	552	90	37[40]	(56)
	Phenyl p-bromobenzenesulfonate	552	86	37[40]	(116)
C_{15}	β-Phenoxyethyl p-toluenesulfonate	552	92	37[32]	(81)
C_{19}	n-Dodecyl p-toluenesulfonate	552	90	37[34]	(25)

For explanations and symbols see pp. xi–xii.

REFERENCES FOR CHAPTER 37

[1] Lee and Dougherty, *J. Org. Chem.*, 5, 83 (1940).

[2] Schreiber and Shriner, *J. Am. Chem. Soc.*, 56, 115 (1934); Wertheim, *Org. Syntheses*, Coll. Vol. II, 471 (1943).

[3] Hubacher, *Org. Syntheses*, Coll. Vol. II, 455 (1943); Fuson et al., *J. Org. Chem.*, 11, 469 (1946); Rheinboldt and Motzkus, *Ber.*, 72, 657 (1939).

[4] Hearst and Noller, *Org. Synthesis*, 30, 58 (1950); *J. Am. Chem. Soc.*, 70, 3955 (1948).

[5] Adams and Marvel, *Org. Syntheses*, Coll. Vol. I, 84 (1941).

[6] Smiles and Stewart, *Org. Syntheses*, Coll. Vol. I, 8 (1941).

[7] Johnson and Sprague, *J. Am. Chem. Soc.*, 58, 1348 (1936), 59, 1837, 2439 (1937).

[8] Weston and Suter, *J. Am. Chem. Soc.*, 61, 389 (1939).

[9] Suter and Weston in *Organic Reactions*, Vol. 3, John Wiley & Sons, New York, 1946, p. 164.

[10] Newton, *J. Am. Chem. Soc.*, 65, 2439 (1943).

[11] Brand, Gabel, and Rosenkranz, *Ber.*, 70, 304 (1937).

[12] Morgan and Cretcher, *J. Am. Chem. Soc.*, 70, 375 (1948).

[13] Shepherd and English, *J. Org. Chem.*, 12, 449 (1947).

[14] Pearl, *J. Org. Chem.*, 10, 205 (1945).

[15] Hodgson and Whitehurst, *J. Chem. Soc.*, 482 (1944).

[16] Barber, *J. Chem. Soc.*, 102 (1943).

[17] Johnson and Douglass, *J. Am. Chem. Soc.*, 61, 2549 (1939).

[18] Huntress and Carten, *J. Am. Chem. Soc.*, 62, 511 (1940); Huntress and Autenrieth, *ibid.*, 63, 3446 (1941).

[19] Kulka, *J. Am. Chem. Soc.*, 72, 1216 (1950).

[20] Demeny, *Rec. trav. chim.*, 48, 1146 (1929).

[21] Bernoulli and Stauffer, *Helv. Chim. Acta*, 23, 640 (1940).

[22] Helberger, Manecke, and Fisher, *Ann.*, 562, 33 (1948).

[23] Backer, *Rec. trav. chim.*, 54, 545 (1935).

[24] Douglass and Johnson, *J. Am. Chem. Soc.*, 60, 1486 (1938).

[25] Folkers, Russell, and Bost, *J. Am. Chem. Soc.*, 63, 3530 (1941).

[26] Bergeim and Braker, *J. Am. Chem. Soc.*, 66, 1459 (1944).

[27] Bauer and Rosenthal, *J. Am. Chem. Soc.*, 66, 611 (1944).

[28] Shepherd, *J. Org. Chem.*, 12, 275 (1947).

[29] Galat, *Ind. Eng. Chem.*, 36, 192 (1944).

[30] Helferich and Grünert, *Ber.*, 73, 1133 (1940).

[31] Kranzfelder and Sowa, *J. Am. Chem. Soc.*, 59, 1490 (1937); Roos, Gilman, and Beaber, *Org. Syntheses*, Coll. Vol. I, 145 (1941), note 4.

[32] Tipson, *J. Org. Chem.*, 9, 235 (1944).

[33] Chapman and Owen, *J. Chem. Soc.*, 582 (1950).

[34] Marvel and Sekera, *Org. Syntheses*, 20, 50 (1940).

[35] Bissinger, Kung, and Hamilton, *J. Am. Chem. Soc.*, 70, 3940 (1948).

[36] Sekera and Marvel, *J. Am. Chem. Soc.*, 55, 346 (1933).

[37] Rossander and Marvel, *J. Am. Chem. Soc.*, 50, 1493 (1928).

[38] Clemo and Tenniswood, *J. Chem. Soc.*, 2550 (1931).

[39] Levaillant, *Ann. chim.*, (11) 6, 494 (1936).

[40] Sekera, *J. Am. Chem. Soc.*, 55, 421 (1933); Hazlet, *ibid.*, 59, 287 (1937).

[41] Marvel, Helfrick, and Belsley, *J. Am. Chem. Soc.*, 51, 1273 (1929).

[42] Ray and Soffer, *J. Org. Chem.*, 15, 1039 (1950).

38

Thioanalogs of Other Oxygenated Compounds

CONTENTS

Thioanalogs of ketones,[1] acetals,[5, 11, 13] carboxylic acids,[3, 4, 8] esters,[6, 7, 9, 10, 12, 15] amides,[17, 18, 50] isocyanates,[20–29] urethanes,[33] and ureas[40–43, 51, 52] are often prepared by reactions similar to those used for the corresponding oxygenated compounds. In Table 117 are listed a few of these compounds. The method numbers are those for the introduction of the corresponding oxygenated group. Sometimes the thioanalogs are obtained directly from the oxygenated compounds by heating with sulfur or compounds of sulfur, for example the preparation of thioamides by the action of phosphorus sulfide on acid amides.[2, 14, 16]

Aryl thiocyanates, ArSCN, are formed by direct thiocyanation of the aromatic nucleus[30, 31, 49] or by treating diazonium salts with metallic thiocyanates.[32, 36] Methods for the thiocyanation of organic compounds have been reviewed.[53]

TABLE 117. SULFUR ANALOGS OF OTHER OXYGENATED ORGANIC COMPOUNDS

C_n	Compound	Method	Yield (%)	Chapter[ref.]	B.p./mm., n_D^t, (M.p.)
			Thioacids and Thiolesters		
C_2	Thioacetic acid (thiolacetic acid)	250	72	38[8]	88–92
C_3	Methyl thiolacetate	286	55 †	38[12]	96/760, 1.4600[25]
	Methyl bromothiolacetate	286	82	38[15]	77/15
C_4	Ethyl thiolacetate	286	70	38[6]	116, 1.4503[28]
		288	92	38[7]	109–115
C_5	Thiofuroic acid	250	62	38[3]	102/16, 1.589[24]
C_6	Isobutyl thiolacetate	....	60	38[9]	152/744
	t-Butyl thiolacetate	286	81	38[10]	38/14, 1.4490[24]
C_7	Ethyl orthothioformate	....	26	38[37]	234
C_{10}	γ-Bromopropyl thiolbenzoate	286	75	38[19]	149/1, 1.5950[25]
C_{13}	Methyl thiolaurate	286	89	38[4]	113/1, 1.4642[25]
			Thioamides		
C_3	Thiopropionamide	....	32	38[16]	(42)
C_6	Thionicotinamide	354	86	38[17]	(181)
C_7	Thioformanilide	....	100	38[38]	
C_8	p-Chlorothioacetanilide	....	54	38[2]	(142)
	p-Nitrothioacetanilide	....	70	38[14]	(175)
			Thioureas		
C_2	S-Methylthiouronium sulfate	....	84	38[46]	(235)
	N-Methylthiourea	416	81	38[42]	(121)
C_3	Ethylene thiourea	....	89	38[44]	(198)
	β-Bromoethylthiourea	416	60	38[40]	(174)
C_5	N-t-Butylthiourea	416	99	38[51]	(171)
C_7	α-Phenylthiourea	....	76	38[45]	(153)
	o-Chlorophenylthiourea	416	43	38[54]	(146)
	o-Nitrophenylthiourea	416	61	38[52]	(136)
C_8	S-Benzylthiouronium chloride	....	100	38[47]	(174)
C_{11}	α-Naphthylthiourea	416	80	38[41]	(194)
			Thiocyanates		
C_4	Isopropyl thiocyanate	413	79	38[26]	150
C_6	n-Amyl thiocyanate	413	85	38[23]	91/16, 1.4620[25]
	α-Furfuryl thiocyanate	413	70	38[24]	112/27, 1.5614
C_7	o-Chlorophenyl thiocyanate	....	53	38[36]	160/45
	o-Nitrophenyl thiocyanate	....	64	38[32]	(136)
C_8	Tetramethylethylene dithiocyanate	413	55	38[25]	(61)
C_9	p-Thiocyanodimethylaniline	....	67	38[49]	(74)

TABLE 117. OTHER SULFUR ANALOGS 829

TABLE 117 (*continued*)

C_n	Compound	Method	Yield (%)	Chapter[ref.]	B.p./mm., n_D^t, (M.p.)
		Isothiocyanates			
C_2	Methyl isothiocyanate	....	76	38[34]	118
C_5	Methallyl isothiocyanate	413	95	38[22]	64/10
C_7	Phenyl isothiocyanate	....	78	38[48]	121/35
	p-Chlorophenyl isothiocyanate	411	81	38[27]	(45)
	o-Nitrophenyl isothiocyanate	411	96	38[29]	(72)
	p-Nitrophenyl isothiocyanate	411	85	38[21]	(113)
C_8	Benzoyl isothiocyanate	414	64	38[35]	135/18
		Other Sulfur Analogs			
C_1	Thiosemicarbazide	416	70	38[39]	(184)
C_3	Formaldehyde dimethyl mercaptal	129	85	38[13]	149
C_5	4-t-Butylthiosemicarbazide	416	90	38[51]	(138)
C_8	Methyl phenyl thiourethane	416	63	38[33]	(93)
C_9	Formaldehyde dibutyl mercaptal	129	60	38[5]	
C_{13}	Thiobenzophenone	222	50	38[1]	174/14, (54)

For explanations and symbols see pp. xi–xii.

REFERENCES FOR CHAPTER 38

[1] Staudinger and Freudenberger, *Org. Syntheses*, Coll. Vol. II, 573 (1943).
[2] Beilenson and Hamer, *J. Chem. Soc.*, 1228 (1936).
[3] Patton, *J. Am. Chem. Soc.*, 71, 3571 (1949).
[4] Ralston, Segebrecht, and Bauer, *J. Org. Chem.*, 4, 502 (1939).
[5] Westlake and Dougherty, *J. Am. Chem. Soc.*, 63, 658 (1941).
[6] Wenzel and Reid, *J. Am. Chem. Soc.*, 59, 1089 (1937); Baker and Reid, *ibid.*, 51, 1568 (1929).
[7] Hurd and Williams, *J. Am. Chem. Soc.*, 58, 965 (1936).
[8] Clarke and Hartman, *J. Am. Chem. Soc.*, 46, 1731 (1924); cf. ref. 55.
[9] Ipatieff and Friedman, *J. Am. Chem. Soc.*, 61, 73 (1939).
[10] Rylander and Tarbell, *J. Am. Chem. Soc.*, 72, 3021 (1950).
[11] Wenzel and Reid, *J. Am. Chem. Soc.*, 59, 1090 (1937); Sjöberg, *Ber.*, 75, 27 (1942).
[12] Arndt, Loewe, and Ozansoy, *Ber.*, 72, 1862 (1939); cf. ref. 6.
[13] Böhme and Marx, *Ber.*, 74, 1672 (1941).
[14] Fries and Wolter, *Ann.*, 527, 71 (1937).
[15] Arens and van Dorp, *Rec. trav. chim.*, 66, 409 (1947).
[16] Erlenmeyer et al., *Helv. Chim. Acta*, 31, 1153 (1948).
[17] Karrer and Schukri, *Helv. Chim. Acta*, 28, 821 (1945).
[18] Ralston, Vander Wal, and McCorkle, *J. Org. Chem.*, 4, 68 (1939).
[19] Karjala and McElvain, *J. Am. Chem. Soc.*, 55, 2966 (1933).
[20] McKee and Bost, *J. Am. Chem. Soc.*, 68, 2506 (1946).
[21] Dyer and Johnson, *J. Am. Chem. Soc.*, 54, 781 (1932).
[22] Bruson and Eastes, *J. Am. Chem. Soc.*, 59, 2012 (1937).
[23] Allen, *J. Am. Chem. Soc.*, 57, 198 (1935).
[24] Kirner and Richter, *J. Am. Chem. Soc.*, 51, 3141 (1929).
[25] Youtz and Perkins, *J. Am. Chem. Soc.*, 51, 3510 (1929).
[26] Shriner, *Org. Syntheses*, Coll. Vol. II, 366 (1943).
[27] Dyson, *Org. Syntheses*, Coll. Vol. I, 165 (1941).
[28] Wagner-Jauregg, Arnold, and Hippchen, *J. prakt. Chem.*, 155, 216 (1940).
[29] Erlenmeyer and Ueberwasser, *Helv. Chim. Acta*, 23, 329 (1940).
[30] Wood and Fieser, *J. Am. Chem. Soc.*, 63, 2323 (1941).
[31] Fichter and Schönmann, *Helv. Chim. Acta*, 19, 1411 (1936).
[32] Wagner-Jauregg and Helmert, *Ber.*, 75, 942 (1942); Dienske, *Rec. trav. chim.*, 50, 407 (1931).
[33] Bost and Andrews, *J. Am. Chem. Soc.*, 65, 900 (1943).
[34] Moore and Crossley, *Org. Syntheses*, 21, 81 (1941).
[35] Ambelang and Johnson, *J. Am. Chem. Soc.*, 61, 632 (1939).
[36] Challenger, Higginbottom, and Huntington, *J. Chem. Soc.*, 29 (1930).
[37] Post, *J. Org. Chem.*, 6, 832 (1941).
[38] Todd et al., *J. Chem. Soc.*, 363 (1937).
[39] Sah and Daniels, *Rec. trav. chim.*, 69, 1547 (1950).
[40] Masters and Bogert, *J. Am. Chem. Soc.*, 64, 2710 (1942).
[41] Berkebile and Fries, *J. Chem. Education*, 25, 618 (1948).
[42] Moore and Crossley, *Org. Syntheses*, 21, 83 (1941).
[43] Cressman, *Org. Syntheses*, 27, 56, 57 (1947).
[44] Allen, Edens, and VanAllan, *Org. Syntheses*, 26, 34 (1946).
[45] Frank and Smith, *Org. Syntheses*, 28, 89 (1948).
[46] Shildneck and Windus, *Org. Syntheses*, Coll. Vol. II, 411 (1943).

[47] Chambers and Watt, *J. Org. Chem.*, **6**, 377 (1941).

[48] Dains, Brewster, and Olander, *Org. Syntheses*, Coll. Vol. I, 447 (1941).

[49] Brewster and Schroeder, *Org. Syntheses*, Coll. Vol. II, 574 (1943).

[50] Chabrier and Renard, *Bull. soc. chim. France*, (5) **16**, D272 (1949).

[51] Schmidt et al., *Ann.*, **568**, 196 (1950).

[52] Erlenmeyer and Ueberwasser, *Helv. Chim. Acta*, **23**, 330 (1940).

[53] Kaufmann in *Newer Methods of Preparative Organic Chemistry*, Interscience Publishers, New York, 1948, p. 369.

[54] Kurzer, *Org. Syntheses*, **31**, 21 (1951).

[55] Ellingboe, *Org. Syntheses*, **31**, 105 (1951).

39

Heterocyclic Compounds

CONTENTS

In this chapter are listed twenty-three methods for the formation of the more common heterocyclic nuclei and several reactions for their modification, namely, reduction, dehydrogenation, and alkylation.

The syntheses of heterocyclic compounds containing various functional groups are discussed in preceding chapters.

The chemistry of the heterocyclic compounds has been reviewed in several excellent works.[18, 19, 222]

554. Reduction of the Heterocyclic Nucleus

Reduction of heterocyclic compounds parallels reduction of aromatic compounds with the added factor that fission of the ring may occur. In most instances, catalytic hydrogenation is preferred to chemical reduction, purer products and more consistent results being obtained.

In the furan series, extensive studies have been made for the catalytic hydrogenation of furan and furfural. Furan is converted to tetrahydrofuran in almost quantitative yields. Catalysts and conditions include palladous oxide at 50° and 7 atm., Raney nickel at 150° and 150 atm., and Raney nickel in butyl alcohol at 50° and atm., pressure.[96] Furfural is hydrogenated quantitatively to furfuryl alcohol upon absorption of one molecular equivalent of hydrogen (platinum oxide) and further reduced to tetrahydrofurfuryl alcohol with traces of ring-cleavage products, namely, 1,2- and 1,5-pentanediols and 1-pentanol.[97] α-Furoic acid gives the tetrahydro compound in a similar way. Important derivatives of furfural like β-(2-furyl)-acrolein, furfuralacetone, and ethyl β-(2-furyl)-acrylate are reduced to tetrahydrofuryl compounds in excellent yields over nickel catalysts at 125–175°.[95, 98] The interaction of Grignard reagents and furfural followed by nuclear hydrogenation is a good route for making alkyltetrahydrofurylcarbinols of the type $(C_4H_7O)CHOHR$.[99] Catalytic dehydration of the alcohols with subsequent hydrogenation furnishes tetrahydrofurylalkanes.[100]

Catalytic hydrogenation of the thiophene nucleus has been successfully accomplished over a supported palladium catalyst at low temperature and pressure.[108]

Pyrroles may be hydrogenated over a platinum catalyst in acetic acid at 4 atm. and 70°[9] or over a nickel catalyst without solvent at 110 atm. and 180°.[75, 109] N-Substituted pyrroles are more reactive.[75, 110, 112] Partial and complete hydrogenation of phenylpyrroles, phenylindoles, carbazoles, and acridines may be accomplished with either a copper chromite or Raney nickel catalyst.[111]

Synthesis of a piperidine compound is commonly carried out by reduction of the corresponding pyridine derivative. An excellent discussion has been presented.[113] Earlier techniques concerned with reduction by the action of sodium and alcohol have been largely replaced by procedures of catalytic hydrogenation. An example is the reduction of pyridine to piperidine in 83% yield over nickel at 170–200°.[95] Reduction of its homologs occurs in the same way. Platinum oxide is poisoned by pyridine bases, but it will catalyze reduction of the hydrochlorides or acetates conveniently at low temperature and pressure. Absolute ethanol, dioxane, and acetic acid are preferred as solvents. In this manner, a number of N-substituted pyridines like N-ethylpyridine, N-β-hydroxyethylpyridine, and N-carbethoxymethylpyridine are reduced.[116] Nicotinic acid is also hydrogenated to piperidine-3-carboxylic acid over platinum oxide catalyst;[117] the corresponding ester is reduced over a nickel catalyst.[95] 3- and 4-Hydroxypyridines are reduced by catalytic hydrogenation and by sodium-ethanol, respectively, to the corresponding hydroxypiperidines, but the 2-isomer is changed to 2-piperidone instead of 2-hydroxypiperidine.[118, 119] The aminopyridines respond to reduction in a way similar to their hydroxy analogs; 3- and 4-aminopiperidine can be made, but 2-iminopiperidine is formed rather than 2-aminopiperidine.[119—121]

Pyridines containing side chains are hydrogenated to piperidine derivatives in good yields over platinum catalyst. The products include, for example, β-(4-piperidyl)-propionic acid,[122] γ-(2-piperidyl)-propionic acid,[123] 1-(α-piperidyl)-2-ethanol,[124] 4-(α-piperidyl)-1-methoxybutane,[125] and 2-aminomethylpiperidine.[126]

The pyridine ring as present in quinoline and its derivatives may be selectively hydrogenated. Thus, quinoline hydrogenated over copper-chromium oxide yields py-tetrahydroquinoline (97%).[95] Partial or complete hydrogenation to py-tetrahydro- or decahydro-quinoline is accomplished with Raney nickel catalyst.[151] Isoquinoline gives py-tetrahydroisoquinoline in 92% yield by means of copper-chromium oxide catalyst and hydrogen.[150] Catalytic hydrogenation of isoquinoline over platinum in glacial acetic acid with sulfuric acid leads to a mixture of cis- and trans-decahydroisoquinolines.[152] The quinolines may also be reduced with sodium and alcohol.[153]

555. Reduction of Cyclic Amides

The reduction of substituted 2-pyridones with sodium and hot n-butyl alcohol represents the final step in a convenient synthesis for certain piperidines having alkyl, aryl, or carbethoxy groups in the 3- or 4-positions. The yields range between 60% and 90%. The starting 2-pyridones are made by the catalytic reduction of γ-cyano esters.[106] For example, hydrogenation of methyl γ-cyano-γ-phenylbutyrate, $C_6H_5CH(CN)CH_2CH_2CO_2CH_3$, over Raney nickel gives 5-phenyl-2-pyridone, $R = C_6H_5$ in above equation, which is then reduced with sodium and n-butyl alcohol to 3-phenylpiperidine (50% over-all).

556. Reduction of Heterocyclic Aldehydes and Ketones

Many heterocyclic compounds are made from aldehydes and ketones by reduction procedures which have been applied in the synthesis of hydrocarbons (method 3). Typical examples are considered here.

2-Methylfuran is best prepared by the vapor-phase hydrogenation of furfural over a copper chromite catalyst at 1 atm. and 200–300°. Full experimental details have been given.[198] Homologs have been made by reduction of 2-acylfurans by the Wolff-Kishner procedure.[181]

2-Ethylthiophene may be obtained in 91% yield by a modified Wolff-Kishner reduction of 2-acetylthiophene. Other thiophene ketones, also aldehydes, have been converted in the same way in 70% to 90% yields.[199] Reduction by the Clemmensen procedure gives 38% to 55% yields.[200]

3-Ethylpyridine is made in 80% yield by heating 3-acetylpyridine by a modified Wolff-Kishner procedure.[204] Other 2- and 3-alkylpyridines have been formed in the same way.[205, 206]

A unique method for preparing 4-alkylpyridines consists in treatment of pyridine with aliphatic anhydrides in the presence of zinc dust. The intermediate 1,4-diacyl-1,4-dihydropyridines are not isolated but are further reduced to the 4-alkylpyridines by the action of zinc dust and acetic acid.[195] The procedure is illustrated by the synthesis of 4-ethylpyridine (38% over-all).[207]

557. Dehydrogenation of Heterocyclic Compounds

Certain heterocyclic compounds, particularly those containing a nitrogen atom, have been prepared in high yields by catalytic dehydrogenation. Several catalysts are available including those employed for hydrogenation (cf. method 2).

Representative compounds having a pyrrolidine or piperidine nucleus have been dehydrogenated in benzene solution under pressure at 250–350° over a nickel catalyst, e.g., 1-(n-amyl)-pyrrolidine to 1-(n-amyl)-pyrrole (88%), indoline to indole (75%), and 1,2,3,4-tetrahydrocarbazole to carbazole (95%).[154] Indole is also prepared by the dehydrogenation of its 2,3-dihydro derivative over palladium in boiling xylene (62%).[111] Partially hydrogenated alkylpyridines are dehydrogenated over palladized asbestos.[105] 2,4-Diphenylpyrrole is synthesized by the selenium dehydrogenation of its 2,3-dihydro compound (46%).[155]

Decahydroquinoline and decahydroisoquinoline are dehydrogenated over palladium to the corresponding bz-tetrahydro derivatives, a valuable procedure for making these compounds.[152, 156] 1-Methylisoquinoline is prepared by refluxing its 3,4-dihydro derivative with excess Raney nickel until the temperature reaches 248°, the boiling point of the desired product (75%).

Chloranil in boiling xylene has been shown to be an excellent dehydrogenation agent for the preparation of carbazoles from 1,2,3,4-tetrahydrocarbazoles (75–95%). By this procedure, carbazoles substituted in the 1-, 2-, and 3-positions with alkyl, halo, alkoxyl, carboxyl, or nitro groups are readily made.[158] The starting materials are available by ring closures of cyclohexanone-m-phenylhydrazones. A palladium-carbon catalyst for the same purpose is also noteworthy, the yields of alkylcarbazoles being 86–100%.[159]

Tetrahydrothiophene can be dehydrogenated to thiophene over platinum in 32% yield.[160]

558. Alkylation of the Heterocyclic Nucleus

Heterocyclic compounds containing a nitrogen atom commonly undergo N-alkylation or C-alkylation. N-Methyl pyrrole can be prepared by interaction of methyl iodide with potassium pyrrole (40%).[170] N-Carbethoxy pyrrole is made from chloroformic ester and potassium pyrrole.[171] The C-alkylation of pyrroles has been discussed.[177] 3-Alkylindoles are made by the alkylation and decarboxylation of indole-2-carboxylic acid.[64] The conditions for alkylation of pyrrolidine are analogous to those employed for the alkylation of a secondary amine. Thus, pyrrolidine on treatment with n-butyl bromide and potassium hydroxide in boiling benzene is converted to the N-butyl derivative in 40% yield.[168] Compounds having functional groups in the side chain are made in the same way. An illustration is the interaction of pyrrolidine and propylene chlorohydrin in the presence of sodium hydroxide to form 1-(1-pyrrolidyl)-2-propanol (77%).[109] Carbazole also undergoes N-alkylation with alkyl sulfates and chlorohydrins in strong caustic solution.[179,180] It reacts with iodobenzene at 200° in the presence of copper-bronze and potassium carbonate to give N-phenylcarbazole (65%).[169]

Alkyl or aryl groups may be joined to pyridine compounds (1) through an active methyl group jn the *alpha* or *gamma* position, (2) directly at a nuclear carbon atom, or (3) at the nitrogen atom to form quaternary alkyl- or aryl-pyridinium salts. A comprehensive discussion of the alkyl- and aryl-pyridines made by these routes has been presented.[178]

In the first instance, excess α- or γ-picoline is treated at low temperatures with sodium amide and an alkyl halide. The yields of C-monoalkylpyridines are lowered by alkylation at the nitrogen atoms, dehydrohalogenation of the alkylating agent, and further alkylation of the product at the site of the remaining active hydrogens.[187]

$$\text{pyridine-CH}_3 \xrightarrow[\text{NaNH}_2]{\text{RX}} \text{pyridine-CH}_2\text{R} \xrightarrow[\text{NaNH}_2]{\text{RX}} \text{pyridine-CHR}_2$$

Long-chain halides undergo this reaction at 100°, no C-dialkylated products being formed.[189] In alkylations with aryl-substituted alkyl halides, $Ar(CH_2)_nX$, $n = 1$ to 3, yields are improved by performing the reaction rapidly in liquid ammonia (56–99%). Also, quinoline methylated in the 2- or 4-position reacts in the same way.[188] A methyl group in the 3-position of pyridine or quinoline is unreactive.

Direct nuclear attachment is accomplished by the interaction of an organometallic compound and pyridine. An example is the synthesis of

$$\text{pyridine} \xrightarrow{\text{C}_6\text{H}_5\text{Li}} \text{(pyridine)}\overset{\text{H}}{\underset{\underset{\text{Li}}{\text{C}_6\text{H}_5}}{\text{N}}} \rightarrow \text{pyridine-C}_6\text{H}_5 + \text{LiH}$$

2-phenylpyridine in 49% yield from phenyllithium and pyridine.[190] The procedure has been applied in the preparation of 2-ethylquinoline (30%).[194] Another procedure consists in coupling aryldiazonium salts with pyridine to form arylpyridines in 20% to 80% yield; however, a mixture of α, β, and γ-isomers results.[191] By heating benzyl chloride and pyridine in the presence of a copper catalyst, a mixture of 2- and 4-benzylpyridines is obtained; these compounds can be separated by fractional distillation.[193]

Extensive studies of the alkylation of thiophene and its derivatives with olefins and alcohols have been made.[196] The catalysts are the same as those employed for the alkylation of hydrocarbons. Alkylation occurs predominently in the 2-position, and the yields are in the range of 60% to 80%.

The interaction of furan and aryldiazonium chlorides in the presence of alkali leads to 2-arylfurans, e.g., 2-phenyl-, 2-p-halophenyl-, and 2-p-nitrophenylfuran; however, the yields are low (15–22%).[197]

559. Decarboxylation of Heterocyclic Acids

A carboxyl group is removed from a heterocyclic nucleus in much the same way as from an aromatic nucleus (method 13), i.e., by thermal decomposition. The pyrolysis is catalyzed by copper or copper salts and is frequently carried out in quinoline solution. The reaction is important in the synthesis of various alkyl[181] and halo furans. Furoic acid loses carbon dioxide at its boiling point (205°) to give furan (85%).[182] A series of halo furans have been made in 20–97% yields by pyrolysis of the corresponding halofuroic acids. The 5-iodo acid decarboxylates at a temperature of 140°,[183] whereas the 3- and 5-chloro acids require copper-bronze catalyst at 250°.[184]

Carboxyl groups on the pyrrole nucleus are removed by the action of superheated steam on aqueous alkaline solutions of the carboxylic acids.[186]

Carboxyl groups adjacent to carbonyl groups in the nucleus present the familiar β-keto acid structure and are decarboxylated by refluxing with hydrochloric acid.[115]

Heterocyclic carboxylic acids have also been decarboxylated by pyrolysis of their calcium,[87] silver,[146] and ammonium[202] salts.

560. Cyclization of 1,4-Glycols and Related Compounds

where Z = O, S, or NH

1,4-Glycols readily lose water in the presence of acid catalysts. 1,4-Butanediol is dehydrated by 1% phosphoric acid at 270° to tetrahydrofuran (95%).[1] Furfural is obtained by acid treatment of carbohydrate materials containing pentoses, $CH_2OH(CHOH)_4CHO$.[6] Analogous furan aldehydes may be prepared from other sugars; e.g., the fructose portion of sucrose yields 5-hydroxymethylfurfural. With hydrochloric acid, the corresponding 5-chloromethylfurfural is obtained.[4] The chloromethyl group in the latter compound may be reduced in the presence of the aldehyde group by stannous chloride. The over-all yield of 5-methylfurfural from cane sugar is 11%.[5]

Elimination of hydrogen bromide from 1,2-dibromo-4-butanol, $BrCH_2CHBrCH_2CH_2OH$, is accomplished with powdered potassium hydroxide in dry ether.[41] The resulting β-bromotetrahydrofuran loses another molecule of hydrogen halide when heated with excess powdered base. The over-all yield of dihydrofuran is 62%.[9] This elimination reaction has been extended to the preparation of β-bromofurans and 2,5-dihydrofurans having two alkyl groups on one of the α-carbon atoms.[40]

For the preparation of tetrahydrothiophenes, 1,4-dihalides are allowed to react with sodium sulfide.[7, 9, 223]

Pyrrole and N-substituted pyrroles are formed by a reaction analogous to the conversion of sugars to furan aldehydes. Ammonium and substituted ammonium salts of mucic acid, $HO_2C(CHOH)_4CO_2H$, are cyclized and decarboxylated by pyrolysis. The yields of pyrrole[10] and its N-phenyl[11] and N-methyl[12] derivatives are about 40%. Tetrahydropyrroles (pyrrolidines) are formed from various 4-substituted amines by elimination of water, ammonia, or hydrogen halide.[14-17]

Similar elimination reactions are employed in the synthesis of the benzologs of five-membered heterocyclic compounds. For example, β-phenylethyl alcohols having hydroxyl, sulfhydryl, and amino groups in the ortho position are cyclized to the dihydro derivatives of benzofuran, benzothiophene, and benzopyrrole, respectively.[46] Likewise, dehydrohalogenation of β-(o-hydroxyphenyl)-ethyl bromide gives dihydrobenzofuran in 72% yield.[48]

The α-methyl derivative is produced from the acetate of o-allylphenol, $HOC_4H_6CH_2CH=CH_2$, by the addition of hydrogen bromide in the absence of peroxides followed by dehydrohalogenation of the free phenol with potassium hydroxide. In the presence of air or peroxides the mode of addition of hydrogen bromide is reversed and cyclization gives benzopyran.[49] β-Keto derivatives are prepared by a similar ring closure.[51]

561. Cyclization of 1,4-Dicarbonyl Compounds

$$RCOCH_2CH_2COR \xrightarrow[NH_3]{H^+ \text{ or } P_2S_5 \text{ or}}$$

HC —— CH
‖   ‖
RC   CR
  \   /
    Z

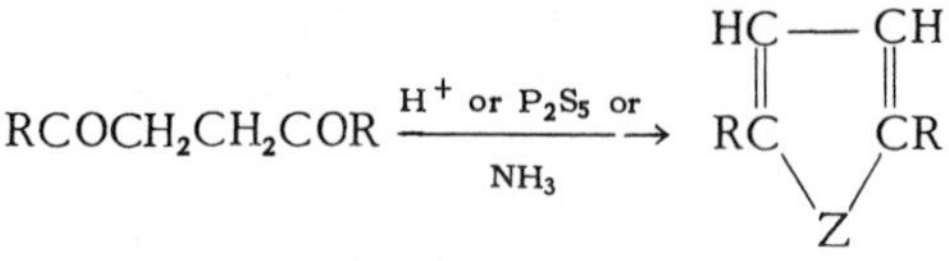

where Z = O, S, or NH

Dienolic forms of 1,4-dicarbonyl compounds are dehydrated by sulfuric acid, phosphorus pentoxide, and like catalysts to substituted furans.[20, 23, 221] Diacylethylenes, RCOCH=CHCOR, undergo similar ring closure in reducing media.[21, 22]

In the thiophene series, phosphorus sulfide converts 1,4-diketones[24, 26, 223] and sodium salts of succinic[25] and alkylsuccinic[27] acids to the five-membered heterocyclic compounds. The yields are low, usually 20–30% from the succinates and 60% from the diketones.

Acetonylacetone, $CH_3COCH_2CH_2COCH_3$, is cyclized to 2,5-dimethylpyrrole by heating to 100° with ammonium carbonate. The yield is 86%. This reaction has been modified and extended to the syntheses of N-alkyl-2,5-dimethylpyrroles by the substitution of amines for ammonia and removal of water by azeotropic distillation with benzene.[30]

Five-membered heterocyclic compounds of the furan, thiophene, and pyrrole series are interconvertible by one-step catalytic processes.[31, 32] For example, at 450° over aluminum oxide catalyst, furan is converted to pyrrole by ammonia and to thiophene by hydrogen sulfide. The yields are 30%.

562. Condensation of α-Chloro Ketones with β-Keto Esters

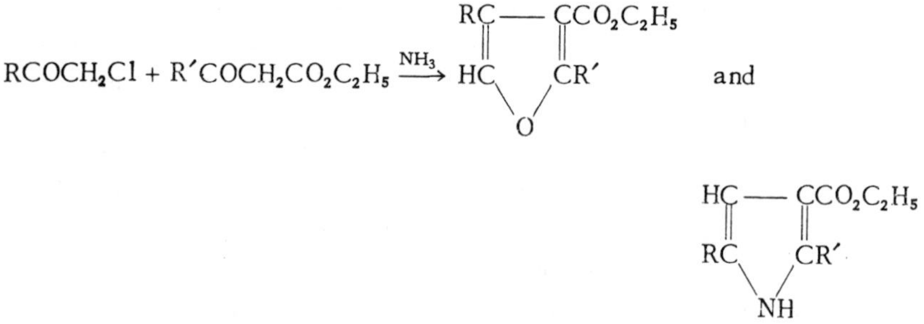

$$RCOCH_2Cl + R'COCH_2CO_2C_2H_5 \xrightarrow{NH_3}$$

RC —— CCO_2C_2H_5
‖   ‖
HC   CR'
  \   /
    O

and

HC —— CCO_2C_2H_5
‖   ‖
RC   CR'
  \   /
    NH

Interaction of α-chloro ketones and β-keto esters in the presence of ammonia leads to both furans and pyrroles.[44] The ring closures are dissimilar, however, in that the positions of the substituent groups on the nuclei are not the same in the two series. The pyrrole ring closure prob-

ably involves an intermediate β-aminocrotonic ester,
$R'C(NH_2) = CHCO_2C_2H_5$.[43] The synthesis of furans by this method has
been improved and extended by substituting pyridine for ammonia as the
condensing agent[42] and by using α,β-dichloroethyl ether as a source of
chloroacetaldehyde.[42, 45]

563. Condensation of α-Amino Ketones and Carbonyl Compounds (Knorr)

$$
\begin{array}{ccc}
R_2 - CO & H_2C - R_3 & R_2C \!\!=\!\!=\!\! CR_3 \\
| & | & \\
R_1 - CH & C - R_4 & \longrightarrow \quad R_1C \quad CR_4 \\
| & /\!\!/ & \diagdown N H \diagup \\
NH_2 & O &
\end{array}
$$

A general reaction for the formation of the pyrrole nucleus consists in
the treatment of an α-amino ketone with another ketone having a reactive
α-methylene group.[37] The α-amino ketone is conveniently prepared from
the ketone by nitrosation and reduction and then, without isolation, it is
allowed to condense with a second carbonyl compound, viz.,
$RCOCH_2R \rightarrow RCOC(=NOH)R \rightarrow RCOCH(NH_2)R$. An example is the
condensation of ethyl α-aminoacetoacetate ($R_1 = CO_2C_2H_5$, $R_2 = CH_3$)
with acetoacetic ester ($R_3 = CO_2C_2H_5$, $R_4 = CH_3$) to give 2,4-dimethyl-3,5-
dicarbethoxypyrrole (64%).[38] The synthesis of 3-acetyl-5-carbethoxy-2,4-
dimethylpyrrole from ethyl acetoacetate and acetylacetone also illustrates
the procedure.[39]

564. Interaction of Grignard Reagents and γ-Chloro Nitriles

$$
\begin{array}{ccc}
H_2C - CHR & H_2C - CHR & H_2C \!\!-\!\! CHR \\
| \quad | & | \quad | & | \\
H_2C \quad C & \xrightarrow{R'MgBr} \quad H_2C \quad CR' & \xrightarrow{NH_3} \quad H_2C \quad CR' \\
| \quad \|\| & | \quad \|\| & \diagdown N \diagup \\
Cl \quad N & Cl \quad NMgBr &
\end{array}
$$

α-Substituted pyrrolines are conveniently made by the action of aliphatic or aromatic Grignard reagents on γ-chloro nitriles followed by
hydrolysis, ammonolysis, or pyrolysis of the intermediate N-bromomag-
nesium ketimine.[36] An example is the conversion of γ-chlorobutyronitrile
and phenylmagnesium bromide to 2-phenylpyrroline (55%).[35] The 1-posi-
tion of the double bond is favored.

565. Sulfurization of Hydrocarbons

$$
\begin{array}{c}
HC \!\!=\!\!=\!\! CH \\
\| \quad \| \\
CH_2 = CH - CH = CH_2 \xrightarrow{S} HC \quad CH \\
\diagdown S \diagup
\end{array}
$$

Thiophene is obtained in 6% yield by passing butadiene into molten sulfur at 320–420°. The reaction is general and affords somewhat higher yields (31–40%) of methylated thiophenes from homologs of butadiene.[8, 223] The free-radical nature of the reaction has been discussed.[13] Dibenzothiophene is conveniently prepared by heating biphenyl and melted sulfur with aluminum chloride at 120°. The yield is 47%.[57]

566. Interaction of 1,2-Dicarbonyl Compounds with Ethers or Sulfides[33, 223]

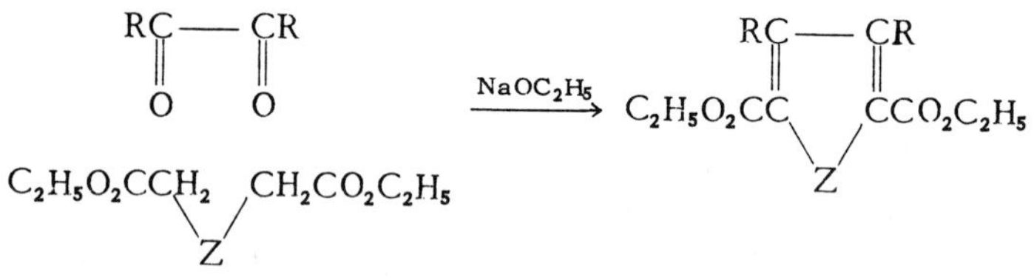

where Z = O or S

567. Elimination of Hydrogen Chloride from N-Chloro Amines[34]

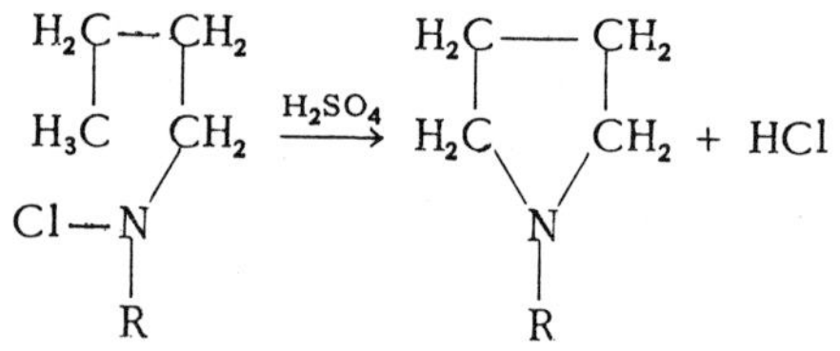

where R = CH$_3$, C$_2$H$_5$, n-C$_3$H$_7$, or n-C$_4$H$_9$ (80%)

568. Catalytic Dehydrocyclization

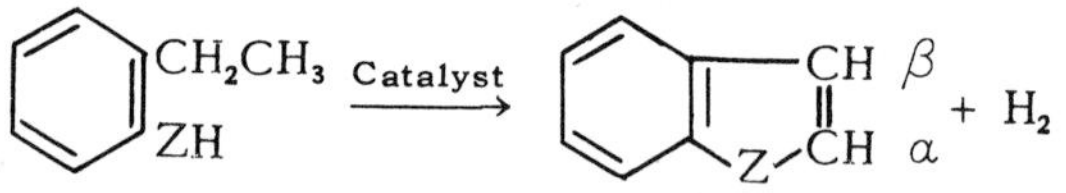

where Z = O or S

Several benzologs of furan and thiophene are conveniently formed by procedures of ring closure over dehydrogenation catalysts. o-Ethylphenol is cyclized at 620° over a palladium catalyst to benzofuran (11%).[53] Chromium oxide on alumina at 450° converts o-ethylthiophenol to benzothiophene (42%).[54] Alkyl groups in the *alpha* and *beta* positions are obtained by suitable variation of structure in the alkyl side chain. For the preparation of benzothiophene, o-ethylthiophenol may be replaced by the more convenient starting materials, hydrogen sulfide and styrene[56] or hydrogen sulfide and ethylbenzene.[55]

569. Cyclodehydration of Aryl Ketones

where Z = O, S, or NH

The formation of these heterocyclic systems by this method of ring closure has been reviewed.[58] Yields in the benzofuran series are poor. A successful application to the synthesis of certain benzothiophenes has been described involving cyclization of arylketosulfides in the presence of zinc chloride or phosphorus pentoxide (85–90%).[59]

The indole system has been the most extensively studied, particularly in regard to the mechanism of cyclization.[78] It is noteworthy that in some instances an isomerization of the anilinoketone occurs, viz., R'CH(NHR)COR'' to R'COCH(NHR)R''. From a preparative standpoint, the method is valuable in the formation of several indoles in excellent yields, e.g., 2,3-dimethylindole (85%)[79] and 2-ethyl-3-methylindole (92%).[80] Condensation of aniline derivatives of 2-chlorocyclohexanone yields the corresponding tetrahydrocarbazoles.[81]

570. Intramolecular Condensation of Substituted Aryl Carbonyl Compounds

where Z = O or S and Y = CH₃ or OR

Benzofurans and benzothiophenes are sometimes obtained by condensation of active methylene and aldehyde groups in *ortho* substituents on the benzene ring.[60-62] The starting materials in the furan series are conveniently prepared *in situ* from phenolic aldehydes and α-halo ketones or α-halo esters.

The Claisen-type condensation of acyl derivatives of o-toluidine furnishes a useful general synthesis of indoles.

where Y = H or R

Cyclization of acetyl-o-toluidine occurs with sodium amide at 250° to give 2-methylindole (83%).[76] The formyl derivative of toluidine requires the presence of potassium ions for condensation to indole (79%).[77] Potassium alkoxide or a mixture of sodium alkoxide and potassium acetate is effective.

571. Elimination of Ammonia from Phenylhydrazones (Fischer Indole Synthesis)

An important general method for preparing indoles involves the catalytic elimination of ammonia from phenylhydrazones of carbonyl compounds having an α-methylene group.[68] Catalysts include zinc chloride,[69] cuprous chloride,[75] boron fluoride etherate,[72] dilute sulfuric acid, alcoholic hydrochloric acid, and glacial acetic acid.[71]

Some ring closures occur rapidly at room temperature, others on heating. As an example (equation above), the phenylhydrazone of acetone on heating with zinc chloride in methylnaphthalene yields 2-methylindole in 80% yield.[69] In a similar manner 2-phenylindole is synthesized (80%).[70] If N-methylphenylhydrazine is employed, the N-methylindole results.[72] The phenylhydrazone of ethyl pyruvate on heating with sulfuric acid in acetic acid forms indole-2-carboxylic acid (58%).[66] When the phenylhydrazone has nuclear substituents like alkyl, halo,[73] or nitro[74] groups, the corresponding 4-, 5-, 6-, or 7-substituted indoles are obtained. When phenylhydrazine is added to a boiling mixture of cyclohexanone and acetic acid, hydrazone formation and ring closure occur in a single operation to yield 1,2,3,4-tetrahydrocarbazole (87%).[71]

572. Intramolecular Condensation of o-Aminobenzyl Ketones and Related Compounds

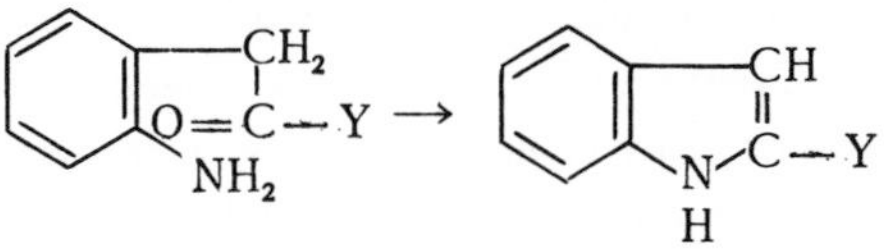

where Y = H, CO_2H, or $CO_2C_2H_5$

This ring closure takes place readily whenever the carbonyl and amino groups occur in the relative positions shown above. Reduction of o-nitrophenylacetonitrile by stannous chloride produces indole rather than the corresponding amino aldehyde.[67] The synthesis is most useful for the preparation of indole-2-carboxylic acid by reduction of o-nitrophenylpyruvic acid with ferrous sulfate and ammonia[63, 66] or with sodium hydrosulfite.[64] The ethyl ester is obtained by a similar reduction with zinc and acetic acid[63] or by catalytic hydrogenation of ethyl o-nitrophenylpyruvate over platinum oxide catalyst.[65]

573. Pyridine Compounds by Ring Closure

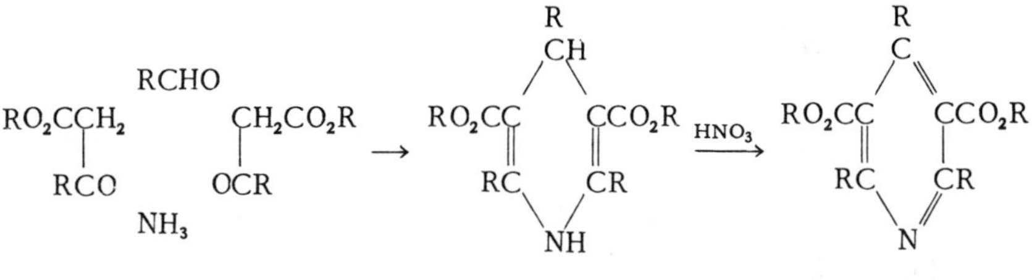

The above equation represents the classical pyridine synthesis of Hantzsch, the starting materials being an aldehyde, a β-keto ester, and ammonia. The over-all yield of 3,5-dicarbethoxy-2,6-dimethylpyridine from formaldehyde, acetoacetic ester, and ammonia is 49–58%.[87] A study of substituted aromatic aldehydes in this synthesis has been made.[92] This is one of many condensations of aliphatic compounds that leads to pyridine derivatives. Although these condensations have been subdivided in various ways for purpose of discussion,[84, 94] the lines of de-

marcation among them are not sharp. The β-keto ester may be replaced
by most 1,3-dicarbonyl compounds or potential 1,3-dicarbonyl compounds.
The nitrogen atom may be a part of a simple organic molecule such as
β-aminocrotonic ester[91] or cyanoacetamide.[90, 93] With cyanoacetamide,
the amide group is active in the condensation and the product is a
3-cyano-2-pyridone. In several of these reactions, formation of a 1,5-
dicarbonyl compound or derivative thereof is possible before ring closure takes place. 1,5-Diketones[89] or cyclohexenones,[88] which are
cleaved to 1,5-diketones, may be used directly in this synthesis.

Simple saturated and olefinic aldehydes condense with ammonia to
give alkylpyridines (Chichibabin), but the products are frequently complex mixtures from which pure compounds are separated with difficulty.[86]
An exception is the preparation of 5-ethyl-2-methylpyridine in 53% yield
from paraldehyde and ammonium hydroxide.[85] In an extensive study of
the reaction, it has been pointed out that other single products can sometimes be obtained in fair yields by proper choice of reagents and conditions.[127]

574. Piperidines by Ring Closure

$$RNH(CH_2)_5OH \xrightarrow[290^\circ]{Al_2O_3} \begin{array}{c} CH_2 \\ H_2C \quad CH_2 \\ H_2C \quad CH_2 \\ N \\ R \end{array} + H_2O$$

A variety of difunctional compounds having groups in the 1,5-positions
undergo intramolecular reaction to give piperidines. Common interacting
groups are halo,[101] hydroxyl,[102] and amino. The yields vary within wide
limits. 1,5-Diamino compounds are cyclized during reduction of the corresponding dicyanides. For example, catalytic hydrogenation of glutaro-
nitrile over a nickel catalyst gives piperidine (22%).[107] Likewise, the
cyclic amides, 2-piperidones, are formed by interaction of amino and
ester groups during the catalytic reduction of γ-cyano esters.[106] 1,4,5,6-
Tetrahydropyridines are sometimes prepared in good yield by the action
of ammonia on δ-bromo ketones.[103, 105]

Ring closure in the 4-position of the piperidine nucleus by an intramolecular Claisen condensation of di-(β-carbethoxyethyl)-amines and related compounds leads to 4-piperidones in excellent yields.[115]

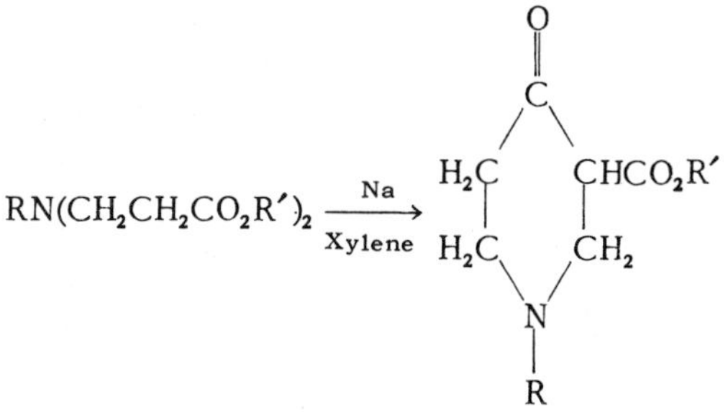

$$RN(CH_2CH_2CO_2R')_2 \xrightarrow[\text{Xylene}]{\text{Na}}$$

(structure shown)

575. Quinoline Compounds by Ring Closure

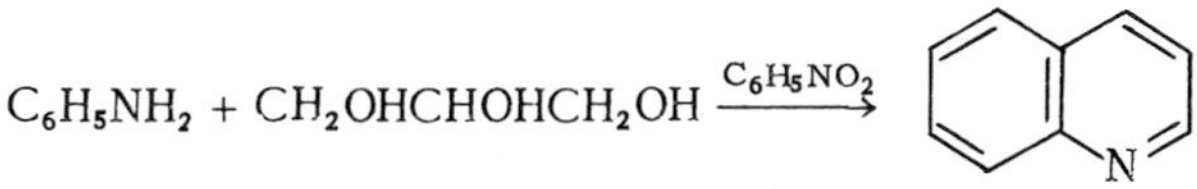

$$C_6H_5NH_2 + CH_2OHCHOHCH_2OH \xrightarrow{C_6H_5NO_2}$$

(quinoline structure shown)

Quinolines are formed by refluxing aniline or substituted anilines with glycerol and nitrobenzene (Skraup). The yield of quinoline from aniline is 84-91%.[136] The nitrobenzene serves as an oxidizing agent and may be replaced by arsenic acid,[133, 137, 145, 147] by nitrobenzenesulfonic acid,[143] or in some modifications of the reaction by ferric chloride.[140] The reaction is exothermic and sometimes difficult to control. Various techniques, catalysts, and solvents have been proposed to alleviate this difficulty.[129, 137, 139] The reaction may proceed by way of the intermediate formation of acrolein and its anil or by the addition of the aniline to the double bond of acrolein. These possibilities have suggested other compounds as starting materials in the synthesis. Thus, the glycerol may be replaced by two molecules of acetaldehyde or glycol (Döbner-Miller),[140] substituted glycerols,[148] pyruvic acid, acetoacetic ester (Conrad-Limpack-Knorr),[132, 142] or various combinations of simple carbonyl compounds.[135, 137, 143] The relationship of these modifications to the original Skraup reaction has been discussed.[161] Many quinoline derivatives have been prepared by these reactions, but most of the compounds are beyond the scope of this book.[128-149, 172, 173] Many functional groups including halo,[143] methoxyl,[128, 133, 140, 147] carboxyl,[131, 138] and nitro[130, 133, 145] have been present in the reactants. Substituents in the *ortho* or *para* positions of the aniline present no problem in orientation. An excellent study of the directive influence of various substituents in the *meta* position has been made.[146] Rearrangement of nuclear substituents is rare but accounts for the failure of at least one Skraup reaction.[141]

Ring closures are also effected from precursors obtained by condensations of o-aminobenzaldehyde and related compounds. These condensations differ from the above reactions in that the number 4 carbon of the quinoline was originally in the *ortho* position of the aniline.[174, 175]

The preparation of isoquinolines by methods of ring closure has been reviewed.[224]

576. Interaction of Grignard Reagents and N-Methyl-α-pyrrolidone[216]

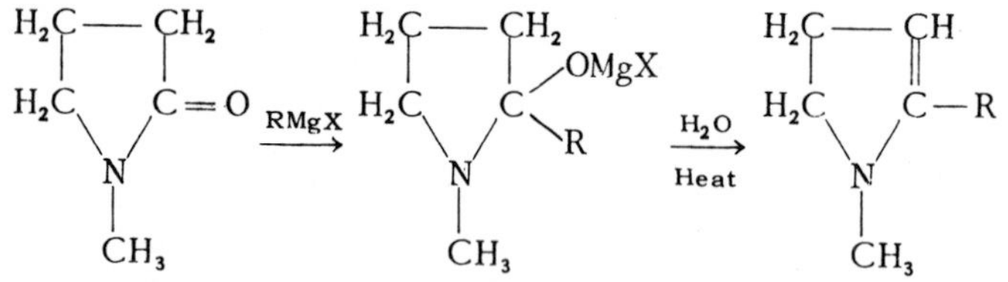

R = Methyl, ethyl, *n*-propyl, *n*-butyl, or phenyl   (50–70% over-all)

TABLE 118. HETEROCYCLIC COMPOUNDS   849

TABLE 118. HETEROCYCLIC COMPOUNDS [†]

C_n	Compound	Method	Yield (%)	Chapter[ref.]	B.p./mm., n_D^t, (M.p.), Deriv.
			Furans		
C_4	Furan	559	71	39[182]	31/760
		....	65	39[185]	
	Dihydrofuran	560	62	39[9]	67/744, 1.4321
	$\triangle^{3,\,4}$-Dihydrofuran	560	28	39[3]	67, 1.428[15]
	Tetrahydrofuran	554	93	39[96]	66
C_5	2-Methylfuran	556	93	39[198]	63/737 *
	α-Methyltetrahydrofuran	554	83	39[95]	
		560	40	39[2]	80
C_6	α-Ethyltetrahydrofuran	554	78	39[100]	108/758, 1.4190[11]
	2,2-Dimethyl-2,5-dihydro-furan	560	60	39[40]	83, 1.4155[17]
	α-Vinylfuran	19	20	2[166]	97/748, 1.4950[25]
		27	73	2[471]	98–101
C_7	2-n-Propylfuran	556	36	39[181]	115, 1.4410[25]
	2-Isopropylfuran	559	55	39[181]	108, 1.4466[25]
	2-Isopropenylfuran	19	56	2[425]	57/75, 1.4966[25]
	α-n-Propyltetrahydro-furan	554	91	39[100]	135/773, 1.4256[10], 1.4230[25]
C_8	2-n-Butylfuran	556	54	39[181]	138, 1.4460[25]
	2-t-Butylfuran	559	60	39[181]	120, 1.4380[25]
	α-n-Butyltetrahydrofuran	554	68	39[100]	160/768, 1.4315[9]
	Benzofuran (coumarone)	559	72	39[201]	60/12
		568	11	39[53]	172, 1.5631[24], 103Pi
	2,3-Dihydrobenzofuran	560	72	39[48]	79/17, 1.5495
C_9	α-n-Amyltetrahydrofuran	554	70	39[100]	71/14, 1.4362[10]
	2-Methylbenzofuran	568	30	39[53]	196/730, 1.5539[24], 74Pi
	2-Methyl-2,3-dihydro-benzofuran	560	30	39[49]	81/15, 1.5309
C_{10}	2-Phenylfuran	558	22	39[197]	95/10, 1.5920
C_{12}	Dibenzofuran	560	95	39[47]	(87)
C_{16}	2,5-Diphenylfuran	561	86	39[22]	(90)
			Thiophenes		
C_4	Thiophene	561	31	39[32]	84
		561	30	39[25]	86
	Tetrahydrothiophene	560	50	39[9]	120/760, 1.5046
		560	64	39[225]	120, 1.5037[21]
		554	71	39[108]	

[†] Heterocyclic compounds containing the common functional groups are listed in the tables in the appropriate chapters.

For explanations and symbols see pp. xi–xii.

TABLE 118 (*continued*)

C_n	Compound	Method	Yield (%)	Chapter[ref.]	B.p./mm., n_D^t, (M.p.), Deriv.
			Thiophenes (continued)		
C_5	2-Methylthiophene	556	78	39[199]	113, 1.5203
		561	11	39[32]	113, 1.5210
	3-Methylthiophene	561	30	39[27]	120
		565	40	39[8]	115/748, 1.5169[25]
C_6	2-Ethylthiophene	556	91	39[199]	134, 1.5122
	2,3-Dimethylthiophene	556	82	39[199]	140, 1.5188
	2,5-Dimethylthiophene	556	78	39[199]	136, 1.5132
		561	58	39[24]	135
	3,4-Dimethylthiophene	565	31	39[8]	148, 1.5187[25]
	α-Vinylthiophene	19	74	2[166]	63/50, 1.5698[25]
		19	100	39[213]	1.5612[23]
		20	44	2[456]	63/50, 1.5710[25]
		29	29	39[214]	73/69, 1.5697[25]
		29	29	2[455]	73/69, 1.5697[25]
C_7	2-*n*-Propylthiophene	556	89	39[199]	159, 1.5050
	2-Isopropylthiophene	558	72	39[196]	154/760, 1.5043
	2,3,5-Trimethylthiophene	561	40	39[26]	165/746, 1.5131
C_8	2-*s*-Butylthiophene	558	48	39[196]	76/24, 1.5013
	2-*t*-Butylthiophene	558	66	39[196]	164, 1.4979
	Benzothiophene (thianaphthene)	568	63	39[56]	221, (31)
		....	30 †	39[83]	104/20
	2,3-Dihydrobenzothiophene	560	100	39[46]	107/13.5, 234
C_9	2-*t*-Amylthiophene	558	80	39[196]	189/760, 1.5007
	3-Methylbenzothiophene	569	85	39[59]	125/25, 1.6229, 120Pi
	5-Methylbenzothiophene	556	49	39[203]	110/13, (22)
C_{10}	2-Phenylthiophene	565	22	39[13]	95/3, (35)
C_{12}	Dibenzothiophene	565	47	39[57]	154/3, (99), 125Pi
			Pyrroles		
C_4	Pyrrole	560	40	39[10]	131
		561	30	39[31]	34/16, 132/756
	Pyrrolidine	554	65	39[9]	89/760, 1.4426
C_5	N-Methylpyrrole	558	50	39[170]	117/749
		560	39	39[12]	114
	α-Methylpyrrole	561	24	39[32]	150, 1.5012
	N-Methylpyrrolidine	554	100	39[110]	78
C_6	1,2-Dimethylpyrrole	559	97	39[12]	140, 1.4913[25]
	2,4-Dimethylpyrrole	559	95	39[186]	72/25
	2,5-Dimethylpyrrole	561	86	39[29]	80/25, 1.500[22]
	α-Methyl-N-methylpyrroline	576	50	39[216]	131

TABLE 118. HETEROCYCLIC COMPOUNDS 851

TABLE 118 (*continued*)

C_n	Compound	Method	Yield (%)	Chapter[ref.]	B.p./mm., n_D^t, (M.p.), Deriv.
			Pyrroles (*continued*)		
C_6	α-Ethylpyrroline	564	46	39[35]	140, 87Pi
	α-Ethylpyrrolidine	560	22	39[16]	123/742, 1.4462[15]
	2,4-Dimethylpyrrolidine	554	68	39[109]	111
	2,5-Dimethylpyrrolidine	554	67	39[109]	105
C_8	2,4-Dimethyl-3-ethyl-pyrrole	3	58 †	39[39]	94/18
	N-*n*-Butylpyrrolidine	554	88	39[110]	124Pi
		558	40	39[168]	88/63, 125Pi
		567	80	39[34]	155/758, 1.437[27]
	2-Isobutylpyrrolidine	560	71	39[14]	164
	Benzopyrrole (indole)	557	75	39[154]	
		557	62	39[111]	133/12, 254, (52)
		559	55	39[66]	120/3, (52)
		570	79	39[77]	144/27, (53)
	2,3-Dihydroindole	572	60	39[111]	231
C_9	2-Methylindole	570	83	39[76]	119–126/3–4, (57)
		571	80	39[69]	
C_{10}	1-(*n*-Amyl)-pyrrole	557	88	39[154]	82/15, 1.4694
	N-Phenylpyrrole	560	43	39[11]	(61)
	2-Phenylpyrrole	....	35	39[11]	(129)
	α-Phenylpyrroline	564	55	39[35]	124/15
	N-Cyclohexylpyrrolidine	554	90	39[95]	214, 1.4792[25]
	N-Phenylpyrrolidine	554	63	39[95]	116/9, 1.5803[25]
	2-Phenylpyrrolidine	554	55	39[111]	116/15, 1.5390[25], 164HCl
		560	78	39[17]	239/756, 149Pi
	3-Ethylindole	558	62	39[64]	156/20, (37)
	2,3-Dimethylindole	569	85	39[79]	(108)
C_{11}	2-Ethyl-3-methylindole	569	92	39[80]	130/2, (66)
	1,2,3-Trimethylindole	569	90	39[79]	284/762, (19)
C_{12}	2,3-Diethylindole	571	46	39[75]	167/15
	Dibenzopyrrole (carbazole)	....	54	39[82]	(246)
		557	95	39[159]	(245)
		557	95	39[154]	
	1,2,3,4-Tetrahydrocarbazole	571	85	39[71]	(116)
C_{13}	N-Methylcarbazole	557	86	39[159]	(88)
	2-Methylcarbazole	557	90	39[159]	(260)
	3-Methylcarbazole	557	99	39[159]	(207)
C_{14}	2-Phenylindole	571	80	39[70]	(188)
C_{16}	2,4-Diphenylpyrrole	557	46 †	39[155]	(176)
C_{18}	N-Phenylcarbazole	558	65	39[169]	(93), 129Pi

For explanations and symbols see pp. xi–xii.

TABLE 118 (continued)

C_n	Compound	Method	Yield (%)	Chapter[ref.]	B.p./mm., n_D^t, (M.p.), Deriv.
			Pyridines		
C_5	Piperidine	554	83	39 [95]	105/740
		574	22	39 [107]	106, 151Pi
C_6	2-Methylpiperidine	554	90	39 [95]	119/740, 1.4495 *
	4-Methylpiperidine (4-pipecoline)	554	60	39 [114]	129, 1.4382 *
C_7	2-Ethylpyridine	5	86	39 [212]	146/12, 1.4966, 111Pi
		556	80	39 [205]	107Pi
	3-Ethylpyridine	556	80	39 [204]	166/760, 130Pi
	4-Ethylpyridine	556	38 †	39 [207]	165/760, 1.5010, 170Pi
	2,3-Dimethylpyridine	557	90	39 [105]	164, 188Pi
	2,6-Dimethylpyridine	573	36	39 [87]	143/743
	β-Vinylpyridine	20	20	2 [457]	144Pi
	2,3-Dimethyl-1,4,5,6-tetrahydropyridine	574	67	39 [105]	154–157, 155Pi
	N-Ethylpiperidine	554	100	39 [116]	127
	3-Ethylpiperidine	555	70	39 [106]	155 *, 140HCl
C_8	4-n-Propylpyridine	556	64	39 [195]	189, 132Pi
	2-Methyl-3-ethyl-pyridine	556	63	39 [208]	69/14, 141Pi
	5-Ethyl-2-methyl-pyridine	573	53	39 [85]	66/17, 1.4971
	2,3,4-Trimethylpyridine	573	20	39 [127]	80/25, 1.5118, 164Pi
	2,4,6-Trimethylpyridine (sym-collidine)	573	37	39 [88]	62/11, 1.4939, 156Pi
	4-Isopropylpiperidine	574	26	39 [101]	63/10
C_9	3-n-Butylpyridine	556	60	39 [206]	39/0.5, 1.4909, 90.5Pi
	4-n-Butylpyridine	556	47	39 [195]	209
	a-s-Butylpyridine	558	59	39 [192]	93/23, 91Pi
	4-Isobutylpyridine	556	30	39 [195]	199
C_{10}	a-Amylpyridine	558	45	39 [187]	110/28
	2-n-Amyl-1,4,5,6-tetrahydropyridine	574	84	39 [103]	95/9
	a-n-Amylpiperidine	554	74	39 [103]	87/10
C_{11}	2-Phenylpyridine	558	49	39 [190]	140/12
	2-Phenyl-1,4,5,6-tetrahydropyridine	574	66	39 [104]	142–150/20, 182Pi
	N-Phenylpiperidine	554	100	39 [116]	260/754
		574	56	39 [102]	256/750, 106/4, 146Pi
	2-Phenylpiperidine	554	80	39 [95]	112/9
	3-Phenylpiperidine	555	57	39 [106]	142/19, (15), 144HCl
	4-Phenylpiperidine	554	85	39 [95]	(50)
		555	60	39 [106]	137–147/21, (60)

TABLE 118. HETEROCYCLIC COMPOUNDS 853

TABLE 118 (continued)

C_n	Compound	Method	Yield (%)	Chapter[ref.]	B.p./mm., n_D^t, (M.p.), Deriv.
		Pyridines (continued)			
C_{12}	2-Benzylpyridine ⎱	558	75	39[193]	277/730, 140Pi
	4-Benzylpyridine ⎰				289/730, 139Pi
	N-Benzylpiperidine	574	33	39[102]	120/11, 166Pi
C_{13}	2-Phenethylpyridine	558	68	39[188]	146/10, 127Pi
	4-Phenethylpyridine	558	94	39[188]	(71)
		Quinolines and Isoquinolines			
C_9	Quinoline	575	60	39[136]	112/14
	py-Tetrahydroquinoline	554	97	39[95]	
		554	100	39[151]	121/13, 1.5897[25]
	bz-Tetrahydroquinoline	557	36	39[156]	103/10, 158Pi
	py-Tetrahydroisoquinoline	554	92	39[150]	236, 1.5749[22], 195Pi *
	bz-Tetrahydroisoquinoline	557	25	39[152]	144Pi
	Decahydroquinoline	554	90	39[151]	90/13, 1.4911[25], (27)
	Decahydroisoquinoline				
	(cis-)	554	80	39[152]	150Pi
	(trans-)		10		177Pi
C_{10}	2-Methylquinoline	575	50	39[143]	247 *
	(quinaldine)				
	3-Methylquinoline	575	49	39[143]	253, 1.6160, 188Pi
		575	80	39[174]	
	4-Methylquinoline	7	87	39[211]	127/15
	(lepidine)	575	73	39[140]	99/3, (9), 1.6197, 212Pi
	6-Methylquinoline	7	87	39[211]	137/12
	8-Methylquinoline	7	90	39[211]	(55)
	1-Methylisoquinoline	557	75	39[157]	126/10, 232Pi
C_{11}	2-Ethylquinoline	558	30	39[194]	130/15, 149Pi
	3-Ethylquinoline	575	54	39[143]	266, 1.5988, 199Pi
	2,3-Dimethylquinoline	575	50	39[166]	(69), 229Pi
	2,4-Dimethylquinoline	575	80	39[135]	150/20
C_{15}	3-Phenylquinoline	575	12	39[148]	(52), 205Pi

For explanations and symbols see pp. xi–xii.

REFERENCES FOR CHAPTER 39

[1] U. S. Dept. Commerce, Office of Technical Services, Repts. PB 1661, 1812.

[2] Bennett and Philip, *J. Chem. Soc.*, 1937 (1928).

[3] Valette, *Ann. chim.*, (12) 3, 674 (1948).

[4] Haworth and Jones, *J. Chem. Soc.*, 667 (1944); Gilman and Dickey, *J. Am. Chem. Soc.*, 52, 2010 (1930); Teunissen, *Rec. trav. chim.*, 49, 788 (1930).

[5] Rinkes, *Org. Syntheses*, Coll. Vol. II, 393 (1943).

[6] Adams and Voorhees, *Org. Syntheses*, Coll. Vol. I, 280 (1941).

[7] Karrer and Schmid, *Helv. Chim. Acta*, 27, 116 (1944); cf. ref. 225.

[8] Shepard, Henne, and Midgley, *J. Am. Chem. Soc.*, 56, 1355 (1934).

[9] Robles, *Rec. trav. chim.*, 58, 111 (1939).

[10] McElvain and Bolliger, *Org. Syntheses*, Coll. Vol. I, 473 (1941).

[11] Allen, Gilbert, and Young, *J. Org. Chem.*, 2, 230 (1937); also ref. 111.

[12] Rapoport and Jorgensen, *J. Org. Chem.*, 14, 664 (1949).

[13] Horton, *J. Org. Chem.*, 14, 767 (1949).

[14] Menschikoff and Schdanowitsch, *Ber.*, 69, 1799 (1936).

[15] Albertson and Fillman, *J. Am. Chem. Soc.*, 71, 2818 (1949).

[16] Müller and Feld, *Monatsh.*, 58, 17 (1931).

[17] Knott, *J. Chem. Soc.*, 186 (1948).

[18] Elderfield, *Heterocyclic Compounds*, Vol. 1, John Wiley & Sons, New York, 1950.

[19] Morton, *The Chemistry of Heterocyclic Compounds*, McGraw-Hill Book Co., New York and London, (1946).

[20] Ref. 18, pp. 127–132.

[21] Lutz, *J. Am. Chem. Soc.*, 51, 3008 (1929).

[22] Lutz and Rowlett, *J. Am. Chem. Soc.*, 70, 1359 (1948).

[23] Gilman and Burtner, *Rec. trav. chim.*, 51, 667 (1932).

[24] Farrar and Levine, *J. Am. Chem. Soc.*, 72, 4433 (1950).

[25] Phillips, *Org. Syntheses*, Coll. Vol. II, 578 (1943).

[26] Youtz and Perkins, *J. Am. Chem. Soc.*, 51, 3511 (1929).

[27] Linstead, Noble, and Wright, *J. Chem. Soc.*, 915 (1937).

[28] Steinkopf and Thormann, *Ann.*, 540, 4 (1939).

[29] Young and Allen, *Org. Syntheses*, Coll. Vol. II, 219 (1943).

[30] Bishop, *J. Am. Chem. Soc.*, 67, 2261 (1945).

[31] Wilson, *J. Chem. Soc.*, 63 (1945); cf. ref. 32.

[32] Jurjew, *Ber.*, 69, 440, 1002 (1936).

[33] Backer and Stevens, *Rec. trav. chim.*, 59, 423, 899 (1940).

[34] Coleman, Nichols, and Martens, *Org. Syntheses*, 25, 14 (1945).

[35] Cloke, *J. Am. Chem. Soc.*, 51, 1174 (1929); Craig, Bulbrook, and Hixon, *ibid.*, 53, 1831 (1931).

[36] Cloke et al., *J. Am. Chem. Soc.*, 67, 1587 (1945); 68, 126 (1946).

[37] Knorr and Lange, *Ber.*, 33, 2998 (1902).

[38] Fischer, *Org. Syntheses*, Coll. Vol. II, 202 (1943).

[39] Fisher, *Org. Syntheses*, 21, 67 (1941).

[40] Colonge and Garnier, *Bull. soc. chim. France*, (5) 15, 432 (1948).

[41] Amstutz, *J. Org. Chem.*, 9, 310 (1944).

[42] Gilman, Burtner, and Smith, *Rec. trav. chim.*, 51, 408 (1932); Blomquist and Stevenson, *J. Am. Chem. Soc.*, 56, 148 (1934); Scott and Johnson, *ibid.*, 54, 2552 (1932).

[43] Korschun, *Ber.*, 38, 1125 (1905).

[44] Feist, *Ber.*, 35, 1545 (1902).

[45] Reichstein and Zschokke, *Helv. Chim. Acta*, 14, 1272 (1931); 15, 270 (1932).

[46] Bennett and Hafez, *J. Chem. Soc.*, 287 (1941).

[47] Cullinane and Davies, *Rec. trav. chim.*, 55, 881 (1936).

[48] Chatelus, *Ann. chim.*, (12) 4, 530 (1949).

[49] Hurd and Hoffman, *J. Org. Chem.*, 5, 218 (1940).

[50] Adams and Rindfusz, *J. Am. Chem. Soc.*, 41, 655 (1919).

[51] Shriner and Witte, *J. Am. Chem. Soc.*, 61, 2328 (1939); Horning and Reisner, *ibid.*, 70, 3619 (1948).

[52] Price and Krishnamurti, *J. Am. Chem. Soc.*, 72, 5335 (1950).

[53] Hansch, Saltonstall, and Settle, *J. Am. Chem. Soc.*, 71, 943 (1949).

[54] Hansch and Blondon, *J. Am. Chem. Soc.*, 70, 1561 (1948).

[55] Hansch and Hawthorne, *J. Am. Chem. Soc.*, 70, 2495 (1948).

[56] Moore and Greensfelder, *J. Am. Chem. Soc.*, 69, 2008 (1947).

[57] Gilman and Nobis, *J. Am. Chem. Soc.*, 67, 1479 (1945); Gilman and Jacoby, *J. Org. Chem.*, 3, 108 (1938).

[58] Bradsher, *Chem. Revs.*, 38, 447 (1946).

[59] Werner, *Rec. trav. chim.*, 68, 509, 518 (1949).

[60] Shriner and Anderson, *J. Am. Chem. Soc.*, 61, 2706 (1939); Stoermer, Chydenius, and Schinn, *Ber.*, 57, 74 (1924).

[61] Reichstein et al., *Helv. Chim. Acta*, 18, 816 (1935).

[62] Fieser and Kennelly, *J. Am. Chem. Soc.*, 57, 1614 (1935).

[63] Johnson et al., *J. Am. Chem. Soc.*, 67, 423 (1945); cf. ref. 64.

[64] Cornforth and Robinson, *J. Chem. Soc.*, 680 (1942).

[65] Brehm, *J. Am. Chem. Soc.*, 71, 3541 (1949); cf. ref. 63.

[66] Elks, Elliot, and Hems, *J. Chem. Soc.*, 629 (1944).

[67] Stephen, *J. Chem. Soc.*, 1876 (1925).

[68] Van Order and Lindwall, *Chem. Revs.*, 30, 69 (1942).

[69] Fischer, *Ber.*, 19, 1564 (1886); Ger. pat. 238,138; *Frdl.*, 10, 332 (1910–1912).

[70] Shriner, Ashley, and Welch, *Org. Syntheses*, 22, 98 (1942).

[71] Rogers and Corson, *Org. Syntheses*, 30, 90 (1950).

[72] Snyder and Smith, *J. Am. Chem. Soc.*, 65, 2452 (1943).

[73] Carlin and Fisher, *J. Am. Chem. Soc.*, 70, 3421 (1948).

[74] Schofield and Theobald, *J. Chem. Soc.*, 796 (1949).

[75] Arbusow, Saizew, and Rasumow, *Ber.*, 68, 1792 (1935).

[76] Allen and Van Allan, *Org. Syntheses*, 22, 94 (1942); Madelung, *Ber.*, 45, 1128 (1912).

[77] Tyson, *Org. Syntheses*, 23, 42 (1943); Galat and Friedman, *J. Am. Chem. Soc.*, 70, 1280 (1948).

[78] Julian et al., *J. Am. Chem. Soc.*, 67, 1203 (1945); Brown and Mann, *J. Chem. Soc.*, 858 (1948).

[79] Janetzky and Verkade, *Rec. trav. chim.*, 65, 699 (1946).

[80] Janetzky and Verkade, *Rec. trav. chim.*, 65, 909 (1946).

[81] Campbell and McCall, *J. Chem. Soc.*, 2870 (1950).

[82] Morgan and Wallis, *J. Soc. Chem. Ind. (London)*, 57T, 358 (1938); 50, 94T (1931); Waterman and Vivian, *J. Org. Chem.*, 14, 295 (1949).

[83] Hansch and Lindwall, *J. Org. Chem.*, 10, 383 (1945).

[84] Bergstrom, *Chem. Revs.*, 35, 91–103 (1944).

[85] Frank, Pilgrim, and Riener, *Org. Syntheses*, 30, 41 (1950); Graf and Langer, *J. prakt. Chem.*, 150, 153 (1938).

[86] Tchitchibabine, *Bull. soc. chim. France*, (5) 4, 1826 (1937).

[87] Singer and McElvain, *Org. Syntheses,* Coll. Vol. II, 214 (1943).

[88] Frank and Meikle, *J. Am. Chem. Soc.,* 72, 4184 (1950).

[89] Merz and Richter, *Arch. Pharm.,* 275, 294 (1937).

[90] Gruber and Schlögl, *Monatsh.,* 81, 83 (1950).

[91] Baumgarten and Dornow, *Ber.,* 72, 563 567, 859 (1939); Dornow, *ibid.,* 72, 1548 (1939); Dornow and Peterlein, *ibid.,* 82, 257 (1949).

[92] Hinkel et al., *J. Chem. Soc.,* 750 (1929); 1835 (1931); Bodforss, *Ber.,* 64, 1108 (1931).

[93] Dornow, *Ber.,* 73, 153 (1940); Wenner and Plati, *J. Org. Chem.,* 11, 751 (1946).

[94] Ref. 18, pp. 452–472; ref. 19, pp. 186–190.

[95] Adkins, *Reactions of Hydrogen,* University of Wisconsin Press, Madison, 1937, pp. 62–68.

[96] Starr and Hixon, *Org. Syntheses,* Coll. Vol. II, 566 (1943).

[97] Kaufmann and Adams, *J. Am. Chem. Soc.,* 45, 3029 (1923); ref. 95.

[98] Hinz, Meyer, and Schücking, *Ber.,* 76, 676 (1943); cf. ref. 95.

[99] Paul, *Bull. soc. chim. France,* (5) 4, 846 (1937).

[100] Paul, *Bull. soc. chim. France,* (5) 5, 1053 (1938).

[101] Piantanida, *J. prakt. Chem.,* 153, 260 (1939).

[102] Scriabine, *Bull. soc. chim. France,* (5) 14, 456 (1947).

[103] Franke and Kroupa, *Monatsh.,* 69, 198 (1936).

[104] Salathiel, Burch, and Hixon, *J. Am. Chem. Soc.,* 59, 984 (1937).

[105] Finkelstein and Elderfield, *J. Org. Chem.,* 4, 365 (1939).

[106] Koelsch, *J. Am. Chem. Soc.,* 65, 2093, 2458, 2459, 2460 (1943).

[107] Henecka, *Chem. Ber.,* 82, 111 (1949).

[108] Mozingo et al., *J. Am. Chem. Soc.,* 67, 2092 (1945).

[109] Reid et al., *J. Am. Chem. Soc.,* 70, 3100 (1948).

[110] Craig and Hixon, *J. Am. Chem. Soc.,* 53, 187 (1931).

[111] Adkins and Coonradt, *J. Am. Chem. Soc.,* 63, 1563 (1941).

[112] Rainey and Adkins, *J. Am. Chem. Soc.,* 61, 1104 (1939).

[113] Ref. 18, pp. 631–642

[114] Elderfied, Pitt, and Wempen, *J. Am. Chem. Soc.,* 72, 1343 (1950).

[115] McElvain et al., *J. Am. Chem. Soc.,* 70, 1822 (1948); 51, 924 (1929); Fuson, Parham, and Reed, *ibid.,* 68, 1239 (1946); Howton, *J. Org. Chem.,* 10, 277 (1945); Cardwell and McQuillin, *J. Chem. Soc.,* 711 (1949).

[116] Hamilton and Adams, *J. Am. Chem. Soc.,* 50, 2260 (1928).

[117] McElvain and Adams, *J. Am. Chem. Soc.,* 45, 2745 (1923).

[118] Cavallito and Haskell, *J. Am. Chem. Soc.,* 66, 1166 (1944).

[119] Koenigs and Neumann, *Ber.,* 48, 956 (1915); Renshaw and Conn, *J. Am. Chem. Soc.,* 60, 745 (1938).

[120] Nienburg, *Ber.,* 70, 635 (1937).

[121] Grave, *J. Am. Chem. Soc.,* 46, 1460 (1924).

[122] Kleiman and Weinhouse, *J. Org. Chem.,* 10, 562 (1945).

[123] Doering and Weil, *J. Am. Chem. Soc.,* 69, 2461 (1947).

[124] Burtner and Brown, *J. Am. Chem. Soc.,* 69, 630 (1947).

[125] Norton et al., *J. Am. Chem. Soc.,* 68, 1572 (1946).

[126] Norton et al., *J. Am. Chem. Soc.,* 68, 1330 (1946).

[127] Frank and Seven, *J. Am. Chem. Soc.,* 71, 2629 (1949).

[128] Kaslow and Raymond, *J. Am. Chem. Soc.,* 68, 1102 (1946); cf. refs. 129 and 149.

[129] Elderfield et al., *J. Am. Chem. Soc.,* 68, 1584 (1946).

[130] Linsker and Evans, *J. Am. Chem. Soc.*, 68, 149, 874 (1946); cf. ref. 145.

[131] Campbell et al., *J. Am. Chem. Soc.*, 68, 1845 (1946).

[132] Reynolds and Hauser, *Org. Syntheses*, 29, 70 (1949).

[133] Mosher, Yanko, and Whitmore, *Org. Syntheses*, 27, 48 (1947).

[134] Price and Roberts, *Org. Syntheses*, 28, 38 (1948).

[135] Vaughan, *Org. Syntheses*, 28, 49 (1948).

[136] Clarke and Davis, *Org. Syntheses*, Coll. Vol. I, 478 (1941).

[137] Yale and Bernstein, *J. Am. Chem. Soc.*, 70, 254 (1948); 69, 1230 (1947).

[138] Jones et al., *J. Am. Chem. Soc.*, 70, 2847 (1948).

[139] Cohn and Gustavson, *J. Am. Chem. Soc.*, 50, 2709 (1928); Cohn, *ibid.*, 52, 3685 (1930).

[140] Campbell and Schaffner, *J. Am. Chem. Soc.*, 67, 86 (1945).

[141] Frisch, Silverman, and Bogert, *J. Am. Chem. Soc.*, 65, 2432 (1943).

[142] Kaslow and Marsh, *J. Org. Chem.*, 12, 457 (1947).

[143] Utermohlen, *J. Org. Chem.*, 8, 544 (1943).

[144] Reitsema, *Chem. Revs.*, 43, 43 (1948), cf. ref. 118.

[145] Le Fevre and Le Fevre, *J. Chem. Soc.*, 1472 (1935).

[146] Bradford, Elliott, and Rowe, *J. Chem. Soc.*, 437 (1947).

[147] King and Sherred, *J. Chem. Soc.*, 415 (1942).

[148] Warren, *J. Chem. Soc.*, 1366 (1936).

[149] Cromwell, Caughlan, and Gilbert, *J. Am. Chem. Soc.*, 66, 401 (1944).

[150] Cromwell and Cram, *J. Am. Chem. Soc.*, 65, 301 (1943).

[151] Palfray, *Bull. soc. chim. France*, (5) 7, 433 (1940).

[152] Witkop, *J. Am. Chem. Soc.*, 70, 2617 (1948).

[153] Allewelt and Day, *J. Org. Chem.*, 6, 384 (1941); Elderfield and Kreysa, *J. Am. Chem. Soc.*, 70, 44 (1948).

[154] Adkins and Lundsted, *J. Am. Chem. Soc.*, 71, 2964 (1949).

[155] Allen and Wilson, *Org. Syntheses*, 27, 33 (1947).

[156] Ehrenstein and Bunge, *Ber.*, 67, 1715 (1934).

[157] Barrows and Lindwall, *J. Am. Chem. Soc.*, 64, 2430 (1942).

[158] Barclay and Campbell, *J. Chem. Soc.*, 530 (1945).

[159] Horning, Horning, and Walker, *J. Am. Chem. Soc.*, 70, 3935 (1948).

[160] Jurjew and Borissow, *Ber.*, 69, 1395 (1936).

[161] Ref. 19, pp. 262–267.

[162] Clemo and Swan, *J. Chem. Soc.*, 869 (1945).

[163] Johnson, Woroch, and Buell, *J. Am. Chem. Soc.*, 71, 1901 (1949).

[164] Renshaw and Friedman, *J. Am. Chem. Soc.*, 61, 3321 (1939).

[165] Briggs and De Ath, *J. Chem. Soc.*, 456 (1937).

[166] Petrow, *J. Chem. Soc.*, 693 (1942).

[167] Andrus and Johnson, *Org. Syntheses*, 23, 90 (1943).

[168] Ochiai, Tsuda, and Yokoyama, *Ber.*, 68, 2291 (1935).

[169] Dunlop and Tucker, *J. Chem. Soc.*, 1945 (1939).

[170] Hess and Wissing, *Ber.*, 47, 1416 (1914).

[171] Tschelinzeff and Maxoroff, *Ber.*, 60, 194 (1927).

[172] Phillips, Elbinger, and Merritt, *J. Am. Chem. Soc.*, 71, 3986 (1949).

[173] Kaslow and Cook, *J. Am. Chem. Soc.*, 67, 1969 (1945).

[174] Willimott and Simpson, *J. Chem. Soc.*, 2809 (1926).

[175] Fuson and Burness, *J. Am. Chem. Soc.*, 68, 1270 (1946).

[176] Fourneau, Trefouel, and Wancolle, *Bull. soc. chim. France*, (4) 47, 738 (1930).

[177] Ref. 18, pp. 295–299, 306–307.

[178] Ref. 18, pp. 487–490.

[179] Buu-Hoi and Royer, *Rec. trav. chim.*, 66, 533 (1947).

[180] Flowers, Miller, and Flowers, *J. Am. Chem. Soc.*, 70, 3019 (1948).

[181] Gilman and Calloway, *J. Am. Chem. Soc.*, 55, 4203 (1933).

[182] Dolliver et al., *J. Am. Chem. Soc.*, 60, 442 (1938); Wilson, *Org. Syntheses,* Coll. Vol. I, 274 (1941); Gilman and Lousinian, *Rec. trav. chim.*, 52, 156 (1933).

[183] Gilman, Mallory, and Wright, *J. Am. Chem. Soc.*, 54, 734 (1932).

[184] Shepard, Winslow, and Johnson, *J. Am. Chem. Soc.*, 52, 2085 (1930); Whittaker, *Rec. trav. chim.*, 52, 354 (1933).

[185] Wilson, *J. Chem. Soc.*, 61 (1945).

[186] Fischer, *Org. Syntheses*, Coll. Vol. II, 217 (1943); Corwin and Krieble, *J. Am. Chem. Soc.*, 63, 1830 (1941).

[187] Chichibabin, *Bull. soc. chim. France*, (5) 3, 1607 (1936); (5) 5, 429, 436 (1938).

[188] Bergstrom, Norton, and Seibert, *J. Org. Chem.*, 10, 452 (1945).

[189] Knight and Shaw, *J. Chem. Soc.*, 682 (1938); Brody and Bogert, *J. Am. Chem. Soc.*, 65, 1075 (1943).

[190] Evans and Allen, *Org. Syntheses*, Coll. Vol. II, 517 (1943).

[191] Haworth, Heilbron, and Hey, *J. Chem. Soc.*, 349 (1940).

[192] Doering and Pasternak, *J. Am. Chem. Soc.*, 72, 143 (1950).

[193] Crook, *J. Am. Chem. Soc.*, 70, 416 (1948).

[194] Woodward and Kornfeld, *J. Am. Chem. Soc.*, 70, 2508 (1948).

[195] Arens and Wibaut, *Rec. trav. chim.*, 61, 59 (1942); cf. ref. 207.

[196] Caesar, *J. Am. Chem. Soc.*, 70, 3623 (1948); Pines, Kvetinskas, and Vesely *ibid.*, 72, 1568 (1950); Kutz and Corson, *ibid.*, 68, 1477 (1946).

[197] Johnson, *J. Chem. Soc.*, 895 (1946).

[198] Schniepp, Geller, and Korff, *J. Am. Chem. Soc.*, 69, 672 (1947); Burnette et al., *Ind. Eng. Chem.*, 40, 502 (1948); cf. Reichstein, *Helv. Chim. Acta*, 13, 347 (1930).

[199] King and Nord, *J. Org. Chem.*, 14, 638 (1949); Buu-Hoi, Hoan, and Khoi, *ibid.*, 15, 959 (1950).

[200] Campaigne and Diedrich, *J. Am. Chem. Soc.*, 70, 391 (1948).

[201] Reichstein and Baud, *Helv. Chim. Acta*, 20, 893 (1937).

[202] Harvey and Robson, *J. Chem. Soc.*, 100 (1938).

[203] Tarbell, Fukushima, and Dam, *J. Am. Chem. Soc.*, 67, 1643 (1945).

[204] Fand and Lutomski, *J. Am. Chem. Soc.*, 71, 2931 (1949).

[205] Furst, *J. Am. Chem. Soc.*, 71, 3550 (1949).

[206] Frank and Weatherbee, *J. Am. Chem. Soc.*, 70, 3482 (1948).

[207] Frank and Smith, *Org. Syntheses*, 27, 38 (1947).

[208] Dornow and Machens, *Ber.*, 73, 355 (1940).

[209] Sawyer and Andrus, *Org. Syntheses*, 23, 25 (1943).

[210] Rinkes, *Org. Syntheses*, Coll. Vol. II, 393 (1943).

[211] Neumann et al., *Org. Syntheses*, 26, 45 (1946), also note 6.

[212] Frank and Phillips, *J. Am. Chem. Soc.*, 71, 2804 (1949).

[213] Nazzaro and Bullock, *J. Am. Chem. Soc.*, 68, 2121 (1946).

[214] Strassburg, Gregg, and Walling, *J. Am. Chem. Soc.*, 69, 2141 (1947).

[215] Gilman and Melstrom, *J. Am. Chem. Soc.*, 70, 1655 (1948); Stoermer and Kahlert, *Ber.*, 35, 1636 (1902).

[216] Craig, *J. Am. Chem. Soc.*, 55, 295 (1933).

[217] Albert and Ritchie, *Org. Syntheses*, 22, 5 (1942); Lehmstedt and Schrader, *Ber.*, 70, 838 (1937); Goldberg and Kelly, *J. Chem. Soc.*, 102 (1946).

[218] Allen and McKee, *Org. Syntheses,* Coll. Vol. II, 15 (1943).

[219] Albert, *J. Chem. Soc.,* 1225 (1948).

[220] Elpern and Hamilton, *J. Am. Chem. Soc.,* 68, 1436 (1946); Fisher and Hamer, *J. Chem. Soc.,* 1907 (1934).

[221] Nowlin, *J. Am. Chem. Soc.,* 72, 5754 (1950).

[222] Hartough, *Thiophene and Its Derivatives,* Interscience Publishers, New York, 1951; Hollins, *The Synthesis of Nitrogen Ring Compounds,* E. Benn, Ltd., London, 1924.

[223] Wolf and Folkers in *Organic Reactions,* Vol. 6, John Wiley & Sons, New York, 1951, p. 410.

[224] Whaley and Govindachari in *Organic Reactions,* Vol. 6, John Wiley & Sons, New York, 1951, pp. 74 and 151; Gensler, *ibid.,* p. 191.

[225] Tarbell and Weaver, *J. Am. Chem. Soc.,* 63, 2940 (1941).

Index

In the interest of economy compounds listed in the tables are not repeated as a separate index. However, compounds and accompanying information may be found in the appropriate tables.